Organogenesis

CONTRIBUTORS

Rodolfo Amprino
Robert Auerbach
Eugene Bell
Helene Charniaux-Cotton
Giovanni Chieffi
Alfred J. Coulombre
Y. Croisille and N. M. Le Douarin
Robert L. DeHaan
L. G. Gallien
T. Adesanya I. Grillo
Terrell H. Hamilton and Ching-sung Teng
Elizabeth D. Hay
Alfred Jost
Bengt Källén
Irwin R. Konigsberg
Rita Levi-Montalcini and Pietro U. Angeletti
E. H. Mercer
J. Milaire
Benjamin Moffett, Jr.
H. W. Mossman
Dorothy Price and Evalina Ortiz
Thomas H. Shepard
Sergei Sorokin
R. W. Sperry
Theodore W. Torrey
J. P. Trinkaus
Heinrich Ursprung
Ray L. Watterson
Lemen J. Wells
Vincent B. Wigglesworth
P. G. Wilkin

Organogenesis

Robert L. DeHaan
Carnegie Institution of Washington
Baltimore, Maryland

Heinrich Ursprung
The Johns Hopkins University
Baltimore, Maryland

EDITORS

Holt, Rinehart and Winston
NEW YORK · CHICAGO · SAN FRANCISCO · TORONTO · LONDON

Fig. 16.3 reprinted from *Physiological Zoology*, Rudnick and Rowles
16:22-42, 1943, by permission of the University of Chicago Press.
Copyright 1943 by the University of Chicago.

Fig. 30.19 from Bartels et al., *Am. J. Obstet. Gynecol.*
84:1714, 1962, published by The C. V. Mosby Co.

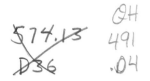

Preface

"Organic form — the architecture and texture
of organisms — is better known than understood."
Weiss, 1960

Those charged with arranging the program of the International Conference on Organogenesis believed that the time had come for re-emphasizing the study of development "beyond the ribosome." Acting under the conviction that ample attention was being given to problems of coding and protein biosynthesis, Professor Etienne Wolff, president of the International Institute of Embryology under whose auspices the conference was held, invited the organizing committee to develop a program that would center attention on supermolecular aggregates, cells, and cell associations. Thus at the conference the primary focus was the behavior and interactions of cells and cell groups in the fashioning of complex, ordered tissues.

Within the International Union of Biological Sciences, the International Institute of Embryology represents developmental biology. In addition to its publishing and research programs, centered in the Hubrecht Laboratory, the institute has convened a series of successful international conferences. Happily, the International Conference on Organogenesis did not prove to be an exception. Its success was attested by the genuine enthusiasm of the four hundred participants and the prompt, willing cooperation of speakers, discussants, and other contributors to this volume.

The conference was held in Baltimore, Maryland, September 6–12, 1964. The International Institute of Embryology and the organizing committee are deeply indebted to the hospitality of the Carnegie Institution of Washington, The Johns Hopkins University, and the local committee, for an attractive setting; and to the National Science Foundation, the International Union of Biological Sciences, and Holt, Rinehart and Winston, Inc., for grants making the meeting possible.

JAMES D. EBERT
Chairman, Organizing Committee

Baltimore
February, 1965

v

Editors' Introduction

"How all's to one thing wrought."
Gerard Manley Hopkins "On a piece of music"

Our purpose as developmental biologists is to understand the causal mechanisms underlying the processes of growth, differentiation, and morphogenesis. It is now accepted as a truism that events occurring at the level of the molecule, the cell, and the cell group or tissue operate simultaneously and coordinately to influence these processes. Thus, we cannot expect to derive satisfying explanations of how an eye or a limb or a heart develops by learning about the inductive interactions of the component tissue layers alone, or by knowing only of the microscopic behavior of the cells involved, or by learning what enzymes are active or what nucleotide sequences are transcribed. Only when we have access to information at all these levels—and can synthesize it—can we truly understand how an organ or an embryo develops.

Fortunately, there is a tendency for information at different levels to interact. When, through advances in instrumentation or techniques, a new approach is introduced, it is at first directed by existing information. What the ultrastructural or molecular biologist initially looked for—the problems he attacked, the questions he asked—was in large part guided by his knowledge of the properties of cells and cell groups previously determined with less refined techniques. However, as we now gain greater insights into the mechanisms of synthesis, interaction, and structural characteristics of macromolecules, these ideas will in turn increasingly direct the questions that are asked at the cellular and supracellular level.

It is our hope that the present volume will act as a catalyst in this interaction of information, leading toward the synthesis of ideas, derived from various levels of investigation, into a more comprehensive understanding of the problems of the development of organs and tissues.

As editors, we have attempted in *Organogenesis* to recognize the needs of three major groups of readers: investigators in developmental biology, advanced students and teachers of embryology, and biologists in other fields. Investigators require definitive review articles covering their own and related areas to aid them in digesting and creatively synthesizing the deluge of literature with which they are inundated today. The other readers also desire critical and comprehensive reviews, but may, in addition, need sufficient introductory material to make these reviews meaningful. We have striven to have the chapters in this book fulfill both of these requirements wherever possible.

The contributing authors of this volume must receive ultimate credit for whatever success it achieves. To them we express our thanks for their promptness in submitting manuscripts, for their willingness to accept editorial suggestions, and above all, for their remarkable expertise in their respective subjects.

ROBERT L. DEHAAN
HEINRICH URSPRUNG
Editors

Baltimore
April, 1965

Contents

SECTION I Basic Mechanisms

1

Genes and Development

HEINRICH URSPRUNG[*]

Department of Biology
Johns Hopkins University
Baltimore, Maryland

When biologists first began to wonder about the role of genes in development, the presence of a gene responsible for a trait could be inferred only if a mutation occurred that led to alteration of the trait. Fortunately for the science of developmental genetics, a fair number of such mutations had been described by breeders, and their mode of inheritance analyzed by geneticists through pedigree studies. In those early days it became evident that the central task of developmental geneticists was to be the analysis of the mode of action of genes, mutant and normal.

At first, gene action was assessed at very different levels of biological expression. The phene "waltzing" of the house mouse (Guaita, 45), for example, is a behavioral one, and the responsible gene (v) expressed itself on a behavioral level. Another factor, Danforth's short tail (Sd) on the other hand, was found to act early in embryonic development on tissue inter-

actions. A refined study revealed the fact that in this mutant the ureters fail to grow, inductive interactions do not occur, and as a consequence, kidneys do not develop (Gluecksohn-Schoenheimer, 39). Yet another gene of the mouse, dwarf (dw) expressed itself on a histological-endocrinological level. The eosinophilic cells of the anterior pituitary of these mice are histologically abnormal and apparently fail to produce thyrotrophic and adrenocorticotrophic hormones. The consequences are dwarfism and sterility (Smith and Macdowell, 93). A fourth category of gene action was measured on the chemical level. A large number of mutants which affect anthocyans and their derivatives in petals (Alston and Hagen, 4) were found in flowering plants. The well-known mutant genes controlling ommochromes and pteridines in the eyes of *Drosophila* also belong in this category (Ziegler, 116).

These studies clearly indicated that gene action can be observed on many different levels of biological organization. But geneticists early postulated that a primary gene action underlay the different phenotypic expressions

[*] The author's research is supported by National Science Foundation grant GB-298. The critical comments of C. L. Markert and S. Suskind are gratefully acknowledged.

3

of a mutation. According to this concept of unity of gene action (Grüneberg, 43), it appeared sufficient to assume that a gene produced one effect, which automatically, through the channels of development, affected subsequent steps and ultimate traits. This concept explained in a very simple fashion the frequent phenomenon of pleiotropic gene action, because it was now easy to picture an entire syndrome of effects as the result of a single shift from normal to mutant on the gene level. Developmental geneticists undertook to build pedigrees of causes, starting at the level of the complicated syndrome, and tracing the elements back in development to the unifying and simple initial genetic defect. However, the existence of this genetic defect was still a prerequisite for such a study because the existence of a normal allele could be inferred only when the consequences of an abnormal allele became manifest.

Soon the concept of unity of gene action was carried an important step further. Not only was it assumed that a given gene brought about its manyfold consequences by a primary action, it was postulated now that the primary action of all genes was of one kind only. This important concept was primarily a result of biochemical studies on mutants of *Drosophila* and *Neurospora* and was highlighted by the well-known one-gene–one-enzyme hypothesis (Beadle, 10). Several new slogans followed the one-gene–one-enzyme hypothesis, until now, after two decades of intensive research, it has metamorphosed to the one-operon–one-messenger theory (Martin, 75).

The present theory of gene action is a result of brilliant genetic research, primarily on microorganisms. It is therefore not surprising that the first speaker of the 1964 International Conference on Organogenesis was not an embryologist, but a microbial geneticist, Francois Jacob of the Institut Pasteur in Paris. Jacob, with his colleague Jacques Monod, is considered the father of the current dogma of gene action, which will be described in the following section.

But before turning to this discussion, we should recapitulate the predogma state of developmental genetics. It has been shown, beyond doubt, that cellular differentiation and development of higher organisms is under genetic control. It was found that the action of genes affecting development is pleiotropic. In the construction of pedigrees of causes, various levels had been reached; a few analyses were successful in tracing pleiotropic systems down to the level of an enzyme deficiency.

This introduction is brief and incomplete and therefore does injustice to many investigators whose thoughts and experiments in the area of cytology, histochemistry, cytogenetics, biochemistry, and other branches of biology helped construct the current view of the sequence leading from DNA via RNA to protein (Caspersson, 29; Brachet, 21; and many others). Their work has been described in a number of monographs and texts and cannot be reviewed here. These books should not be put on the shelf however, for soon developmental biologists will want to use monographs such as those by Grüneberg (43, 44), Hadorn (47), and Waddington (109, 110) when it will be important again to build predigrees of causes — leading from genes to phenes, this time.

The Dogma of Gene Action

The concept of gene action, as presented by Jacob and Monod (59) in 1961, consists of two major parts. First, it states that the genetic information of an organism, encoded in the nucleotide sequence of DNA, is transcribed into a complementary nucleotide sequence called messenger-RNA (m-RNA). This m-RNA then establishes a temporary union with ribosomes, and the nucleotide sequence is translated into the amino acid sequence of a specific polypeptide. Second, the dogma states that the synthesis of m-RNA is regulated by specific repressors which are products of regulator genes. The repressors are thought to act by becoming engaged with the operator site of the gene, their affinity to the operator being determined by the concentration of metabolites, so-called effectors. An operator is the control site of a cluster of structural genes. When the operator is open, all genes of the operon synthesize m-RNA; when it is closed, none do.

We shall describe some of the evidence advanced in favor of the dogma, and point out some of the difficulties that await solution. This discussion will deal with microbes, for the most part. A special section discusses the dogma's applicability to higher organisms.

Transcription

When a culture of *Escherichia coli* is infected with T_2 bacteriophage in the presence of P^{32} orthophosphate, within a few minutes label can be recovered that has become incorporated into RNA (Volkin and Astrachan, 108). The ratio $A + U/C + G$ of this RNA is about 1.7—that is, almost identical to the base-ratio of T_2 DNA (1.8), but quite different from that of *E. coli* DNA (1.0). From this observation it appeared that the phage DNA primed the rapid synthesis of a specific, complementary RNA. This notion has since been substantiated by a number of elegant experiments. Hall and Spiegelman (49) prepared P^{32}-labeled m-RNA from T_2-infected *E. coli* and mixed this preparation with H^3-labeled T_2 DNA, the two strands of which had previously been separated from one another by heat. The mixture was cooled and centrifuged through a cesium chloride density gradient. Three bands formed and the analysis showed that one of them was DNA, the second, RNA, and the third, a molecular hybrid containing both H^3 and P^{32} labels and having a density intermediate between DNA and RNA. When, as a control, bacterial DNA was used as the partner of the m-RNA in the mixing experiment, no such hybrid DNA-RNA molecules were detected. It is thus apparent that the T_2 DNA primed the synthesis of a specific m-RNA which by virtue of its complementary base sequence hybridizes with the DNA. Such a synthesis is also possible in vitro, using bacterial RNA polymerase in the presence of ribonucleotide triphosphates (Weiss and Nakamoto, 111; Hurwitz et al., 57). Depending on the type of DNA primer utilized in such an experiment, the base sequence of the newly synthesized RNA varied. This base sequence can be determined only indirectly at the present time by a procedure called nearest neighbor sequence analysis (see Kornberg, 62, for review), which does not permit determination of the complete nucleotide sequence. However it was found, for example, that the position of cytidylate in the new RNA was specifically determined by the DNA that was used as primer, which strongly indicates that the exact base sequence of the m-RNA is primed by DNA. Methods are now becoming available that, hopefully, will permit a direct visualization of nucleotide sequence by electron-microscopy (Beer, 12; Moudrianakis and Beer, 81).

With these facts apparent, it became important to find out in more detail how transcription operates. DNA is a double helix of two strands with complementary base sequences. If the base sequence of m-RNA determines the specificity of the message, then two quite different messages could be read, one from each DNA strand. A number of experiments have shown, however, that the genetic information is read from only one of the two strands of the DNA double helix (Champe and Benzer, 30; Bautz and Hall, 9). Using the RNA-DNA hybridizing technique, it was possible (9) to prepare phage DNA-specific m-RNA. A quantitative analysis of nucleotides present in this RNA was then done. If both DNA strands had been read during transcription, and if they both produced an equally stable copy, then the RNA should have contained equal amounts of, for example, guanine and cytosine. This was not the case, however. There was more guanine present than cytosine, which indicated that only one strand of the DNA had been read. This notion has since been confirmed by a variety of experimental procedures (Hayashi et al., 51).

Translation

Pardee (88) had shown that protein synthesis comes to a halt when RNA synthesis is stopped. Through the use of radioactive amino acids it was then found that amino acids become first incorporated into protein associated with ribosomes (Littlefield et al., 68). Nomura and co-workers (87) showed that newly formed m-RNA is associated with ribosomes. From these observations the idea arose that ribosomes function as assembly plants, where m-RNA encounters amino acids, precursor molecules for polypeptide synthesis, and where new proteins are synthesized. The question then arose as to whether ribosomes carry any information themselves, or whether they are unspecific workbenches. This query was answered in an experiment by Brenner and co-workers (23). These authors prepared "heavy" ribosomes by growing $E.$ $coli$ in a medium containing N^{15} and C^{13}. These heavy ribosomes can be recognized and separated from "light" ribosomes by centrifugation. Bacteria containing heavy ribosomes were then infected with T_2 phage and immediately transferred to a light medium containing radioactive nucleic acid and protein precursors. When the ribosomal populations of such cultures were examined, it was found that no light ribosomes had formed. Furthermore it was seen that the newly formed m-RNA and protein were associated with heavy ribosomes. These had previously been involved in the synthesis of bacterial proteins, and were now used to fabricate phage protein under the direction of the phage m-RNA. Thus the specificity for protein synthesis resides in the m-RNA, not in the ribosomes.

This does not imply that their RNA sequence is unspecific. In fact it has been shown by the molecular hybridization technique (Yankofsky and Spiegelman, 114) that ribosomal RNA is complementary to the nucleotide sequence of two cistrons in the bacterial genome.

The actual translation mechanism has been studied in more detail by Hoagland and co-workers (53) in rat liver, and by Berg and Ofengand (15) in bacteria. When amino acids are added to a high spin supernatant containing ATP and soluble-RNA (s-RNA), complexes form between s-RNA and amino acids, under the guidance of amino acid-specific activating enzymes. The complex is then transferred to ribosomes, a step that depends on the presence of GTP. Because of this function in protein synthesis, s-RNA is also called transfer-RNA (t-RNA). There is at least one t-RNA species for each amino acid. The t-RNA–amino acid complexes become attached to m-RNA on the ribosomes, peptide bonding occurs, and t-RNA is released. Apparently m-RNA recognizes the t-RNA moiety of the complex, not the amino acid. This was proved by an ingenious experiment (Chapeville et al., 31). First, cysteine was complexed to its t-RNA. The cysteine was then desulfhydrylated to alanine by Raney nickel. Thus an unusual complex was produced, namely, a t-RNA carrying the wrong amino acid. This complex was introduced into a protein synthesizing system containing a synthetic messenger, polyuridylicguanylic acid (poly-UG), which from other work is known to direct the incorporation into protein of cysteine, but not of alanine. Would this messenger now recognize the cysteine-specific t-RNA of the complex and incorporate alanine? Or would it recognize alanine, and therefore not incorporate it? The first alternative was observed, thereby proving that the recognition occurs between messenger and the transfer-RNA moiety of the complex.

The next, very important question to be solved was a language problem. Which are the words used in the process of translation? In molecular terms, which nucleotide sequence of the message is translated into which amino acid in the protein?

Artificial messengers have been instrumental in solving this important question of the code. The letters of m-RNA are known; they are A, U, G, and C. In order to specify 20 words, the letters must be written in groups of at least three, a code that would actually allow 64 words. But the next shorter code – that is, two letters per word, would specify only 16 words. A frontal attack on the problem was initiated by Nirenberg and Matthaei (85) and by Lengyel, Speyer, and Ochoa (66). A bacterial homogenate containing ribosomes, t-RNA, an energy source, and enzymes can incorporate radioactive amino acids into polypeptides in the presence of synthetic polynucleotides. When poly-U was used as the messenger in this system, phenylalanine – and only phenylalanine – was incorporated into a polypeptide, polyphenylalanine. Assuming a triplet code, this would mean that the message word UUU means "phenylalanine" on the level of the amino acid. This message word is transcribed from a sequence AAA in the DNA. Extensive work on the code (see Nirenberg and Leder, 86, for a recent review) has confirmed the notion that code words are triplets, and has further characterized the properties of the code to a remarkable degree. The code has also been studied in less synthetic systems, using natural, rather than synthetic messengers. Nathans and co-workers

(83) showed that a viral RNA message is translated by *E. coli* extracts into normal viral coat protein.

Regulation

Let us examine briefly the constituents of the regulatory circuitry as proposed in the gene action dogma. Jacob and Monod (59) defined the operon as a "genetic unit of coordinated transcription." It contains a cluster of cistrons, closely linked on the genetic map, each coding for a particular enzyme of a common pathway. In recent years much evidence has been produced showing that the synthesis of the enzymes coded in an operon can be coordinately induced by the common substrate, which acts as an effector. The adverb "coordinately" is the basis for the concept of the functional unit, and it calls for a master switch, the operator. In inducible strains, mutants were isolated that produced all the enzymes of an operon, even in the absence of inducer. Such mutations mapped outside the cistron did not appear to alter the structure of the enzymes, and were therefore interpreted as mutations of a regulator gene. The mutant regulator allele fails to produce a repressor; consequently, the operator is open and the operon functions. In a normal strain, regulation was thought to be controlled ultimately by effectors, metabolites of the pathway of the cognate operon. These effectors were thought to control the affinity of the repressor to the operator, which would again lead to an open or closed operon.

Very intensive research on the regulation problem has produced a substantial amount of evidence in support of the idea of coordinate control (see Ames and Martin, 6, for review). The importance and specificity of effectors was demonstrated by Attardi and co-workers (8) and by Hayashi and co-workers (52). The question to be answered was: Does the presence of inducer (effector) increase the production of a message cognate to the relevant genetic region? The answer appears to be "yes." When the synthesis of β-galactosidase was induced in an *E. coli* culture, the rate of synthesis of a specific β-galactosidase message increased, as shown by the presence of increased molecular hybridization with the corresponding DNA (52).

This result leaves little doubt that regulation can occur at the transcription level. So far, however, no one has succeeded in isolating the intermediate repressor that has been postulated in the sequence of effector-operator, although its proteinaceous nature is widely taken for granted (Jacob and Monod, 60) Furthermore, the fact that regulation can occur on the transcription level does not imply that regulation does not also occur during translation. In fact, a number of observations suggest regulatory mechanisms on the level of translation. McAuslan (76) found that protein synthesis can be regulated experimentally long after the synthesis of the cognate m-RNA is completed. Ames and Hartman (5) discuss so-called polarity mutants, which affect a structural gene of the operon and at the same time alter the rate of synthesis of enzymes cognate to cistrons distal of the mutant cistron, but not of those that are located proximal of the mutant site (toward the operator). This effect has led to the modulation concept (5), which proposes regulation of protein synthesis on the translation level, possibly involving t-RNA binding and ribosomes.

On the whole, the regulation part of the dogma is the least understood and an object of intensive research and thought (see Stent, 97, for review). As we shall see, its solution is of paramount importance for the understanding of the genetic control of development.

The Dogma in Higher Organisms

Comparative biologists have demonstrated over and over again principles of uniformity in living matter. On the morphological level, comparative anatomists have traced the extremities of vertebrates to a common and unifying building plan. On the chemical level, comparative biochemists have discovered the universality of such common pathways as the Krebs cycle. Many biologists therefore were tempted, in the absence of evidence, to believe a priori that the dogma of gene action was applicable to higher organisms. This belief has one very distinct advantage. It enables the investigator to ask very precise chemical questions in experimentation with higher forms. The developmental geneticist with this belief does not have to rely on mutations in his attempt to explain the genetic control of normal development. He takes the mere synthesis of an m-RNA species as certain evidence of gene action.

During the last few years, several lines of evidence have supported the idea of the universal applicability of the dogma in living matter. Although the picture is not as complete in higher organisms as in microbes, several parallels to microbial protein synthetic systems have been postulated or detected or postulated and detected in higher forms also. Thus, McClintock (78) pointed out shortly after Jacob and

Monod's (59) review that a system similar to the bacterial operator-regulator system had long been known in maize. Subsequent analyses in higher organisms have for the most part been carried out on the biochemical problems of protein synthesis and its regulation.

Mechanisms of Protein Synthesis

Transcription and translation of genetic information appear to follow the same pathway in higher organisms as in microbes. This has been demonstrated recently in vivo and in vitro by a number of investigators. Using pea seedlings, Huang and co-workers (56) were able to extract an enzyme system capable of incorporating C^{14}-labeled ATP into RNA in the presence of GTP, CTP, and UTP. This reaction was shown to be DNA-dependent; deoxyribonuclease pretreatment destroyed the capacity to synthesize RNA. Within only a few years, workers in the same laboratory (Bonner et al., 18) carried this experiment an important step further. They succeeded in coupling the DNA-dependent m-RNA synthesizing system to m-RNA-dependent protein synthesis, and thus obtained DNA-primed proteins as follows. Again, chromatin prepared from pea seedlings was able to synthesize RNA. The addition of bacterial RNA polymerase was found to enhance this reaction greatly, so that the pea DNA yielded increased amounts of m-RNA. Now, a bacterial ribosome system was added, and the m-RNA-dependent incorporation of leucine-C^{14} into protein determined. Protein synthesis occurred. By means of immunochemical techniques, the proteins synthesized in this system were partially identified as seed reserve globulins. The fact that pea DNA can be transcribed to pea m-RNA under the guidance of *E. coli* polymerase, and that the pea message can be translated on *E. coli* ribosomes into pea protein supports the idea of universal applicability of the dogma. Hopefully, similar hybrid systems will be analyzable soon; if they are successful, our optimism would be substantiated.

There are a fair number of other observations available already that point to the universality of the dogma. In fact, many major contributions to our present understanding of protein synthesis stem from the study of higher organisms. Rich and co-workers (91) in work on rabbit reticulocytes made the very important discovery that protein synthesis occurs on clusters of ribosomes. Assuming a triplet code, it can be calculated that the m-RNA necessary for coding the 150 amino acids of the hemoglobin molecule would have to be about 1500 A long (assuming a 3.4 A internucleotide spacing). Ordinary ribosomes, sedimenting at 70 S, have a diameter of only about 200 A. Thus there would appear to be room for more than one ribosome per messenger. When lysates of reticulocytes were subjected to sucrose density gradient centrifugation, several ribosome fractions were isolated, each containing either single ribosomes, or ribosome tetramers, pentamers, and hexamers, respectively. These polymers were identified in the electron microscope as ribosome clusters in which the individual ribosomes were held together by thin strands of 10–15 A diameter. In view of the finding that m-RNA is associated with ribosomes (87), it is logical to assume that the thin strands represent m-RNA. Polyribosomes, or polysomes, have since been observed in a variety of other mammal-

ian tissues, such as liver, HeLa cells, but also in chick muscle, slime molds, and bacteria (see 91 for review).

Other investigations in higher organisms have been concerned with transfer-RNA. Von Ehrenstein and co-workers (37) demonstrated the amino acid specificity of t-RNA in a cell-free system using ribosomes from rabbit reticulocytes. Their experiment is very similar to the one which we described earlier (31), in which microbial systems were utilized. Chipchase and Birnstiel (32), using isolated pea nuclei, found that the synthesis of t-RNA is DNA-dependent. Using rabbit reticulocytes, Dintzis (35) demonstrated that the assembly of amino acids into protein starts at the free amino end and terminates at the free carboxyl end.

These are but a few examples of the experiments dealing with the nature of protein synthesis in higher organisms. Taken as a whole, they indicate strongly that gene action, that is, m-RNA synthesis followed by the synthesis of specific protein, follows similar pathways in all branches of living matter so far investigated.

Regulation of Gene Function

The criterion most widely used in distinguishing lower from higher organisms is the fact that the latter are composed of different kinds of cells. These cellular differences can be expressed using morphological or biochemical vocabularies. Description is simpler and often more precise if it is done in biochemical terms. A reticulocyte is characterized by its hemoglobin synthesis, for example, and a melanocyte can be recognized by its production of tyrosinase.

If one considers the cell-specific patterns of protein or m-RNA syntheses sufficient to describe the differentiated state of a cell, then the process of cellular differentiation can be explained by assuming that gene activities are differentially regulated.

A number of investigators have therefore begun to study gene regulation in higher organisms (see Ursprung, 105, for review) under the assumption that gene action and regulation proceeds in ways very similar to bacterial schemes. It was realized that regulation may occur either on the level of transcription or on the level of translation. Thus far, none of these investigations has yielded clear-cut evidence on the mechanism of in vivo gene regulation as it occurs in higher organisms. Nevertheless we should like to present some of the assay systems used, for we believe that the study of gene regulation represents one of the key problems of contemporary biology.

In a search for regulation on the level of transcription, Bonner's group (18, 56) utilized the pea system already mentioned. Decisive for their experiment was the fact that in vivo, seed reserve globulin is synthesized by cotyledons, but not by buds, and the observation that in vitro, chromatin prepared from cotyledons does prime the synthesis of this globulin, whereas chromatin prepared from buds does not. It was assumed now that histones, basic proteins complexed with chromosomal DNA (see Bloch, 16 for review), act as repressors of gene function. According to the authors, when histones were removed from a pea bud chromatin preparation, the resulting DNA started to prime reserve globulin synthesis in vitro. Further exploration of this system promises valuable insight into regulatory mechanisms, particularly with regard to the question of histone specificity in repression.

A similar assay system has been used by Allfrey and Mirsky (1, 2) for several years. These authors demonstrated DNA-dependent RNA synthesis in a variety of mammalian nuclear preparations, primarily of the thymus. They found that this synthesis is repressed by added histones, and that it can be derepressed by tryptic removal of the histones. Furthermore, it was demonstrated that the repressing activity of the histones was dependent on their degree of acetylation (3). It must be kept in mind, however, as the authors point out themselves, that this system measures the capacity of nuclei or extracts to synthesize m-RNA in general. It is very questionable thus far whether the histones act in a locus-specific way. In fact, other polycations, such as polylysine, mimic the effect of histone in this assay system.

The same reservation probably applies to a still different assay system, in which gene action is measured at an embryological level (Markert and Ursprung, 74). We assumed that gene function can be regulated by chromosomal macromolecules. If such macromolecules were involved in gene regulation, the macromolecular composition of nuclei of different cell types would be different. The plan of our experiments therefore was to prepare nuclear macromolecules from one cell type and make them available to the genome of a different cell type. Abnormal complexes might form between DNA and the foreign macromolecules, and the abnormality might express itself in the genetic output of this combination. In the actual experiment we prepared several fractions from adult frog liver — namely, globulin, albumin, nucleoprotein, histones, and alkali soluble proteins. These fractions were then injected into frog eggs, and the development of the animals observed. Albumins, and to a much lesser degree histones, produced one effect—the embryos arrested at the late blastula stage and failed to gastrulate. Since gastrulation from a considerable amount of indirect evidence appears to be a critical phase of development where gene action becomes essential for subsequent embryonic development (Moore, 80) it appeared possible that the injected material had actually interfered with the genome. In fact, nuclear transplantation showed that the effect produced was inherent in the nuclei and irreversible. Unfortunately a karyotype analysis showed that the nuclear effect involved gross chromosomal damage, which was always associated with developmental arrest and perhaps sufficient to account for it. More recent experiments have shown, however, that gross chromosomal damage is not always followed by arrest at gastrulation. Thus the chromosomal damage may be a coincident result of abnormal complexes between DNA and the injected protein, and therefore neither the primary nor a sufficient cause of developmental arrest. Furthermore, no nuclease or protease activity of the injected extracts could thus far be made responsible for the arrest (see Ursprung, 106 for review). Thus it is still unclear whether this developmental effect can be attributed to an abnormal complexing of the egg's DNA with the injected protein. If such complexes do occur, then it would seem particularly interesting that nonhistone proteins (albumins) are the most active in producing these abnormal developmental effects.

This class of proteins has attracted very little attention. The few investigations on nonhistone proteins all agree that they are highly cell specific (Mirsky and Osawa, 79). They may very well represent the differential responsible for cell-specific gene regulation. Their mode of action could be competition with histones for complex formation with DNA. This appears to be possible from a chemical point of view (Busch et al., 27).

Some indirect evidence for the role of nonhistone proteins stems from recent observations in puffs of giant chromosomes of dipteran salivary glands (Swift, 99). By cytochemical methods it was found that the histone moiety of a genetic region on the salivary chromosomes remains unchanged in the process of puffing, whereas a nonhistone protein accumulates. According to our scheme, we would interpret this observation to mean that the nonhistone protein moves onto the chromosome from outside.

That a transport of protein from cytoplasm to nucleus actually occurs has been postulated by Goldstein (40). When a nucleus of a donor amoeba labeled by incorporated radioactive amino acids was introduced into a host amoeba, within a few hours the radioactivity became distributed among the two nuclei of the host amoeba. The cytoplasm contained little label. These results are interpreted to mean that label left the donor nucleus, entered the cytoplasm, and then re-entered the two nuclei at random. The ratio of grains in donor to grains in host nucleus equals about 2.6 : 1, which indicates that the nucleus contains a nonmigrating as well as a migrating fraction of label. Goldstein (40) has good evidence that the label actually represents protein, and furthermore believes that histone is not a substantial part of it.

It is evident from the few examples mentioned that the role of histones and nonhistone proteins in gene regulation awaits further clarification. Other molecules that have been invoked as candidates for repressor function in higher organisms are hormones (see Clever, 34 for review). Ecdysone, the steroid growth and differentiation hormone of many insects, has been found to control the formation of puffs in dipteran giant chromosomes. As we shall see later, much evidence has accumulated which indicates that puffing is a reflection of gene action. The formation of some puffs is clearly controlled by the ecdysone titer, and it has been inferred from these observations that ecdysone acts as an effector. Its precise mode of interference with gene action is unknown, although there is some indirect evidence that ecdysone affects gene action at the transcription level. It was found, for example, that actinomycin-D, which is known to inhibit DNA-dependent synthesis of m-RNA (Reich et al., 90), prevents the regulatory action of ecdysone, whereas puromycin, which interferes with protein synthesis at the translation level (Yarmolinsky and de la Haba, 115) does not influence the activity of ecdysone. The ecdysone puff assay system has a great potential, although some recent reports point out a high degree of lability of puff formation, which calls for careful exploration before definite conclusions are drawn. Kroeger (63, 64) warns that puff formation is influenced by the ratio of sodium and potassium ions in the nuclear sap, and furthermore that Zn^{2+} may mimic the action of ecdysone.

The experiments on regulation described thus far were aimed to detect regulation on the level of transcription. A different series of observations, which point to regulation during translation, were made by Wilt (113), Nemer (84), Gross (42), and Tyler (103). The material used by these workers was the sea urchin embryo. When unfertilized mature eggs are incubated with radioactive amino acids, scarcely any label is incorporated into protein. Neither do unfertilized eggs synthesize RNA. At fertilization, however, a burst of protein synthesis occurs which is not paralleled by a burst of RNA synthesis, although some new RNA is made at that stage. Interestingly enough, the postfertilization incorporation of amino acids into protein is actinomycin-insensitive, that is, addition of actinomycin-D does not block this early protein synthesis, although it blocks m-RNA synthesis. This fact has been interpreted to mean that the postfertilization burst of protein synthesis is directed by preformed, stable messenger-RNA that was already present in the unfertilized egg. Mechanically enucleated eggs proceed to synthesize the postfertilization protein, which supports the idea of the stable messenger. The question of why the unfertilized egg does not synthesize protein then arises. At first it was assumed that its ribosomes are incompetent, for the egg does contain t-RNA, activating enzymes, and amino acid pools in addition to the stable m-RNA. But when ribosomes from unfertilized eggs were incubated with synthetic messenger (poly-U) they were found to support synthesis of polyphenylalanine, indicating that they are competent, at least in this synthetic system. Perhaps the m-RNA of the egg is not accessible to ribosomes prior to fertilization. The process of fertilization could trigger the release of the preformed m-RNA, thereby initiating protein synthesis. At the same time, polysomes appear, as indicated by the fact that protein label is found associated with RNA sedimenting at 100 S or above. When these heavy polysome fractions are treated with ribonuclease, they peak at about 70 S, where single ribosomes are expected. Thus in the unfertilized sea urchin egg, regulation does not appear to operate on the transcription level, since the messenger is present. However, it is not clear yet how the postulated regulation at the translation level actually operates; maybe it involves t-RNA.

At later stages, protein synthesis becomes actinomycin-D-sensitive, indicating the need for newly formed m-RNA. This m-RNA appears to be rather stable also, as shown by timed applications of actinomycin-D and parallel measurements of protein and RNA synthesis. This stability of m-RNA has been reported in other higher organisms also. It contrasts with the lability of this RNA species in microbes, and brings an important feature of differentiated cells to mind, namely, their apparent stability.

The Stability of the Differentiated State

A liver cell remains a liver cell in vivo and is not as readily changed by alteration of the medium as a bacterium. It has been postulated repeatedly, therefore, that a theory of differentiation must provide for stabilizing factors that make differentiation irreversible.

A series of experiments of great heuristic and dialectic value, by Briggs and King (24), indicated that this stabilization occurred at the level of the cell nucleus. In a typical experiment, nuclei were removed from *Rana pipiens* embryos at various developmental stages, and their ability to promote development tested by implantation into a previously enucleated egg. The development of this host egg was observed. With increasing age of the donor, an increasing percentage of nuclei failed to promote normal development of the host egg. This finding was taken as an indication that nuclear differentiation had occurred. Through serial transfer experiments it was shown, furthermore, that this nuclear differentiation was irreversible.

The inherent difficulty of this system is that it is difficult to decide whether the nuclear alterations occurred in the course of normal development of the donor, or only as a consequence of transplantation. Certainly, an increased susceptibility of older nuclei to the transplantation procedure could be responsible for their decreased developmental potencies. This is especially true because nuclear differentiation in this assay system is measured as a loss of potency, rather than a gain of specificity—a negative criterion is used.

More recently, Gurdon (46) presented evidence that a large percentage of nuclei of differentiated intestinal cells of *Xenopus* are able to promote normal development of host eggs in the transplantation experiment. Such eggs developed into feeding tadpoles with normally differentiated nerve and muscle cells. This positive result is impressive and strongly points to the possibility that the earlier results are attributable to nuclear changes during or after transplantation. In view of Gurdon's findings, nuclear differentiation, if it occurs, is reversible.

Nuclear differentiation almost certainly does occur. For as we shall discuss later, the syntheses of macromolecules are regulated cell and time specifically, and at least part of this regulation seems to operate on the level of nuclear DNA. But as was pointed out in several models (Jacob and Monod, 60; Grobstein, 41; Ursprung, 105), this regulation need not be irreversible.

In fact, several lines of recent evidence agree with the idea that differentiation is reversible. In the tobacco plant, for example, it was shown that a single parenchymatous cell is able to develop into an entire tobacco plant (Braun, 22). Furthermore, under conditions of tissue culture, the differentiated state of cells is often lost (Grobstein, 41; Holtzer et al., 54; Konigsberg, 61). This has also been observed during "tissue culture in vivo" in a series of recent experiments by Hadorn (48). This author cultures fragments of larval *Drosophila* primordia in the body cavity of adult flies, a culture condition allowing the implanted cells to divide, but not to differentiate into adult structures, apparently for hormonal reasons (Bodenstein, 17). By serial transplantations of aliquots of this proliferating tissue, cell lines derived from a variety of primordia can be carried in adult hosts over periods of months or years. When the investigator wants to assess the developmental capacity of the cultured cells after a given time of proliferation, he simply transfers an aliquot of a cell line into a larval host. This implant then undergoes metamorphosis simultaneously with its host, and can be removed from the abdomen of the metamorphosed fly for microscopic examination. Two major phenomena have been observed in this system thus far. First, the longer a primordium had been cultured by repeated fragmentation and proliferation, the narrower were the developmental capacities of a given aliquot. This can be explained on a statistical basis, for it is known that the original primordium represents a mosaic of organ-forming areas. By repeated fragmentation and culture, individual organ-forming areas inadvertently are selected and form monocultures. Second, and more important, a switch of developmental capacities was seen to occur in such monocultures. It was observed, for example, that a monoculture derived from genital primordia and forming a given genital structure only, after a few cell divisions switched to form head structures that are normally formed by a different primordium. The only obvious alteration in the life history of these cultured cells is the total number of cell divisions undergone prior to differentiation. The system thus represents an example of dedifferentiation (or dedetermination) by cell division, and argues strongly against irreversibility of differentiation or determination.

Still, it is not certain whether stability or reversibility of the differentiated state are "either-or" questions. Nor is it understood how the reversible regulation of gene activities in higher organisms operates. What is known, however, is that it does operate. This will be illustrated in the three following sections.

Differential Synthesis of RNA

As a result of a recent careful analysis, Brown (25) presents a catalog of

RNA synthesis during early amphibian development. By timed administration of labeled precursor, and extraction of total RNA followed by gradient centrifugation, he found that the three functional classes of RNA are synthesized time specifically. Synthesis of ribosomal RNA (28 S and 18 S) is intense during oogenesis, but almost zero in the mature oocyte. The ribosomal RNA formed during oogenesis is very stable. Only at the onset of gastrulation is new ribosomal RNA synthesized again; at this stage, nucleoli first appear. However, an actual need for new ribosomes does not seem to exist until the swimming stages, as evidenced by the fact that the anucleolate mutant of *Xenopus* (26) develops normally up to the swimming stage in the absence of new ribosome synthesis. Soluble RNA is synthesized at a low rate in the immature oocyte and then again in the late cleavage stages. At the same time, heterogeneous RNA with a DNA-like base composition is synthesized.

The importance of these observations lies in the fact that the synthesis of the various RNA types *is* regulated. Further experimentation may reveal *how* this regulation operates. Measurements of synthetic rates under variable experimental conditions may yield very important facts for our understanding of gene regulation. This is especially true for the 28 S and 18 S ribosomal RNA, whose synthesis has been shown to be under genetic control in a coordinate fashion, resembling a microbial operon. It may turn out that ribosomal RNA synthesis is a much easier assay system than the synthesis of messenger-RNA, particularly in view of the stability of ribosomal RNA, because it does not require

correction of the results for rapid degradation.

While Brown's (25) study describes the stage specificity of RNA synthesis, recent work by McCarthy and Hoyer (77) deals with its tissue specificity. These authors prepared nuclei from a variety of adult mouse tissues and extracted DNA. From the same tissues, RNA was also prepared. In a typical experiment, the DNA was then made single stranded by a heat treatment followed by quick cooling. The separated strands of DNA are kept isolated from one another in agar. When liver RNA is added to such a preparation, DNA-RNA hybrid molecules will form wherever complementary nucleotide sequences exist. When saturation is reached, the addition of more liver RNA will not lead to the formation of more hybrids. However, when kidney RNA was added after saturation had been reached with liver RNA, more hybrid molecules were formed, indicating that at least some of the kidney RNA had different nucleotide sequences than the liver RNA. In these experiments, rapidly labeled RNA (m-RNA) was used for the hybridization, and the results obtained showed clearly that the two tissues synthesize different types of m-RNA.

DNA of various tissues was also tested in this hybridization system, and it was found that DNA of the various cell types is identical. The old, well-established assumption that all cells of a higher organism are genetically identical has thus been confirmed at the molecular level. For more detailed description of the ingenious technique utilized in these experiments, see a recent review by Hoyer, McCarthy, and Bolton (55).

Differential Synthesis of Proteins

When the titers of given enzymes in various tissues are measured, it is found that they cover a wide range from probably millions of molecules per cell to none at all—or at least to a number so small as to not be detected by our most sensitive assay methods. We have mentioned tyrosinase, which is an enzyme characteristic for melanocytes, and hemoglobin, a protein characteristic for reticulocytes. Such enormous differences in prevalence of given enzymes or proteins are best interpreted by assuming different rates of synthesis. It must be kept in mind, however, that many investigations concerned with the cell specificity of proteins do not actually measure the synthesis of a protein directly, but rather, assess its presence. The reason why presence rather than synthesis is usually measured is the difficulty involved in the isolation of minute amounts of a given species of newly synthesized proteins from the vast number of other proteins present in the cell. Noteworthy exceptions have been mentioned earlier in the case of incorporation of radioactive amino acids into seed-reserve protein of the pea by extracts from seedlings (Bonner et al., 18), and in the much more refined investigation on hemoglobin synthesis (Dintzis, 35).

But even in the absence of much evidence of differential synthesis of proteins, differential presence of proteins can be interpreted as reflecting differential synthesis, since it seems much easier to imagine a control mechanism operating at the transcription or translation level (that is, controlling the synthesis) rather than at the level of the finished protein (controlling its rate of degradation). How-

ever, evidence for the latter mode of control has been produced in clear-cut experiments by Schimke (91b).

Cell and time specificity of protein patterns has been studied in a number of cases, but probably the best known is the enzyme lactate dehydrogenase (LDH). (See Markert, 70 for review.) When vertebrate tissue extracts are electrophoresed on starch gels or similar supporting media, and the gels then stained for LDH activity, this enzyme is seen to be present in several molecular forms of different charge. Such multiple forms of a given enzyme with similar substrate specificity have been termed isozymes. About one hundred enzymes have so far been found to exist in isozymic forms. In mouse tissues, after electrophoretic separation, five isozymes of LDH are commonly seen with LDH-1 at the anodal end of the spectrum, LDH-5 at the cathodal end. The isozyme patterns of LDH are tissue and stage specific (Markert and Ursprung, 73). In the embryo, isozymes at the LDH-5 end of the spectrum are predominant. During development, the patterns alter in a tissue-specific fashion. Thus, in the development of the heart, LDH-1 and LDH-2 gradually become predominant, whereas in skeletal muscle, the embryonic predominance of LDH-5 is maintained throughout development. The fact that in many vertebrates five forms of LDH are consistently found was interpreted to mean that the LDH molecule is a tetramer consisting of two types of polypeptide subunits assembled in the five possible groups of four, and that the two polypeptide subunits are under the control of two different genes. This hypothesis has been substantiated beyond doubt. First, when intact LDH of a molecular weight of 135,000 is dissociated by hydrogen bonding agents such as urea, a subunit with MW = 35,000 is found. Second, when dissociated LDH is electrophoresed, two enzymatically inactive protein fractions of different charge are seen. Third, the amino acid composition of purified LDH-1 differs from that of LDH-5, the latter being richer in basic amino acid residues. Fourth, when equal amounts of LDH-1 and LDH-5 were mixed, dissociated into subunits and then reaggregated, the results clearly showed that the two subunits had become reaggregated in the expected ratio of $1:4:6:4:1$ (Markert, 71). Fifth, mutants of LDH subunits have been found in mice (Shaw and Barto, 92) and humans (Boyer, 20). A mouse heterozygous at one of the LDH loci carries the information for three types of subunits and accordingly synthesizes 15 different LDH molecules. Sixth, in vitro hybridization of LDH from different animals (for example, mouse and rabbit) yields zymograms according to expectation if four different subunits participated in the formation of the isozymes (Markert, 72).

From this evidence, it appears that the various polypeptide subunits are each under the control of a separate gene. The observation of stage and cell specificity of isozyme patterns is best interpreted by the assumption that the various genes involved are differentially active.

In hemoglobins, a very similar situation exists (Ingram, 58). During development, fetal hemoglobin is gradually replaced by adult hemoglobin. Again, in this case, the relative abundance of related protein tetramers appears to be determined by regulation of the relative rates of gene activity.

Differential Chromosomal Activities

We have mentioned the puffs of dipteran giant chromosomes and wondered how regulation of gene action functioned in higher organisms. Now, we simply want to emphasize again that it does operate in these polytene chromosomes. An account of parallel observations in lampbrush chromosomes of amphibian oocytes can be found in recent reviews by Callan (28) and Gall (38).

From extensive investigation, primarily by Beermann (13, 14), Clever (33, 34) and Pelling (89), it is certain that puffs represent active gene loci. In pulse experiments with tritiated uridine, RNA is formed rapidly at the puffs, as seen by radioautography. Puff RNA is characterized by strong asymmetry in A/U ratio, which, together with the rapid synthesis, is suggestive of messenger RNA formed at one of the DNA strands. In view of these recent results, the earlier observations on time and cell specificity of puff formation gain in importance, since it now appears certain that these specificities represent differential gene function. Probably the most beautiful demonstration is that of Beermann (13) relating the activity of a puff directly to the formation of a specific cytoplasmic product. This author observed that two sibling species of a midge, *Chironomus tentans* and *Chironomus pallidivittatus* differ in a small lobe of the salivary gland. In *C. pallidivittatus*, this lobe is characterized by a granular component of the cytoplasm; the granules are absent in *C. tentans*. The trait granule is inherited in a simple Mendelian way, as shown

by crosses between the two sibling species. Furthermore, the locus could be mapped to the fourth Balbiani ring, near the end of a chromosome of *C. pallidivittatus*. In *C. tentans*, this Balbiani ring is absent. These observations link the puff to the final cytoplasmic product, and demonstrate that presence or absence of gene action, as observed on the chromosomal level, is reflected by presence or absence of a cytoplasmic product. Similar studies linking chromosomal puffs with cytoplasmic constituents are those of Laufer and co-workers (65). These authors found that several enzyme activities are reduced in salivary glands after treatment of the animals with actinomycin-D, which inhibits the formation of puffs.

Regulation of gene activity on the chromosomal level has also been found in mammals, including man (see Lyon, 69a, for review). Female mammals differ from males by one X chromosome, and one often wondered how this difference in gene dosage is compensated in the two sexes. When it became known that mice of the constitution XO, that is, animals carrying only one X chromosome, are fully viable females, it was speculated that possibly only one active X chromosome is needed for normal development. A number of findings support this idea. Female mice heterozygous for sex-linked coat color mutations show mosaic phenotypes with wild-type and mutant patches on their body. This mosaicism could easily be explained by the assumption that one of the X chromosomes became inactivated at some stage in development, and that descendant cells would all carry this one inactivated X chromosome together with its active partner.

If one assumes, furthermore, that paternal or maternal X chromosomes become inactivated at random, mutant or wild-type gene expression, respectively, would be accounted for. Cytogenetic studies lend strong support to this idea, commonly known as the Lyon hypothesis. Various mouse tissues were found to contain a heteropycnotic – and presumably genetically inactive – chromosome, and there is good evidence that this heteropycnotic chromosome is an X chromosome. In multi-X individuals, all X chromosomes in excess of one seem to be inactivated; they appear as so-called sex chromatin or Barr bodies. Again, it is obvious that regulation does operate in this case; but the *modus operandi* is as yet unknown.

A possibly similar type of regulation at the chromosomal level is encountered in so-called variegated position effects (see Baker, 8a, for review). This effect is characterized by a mottling, due to instability of the expression of genes placed in close proximity to heterochromatin (Schultz, 91a). It appears that the mottling is a consequence of a gene being either turned on or off in a given cell, indicating that variegation is due to a malfunction of the regulatory mechanism. But thus far all theories advanced for the explanation of variegated position effects have left much unexplained. This is also true for the possibly analogous but not understood phenomenon of paramutation in maize (Brink, 24a), which will not be discussed here.

Omnis Morphe e DNA?

In the previous sections we have defended the notion that the dogma of gene action is universal and applies to higher organisms. In particular we have attempted to demonstrate that DNA carries the information necessary for the synthesis of specific proteins. Much earlier, classical developmental genetics had demonstrated that development itself is under genetic control. It was observed that genes determine whether kidneys are formed in a mouse, or whether the tail of the animal is crooked or straight.

Does this imply that DNA explains everything? This question is more difficult than it might appear at first sight, and we should like to defer the answer, if we can reach any, to the end of this section.

The Order of Structure of Proteins

Some relevant information comes from physical chemistry (see Anfinsen, 7). The structure of only a few proteins has been analyzed, however, and therefore a generalized conclusion is not warranted at the present time. But we can state with confidence that the primary amino acid composition of a protein (that is, the linear arrangement of amino acids) autonomously leads to its secondary structure (that is, to the first order of coiling of the amino acid chain). The secondary structure, in turn, autonomously defines the tertiary structure (that is, higher orders of coiling). The next step is more questionable. For as we have seen earlier, a subunit of LDH-1, certainly of different primary structure than a subunit of LDH-5, can reaggregate with its like or its unlike and form any of the five possible tetramers. Depending on the availability of subunits, various amounts of the different tetramers will form. Thus the behavior of the subunits is nonauton-

omous in the sense that they enter into different quaternary structures, depending on the availability of the two partners involved. Also it is known that the quaternary structure can be disrupted by reagents such as urea, which clearly shows that the formation of a higher-order structure is influenced by stimuli not intrinsic to the polypeptide itself. On the other hand, every macromolecule has a tendency to assume the energetically most stable form, and groups of macromolecules tend to become stabilized autonomously in energetically most stable configurations for any given ionic condition. The question is whether they do reach this state in the living cell. At the present time, all one can say is that molecules can achieve higher orders of structure on their own, although the ionic environment influences and modifies the formation of these higher orders of structure.

Very valuable information on this fundamental problem is also to be expected from investigations on artificial membranes. Thompson (100) has succeeded in constructing phospholipid films 61 A thick, which form automatically under appropriate experimental conditions. It will be interesting to see how much automatism is involved in the formation of the more complicated biological membranes, and to what degree the nature of the membranes formed in such artificial systems can be influenced by the environment. Does DNA provide the information carried on the cell surface that so specifically determines the behavior of the cell when it encounters another cell (Steinberg, 96; see Trinkaus, 102 for review)? Furthermore, can the information that is required for the formation of tissues and organs be traced back to DNA?

Cytoplasmic DNA

In order to lessen the burden on DNA, we should modify the question to some extent. Can this information be traced back to the dogma—that is, the DNA-RNA-proteins relation with the regulatory circuitry?

The recent findings that DNA does not only occur in the nucleus, but also in mitochondria (Nass and Nass, 82) is not entirely relevant in this connection, but might at least reduce the problem of information transfer in the cell. Mitochondria not only contain DNA but also a polymerase necessary for the synthesis of RNA copies. It will no doubt be known shortly whether this mitochondrial DNA is identical to the nuclear DNA in base sequence; it is already known that the buoyant densities of the two varieties of DNA in *Neurospora* are different (Luck and Reich, 69). If this newly discovered DNA were different from nuclear DNA, the cell would have more than one source of replicable information, and the types of information would be different. The problem of autonomy or nonautonomy of the achievement by macromolecules of higher orders of structure remains the same, however.

The Genetic Control of Shape

The various cell types characterizing a higher organism do not occur at random throughout the body. A higher organism has shape. In many instances shape may arise epigenetically by cell movements (see Trinkaus, 102, for review). But in other cases it appears that a given type of differentiation is initiated in a nonrandom fashion in the absence of prior cell movements. This is probably true in the formation of scales on the wing of a butterfly, or of bristles and hairs covering the surface of a fly (see Ursprung, 104, for review). Are these patterns under genetic control?

They apparently are. Stern (98) has reported several mutant strains of *Drosophila* that are characterized by different arrangements of bristles— that is, pattern mutants. He has furthermore obtained some information on the nature of this genetic control (98; also Tokunaga, 101). The assumption underlying these experiments was that the nonrandom initiation of a given type of differentiation is preceded by a nonrandom distribution of physical or chemical factors, or both, which through interaction with the genome of a cell lead to the particular type of differentiation; in other words, a prepattern was postulated. The question, then, was this: Does the pattern mutation exert its effect by altering this prepattern, that is, the general organization of the tissue? In other words, are wild type and mutant different in their prepatterns? In an attempt to answer this question, the authors produced mosaic flies carrying both wild-type and pattern-mutant patches of tissue in various proportions. (In order to recognize cells derived from the pattern mutant in the mosaic, the mutant tissue was labeled with a genetic color marker.) To the surprise of the authors, any pattern trait examined thus far always formed autonomously in such mosaics, no matter what the proportion of wild-type or mutant tissues were. This strongly indicates that both wild type and mutant carry the same prepattern. The mutation apparently does not affect the over-all organization of the tissue, but the competence of the individual cell to respond to this overall organization with formation of the respective structure. A mutation in the DNA in this case can apparently lead to a pattern difference simply by acting on the individual cell. Shape, in this case, is under rather direct genetic control.

Preformed Structure in *Paramecium*

The question of whether all form originates with DNA is answered in the negative most impressively by Sonneborn's (94) work on ciliated protozoans. One of the most decisive observations will be described briefly. Singlet exconjugants of matings involving singlets and doublets in several cases bore a very conspicuous extra piece of the doublet's paroral cortex. The doublet mate showed a corresponding nick. The extra piece on the singlet flattened out shortly, but the resulting organism remained clearly distinguishable from either normal singlets or normal doublets. When this new organism divided, one of the fission products gave rise to a clone of cells all of which were clearly different from normal singlets or doublets. In particular, this new type has a secondary oral segment, which however, is not 180° apart from the primary oral segments as in normal doublets, but only about 90°. Thus a piece of paroral cortex of one cell, incorporated onto the surface of another cell, has led to the development of an additional oral segment on the host and, more importantly, to the inheritance of this new trait. This formation of a new clone occurred in the absence of any information transfer of nuclear or endoplasmic nature. The cortical structure itself is decisive for morphogenesis and inheritance in this case. Such a cortical structure, or the information leading to its formation, may be termed a cytoplasmic gene. In a recent analysis of a different trait of *Paramecium*, the cytoplasmic genes have been found to represent stable m-RNA molecules (metagons) that replicate (Gibson and Sonneborn, 38a).

Our question, then, again is not an "either-or" question. Clearly, primary amino acid composition can account for much structure of higher order. But clearly also, morphogenetic transformations and their inheritance can be achieved in the absence of immediate nuclear information transfer.

It may be that preformed structure in the sense just described is unique for protozoans. But in a different sense, preformed structure certainly plays a key role in the genetic control of shape, for an egg cell is exposed to preformed structures of the maternal organism and genes have to face nonrandomly arranged molecules, particles, and organelles in the cell. Thus in a developing organism, autonomous formation of structures of higher order may often not be an issue at all, because the timing of developmental processes may make preformed structures available to guide direct and more remote gene products into the proper positions and arrangements. Subsequent chapters in this book, especially the one by Trinkaus (102), will deal more with these questions conventionally earmarked "embryological."

Summary

Classical developmental genetics has established, beyond doubt, that both cellular differentiation and development of higher organisms are under genetic control. A single primary genetic alteration is amplified and diversified in its effects through the pathways of subsequent development.

In the present article, the current concept of gene action as derived from studies in microbial systems is briefly described. It is then postulated that the same genetic mechanisms may operate in higher organisms, and evidence is cited supporting the notion of universality of the pathways transcribing and translating genetic information in living matter.

Particular emphasis is placed on the problem of the regulation of gene function during development, since it is believed that an understanding of genetic regulatory mechanisms would provide adequate explanations of cellular differentiation. The stability of the differentiated state is discussed.

Finally, the question whether information encoded in DNA is sufficient to account for higher orders of organization—that is, shape, is discussed.

References

1. Allfrey, V. G., and A. E. Mirsky, "Evidence for the Complete DNA-Dependence of RNA Synthesis in Isolated Thymus Nuclei," *Proc. Natl. Acad. Sci. U.S.* 48:1590–1596 (1962).

2. ——, and ——, "Mechanisms of Synthesis and Control of Protein and Ribonucleic Acid Synthesis in the Cell Nucleus," *Cold Spring Harbor Symp. Quant. Biol.* 28:247–263 (1963).

3. ——, R. Faulkner, and A. E. Mirsky, "Acetylation and Methylation of Histones and Their Possible Role in the Regulation of RNA Synthesis," *Proc. Natl. Acad. Sci. U.S.* 51:786–794 (1964).

4. Alston, R. E., and C. W. Hagen, "Chemical Aspects of the Inheritance of Flower Color in *Impatiens balsamina*," *Genetics* 43:35–47 (1958).

5. Ames, B. N., and P. E. Hartman, "The Histidine Operon," *Cold Spring Harbor Symp. Quant. Biol.* 28:349–356 (1963).

6. ——, and R. G. Martin, "Biochemical Aspects of Genetics: the Operon," *Ann. Rev. Biochem.* 33:235–258 (1964).

7. Anfinsen, C. B., "On the Possibility of Predicting Tertiary Structure from Primary Sequence," *New Perspectives in Biology*, M. Sela, ed. Amsterdam: Elsevier, pp. 42–50 (1964).

8. Attardi, G., S. Naono, J. Rouviere, F. Jacob, and F. Gros, "Production of Messenger RNA and Regulation of Protein Synthesis," *Cold Spring Harbor Symp. Quant. Biol.* 28:363–372.

8a. Baker, W. K., "Genetic Control of Pigment Differentiation in Somatic Cells," *Am. Zoologist* 3:57–69 (1963).

9. Bautz, E. F. K., and B. D. Hall, "The Isolation of T₄-Specific RNA on a DNA-Cellulose Column," *Proc. Natl. Acad. Sci. U.S.* 48:400–408 (1962).

10. Beadle, G. W., "Biochemical Genetics," *Chem. Rev.* 37:15–96 (1945).

11. Becker, H. J., "Die genetischen Grundlagen der Zelldifferenzierung," *Naturwissenschaften* 51:205–211, 230–35 (1964).

12. Beer, M., "Electron Microscopy of Unbroken DNA Molecules," *J. Mol. Biol.* 3:263–266 (1961).

13. Beermann, W., "Ein Balbiani-Ring als Locus einer Speicheldruesen-Mutation," *Chromosoma* 12:1–25 (1961).

14. ——, "Control of Differentiation at the Chromosomal Level," *J. Exptl. Zool.* 157:49–62 (1964).

15. Berg, P., and E. T. Ofengand, "An Enzymatic Mechanism for Linking Amino Acids to RNA," *Proc. Natl. Acad. Sci. U.S.* 44:78–ff. (1958).

16. Bloch, D. P., "Genetic Implication of Histone Differentiation," *The Nucleohistones*, D. Bonner and P.O.P. Ts'o, eds. San Francisco: Holden-Day, pp. 335–342 (1964).

17. Bodenstein, D., "Humoral Dependence of Growth and Differentiation in Insects," *Recent Advan. Invertebrate Physiol. Symp.* 1955:197–211 (1956).

18. Bonner, J., R. C. Huang, and Ray V. Gilden, "Chromosomally Directed Protein Synthesis," *Proc. Natl. Acad. Sci. U.S.* 50:893–900 (1963).

19. ——, and P.O.P. Ts'o, eds. *The Nucleohistones*, San Francisco: Holden-Day (1964).

20. Boyer, J. H., D. C. Fainer, and E. J. Watson-Williams, "Lactate Dehydrogenase Variant from Human Blood: Evidence for Molecular Subunits," *Science* 141:642–643 (1963).

21. Brachet, J., "The Biological Role of Pentose Nucleic Acids," *The Nucleic Acids*, E. Chargaff and J. N. Davidson, eds. New York: Academic Press, vol. II, pp. 476–519 (1955).

22. Braun, A. C., "A Demonstration of the Recovery of the Crown-Gall Tumor Cell with the Use of Complex Tumors of Single-Cell Origin," *Proc. Natl. Acad. Sci. U.S.* 45:932–938 (1959).

23. Brenner, S., F. Jacob, and M. Meselson, "An Unstable Intermediate Carrying Information from Genes to Ribosomes for Protein Synthesis," *Nature* 190:576 (1961).

24. Briggs, R., and T. J. King, "Nuclear Transplantation Studies on the Early Gastrula (*Rana pipiens*). I. Nuclei of Presumptive Endoderm," *Develop. Biol.* 2:252–270 (1960).

24a. Brink, R. A., "Genetic Repression of R Action in Maize," *The Role of Chromosomes in Development*, M. Locke, ed. New York: Academic Press, pp. 183–230 (1964).

25. Brown, D. D., "RNA Synthesis during Amphibian Development," *J. Exptl. Zool.* 157:101–114 (1964).

26. ——, and J. B. Gurdon, "Absence of Ribosomal RNA Synthesis in the Anucleolate Mutant of *Xenopus laevis*," *Proc. Natl. Acad. Sci. U.S.* 51:139–146 (1964).

27. Busch, H., W. J. Steele, L. S. Hnilica, C. W. Taylor, and H. Marioglu, "Biochemistry of Histones and the Cell Cycle," *J. Cellular Comp. Physiol.* 62, Suppl. 1:95–110 (1963).

28. Callan, H. G., "The Nature of Lampbrush Chromosomes," *Intern. Rev. Cytol.* 15:1–34, New York: Academic Press (1963).

29. Caspersson, T. O., *Cell Growth and Cell Function*, New York: Norton (1950).

30. Champe, S. P., and S. Benzer, "Reversal of Mutant Phenotypes by 5-Fluorouracil: An Approach to Nucleotide Sequences in Messenger RNA," *Proc. Natl. Acad. Sci. U.S.* 48:532–546 (1962).

31. Chapeville, F., F. Lipman, G. von Ehrenstein, B. Weisblum, W. J. Ray, and S. Benzer, "On the Role of Soluble Ribonucleic Acid in Coding for Amino Acids," *Proc. Natl. Acad. Sci. U.S.* 48: 1086–ff. (1962).

32. Chipchase, M. I. H., and M. L. Birnstiel, "Synthesis of Transfer RNA by Isolated Nuclei," *Proc. Natl. Acad. Sci. U.S.* 49:692–699 (1963).

33. Clever, U., "Genaktivitaeten in den Riesenchromosomen von *Chironomus tentans* und ihre Beziehungen zur Entwicklung. II. Das Verhalten der Puffs waehrend des letzten Larvenstadiums und der Puppenhaeutung," *Chromosoma* 13:385–436 (1962).

34. ——, "Puffing in Giant Chromosomes of Diptera and Mechanism of Its Control," *The Nucleohistones*, J. Bonner and P.O.P. Ts'o, eds. San Francisco: Holden-Day, pp. 317–334 (1964).

35. Dintzis, H., "Assembly of the Peptide Chains of Hemoglobin," *Proc. Natl. Acad. Sci. U.S.* 47:247–261 (1961).

36. Edström, J. E., and W. Beermann, "The Base Composition of Nucleic Acids in Chromosomes, Puffs, Nucleoli, and Cytoplasm of *Chironomus* Salivary Gland Cells," *J. Cell Biol.* 14:371–380 (1962).

37. von Ehrenstein, G., B. Weisblum, and S. Benzer, "The Function of S-RNA as Amino-Acid Adaptor in the Synthesis of Hemoglobin," *Proc. Natl. Acad. Sci. U.S.* 49:669–675 (1963).

38. Gall, J. G., "Chromosomes and Cytodifferentiation," *Cytodifferentiation and Macromolecular Synthesis*, M. Locke, ed. New York: Academic Press, pp. 119–143 (1963).

38a. Gibson, Ian, and T. M. Sonneborn, "Is the Metagon an m-RNA in *Paramecium* and a Virus in *Didinium*?" *Proc. Natl. Acad. Sci. U.S.* 52:869–875 (1964).

39. Gluecksohn-Schoenheimer, S., "The Embryonic Development of Mutants of the *Sd* Strain in Mice," *Genetics* 30:29–38 (1945).

40. Goldstein, L., "RNA and Protein in Nucleocytoplasmic Interactions," *Cell*

Growth and Cell Division, R. J. C. Harris, ed. New York: Academic Press, pp. 129–151 (1963).

41. Grobstein, C., "Cytodifferentiation and Macromolecular Synthesis," *Cytodifferentiation and Macromolecular Synthesis*, M. Locke, ed. New York: Academic Press, pp. 1–14 (1963).

42. Gross, P. R., "The Immediacy of Genomic Control during Early Development," *J. Exptl. Zool.* 157:21–38 (1964).

43. Grüneberg, H., *The Genetics of the Mouse*, Cambridge: Cambridge University Press (1943).

44. ——, "Developmental Genetics in the Mouse," *J. Cellular Comp. Physiol.* 56, Suppl. 1:49–60 (1960).

45. Guaita, G.v., "Versuche mit Kreuzungen von verschiedenen Rassen der Hausmaus," *Ber. Nat. Ges. Freib.* 10:317–332 (1898).

46. Gurdon, J. B., "Nuclear Transplantation in Amphibia and the Importance of Stable Nuclear Changes in Promoting Cellular Differentiation," *Quart. Rev. Biol.* 38:54–78 (1963).

47. Hadorn, E., *Developmental Genetics and Lethal Factors*. New York: Wiley (1961).

48. ——, "Bedeutungseigene und bedeutungsfrende Entwicklungsleistungen proliferierender Primordien von *Drosophila* nach Dauerkultur in vivo," *Rev. Suisse Zool.* 71:99–115 (1964).

49. Hall, B. D., and S. Spiegelman, "Sequence Complementation of T_2 DNA and T_2-Specific RNA," *Proc. Natl. Acad. Sci. U.S.* 47:137–146 (1961).

50. Hartman, P. E., and S. Suskind, *Gene Action*. Englewood Cliffs, N.J.: Prentice-Hall (1965).

51. Hayashi, M., M. N. Hayashi, and S. Spiegelman, "Restriction of *in vivo* Genetic Transcription to One of the Complementary Strands of DNA," *Proc. Natl. Acad. Sci. U.S.* 50:664–672 (1963).

52. ——, S. Spiegelman, N. C. Franklin, and S. E. Luria, "Separation of the RNA Message Transcribed in Response to a Specific Inducer," *Proc. Natl. Acad. Sci. U.S.* 49:729–736 (1963).

53. Hoagland, M. B., M. L. Stephenson, J. F. Scott, R. J. Hecht and P. Zamecnik, "A Soluble Ribonucleic Acid Intermediate in Protein Synthesis," *J. Biol. Chem.* 231:241–257 (1958).

54. Holtzer, H., J. Abbot, J. Lash, and S. Holtzer, "The Loss of Phenotypic Traits by Differentiated Cells *in vitro*. I. Dedifferentiation of Cartilage Cells," *Proc. Natl. Acad. Sci. U.S.* 46:1533–1542 (1960).

55. Hoyer, B. H., B. J. McCarthy, and E. T. Bolton, "A Molecular Approach to Systematics in Higher Organisms," *Science* 144:959–967 (1964).

56. Huang, R. C., N. Maheshwari, and J. Bonner, "Enzymatic Synthesis of RNA," *Biochem. Biophys. Res. Comm.* 3:689–694 (1960).

57. Hurwitz, J., J. J. Furth, M. Anders, P. J. Oritz, and J. T. August, "The Enzymatic Incorporation of Ribonucleotides into RNA and the Role of DNA. *Cold Spring Harbor Symp. Quant. Biol.* 26:91–100 (1961).

58. Ingram, V. M., *The Hemoglobins in Genetics and Evolution*. New York: Columbia University Press (1963).

59. Jacob, F., and J. Monod, "Genetic Regulatory Mechanisms in the Synthesis of Proteins," *J. Mol. Biol.* 3:318–356 (1961).

60. ——, and ——, "Genetic Repression, Allosteric Inhibition, and Cellular Differentiation," *Cytodifferentiation and Macromolecular Synthesis*, M. Locke, ed. New York, Academic Press, pp. 30–57 (1963).

61. Konigsberg, I. R., "Clonal Analysis of Myogenesis," *Science* 140:1273–1284 (1963).

62. Kornberg, A., "Biologic Synthesis of Deoxyribonucleic Acid," *Science* 131:1503–ff. (1960).

63. Kroeger, H., "Chemical Nature of the System Controlling Gene Activities in Insect Cells," *Nature* 200:1234–1235 (1963).

64. ——, "Zellphysiologische Mechanismen bei der Regulation von Genaktivitaeten in den Riesenchromosomen von *Chironomus thummi*," *Chromosoma* 15:36–70 (1964).

65. Laufer, H., Y. Nakase, and J. Vanderberg, "Developmental Studies on the Dipteran Salivary Gland. I. The Effect of Actinomycin-D on Larval Development, Enzyme Activity, and Chromosomal Differentiation in *Chironomus thummi*," *Develop. Biol.* 9:367–384 (1964).

66. Lengyel, P., J. F. Speyer, and S. Ochoa,

"Synthetic Polynucleotides and the Genetic Code. *Proc. Natl. Acad. Sci. U.S.* 47:1936–1942 (1961).

67. Lewis, E. B., "Genetic Control and Regulation of Developmental Pathways," *The Role of Chromosomes in Development*, M. Locke, ed. New York: Academic Press, pp. 231–252 (1964).

68. Littlefield, J. W., E. B. Keller, G. Gross, and P. Zamecnik, "Studies on Cytoplasmic Ribonucleoprotein Particles from the Liver of the Rat," *J. Biol. Chem.* 217:111–124 (1955).

69. Luck, D. J. L., and E. Reich, "DNA in Mitochondria of *Neurospora crassa*," *Proc. Natl. Acad. Sci. U.S.* 52:931–ff. (1964).

69a. Lyon, M. F., "Sex Chromatin and Gene Action in the Mammalian X-chromosome," *Am. J. Human Genet.* 14:135–148 (1962).

70. Markert, C. L., "Epigenetic Control of Specific Protein Synthesis in Differentiating Cells," *Cytodifferentiation and Macromolecular Synthesis*, M. Locke, ed. New York: Academic Press pp. 67–81 (1963).

71. ———, "Lactate Dehydrogenase Isozymes: Dissociation and Recombination of Subunits," *Science* 140:1329–1330 (1963).

72. ———, "Cellular Differentiation — An Expression of Differential Gene Function," *Second Intern. Conf. Congenital Malformations*. New York: International Medical Congress, Ltd. pp. 163–174 (1964).

73. ———, and H. Ursprung, "The Ontogeny of Isozyme Patterns of Lactate Dehydrogenase in the Mouse," *Develop. Biol.* 5:363–381 (1962).

74. ———, and ———, "Production of Replicable Persistent Changes in Zygote Chromosomes of *Rana pipiens* by Injected Proteins from Adult Liver Nuclei," *Develop. Biol.* 7:560–577 (1963).

75. Martin, R. G., "The One Operon–One Messenger Theory," *Cold Spring Harbor Symp. Quant. Biol.* 28:357–361 (1963).

76. McAuslan, B. R., "The Induction and Repression of Thymidine Kinase in the Poxvirus-Infected HeLa Cell," *Virology* 21:383–389 (1963).

77. McCarthy, B. J., and B. H. Hoyer, "Identity of DNA and Diversity of Messenger RNA Molecules in Normal Mouse Tissues," *Proc. Natl. Acad. Sci. U.S.* 52:915–922 (1964).

78. McClintock, B., "Some Parallels between Gene Control Systems in Maize and in Bacteria," *Am. Naturalist* 95:265–277 (1961).

79. Mirsky, A. E., and S. Osawa, "The Interphase Nucleus," *The Cell*. New York: Academic Press, vol. 2, pp. 677–770 (1961).

80. Moore, J. A., "Nuclear Transplantation and Problems of Specificity in Developing Embryos," *J. Cellular Comp. Physiol.* 60, Suppl. 1:19–34 (1962).

81. Moudrianakis, E. N., and M. Beer, "Base Sequence Determination in Nucleic Acids with the Electron Microscope. III Chemistry and Microscopy of Guanine Labeled DNA," *Proc. Natl. Acad. U.S.* 53:564–571 (1965).

82. Nass, M. M. K., and S. Nass, "Intramitochondrial Fibers with DNA Characteristics. I. Fixation and Electron Staining Reactions," *J. Cell Biol.* 19:593–611 (1963).

83. Nathans, D., G. Notari, J. H. Schwartz, and N. D. Zinder, "Biosynthesis of the Coat Protein of Coliphage F₂ by *E. coli* Extracts," *Proc. Natl. Acad. Sci. U.S.* 48:1424–1431 (1962).

84. Nemer, M., "Old and New RNA in the Embryogenesis of the Purple Sea Urchin," *Proc. Natl. Acad. Sci. U.S.* 50:230–235 (1963).

85. Nirenberg, M. W., and J. H. Matthaei, "The Dependence of Cell-Free Protein Synthesis in *Escherichia coli* upon Naturally Occurring or Synthetic Polyribonucleotides," *Proc. Natl. Acad. Sci. U.S.* 47:1588–ff. (1961).

86. ———, and P. Leder, "RNA Codewords and Protein Synthesis," *Science* 145:1399–1407 (1964).

87. Nomura, M., B. D. Hall, and S. Spiegelman, "Characterization of RNA Synthesized in *Escherichia coli* after Bacteriophage T₂ Infection," *J. Mol. Biol.* 2:306–326 (1960).

88. Pardee, A., "Nucleic Acid Precursors and Protein Synthesis," *Proc. Natl. Acad. Sci. U.S.* 40:263–ff. (1954).

89. Pelling, C., "Ribonukleinsaeuresynthese der Riesenchromosomen. Autoradiographische Untersuchungen an *Chironomus tentans*," *Chromosoma* 15:71–122 (1964).

90. Reich, E., R. M. Franklin, A. J. Shatkin, and E. L. Tatum, "Action of Actinomycin-D on Animal Cells and Viruses," *Proc. Natl. Acad. Sci. U.S.* 48:1238–1245 (1962).

91. Rich, A., J. R. Warner, and H. M. Goodman, "The Structure and Function of Polyribosomes," *Cold Spring Harbor Symp. Quant. Biol.* 28:269–285 (1963).

91a. Schultz, J. "Variegation in *Drosophila* and the Inert Chromosome Regions," *Proc. Natl. Acad. Sci. U.S.* 22:27–33 (1936).

91b. Schimke, R. T., E. W. Sweeney, and C. M. Berlin, "The Role of Synthesis and Degradation in the Control of Rat Liver Tryptophan Pyrrolase," *J. Biol. Chem.* 240:322–331 (1965).

92. Shaw, C. R., and E. Barto, "Genetic Evidence for the Subunit Structure of Lactate Dehydrogenase Isozymes," *Proc. Natl. Acad. Sci. U.S.* 50:211–214 (1963).

93. Smith, Ph. E., and E. C. Macdowell, "An Hereditary Anterior-Pituitary Deficiency in the Mouse," *Anat. Record* 46:249–257 (1930).

94. Sonneborn, T. M., "Does Preformed Cell Structure Play an Essential Role in Cell Hereditary?" *The Nature of Biological Diversity*, J. M. Allen, ed. New York: McGraw-Hill, pp. 165–219 (1963).

95. Stahl, F. W., *The Mechanics of Inheritance*. Englewood Cliffs, N.J.: Prentice-Hall (1964).

96. Steinberg, M. S., "The Problem of Adhesive Selectivity in Cellular Interactions," *Cellular Membranes in Development*, M. Locke, ed. New York: Academic Press, pp. 321–366 (1964).

97. Stent, G. S., "The Operon: On Its Third Anniversary," *Science* 144:816–820 (1964).

98. Stern, C., "Two or Three Bristles," *Am. Scientist* 42:213–47 (1954).

99. Swift, H., "The Histones of Polytene Chromosomes," *The Nucleohistones*, J. Bonner and P.O.P. Ts'o, eds. San Francisco: Holden-Day pp. 169–181 (1964).

100. Thompson, T. E., "The Properties of Bimolecular Phospholipid Membranes," *Cellular Membranes in Development*, M. Locke, ed. New York: Academic Press, pp. 85–96 (1964).

101. Tokunaga, C., "The Differentiation of a Secondary Sex Comb under the Influence of the Gene Engrailed in *Drosophila melanogaster*," *Genetics* 46:157–176 (1961).

102. Trinkaus, J. P., *Organogenesis*, DeHaan and Ursprung, eds. New York: Holt, Rinehart and Winston, Chapter 3 (1965).

103. Tyler, A., "The Manipulation of Macromolecular Substances during Fertilization and Early Development of Animal Eggs," *Am. Zool.* 3:109–126 (1963).

104. Ursprung, H., "Development and Genetics of Patterns," *Am. Zoologist* 3:71–86 (1963).

105. ——, "Genetic Control of Differentiation in Higher Organisms," *Federation Proc.* 23:990–993 (1964).

106. ——, "Kernproteine und Genfunktion," *Naturwissenschaften*. In press (1965).

107. Volkin, E., "Biosynthesis of RNA in Relation to Genetic Coding Problems," *Mol. Genet.*, J. H. Tayler, ed. New York: Academic Press, pp. 271–289 (1963).

108. ——, and L. Astrachan, "Phosphorus Incorporation in *Escherichia coli* Ribonucleic Acid after Infection with Bacteriophage T_2," *Virology* 2:149–161 (1956).

109. Waddington, C. H., *Organizers and Genes*, Cambridge, Cambridge University Press (1947).

110. ——, *The Strategy of the Genes*, London: Allen and Unwin (1957).

111. Weiss, S. B., and T. Nakamoto, "On the Participation of DNA in RNA Synthesis," *Proc. Natl. Acad. Sci. U.S.* 47:694–697 (1961).

112. Willier, B. H., P. Weiss, and V. Hamburger, *Analysis of Development*, Philadelphia: Saunders (1955).

113. Wilt, F., "Ribonucleic Acid Synthesis during Sea Urchin Embryogenesis," *Develop. Biol.* 9:299–313 (1964).

114. Yankofsky, S. A., and S. Spiegelman, "The Identification of the Ribosomal RNA Cistron by Sequence Complementarity II. Saturation of and Competitive Interaction at the RNA Cistron," *Proc. Natl. Acad. Sci. U.S.* 48:1466–1472 (1962).

115. Yarmolinsky, M. B., and C. L. de la Haba, "Inhibition by Puromycin of Amino Acid Incorporation into Protein," *Proc. Natl. Acad. Sci. U.S.* 45:1721–1729 (1959).

116. Ziegler, Irmgard, "Genetic Aspects of Ommochrome and Pterin Pigments," *Advan. Genet.* 10:349–403 (1961).

2

Intercellular Adhesion and Histogenesis

E. H. MERCER*

John Curtin School of Medical Research
Australian National University
Canberra, Australia

The molecular embryologist has before him two problems: (1) As a *biochemist* he is concerned with cellular differentiation; that is, how it comes about that cells, similarly endowed genetically, can make many different products in accordance with an inherited plan. We have a good working hypothesis of how this happens (Ursprung, Chapter 1). (2) As a *morphologist* he is concerned with what role the products of cells play in tissue construction. To determine how a material is made, is one thing, how it is used in construction, another, and to find out how this construction affects all the cells involved is still a third.

Whatever the detailed internal biochemical circuitry, we would all agree that the signals which operate the switches must be either molecules emitted by other cells or the physical contact of one cell or structural cell product with another (Abercrombie, 1; Grobstein, 13, 14; Waddington, 34;

Wessels, 40). It is the step-by-step construction of the organism that creates, step-by-step, the special environments that induce and maintain differentiation. These macromolecular and supermolecular events can only be unraveled by examining the organism in detail.

Obviously we lack a molecule-by-molecule description of the development of any organism and are likely to lack it for some time. Nevertheless, we possess today methods of microscopy that promise to give us precisely this sort of information about structural materials. When we consider the labor involved in elucidating the near-molecular structure of even a small and simple developing system by microscopy, it is clear that progress can only be made by the selection of special and limited problems whose solution will clarify a wider issue. It is for this reason that I, with various colleagues, have for some years studied the evidence for the effects of intercellular adhesion in histogenesis by means of electronmicroscopy.

Tissues may be divided into cellular tissues in which the cells are effec-

* The author wishes to acknowledge that much of the work described here was carried out in collaboration with various colleagues, including L. Wolpert, G. C. Easty, and M. S. C. Birbeck.

29

tively in close, adhesive contact over most of their surfaces and the amount of intercellular space is very small, and open or paucicellular tissues in which the intercellular volume predominates, cells are rare, and intercellular secretions are conspicuous. Epithelium is a typical cellular tissue, and the enclosure of volumes by the growth of epithelia is one of the commonest maneuvers in embryogenesis.

In vertebrates, typically, the cellular epi- or endothelium is backed by a deposit of collagen fibrils contributed by mesodermal fibrocytes. There are many experiments which demonstrate cooperation between the two cell systems (epidermal and mesodermal) in the formation of this complex and it is with this problem that we are partly concerned. A brilliant light has been cast on the spontaneous structure-forming properties of the isolated intercellular substance, collagen, by the work of Schmitt (30), Hodge (17), and Gross (15, 16) to mention only a few names. Furthermore, something is known about the formation of collagen in the organism and of the manner in which it enters into the construction of growing tissues. Among the most valuable contributions in this field, those of Weiss and Ferris (35, 36), Porter (28), Kemp (20), Gross (15, 16), Jackson (19), Parakkal and Matoltsy (23), Chapman and Dawson (3), Leeson and Threadgold (21), and Edds and Sweeny 6–7), have been concerned with the formation of the strikingly regular orthogonal meshwork of collagen fibrils beneath the epidermis of larval amphibians. The important studies (mentioned earlier) of the spontaneous growth of collagen fibrils in vitro have established that, once synthesized and secreted in the appropri-

ate conditions, the soluble precursor of collagen (tropocollagen) is capable of forming the filamentous structures observed. The next problem is to discover the factors which in vivo cause the fibrils to be deposited beneath the epidermis and to assume their characteristic orthogonal arrangement. I cannot add much to what these investigators have had to say, but I believe that one approach to the solution is to consider the constructional events immediately preceding the deposition of the first collagen — that is, the events leading to the formation of the cellular epithelium, the foundation on which the collagen is laid. Therefore, we turn to examine the somewhat earlier event: the establishment of a coherent cellular layer, which forms the substratum for the subsequent deposition of the collagen. In cellular tissues the cell membranes adhere, for without this the tissues would fall apart; thus we are primarily concerned with the nature and morphology of cell contacts, and with their ontogeny.

The classical works of Holtfreter (18, 18a, 32) in this field are still the most stimulating; there are excellent reviews by Weiss (37, 38, 39) and DeHaan (5) and a series of useful papers in the volume *Cell Movement and Cell Contact* published as a supplement to *Experimental Cell Research* (4, 11).

I shall illustrate my remarks with observations based on three different developing systems which, with various colleagues (M. S. C. Birbeck, L. Wolpert, and G. E. Easty, 2, 24, 41), I have been studying for some years. These are the epidermis of the larval amphibian tail, the ectoderm of sea urchin blastula and gastrula, and the mammalian hair follicle. The first two are embryonic systems. The third, a constantly growing tissue, has conserved an embryonic character. In each of these systems we have observed morphological changes due to intercellular adhesion, which appear to be initiated by the appearance of intercellular adhesive substances.

Amphibian Tadpole Tail (Xenopus *and* Rana)

The epidermis of the tail of larval amphibians has proved an ideal material for this type of study (Shumway, 31). The organisms are small and easy to cultivate; the structures are relatively simple and there is little problem in establishing the stages of development. The histology and fine structure of the tissues has been described by several authors (Chapman and Dawson, 3; DeHaan, 5; Edds, 6, 7; Leeson and Threadgold, 21; Matoltsy and Parakkal, 23; Porter, 28; Rosin, 29; Weiss and Ferris, 35, 36). Figure 2.1 will recall the major features of its histology.

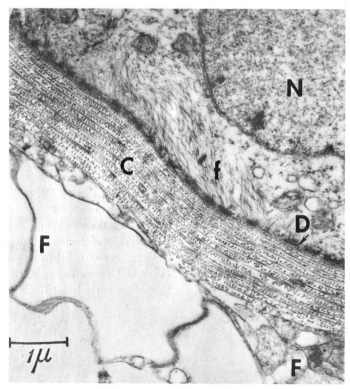

Fig. 2.1 Portion of a basal layer cell of tail epidermis of a *Rana* tadpole soon after hatching. N, nucleus; F, fibrocytes in dermis with long processes extending to the base of the collagen lamellae, C; f, prekeratin filaments in basal layer cells; D, half-desmosomes associated with plasma membrane of basal layer cell. Fixation O_sO_4; embedding, Araldite; stain, phosphotungstic acid (PTA). In all micrographs magnification is indicated by a line of marked length.

Here the problem is posed with diagrammatic simplicity. The epidermis consists of two layers of cells. The outer layer is mostly mucin-secreting cells, with lesser numbers of ciliated cells. The inner layer of cells (germinal) is less clearly differentiated. Beneath them the dermal collagen is disposed in strikingly regular lamellae and in each lamella the individual collagen fibrils are arranged parallel and at right angles to those of adjacent lamellae (28, 35, 36). Immediately beneath the layers of collagen one encounters isolated fibrocytes. This epidermal-dermal complex is established over most of the body surface before hatching.

The appearance of ectoderm and its development into a typical epithelium (epidermis) could not be followed in the amphibian from the egg onward. (However, we have done this in the sea urchin. The amphibian egg is so loaded with yolk that a variety of practical difficulties arose. It was found convenient, therefore, to take advantage of the fact that immediately after hatching, the epidermis at the tip of the tail lags behind the rest of the surface in its development. In this site (Figs. 2.2 and 2.3) the epithelium is still a single layer, there is no basement membrane and no collagen. Immediately anterior to the tip, stages

leading to the normal condition are found. This terminally situated tissue readily separates into individual cells when the tail is cut off and immersed in calcium-free solutions.

In this material, three steps in the establishment of the dermoepidermal complex can be distinguished and are illustrated in the electronmicrographs shown in Figures 2.1, 2.4–2.7.

STEP 1. The single layer of ectodermal cells is held together only by the cohesion of small areas of cell membrane at the outer edges of the cells (Fig. 2.2,A and Fig. 2.4). Elsewhere (Fig. 2.2,B) the cell surfaces are smoothly but irregularly convoluted, as they often are in isolated cells. In life these surfaces are actively in movement. The nature of the limited contacts between the cells at their exposed faces should be noted. The two participating plasma membranes are smooth and parallel over a limited area and are located 100–200 A apart. There are as yet no special adhesive devices.

The inner faces of the cells facing the narrow cavity (Fig. 2.4,V), which is continuous with the mesodermal space further along the tail, are rounded and free of basement membrane. The condition of the ectoderm cells at this point may be likened to that of an early blastula.

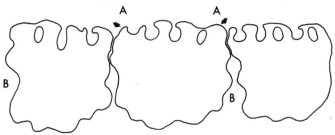

Fig. 2.2 Epithelial cells of tip of tail of amphibian larva showing localized adhesions, A, at external edges of cells, which form a single layer at this stage. The surfaces of the cells are covered with mucin pockets. Nonadhesive convoluted membranes are shown at B.

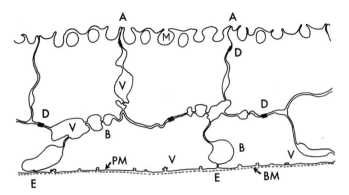

Fig. 2.3 The epithelium at a later stage than that in Fig. 2.2, showing two layers of cells and a basement membrane, BM. A, tight contact; D, desmosomes; V, intercellular cavities; E, contacts at inner surface of basal layer cells; PM, plasma membrane; B, nonadhesive cell membranes; M, mucin pocket.

Fig. 2.4 Cross section of a portion of one of the two layers of epithelial cells comprising the tip of the tail of a *Xenopus* tadpole immediately upon hatching. N, nucleus; PM, plasma membrane; O, external space; A (arrow), close contact of two cells at their outer edges; B, convoluted cell surfaces; V, intercellular gap; p, cell processes; W, phospholipid whorls; M, mitochondria. There is no collagen and no basement membrane. Fixation as in Fig. 2.1. No stain.

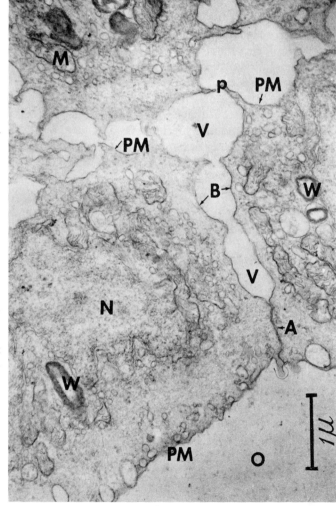

STEP 2. The epithelium consists of two layers of cells; the deposition of collagen has begun (Fig. 2.3). The cells have lost their rounded shape and in their intercellular relations resemble the more mature epithelium found elsewhere. Elaborate contacts have developed at the outer edges of the cells and the inner face of the cell sheet has become remarkably smooth and flat.

The specialized contacts at the external lips of the cells are of the type described by Farquar and Palade (9) in numerous epi- and endothelia. Proceeding from without, we note (Fig. 2.5) that at the point where the intercellular contact reaches the outer surface, the plasma membranes are raised to form small projections (or ridges in two dimensions). The intercellular space here is very narrow (100 A), as in Figure 2.5,A; the dense outer lines of the triple-layered surface membranes are effectively in contact, forming a five-layered complex. This structure Farquar and Palade refer to as a "tight contact" (9) and they marshal evidence to show that it is indeed "water-tight!" The implications of the establishment at this stage of a water-tight surface separating an inner from an outer space of the embryo are obvious. Further inward, the contact surfaces separate slightly (250A), grow denser, and become backed with an intercellular deposit to form one or more typical localized desmosomes (Fig. 2.5,D). It is believed that such deposits represent sites of enhanced mechanical cohesion (Fawcett, 10, 11; Weiss, 39). A dense material occupies the intercellular gap.

When a tail tip is cut off and immersed in Ca-free buffer the membranes separate in the reverse order, the tight contact persisting longest. The intercellular material covering the surface of the adhering cells is less evident after they separate.

The desmosomal area is followed by the type of intercellular contact most commonly observed in cellular tissues: the membranes run parallel, about 200 A apart. A further peculiarity of this region of contact is the irregular clusters and strings of dense, intracellular material seen in close proximity to the cell surfaces (Fig. 2.5,E). Beyond this point, the membranes may separate widely to give the large interconnected, intercellular cavities (V) which are characteristic of adult amphibian skin (Matoltsy and Parakkal, 23). These intercellular spaces are prominent between the cells of the two layers. They are frequently bridged by fingerlike projections of both surfaces which establish contact with the opposing cell face.

The superficial cells are differentiated as either mucinogenic cells, characterized by numerous pockets containing mucin, both open and closed, bordering the outer surface (Figs. 2.4, 2.5 and 2.6,M), ciliated cells, or more rarely, cells lacking either of these surface specializations. Cells of mixed characteristics occur and most contain small bundles of filaments of the prekeratin type.

The inner surfaces of the epithelium facing the inner cavity are quite smooth (Figs. 2.7–2.9), a surface clearly prepared to receive its carpet of collagen fibrils. In the stage illustrated, fibrils of the first lamella are already present in a somewhat irregular and loosely packed array. A diffuse surface, separated from the plasma membranes of the cells by a clear space (about 300–400 A), which we shall refer to as the

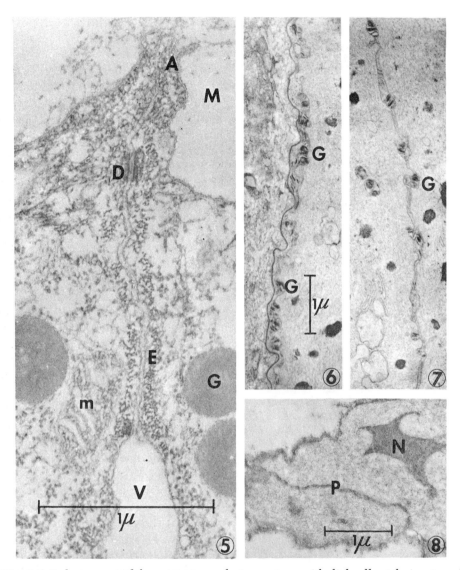

Fig. 2.5 Enlargement of the contact zone between two epithelial cells at their external edges. A, external end of contact showing narrow or tight contact; M, portion of mucin pocket; D, desmosome; E, extension of contact (normal type of intercellular gap). Note dense intracellular deposits on each side of contact; m, mitochondrion; G, pigment granule; V, widened intercellular gap. *Xenopus* tadpole tail as for Fig. 2.4. **Figs. 2.6 and 2.7** Two successive contacts between keratinocytes in marsupial skin (kangaroo) to show secretion of membrane-coating granules, G (see text). O_sO_4 fixation, Pb stain. (Micrograph by A. G. Matoltsy made at John Curtin School of Medical Research, Canberra, Australia.) **Fig. 2.8** Resistant membranes bonded by intercellular cement in hair cells after keratin has been removed (see references 23, 24) O_sO_4 fixation. Uranyl stain. N, nuclear remnant; P, membrane.

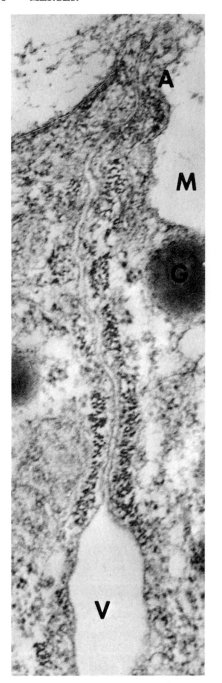

basement membrane (BM), is now present. Collagen fibrils are deposited outside this membrane.

There is a difference here between the condition of these primary deposits of collagen in my material and that described by earlier workers who report (and illustrate) that the first deposited fibrils are irregularly arranged in the plane parallel to the epidermal surface. My impression (see Fig. 2.5) is that after a very diffuse phase of indefinite fibrils (Figs. 2.10 and 2.11), most defined fibrils form a parallel array and lie on the head-tail axis (Figs. 2.12 and 2.13) from the very beginning. The packing of these fibrils is less dense than it becomes later.

The thin basement membrane appears in patches (Figs. 2.10 and 2.11) as indefinite particles or filaments, which condense to yield a distinct surface about 200 A from the plasma membrane of the basal layer cell. One of the several peculiar features of this membrane is that although it follows the broad contours of the cell membranes, it does not follow them in their finer detail. While the lower surfaces of the basal cells are flattened, they are marked by numerous small indentations (Figs. 2.12 and 2.13). Also, fairly often a wide gap may occur at a contact between one cell and the next. These small irregularities are not reflected in the contours of the basal membranes facing them.

Since there is little chemical knowledge of these basement membranes, which underlie the epithelia everywhere, we can only speculate about their structural peculiarities. I have elsewhere (24) offered the guess that this denser surface is a region of contact between some surface layer of the

Fig. 2.9 Specialized contact zones at edge of developing epithelium in *Xenopus* to display variety of appearance. Preparation and lettering as for Fig. 2.5.

epithelial cells and a product of meso-dermal provenance. Antigens to epi- and endothelial cells are recognized in the analogous membrane in kidney. An elaboration of the idea that these cavities are filled and distended by weak hydrophilic gels (Grobstein, 13, 14; Meyer, 25; Picken, 27) is that this surface is none other than the surface of such a gel outlined by a reaction precipitate formed with a product of the epidermal cells. An expanding gel could compress and flatten the faces of the basal layer cells, and distend the whole cavity, but owing to its finite yield point would be unable to flow into the smaller cavities of these sur-faces. This assumption would also ex-plain why evidence of membrane ad-hesion between cells facing the cavity is slight and why so many large vac-uoles persist. The expanding gel has simply pressed flat the irregular, partly adhering cells of the previous phase.

At this stage small segments of fibrils are also encountered in the mesoderm cavity and are apparently unrelated to the subepidermal deposits. Cells are present (presumably fibrocytes), char-acterized by the cytoplasmic pattern of ribosomes associated with mem-branes of the protein-secreting cell. These are, however, still rounded and lack the exaggeratedly extended forms found in areas of presumably vigorous collagen deposition in other portions of the skin; nor does one observe the mushroomlike processes extending from fibrocytes and applied to the underface of the collagen meshwork (Fig. 2.1).

STEP 3. A more massive deposi-tion of collagen follows, leading to the formation of as many as 20 plies. Weiss and Ferris (35, 36) Kemp (20), Edds and Sweeny (6, 7) and others (Gross 15; Leeson and Threadgold, 21; and Lowther, 22) have speculated on the mechanism controlling this deposi-tion. Two distinct concepts have been advanced. In one, the controlling fac-tor comes from the epidermis, in the other it is some intrinsic property of the collagen. Very little can be added to the comments of these authors, but it is worth mentioning that although the regularity of the orthogonal array is striking, it is not of a crystalline perfection. Neither the number of lamellae nor the number of fibrils composing each are fixed and constant. Any proposed mechanism must be flexible enough to allow for consider-able imperfection in detail. Dimen-sions, such as the spacing of the fibrils from each other (400–600 A), are not easy to measure with confidence after fixation; nevertheless it appears that this distance could be a constant of the system.

The first group of fibrils (Figs. 2.12 and 2.13) to be deposited are, on the whole, parallel to the major axis of the animal and to the flattened surface of the epithelium. These two major fea-tures then clearly impose an over-all orientation.

What is more interesting, is that the density of packing of the earlier crop of fibrils is far less than in the better-established areas. This is shown in cross sections of the fibrils, made at right angles to the head-tail axis in an area in which deposition has not pro-gressed very far (compare Figs. 2.14 and 2.1). The actual numbers of fibrils recorded in the figure need not be taken too seriously since there is con-siderable variation from site to site. However, a problem arises when we

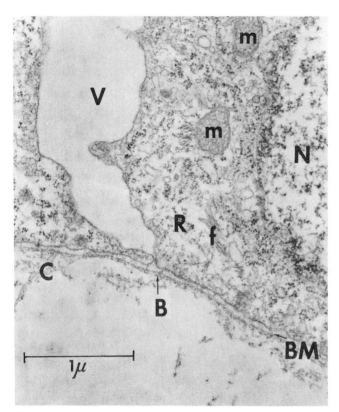

Fig. 2.10

Figs. 2.10, 2.11, 2.12, and 2.13 Details of basal layer cell contacts and early deposition of collagen fibrils. *Xenopus* tadpole immediately after hatching. Notice the flatness of the lower surfaces in contrast to the lateral surfaces of cells. BM, basement membrane; C, collagen; V, intercellular gaps; N, nucleus; B, intercellular contact. In Fig. 2.10 a large gap, V, and an imperfect contact, B, between cell processes is visible; the BM has formed, the collagen deposits are still diffuse. R, ribosomes; f, intracellular filaments. Fig. 2.11 represents a cell adjacent to that of Fig. 2.10 in which ribosome-covered mem-

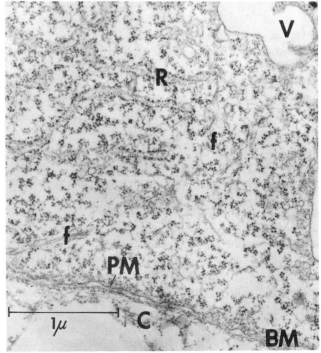

Fig. 2.11

38

branous sacs (containing fibrillar material), R, are visible. In Fig. 2.12 a cell from a more rostral position is shown. Collagen deposits beneath the basement membrane are well advanced. Notice loose packing of collagen and both transverse and longitudinal fibrils. Fig. 2.13 shows a site further anterior than that in Fig. 2.12. Here the irregularities in the cell membrane, v, are very obvious; fibrous strands seem to cross the space between the BM and PM. Note that the BM does not follow the small irregularities of the PM. U, nucleolus of N, nucleus. Pb stain.

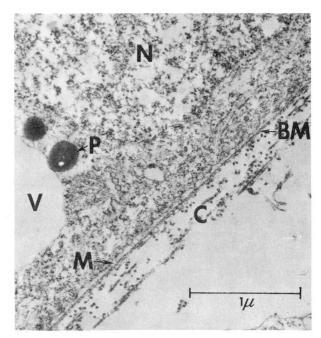

Fig. 2.12

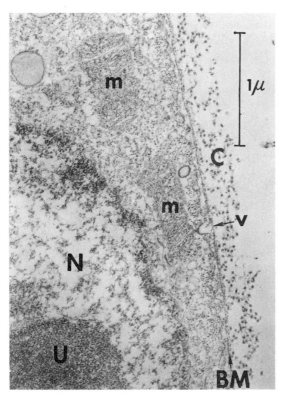

Fig. 2.13

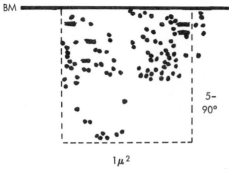

BM

5–90°

1μ²

Fig. 2.14 Tracing of sections of collagen fibrils packing against the basement membrane, BM, in an early stage of collagen deposition; fibrils running in head-tail direction shown in cross section; oblique sections of fibrils at right angles to AP axis.

ask where the later filaments are added. One might think they could be added either at the epidermal surface (under epidermal control) or on the dermal face of the growing formation (guided by existing deposits). In area A ($1\mu^2$) there are already enough fibrils to make about three layers running parallel to the head-tail axis, if packed down as in Figure 2.1. There are insufficient fibrils running in the direction at right angles to provide for the lamellae containing fibrils running this way in Figure 2.1. These could not be added later to either the inner or outer faces of the whole formation; the only conclusion seems to be that fibrils can grow within the interstices of the mesh wherever there happens to be an unoccupied niche. This could be possible if their immediate precursor were of molecular dimensions (for example, tropocollagen); it would hardly be possible if aggregation had proceeded very far. These fibrils also grow in diameter from about 100 A to 400 A. (cf. Fitton-Jackson, 19).

During the early phases of deposition (as in Figs. 2.10–2.12) fibrocytes are not found closely adjacent to the basement membrane, and occasional wispy filaments are encountered throughout the dermal volume immediately underlying the epidermis. As noted some years ago by Porter (28), many of the basal cells of the epidermis (Fig. 2.11) contain particle-covered membranes, the organelle of protein secretion. This feature, taken along with Hay and Revel's finding of proline incorporation in such cells (Chapter 13) could mean that they are at this time secreting collagen, another indication of an uncertain differentiation.

Somewhat later, fibrocytes gather more closely and project mushroom-shaped processes, which apply themselves closely against the collagen formation (Fig. 2.1). It has proved difficult in our pictures to recognize a plasma membrane in areas where these processes are spread out over the collagen mesh; one recalls the observation of Porter and Pappas (28a) that the process of fibril formation seems somehow closely involved with the membrane.

The Sea Urchin Blastula

A cohesive ball of cells, the blastula, is established before hatching. Here we are concerned with a layer only one cell thick, and the fibrous deposits on the inner face of these cells are less prominent than in the vertebrates. The effects of cellular adhesion are, however, very similar to those noted in amphibian tail (Wolpert and Mercer, 41).

Adhesion is apparent first at the outer edges of the contacting cells; division furrows run outward radially from the inner faces, and the cells, although cleaved, never quite lose contact at the outer edge. A special variety of adhesive device develops immediately inward from the outer edges of the zone of contact—the so-called "septate desmosome," a device common (as far as is known) in invertebrates (Wood, 43). The intercellular gap (200 A) is crossed by several (up to 12) septa (Figs. 2.15 and 2.16A)

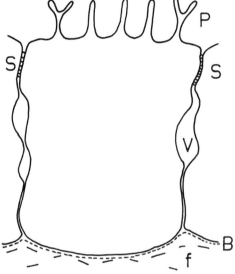

Fig. 2.15 Cell of late blastula of sea urchin showing position of septate desmosomes, S. P, microvilli derived from bursting of sacs containing fertilization granules; B, basement membrane; V, intercellular gaps; and f, filaments in blastocoel cavity.

which appear to run round the edges of the cells, sealing off the contact. There are no intracellular deposits backing this kind of attachment area (as in the vertebrate desmosome) and no intracellular fibrils converge on the site.

Although the cell membranes may lose close contact in places and separate more or less widely beyond the desmosome, close contact and parallelism is the common condition of the membranes, suggesting that the surfaces are somewhat adhesive. The inner surfaces of the cells facing the blastocoele smooth out and a rather flimsy deposition of fibrous material occurs as gastrulation approaches. Collagen occurs in the echinoderms, but these fibrils cannot be identified with certainty in our pictures. While the ontogeny of epithelial contacts has not been studied in detail in other embryos, similar specialized junctions have been noted in older chick embryos (Mercer, 24).

Morphogenesis in the Hair Follicle

The hair and its enclosing sheaths consist entirely of epidermal cells. A stream of cells, generated by division of germinal cells seated on the dermal papilla (Birbeck and Mercer, 2; 24), moves outward toward the surface, differentiating into six different cell types. These form as many concentric cylinders, each characterized by a distinctive cell shape and intercellular product. The fibrous cells of the cortex form the bulk of the hair shaft, and in nonmedullated hairs, occupy the center of the formation. Two cuticles, whose cells flatten and become imbricated as the cell stream narrows to form the neck of the follicle, closely invest the cortical shaft. These in turn are enclosed and closely packed by the remainder of the inner root sheath and an outer sheath.

All the cells in the lower part of the follicle appear identical; they are rounded, have irregularly convoluted surfaces, a large nucleus, and the simple undifferentiated cytoplasm typical of the germinal or embryonic cell (few mitochondria, few membranes,

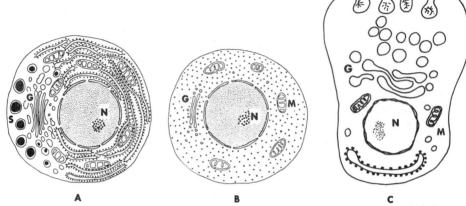

Fig. 2.16 Idealized types of cells engaged in synthesis. A. Protein secretory cell. Characteristic organelle, the particle-covered reticulum. N, nucleus; G, Golgi region of smooth membrane stacks and vacuoles; S, secretory granules. B. Protein-retaining cell. Free ribosomes and poorly developed Golgi cluster, G. M, mitochondrion. C. Polysaccharide (mucopolysaccharide) secreting cells. Small development of particle-covered membranes, elaborately developed Golgi cluster, G; m, pockets of secretion being discharged.

and large numbers of free ribosomes, Fig. 2.16). A little above the middle of the bulb, the presumptive cuticle cells become distinguishable by a change in shape and a closer knitting together of their membranes. Intercellular spaces are effaced, surface irregularities are smoothed out, and the cells assume a rectangular shape in longitudinal section. The plasma membranes run parallel in the familiar pattern of close contact, and some tightly contacted areas are seen. Henceforth these two layers of cells remain closely bonded and form a cylinder enclosing the presumptive cortical cells, which remain irregular in shape and between which intercellular gaps persist. Higher in the follicle, where the advancing cell mass narrows, the cells of the two cuticles tilt over together and assume their familiar imbricated condition. At this level, the cortical cells elongate and their surfaces become more closely applied to each other.

These morphological changes can be accounted for in part by assuming that intercellular adhesion first develops between the cuticle cells and knits them into a definite cylinder having characteristics similar to an epithelium. Within this cylindrical enclosure, the cortical cells persist for a time in a nonadhesive condition, in some way shielded from influences emanating from the surroundings. The morphogenetic effect arises from the differential timing of cellular adhesion —that is, from the fact that adhesion develops between one group of cells before it develops between others (Birbeck and Mercer, 2; Chapman and Dawson, 3).

The Cytology of Developing Cells

Certain intracellular patterns characteristic of distinct cellular activities are now well recognized from the fine structural studies of differentiated cells (Mercer, 24; Palay, 26). Which of these patterns is found in early developing epidermal cells? The superficial layer of cells contains more differentiated features than the inner layer. In addition to the ubiquitous nuclei and mitochondria we find: small amounts of particle-covered membranes; many smooth-walled vesicles, including large numbers near to and opening into the outer surface of the cells and containing mucin filaments and bundles; filaments (prekeratin); quantities of dense stringy material referred to above (Fig. 2.5,E); and cilia. It may happen that a cell has all of these differentia. The conclusion one is forced to draw is that although as a class these differentiated features are typical of superficially placed cells, the cells themselves are not committed to the exclusive production of any of them; they are not differentiated in an exclusive manner.

The inner layer of epidermal cells contain no smooth-surfaced mucinogenic vesicles; free ribosomes (Figs. 2.10–2.13,R) are common; a small number of flattened particle-covered vesicles (Fig. 2.11,R) and fine filaments (f) which are often associated with desmosomes are found (Figs. 2.10–2.13).

In the mesodermal space, cells are rounded and mostly of indeterminate character. Some have well-developed particle-covered membranes in part of their cytoplasm and are (presumably) maturing fibrocytes producing the collagen already collecting in the subepidermal lamellae.

It may be advantageous to insert here a description of certain of the cytological structural patterns and their functional implications (Fig. 2.16). The classical pattern of the secretory cell, which we owe largely to Palade, is that of the pancreatic cell. This specialized cell is frequently illustrated in undergraduate textbooks,

and referred to as typical of cells in general. The definitive organelle of the secretory cell is the particle-covered membrane, the cytoplasmic reticulum associated with ribosomes (Fig. 2.16A). Protein is thought to be assembled on ribosomes, from whence it passes across the associated membrane to accumulate in enclosed sacs. Secretion from the cell is later effected by the membranes enclosing the product first shedding their ribosomes, and then, after an uncertain migration, opening onto the cell surface to discharge their contents (Fig. 2.16A).

The type of cell which synthesizes protein, but does not secrete it, is quite different. Most ribosomes are free and there are few particle-covered membranes. The protein assembled on the ribosomes is released directly into the cell sap (Fig. 2.16B). Eggs and early embryonic cells are predominantly retaining cells. The specialized cytology of differentiated cells is due to the elaboration of such cytological components as membranes and filaments (see Konigsberg, Chapter 14). Some cells, for example, keratinocytes and reticulocytes, remain retaining cells (free ribosomes and few membranes); in others (protein-secreting cells) the ribosomes attach to expanding membranes and their protein enters the sacs formed by these membranes. Enzymes able to release these proteins from ribosomes are perhaps located on these membranes.

The cytology of cells which secrete polysaccharide (or polysaccharide-protein) differs from that of cells secreting protein. They contain numerous vesicles enclosed by smooth (ribosome-free) membranes in which the secretion accumulates and is discharged as shown in Figure 2.16C. A few mem-

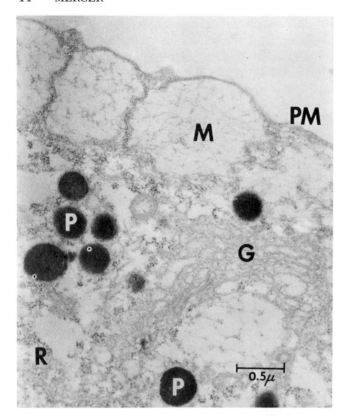

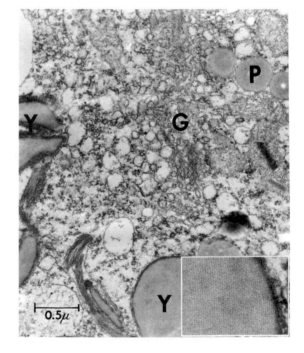

Fig. 2.17 Mucinogenic cell on surface of epithelium of developing *Xenopus* tadpole. M, mucin-containing vacuoles at surface; PM, plasma membrane; G, Golgi zone of smooth membrane clusters; R, ribosome-covered membranes (sac of reticulum); P, pigment granule. Preparation as for Fig. 2.5. Pb stain.

Fig. 2.18 Mucinogenic cell as in Fig. 2.17, showing Golgi zone and yolk granules, Y, in course of dissolution. Preparation as for earlier material. Uranyl stain. Inset: Enlargement of yolk granule to reveal internal crystalline order.

branes associated with ribosomes are present at the opposite pole of such cells. Most of the superficial epidermal cells of the tadpole tail are of this kind (Figs. 2.17 and 2.18). The protein moiety of the secretion and perhaps the enzymes involved in polymerizing sugars are probably formed in the particle-covered sacs and the polysaccharide added in the smooth-walled vesicles.

The production line in each of these cells has been summarized in a severely diagrammatic manner in Figure 2.19. In each case a messenger RNA (m) is supposed to move from the nuclear DNA to a ribosome (R) where it controls the synthesis of a protein. In the simplest case, the retaining cell (Fig. 2.19A), this protein is then released into the cytoplasmic space where it accumulates. This is the case, for example, in the epidermal cell, where prekeratin fibrils are formed. In the cell which secretes protein (Fig. 2.19B), it is supposed that the ribosome (R) must be in contact with a cytoplasmic membrane (M) to effect the release of its assembled protein. The protein in this case accumulates in the sacs of particle-covered membranes (M). It is next found in smooth-walled vesicles and then as distinct secretion granules (S) near the cell apex, from which point it ultimately escapes into the extracellular space. The polysaccharide-forming cell (Fig. 2.19C) is similar to the protein-secreting cell in its early stages, but it is supposed that the protein accumulating in the cytoplasmic sacs is the enzyme responsible for the synthesis of the saccharide from precursors (T).

Using these morphological criteria of the idealized "types," the epidermal cells of the tadpole tail clearly exhibit

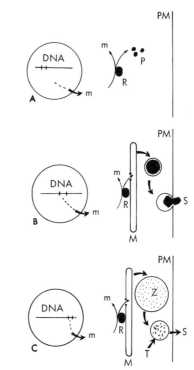

Fig. 2.19 Biochemical mechanisms involved in the three types of cells described in Fig. 2.16. A. Retaining cell; m, messenger-RNA; R, ribosome with associated messenger and protein, P, being produced and released into cell cytoplasm. B. Protein secretory cell. Lettering as for A. The protein is passed into the sac of the reticulum (particle-covered membrane), M, perhaps aided by a releasing enzyme located on surface. PM, plasma membrane; S, secretion of granule after it has passed through the Golgi region. C. The polysaccharide-synthesizing cell. In this case the enzyme for polymerizing the polysaccharide from its monomers, T, is thought to accumulate in smooth-walled sacs as in B and to effect polymerization prior to secretion at S.

mixed characteristics. The superficial cells may exhibit cilia. They have numerous smooth-walled vesicles containing mucin, fine filaments, and some free ribosomes which suggest the synthesis and retention of protein (prekeratin). The basal layer cells have numerous free ribosomes, some filaments, and often a few flattened sacs of particle-covered membranes suggesting secretory activity. These cells, viewed as a whole, have no well-defined structural differentiation; their mixed characteristics may be temporary, awaiting contact with other tissue components capable of impressing a definite differentiated state on them. Very similar comments could be made about the cytology of sea urchin blastomeres (Wolpert and Mercer, 41).

Intercellular Substances and Adhesion

The preceding account of the course of events in the establishment of epithelia suggests that the time at which intercellular adhesion sets in is a factor of decisive morphogenetic influence. This differential adhesion may concern different areas of the same cell surface or it may involve different cells.

In the tail epithelia of the tadpole it is the external edges of cells which first adhere, and which later adhere most strongly and exhibit the most specialized structural features (tight contacts, desmosomes, and associated filaments). The adhesion travels inward, drawing the cells together. Adhesive patches appear on these more deeply placed cell surfaces, drawing the surfaces together; in this way the epithelial pattern is established, while still leaving many intercellular gaps. The intercellular contacts, where they emerge on the inner face of the epithelium facing the mesoderm, are less firmly adherent, less tight, and less mechanically reinforced than on the external face. The inner face seems less in need of mechanical reinforcement; its flatness suggests that it is

under some form of compression which may squeeze loose edges of cells together and render the reinforcement of contacts unnecessary. The enclosed mesodermal cells have rounded surfaces, which suggests that at this time their surfaces are not adhesive.

Essentially the same sequence of events was traced in the somewhat simpler system, the sea urchin blastula and gastrula: limited areas of strong adhesion at the exposed external edges of the contacting cells, patchy adhesion between the more deeply placed intercellular contacts, and a flattening of the cell surfaces facing the blastocoele with a deposition of fibrils. The cells of the primary mesenchyme are recruited from the vegetal pole of the blastula, where cells in the surface sheet fail to develop adhesion, round up, and slip into the blastocoele. These are at first almost spherical in shape, but soon extend long fine processes which find and adhere to sticky areas on the inner surface of the ball of cells (Gustafson and Wolpert. Referred to in 41).

In a purely cellular epidermal derivative hair, we concluded (Birbeck and Mercer, 2; Mercer, 24) that the molding of the complicated structure of the hair and hair follicle owed its inception to the appearance of intercellular adhesion between the presumptive cuticle cells before it appeared between those of the presumptive cortex.

It will be recalled that Curtis (4) concluded that a timing mechanism was responsible for the apparently specific adhesiveness of certain cells in cell mixtures. His experiments were carried out on cells obtained by dispersing *Xenopus* larvae. He noted that ectodermal cells normally became adhesive before meso- or endodermal cells. He rejected the idea of a cell-specific adhesive substance, and concluded that it is not necessary to assume specificity to explain the change in cell relationships and shape. It seems to be largely a matter of the timing of the adhesion which brings about the cellular pattern of the tissue (cf. Tyler, 33).

Nature of Intercellular Adhesion

To carry this discussion further it is necessary to have some more definite ideas about the mechanism of intercellular adhesion. It is necessary to ask: What is the physical basis of adhesion and what controls its appearance? It would be convenient at this point if there were wide agreement concerning the nature of adhesion. Unfortunately, there is not. The situation has not greatly altered since the appearance of the symposium on adhesion published as *Cell Movement and Cell Contact* (4, 11) to which reference may be made for a fuller account of the various theories. I can only argue here the case for supposing that adhesion is due to the appearance of substances on the outside surfaces of cells which causes them to stick to other such surfaces. The evidence for such an intercellular adhesive must be largely derived from the analysis of micrographs, although there are many reports that cells in general produce surface exudates.

The image of an intercellular contact seen in sections of fixed material in the electron microscope is the main source of information (Figs. 2.5–2.8). The two dense double-profiled lines seen in tissues fixed in osmium tetroxide are usually taken to be the images of components of the plasma membranes of the two adhering cells. Between these lines is a more or less dense image which represents the intercellular space. The density of the material in this gap depends on several factors. The first of these is the technique of preparation: fixing, staining, and embedding. In osmium-fixed material it appears very light. After further staining by lead or uranium solutions, its density may be increased substantially. After formaldehyde or glutaraldehyde fixation, the membranes are less dense (no deposited osmium) and the intercellular material relatively more dense.

This intercellular material is the postulated adhesive; it may be regarded either as an extracellular substance or as a superficial component of the membrane. At desmosomes it is more abundant and denser. It differs from the abundant extracellular secretions characteristic of the mesoderm in that it is small in amount and is closely associated with the surfaces of cells. But chemically it may be a polysaccharide-protein complex like many extracellular secretions. These substances react weakly with the usual chemical fixatives and stains. I have found by tests on model membranes of cellulose derivatives – agar and bacterial capsules, and so on – that they yield very faint images in the electron microscope, owing to their feeble scattering power for electrons.

Whatever their chemical nature, these layers can exert effects on relative intercellular motion varying from lubrication to complete immobilization. Since COO^- groups are present, we can understand the effect of Ca^{2+} ions linking these, or of proteins bearing excess positive charges, to cause an increased viscous drag. The local secretion of proteins of this type could increase local adhesion.

Little is known about the formation and secretion of intercellular adhesive. In Figures 2.5, 2.9, 2.20, and 2.21 an unusual material (E) may be seen beneath the cell surfaces in the vicinity of areas of adhering membrane, but it cannot be inferred that this is necessarily related to the formation and secretion of intercellular substances.

There is a special instance of enhanced cellular adhesion in which the presence and active secretion of intercellular adhesive material is readily observed. In keratinizing epidermis the intercellular gap, at first normal (about 200 A), widens to some 400–600 A and denser deposits appear between the cells as these keratinize (Birbeck and Mercer, 2, 24). Matoltsy and co-workers (23) have demonstrated the formation within the cells of membrane-enclosed secretion-granules. These "membrane-coating granules" are expelled from the cells into the intercellular spaces, where they yield dense deposits which spread out to cover the cell surface (Figs. 2.6–2.8).

The keratinized tissues are exceptional in being more strongly bonded than other epithelia; nevertheless such exceptions, by exaggerating the normal, are often informative.

To conclude, what information does a detailed morphological analysis provide the biochemist in his search for the structural substances involved in differentiation and the clues promoting their formation? The first event in time pointing toward epithelial differentiation is the adhesion of the external edges of the presumptive epidermal cells. These cells, previous to this step, have expressed a number of what may be recognized as their epithelial potentialities. However, since many free cells, including protozoa, produce the same structures, these differentia (cilia, mucin, prekeratins) may be thought to be induced by exposure to the environment. Adhesion is the first step toward multicellularity. Since the nature of intercellular adhesive material is not known, it is only possible to say that cells must be induced to synthesize the components as an early and necessary step in tissue formation.

The adhering edges rapidly develop specialized features and it would seem that these serve at least two functions: (1) holding the cells (and embryo) together against dispersion and pressure building up from within; and (2) creating the internal and external milieu. Since tight contacts are found only where an intercellular contact opens at an external surface, it is possible that this form of adhesion may require some component supplied from the environment (Ca^{2+} or Mg^{2+}).

The morphological changes in the basal layer cells suggest that another early product is a space-filling and expanding gel whose synthesis precedes that of the precursors of collagen.

The Desmosome

The desmosome appears to be a device of enhanced and semipermanent adhesion, and to consist of several components, each of which must be synthesized simultaneously by the two participating cells. It is also the site to which intracellular filaments attach. In the light microscope it appears that bundles of these filaments stretch from desmosome to desmosome and thus brace the cell—that is, they are tonofilaments, truly morphogenetic structural elements maintaining cell shape. Synthesis of these

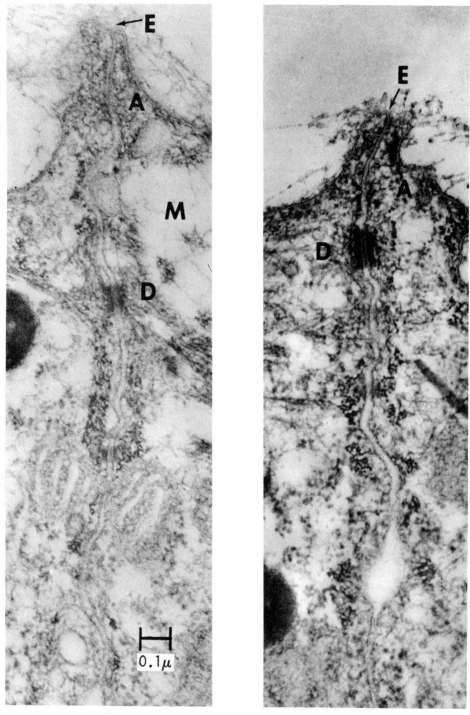

Figs. 2.20 (left) and 2.21 (right) The contact zones between two epithelial cells at their external edges. Compare with Fig. 2.5.

filaments could be promoted by the withdrawal of their soluble precursors from the cell sap by crystallization on the desmosomal sites. These sites are not placed haphazardly, nor are filaments simply dumped in the cell. The system of braces transmitting forces from cell to cell is an intimate part of the histology.

What determines the site of a desmosome? There is evidence of a desmosomal pattern on the surfaces of cells. A hexagonal disposition is revealed in sections running parallel to the face of basal layer cells. Elsewhere the surfaces are too convoluted to reveal such a pattern in sections, but suggestive groups of desmosomes are often apparent. Such patterns may prove to be integral and inherited structures within the plasma membrane, with a well-defined molecular basis, which could be transmitted from cell to cell as surely as are the genes. Possibly the sites of these deposits may mark permeable areas through which appropriately shaped molecules may escape to the outer surface; such areas on cytoplasmic membranes were postulated earlier to explain the penetration of proteins into sacs of the reticulum (Fig. 2.8*B*).

The Basal Cells and Basal Membrane

The cells of the inner layers of the epidermis (even in adult skins) are linked by cell processes, some bearing desmosomes, others not. Large vacuoles are common. The contacts facing the basement membrane are often poorly adhesive in early stages. The impression gained from these micrographs is of loosely adhering cells pressed together by some semirigid gel whose upper surface is per-

haps marked by the surface referred to as the basement membrane. This gel material may be synthesized by mesodermal cells before the more noticeable collagen. If it plays a part in the subsequent organization of the collagen (as has been suggested), there is no obvious evidence of this, other than that the basement membrane seems to be a barrier against which the collagen lamellae are packed.

The basement membrane itself is a structure of some importance. It is a sieve of macromolecular texture. Once formed, it isolates henceforth the epithelial and mesodermal domains, and may influence the exchange of molecules between them.

Summary

The histogenesis of an epithelium, with special reference to the ontogony of adhesive surfaces, is discussed, using as a model tissue the epidermis of the tails of the larval forms of *Xenopus* and *Rana*.

The single layer of loosely adhering cells comprising the presumptive epithelium at first develops adhesive contacts at their outside edges; these contacts then develop specialized features: a tight contact (cell membranes virtually fused) at the external exposed edge of the contact, and further inward, one or more desmosomes followed by an area of the more normal type of intercellular junction (parallel membranes spaced at about 200 A). The inward facing portions of the cell membranes remain convoluted and poorly adhesive.

A further layer of cells next appears on the inner face. Contact with the outer layer is patchy and limited largely to encounters between small processes projecting from the cells. No specialized areas of contact appear on the opposed faces of the inner (basal) cells.

The inward face of the basal layer cells smooths out and a thin basement membrane (400 A thick) appears as a fuzzy layer about 200–400 A from their plasma membranes. Collagen fibrils next build up against the basement membrane.

The earlier fibrils of the system of lamella are parallel to the head-tail axis but not closely packed. Consideration of numbers, sizes and arrangement of these fibrils suggest that new fibrils are added in the interstices of those deposited earlier.

The close contacts of the superficial cells are needed to maintain the tissue mechanically, and separate the internal and external environments. The flat surfaces of the basal layer cells, the appearance of large trapped vacuoles, and the absence of close contacts suggests that this layer is compressed against a gellike mesodermal component. Similar structures occur in the late blastula of the sea urchin.

The fine cytology of the epidermal cells is of the epidermal type, although mixed in character (cilia, mucin, and prekeratin may be produced by the same cell). The ontogeny of fine cytology is discussed.

References

1. Abercrombie, M., "Exchanges between Cells," *Chemical Basis of Development*, W. D. McElroy and B. Glass, eds. Baltimore: The Johns Hopkins Press, p. 318 (1958).
2. Birbeck, M. S. C., and E. H. Mercer, "The Role of Cell Membranes in Morphogenesis," *Proc. Stockholm Conf. Electron Microscop.* pp. 156–158 (1956).
3. Chapman, G. B., and A. B. Dawson, "Fine Structure of Larval Anuran Epidermis," *J. Biophys. Biochem. Cytol.* 10: 425 (1961).
4. Curtis, A. S. G., "Timing Mechanisms in the Specific Adhesion of Cells," *Exptl. Cell Res. Suppl.* 8:107–122 (1961).
5. DeHaan, R. L., "Cell Migration and Morphogenetic Movements," *Chemical Basis of Development*, W. D. McElroy and B. Glass, eds. Baltimore: The Johns Hopkins Press, p. 339 (1958).
6. Edds, M. V., "Development of Collagen in Frog Embryo," *Proc. Natl. Acad. Sci. U.S.* 44:296–305 (1958).
7. ——, and P. R. Sweeny, "Chemical and Morphological Differentiation of the Basement Lamella," *Synthesis of Molecular and Cellular Structure*, D. Rudnick, ed. New York: Ronald, p. 111 (1961).

7a. ——, and ——, "Development of the Basement Lamella," *5th Intern. Congr. Electron Microscop. Philadelphia.* New York: Academic Press, p. QQ2 (1962).
8. ——, "Origin and Structure of the Intercellular Matrix," *Chemical Basis of Development*, W. D. McElroy and B. Glass, eds. Baltimore: The Johns Hopkins Press, pp. 157–173 (1958).
9. Farquar, M. G., and G. E. Palade, "Junctional Complexes in Various Epithelia." *J. Cell Biol.* 17:375 (1963).
10. Fawcett, D. W., "Structural Specializations of the Cell Surface," *Frontiers in Cytology*, S. L. Palay, ed. London: Oxford University Press, p. 19 (1959).
11. ——, "Intercellular Bridges," *Exptl. Cell Res. Suppl.* 8:174 (1961).
12. Gersh, I., and H. R. Catchpole, "Nature of Ground Substance of Connective Tissue," *Perspectives Biol. Med.* 3:282–319 (1960).
13. Grobstein, C., "Cell Contact in Relation to Embryonic Induction," *Exptl. Cell Res. Suppl.* 8:234–245 (1961).
14. ——, "Tissue Interaction in Morphogenesis of Mouse Embryonic Rudiments in vitro," *Aspects of Synthesis and Order in Growth*, D. Rudnick, ed. Princeton,

N.J.: Princeton University Press, pp. 233–256 (1955).

15. Gross, J., "Behavior of Collagen Units as a Model in Morphogenesis," *J. Biophys. Biochem. Cytol. Suppl.* 2:261–274 (1956).

16. ———, "Studies on the Formation of Collagen," *J. Exptl. Med.* 107:247; 108:215 (1958).

17. Hodge, A. J., and F. O. Schmitt, "The Charge Profile of the Tropocollagen Macromolecule and the Packing Arrangements in Native Type Collagen Fibrils," *Proc. Natl. Acad. Sci. U.S.* 46:186–187 (1960).

17a. ———, and J. A. Petruska, "Recent Studies with the Electron Microscope on Ordered Aggregates of the Tropocollagen Molecule," *Aspects of Protein Structure*, G. N. Ramachandran, ed. New York: Academic Press, p. 289 (1963).

18. Holtfreter, J., "A Study of the Mechanics of Gastrulation," *J. Exptl. Zool.* 94:261 (1943).

18a. ———, "The Significance of the Cell Membrane in Embryological Processes," *Ann. N.Y. Acad. Sci.* 49:9 (1948).

19. Jackson, S. Fitton-, "The Morphogenesis of Avian Tendon," *Proc. Roy. Soc. London Ser. B* 144:556–572 (1956).

20. Kemp, N. E., "Development of the Basement Lamella of Larval Anuran Skin," *Develop. Biol.* 1:459–476 (1959).

21. Leeson, C. R., and L. T. Threadgold, "The Differentiation of the Epidermis in *Rana pipiens*," *Acta Anat.* 44:159 (1961).

22. Lowther, D. A., "Chemical Aspects of Collagen Fibrillogenesis," *Intern. Rev. Conn. Tissue Res.*, D. A. Hall, ed. New York: Academic Press, vol. 1, p. 64 (1963).

23. Matoltsy, A. G., and P. Parakkal, "Membrane Coating Granules of Keratinizing Epithelia," *J. Cell Biol.* 24(2):295 (1965).

23a. ———, and ———, "A Study of the Fine Structure of the Epidermis of *Rana pipiens*," *J. Cell Biol.* 20:85 (1964).

24. Mercer, E. H., *Keratin and Keratinization—An Essay in Molecular Biology*. New York: Pergamon Press (1961).

25. Meyer, K., "Nature and Function of Mucopolysaccharides of Connective Tissue," *Mol. Biol.* D. Nachmansohn, ed. New York: Academic Press, pp. 69–76 (1960).

26. Palay, S. L., ed., "Morphology of Secretion," *Frontiers in Cytology*. New Haven, Conn.: Yale University Press, chap. 11, p. 305 (1958).

27. Picken, L., "The Organization of Cells and Other Organisms," London: Oxford University Press, p. 407 (1960).

28. Porter, K. R., "Structure of Cell and Body Walls," *Proc. Intern. Conf. Electron Microscop. London*. London: Williams and Clowes, p. 125 (1956).

28a. ———, and G. D. Pappas, "Collagen Formation by Fibroblasts of Chick Embryo Dermis," *J. Biophys. Biochem. Cytol.* 5:143–166 (1959).

29. Rosin, S., "Über Bau und Wachstum der Greuzlamelle der Epidermis bei Amphibienlarven; Analyse einer Orthogonalen Fibrillenstructur," *Rev. Suisse Zool.* 53:133–201 (1946).

30. Schmitt, F. O., J. Gross, and J. H. Highberger, "States of Aggregation of Collagen," *Symp. Soc. Exptl. Biol.* 9:148 (1955).

31. Shumway, W., "Stages in the Normal Development of *Rana pipiens*," *Anat. Record* 78:139 (1940).

31a. ———, P. G. Nieuwkoop, and J. Faber, *Normal Tables of Xenopus laevis (Daudin)*. Amsterdam: North-Holland Publishing Co., (1956).

32. Townes, P. L., and J. Holtfreter, "Directed Movement and Selective Adhesion of Embryonic Amphibian Cells," *J. Exptl. Zool.* 128:53 (1955).

33. Tyler, A., "An Auto-antibody Concept of Cell Structure, Growth and Differentiation," *Growth 10* (Suppl. 6th Symp.) 7–19 (1946).

34. Waddington, C. H., *Principles of Embryology*. London: Allen & Unwin (1956).

35. Weiss, P., and W. Ferris, "Electronmicrograms of Larval Epidermis," *Exptl. Cell Res.* 6:546–549 (1954).

36. ———, and ———, "Electron-Microscopic Study of the Texture of the Basement Membrane of Larval Amphibian Skin," *Proc. Natl. Acad. Sci. Wash.* 40:528–540 (1954).

37. ———, "Macromolecular Fabrics and Patterns," *J. Cellular Comp. Physiol.* 49, *Suppl.* 1:105–112 (1957).

38. ———, and A. Moscona, "Film on Cell Adhesion," London: (1958).

39. ——, "Cell Contact," *Intern. Rev. Cytol.* 7:391 (1958).

40. Wessels, N. K., "Tissue Interactions during Skin Histodifferentiation," *Develop. Biol.* 4:87–107 (1962).

41. Wolpert, L., and E. H. Mercer, "An Electron Microscope Study of the Development of the Blastula of the Sea Urchin Embryo and Its Radial Polarity," *Exptl. Cell Res.* 30:280–300 (1963).

42. Wood, G. C., "Formation of Fibrils from Collagen," *Biochem. J.* 75:598–605 (1960).

43. Wood, R. L., "Intercellular Attachment in the Epidermis of *Hydra*," *J. Biochem. Cytol.* 6:343 (1959).

3

Mechanisms of Morphogenetic Movements

J. P. TRINKAUS*

Department of Biology
Yale University
New Haven, Connecticut

Morphogenetic movements range from an in situ change in form of a discrete structure, as in the indentation of an optic vesicle or auditory placode, to the translocation of cells over long distances, as in the invagination of prechordal material or the emigrations of cells from the neural crest and early germinal areas. Even though much small-scale movement remains to be charted, the broad outlines of these movements are now well known for gastrulation and organogenesis in a number of organisms. This knowledge, combined with our growing understanding of the movements of cells in culture and in mixed aggregates, has created a situation in which analysis of the mechanism of morphogenetic movements will be an increasingly profitable pursuit. Until now, however, attempts at such analysis have been largely disjoined from parallel studies of cell movement under the more controlled conditions of cell and organ culture. It is the purpose of this chapter to try to pull these separate efforts more closely together, hopefully to their mutual benefit.

A Catalog of the Movements

Migrations of Individual Cells during Embryogenesis

CONDENSATIONS OF MESENCHYME. Increase in cell population density often precedes histogenesis. Examples may be found in the condensation of presomite and prenotochordal mesenchyme, and in the formation of chondrogenic and myogenic blastemata.

* The original work of the author and the writing of this chapter have been supported by grants from the National Science Foundation. The Higgins Fund of Yale University supported some of the earlier work on *Fundulus* epiboly.

These condensations could result from aggregative cell movements, contraction of the whole cellular mass, or a local increase in cell division. The importance and ubiquity of such condensations is undeniable, but evidence on the mechanisms of their formation is largely lacking. An exception is the dermal condensation that precedes formation of a feather germ. Wessells (153a) has recently shown it to be due to local increases in mitotic rate.

PRIMORDIAL GERM CELLS. The migrations of the primordial germ cells are at the same time one of the most spectacular and most intimately studied of all cell movements. In the chick embryo, they are first detected as large cells in the endoderm anterior to the embryo in the head-process stage, whence they travel posteriorward, eventually to reach the gonadal area. Simon (115) has shown that if a blastoderm whose germinal crescent has been removed is parabiosed in culture with a normal blastoderm, gonads of the former will be colonized by germ cells of the latter. If both germinal crescents are excised, both blastoderms remain sterile. Simon went on to note that the invasion will occur only if yolk sac blood vessels of the two blastoderms anastomose. Otherwise the gonads remain sterile. It appears, therefore, that germ cells migrate most readily through or in blood vessels. Whether they are passively carried in the circulating blood or are guided in their migrations by the walls of the blood vessels could only be settled by tracing the cells. This has been done very recently by Meyer (81), taking advantage of their high glycogen content. He found these PAS-positive cells first appeared within the embryo at the onset of cardiac propulsion and

blood circulation. Hence they are apparently wafted passively in the circulation. Initially, they are observed throughout the existing vascular channels, but by stages the majority are concentrated in the future gonadal regions, where they accumulate in the small vessels leading from the dorsal aorta. They may accumulate there because of lack of passage due to the small size of the vessels, as Meyer suggests, or because of more subtle factors, such as differential adhesiveness. Primordial germ cells are particularly easy to identify in the mouse, because of their high alkaline phosphatase activity, and Mintz (83) has taken advantage of this to trace them into the germinal epithelium with great precision. But neither here, nor in the chick, is the mechanism or the direction of the movements through tissues yet understood.

THE NEURAL CREST. Because of the importance and dispersion of its products, the neural crest has attracted the attention of many investigators during the last half century. During this period the list of histological end products has lengthened to the point where this transitory primordium stands unchallenged for the diversity of its derivatives (Hörstadius, 65). Among these, the wandering pigment cells have been the subject of so much intensive study that we now possess a richer knowledge of the extent, direction, and control of their movements by genetic factors and tissue environment than of any other migratory cell (see Rawles, 99; Reams, 100; Twitty, 140; Lehman and Youngs, 73). Yet many critical questions remain unanswered. Do all cells of the neural crest find their mark, or do many of them disperse at random into other areas where they either cytolyze, divide little, remain undifferentiated, or are incorporated in undetectably small numbers into other organs? Do neural crest cells migrate at random from the dorsal surface of the neural tube out into the embryo, or do they move along certain pathways? If they move along pathways, are these characteristic and well defined, and, if so, what features of the cells or their environment direct their movements? What causes the cells to begin emigrating and what causes them to stop?

None of these questions could be answered until a cell-specific, nontoxic, long-term cell marker had been developed. This finally became available with the synthesis of tritiated thymidine (Hughes, 66; Messier and LeBlond, 80; Trinkaus and Gross, 137). Application of this marker to the chick embryo has provided answers to some of the questions (Weston, 154). Cells of the trunk neural crest emigrate in two rather well-defined streams of cells — one leading ventrad into the mesenchyme between the neural tube and the myotome to form spinal and sympathetic ganglia. The other leads in a dorsolateral direction into the superficial ectoderm (Fig. 3.1A). The migration is in no sense random. The cells obviously follow favored pathways and then, for reasons not yet understood, cease moving and accumulate rapidly in known destinations. The dorsal stream moves directly into the ectoderm, rather than into the dermis, contrary to prior thinking. These cells are apparently promelanoblasts, for ectoderm containing them yields pigment cells if grafted to a nonpigmented host.

Interestingly, the orientation and direction of the ventral migration is in-dependent of the mesenchyme through which it moves. It is somehow related to the orientation of the neural tube. When a tube with labeled neural crest is inverted, crest cells continue to migrate ventrad relative to the neural tube, which of course is dorsad relative to the host embryo. Metamerism of sensory and sympathetic ganglia, on the other hand, is strongly influenced by the mesodermal somites, possibly due to the preferential migration of neural crest cells within, rather than between, somites.

The use of tritiated thymidine has thus given impressive confirmation of the neural crest origin of certain derivatives, a testimony to the care and accuracy with which early workers drew their conclusions from the circumstantial evidence provided by grafting and deletion experiments. Certain of the questions we have posed have been answered, others not. But we are now in a position to hope realistically that these too may soon be attacked with profit.

BLASTULATION AND GASTRULATION. Disappearance of stained material from the vegetal pole of amphibian blastulae once suggested that vegetal blastomeres slip inside in a new morphogenetic movement of unipolar ingression (Schectman, 111; Nicholas, 91). However, a study in which cell lineage was meticulously followed showed that no cells leave the surface (Ballard, 14). Stain is carried inside by the expanding cortex of the large vegetal blastomeres as they divide. At the onset of gastrulation, on the other hand, individual cell movements are very much in evidence. Elongate bottle cells move into the interior at the site of the future blastopore. They presage the invagination of the prospective endoderm and mark the beginning of gastrulation.

In sea urchin blastulae, primary mesenchyme cells also leave the vegetal plate precisely at the point where invagination will occur and migrate on the inner surface of the blastocoel wall. Later on, secondary mesenchyme cells emerge from the tip of the advancing archenteron and attach by long filopodia to the blastocoel wall. The significance of these cells and of the amphibian bottle cells for gastrulation movements will be discussed later.

Fig. 3.1 A. Radioautograph of a transverse section through a nonlabeled host chick embryo, showing a grafted neural tube labeled with tritiated thymidine and labeled neural crest derivatives which have emigrated from it. Note labeled cells in the ectoderm, in the condensed spinal ganglia, and in the sympathetic ganglia (at the bottom). In the lower left corner are labeled sheath cells on a motor nerve. (From Weston, *Develop. Biol.* 6:279–310, 1963.) B. Schematic drawings of fibroblasts in dark field surface contact microscope (lines are illuminated areas which appear to be in continuous undulating movement). a, single fibroblast; b, streaming group; c, interpretation of image; U, undulating contacts. (From Ambrose, *Exptl. Cell Res. Suppl.* 8:54–73, 1961.)

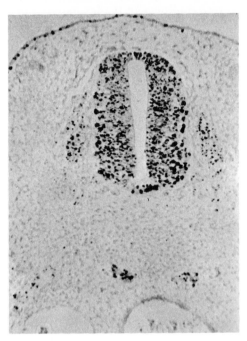

A

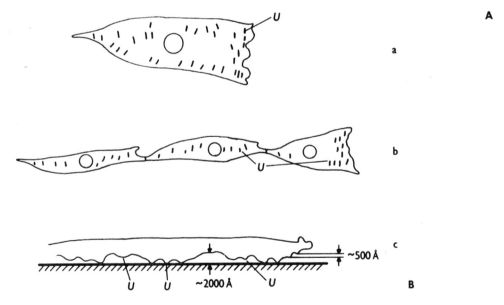

a

b

c

B

Movements of Individual Cells in Adults

Movements of individual cells are of course not confined to embryos. Amoebocytes of various kinds have extraordinary migratory powers in adults (as well as in embryos) and can move to, and accumulate rapidly in great numbers at an area of inflammation. They move to all parts of the organism mainly in the blood and lymph, in which they are probably transported passively. But they also squeeze out of these vessels and can actively propel themselves through tissues. Their manner of movement under such circumstances is not understood.

Chick melanoblasts, which migrate extensively during early embryogenesis (see Rawles, 99), likewise retain their migratory powers in postembryonic stages. This has been shown by two kinds of experiments. If pigment-free skin is grafted to a pigmented host just after hatching, it is invaded by host melanoblasts which deposit a host-type pigment pattern in the forming feathers (Rawles, 98a). If pigmented barb ridges from feather germs of an adult chicken are grafted to the base of the wing bud of a 3-day embryo, melanoblasts migrate from the graft and pigment feather germs of the wing (Nickerson, 91a; Trinkaus, 131a).

The presence of pluripotent migratory cells in the adult has long been postulated to account for regeneration and cancer. I speak of the so-called neoblasts, which are supposed to have the capacity for directed migration over long distances to the site of the neoformation (DuBois, 46). However, since the very existence of these cells is still unsettled (Butler and O'Brien, 22; Flickinger, 47), their presumed migratory powers do not merit discussion.

The metastasis of neoplastic cancer cells over long distances to other tissues and organs is one of the most spectacular examples of movement by individual cells and small cell clusters in the adult and a major reason for interest in cell movements. Apparently because of decreased adhesiveness (Coman, 26), cells slough off from the invading tongues of a malignancy to be carried away in the circulation. Neoplastic cells often show great motility in culture, but to what extent individual tumor cells can actively migrate through tissues is still a moot question. In this regard, it is notable that certain carcinoma cells are much more invasive in organ culture than are normal mesonephric cells (Wolff and Schneider, 158) and are not inhibited in their movements by contact with fibroblasts (Abercrombie et al., 7).

Whether normal mesenchyme cells and tissue fibroblasts shift their positions in embryos or adults is unknown. Their looseness of organization in vivo and their high degree of motility in vitro is suggestive, but is not sufficient evidence. It is certainly a subject which invites investigation with isotopic labeling.

Spreading and Folding of Cell Sheets

The importance of movements of individual cells in development is well established, but in fact the bulk of the movements that mold the organism are not movements of individual cells. They involve the spreading and folding of sheets of cells. I don't take time to consider these movements because they are well known to all students of development. At first there is gastrulation: invagination and involution, medial convergence, lateral divergence and anteroposterior extension, and epibolic spreading. Then there are the movements of organogenesis: the medullary plate rolls up to form the neural tube; it expands to form the brain; the forebrain invaginates and the optic cups are formed; the ureteric bud and the nephrogenic blastema branch and join; and the foregut balloons into branchial pouches. As an adult, the organism readily responds to wounding by an epithelial spreading sufficient to cover wound surfaces of considerable magnitude.

Mechanisms of Cell Movement

Amoeboid Movement

Studies of cell movement have revealed at least two quite different mechanisms — the pseudopodial propagated movement of amoeboid cells and the gliding movement of fibroblasts and epithelial cells. Amoeboid movement has been intensively studied in the giant amoebae of the Sarcodina and considerable detailed information accumulated. There is actually much agreement on the location and timing of the important sol-gel changes that occur during amoeboid movement, but disagreement on the source of the motive force (cf. Goldacre, 49; Allen, 8). This work is of much interest, but I will not take the considerable space required to describe it, because it is not yet clear whether the so-called amoeboid tissue cells of metazoa, such as leukocytes and histiocytes, move in a similar fashion (see Allen, 9; Robineaux, 103). More intensive study of the mechanism of movement in these cells in the light of work on the free-living amoebae and fibroblasts is a pressing need, and now possible with modern microscopy, microsurgery, and methods of cell culture (see Wohlfarth-Botterman, 157).

Gliding Movement

Other kinds of tissue cells, such as fibroblasts and epithelial cells, whose position in vivo seems ordinarily to be fixed or to change little, will nevertheless move readily in culture and under conditions of wound healing. The movement of these cells is of great interest in the context of this chapter, since it seems likely that most cells participating in morphogenetic movements move in a similar way. The tissue fibroblasts or mechanocytes (Willmer, 155) have been studied the most. They do not move by amoeboid movement. They flatten and adhere to a solid or semisolid substratum and glide across it without pseudopodial formation or other gross deformation of cell form. Such cells can move off the substratum across a fluid gap only if they can first attach extensions of themselves to a surface on the other side. They appear to move by waves of adhesive contact with the substratum, as in Figure 3.1*B*. (Ambrose, 10; Abercrombie, 1; Abercrombie and Ambrose, 3, 4). There is no evidence that protoplasmic flow is involved. Phase and interference microscopy have revealed the leading edge of a moving fibroblast to consist of an exceedingly thin, fanlike membrane, 5–10 μ wide and closely applied to the substratum. This membrane undergoes, on its upper surface, continual folding movements which beat inward. These so-called ruffles occur rapidly enough to be seen without the aid of time-lapse cinemicrography. Part of their undersurface is obviously stuck to the glass substratum, for they leave fine cytoplasmic filaments behind when they withdraw. The surface contact microscope reveals intermittent attachments to the substratum at the leading edge during movement. A few are also seen under the nuclear region and the trailing edge. These attachments are in a constant state of flux. The exact relation between them and the ruffled membrane is unknown, but both appear to be expressions of the same surface activity. Usually where a large ruffled membrane is seen, the cell is traveling in that direction, and when a new one forms, the cell soon begins to move in the new direction. It appears from all this that the ruffled membrane, and its accompanying attachments, is the locomotive organ of the cell. Compression waves between the attachments probably assure cell movement, but they have not yet been detected. It is possible that contractile proteins energized by ATP may be involved in this postulated compression. Glycerol-extracted fibroblasts contract in the presence of ATP in a manner reminiscent of skeletal muscle fibers (Hoffmann-Berling, 57). Epithelial cells have been much less studied than fibroblasts, but it appears that they too move at the edge, by a similar mechanism.

CONTACT INHIBITION. When a moving fibroblast encounters another fibroblast, if forms a contact with it, its ruffled membrane is paralyzed and movement in that region of the cell stops. Abercrombie (5, 6) has termed this phenomenon "contact inhibition" and has documented its importance in the control of fibroblast movement in culture. For example, it provides a probable explanation for the "zone of outgrowth" around an explant. Cells at the periphery of an explant have free surface at which new ruffled membranes may form. This eventually provides sufficient momentum to pull a cell away from its fellows, freeing one surface of the cell behind, so that it can now break away. Thus a slow exodus of fibroblast occurs. As long as there is some cell-free space, a fibroblast will move into it until it either overtakes or is overtaken by another fibroblast. They will then "contact inhibit" each other, but may break away again, if a new ruffled membrane forms. But this outward movement does not necessarily mean that eventually they will form a population of separate cells. At first, when cells leave the explant they will move outward. Soon, however, their direction of movement will become random. Separated cells will then tend to be overtaken by the outward-moving cells that have just left the explant. When the only surface available is that of its neighbor cells, a fibroblast will come to a standstill. It usually will not crawl over other fibroblasts. Thus, cells in the zone of outgrowth tend to become arranged in an ever-widening monolayer. The possible significance of contact inhibition for cell movements in vivo received a heavy boost when Abercrombie and co-workers (7) showed that invasive sarcoma cells are not contact inhibited by fibroblasts in culture. The means by which one fibroblast inhibits the movement of another is not understood. Abercrombie (1) has listed a number of possible explanations, but we are not yet in a position to distinguish among them (see also Taylor, 130).

ADHESION TO THE SUBSTRATUM. Since fibroblasts move by a process of making and breaking adhesions to the substratum, the adhesion must be firm enough for a cell to get a grip and pull itself along, but not too strong, else cells could become completely immobilized. If the adhesion is too weak, cells will slip, become rounded, and cease movement. It is obvious that a knowledge of the adhesiveness of cells is essential for an understanding of their locomotion.

The analysis of the relation between cellular adhesiveness and locomotion is still in its infancy. It is known, however, that moving cells are usually flattened on the substratum. If it could be established that degree of flattening were a direct measure of adhesiveness, we would have a convenient means of studying the relation between adhesiveness and locomotion. There is some crude indication that this is so. Cells which are flattened on glass are less readily detached than more rounded cells, when they are subjected to turbulence in the medium (Lieberman and Ove, 76; Taylor, 129). Moreover, rounded anaplastic cancer cells are less adhesive to a fibrin substratum than flattened fibroblasts (Ludford, 78).

Since we know that cells will not move unless they adhere to a substratum and that this adhesion varies, it would be of interest to know just how these variations affect the motility of cells. Aside from a demonstration that an increase in adhesiveness, as indicated by increased flattening of blastomeres, occurs during the transition from blastula to gastrula in *Fundulus* and is associated with acquisition of the capacity to move (Trinkaus, 135), we have little to say on the matter. This is an area of importance, needing quantitative studies of rate of locomotion, degree of flattening, and degree of adhesion.

The adhesiveness of the cell surface is obviously not the only factor to be considered. The nature of the substratum is just as important. This has been amply demonstrated in vitro, where controlled modifications of nonliving substrata drastically affect the adhesion of cells (Rappaport et al., 98; L. Weiss, 146a; Rosenberg, 106). Within the organism, other cells usually serve as the substrata; hence we would expect the substratum to vary with different cell types and their stage in development. This is indeed the case. Ectoderm of an amphibian gastrula adheres readily to both mesoderm and endoderm at first, but after a day or so much less readily to endoderm (Holtfreter, 59). Epidermis of an advanced larva adheres to other epidermis and to normally contiguous tissues like buccal epithelium and cornea by a cellular intermixing at the juncture. With noncontiguous epithelia such as esophagus, however, the adhesion is different and involves spreading of one epithelium over the other (Chiakulas, 24).

CONTACT GUIDANCE. Perhaps the most impressive evidence that the substratum plays an important role in the movements of cells is provided by the phenomenon of contact guidance (Harrison, 56; P. Weiss, 149, 151, 152; Weiss and Garber, 153), in which cells are apparently oriented by features of the substratum. The evidence is derived mainly from the behavior of fibroblasts in culture. This must be kept in mind, since it does not necessarily follow that all tissue cells behave similarly. An explant always digests a plasma clot a little and imposes stresses which may line up the colloidal micellae in particular orientations. When two explants are placed near each other, lines of stress are most pronounced between the two explants.

This has a profound effect on the fibroblasts (P. Weiss, 149). They orient preferentially in the in-between region to form a densely populated cellular bridge connecting the two explants. An even greater regimentation occurs if the cells are presented with glass or plastic fibers or with a glass substratum which has been scored with fine parallel grooves. Individual cells assume elongate spindle shapes in their efforts to conform precisely to the longitudinal axis of the fibers or to the grooves (P. Weiss, 151). But why would cells orient on glass or plastic? There is no reason to believe that glass or plastic surfaces offer orientations to which a cell could respond. Weiss suggests that the answer lies in the macromolecular materials that exude from cells. On a cylindrical fiber, for example, the exudate would advance mainly along the axis of the fiber. This could stretch the meshes of the micellar network in a lengthwise orientation. The leading edge of the cell may then trace these tracks and orient the rest of the cell. It is also possible that orientation could be simply the result of greater probability for contact of ruffled membranes in the long axis of the fiber. Similarly, cells might accumulate in concave surfaces merely because more substratum surface is available. If this explanation were valid, cells would be guided by contact, but not necessarily because of micellar orientations of the contacted surface.

Thus far, the intact organism has resisted efforts to find indisputable evidence for contact guidance, but many observations find their readiest explanation in this hypothesis: the migration of pigment cells along blood vessels; the movement of nerve axons along blood vessels, myotome boundaries and the remains of degenerating nerve fibers; the posteriad movement of the lateral line organ and the Wolffian duct; the oriented protrusion of dendritic extensions of melanocytes along oriented rows of barbule cells in a feather germ; the movement of clusters of heart-forming cells on an oriented endodermal substratum (De-Haan, 35); the movement of neural crest cells ventrad along the neural tube (Weston, 154). Contact guidance appears therefore to be a probable mechanism for orienting the movement of cells in vivo. It must be emphasized, however, that although it may give orientation, it does not in itself provide direction.

Mechanism of Cell Movements in vivo

We know very little about the mechanism whereby cells move within the organism, except by inference from in vitro studies. Technical problems which impede effective use of modern optical methods have been the main obstacles.

Despite these limitations, Gustafson and co-workers (50, 52, 70) and Dan and Okazaki (32) have made some remarkably detailed observations on the movements of individual mesenchyme cells of transparent sea urchin blastulae. Just prior to invagination, primary mesenchyme cells slip out of the vegetal plate and move into the blastocoel. Their liberation from their neighbors is accompanied by assumption of a spheroid form and by lively pulsatory activity of their inner surfaces. A decrease in adhesiveness could be the primary event, releasing cells so that they may be pushed into the blastocoel. It is of interest that cells of many tissues and organs, when freed from their fellows by EDTA or trypsin, also become spherical and pulsate. When primary mesenchyme cells are completely free, they spin out long dendritic filopodia whose tips make adhesive contact with the inner surface of the blastocoel wall. When these filopodia contract, they pull the cell along, providing a mechanism of movement somewhat in the manner of an inchworm. It appears to be an exaggerated variant of the familiar crawling of fibroblasts; but here the protoplasmic contractions are clearly evident. Concomitant decreased adhesiveness of the cell body may allow it to be more easily dislodged from its anchorage. As with a fibroblast, the adhesive contacts of these cells are not permanent; they slowly break and re-form, thus permitting changes in cell position. Gustafson and Wolpert (52) and Okazaki and co-workers (92) suggest that local differences in adhesiveness of the blastocoel wall could cause the ultimate arrangement of the mesenchyme cells.

Mechanism of Spreading of Cell Sheets

Epithelial cells characteristically unite to form a flat, cohesive sheet. Such a sheet will invariably spread, whether in vitro or in vivo, provided it adheres to the substratum and possesses a free edge. Accompanying the advance of the free edge and thoroughly integrated with it is a similar advance of the sheet behind it. A cell sheet spreads as a unit. Apparently cells do not need to break away from their neighbors in order to move, for cells within the sheet neither climb over each other nor lag behind as the sheet spreads. It is possible that areas of mutual cellular adhesion are reduced intermittently during spreading, but at present we lack evidence on this point.

Even though a sheet spreads as a unit, it is apparently the activity of the individual cells which provides the momentum. Lash (72) observed that at the onset of spreading of a wound epithelium only marginal cells show movement. Cells behind the border join the advance at progressively later times, the delay in their mobilization increasing with their distance from the cut edge of the wound. Galtsoff (48) and Holtfreter (64) have also seen a coordination of movements of individual cells within small groups of sponge cells and amphibian embryonic cells that causes the group to move as a unit; and I have observed something similar in small aggregates of blastomeres from *Fundulus* blastulae (Unpublished observations). When the cohering *Fundulus* cells are strung out in a chain, the lobopodial activities of the individual cells can be easily observed. In such a situation the collective movements of the pseudopods are translated into group activity, and the entire chain writhes and twists as a unit. Thus, small clusters of cells may move, but there is no direction to the movement, presumably because the entire edge of the aggregate is free. The directional quality of the movement of precardiac cell clusters in the chick blastoderm (DeHaan, 35) may in part be due to contact guidance.

It has been known for a long time that spreading of an epithelial sheet both in culture and in wound healing is stopped by contact with another epithelial edge. This is apparently a form of contact inhibition. If indeed contact inhibition is at work here, perhaps it also acts to prevent overlap of the cells within the sheet and coordinate their spreading movements. In the case of fibroblasts, which have been more carefully studied, spreading of a cell sheet may be completely accounted for by contact inhibition (Abercrombie and Ambrose, 4). Marginal cells will tend to move centrifugally, away from contact with other cells. As this exposes edges of neighboring cells, they too will tend to move. In this way centrifugal movement will be propagated centripetally. Of course, the more neighboring cells a fibroblast adheres to, the slower its speed of locomotion. Contact inhibition will greatly reduce the mobility of a cell; but if a cell to which it adheres is moving, it will tend to move with it. Therefore, along with the reduced speed will be an improved consistency of movement, so that the net displacement over a given period of time will be much greater for a coherent fibroblast sheet than for isolated cells (Abercrombie and Ambrose, 4). As Abercrombie has emphasized (4, p. 528), "For a cell to become anchored it must adhere firmly to something which does not itself move." This could explain the gradual mobilization of cells back of the edge of an advancing wound epithelium and their abrupt immobilization when the marginal cells stop (Lash, 72), for now they would be anchored to something which does not itself move. As far as epithelial cells are concerned, the proposed mechanism of spreading is mostly conjecture. The detailed observations required are still to be made.

One frequent observation must be taken into account by any theory of the spreading of cell sheets. When the margin of an epithelial sheet is detached from glass, the whole sheet usually retracts. This indicates that the sheet is under considerable contractile tension, and that its attachment to the substratum is firmest at the margin. Indeed, in some cases it is not certain that there is any attachment at all back of the marginal region. If attachment is confined to the margin, spreading could be due to an active centrifugal movement of marginal cells, followed by either active or passive accomodation of the rest (as emphasized years ago by Holmes, 58). This could provide an alternative explanation for the gradual involvement of nonmarginal cells and their abrupt cessation, when the marginal cells stop moving (Lash, 72).

The unitary behavior of a spreading cell sheet could also depend on the presence of a cohesive intercellular material forming a sort of continuum in which all cells are embedded (see Holtfreter, 62; Grobstein, 49a). If this material had the proper adhesive and elastic properties, it could help regiment cell movements within a sheet, coordinating them in one area and gradually transmitting them to other areas. That intercellular materials are present in varying amounts in certain tissues is undeniable. Whether or not they are essential for coordinating cell movements in sheets, however, is unsettled.

Cellular Segregation

There are many instances of cells moving directionally and segregating in specified regions. Cells of the teleost germ ring converge dorsally to form the embryonic shield. Neural crest cells move to their destinations along defined routes. Amoebae of the cellular slime molds form streams and converge on a center. Leukocytes accumulate at a site of inflammation. Sperm of a bracken fern gather in the archegonial pores. The directional movement of cells is obviously a widespread phenomenon of decided developmental and functional significance.

We have already discussed the possible importance of the substratum in giving orientation to cell movements. But contact guidance of itself does not impose directionality. Nor does it account for the cessation of movement and accumulation of cells at the destination. Cells could be attracted chemotactically by a diffusible chemical agent. Cells might also become concentrated at a given locus after completely random movements, if they are selectively eliminated elsewhere, or if there is some means of trapping those that by chance reach the proper region. One can imagine several possible mechanisms for such trap action: selective adhesion or "selective fixation" (Weiss, 150), slowing down or cessation of movement, the presence of a more favorable nutritional environment which stimulates cell division. Selective adhesion and other mechanisms of trap action will be discussed at length presently. We will concentrate first on chemotaxis.

Chemotaxis

When the direction of movement of cells is influenced by a gradient in concentration of substances in solution, chemotaxis is involved. In spite of frequent conviction to the contrary, it is not an easy matter to decide whether chemotaxis is at work. Not only must cells accumulate at the destination, but it must be shown that their movement has actually been turned in that direction. A cell must be able to detect a concentration difference over a distance corresponding to its own diameter and move parallel to the gradient. Contact guidance must be excluded. A classical method of testing for chemotaxis has been to insert a capillary tube containing the suspected chemotactic agent into a medium in which responsive cells are present. If cells accumulate in the tube, chemotaxis is inferred. This is not a critical experiment. Cells may be drawn to the tube by convection currents (resulting from physicochemical differences between the medium inside and outside the tube) or by a pumping or sucking action due to capillarity. Or, cells moving into the tube by chance may not readily leave because of one or another kind of trap action, such as the mouth of the tube being too small to permit random movement. Because of insufficient attention to pitfalls like these, there are not many claims for chemotaxis which exclude other interpretations. On the other hand, because of the difficulty of obtaining the necessary proofs, chemotaxis often cannot be excluded either, and so persists as a possibility by default in many situations where it probably is not at work. Where exceedingly short distances are involved, it is especially difficult to distinguish between trap action and chemical attraction and the distinction becomes semantic.

The best-known and most clearly established cases of chemotaxis are the attraction of bracken sperm to the archegonium (Pfeffer, 96) and the attraction of myxamoebae of the cellular slime molds to an aggregation center (Bonner, 18). Each of these involves the behavior of free-living cells and has been subjected to intensive analysis in recent years (Rothschild, 107; Brokaw, 21; reviews by Sussman, 128; Shaffer, 110).

There have been many claims of chemotaxis for animal cells, based largely on the end result—an accumulation of cells (see Rosen, 104). For example, Wilhelm Roux (108) teased apart the cells of early amphibian embryos and observed that they tended to aggregate in culture. He assumed this to be due to "cytotropic" factors released by the cells and concluded that such factors could play an important role in morphogenesis. His conclusion remained unchallenged for decades until finally re-examined by Voightlander (144), Kuhl (71), and Lucey and Curtis (77). They traced individual amphibian cells and found their movements to be entirely random. With but two exceptions, this has been the fate of all other suspected cases of chemotaxis of animal cells which have been subjected to careful analysis. The possibility that *Triturus* pigment cells mutually repel one another was supported when it was found that two or three cells confined in a capillary tube move apart. A single cell remains stationary (Twitty and Niu, 141). That leukocytes and lymphocytes are chemotactically attracted to a focus of infection has been suspected for a long time. It is only in recent years, however, that each of these has been examined under controlled conditions. By culturing cells under a cover slip in a viscous medium, Harris (55) was able to show that individual polymorphonuclear leukocytes, eosinophil leukocytes, and monocytes are

chemotactically responsive to a wide variety of microorganisms. Lymphocytes are not. There is no information on the mechanism of the cellular response or the nature of the diffusible agents (but see Boyden, 19, for hopeful progress on this problem).

Trap Action

Contact inhibition seems at first thought to be a likely means by which migratory cells could be immobilized and trapped within the organism. This is a distinct possibility, but an improbable one, in view of its apparent nonselectivity (Abercrombie et al., 7). Wandering cells, such as those from the neural crest, don't stop just anywhere. They cease movement and adhere to particular cells in particular regions of the embryo. This brings us to selective adhesion as a possible means of trapping cells during development. This possibility has been dramatized in recent years by the remarkable behavior of aggregates of dissociated cells. It is appropriate therefore that we give these studies extended treatment.

Cellular Segregation and Selective Adhesion

The questions to which we will now devote out attention were posed implicitly near the beginning of the century in the well-known studies of reconstitution by dissociated sponge cells (Wilson, 156). For all the interest excited by these studies, the tissue origin of the various cell types in the reconstituted sponges remains a mystery. Some thought that cell transformation occurred, others that cells sorted out according to type. Unfortunately, sponge cells are largely indistinguishable in the dissociated state and cannot be followed during reconstitution. Moreover, the various kinds of cells are so intermingled in sponges that workers have been discouraged from separating them. Unless this is done, different cell types cannot be marked and followed; and conclusions regarding cell transformation or sorting out will rest less on evidence than on preconceived notions of the degree of fixity of differentiated cells.

Modern investigations of tissue and organ reconstitution began with Holtfreter's discovery in 1944 (63) that dissociated prospective pronephric cells of an amphibian gastrula form pronephric systems, when allowed to re-aggregate in culture. When soon after, Moscona (84, 88) obtained characteristic tissue reconstitution in aggregates of mesonephric or chondrogenic cells of 4-day chick embryos (dissociated with trypsin), it appeared that reconstitution is a phenomenon of general biological significance, not at all confined to primitive invertebrates, as was thought for so long. As such, it greatly needed explanation. For this purpose vertebrate embryos were more hopeful material than sponges, because of the ease of separating organs and even certain tissues.

In an effort to see if partly differentiated cells from diverse sources could influence each other's differentiation, Groves and I (138) mixed dissociated cells of the chick mesonephros and wing bud. In spite of the fact that cells of one type were in intimate contact with those of another type within the aggregate, no new modes of differentiation appeared. Both mesonephric and limb bud tissues were reconstituted, often in characteristic arrangements: keratinizing epidermis on the periphery, cartilage in the center and mesonephric tubules between the two (Fig. 3.2A). Since no way had yet been found to mark the cells, the origin of each cell in the differentiated aggregate remained unknown. At this time Holtfreter, in collaboration with Townes (131), was extending his studies with amphibian material. They took advantage of differences in pigmentation and cell size of the germ layers in a brilliant way to provide the first critical evidence of cell origin in mixed cell aggregates, and thus launched the analysis of reconstitution. In an extensive series of experiments with cells from gastrula and neurula stages, they found that cells move within the aggregate, with ectodermal cells always accumulating at the periphery and endodermal cells in the interior or at the surface, depending on the mixture. Mesoderm cells move to the interior (Fig. 3.2B). Even though precise cell origin was not established in all instances, these experiments provided conclusive proof that the cells tended to segregate according to type and re-establish their former associations. Soon after, Moscona (85) took advantage of the different staining properties of mouse and chick cells (Wolff and Weniger, 159) to show that here, too, cells from one organ sort out from those of another (in this case irrespective of taxonomic differences), as shown in Figure 3.2C.

Natural cell markers made possible the discovery of sorting out, but further analysis required labels of more general applicability. The best candidates were radioactive isotopes. After early attempts to use S^{35} (Trinkaus, 134), tritiated thymidine became available and we found (Trinkaus and Gross, 137) that it is a label par excellence for tracing cells in mixed aggregates. When it was applied to the problem, we were able to confirm previous work and establish that chick cells derived from several organs segregate from other kinds of chick cells.

It appears from these several studies that affinities demonstrated as important at the tissue and organ level (Holtfreter, 59; Chiakulas, 24) apply also at the cell level. Cells of germ layers and

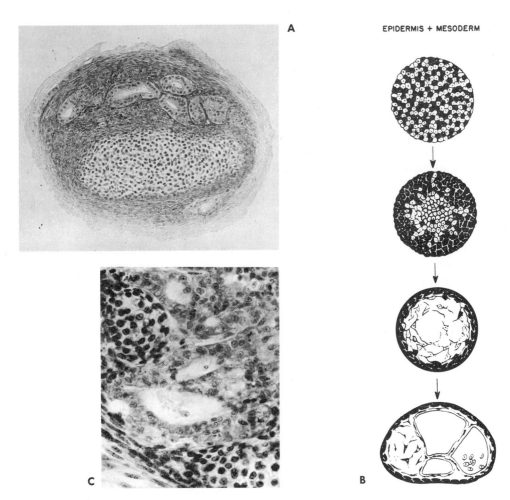

A

EPIDERMIS + MESODERM

Fig. 3.2 A. Mixed aggregate of 5-day chick mesonephros and 5-day chick wing bud cells in a ratio of 1 : 1, after 10 days in culture. Note the regional arrangement of the reconstituted tissues: keratinizing epidermis at the periphery, cartilage toward the center and mesonephric tubules between the two. (From Trinkaus and Groves, *Proc. Natl. Acad. Sci. U.S.* 41:787–795, 1955.) B. Mixed aggregate of prospective epidermal cells and mesodermal cells from an amphibian neurula, showing sorting out by outward movement of epidermal cells and inward movement of mesodermal cells. The latter eventually form mesenchyme, coelomic cavities, and blood cells. (From Townes and Holtfreter, *J. Exptl. Zool.* 128:53–118, 1955.) C. Mixed aggregate of 4-day chick mesonephric cells and 12-day mouse chondrogenic cells, showing sorting out according to histological type. (Courtesy of A. A. Moscona.)

of embryonic organs eventually adhere to cells of like origin. However, since studies of advanced stages invariably utilized cells derived from whole organs, they of course gave no information on specificity at the tissue level. In most organs the tissues are so intermingled that it is virtually impossible to disentangle them and obtain preparations of a single cell type. One place where this can be done is in the eye. The retinal pigment layer consists exclusively of cells of one type and can be easily isolated. Moreover, its cells are readily distinguished because of their black melanin protein granules. We found that when these cells are dissociated and mixed with cell suspensions from a variety of organs they sort out efficiently (Trinkaus, 134, 136). It can be said, therefore, that for the retinal pigment layer, at least, segregation is tissue specific. It would naturally be of interest to know if such selectivity operated in the reconstitution of organs—whether, for example, in an aggregate of mesonephric cells the epithelial tubules are derived exclusively from former tubule cells, the mesenchyme from former mesenchyme cells, and so on. Everyone assumes that this is what happens. But, at the risk of belaboring the obvious, it must be emphasized that the evidence for this assumption is largely lacking. It will come only as we find ways of separating the tissues of complex organs. We already possess an adequate label in tritiated thymidine. It is not impossible that when the experiments are finally performed we shall have a few surprises.

Even though the picture is incomplete, sorting out of cells of like type has obvious histogenetic significance. Some (or most) tissue cells have migratory ability when dissociated and presented with unfamiliar cellular environments. They seem to remain immobile only when adherent to their normal cellular associates. The integrity of cellular contacts in tissues and organs, therefore, does not necessarily depend on intrinsic inability of the cells to move. The immobility of cells in tissues, and hence the topographic stability of the tissues, may rest on the selective adhesion of cells to each other. (Conversely, the mobility of metastatic cancer cells may not be due so much to a newly acquired capacity to move as to a diminution of cellular adhesion.) The possible selective nature of this adhesion, suggested by sorting out, thus emerges as a question of first rank developmental and histological importance. Because of this there has been much effort to explain what is going on.

THEORIES OF CELLULAR SEGREGATION. An adequate theory of sorting out must explain both the eventual cohesion of like cells to form sectors within an aggregate and the positioning of these sectors in a concentric pattern peculiar to each combination (Townes and Holtfreter, 131; Trinkaus and Groves, 138; Moscona, 85). Until recently, the most popular proposals for sorting out assumed random cell movement followed by qualitatively specific adhesion of like cells (Townes and Holtfreter, 131). It is most difficult, however, to explain positioning on the basis of such a mechanism. On the other hand, any mechanism which accounts for positioning will account equally well for sorting out. Three hypotheses have been proposed recently to account for positioning. All three assume all cells to be mutually adhesive at first.

1. *Chemotaxis.* Stefanelli and co-workers (121) and Townes and Holtfreter (131) have suggested that cells respond to and migrate along gradients in concentration of metabolites within an aggregate, either toward or away from the point of highest concentration. (1) The agent could be produced by all cells in the aggregate, in which case the highest concentration would be in the center. This would attract the most sensitive cells to the center of the aggregate and would result in an inner and an outer component. (Alternatively, one cell type could be attracted toward the periphery by a metabolite which is available in the medium.) (2) Another form of chemotaxis would involve migration of one type of cell toward a substance which they, and only they, produce. In a random mixture the concentration of this substance would be highest in the center of the aggregate and so the sensitive cells would move in that direction. Conceivably, they could also form foci of attraction eccentrically, if the cell mixture is not entirely random.

2. *Timing.* Curtis (27, 28, 29) makes the not unreasonable suggestion that the cell surface is modified by dissociating agents. He proposes that tissue cells become migratory because their surface is so modified and that they continue to migrate at random within an aggregate until they recover. With this their adhesiveness rises. It is further assumed that cell movement is promoted by the shearing effects of cells moving over each other. At the surface of the aggregate, cells are in contact over only part of their surface, hence there is less shear. As the cells which first regain adhesiveness reach the surface by random movements, the combined effect of increased adhesiveness and reduced shear will trap them there. As other cells of the same type, also with increased adhesiveness, contact these immobile cells, they will cease movement, trapped by contact inhibition. By this means, cells of the first type to recover will gradually become trapped in the cortex of the aggregate and other cells will be herded by them toward the center. As successive cell types recover, they will become trapped and build up layers of cells. Accordingly, both sorting out and positioning is achieved.

3. *Differential adhesion.* This hypothesis has been promoted recently by Steinberg (122, 123, 124, 126, 127). It assumes that sorting out results entirely from random mobility and quantitative differences in the general adhesiveness of cells and that an aggregate containing cells of more than one kind may be treated as if it were a multiple phase system of immiscible liquids. It further assumes that thermodynamic relationships which govern miscibility and surface spreading in liquids would apply, if by analogy the place of the molecules in the physical system is taken by the cells in the biological system. In order to achieve equilibrium, there must be maximal adhesion of cell surfaces. If these conditions obtain and the cells are motile, they will tend to exchange weaker for stronger adhesions. The distribution of tissue-phases which comes about in a heterogeneous population should then reflect the strengths with which the differing kinds of cells adhere to partners of like and unlike kind. On the basis of this model, Steinberg was able to make predictions which could be checked against cell behavior. Let us assume that an aggregate is composed of two cell types, A and B, and

that A cells cohere more strongly than B cells. If A-B adhesions are intermediate in strength between A-A and B-B adhesions, but weaker than the average of the two, then a population containing A and B cells will tend to form an inside core composed of A cells with the surface occupied exclusively by B cells. (Calculation shows this set of adhesive relationships to be that which should obtain if adhesion between two cells depends simply on the product of the frequencies of adhesive spots on their respective surfaces). Whenever, in a mixture, A cells make the smallest contact with other A cells, they will tend to extend that contact. In this way there will be a continual exchange of heteronomic A-B adhesions for homonomic A-A and B-B cohesions until segregation of the two cellular phases approaches comple-

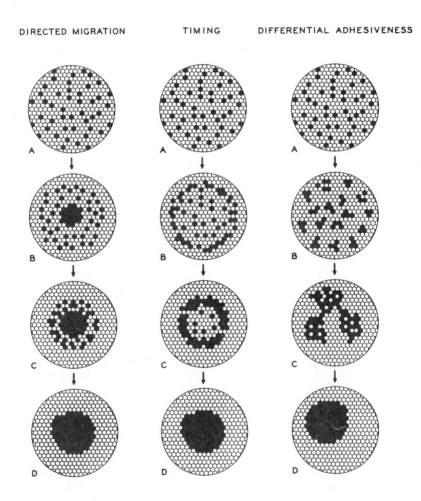

DIRECTED MIGRATION   TIMING   DIFFERENTIAL ADHESIVENESS

Fig. 3.3 The time course of segregation, as it would appear ideally, if brought about through directed migration (chemotaxis), timing, or differential adhesiveness. (From Steinberg, pp. 321–366 in *Cellular Membranes in Development*, M. Locke, ed. Academic Press, 1964.)

tion. The more cohesive A cells will tend to exclude the less cohesive B cells toward the periphery. By default then, the surface of the aggregate will come to be composed entirely of the more weakly cohering B cells. In short, the more cohesive A cells will form the internal component, engulfed by and embedded in a continuous tissue component composed of the less cohesive B cells. Minimization of the area of contact between the concentric phases will cause the boundary area between them to shift toward a spherical form. In summary, by means of cell motility and quantitative differences in general cellular adhesiveness, both sorting out and positioning are achieved. Qualitatively specific adhesion is not a necessary postulate.

We are certainly not yet in a position to decide definitively which of these three hypotheses (or other possible hypotheses) provides the proper explanation, for in no instance have those measurements been made which would provide direct evidence of the postulated differences in cell behavior. There are, nevertheless, certain lines of indirect evidence that permit arguments for and against each.

The first variety of chemotaxis would ideally result in the inner component taking a position in the center of the aggregate in a single cluster. But the inner component, in fact, is usually neither central nor single. Nor does the course of sorting out favor this mechanism (Fig. 3.3), for the first small clusters of the internal component are randomly located within the aggregate (Trinkaus, 134; Steinberg, 126, 127). The facts therefore weigh against chemotaxis of the first variety. This is not to say that cells may not be attracted along chemical gradients. The phe-

nomenon simply is not sufficient to explain sorting out and therefore is not at present the most useful working hypothesis. The second variety of chemotaxis, based on self-produced attractants, does not necessarily require a single central cluster of the internal component and so could give some of the results obtained.

To test the timing hypothesis, Curtis varied the interval between dissociation and reaggregation (28). If the surface position of ectoderm in aggregates of amphibian gastrula cells is due to faster recovery from dissociation, their position should be altered if endoderm cells are allowed to recover first. This is exactly what was found. Endoderm cells dissociated with EDTA 6 hours before ectomesoderm assumed a cortical position when all were mixed. In a similar experiment with several species of sponges, Curtis (30) found that dissociated cells from different species reaggregate at different rates. Cells from two such species sort out when mixed. If the slower aggregating cells are dissociated some hours prior to mixing with cells of the faster species, sorting out does not occur. When cells from sponges with similar rates of aggregation are mixed, they likewise do not sort out.

All of this supports the timing hypothesis, but it is not the whole story. Like chemotaxis, this hypothesis ideally requires the inner component to form a single central cluster (Fig. 3.3), and of course this does not always occur. In fact, when the proportion of cells is small, they sort out poorly and are often distributed at random within the aggregate (an argument against chemotaxis as well).

The most damaging evidence against the timing hypothesis is that the same patterns of positioning obtained in mixed aggregates are duplicated if intact pieces of the same organs or tissues are joined in vitro (Townes and Holtfreter, 131; Steinberg, 124; Bresch 20) (see below). Whatever may be the factors that cause one component to move over the other in these experiments, they are not related to recovery from dissociation. It seems unlikely that peripheral injury from cutting could have differential effects on all the cells. At this time we can say no more than that these contradictory findings await resolution. In the meantime, it must be emphasized that there "is not yet sufficient experimental evidence to decide how changes in surface viscosity under shear affect adhesion and cell motility . . ." (Curtis, 28, p. 121). The timing hypothesis has been damaged, but not eliminated. There is still a possibility that the effects it postulates may on occasion have an important modifying influence on cell segregation. Incidentally, Curtis' experiments with ectoderm and endoderm provide additional evidence against the operation of chemotaxis.

The differential adhesion hypothesis is consistent with and provides an explanation for all features of sorting out that we have described (Fig. 3.3), with the exception of some of Curtis' results. Steinberg has tested his hypothesis in three ways. (1) The hypothesis requires that cells of the internally segregating component only leave the surface of the aggregate. They need not move deep inside. When the proportion of the internally segregating component is reduced, they leave the surface, but once inside tend to remain scattered throughout the interior, with some remaining just beneath the surface, as predicted. (2) Since, accord-

ing to Steinberg, positioning is due to quantitative differences in adhesiveness, it should vary in different cellular combinations. This was demonstrated to be so by mixing cells from several organs in binary combinations. Thus, if in a mixture of types A and B, A cells form the cortex and B cells the core, and of B and C, B cells form the cortex and C the core, then in a mixture of A and C, A should form the cortex and C the core. This occurs, and in this way one can construct a hierarchy in which those lower on the scale (more adhesive) always segregate internally to those higher up. (3) Finally, Steinberg has shown that cells need not be dissociated in order to achieve the equilibrium positioning proper for each combination. Intact pieces of tissue behave in the same way. A chunk of cartilage will be surrounded by a piece of pigmented retina and heart will be engulfed by embryonic liver. Townes and Holtfreter (131) obtained similar results with intact germ layer explants from amphibian gastrulae and neurulae.

Even with the impressive support that these observations give to the differential adhesion hypothesis there are several questions that remain.

1. We do not know whether the postulated differences in adhesiveness actually exist. Nor is it easy to gain information on this question. The adhesiveness of cell surfaces is difficult to measure and the results have not yet yielded to undisputed interpretation (Taylor, 129; L. Weiss, 148). Furthermore, it is not really required that adhesion between molecules be represented in aggregates by adhesion between cells. Abercrombie (2) has pointed out that any cellular behavior which reduces the probability of sepa-

ration, once cells have collided, will in theory serve instead of adhesion. L. Weiss (147) has repeatedly emphasized that what keeps cells together may not really be their adhesion, which may be essentially complete, but the resistance of their membranes to rupture. One could also substitute an inhibition of locomotion for adhesiveness. For the moment, it seems profitable to go along with Steinberg and consider that adhesiveness is really involved. But the question awaits direct measurements for an answer.

2. Another question concerns the manner of cluster formation by the internally segregating component. It is known from histological analysis of mixed aggregates of chick cells that during the first day the potentially internal cells form small homonomic clusters which are randomly distributed. Toward the end of the second day, almost all cells become concentrated in a smaller number of larger clusters, but seldom in a single large cluster. This is more readily explained by the differential adhesion hypothesis than by the other two hypotheses. Sometimes, however, segregation is very incomplete indeed, and ceases when the internal component is still distributed in several clusters. This raises a serious question. If cell clusters as well as individual cells can move and join within the aggregate and if the process of exchange of heteronomic for homonomic adhesions proceeds to completion (as is required by the hypothesis), all cells of the internally segregating component should ultimately come to cohere in a single large internal mass. It is therefore essential to know whether clusters of the internally segregating cells can move. But an exchange of heteronomic for

homonomic adhesions is not the only conceivable mechanism for cluster enlargement. A possibility which has not been eliminated is an exchange of homonomic adhesions for heteronomic ones at one phase of the process, with certain small clusters composed of more weakly cohering homonomic cells tending to disaggregate. The cells thus freed would resume migratory movements within the aggregate and eventually contact and cohere more firmly with those homonomic clusters which have persisted. By this means the latter would enlarge. If the internally segregating component of a mixed aggregate is indeed the more cohesive one, this should not occur.

3. Both the directed migration and timing hypotheses demand considerable migratory ability on the part of the cells. The differential adhesion hypothesis, on the contrary, does not demand cell migrations of long distances. There are only two reasons for movement to occur. More adhesive cells will tend to leave the surface of the aggregate. But they need not go far. There will also be an exchange of weaker heteronomic adhesions for stronger homonomic cohesions. Cells will tend to spread maximally over adjacent cells for maximum adhesive contact. This will cause them to move a short distance and increase the probability of their contacting homonomic cells. This could explain the dendritic shapes assumed by retinal pigment cells during the migratory phase (Trinkaus, 134, 136). Then, as homonomic cells cohere and pack together, they will tend to lose the spread-out condition and take on a more polyhedral form, as indeed is the case with retinal pigment cells. If internally segregating cells do not have homonomic cells in

the vicinity and thus fail to contact them, they may exhibit no translocation and sorting, simply exercising in place. In such a situation they might retain the spindle or dendritic shape. Significantly, individual retinal pigment cells which have failed to find a mate tend to remain dendritic.

It is evident that detailed knowledge of the movements of cells and cell clusters within the aggregate would answer some critical questions and provide a further test of the hypotheses. To gain this information, it is necessary to observe segregation directly. All conclusions reached up to this point had a strong element of extrapolation in them, based as they were solely on fixed material. One must study sorting out at closely timed intervals in individual living cell aggregates, in which the internally segregating cells are visually distinguishable. Moreover, the aggregates must be three-dimensional systems in which sorting out occurs in an exclusively cellular environment, rather than on an inert substratum, such as glass. Lentz and I (139) decided to make such a study and chose as our system mixed aggregates of retinal pigment cells and heart cells of the chick embryo. In this combination the pigment cells constitute the internally segregating component and are readily visible because of their melanin-protein granules. We varied the proportions of the two cell types and followed the entire process of sorting out photographically, at closely timed intervals.

The onset of sorting out of retinal pigment cells is already evident within a few hours after segregation. It continues steadily and is almost complete by 48 hours. During this phase, individual cells appear to move only very short distances (10–30 μ). The movements seem to be random, except, of course, for those cells which were initially at the surface. These move internally. Sorting out is less complete when the proportion of pigment cells to heart cells is reduced to less than 1 : 4, and very incomplete when it is reduced to 1 : 16.

With a sufficient proportion of pigment cells, small clusters form internally at random within a few hours. No clusters have been observed to move except those so tiny as to be just distinguishable from individual cells. Clusters enlarge by accretion, the adhesive addition of individual cells and tiny clusters (Fig. 3.4). As they enlarge, they often contact adjacent clusters and fuse. Clusters also change shape constantly, presumably because of pigment cells spreading over each other, and by this means adjacent clusters also abut and fuse (Fig. 3.5). Once small clusters of pigment cells have formed, they persist, and it is possible to trace them from hour to hour and day to day, unless they lose their identity by fusing with adjacent clusters. There is no sign of disaggregation into still smaller clusters or individual cells. One would predict from these observations that the higher the proportion of pigment cells, the smaller the number and the larger the size of the clusters they form. This is in fact the case. During the final phases of sorting out (after approximately 48 hours), the clusters which have increased in size, due to accretion and fusion with other clusters, now round up and become more compact, as expected if the cells cohere maximally. There is also a contraction of networks of interconnected clusters of pigment cells to form more compact cell masses. As clusters be

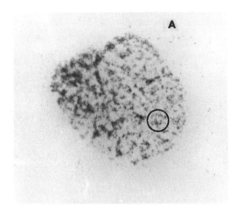
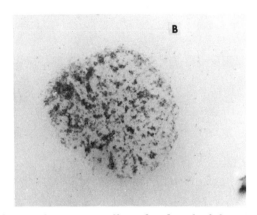

Fig. 3.4 Mixed aggregate of 5½-day chick retinal pigment cells and 4-day chick heart cells in the proportion of 1 : 4. Note pigment cell clusters forming by the aggregation of loose groups of pigment cells (for example, inside circle). A. 23 hours in culture. B. 34 hours in culture. (From Trinkaus and Lentz, *Develop. Biol.* 9:115–136, 1964.)

come more compact, some of those in contact pull apart, as expected if their cohesive contact is tenuous. This is not readily explained by the second form of chemotaxis and constitutes evidence against it.

These results clearly favor the selective adhesion hypothesis, at least insofar as the sorting out of retinal pigment cells from heart cells is concerned. Pigment cells move internally over very short distances and, as predicted, segregate poorly when the proportion of them is low. Clusters of pigment cells do not disaggregate, do not move, and fuse only when brought into contact by accretion or form changes. This explains why (in the range where sorting out occurs) the smaller the proportion of pigment cells, the smaller the size and the larger the number of clusters. In view of all this, the selective adhesion hypothesis seems the most likely mechanism of sorting out in mixed cell aggregates.

There are, however, still other questions — most immediate is why clusters of retinal pigment cells do not move.

DeHaan (35) has observed the movement of clusters of heart cells in an exclusively cellular environment in the chick blastoderm. Perhaps lack of movement of pigment cell clusters is related to the low mobility of individual pigment cells (p. 96).

Although retinal pigment cells show surprisingly low migratory powers when mixed with heart cells (and this fits the differential adhesion hypothesis), it would be premature to generalize. They might migrate more actively on other cellular substrata. Also, other kinds of cells may have greater powers of movement. Heart cells, for example, may migrate more actively than pigment cells, as suggested by their behavior on glass (Trinkaus and Lentz, 139). In point of fact, however, we know nothing about their movements in these aggregates. The problem will be to find a means of following them.

Since it has been thought that cells cease moving as they sort out, it has been suggested that contact inhibition is at work (Curtis, 27). Because of the

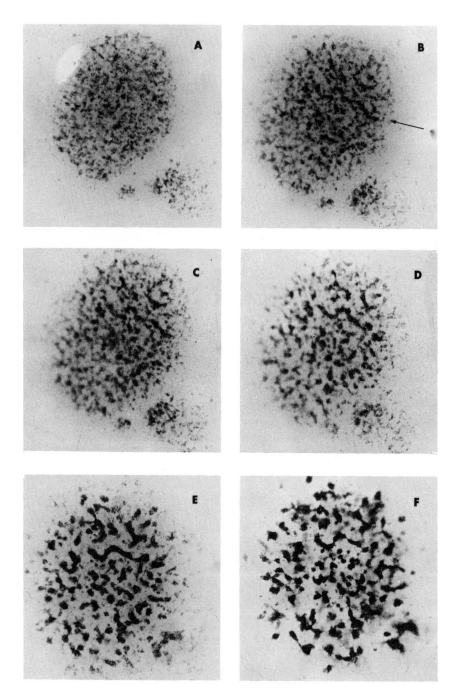

Fig. 3.5 Mixed aggregate of 5½-day chick retinal pigment cells and 4-day heart cells in a ratio of 1 : 4, showing the formation of small clusters of pigment cells and their gradual fusion to form larger clusters. Note in particular the fusion of several randomly arranged clusters to form a single, large, elongate cluster (arrow on *B*). Clusters do not move. In *E* and *F*, clusters are condensing. This causes some clusters to pull apart (see text). *A*. 12 hours in culture. *B*. 20 hours in culture. *C*. 23 hours in culture. *D*. 34 hours in culture. *E*. 68 hours in culture. *F*. 5 days in culture. (From Trinkaus and Lentz, *Develop. Biol.* 9:115–136, 1964.)

relative ease of studying cell behavior on a transparent inert substratum, the possible similarity of contact inhibition and segregation has much experimental interest. No direct test has yet been made, but certain observations are pertinent. Clusters of retinal pigment cells continually change shape, suggesting that cells are not immobilized but are changing position within the clusters. Weiss (151) observed that cell movement continues in homonomic aggregates of liver, lung, and kidney cells. If contact inhibition is at work in these cell clusters, surely it is at reduced intensity in comparison with its operation at the glass-medium interface. Another characteristic of a contact-inhibited system is the continual pulling away of the marginal cells. In contrast, once retinal pigment cells have cohered within a mixed aggregate, we have never observed them to break away again.

An appealing feature of the differential adhesion hypothesis is the fact that it simultaneously provides a basis for adhesion of like and unlike cells, and sets the stage for an analysis of the genesis and maintenance of organ architecture. The cohesion of like with like (isoaffinity) is necessary to establish and maintain the integrity of individual tissues. But it is the adhesion of unlike cells (heteroaffinity) that binds different tissues together to form organs (Holtfreter, 59). Heteroadhesion is clearly a subject that deserves more consideration. Additional means must be found for separating organs into their constituent tissues (cf. Trinkaus, 134) and for studying contact behavior of more mature cells (cf. Moscona, 87). And, more attention must be paid to the best-known heteroadhesion of all — sperm and egg. Recent evidence that egg and sperm membranes actually fuse to form a continuous membrane during fertilization (Colwin and Colwin, 25) is most suggestive in the light of proposals that cell surfaces differ only quantitatively.

Finally, all of this work on the adhesiveness of cells to each other and various other substrata raises fascinating problems of mechanism which go beyond the scope of this chapter. How may the image of the cell surface revealed by the electron microscope (Overton, 93; Robertson, 102) be accounted for in chemical terms (Abercrombie and Ambrose, 4)? How may one measure cellular adhesiveness (L. Weiss, 148; Steinberg, 127)? What are the physical and chemical forces that hold cells together and push them apart (Curtis, 27, 29; Pethica, 95; L. Weiss, 147, 148; Rosenberg, 105; DeHaan and Ebert, 37)? Are cells bound together directly at their surfaces or by a stable intervening intercellular material (Grobstein, 49a, 49b; Moscona, 86, 87; Humphreys, 66a; Steinberg, 125)? These questions represent areas which at present are richer in speculation than in firm conclusions, because of a paucity of hard facts. Nevertheless, they are basic to all that we discuss in this chapter and will attract increasing research effort with each passing year.

Mechanisms of Gastrulation

Although gastrulation may be conveniently divided into a number of particular movements for convenience of analysis, it is essentially a phenomenon of the whole, whose cardinal feature is integration. It is a system par excellence where understanding of the whole process is necessary for a meaningful comprehension of each separate part. I will therefore not attempt a comparative or horizontal approach, in which each constituent movement is idealized. In my opinion, this is not at present the most profitable tack. The temporal sequence and geographical extent of the different movements vary so greatly from one group to another that, in a sense, each organism is a special case whose particular characteristics must be appreciated before we can even begin an analysis. Accordingly, I will take a vertical approach and consider, each in its turn, several organisms whose gastrulation has been subjected to analysis. Hopefully, certain general features, which may apply across the board, will emerge from the presentation.

Amphibian Gastrulation

In modern times the analysis of the mechanism of amphibian gastrulation has rested largely in the hands of one man, Johannes Holtfreter (60, 61, 62, 64, 131), and, indeed, if it were not for his extensive investigations we would have little to say about these movements today. It is also questionable how much we would have to say about mechanisms of morphogenetic movements in other forms; for his was the first concerted attack on the problem and it has kindled the interest of many.

Holtfreter (60) placed great emphasis on his concept that all superficial cells are united by a gelated extracellular "surface coat." Electronmicrographs, however, have cast doubt on its existence. Some workers find no unifying extra layer applied to the electron dense boundaries of superficial cells (Karasaki, 68; Balinsky, 12). Others, however, find a layer of variable density and thickness applied to the surface of early blastomeres of some forms (Wartenberg and Schmidt, 146; Dollander, 44). The meaning of these con-

tradictory results is not clear, but it should be pointed out that if the coat consisted of mucopolysaccharides, as would seem likely (Bell, 15), it would have very low electron density and be very difficult to detect in the electron microscope. What then is the status of the surface coat? Even though it is in doubt, Holtfreter's observations on the properties of the superficial cell layer remain valid. In the absence of positive and repeatable demonstrations of the coat, it seems wisest to assume provisionally that the "surface coat" is a logical artifact, in that its several characteristics probably depend on different structures. Its low adhesiveness could depend on the outer surfaces of the superficial cells or on a thin layer of extracellular material. The tight cohesion of these cells could be due to close adhesion of their lateral boundaries. It is significant in this regard that the lateral boundaries of these cells are more electron dense near their distal ends, suggesting desmosomelike differentiations (Dollander, 45), and closer to the boundaries of the next cell (70–90 A, as opposed to 110–200 A more proximally) (Balinsky, 12).

The first sign of invagination is the deformation of certain vegetal cells into an elongate bottle shape in the prospective blastopore region. These bottle cells progressively attenuate until the bulk of each cell has moved completely into the interior. Significantly, their outer surfaces remain in contact at the egg surface, even though the neck of the bottle becomes stretched enormously (Fig. 3.6). These cells have attracted attention for years, but it is Holtfreter's analysis (61, 62), which has led us closest to a correct concept of their function. Wherever bottle cells appear, the egg surface is

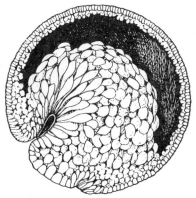

Fig. 3.6 Schematized section through an amphibian gastrula showing elongate bottle cells. (From Holtfreter, *J. Exptl. Zool.* 94: 261–318, 1943.)

slightly indented. As they become more and more attenuated and as their number increases, the indentations deepen and merge to form the beginning blastopore. They are confined to the anterior front of the invagination mass and their attenuation reaches its maximum when the archenteron has penetrated halfway into the blastocoel. Bottle cells are obviously deeply involved in invagination. The question is how. Do they play a causal role or are they simply a natural consequence of infolding?[1]

Holtfreter followed Rhumbler (101) in proposing that the bottle cells initiate invagination and in suggesting that the expansion of their inner membranes is due to low surface tension, caused by the high pH of the blastocoelic fluid (Buytendijk and Woerdeman, 23). These ideas on membrane expansion have been seriously questioned by Stableford (120), who showed that invagination continues in eggs whose blastocoel has been

[1] Baker (10a) has recently shown that bottle cells protrude long microvilli at their distal surfaces, which interdigitate tightly with adjacent cells. These may well anchor bottle cells at the archenteron surface. No surface coat is evident.

opened and exposed to widely varying pH's. On the other hand, Shapiro (114) has found that perfusion with Holtfreter's solution at pH 7–8 suppresses invagination, while solutions at pH 6–7 and pH 8–9 favor it. The solution is obviously confused. This is not to say, however, that bottle cells are not important in invagination. Holtfreter has presented very impressive evidence that they are, but only if they cohere at their outer ends. A group of blastoporal endoderm cells placed on blastocoelic endoderm immediately adheres and sinks in. Dissections reveal that bottle cells have squeezed between cells of the substratum. They retain their outer connections, but the active pulling force of the deeply rooted bottle cells is so great that the surface is partly dragged into the substratum and a small blastopore forms. Beginning invagination is beautifully simulated. If the graft is deep endoderm, cells slip in but no blastopore is formed (Fig. 3.7).

It appears, therefore, that bottle cells are responsible for beginning invagination. Tight cohesion at their outer ends probably communicates the pull to other endoderm and to mesoderm cells. Since bottle cells may arise independently of the pH of the medium (Stableford, 120), their formation appears to depend on ill-understood interactions with their cellular substratum. In line with the differential adhesion hypothesis, we would expect bottle cells to possess greater adhesiveness than inner endoderm cells. But then, why would they be in the surface layer? Actually, we don't know the answer, but perhaps they are held there by the very low adhesiveness of their outer surfaces. Incidentally, this property of the outer surface probably prevents the mutual adhesion of the mar-

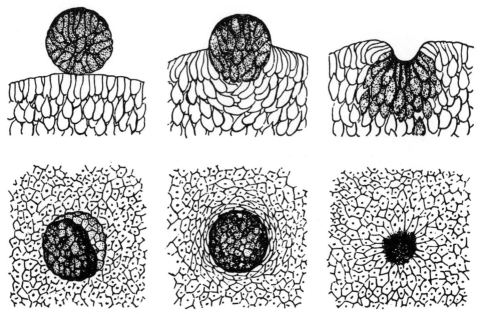

Fig. 3.7 A graft of amphibian blastoporal cells sinking into an endodermal substratum (left to right) to form a blastoporal groove. Upper row, sections; lower row, surface views. (From Holtfreter, *J. Exptl. Zool.* 95:171–212, 1943.)

ginal zone and yolk plug at points where they contact each other, as both slip into the interior.

Once invagination is begun, what forces cause it to continue? Schechtman (111) and Holtfreter (62) found that if presumptive chordamesoderm from the dorsal lip is grafted to inner endoderm, both the graft and its cells elongate along their anteroposterior axes, which suggests that they are endowed with an autonomous capacity for oriented stretching. Holtfreter then found that if surface presumptive mesoderm is grafted to deep endoderm, cells of the graft move into the surrounding endoderm and form a short archenteron. This is a puzzling result, because mesoderm does not normally penetrate the endoderm; it glides on its surface. One possible explanation is that invagination movement normally

is prevented by adhesion of the mesoderm to the undersurface of the ectoderm. Sure enough, when ectoderm of a neurula is removed, the mesoderm contracts into patches and sinks into the endoderm. The orderly, integrated involution of mesoderm obviously is poorly understood, but it seems to be due to a number of factors, involving all three germ layers.

Meanwhile, back at the surface of the egg, the ectoderm is spreading in epiboly. What forces are responsible for this spreading? Is the ectoderm pulled and stretched by the invaginating marginal zone or does it have spreading properties of its own, like an epithelial sheet in culture? The latter is definitely the answer, for an isolated piece of superficial ectoderm will spread over any deep cells of the same age. This is most suggestive and possibly due to its low adhesiveness. As a matter of fact, ectoderm deprived of its superficial layer behaves very differently; it moves underneath superficial ectoderm and invades endoderm. The independent spreading of pieces of ectoderm suggested that individual ectoderm cells may be endowed with the capacity to spread independently. To test for this, Holtfreter dissociated ectoderm and cultured the cells in Holtfreter's solution on glass. The cells adhere to each other and to the substratum almost immediately and then, after about 30 minutes, flatten, and spread on the glass. Not all ectoderm cells show this behavior, but Holtfreter contends that they do it more frequently than isolated mesoderm or neural cells (cf. Jones and Elsdale, 67). Although a really quantitative comparison would be desirable, one is justified in drawing a provisional conclusion. The spreading of the ectodermal sheet appears to depend on the spreading activities of its constituent cells. Just how this comes about within the sheet is not at all understood (cf. Jones and Elsdale, 67). The regimentation of the spreading of individual cells into the coordinate spreading of a sheet is no doubt dependent upon their tight cohesion.

In the light of these studies, the strikingly different behavior of superficial and inner ectoderm layers requires further study. It would be of great interest to know, for example, whether dissociated deep ectoderm cells behave like outer ectoderm cells, both on glass and in mixed aggregates. Superficial ectoderm cells move to the surface of an aggregate of dissociated cells (Townes and Holtfreter, 131). Would inner ectoderm do the same?

Since a grafted piece of ectoderm spreads centrifugally in all directions, it lacks polarity. How then account for its oriented spreading in epiboly? Contact guidance by an oriented substratum is possible, but not really necessary. By replacing the mesoderm and endoderm as they undergo involution, the spreading ectoderm merely follows the path of least resistance and through no effort of its own is bound to spread in an oriented fashion. This is a nice illustration of how a directional movement of one layer can impose direction on another, so that its movement is coordinated with the pattern of the whole gastrula.

Endoderm is also a spreading layer and much of what has been said about ectoderm applies to it as well. Superficial presumptive endoderm spreads over deeper cells. If ectoderm is removed from a neurula, endoderm spreads out of the blastopore over the mesoderm, in reversed epiboly. This is normally prevented by the spreading ectoderm. In a sense, the two layers are in competition. Here again, the integration of a spreading layer with the pattern of the whole gastrulae depends on its relation to another layer. The extensive spreading capacity of the endoderm is limited by the spreading ectodermal sheet to just that amount proper for coordinated gastrulation. In short, epiboly of the ectoderm is necessary to maintain the archenteron!

Expansion of an endodermal sheet seems, as in the case of the ectoderm, to rest on the spreading activities of its individual cells, as shown by their tendency to flatten in culture. But a number of questions must be raised. Some are the same as for the ectoderm; others are distinctive to the endoderm. For example, how may we explain the contraction of endoderm as invagination begins and its subsequent expansion within the archenteron?

During his analysis, Holtfreter (61, 62) anticipated Steinberg (127) by pointing to the possible importance of adhesiveness in determining whether cells will infiltrate or spread. He showed that mesoderm is engulfed by endoderm and concluded that mesoderm is more cohesive. Deep endoderm is in turn engulfed by superficial ectoderm. If differences in adhesiveness are indeed critical, superficial ectoderm would then be the least cohesive of all and mesoderm should be engulfed by it, which of course it is. This gives a hierarchy of increasing adhesiveness: ectoderm, endoderm, mesoderm. But mesoderm, which should be interior to endoderm, is of course between ectoderm and endoderm at the end of gastrulation. The modifying effect of the nonadhesive ectoderm surface could be crucial. Ectoderm stripped of its superficial layer in fact is engulfed by endoderm. It would be of great interest to know if inner ectoderm would likewise be engulfed by mesoderm. This has not been done, but if we assume the predicted result, we could solve the problem of gastrulation by assuming that the ectoderm cells are actually the most cohesive of all on their inner surfaces, but have their over-all cohesiveness drastically reduced by their nonadhesive outer surfaces. According to Steinberg (127), this would put the ectoderm at the periphery, because its average cohesiveness is the lowest. But since the inner surface of the ectoderm is most cohesive, mesoderm, which is more cohesive than endoderm, would take the intermediary position and adhere to the inner surface of the ectoderm and

spread on it. This would account for expansion of the roof of the archenteron and in part for mesodermal invagination. Endoderm would then spread on the inner surface of the more cohesive mesoderm in gut formation. All this would partially explain the disposition of the germ layers. Everything depends on the postulated properties of the ectoderm.

In summary, we now possess a working picture of the mechanism of amphibian gastrulation (see review of Picken, 97). Gastrulation begins as the superficial endodermal cells of the blastoporal region actively sink into the deep endoderm to form bottle cells. Because their outer ends are tightly coherent, the surface is indented, other endoderm cells are dragged in, and a beginning archenteron is formed. The prospective mesoderm follows, apparently in part because of an inherent tendency to stretch in an anteroposterior direction, and spreads on the highly adhesive undersurface of the ectoderm. Meanwhile, the ectoderm cells display their inherent spreading capacity by expanding over the invaginating mesoderm and replacing it as it disappears from the surface. Ectoderm cells gain their lower average cohesiveness from their nonadhesive outer surfaces. The superficial endoderm possesses properties similar to the ectoderm and in consequence spreads extensively to line the archenteron and aid in its enlargement. The greater spreading tendency of the ectoderm confines the spreading of the endoderm to the lining of the archenteron and thus prevents a reversal of involution.

It is a rather neat picture, internally consistent and profusely documented. It provides a sound basis for continuing investigation. However, we need to know more about the ectoderm. If it does not play the role assigned to it, the whole structure collapses. Then there is the difficult problem of cell surface adhesiveness. Do the postulated quantitative differences actually exist? How can we account for regional differences in the behavior of marginal zone and yolk plug endoderm cells, some forming bottle cells, others not (cf. Dan, 31)? By what mechanism do cells adhere to each other during these extensive movements? When in development do isolated ectoderm and endoderm cells begin to spread? Jones and Elsdale (67) have recently made a most interesting observation. Differentiation of gastrula cells in culture into the first tissue types is preceded by flattening on the substratum. Does this mean that both gastrulation and histogenesis are initiated by an increase in cellular adhesiveness?

Echinoderm Invagination

In echinoderm eggs the archenteron forms in a classical textbook fashion from a cell sheet one cell layer thick. The vegetal plate invaginates into the blastocoel with little or no involution and little growth or cell division. Invagination continues until the tip of the archenteron reaches the animal pole and turns ventrally to fuse with the future mouth region. The process appears so similar in the several species that have been studied that it seems justifiable to combine the evidence.

The modern attack began with the observation of Moore and Burt (89) that the first $\frac{1}{4}$–$\frac{1}{3}$ of invagination can occur in the absence of the animal half of the egg. Forces intrinsic to the vegetal plate appear to be responsible. Kinnander and Gustafson (70), using time-lapse cinemicrography, found that during this first phase the columnar cells of the vegetal plate round up on their inner borders, indicating reduced contact with each other. However, they retain full contact with the hyaline plasma layer at their outer surfaces. The rounded inner surface shows pulsatile activity. If contact between columnar cells is reduced, the sheet is bound to increase in area. Gustafson and Wolpert (54) postulate that the vegetal plate is confined by the tightly constructed blastocoel wall (Balinsky, 11) and therefore cannot spread as a flat sheet. The alternative is to curve. Since reduced cellular contact occurs at the inner surface, curvature will be in that direction and invagination will begin. This is a neat idea and could well be correct.

Primary invagination eventually stops. Beginning of the second phase is always associated with the formation of filopodia spun out from the secondary mesenchyme cells at the tip of the archenteron. These filopodia eventually reach the inner aspect of the blastocoel wall, where they adhere intermittently and exert contractile tension (resembling in exaggerated form the ruffled membrane of fibroblasts) (Fig. 3.8). It has been proposed that these filopodia exert sufficient tension to stretch and pull the archenteron to the animal pole (Dan and Okazaki, 32; Gustafson and Kinnander, 50).

The evidence must provide affirmative answers to two questions, if the proposal is valid: (1) Do the filopodia exert sufficient force to stretch the archenteron to double or more of its length? (2) Is the contractile pull of the filopodia indispensable for the second phase of invagination? The answer to the first question appears to be positive.

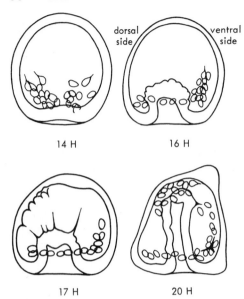

14 H   16 H

17 H   20 H

Fig. 3.8 Diagrammatic representation of gastrulation in the sea urchin, *Psammechinus miliaris*. Approximate age in hours is indicated. 14 H. Mesenchyme blastula at the onset of gastrulation. 16 H. Profile of an early gastrula—at the end of primary invagination—showing beginning dorsoventrality and the ring of primary mesenchyme. 17 H. Gastrula at the onset of the second phase of invagination, showing filopodial activity of secondary mesenchyme cells at the tip of the archenteron rudiment. 20 H. Gastrula at the end of invagination showing release of secondary mesenchyme from the archenteron tip, and pronounced dorsoventrality. (From Gustafson and Wolpert, *Intern. Rev. Cytol.* 15:139–214, 1963.)

Dan and Okazaki (32) and Dan (31) showed by the following evidence that filopodia exert enough contractile tension to pull the blastocoel wall inward at the animal pole. When gastrulae are caused to exogastrulate, no filopodial attachments are in evidence. Reinvagination of such an exogastrula will only occur if the archenteron is reattached to the blastocoel wall by filopodia. In these "entoexogastrulae" the force exerted may be so great that it stretches the archenteron wall to the

breaking point, the upper part then being pulled to the animal pole. From all this, it is evident that secondary mesenchyme filopodia collectively exert considerable contractile tension, probably sufficient to account for secondary invagination.

Gustafson and his colleagues have provided the main evidence on the second question. Taking full advantage of time-lapse photography, they have followed all of invagination in exquisite detail. The second phase of invagination is always accompanied by attachment of the archenteron tip to the blastocoel wall by filopodia. After completion of the primary phase, invagination stagnates somewhat and recommences or accelerates only when filopodial attachments are made. If secondary mesenchyme cells pull out of the tip of the archenteron, invagination slows down or stops and does not begin again until new filopodia attach. In gastrulae vegetalized with lithium chloride (Gustafson and Wolpert, 51), good secondary invagination is always associated with good filopodial attachments, and poor invagination with poor attachments.

This evidence is very impressive, but we are reminded by Gustafson and Wolpert (54, p. 142) that correlations of this sort can only support or disprove a hypothesis, they cannot constitute proof. Actually the correlation between the beginning of the second phase and the presence of connecting filopodia is not always clear. Could there be some autonomous extension of the archenteron at the beginning of the second phase? The attachments of filopodia have been carefully traced and conform to the demands of the hypothesis during the last half of invagination. But at the completion of the first phase the archenteron tip is only approximately ⅓ the way to the animal pole and is, in fact, nearest the lateral and even vegetal areas of the blastocoel wall. Filopodia might accordingly be expected to attach preponderantly to these regions. Published photographs appear to fulfill this expectation (Gustafson and Wolpert, 54, p. 186, Fig. 19c), and we ourselves have observed a similar situation in another sea urchin (*Lytechinus*). In such circumstances, secondary invagination should be opposed by the tension exerted by many or even most of the filopodia. Nevertheless, invagination proceeds. This suggests that some autonomous extension may be occurring at this time. A characteristic feature of the second phase is the thinning of the archenteron wall, as of any expanding epithelial sheet. Does this thinning begin before filopodial attachments are evident? In *Lytechinus* it does. At the moment these observations permit only questions about the middle phase. Is it possible that some autonomous extension of the archenteron wall occurs at this time? If so, the filopodia would have a dual role. They would exert both a pulling force and at the same time anchor the archenteron in place, so that as it extends it is not in danger of retracting.

Wolpert and Gustafson (53, 54) are much impressed by the apparent similarities of several morphogenetic processes in early echinoderm development and have made an inviting attempt to explain all in terms of three cell properties: random motility, differential adhesiveness, and filopodial contraction. Since thus far the evidence is mostly descriptive, these postulates at present lack proof. Nonetheless, the arguments are persuasive and a careful examination of the reasoning will profit anyone interested in morphogenesis. At the very least, the effort is noteworthy and refreshing in contrast to the usual pessimistic attitude that such processes are so complex as almost to resist analysis (see Spiegelman, 116, p. 491).

Teleost Epiboly

Teleost eggs have attracted attention for the analysis of gastrulation because of the spectacular extent of their epiboly. For this reason, and because the germ layers are not easily separated, research on mechanism has been devoted almost entirely to epiboly.

The first concerted study of teleost epiboly was by Warren H. Lewis (74, 75). Inasmuch as his hypothesis was the point of take-off for other studies, it is appropriate that we consider it first. Lewis worked mainly on the egg of *Brachydanio rerio* and became impressed by the contractility of the surface gel layer of the yolk. His observations have been confirmed and extended by Devillers for *Salmo* (38, 39) and by myself for *Fundulus* (132, 133). The yolk gel layer constitutes the membrane of the fluid yolk sphere. It connects at first to the margin of the early blastoderm and later to the margin of the syncytial periblast, as the latter extends peripherally to the blastoderm. The gel layer is nonadhesive on its outer surface and sticky on its inner. When it is punctured, the wound widens within seconds, demonstrating that the membrane is under considerable contractile tension. Then, as the edges of the wound thicken, the gap closes in a few minutes. If the blastoderm margin is near, it is pulled toward the point of wound closure. Afterward, the semispherical shape of the egg is restored, indicating that the layer exerts contractile tension tangentially and uniformly in all directions. This is confirmed by the fact that two or three wounds widen simultaneously in different parts of the same yolk gel layer.

On the basis of such evidence, Lewis (74, 75) proposed that the yolk gel layer is the prime mover in epiboly. His hypothesis assumes that before epiboly begins the contractile tension of the yolk gel layer is balanced by that of the blastoderm and periblast. Then, the contractile tension of the latter two is presumed to decrease and upset the balance, allowing the yolk gel layer to pull the blastoderm to the vegetal pole. The gel layer is thought also to exert pressure on the yolk mass, causing it to act as a sort of hydrostatic cushion compressed against the periblast and blastoderm and expanding them.

In testing this hypothesis, it must be shown first of all that the yolk gel layer exerts sufficient tension to stretch the blastoderm over the yolk in epiboly. There is no information on the amount of this tension other than what has already been described. This does not indicate whether it is adequate. Secondly, it must be shown that the contractile tension exerted by the yolk gel layer is directly responsible for epiboly. In *Fundulus*, the periblast begins to spread prior to the blastoderm (Trinkaus, 133). In consequence, the blastoderm begins epiboly by spreading over the periblast. Similarly, at the end of epiboly the periblast moves ahead and closes its blastopore prior to the blastoderm. With this the yolk gel layer ceases to exist. Nevertheless, the blastoderm completes its epiboly by spreading over the periblast. Blastoderm epiboly thus begins and ends without a connection to the yolk gel layer.

If now the marginal connection of the blastoderm to the periblast is severed, the blastoderm retracts immediately, then slowly reattaches to the periblast substratum and resumes its expansion (Trinkaus, 133). In early to middle epiboly the reattached blastoderm spreads faster than the periblast and catches up to its margin. It then moves ahead with the periblast (Fig. 3.9). If the experiment is performed during late epiboly, the blastoderm behaves differently. Its margin contracts with such force that in closing its blastopore it pinches off the remaining uncovered yolk. As the yolk is constricted, contractile tension in the yolk gel layer would tend to oppose constriction of the periblast. The latter continues anyway, demonstrating that its force is greater than that of the yolk gel layer. The blastoderm readheres to the periblast and spreads over it to close its own blastopore.

Since the blastoderm may spread epibolically, even though it lacks a connection to the yolk gel layer, it is clear that the contractile pull of the layer is not necessary to stretch the blastoderm in epiboly. Accordingly, the yolk gel layer hypothesis is not supported by the facts and has lost its usefulness as a guide to the study of teleost epiboly (Trinkaus, 133). Devillers does not share this opinion. He considers the yolk gel layer to be a "supplementary force which is not negligible" (Devillers, 42 p. 414). This is still a possibility, but there is no proof.

These experiments directed attention to certain remarkable properties of the blastoderm and the syncytial periblast. The blastoderm clearly has an intrinsic capacity to spread, using the periblast as a substratum. And

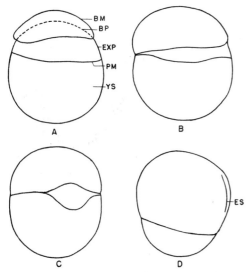

Fig. 3.9 Re-expansion of a reattached blastoderm of an early gastrula over the periblast in *Fundulus heteroclitus*. Time intervals since severance of the marginal connection of the blastoderm to the margin of the periblast: A. 30 minutes. B. 105 minutes. C. 330 minutes. D. 480 minutes. BM, blastoderm; BP, periblast underneath blastoderm; ES, embryonic shield; EXP, exposed periblast; PM, margin of periblast; YS, yolk sphere. (Modified from Trinkaus, *J. Exptl. Zool.* 118:269–319, 1951.)

The blastoderm pushes up a perpendicular protuberance instead, thus expressing its intrinsic capacity for expansion. A similar dependence of blastoderm on periblast is found in *Fundulus*. Even though a reattached blastoderm spreads faster than the periblast, it slows down to the rate of the latter when their margins coincide. It never pushes beyond to move over the yolk.

It is obvious from all this that the manner of adhesion between blastoderm and periblast is a matter of some importance. It is therefore of interest that when the marginal adhesion of a gastrula blastoderm to the periblast is severed, the blastoderm promptly retracts, indicating that it is under tension and that marginal cells adhere more strongly to the periblast than do more central cells. This recalls other spreading epithelial sheets (see pp. 64–65 and p. 93, this chapter), and suggests that marginal cells may be the prime movers in epiboly, exerting tension on the blastoderm by their outward spreading. This could explain why rate of linear marginal advance is the best parameter of blastoderm epiboly (Milkman and Trinkaus, 82). The spreading activity of the marginal cells is clearly of crucial importance and requires closer study. The capacity for strong adhesion is not an exclusive property of normal marginal cells, however, for removal of either the dorsal or ventral half of a *Fundulus* blastoderm results in adhesion of the cells of the cut surface to the periblast. In other words, when central cells become marginal, they too adhere more tightly. The partial blastoderm now spreads over the exposed periblast.

Such a partial blastoderm often approximately doubles its normal extent

the periblast is an ideal substratum, because it also spreads. Moreover, its spreading is independent of the blastoderm. It can not only spread ahead of the blastoderm, it can even complete epiboly in the total absence of the blastoderm (Trinkaus, 133). Evidence that an expanding periblast substratum is essential for blastoderm epiboly is provided in a pretty experiment of Devillers (41). If an early gastrula blastoderm of the trout is grafted to a periblast of the same stage, the blastoderm spreads with the expanding periblast. If a gastrula blastoderm is grafted to a periblast of a blastula stage, however, no epiboly occurs.

of expansion and succeeds in finally closing its blastopore, a dramatic demonstration that the capacity of the blastoderm for spreading is much greater than is normally expressed. The spreading of parts of the blastoderm impelled analysis on the cellular level. In *Salmo*, spreading activity in culture is confined to the outer enveloping layer or Deckschicht. Explants of this layer spread; explants of inner cells do not (Devillers et al., 40, 43). In *Fundulus* we have not yet succeeded in separating the layers and so adopted a different approach. We dissociated blastoderms into cell suspensions with EDTA and cultured the cells in standing drops of a nutrient medium. Blastula cells remain spheroid and protrude lobopodia; early gastrula cells flatten and spread extensively on the glass (Trinkaus, 135). This correlation of cell spreading in vitro with the onset of epiboly indicates that blastoderm epiboly is due in part to the activities of its constituent cells. Late blastula cells behave differently from early blastula cells. They flatten more extensively with increased time in culture, when control eggs are beginning epiboly. This observation is of some significance, for it suggests that the process which changes cell behavior in vivo continues in vitro, independently of the change in environmental conditions.

The flattening of *Fundulus* gastrula cells is probably due in part to an increase in their surface adhesiveness (135, p. 11), over and above that of the blastula cells, whose rounded appearance implies low adhesiveness. Since some degree of adhesion to the substratum is essential for movement to occur, this increase in adhesiveness could well be a necessary condition for the spreading movements of the gastrula cells in epiboly.

This is certainly not the whole story. There are at least two components of cell motility: (1) adequate adhesion to the substratum, and (2) the presence of an active ruffled membrane. Flattening depends on adhesion, but perhaps not solely. An active ruffled membrane could also promote flattening by causing a cell to crawl out on and stretch itself over the substratum. Whether flattening of *Fundulus* cells is accompanied by formation of ruffled membranes or other locomotor specializations, both in vivo and in vitro, is yet to be determined.

Emphasis on cellular activities should not divert attention from the substrata on which cells move. The deep cells are surrounded by one another and hence serve as substrata for each other. An increase in their adhesiveness would cause a closer packing of cells and facilitate their movements over each other. The top layer of deep cells serves as the substratum for the extensive flattening of the enveloping layer. The hypoblast cells and marginal cells of the enveloping layer apparently have high adhesiveness for their substratum, the syncytial periblast, for they flatten on it. This flattening might be facilitated by increased adhesiveness of the periblast surface, but we have no evidence on this matter.

Although cells of both the trout and *Fundulus* spread autonomously in culture, there is an important difference. In the trout only the enveloping layer flattens, while in *Fundulus* over 90 percent of the cells from early gastrula blastoderms flatten. Clearly, deep cells as well as surface cells must be involved. Devillers (42) suggests that in *Salmo* the deep blastomeres are simply passively rearranged during epiboly to compensate for increase in the surface of the blastoderm. This appears unlikely for *Fundulus* (and probably for *Salmo* as well). Deep cells of normal early gastrulae have lost their spheroid form (in fixed material) and have become rhomboid or fusiform and more tightly packed. The enveloping layer has flattened on the deep cells and the hypoblast on the periblast. These conformations would be expected of cells which have high adhesiveness, and are consistent with their changed behavior in culture. It therefore seems probable that their role in blastoderm expansion is an active one. Time-lapse cinemicrography has recently shown this to be a valid conclusion. Deep cells translocate actively and continuously throughout epiboly (Trinkaus and Ebstein, unpublished observations).

How then do we deal with the problem posed by tighter adhesion to the periblast of the marginal cells? This problem is as yet unresolved, both in this instance and for epithelial sheets in general. Readherance and spreading of the sheet at new margins, after it has been cut, is consistent with the operation of a form of contact inhibition, whereby cells migrate centrifugally because their margin is free.

This is where matters stand. There are outstanding unsolved problems, but it is encouraging to note that almost all of them are outgrowths of our partial understanding of what was previously quite unknown. Epiboly apparently begins with an increase in the adhesiveness of cell surfaces and probably an activation of the locomotory mechanisms as well. Cell division plays no role (Kessel, 69). The blastoderm margin appears to be the prime

mover, exerting tension on the blastoderm. But all cells actively participate. They move over each other to rearrange in fewer layers and thus actively respond to the tension exerted by the spreading marginal cells. These changes in cell activity not only make epiboly possible, but probably concurrent morphogenetic movements as well (convergence, extension, involution). The relative importance of the different cell categories remains to be analyzed.

The periblast is the substratum for the spreading of the blastoderm toward the vegetal pole. It is fitted for this role both by its subjacent position and by its capacity for epiboly independently of the blastoderm. It is not necessary to postulate any orientation of its surface. As the normal substratum, it limits the rate and extent of blastoderm epiboly. Hence, even though the blastoderm has greater capacity for spreading than normally realized, its rate becomes that of the periblast as soon as their margins coincide.

The mechanism of periblast spreading during pre-equatorial epiboly is unexplained. After epiboly passes the egg's equator, the gelated ring of the thickened marginal periblast could provide considerable force, as suggested by the periblast surging ahead of the blastoderm toward the end of normal epiboly. The increased rate of periblast epiboly, when the blastoderm is detached, indicates that the stretched blastoderm normally acts as a restraining influence, perhaps accommodating the rate of periblast epiboly to the size of the yolk sphere to be encompassed. This does not imply necessarily that the blastoderm is now passively pulled to the vegetal pole by the contracting periblast margin. Increase in tension is characteristic of spreading cells and cell sheets and forces outside the cell substratum system are not necessary for its genesis.

Even though different regions of the blastoderm differ greatly in the degree of expansion in *Salmo* (Devillers, 42) and somewhat in *Fundulus* (Trinkaus, 133), epiboly is a coordinated, unitary process. It seems probable that the enveloping layer, with its tightly cohering cells, plays a primary role in this regimentation (Devillers, 40). The yolk gel layer exerts contractile tension tangentially and thus aids epiboly indirectly, by maintaining the spherical shape of the egg and the turgor of the yolk. This provides the periblast with a substratum. In pre-equatorial epiboly it is possible that the contractile tension of the yolk gel layer may impede contraction of the marginal periblast, and thus assist its epiboly. The periblast contracts vigorously when the connection between the two is severed. Although the relative importance of the various epibolic forces doubtless varies during the course of epiboly of any one teleost species and from one species to another, the overall mechanisms are in all likelihood the same (Trinkaus, 135). The mechanisms of the other gastrulation movements in teleosts have not been investigated. Except for the enveloping layer, cells are not conveniently organized in well-defined sheets. This renders analysis more difficult, even where the movements are known to be extensive, as in dorsal convergence and anteroposterior extension.

Chick Gastrulation and Other Movements

Analysis of the mechanisms of morphogenetic movements during early chick development has dealt principally with three rather distinct processes. It is convenient to consider them separately.

EPIBOLY OF THE AREA OPACA. It has been known for some time that chick blastoderms do not expand when cultured on plasma or agar substrata (Waddington, 145; Spratt, 117). This is a notable deviation from normal development and lies at the basis of an important controversy on the interpretation of in vitro studies of gastrulation (Malan, 79; Vakaet, 142; Spratt and Haas, 119). With our present appreciation of the importance of the substratum in the expansion of cell sheets it is no surprise to learn that the fault lay, not in injury to the blastoderm, but in lack of a proper substratum. New (90) found that when a cultured blastoderm is supplied with its normal substratum (the inner surface of its vitelline membrane) it adheres and expands over it at the normal rate.

The precise nature of this substratum was thought at first to be quite critical. A blastoderm would adhere to many surfaces, including the outer surface of a vitelline membrane, but would expand only over the inner surface of the membrane (New, 90). However, Spratt (118) has recently shown that a cellulose ester polypore filter will support blastoderm expansion almost as well. The tautness of the membrane seems to be very important. A flaccid vitelline membrane will not support expansion. A local increase in membrane tension will cause increased local spreading, raising the possibility that the blastoderm may be guided by stress lines in its substratum. However, there is no evidence of an animal-vegetal orientation normally in the membrane, and even if there is

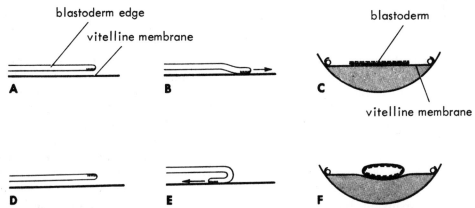

Fig. 3.10 Behavior of a chick blastoderm explanted with normal orientation onto a vitelline membrane (*A, B,* and *C*). *B.* Adhesive undersurface attaches to the vitelline membrane. *C.* Normal expansion follows, as shown by diagram of whole preparation. *D, E,* and *F* show behavior of a blastoderm inverted on a vitelline membrane. *E.* The blastoderm edge curls under to bring adhesive surface against the vitelline membrane. *F.* Expansion in this case is reversed in direction and results in formation of a hollow vesicle. In *A, B, D* and *E* shading indicates adhesive surface. In *C* and *F* thick line denotes ectoderm, broken line endoderm. (From New, *J. Embryol. Morphol.* 7:146–164, 1959.)

one, it is unimportant for the directionality of epiboly. A blastoderm placed endoderm-down on a vitelline membrane will curl under at the edge so that the ectoderm adheres, and then spread in the opposite direction (Fig. 3.10). Presumably the normal slow contraction of the vitelline membrane causes tension to be the same in all tangential directions.

Only the extreme edge of the blastoderm adheres strongly to the vitelline membrane. The remainder is either unattached or very lightly attached. This recalls *Fundulus* epiboly. In the chick, however, the only cells to adhere and spread are those *normally* at the margin, suggesting that these cells are intrinsically different. The marginal cells are obviously of vital importance and their surface activity deserves careful study. In this regard it is interesting that these cells are also highly phagocytic (Bellairs and New, 17). It is New's opinion that the

mechanical tension imposed by the spreading margin is necessary for blastoderm expansion. He points out that if tension were not necessary, one should find instances where rate of expansion had overtaken rate of movement of the attached edge. This has not occurred. The similarity to *Fundulus* epiboly and to the expansion of epithelial sheets in culture is striking and suggests that similar mechanisms are at play. [In the trout, on the other hand, some expansion of the central blastoderm continues in spite of an immobilized margin (Devillers, 39).]

Spratt (118, see below) has placed great emphasis on the morphogenetic role of rapidly dividing growth centers, which he thinks cause spreading by pushing from behind. Studies on chick epiboly give no support to this hypothesis. Marginal pieces continue to expand, even though isolated from more central regions (Schlesinger, 113). Moreover, during epiboly the highest rate of cell division is not centrally located, but is in fact very near the margin. It is difficult to see how this could provide the postulated push. But even if it could, it is not at all necessary. Bellairs (16) has found that blastoderm spreading continues even after mitoses have been inhibited. One can also obtain full blastoderm expansion with no increase in protein (New, 90), indicating that an increase in protoplasm is not necessary for expansion. But even if an increase in protoplasm occurs, it does not lead to expansion unless the substratum is proper. Cell division continues when a blastoderm adheres to the outer surface of the vitelline membrane, but no expansion occurs. Instead, the ectoderm near the margin increases in thickness, from one cell to three to four cells thick. This result is consistent with New's thesis (90) that cells cannot arrange themselves in flat sheets unless subjected to tension.

ENDODERM AND MESODERM FORMATION.   The unincubated chick blastoderm is composed of a cohesive layer of epiblast, underlaid by a ring of loosely packed hypoblast cells. Spratt and Haas (for references see Spratt, 118) have shown by carbon marking that during the first few hours of incubation the hypoblast moves forward and radially over the under surface of the epiblast from a posteriorly located thickened region. Since hypoblast cells do not migrate on the upper surface of the epiblast, the inner or outer surface of the vitelline membrane, or on agar or glass, the lower epiblast surface could well be a specific and necessary substratum. But it does not orient or give direction to hypoblast movement. By simply changing the position of its thickened posterior region, the hypoblast can be made to traverse the epiblast in any direction.

The questions before us are: What causes the hypoblast cells to migrate and what gives them direction? According to Spratt and Haas, intensive cell division in the thickened posterior region of the hypoblast is the cause. Cells are thought to begin moving passively as a result of a push due to increased population density of the rapidly dividing growth center and to continue movement anteriorward because of a continuation of this pressure from behind. This conclusion rests principally on two observations: Hypoblast movement stops in the anterior part of the blastoderm, if it is isolated from the posterior half, and begins in any part of the blastoderm, if a growth center forms in it. This idea excites interest because of its general implications. Cellular proliferation has often been proposed as the motive force for morphogenetic movements. Although such hypotheses have not fared well in the past (see discussions of Holtfreter, 61, and DeHaan, 33), each case deserves close scrutiny in its own right.

The conclusion of Spratt and Haas seems premature. No mitotic counts or other evidence of cell division are submitted in support of the contention that the posterior region is in fact a center of cellular proliferation. Indeed, Vakaet (143), who has also studied hypoblast formation, states explicitly that he found no evidence of a high rate of proliferation. According to his results, the hypoblast forms primarily by polyinvagination. If continual proliferation does occur in the posterior region, blockage of the forward migration should cause a piling up of cells. Obstruction by several means causes no such accumulation (Spratt and Haas,

119). The classic test of whether cell division is essential for a process is, of course, to apply a mitotic inhibitor. When mitoses were blocked in the chick and *Fundulus* blastoderms (Bellairs, 16; Kessel, 69), epibolic spreading continued unabated. No such test has been applied to the spreading of the chick hypoblast. In an elaboration of his explanation, Spratt (118, p. 61) points out ". . . that cells or cell sheets can be 'pushed' only over an 'appropriate' substratum, for example, one permitting cells to attach and spread." But it is now well established that attachment and spreading of cells is an active process, requiring no push from behind.

In view of these reflections, the proposal of Spratt and Haas is unproved. For the present, it seems more likely that the accumulation of hypoblast cells in the posterior region merely provides a source of cells for the ensuing spreading movements. It is possible that changes in cellular motility and surface adhesiveness occur at this time within this cell mass and cause the cells to spread over the epiblast. Hypoblast cells are bound to spread anteriorward, because they have nowhere else to go. This hypothesis could be tested by appropriate studies on cell behavior in culture.

The convergence of the epiblast cells to the primitive streak to undergo involution and form mesoblast has been established for some years now (Pasteels, 90; Spratt, 117; Malan, 79). In addition, we now possess a preliminary picture of cell relations at the fine structure level (Balinsky and Walther, 13). Cells of the epiblast and primitive streak appear to be tightly adhesive, with opposed regions of their membranes electron dense. Many primitive streak cells are flask-shaped. Mesoblast cells are more loosely joined. With this accumulated information it is puzzling that virtually no attention has yet been paid to the mechanism of these movements. The stage is clearly set for such an analysis. Hopefully, with the models now provided by other studies, advances will not be long in coming.

MIGRATION OF PRECARDIAC MESODERM. Between the primitive streak stage and the appearance of the first somites, the precardiac mesodermal cells migrate from the paired precardiac regions to the midline site of heart formation. DeHaan (34, 35) has studied this process with time-lapse cinemicrography. The process is exceptional in that it involves neither the migrations of discrete cells nor the spreading of cell sheets. The precardiac mesoderm first aggregates into small cell clusters which adhere to the endoderm. These clusters then migrate independently of one another over the endoderm eventually to reach the midline. Initially, their directions of movement are random, bearing no relation to their anteromedial point of convergence. After formation of the head fold, however, the clusters begin to follow oriented, parallel paths toward their goal (Fig. 3.11).

The possibility that the substratum may give orientation to these clusters focused attention on the conformation of the endoderm cells. Sure enough, at just about the head-fold stage the endoderm cells of these regions lose their irregular polygonal shape and assume a spindle or lunate form, oriented in the direction of the site of heart formation. The coincidence of time and place is striking and suggests strongly that the oriented lines of the

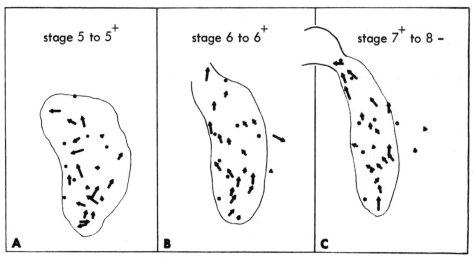

stage 5 to 5⁺   stage 6 to 6⁺   stage 7⁺ to 8 –

A   B   C

Fig. 3.11 Active migration of clusters of precardiac mesoderm cells during selected 1-hour periods. *A.* Movement during the head-process stage (5–5⁺). *B.* Movement during the head-fold stage (6–6⁺). *C.* Movement during formation of the first somites (7⁺–8⁻). (From DeHaan, *Exptl. Cell Res.* 29:544–560, 1963.)

endodermal cell junctions, or other linear structures at the cell surfaces which become aligned with the alteration of cell shape, may give orientation to the mesodermal clusters. Inasmuch as this would suffice only to give orientation and not direction, DeHaan (36) suggests a complementary mechanism. He proposes that clusters may be oriented by filopodial extensions which adhere to the endoderm (cf. Gustafson and Wolpert, 54). If the endoderm were increasingly adhesive in an anteriorward gradient, the filopodia would adhere more frequently on the anterior side, and thus the clusters would be directed toward the site of heart formation. Rumery and others (109) have observed 2-day heart cells to protrude elongate filopodia in culture and DeHann (36) reports the same for 4-day heart cells, with occasional filopodia up to more than 50 μ long. Every now and then one of these establishes a firm connection with the substratum and enlarges as the cell

flows into it. This is plainly a provocative proposal, and the argument is seductive, but acceptance awaits studies on the system in question. Appropriate observations have not yet been made on precardiac cells; nor has endodermal adhesiveness been measured.

Whatever may be the mechanism of cluster translocation, it is essential to know how much it depends on the activities of the component cells. In this connection it is pertinent to contrast the mobility of precardiac clusters with the immobility of clusters of retinal pigment cells (Trinkaus and Lentz, 139). Since the immobility of pigment cell clusters correlates with low mobility of individual pigment cells, it is possible that the mobility of precardiac clusters correlates with high mobility of individual precardiac cells. This would be an exceedingly interesting point to establish, for, if confirmed, it would constitute strong evidence that the movement of a cell cluster does indeed depend on the collective migratory activities of its constituent cells.

Concluding Remarks

Although analysis of morphogenetic movements is as yet in a rudimentary state, it has already revealed certain modes of behavior that may apply generally. Epithelial layers expand primarily at the margin in a number of systems. How the marginal cells do this and how the central cells respond to the tension thus created are urgent problems. The behavior of individual gastrula cells in vitro sufficiently resembles their collective behavior in vivo to encourage belief that changes in particular cell properties, such as surface adhesiveness, are fundamental to both mass movements and the beginnings of histogenesis. This also bolsters the conviction that cell culture, with the opportunities it offers for control of cellular environment, will be increasingly useful in the analysis of morphogenetic movements. Initial explorations of cell relations at the fine structure level during episodes of high locomotory activity have revealed intriguing correlations of structure with function. This is an exciting beginning and a reminder that we still await concerted application of the electron microscope and modern optical methods to the study of mass movements.

Actually, when one contrasts the similarities and the simplicities that have emerged from our comparative study of cell movements — in culture, in mixed aggregates, and in the developing embryo — with earlier notions of the mystery and intricacy of it all, a cautious optimism is justified. It now seems possible that organisms may achieve cellular rearrangements unrivaled for their complexity without recourse to highly specific surface interactions, delicately oriented substrata, long-range taxes and the like. Conceivably they might manage all this by means of quantitative differences in a few properties, such as cellular adhesiveness and motility, expressed in a system of simple, but defined topography.

References

1. Abercrombie, M., "The Bases of the Locomotory Behaviour of Fibroblasts," *Exptl. Cell Res. Suppl.* 8:188–198 (1961).
2. ——, "Cell Contacts in Morphogenesis," *Arch. Biol.* In press (1965).
3. ——, and E. J. Ambrose, "Interference Microscope Studies of Cell Contacts in Tissue Culture," *Exptl. Cell Res.* 15: 332–345 (1958).
4. ——, and ——, "The Surface Properties of Cancer Cells," *Cancer Res.* 22:525–548 (1962).
5. ——, and J. E. M. Heaysman, "Observations on the Social Behaviour of Cells in Tissue Culture. I. Speed of Movement of Chick Heart Fibroblasts in Relation to Their Mutual Contacts," *Exptl. Cell Res.* 5:111–131 (1953).
6. ——, and ——, "Observations on the Social Behaviour of Cells in Tissue Culture. II. Monolayering of Fibroblasts," *Exptl. Cell Res.* 6:293–306 (1954).
7. ——, ——, and H. M. Karthauser, "Social Behaviour of Cells in Tissue Culture. III. Mutual Influence of Sarcoma Cells and Fibroblasts," *Exptl. Cell Res.* 13:276–291 (1957).
8. Allen, R. D., "A New Theory of Ameboid Movement and Protoplasmic Streaming," *Exptl. Cell Res. Suppl.* 8:17–31 (1961).
9. ——, "Ameboid Movement," *The Cell,*

J. Brachet and A. E. Mirsky, eds. New York: Academic Press, vol. II, pp. 135–216 (1961).

10. Ambrose, E. J., "The Movements of Fibrocytes," *Exptl. Cell Res. Suppl.* 8:54–73 (1961).

10a. Baker, Patricia A., "Fine Structure and Morphogenetic Movements in the Gastrula of the Tree Frog, *Hyla regilla*," *J. Cell Biol.* 24:95–116 (1965).

11. Balinsky, B. I., "An Electron Microscopic Investigation of the Mechanisms of Adhesion of the Cells in a Sea Urchin Blastula and Gastrula," *Exptl. Cell Res.* 16:429–433 (1959).

12. Balinsky, B. I., "Ultrastructural Mechanisms of Gastrulation and Neurulation," Symp. on Germ Cells and Develop., *Inst. Intern. Embryol. Fondaz. A. Baselli*, pp. 550–563 (1960).

13. ———, and H. Walther, "The Immigration of Presumptive Mesoblast from the Primitive Streak in the Chick as Studied with the Electron Microscope," *Acta Embryol. Morphol. Exptl.* 4:261–283 (1961).

14. Ballard, W. W., "Cortical Ingression during Cleavage of Amphibian Eggs, Studied by Means of Vital Dyes," *J. Exptl. Zool.* 129:77–98 (1955).

15. Bell, E., "Some Observations of the Surface Coat and Intercellular Matrix Material of the Amphibian Ectoderm," *Exptl. Cell Res.* 20:378–383 (1960).

16. Bellairs, R., "The Effects of Folic Acid Antagonists on Embryonic Development," *Chemistry and Biology of Pteridines*, Ciba Foundation Symposium, G. E. W. Wolstenholms and M. P. Cameron, eds. London: Churchill, pp. 356–365 (1954).

17. ———, and D. A. T. New, "Phagocytosis in the Chick Blastoderm," *Exptl. Cell Res.* 26:275–279 (1962).

18. Bonner, J. T., "Evidence for the Formation of Cell Aggregates by Chemotaxis in the Development of the Slime Mold *Dictyostelium discoideum*," *J. Exptl. Zool.* 106:1–26 (1947).

19. Boyden, S., "The Chemotactic Effect of Mixtures of Antibody and Antigen on Polymorphonuclear Leucocytes," *J. Exptl. Med.* 115:453–466 (1962).

20. Bresch, D., "Recherches Préliminaires sur des Associations d'Organes Embryonnaires de Poulet en Culture *in vitro*," *Bull. Biol. Fr. Belg.* 89:179–188 (1955).

21. Brokaw, C. L., "Chemotaxis of Bracken Spermatozoids," *J. Exptl. Biol.* 35:192–196 (1958).

22. Butler, E., and J. P. O'Brien, "Effects of Localized X-radiation on Regeneration of the Urodele Limb," *Anat. Record* 84:407–413 (1942).

23. Buytendijk, F. J. J., and M. W. Woerdeman, "Die Physico-chemischen erscheinungen während der Eientwicklung. I. Die messung der wasserstoffionenkonzentration," *Arch. Entwicklungsmech. Org.* 112:387–410 (1927).

24. Chiakulas, J. J., "The Role of Tissue Specificity in the Healing of Epithelial Wounds," *J. Exptl. Zool.* 21:383–417 (1952).

25. Colwin, A. L., and L. H. Colwin, "Role of the Gamete Membranes in Fertilization," *Cellular Membranes in Development*, M. Locke, ed. New York: Academic Press, pp. 233–279 (1964).

26. Coman, D. R., "Decreased Mutual Adhesiveness, a Property of Cells from Squamous Cell Carcinomas," *Cancer Res.* 4:625–629 (1944).

27. Curtis, A. S. G., "Cell Contacts: Some Physical Considerations," *Am. Naturalist* 94:37–56 (1960).

28. ———, "Timing Mechanisms in the Specific Adhesion of Cells," *Exptl. Cell Res. Suppl.* 8:107–122 (1961).

29. ———, "Cell Contact and Adhesion," *Biol. Rev. Cambridge Phil. Soc.* 37:82–129 (1962).

30. ———, "Pattern and Mechanism in the Reaggregation of Sponges," *Nature* 196:245–248 (1962).

31. Dan, K., "Cyto-embryology of Echinoderms and Amphibia," *Intern. Rev. Cytol.* 9:321–367 (1960).

32. ———, and K. Okazaki, "Cyto-embryological Studies of Sea Urchins. III. Role of the Secondary Mesenchyme Cells in the Formation of the Primitive Gut in Sea Urchin Larvae," *Biol. Bull.* 110:29–42 (1956).

33. DeHaan, R. L., "Cell Migration and Morphogenetic Movements," *A Symposium on the Chemical Basis of Development*, W. D. McElroy and B. Glass, eds. Baltimore: The Johns Hopkins Press, pp. 339–374 (1958).

34. ———, "Oriented Cell Movements in

Embryogenesis," *Biological Organization at the Cellular and Supercellular Level*, R. J. C. Harris, ed. New York: Academic Press, pp. 147–165 (1963).

35. ——, "Migration Patterns of the Precardiac Mesoderm in the Early Chick Embryo," *Exptl. Cell Res.* 29:544–560 (1963).

36. ——, "Cell Interactions and Oriented Movements during Development," *J. Exptl. Zool.* 157:127–138 (1964).

37. ——, and J. D. Ebert, "Morphogenesis," *Ann. Rev. Phys.* 26:15–46 (1964).

38. Devillers, C., "Le Cortex de l'Oeuf de Truite," *Ann. Stat. Centr. Hydrobiol. Appl.* 2:229–249 (1948).

39. ——, "Mécanisme de l'Épibolie Gastruléenne," *Compt. Rend. Acad. Sci.* 230:2232–2234 (1950).

40. ——, "Les Mouvements Superficiels dans la Gastrulation des Poissons," *Arch. Anat. Microscop. Morphol. Exptl.* 40:298–309 (1951).

41. ——, "Coordination des Forces Épiboliques dans la Gastrulation de *Salmo*," *Bull. Soc. Zool. France* 77:304–309 (1952).

42. ——, "Structural and Dynamic Aspects of the Development of the Teleostean Egg," *Advances in Morphogenesis*, M. Abercrombie and J. Brachet, eds. New York: Academic Press, vol. I, pp. 379–428 (1960).

43. ——, J. Colas, and L. Richard, "Différenciation *in vitro* de Blastodermes de Truite (*Salmo irideus*) Dépourvus de Couche Enveloppante," *J. Embryol. Exptl. Morphol.* 5:264–273 (1957).

44. Dollander, A., "Conceptions Actuelles et Terminologie Relatives a Certains Aspects de l'Organisation Corticale de l'Oeuf d'Amphibien," *Arch. Anat. Histol. Embryol. Suppl.* 44:93–103 (1961).

45. ——, "De Cortex de l'Oeuf d'Amphibien," *Anat. Anz.* Suppl. 109:274–306 (1962).

46. Dubois, F., "Contribution à l'Étude de la Migration des Cellules de Régénération chez les Planaires Dulcicoles," *Bull. Biol. Fr. Belg.* 83:213–283 (1949).

47. Flickinger, R. A., "Isotopic Evidence for a Local Origin of Blastema Cells in Regenerating Planaria," *Exptl. Cell Res.* 34:403–406 (1964).

48. Galtsoff, P. S., "The Amoeboid Movement of Dissociated Sponge Cells," *Biol. Bull.* 45:153–161 (1923).

49. Goldacre, R. J., "The Role of the Cell Membrane in the Locomotion of Amoebae, and the Source of the Motive Force and Its Control by Feedback," *Exptl. Cell Res. Suppl.* 8:1–16 (1961).

49a. Grobstein, C., "Tissue Interaction in the Morphogenesis of Mouse Embryonic Rudiments *in vitro, Aspects of Synthesis and Order in Growth*, Dorothea Rudnick ed. Princeton, N.J.: Princeton University Press, pp. 233–256 (1954).

49b. Grobstein, C., "Cell Contact in Relation to Embryonic Induction," *Exptl. Cell Res., Suppl.* 8:234–245 (1961).

50. Gustafson, T., and H. Kinnander, "Microaquaria for Time-lapse Cinematographic Studies of Morphogenesis in Swimming Larvae and Observations on Sea Urchin Gastrulation," *Exptl. Cell Res.* 11:36–51 (1956).

51. ——, and L. Wolpert, "Studies on the Cellular Basis of Morphogenesis in the Sea Urchin Embryo. Gastrulation in Vegetalized Larvae," *Exptl. Cell Res.* 22:437–449 (1961).

52. ——, and ——, "Studies on the Cellular Basis of Morphogenesis in the Sea Urchin Embryo. Directed Movements of Primary Mesenchyme Cells in Normal and Vegetalized Larvae," *Exptl. Cell Res.* 24:64–79 (1961).

53. ——, and ——, "Cellular Mechanisms in the Morphogenesis of the Sea Urchin Larva. Change in Shape of Cell Sheets," *Exptl. Cell Res.* 27:260–279 (1962).

54. ——, and ——, "The Cellular Basis of Morphogenesis and Sea Urchin Development," *Intern. Rev. Cytol.* 15:139–214 (1963).

55. Harris, H., "Chemotaxis," *Exptl. Cell Res. Suppl.* 8:199–208 (1961).

56. Harrison, R. G., "The Reaction of Embryonic Cells to Solid Structures," *J. Exptl. Zool.* 17:521–544 (1914).

57. Hoffman-Berling, H., "The Role of Cell Structures in Cell Movements," *Cell, Organism and Milieu*, D. Rudnick, ed. New York: Ronald, pp. 45–62 (1959).

58. Holmes, S. J., "The Behavior of the Epidermis of Amphibians when Cul-

tured Outside the Body," *J. Exptl. Zool.* 17:281–295 (1914).

59. Holtfreter, J., "Gewebeaffinität, ein Mittel der Embryonalen Formbildung," *Arch. Exptl. Zellforsch.* 23:169 (1939).

60. ———, "Properties and Functions of the Surface Coat in Amphibian Embryos," *J. Exptl. Zool.* 93:251–323 (1943).

61. ———, "A Study of the Mechanics of Gastrulation: Part I," *J. Exptl. Zool.* 94: 261–318 (1943).

62. ———, "A Study of the Mechanics of Gastrulation: Part II," *J. Exptl. Zool.* 95: 171–212 (1943).

63. ———, "Experimental Studies on the Development of the Pronephros," *Rev. Can. Biol.* 3:220–250 (1944).

64. ———, "Observations on the Migration, Aggregation and Phagocytosis of Embryonic Cells," *J. Morphol.* 80:25–55 (1947).

65. Hörstadius, S., *The Neural Crest*, New York: Oxford (1950).

66. Hughes, W. L., "Chromosomal Replication and the Dynamics of Cellular Proliferation — Some Autoradiographic Observations with Tritiated Thymidine," *The Chemical Basis of Development*, W. D. McElroy and B. Glass, eds. Baltimore: The Johns Hopkins Press, pp. 136–152 (1958).

66a. Humphreys, T., "Chemical Dissolution and *in vitro* Reconstruction of Sponge Cell Adhesions," *Develop. Biol.* 8:27–47 (1963).

67. Jones, K. W., and T. R. Elsdale, "The Culture of Small Aggregates of Amphibian Embryonic Cells *in vitro.*" *J. Embryol. Exptl. Morphol.* 11:135–154 (1963).

68. Karasaki, S., "Electron Microscopic Studies on Cytoplasmic Structures of Ectoderm Cells of the *Triturus* Embryo during the Early Phase of Differentiation," *Embryologia* 4:247–272 (1959).

69. Kessel, R. G., "The Role of Cell Division in Gastrulation of *Fundulus heteroclitus,*" *Exptl. Cell Res.* 20:277–282 (1960).

70. Kinnander, H., and T. Gustafson, "Further Studies on the Cellular Basis of Gastrulation in the Sea Urchin Larva," *Exptl. Cell Res.* 19:278–290 (1960).

71. Kuhl, W., "Untersuchungen über das Verhalten Kunstick Getrennter Fur-

chungszellen und Zellaggregate einiger Amphibienarten mit Hilfe des Zeirafferfilms (Laufbild- und Teilbild-analyse)," *Arch. Entwicklungsmech. Or.* 139: 393–671 (1937).

72. Lash, J. W., "Studies on Wound Closure in Urodeles," *J. Exptl. Zool.* 128: 13–28 (1955).

73. Lehman, H. E., and L. M. Youngs, "Extrinsic and Intrinsic Factors Influencing Amphibian Pigment Pattern Formation," *Pigment Cell Biology*, M. Gordon, ed. New York: Academic Press, pp. 1–36 (1959).

74. Lewis, W. H., "Superficial Gel Layers of Cells and Eggs and Their Role in Early Development," *Sobretiro Anales Inst. Biol.* 20:1–14 (1949).

75. ———, "Gel Layers of Cells and Eggs and Their Role in Early Development," *Lecture Ser. Roscoe B. Jackson Mem. Lab.* pp. 59–77 (1949).

76. Lieberman, I., and P. Ove, "A Protein Growth Factor for Mammalian Cells in Culture," *J. Biol. Chem.* 233:637–642 (1958).

77. Lucey, E. C. A., and A. S. G. Curtis, "Time-lapse Film Study of Cell Reaggregation," *Med. and Biol. Illust.* 9:86–93 (1959).

78. Ludford, R. J., "Differences in the Growth of Transplantable Tumours in Plasma and Serum Culture Media," *Proc. Roy. Soc. London Ser. B* 112:250–263 (1932).

79. Malan, M. E., "The Elongation of the Primitive Streak and the Localization of the Presumptive Chorda-mesoderm on the Early Chick Blastoderm Studied by Means of Coloured Marks with Nile Blue Sulphate," *Arch. Biol. Paris* 64: 149–182 (1953).

80. Messier, B., and C. P. LeBlond, "Preparation of Coated Radioautographs by Dipping Sections in Fluid Emulsion," *Proc. Soc. Exptl. Biol. Med.* 96:7–10 (1957).

81. Meyer, D. B., "The Migration of Primordial Germ Cells in the Chick Embryo," *Develop. Biol.* 10:154–190 (1964).

82. Milkman, R., and J. P. Trinkaus, "Site of Action of Epibolic Forces in the Egg of *Fundulus heteroclitus,*" *Anat. Record* 117:558–559 (1953).

83. Mintz, B., "Continuity of the Female

Germ Cell Line from Embryo to Adult," *Arch. Anat. Microscop. Morphol. Exptl.* 48:155–172 (1959).

84. Moscona, A. A., "Cell Suspensions from Organ Rudiments of Chick Embryos," *Exptl. Cell. Res.* 3:536–539 (1952).

85. ———, "The Development *in vitro* of Chimaeric Aggregates of Dissociated Embryonic Chick and Mouse Cells," *Proc. Natl. Acad. Sci. U.S.* 43:184–194 (1957).

86. ———, "Patterns and Mechanisms of Tissue Reconstruction from Dissociated Cells," *Developing Cell Systems and Their Control*, D. Rudnick, ed. New York: Ronald, pp. 45–70 (1959).

87. ———, "Analysis of Cell Recombination in Experimental Synthesis of Tissues *in vitro*," *J. Cellular Comp. Physiol.* Suppl. 1, 60:65–80 (1962).

88. ———, and H. Moscona, "The Dissociation and Aggregation of Cells from Organ Rudiments of the Early Chick Embryo," *J. Anat.* 86:287–301 (1952).

89. Moore, A. R., and A. S. Burt, "On the Locus and Nature of the Forces Causing Gastrulation in the Embryos of *Dendraster excentricus*," *J. Exptl. Zool.* 82:159–171 (1939).

90. New, D. A. T., "The Adhesive Properties and Expansion of the Chick Blastoderm," *J. Embryol. Morphol.* 7:146–164 (1959).

91. Nicholas, J. S., "Blastulation, Its Role in Pregastrular Organization in *Amblystoma punctatum*," *J. Exptl. Zool.* 100:265–299 (1945).

91a. Nickerson, Mark, "An Experimental Analysis of Barred Pattern Formation in Feathers," *J. Exptl. Zool.* 95:361–397 (1944).

92. Okazaki, K., T. Fukushi, and K. Dan, "Cyto-embryological Studies of Sea Urchins. IV. Correlation between the Shape of Ectodermal Cells and the Arrangement of the Primary Mesenchyme Cells in Sea Urchin Larvae," *Acta Embryol. Morphol. Exptl.* 5:17–51 (1962).

93. Overton, J., "Desmosome Development in Normal and Reassociating Cells in the Early Chick Blastoderm," *Develop. Biol.* 4:532–548 (1962).

94. Pasteels, J., "Analyse des Mouvements Morphogénétiques de Gastrulation Chez les Oiseaux," *Bull. Cl. Sci. Acad. Roy. Belg.* 22:737–752 (1936).

95. Pethica, B. A., "The Physical Chemistry of Cell Adhesion," *Exptl. Cell Res. Suppl.* 8:123–140 (1961).

96. Pfeffer, W., "Locomotorische Richtungsbewegungen durch Chimische Reize," *Unt. Bot. Inst. Tubingen* 1:363–482 (1884).

97. Picken, L., *The Organization of Cells and Other Organisms*, London: Oxford, pp. xxxvii, 629 (1960).

98. Rappaport, C., J. C. Poole, and H. P. Rappaport, "Studies on Properties of Surfaces Required for Growth of Mammalian Cells in Synthetic Medium. I. The HeLa Cell," *Exptl. Cell Res.* 20:465–479 (1960).

98a. Rawles, Mary E., "The Migration of Melanoblasts after Hatching into Pigment-free Skin of the Common Fowl," *Physiol. Zool.* 17:167–183 (1944).

99. Rawles, M. E., "Origin of Melanophores and Their Role in Development of Color Patterns in Vertebrates," *Phys. Rev.* 28:383–408 (1948).

100. Reams, W. M., Jr., "An Experimental Study of the Development of Pigment Cells in the Coelomic Lining of the Chick Embryo," *J. Morphol.* 99:513–548 (1956).

101. Rhumbler, L., "Zur Mechanik des Gastrulationsvorganes, insbesondere der Invagination," *Arch. Entwicklungsmech. Or.* 14:401–476 (1902).

102. Robertson, J. D., "Unit Membranes: A Review with Recent New Studies of Experimental Alterations and a New Subunit Structure in Synaptic Membranes," *Cellular Membranes in Development*, M. Locke, ed. New York: Academic Press, pp. 1–81 (1964).

103. Robineaux, R., "Movements of Cells Involved in Inflammation and Immunity," *Primitive Motile Systems in Cell Biology*, R. D. Allen and N. Kamiya, eds. New York: Academic Press, pp. 351–364 (1964).

104. Rosen, W. G., "Cellular Chemotropism and Chemotaxis," *Quart. Rev. Biol.* 37:242–259 (1962).

105. Rosenberg, M. D., "Long-range Interactions between Cells and Substratum," *Proc. Natl. Acad. Sci. U.S.* 48:1342–1349 (1962).

106. ———, "Cell Guidance by Alterations in Monomolecular Films," *Science* 139: 411–412 (1963).

107. Rothschild, L., *Fertilization.* New York: Wiley (1956).

108. Roux, W., "Über den Cytotropismus der Furchungszellen des Grasfrosches (*Rana fusca*)," *Arch. Entwicklungsmech. Or.* 1:43–68 (1894).

109. Rumery, R. E., R. J. Blandau, and P. W. Hagey, "Observations of Living Myocardial Cells from Cultured 48-hour Chick Hearts," *Anat. Record* 141:253–261 (1961).

110. Shaffer, B. M., "The Acrasina," *Advances in Morphogenesis*, M. Abercrombie and J. Brachet, eds. New York: Academic Press, vol. II, pp. 109–182 (1962).

111. Schechtman, A. M. "Unipolar Ingression in *Triturus torosus*: A Hitherto Undescribed Movement in the Pregastrular Stages of a Urodele," *Univ. Calif. Publ.* 39:303–310 (1934).

112. ———, "The Mechanism of Amphibian Gastrulation. I. Gastrulation-promoting Interactions between Various Regions of an Anuran Egg (*Hyla regilla*)," *Univ. Calif. Publ. Zool.* 51:1–40 (1942).

113. Schlesinger, A. G., "The Structural Significance of the Avian Yolk in Embryogenesis," *J. Exptl. Zool.* 138:223–258 (1958).

114. Shapiro, B. E., "Influences of the Salinity and pH of Blastocoelic Perfusates on the Initiation of Amphibian Gastrulation," *J. Exptl. Zool.* 139:381–401 (1958).

115. Simon, D., "Contribution à l'Étude de la Circulation et du Transport des Gonocytes Primaires dans les Blastodermes d'Oiseau Cultivés *in vitro*," *Arch. Anat. Microscop. Morphol. Exptl.* 49:93–176 (1960).

116. Spiegelman, S., "Remarks in Discussion," *The Chemical Basis of Development*, W. D. McElroy and B. Glass, eds. Baltimore: The Johns Hopkins Press, p. 491 (1958).

117. Spratt, N. T., Jr., "Formation of the Primitive Streak in the Explanted Chick Blastoderm Marked with Carbon Particles," *J. Exptl. Zool.* 103:259–304 (1946).

118. ———, "Role of the Substratum, Supracellular Continuity, and Differential Growth in Morphogenetic Cell Movements," *Develop. Biol.* 7:51–63 (1963).

119. ———, and H. Haas, "Morphogenetic Movements in the Lower Surface of the Unincubated and Early Chick Blastoderm," *J. Exptl. Zool.* 144:139–158 (1960).

120. Stableford, L. T., "The Blastocoel Fluid in Amphibian Gastrulation," *J. Exptl. Zool.* 112:529–546 (1949).

121. Stefanelli, A., A. M. Zacchei, and V. Cheherini, "Ricostituzioni Retiniche *in vitro* dopo Disagregazione dell' Abozzo Oculare di Embrione di Pollo," *Acta Embryol. Morphol. Exptl.* 4:47–55 (1961).

122. Steinberg, M. S., "On the Mechanism of Tissue Reconstruction by Dissociated Cells. I. Population Kinetics, Differential Adhesiveness, and the Absence of Directed Migration," *Proc. Natl. Acad. Sci. U.S.* 48:1577–1582 (1962).

123. ———, "On the Mechanism of Tissue Reconstruction by Dissociated Cells. II. Time-course of Events," *Science* 137: 762–763 (1962).

124. ———, "On the Mechanism of Tissue Reconstruction by Dissociated Cells. III. Free Energy Relations and the Reorganization of Fused, Heteronomic Tissue Fragments," *Proc. Natl. Acad. Sci. U.S.* 48:1769–1776 (1962).

125. ———, "ECM: Its Nature, Origin and Function in Cell Aggregation," *Exptl. Cell Res.* 30:257–279 (1963).

126. ———, "Reconstruction of Tissues by Dissociated Cells," *Science* 141:401–408 (1963).

127. ———, "The Problem of Adhesive Selectivity in Cellular Interactions," *Cellular Membranes in Development*, M. Locke, ed. New York: Academic Press, pp. 321–366 (1964).

128. Sussman, M., "A Developmental Analysis of Cellular Slime Mold Aggregation," *The Chemical Basis of Development*, W. D. McElroy and B. Glass, eds. Baltimore: The Johns Hopkins Press, pp. 264–317 (1958).

129. Taylor, A. C., "Attachment and Spreading of Cells in Culture," *Exptl. Cell Res. Suppl.* 8:154–173 (1961).

130. ———, "Responses of Cells to pH Changes in the Medium." *J. Cell Biol.* 15:201–209 (1962).

131. Townes, P. L., and J. Holtfreter, "Directed Movements and Selective Adhesion of Embryonic Amphibian Cells," *J. Exptl. Zool.* 128:53–118 (1955).

131a. Trinkaus, J. P., "Factors Concerned in the Response of Melanoblasts to Estrogen in the Brown Leghorn Fowl," *J. Exptl. Zool.* 109:135–170 (1948).

132. ———, "The Surface Gel Layer of *Fundulus* Eggs in Relation to Epiboly," *Proc. Natl. Acad. Sci. U.S.* 35:218–225 (1949).

133. ———, "A Study of the Mechanism of Epiboly in the Egg of *Fundulus heteroclitus*," *J. Exptl. Zool.* 118:269–319 (1951).

134. ———, "Affinity Relationships in Heterotypic Cell Aggregates," *La Culture Organotypique.* Paris: Colloq. Intern. Centre Natl. Rech. Sci. no. 101, pp. 209–226 (1961).

135. ———, "The Cellular Basis of *Fundulus* Epiboly. Adhesivity of Blastula and Gastrula Cells in Culture," *Develop. Biol.* 7:513–532 (1963).

136. ———, "Behavior of Dissociated Retinal Pigment Cells in Heterotypic Cell Aggregates," *Ann. N.Y. Acad. Sci.* 100: 413–434 (1963).

137. ———, and M. C. Gross, "The Use of Tritiated Thymidine for Marking Migratory Cells," *Exptl. Cell Res.* 24:52–57 (1961).

138. ———, and P. W. Groves, "Differentiation in Culture of Mixed Aggregates of Dissociated Tissue Cells," *Proc. Natl. Acad. Sci. U.S.* 41:787–795 (1955).

139. ———, and J. P. Lentz, "Direct Observation of Type-specific Segregation in Mixed Cell Aggregates," *Develop. Biol.* 9:115–136 (1964).

140. Twitty, V. C., "Developmental Analysis of Amphibian Pigmentation," *Growth* 9:133–161 (1949).

141. ———, and M. C. Niu, "The Motivation of Cell Migration, Studied by Isolation of Embryonic Pigment Cells Singly and in Small Groups *in vitro*," *J. Exptl. Zool.* 125:541–574 (1954).

142. Vakaet, L., "Quelque Précisions sur la Cinématique de la Ligne Primitive Chez la Poulet," *J. Embryol. Exptl. Morphol.* 8:321–326 (1960).

143. ———, "Some New Data Concerning the Formation of the Definitive Endoblast in the Chick Embryo," *J. Embryol. Exptl. Morphol.* 10:38–57 (1962).

144. Voightlander, G., "Neue Untersuchungen uber den Cytotropismus der Furchenzellen," *Arch. Entwicklungsmech. Or.* 127:151–215 (1932).

145. Waddington, C. H., "Experiments on the Development of Chick and Duck Embryos Cultivated *in vitro*," *Phil. Trans. Roy. Soc. London Ser. B* 221:179–230 (1932).

146. Wartenberg, H., and W. Schmidt, "Elektronemikroskopische Untersuchungen der strukturellen Veränderungen im Rindenbereich des Amphibieneies im Ovar und nach der Befruchtung," *Z. Zellforsch.* 54:118–146 (1961).

146a. Weiss, L., "The Measurement of Cell Adhesion," *Exptl. Cell Res. Suppl.* 8: 141–153 (1961).

147. Weiss, L., "Cell Movement and Cell Surfaces: A Working Hypothesis," *J. Theoret. Biol.* 2:236–250 (1962).

148. ———, "The Mammalian Tissue Cell Surface," *Biochem. Soc. Symp.* 22:32–54 (1962).

149. Weiss, P., "Experiments on Cell and Axon Orientation *in vitro*: The Role of Colloidal Exudates in Tissue Organization," *J. Exptl. Zool.* 100:353–386 (1945).

150. ———, "The Problem of Specificity in Growth and Development," *Yale J. Biol. Med.* 19:235–278 (1947).

151. ———, "Cell Contact," *Intern. Rev. Cytol.* 7:1–30 (1958).

152. ———, "Guiding Principles in Cell Locomotion and Cell Aggregation," *Exptl. Cell Res. Suppl.* 8:260–281 (1961).

153. ———, and B. Garber, "Shape and Movement of Mesenchyme Cells as Functions of the Physical Structure of the Medium," *Proc. Natl. Acad. Sci. U.S.* 38:264–280 (1952).

153a. Wessells, N. K., "Morphology and Proliferation during Early, Feather Development," *Develop. Biol.* In press. (1965).

154. Weston, J. A., "A Radioautographic Analysis of the Migration and Localization of Trunk Neural Crest Cells in the Chick," *Develop. Biol.* 6:279–310 (1963).

155. Willmer, E. N., *Cytology and Evolution.* New York: Academic Press, (1960).

156. Wilson, H. V., "On Some Phenomena

of Coalescence and Regeneration in Sponges," *J. Exptl. Zool.* 5:245–258 (1907).

157. Wohlfarth-Botterman, K. E., "Cell Structures and Their Significance for Ameboid Movement," *Intern. Rev. Cytol.* 16:61–131 (1964).

158. Wolff, E., and N. Schneider, "La Culture d'un Sarcome de Souris sur des Organes de Poulet Explantés *in vitro*," *Arch. Anat. Microscop. Morphol. Exptl.* 46:173–197 (1957).

159. ———, and J. P. Weniger, "Recherches Préliminaires sur les Chimères d'Organes Embryonnaires d'Oiseaux et de Mammifères en Culture *in vitro*," *J. Embryol. Exptl. Morphol.* 2:161–171 (1954).

SECTION II The Nervous System

4

Early Morphogenesis and Pattern Formation in the Central Nervous System

BENGT KÄLLÉN

Tornblad Institute of Comparative Embryology
Lund, Sweden

The central nervous system is formed from the ectoderm of the vertebrate embryo. Since the initial experiments done 40 years ago, it has been demonstrated repeatedly that an inductive influence from the underlying archenteron roof triggers neural differentiation in the ectoderm, resulting in the formation of the neural plate (Fig. 4.1A,B). The plate soon folds into a neural groove, bounded by the thickened neural folds. The groove then deepens and narrows until the neural folds meet, thereby rolling the original plate into a neural tube. At the completion of the process, the tube lies below the surface of the epidermis, and has detached from it.

As the neural plate and early tube form, the anteriormost part is wider than that which is posterior, and forms the rudiment of the brain. The caudal part elongates markedly to form the spinal cord. Within the brain rudiment itself, local swellings soon separate

off three brain regions: (1) the prosencephalon (forebrain), (2) the mesencephalon (midbrain), and (3) the rhombencephalon (hindbrain). When the brain becomes a closed tube, these divisions are referred to as the primary brain vesicles (Fig. 4.2). Soon, the prosencephalon and rhombencephalon become further subdivided, each giving rise to two secondary vesicles. The forebrain divides into the telencephalon, from which the olfactory lobes and cerebral cortex will develop; and the diencephalon, which bears the optic vesicles and thalamic regions. The mesencephalon remains permanently undivided. Somewhat later, the hindbrain specializes into the metencephalon, or future region of the cerebellum and pons, and the myelencephalon or medulla oblongata, from which the brain stem and upper spinal cord develop.

There is much variation among the vertebrate species as to how distinct or

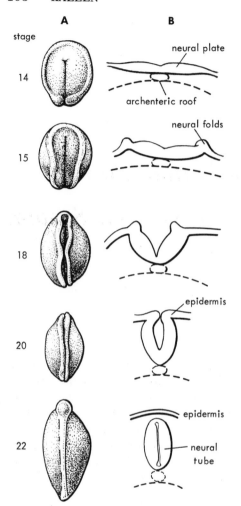

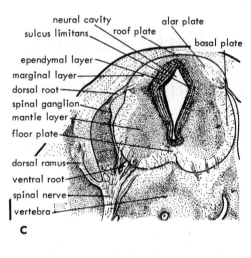

Fig. 4.1 Early stages in the morphogenesis of the brain and spinal cord. A. Formation of the neural tube in the urodele *Ambystoma*. B. Diagrammatic transverse section of the stages shown in *A*. *C*. Diagrammatic section of a 6-week-old human embryo spinal cord.

well defined are the different brain regions; and it is such differences in formative processes that result in the different morphologies seen in adult brains. However, during early embryogenesis, the morphogenetic processes that mold the central nervous system (CNS) are very similar among all vertebrates. It is for this reason that the brains of different species at early stages can be compared directly.

When the neural tube is first formed, it is made up of a pseudostratified cylindrical epithelium, the neural epithelium, also called the primitive ependymal layer or the matrix layer (Fig. 4.1*C*). In later stages, a cell layer called the mantle layer develops laterally. Still lateral to this, the cell-free marginal layer can be seen. The mantle layer is formed by migration of cells from the neural epithelium. The mantle cells differentiate into neuroblasts and neurons, and into spongioblasts and neuroglial cells which later form the astrocytes and oligodendrocytes. Ependymal cells are formed in the gradually disappearing neural epithelium. From surrounding mesenchyme, cells enter the CNS to form blood vessels and the microglial cell population.

The neuroblasts of the mantle layer are not evenly distributed. Instead, they are aggregated into clusters which form the brain nuclei, or the strata of the cortical layers. In some species, such as the urodeles, these aggregations are only weakly developed. However, among mammals, the morphology of the brain nuclei and cortical layers is very complicated. There has been much discussion regarding the correspondences (homologies) among the brain nuclei of different vertebrates, and many problems are yet unsolved.

From maturing neuroblasts, nerve fibers grow out. They do so in distinct patterns, the fibers giving rise to well-defined fascicles, growing in specific directions at specific locations. They terminate at specific regions of the central nervous system, or outside it. The formation of these connections — the wiring of the central nervous system — produces the functional qualities of the CNS, and turns the brain and spinal cord into a working unit (see Sperry, Chapter 6).

The process of neurogenesis is thus complicated and not a one-step process. It has to be analyzed on various levels. How does the primary induction of the neural tissue in the ectoderm take place, and how much information is laid down in the induced neural plate leading to the further development of the brain and spinal cord? A very extensive literature exists on this problem and can hardly be touched upon in the present context. Relatively recent reviews have been published by, among others, Holtfreter and Hamburger (19), Dalcq (7),

and Saxén and Toivonen (46). The developmental potencies of the induced neural plate have been studied under numerous different experimental conditions. Usually, the results obtained have been interpreted in fairly broad outlines, only in terms of which of the different brain parts or spinal cord tissue is formed. Little attention has been paid to the internal organization of the modified structures.

The formation of the extremely complicated structures of the adult central nervous system undoubtedly occurs according to some general principles, similar — although modified in different ways — in various vertebrate groups. The morphogenetic processes determining both gross morphology and internal structure are initially quite similar in various vertebrates. In the neural tube of early stages, a pattern of cellular proliferation and migration develops which gives rise to a skeleton of embryonic structures. This may later be modified in various directions, often in a very complicated way. The origin and appearance of these basic patterns will be the theme of this review.

The well-known and important works of Hamburger, Levi-Montalcini and their co-workers have taught us much about the further modification of the central nervous system, especially the spinal cord of the chick embryo. The importance of the interactions within the central nervous system, and between it and the periphery has been clarified. However, these investigations have been summarized earlier (for example, by Hamburger and Levi-Montalcini, 15; Weiss, 53; and Hamburger, 12, 13, 14) and will be further discussed by Sperry in this volume.

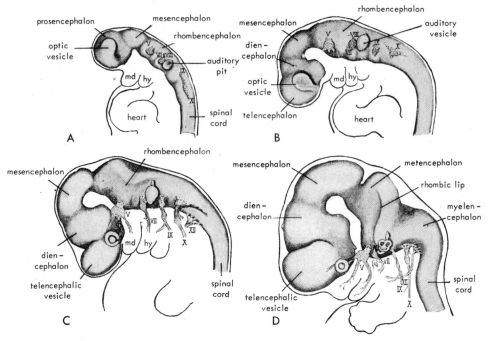

Fig. 4.2 Four stages in the early development of the brain to show formation of the primary brain vesicles. hy, hyoid arch; md, mandibular arch; V, trigeminal; VII, facial; VIII, acoustic; IX, glossopharyngeal; X, vagus; XII, hypoglossal. (After Patten, *Human Embryology*, p. 340, Fig. 203, McGraw-Hill, 1953.)

Early Morphogenesis of the Brain

At neural induction in amphibians, an ovoid neural plate is formed. This plate rapidly elongates and is transformed into a tube through the process of neurulation. The early elongation is important in changing the shape of the plate to yield a wide rostral part—the brain—and a comparatively narrow caudal part—the spinal cord. Its mechanics have recently been studied by Jacobson (23) who placed stain marks at the neural plate stage, and followed the movement of these marks during the process of neural folding (stage 13–16 according to Harrison, using *Ambystoma* material). Movements were also followed with the aid of time-lapse cinematography. Cells were

seen to stream toward the midline and then diverge caudally and to some extent also rostrally, producing an elongation of the neural plate. In other experiments, Jacobson removed the neural plate and placed stain marks on the underlying mesodermal archenteric roof. The same type of cell streaming could also be observed in that structure.

Numerous investigators have tried to analyze the factors responsible for normal neurulation. Factors intrinsic to the neural plate as well as extrinsic to it have been suggested as causal, as have differences in water uptake, mitotic activity, cell death, and so on. The medially directed cell movements just mentioned result in a narrowing of the neural folds. Jacobson showed that the embryo undergoes neurula-

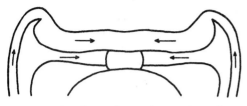

normal embryo (normal neurulation)

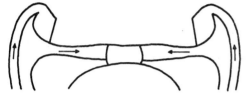

neural plate removed (normal neurulation)

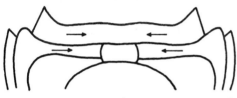

neural folds removed (normal neurulation)

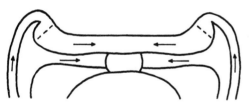

neural plate turned upside - down
(normal neurulation)

neural plate killed (no neurulation)

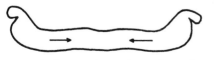

neural plate isolated (neurulation)

tion even after extirpation of the neural plate or the neural folds (Fig. 4.3). Furthermore, it has long been known (Holtfreter, 18), that an isolated neural plate can undergo neurulation. By turning the plate upside down in situ, Jacobson demonstrated that the folding tendency of the substratum was stronger than that of the plate. When the neural plate was killed by excessive staining with vital stains, neurulation was prevented. Jacobson suggested that neurulation is brought about by an increased adhesiveness between the neural epithelial cells, which are firmly attached to the underlying substratum (Fig. 4.4). The isolated neural plate apparently has sufficient tendency for normal curving. When attached to the substratum of the archenteric roof, the increase in adhesiveness between the neural plate cells, illustrated in Figure 4.4, determines the folding process. When the neural plate is turned upside down, the originally apical surfaces of the cells adhere to the substratum, and the folding occurs in a way opposite to that inherent in the plate.

Cell streaming thus results in the narrowing of the plate, while its curvature appears to be caused, at least partly, by changes in cell adhesion.

At about the time of closing of the neural folds to form a tube, a phenomenon appears which was first described in 1828 by von Baer (1) as "neuromery," segmental arrangement of transverse bulges along the neuraxis. The existence of these neuromeres has sometimes been denied—they have

Fig. 4.3 Diagrams showing the effect on neurulation of various operations at the neural plate stage. Arrows mark cell streamings. (Adapted from Jacobson, *Zool. Bidrag Uppsala* 35:433–449, 1962.)

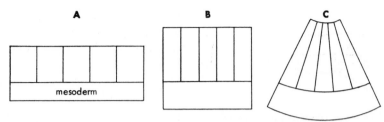

Fig. 4.4 Diagram to show cells from the axolotl neural plate in transverse sections. A. Stage 12. B. Stage 14—increased adhesion between the cells; marked fixation to the mesoderm, which contracts at the same time. Neural tube cells become cylindrical. C. Stage 17—increased intercellular adhesion; still strong attachment to the mesoderm, which does not contract further. As a result, the neural cells become pyramidal in shape. (Reproduced from Jacobson, *Zool. Bidrag Uppsala* 35:433–449, 1962.)

been regarded as shrinkage artifacts, due to fixation. However, many authors have reported their existence even in living embryos, especially of the chick (Fig. 4.5). The extent of neuromery varies greatly in different species. It is most easily observed in embryos with a wide neural tube, such as shark, bird, reptile, and mammalian embryos. It is very difficult to observe in embryos with a massive neural tube, for instance in amphibians, bony fishes, and cyclostomes. Detailed analyses of wax-plate and graphic reconstructions have, however, demonstrated that such bulges exist in all species investigated (Bergquist, 3; Saetersdal, 45; Wedin, 52).

Analysis of closely spaced stage series of mouse and chick embryos (Källén and Lindskog, 36; Källén, 27), and observations on living chick embryos maintained in vitro (Källén, 27), have shown that neuromery develops in an orderly, but complicated way (cf. Fig. 4.17). For a short time, neuromeres occur as far back as the spinal cord. The bulges apparently develop in a rostrocaudal sequence and disappear in a caudorostral sequence. Furthermore, bulges begin to disappear early in the region just caudal to the otic

vesicles. These findings were verified by Wedin (52). Three successive sets of bulges can be observed and have been called proneuromery, neuromery, and postneuromery, respectively.

In young stages (proneuromery and early neuromery stages) the bulges form the dominating morphological characteristic of the brain (Fig. 4.5). In late neuromery and postneuromery stages, they are often only poorly seen, as the brain wall begins to thicken and the boundary fissures become indistinct. Optic evaginations develop very early in the rostral part of the neural tube. By extirpation of the prechordal mesoderm in young *Ambystoma* neurulae, eye development may be prevented, but rostral neuromeres form, nonetheless, as described by Bergquist and Källén (6). Later, hemispheric evaginations are formed, the mesencephalic region widens, and various specializations of the brain appear. The mechanics of these processes are poorly understood. However, these hemispheric evaginations are apparently already determined in the newly formed neural tube, as isolation experiments do not prevent their development (von Woellwarth, 54).

One prominent feature of early

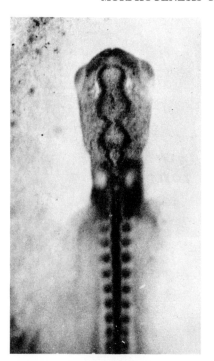

Fig. 4.5 Photograph of an unfixed chick embryo, 12 somites. Neuromere bulges are distinctly seen.

morphogenesis of the brain is that the floor of the neural plate folds down around the notochordal tip to form the hypothalamic protuberance. Jacobson (24) studied this process in *Ambystoma* embryos, in which part of the neural plate had been rotated 180°. The rotation of the hypothalamic rudiment results in a rostrally directed diverticulum. Jacobson concluded that the formation of the hypothalamic bulge is the result of an autonomous process within the neural plate blastema.

A morphogenetic specialization of another type occurs in the early neural tube: the formation of the nonnervous roof and floor plates. In the roof of the third and fourth ventricles ependymal tela develop. In other parts of the brain, transformation of neural to

ependymal tissue takes place, for example, in the roof of the hypothalamic protuberance in many species, or medial wall of the hemispheres. The well-known studies of Holtfreter (17, 18) and Takaya (48), have stressed the importance of the surrounding tissue for such transformation processes (Dalcq, 7). When Jacobson (24) rotated rhombencephalic parts of the neural plate in *Ambystoma* 180°, the rotated region gave rise to a normally structured brain. Its gross development was determined by its surroundings.

The topogenesis of the brain is thus partly determined in the neural plate; however, it can still be influenced by its surroundings. Each formative process must be analyzed separately.

Histogenesis of the Neural Tube Wall in Early Stages

The wall of the early neural tube is made up of a pseudostratified cylindrical epithelium, the neural epithelium. Mitotic figures are found along the ventricular surface exclusively. It was originally thought that these ventricular cells represented a special germinal layer. However, as discussed in detail by Watterson (Chapter 5), it is now known that when a cell divides in the neural epithelium, its nucleus moves to the ventricular lumen, there enters mitosis, and the daughter cells again move lateralwards.

As mentioned previously, a specialized zone appears during development in the lateral part of the neural wall, the stratum zonale. This is a cell-free zone of fairly homogenous appearance. In chicks it is formed at about Hamburger and Hamilton's stage 13–25, varying with the part of the brain (Fig. 4.6). When studied in electron-

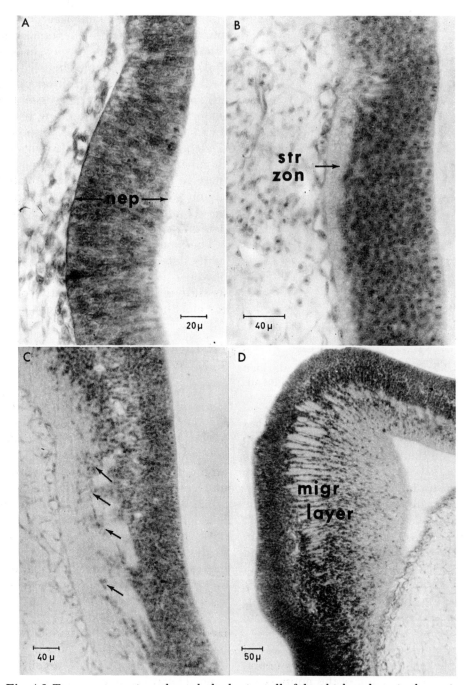

Fig. 4.6 Transverse sections through the brain wall of the chick embryo in the region of the posterior commissure. *A*. Hamburger-Hamilton stage 17 — the whole wall filled with neural epithelium, nep. *B*. H-H stage 18 — a stratum zonale has appeared. *C*. H-H stage 20 — single cells (at arrows) begin to migrate laterally. *D*. H-H stage 28 — large migrated layer (migr. layer).

micrographs (Bergquist, unpublished observations) it is seen that the zone initially is composed of cytoplasmic extensions from the epithelium. This zone broadens, and is further enlarged by the addition of neurites from maturing neuroblasts within the epithelium. After some time, cells begin to detach from the neural epithelium and migrate radially into the zonal layer. In some species, the lateral migration of cells gives rise to a cell layer which is not completely detached from the epithelium (for example, in urodeles), in other species this migrated layer becomes separated from the epithelium by a more or less well-defined cell-free zone. The time schedule for this differentiation of the brain wall is very different in different parts of the central nervous system. It begins early, for instance, in the rhombencephalon and spinal cord, whereas it is late in the dorsal parts of the hemispheres and the mesencephalic bulges.

The radial migration does not take place in a random fashion in the brain. On the contrary, it is patterned in a manner which is practically identical in all species studied. In Figure 4.7, localized areas of high migratory activity are demonstrated. We have called such areas "migration areas," each of which also represents a center of increased mitotic activity (Bergquist, 2).

The radial migration from the neural epithelium outward may be a continuous process, leading to a gradually thickening layer of migrated cells. In many regions, however, especially in the brains of higher vertebrates, migration is discontinuous. This produces a stratification of the migrated cells into concentric layers (Fig. 4.8). Bergquist (5) showed that with each

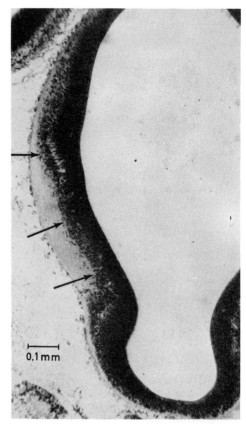

0.1 mm

Fig. 4.7 Transverse section through the diencephalic wall of a chick embryo, H-H stage 26. Note well-limited areas of migratory activity. Borders marked with arrows.

wave of migration, corresponding changes in mitotic activity could be seen at the ventricular lumen, the formation of each layer corresponding to a peak of mitotic activity.

During the gradual progression of embryonic development, the migrated cell layer increases in thickness, while the neural epithelium decreases and finally disappears. Radioautographic studies on DNA synthesis (Källén and Valmin, 38) have shown that cellular multiplication does occur in the migrated layer, despite the fact that mitotic figures in that stratum are ex-

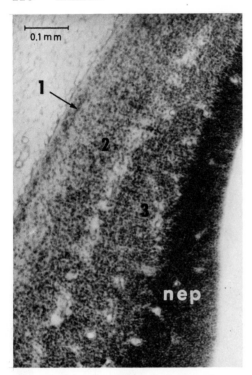

0.1 mm

1

2

3

nep

Fig. 4.8 Frontal section through a hemisphere of a chick embryo, H-H stage 30. Note three layers (1–3) of migrated cells lying outside the neural epithelium, nep.

ceedingly rare. The migrated layers of cells are later transformed to nuclear rudiments or cortical layers after histodifferentiation. Very often the layers can be traced in stained sections, through a series of subdivisions or fusions until cell groups, which correspond to the adult brain nuclei, can be identified. Several authors have analyzed the development of various regions of the brain in this way— Källén studied telencephalic development in various species (27, 33), Bergquist has followed the diencephalic nuclei (2, 4), Rüdeberg (43) the cerebellar nuclei, and Hugosson (21) the rhombencephalic motor and sensory nuclei. In Figure 4.9 the gradual appearance of the dentate cerebellar nucleus within such migrated layers

is shown in embryos of man. Often the various cell groups are not clearly distinguishable in routinely stained sections and some authors, for instance Goldby and Gamble (10), have questioned the reliability of this method. However, with specific histochemical stains, the various cell groups can often be distinguished very clearly (Fig. 4.10). By studies of this kind it has been possible to analyze in detail nuclear development and to describe an embryological "Bauplan" of various brain regions. Thus it is now possible to compare brains of various species and draw conclusions regarding homologies.

Cell migration processes other than the radial migrations just discussed also occur. In an experimental analysis by Harkmark (16), extensive migration of cells in the region of the rhombic lip was demonstrated. Also in the cerebellum, Rüdeberg (43) described a nonradial migration of cells from the attachment of the tela at the external surface of the brain, ventrally to form the superficial granular layer. Another type of cell migration, called "group migration" by Hamburger and Levi-Montalcini (15) consists of movements of whole nuclei or even nuclear groups. Jones and Levi-Montalcini (25) described such movements in the chick telencephalon, basing their observations on silver-stained material. Migration of the facial nucleus with the formation of the genu n. facialis is another well-known example.

It seems reasonable to conclude, then, that a skeleton of nuclear and cortical rudiments is formed as a result of radial and other types of migration. This skeleton is later molded into a definitive pattern by a series of complex modifying processes.

Among the modifying processes

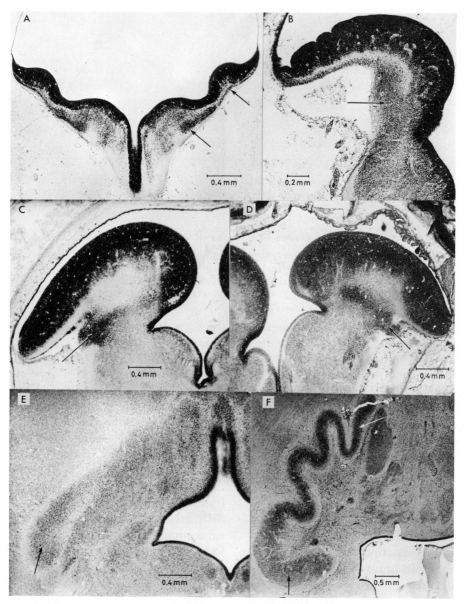

Fig. 4.9 Sections through the cerebellum of human embryos showing the formation of the dentate nucleus from migrated cells. *A*. 13.3-mm length—distinct superficial migrated layer. *B*. 21-mm length—thickening of migrated layer by cells streaming from the ventricular surface. *C*. 25.5-mm length—thick cluster of laterally migrated cells. *D*. 29-mm length—beginning subdivision of migrated cell cord. *E*. 92-mm length—detachment of crescent-shaped lateral cell group. *F*. 350-mm length—dentate configuration of lateral cell group. In *E* the cerebellar ridges have fused in the midline. Arrows mark cell groups mentioned. Further details in Rüdeberg (44).

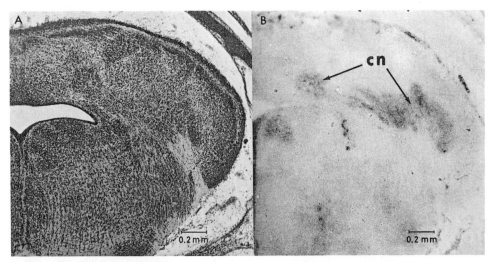

Fig. 4.10 Sections through the cerebellar region of a 17-day-old mouse embryo. *A.* Stained with H and E—cerebellar nuclei hardly visible. *B.* Stained for nonspecific esterase—cerebellar nuclei, cn, distinct. For further details see Rüdeberg (44).

which are important, cell degeneration may be mentioned (35). The best-known example is the selective degeneration in the developing spinal cord, described by Hamburger and Levi-Montalcini (15), by which the motor cell column in the cervical region is reduced. Massive cellular degeneration also apparently plays a role in early morphogenesis (Källén, 28).

Formation of Proliferative and Migratory Patterns

If the migration areas of a vertebrate embryonic brain are reconstructed, a checkered pattern made up of transverse bands and longitudinal bands or columns (Fig. 4.11) is seen. The former represent a direct continuation of the postneuromeres, discussed above. They are most pronounced in the cranial part of the brain, becoming less distinct caudally to disappear in the spinal cord. In the rhombencephalon

they are discernible for a brief period only.

The longitudinal bands appear slightly later than the transverse ones. They are best developed in the rhombencephalon, where four separate and fairly distinct columns can be seen (Fig. 4.12). If such stages are studied histochemically, very definite borderlines can be obtained. In the chick, the two ventral columns—together forming the classical basal plate—are distinctly separated from the two dorsal columns (Fig. 4.13), which together form the alar plate. In the mouse, the ventrolateral column in certain stages is strongly phosphatase positive, the ventral column being negative. Further rostrally, in the mesencephalon, only three columns are seen—the dorsalmost is lacking. In the prosencephalon there are only two, the ventralmost having also disappeared. The boundary between the two middle columns, that is, between the alar plate

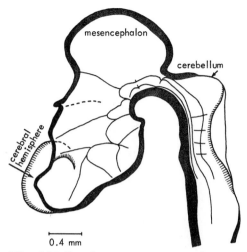

Fig. 4.11 Graphic reconstruction of migration areas in a chick embryo, H-H stage 21–22, seen in medial view. Borders between areas marked with thin lines.

and the basal plate, ends at the optic chiasma. This is apparent from the pattern of the migration areas and also the distribution of alkaline phosphatase (Källén and Valmin, 37).

The fate of these four bands of high mitotic activity was studied by Hugosson (21) who found that they give rise approximately to the longitudinal columns of Herrick: somato-sensory, vis-cero-sensory, viscero-motor and somato-motor. Minor discrepancies were found, however.

The origin of the transverse and longitudinal pattern is a subject of great interest, closely related to the general problem of the cause and significance of neuromere formation. As mentioned previously, opinion has differed in this matter. Some authors have suggested that the neuromeres are artifacts caused by mesodermal segmentation, others believe that they represent the segmental unit of the central nervous system, comparable to myotomes and branchial pockets. We have noted earlier that each neuromeric bulge centers around a region of high mitotic activity. Evidence from colchicine experiments (33) in fact suggests that neuromere formation may be secondary to this mitotic activity. Accumulation of cells in mitotic arrest results in monstrous enlargement of the neuromeric bulges, even in the spinal cord (Fig. 4.14). Apparently the increased number of arrested cells and consequent decrease in interphase cells results in a thinning of the neural wall and enlargement of the ventricular surface. Since this is

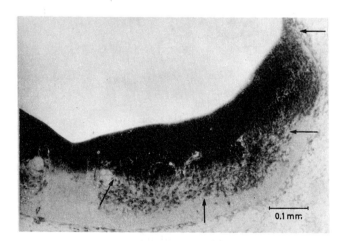

Fig. 4.12 Transverse section through the brain of a chick embryo, H-H stage 26. The section cuts the rhombencephalic anlage. Longitudinal cell columns are visible. Arrows mark borderlines.

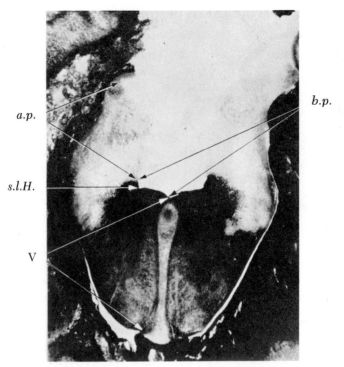

Fig. 4.13 Section through the hindbrain of a chick embryo, age 7 days, stained for alkaline phosphatases; a.p., alar plate; b.p., basal plate; s.l.H., sulcus limitans His; V, ventral cell column. (Reproduced from Källén and Valmin, *Z. Anat. Entwicklungs-geschichte* 121:376–387, 1960, with permission from Springer-Verlag, Berlin, Göttingen, Heidelberg.)

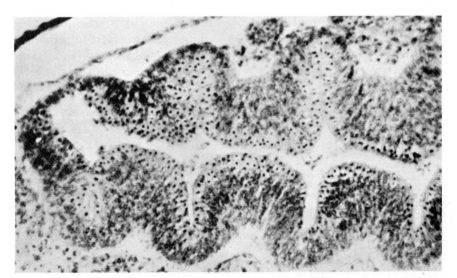

Fig. 4.14 Horizontal section through the spinal cord of a chick embryo, treated at age 2 days 12 hours for 4 hours with colchicine. Note monstrous neuromerelike bulges. (Reproduced from Källén, *Z. Anat. Entwicklungsgeschichte*, 123; 309–319, 1962, with permission from Springer-Verlag, Berlin, Göttingen, Heidelberg.)

most marked at the center of each neuromere, these tend to bulge more than normally. This process has been discussed in detail by Källén (29, 33).

We thus have every reason to believe that the formation of neuromeres is an expression of the existence of proliferative patterns in the neural tube. In 1956 (30) I studied the changes in mitotic rate during formation of the neuromeric bulges, and demonstrated an increase with the appearance of each set of neuromeres.

How then, does this mitotic pattern arise? No definite answer can be given. However, it should be noted that the mitotic centers of the three sets of neuromeric bulges do not coincide topographically. Thus, repeated activation of certain regions of the neural tube with inherently high mitotic rates would not suffice to explain the successive production of neuromeres in different parts of the brain. This is shown schematically in Figure 4.15. It seems more reasonable to think of the patterns as secondary to a generalized increase in mitotic activity of the neural tube. The extent and appearance of the patterns might be related to the dimensions of the tube. That is, the length of each neuromere bulge is related roughly to the diameter of the neural tube at that level. Furthermore, in regions such as the prosencephalon, where specially active growth occurs, the number of bulges increases for each set of neuromeres. A parallel may be drawn to the observation of Waddington and Deuchar (51) that the dimensions of somites are determined by the thickness of the mesoblast. How the patterning occurs is obscure. Turing (50) presented a mathematical theory for the formation of patterns of this type, which has recently been utilized by Maynard-Smith

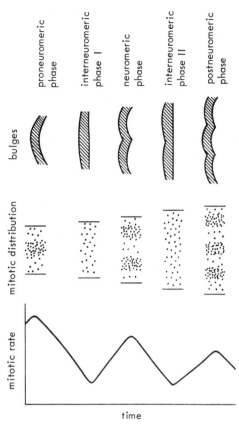

Fig. 4.15 Schematic drawing showing relationship of the three successive mitotic patterns. Top: The appearance of the bulges within a certain brain region. Middle: That of the mitotic distribution. Bottom: mitotic rate curve. (Reproduced from Källén, Z. *Anat. Entwicklungsgeschichte* 123:309–319, 1962, with permission from Springer-Verlag, Berlin, Göttingen, Heidelberg.)

and Sondhi (39) in their analysis of the bristles and ocelli in *Drosophila*. It might also be applicable to the neuromere system.

Hugosson (21) has shown that the longitudinal bands show the same type of association with increased mitotic activity as the transverse neuromere system. I have verified this with colchicine experiments (33). Why do the bands then appear at right angles to the earlier transverse bands? Perhaps this is related to the fact that the tube changes from a closed system to a partly open system when the thin dorsal ependymal roof is formed.

Determination of Neural Patterns

Let us turn to a causal analysis of the origin of neural patterns. Numerous investigations since the time of Mangold and Spemann's original work on neural induction have demonstrated regional specific induction processes which give rise to the various parts of the CNS: archencephalon, deuterencephalon, and spinal cord and its subdivisions. Evidence for the action of regionally specific inductor systems has been presented by many authors, and is discussed at length by Dalcq (7) and by Saxén and Toivonen (46). The group working with Nieuwkoop (40) has shown the importance of temporal differences in the influence of the substratum on the brain anlage; an initial activation being followed by a transformation process. Common to all these studies is the fact that the materials obtained in the various experiments were analyzed only in relatively broad outlines: prosencephalon, and so on.

Are the more detailed patterns of the differentiation of the nuclear centers already present in the neural plate when induction is completed? This problem has been investigated with a variety of methods. Many authors have studied the regenerative capacity of the brain in various stages and species. Even in neural tube stages of amphibians and birds, regulation of an extirpated part may take place and a normal, though hypoplastic brain region may form (36). However, evidence has been presented that certain nuclear groups may be lacking in the regenerated part, which could therefore be regarded as irreversibly determined at the stages of operation, (Holtzer, 20, Stefanelli, 47 and Romanovski and Sládeček, 42).

Another approach has involved the rotation of a piece of the neural plate in amphibian embryos, followed by study of the topography of the nuclei in the rotated part. The most extensive analysis of this kind is that of Jacobson (24), using *Ambystoma* embryos. In an earlier paper (22), Jacobson mapped the neural plate with respect to the different brain regions, as described by Herrick. In this way he was able to determine the position of various histological structures before and after the rotation. Most studies were made on the rhombencephalon, but adjacent parts were sometimes included. When mesencephalic or even diencephalic parts were included in the rotated piece, they developed caudally, that is, according to their original orientation. Similarly, when large enough parts were rotated, it could be demonstrated that even the rhombencephalic motor nuclei retained their original spatial relationships. Only when very small grafts were rotated were the parts influenced by their new location. Mauthner's cells also developed in accordance with their original topology, although some nonspecific twinning and extra Mauthner's cells appeared, which were attributed to the surgical intervention. It should be stressed that the ectopic nuclei in the experimental larvae showed quite abnormal fiber connections; little specificity in the motor innervation could be found.

Jacobson interprets his findings as evidence for the existence in the neural plate of a nearly rigid mosaic of the nuclear anlagen studied; however, equipotential fields exist outside the exact prospective area of each nucleus. Thus, for instance, division of Mauthner's cell area could result in two cells — one lying in a normal position, the other located according to its original development.

Jacobson also analyzed the outgrowth of nerve fibers from the ectopic nuclei. He found strong evidence for a directing influence on the fiber growth present in the polarization of the graft. Ingrowing neurites were oriented in the direction they would have grown in the graft before rotation. Furthermore he showed that there is no specificity in the peripheral connections made by the motor fibers, growing out from an ectopic motor nucleus; not even specificity for somatic versus visceral muscles. We may conclude that the position of motor nuclei, Mauthner's cells and other structures is thus largely determined in the neural plate, whereas their functional properties are not.

Jacobson also demonstrated that certain regions of special ependymal differentiation develop according to their original situation after rotation. Such structures may be of importance for the organization of brain nuclei and fiber tracts, for example the typical splitting of the medial forebrain bundle in the mesencephalon. Also the medullary septum — an ependymal structure — developed according to its position before rotation, in spite of the fact that earlier investigators have shown that the presence of an underlying notochord may be of importance for the formation of this structure (Holtfreter, 17).

It should be stressed that Jacobson's findings agree with the earlier studies by Detwiler (8) and others, that the topogenesis of the rhombencephalon, as mentioned earlier, is modified according to its new surroundings to produce a brain of normal external appearance. Histogenesis is therefore apparently more rigidly determined than topogenesis in the rhombencephalic anlage of the amphibian neural plate.

Isolation experiments by Hugosson (21) of the rhombencephalic anlage of the *Xenopus* neural plate demonstrated that the difference in basal plate and alar plate development was already determined at the neural plate stage. The difference between these two regions is primarily characterized by an earlier maturation of the basal plate cells, and an earlier formation of a peripheral migrated layer. Therefore the neural epithelium is thinner, and the number of mitoses found adjacent to the ventricular lumen is lower, compared to that found in the alar plate (cf. Hamburger, 11).

There is thus good evidence for the idea that many later processes of neural differentiation are already established in the neural plate; for example the formation of ependymal specializations, of motor cells, of Mauthner's cell differentiation. However, this mosaic is not absolutely rigid, and certainly does not mean that later differentiation of nuclear centers may not be influenced by interactions with other structures such as ingrowing fiber tracts. Here the results of Hamburger and his co-workers may be referred to, in which it was demonstrated that although initial development of a nucleus may occur in the absence of peripheral target tissue, later degeneration may occur (for example, Hamburger, 18, Dunnebacke, 9).

Let us then recapitulate the evidence for continued interaction of surrounding structures with the developing neural tube. The investigations of Holtfreter (17, 18) and Takaya (48) demonstrated the importance of surrounding tissues for the gross and histological organization of the neural tube. Källén (31) and Hugosson (21) selected a more isolated developmental process for analysis, namely the formation of proliferative patterns, manifested as neuromeric structures and longitudinal cell columns. When portions of neural plate corresponding to the rhombencephalic anlage were explanted, it was found that mitotic patterns did not develop in the absence of underlying chordamesoderm. We explained this by postulating an inductive influence — possibly of a general mitotic-stimulating nature — from the chordamesoderm on the neural tube. Later studies by Bergquist and Källén support this opinion (see 34). If the normal relationship between the tip of the notochord and the brain anlage is disturbed, it may result in hyperplastic growth of the brain at some distance from the operation site.

It is thus possible that for the early control of growth and other developmental processes, a continued interaction between the chordamesoderm and the neural tube is necessary, at least for some time. This interaction would be of great importance for the initial formation of migratory patterns and therefore for the whole skeleton of nuclear development. In this connection it might be of interest to recall the observation of Ragozina (41) and Takaya (49) that the notochord plays a role in the segmentation of the mesoblast into somites.

This neuromere-inducing factor, whatever its nature, is not regionally

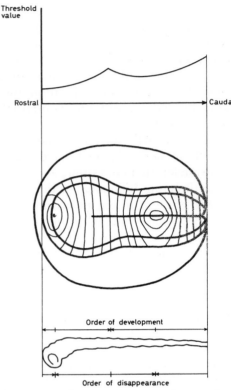

Fig. 4.16 Schematic drawings showing hypothesis of different susceptibility for mitotic-stimulating agents from the substratum. Bottom: Neural tube showing order of appearance and disappearance of neuromere bulges. Middle: Neural plate stage showing fields of different threshold levels. Top: Diagram showing threshold levels.

specific, since any part of the substratum can produce normal neuromeres in an overlying section of neural tube. The specific order of appearance and disappearance of the neuromeres is therefore probably due to differences in reactivity in the neural plate. From the known order of this sequence of appearance and disappearance, hypothetical reactivity thresholds for different parts of the neural tube can be calculated and transcribed to the neural plate. The parts of the nervous system where neuromeres develop early and disappear late would show the lowest threshold values, the parts with late-developing and early-disappearing neuromeres would show the highest threshold values. The hypothetical appearance of the variation of threshold levels along the neuraxis and its transcription to a neural plate stage is shown in Figure 4.16. Two fields would appear to exist. It can be pointed out that the proliferation patterns of the neural tube also extend into the neural crest as long as connection between the two structures exist—the cranial neural crest portions are formed in this way.

Summary

Neurogenesis is an extremely complicated process. Many studies have been made on the problem of neural induction and on later processes. Few exist on the formation of basic patterns in the central nervous system. In order to be able to deepen our knowledge on this point, I think it is wise to analyze early neurogenesis in terms of defined developmental processes instead of resorting to terms such as "competence" for differentiation of whole brain sections and other ill-defined terms. How much information is laid down during neural induction regarding basic cellular processes? Are proliferation rates, time schedule for cellular differentiation, capacity for free motility—processes which are fundamental for early pattern formation in the central nervous system—already established? To what extent may these be modified by or dependent upon influences from surrounding structures? Let me point out a few possibilities for analysis.

From a neural plate map of prospective areas (Fig. 4.17) it can be seen that the alar and basal plates form parallel strips on either side of the notochord. We know that these two structures are already determined in the neural plate. The primary difference between these two areas, in my opinion, is the time of initiation of neuroblast differentiation, the basal plate beginning first. The neural crest forms the outermost structure. Its cells begin neural differentiation still later, and not all of its cells develop into

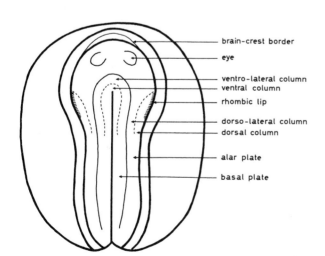

brain-crest border
eye
ventro-lateral column
ventral column
rhombic lip
dorso-lateral column
dorsal column
alar plate
basal plate

Fig. 4.17 Neural plate of an amphibian embryo with prospective areas for eyes, alar plates, and basal plates. Approximate extension of borderlines between the longitudinal columns marked with dashed lines. Hatched parts mark prospective areas for cell regions with a strong nonradial migratory activity.

neural elements. These facts suggest the presence of a gradient in the induced neural field decreasing mediolaterally with respect to starting time of neural differentiation. Such a gradient would reach threshold levels at the border between basal plate and alar plate, between alar plate and neural crest, and between neural crest and epidermis.

On the other hand, the neural crest cells have a marked capacity for free migration. In the outermost part of the neural plate we find cells showing the strongest tendency toward nonradial intraneural migration, in the cerebellar cortical cells and the rhombic lip cells. It would be of interest to study this process in isolation or transplantation experiments, which has not yet been done.

The subdivision of the neural tube into areas of high mitotic and radial migratory activity, according to the results presented above, is due to interaction between continuing influences from the substratum and properties laid down in the neural plate at induction, such as the dimensions and reactivity of the plate and tube.

The rotation experiments of Jacobson demonstrated that many histological structures are already determined at neural plate stage. Of special interest is the existence in the neural plate of regions determined to be ependymal structures in the neural tube. These may be of great importance for the later arrangement of fiber tracts, as demonstrated by Jacobson, and the organization of nuclear centers. Even special neuron groups have been shown to be determined in the neural plate, for example the mauthnerian cells. The functional qualities of the nuclei, however, are apparently not determined. How the different nerve cell characteristics are established at neural induction is a question which awaits further study.

References

1. Baer, K. E. von, "Über Entwicklungsgeschichte der Thiere," Part 1. Königsberg (1828).
2. Bergquist, H., "Zur Morphologie des Zwischenhirns bei niederen Wirbeltieren," *Acta Zool., Stockholm* 13:57-304 (1932).
3. ———, "Studies on the Cerebral Tube in Vertebrates. The Neuromeres," *Acta Zool., Stockholm* 33:117-188 (1952).
4. ———, "Ontogenesis of Diencephalic Nuclei in Vertebrates. A Comparative Study," *Lunds Univ. Årsskr. N.F. Avd. 2. Bd. 50. Nr. 6 Kgl. Fysiograf. Sällskap. i Lund, Handl. N.F. Bd. 65.* Nr. 6: pp. 1-34 (1954).
5. ———, "Mitotic Activity during Successive Migrations in the Diencephalon of Chick Embryos," *Experientia* 13:84 (1957).
6. ———, and B. Källén, "The Archencephalic Neuromery in *Ambystoma Punctatum.* An Experimental Study," *Acta Anat.* 24:208-214 (1955).
7. Dalcq, A. M., "Germinal Organization and Induction Phenomena," *Fundamental Aspects of Normal and Malignant Growth*, W. W. Nowinski, ed. Amsterdam: Elsevier, pp. 305-494 (1960).
8. Detwiler, S. R., "Structural and Functional Adjustments Following Reversal of the Embryonic Medulla in *Ambystoma*," *J. Exptl. Zool.* 116:431-446 (1951).
9. Dunnebacke, T. H., "The Effects of the Extirpation of the Superior Oblique Muscle on the Trochlear Nucleus in the Chick Embryo," *J. Comp. Neurol.* 98:155-178 (1953).
10. Goldby, F., and H. J. Gamble, "The

Reptilian Cerebral Hemispheres," *Biol. Rev.* 32:383–420 (1957).

11. Hamburger, V., "The Mitotic Patterns in the Spinal Cord of the Chick Embryo and Their Relation to Histogenetic Processes," *J. Comp. Neurol.* 88:221–284 (1948).

12. ——, "Development of the Nervous System," *Ann. N. Y. Acad. Sci.* 55, nr. 2: 117–132 (1952).

13. ——, "Regression versus Peripheral Control of Differentiation in Motor Hypoplasia," *Am. J. Anat.* 102:365–410 (1958).

14. ——, "Specificity in Neurogenesis," *J. Cellular Comp. Physiol.* 60, Suppl. 1:81–92 (1962).

15. ——, and R. Levi-Montalcini, "Some Aspects of Neuroembryology," *Genetic Neurology*, P. Weiss, ed. Chicago: University of Chicago Press, pp. 128–160 (1950).

16. Harkmark, W., "Cell Migrations from the Rhombic Lip to the Inferior Olive, the Nucleus Raphe and the Pons. A Morphological and Experimental Investigation on Chick Embryos," *J. Comp. Neurol.* 100:115–210 (1954).

17. Holtfreter, J., "Formative Reize in der Embryonalentwicklung der Amphibien, dargestellt an Explantationsversuchen," *Arch. Exptl. Zellforsch.* 15:281–301 (1934).

18. ——, "Gewebeaffinität, ein Mittel der Embryonalen Formbildung," *Arch. Exptl. Zellforsch.* 23:169–209 (1939).

19. ——, and V. Hamburger, "Embryogenesis: Progressive Differentiation. Amphibians," *Analysis of Development*, B. H. Willier, P. Weiss, and V. Hamburger, eds. Philadelphia: Saunders, pp. 230–296 (1955).

20. Holtzer, H., "Reconstitution of the Urodele Spinal Cord Following Unilateral Ablation. Part 1. Chronology of Neuron Regulation," *J. Exptl. Zool.* 117: 523–558 (1951).

21. Hugosson, R., "Morphologic and Experimental Studies on the Development and Significance of the Rhombencephalic Longitudinal Cell Columns." M.D. thesis, University of Lund (1957).

22. Jacobson, C.-O., "The Localization of the Presumptive Cerebral Regions in the Neural Plate of the Axolotl Larva," *J. Embryol. Exptl. Morphol.* 7:1–21 (1959).

23. ——, "Cell Migration in the Neural Plate and the Process of Neurulation in the Axolotl Larva," *Zool. Bidrag Uppsala* 35:433–449 (1962).

24. ——, "Motor Nuclei, Cranial Nerve Roots, and Fibre Pattern in the Medulla Oblongata after Reversal Experiments on the Neural Plate of Axolotl Larvae. 1. Bilateral Operations," *Zool. Bidrag Uppsala* 36:73–160 (1964).

25. Jones, A. W., and R. Levi-Montalcini, "Patterns of Differentiation of the Nerve Centers and Fiber Tracts in the Avian Cerebral Hemispheres," *Arch. Ital. Biol.* 96:231–284 (1958).

26. Källén, B., "Embryological Studies on the Nuclei and Their Homologization in the Vertebrate Forebrain," *Lunds Univ. Årsskr. N.F. Avd. 2. Bd. 47. Nr. 5. Kgl. Fysiograf. Sällskap. i Lund, Handl. N.F. Bd. 62. Nr. 5*:1–34 (1951).

27. ——, "Neuromery in Living and Fixed Chick Embryos," *Kgl. Fysiograf. Sällskap. i Lund, Handl. 25. Nr. 9*:73–78 (1955).

28. ——, "Cell Degeneration during Normal Ontogenesis of the Rabbit Brain," *J. Anat.* 89:153–161 (1955).

29. ——, "Contribution to the Knowledge of the Regulation of the Proliferation Processes in the Vertebrate Brain during Ontogenesis," *Acta Anat.* 27:351–360 (1956).

30. ——, "Studies on the Mitotic Activity in Chick and Rabbit Brains during Ontogenesis," *Kgl. Fysiograf. Sällskap. i Lund, Handl. 26*, Nr. 17:171–184 (1956).

31. ——, "Experiments on Neuromery in *Ambystoma punctatum* Embryos," *J. Embryol. Exptl. Morphol.* 4:66–72 (1956).

32. ——, "Embryogenesis of Brain Nuclei in the Chick Telencephalon," *Ergeb. Anat. u Entwicklungsgeschichte* 36:62–82 (1962).

33. ——, "Mitotic Patterning in the Central Nervous System of Chick Embryos; Studied by a Colchicine Method," *Z. Anat. Entwicklungsgeschichte* 123: 309–319 (1962).

34. ——, "Overgrowth Malformation and Neoplasia in Embryonic Brain," *Confinia Neurol.* 22:40–60 (1962).

35. ——, "Degeneration and Regeneration in the Vertebrate Nervous System during Embryogenesis," *Progress in*

Brain Research, M. Singer and J. P. Schadé, eds. Amsterdam: Elsevier, vol. 14, in press (1965).

36. ———, and B. Lindskog, "Formation and Disappearance of Neuromery in Mus musculus," *Acta Anat.* 18:273–282 (1953).

37. ———, and K. Valmin, "Morphogenetic Aspects on the Alkaline Phosphatase Distribution in Embryonic Chick Brains," *Z. Anat. Entwicklungsgeschichte* 121:376–387 (1960).

38. ———, and ———, "DNA Synthesis in the Embryonic Chick Central Nervous System," *Z. Zellforsch. Mikroskop. Anat.* 60:491–496 (1963).

39. Maynard, Smith, J., and K. C. Sondhi, "The Genetics of a Pattern," *Genetics* 45:1039–1050 (1960).

40. Nieuwkoop, P. D., "Activation and Organization of the Central Nervous System in Amphibians. III. Synthesis of a New Working Hypothesis," *J. Exptl. Zool.* 120:83–108 (1952).

41. Ragozina, M. N., "The Influence of the Neural Plate and the Chord on the Development of the Axial Mesoderm in Amphibians," *Dokl. Akad. Nauk SSSR* 51:245–247 (1946).

42. Romanovský, A., and F. Sládeček, "Influence of Early Brain Restitution on Swimming Capacity in the Larvae of Axolotl," *Folia Biol. (Praha)* 6:420–425 (1960).

43. Rüdeberg, S.-I., "Morphogenetic Studies on the Cerebellar Nuclei and Their Homologization in Different Vertebrates Including Man." Ph.D. thesis, University of Lund (1961).

44. ———, "Topographic Distribution of Non-specific Esterase during Cerebellar Development in Mouse," *Z. Anat.*

Entwicklungsgeschichte 124:226–233 (1964).

45. Saetersdal, T. A. S., "On the Development of the Neural Chord in *Trichogaster trichopterus* (Pallas) and *Gadus callarias*," *L. Univ. i Bergen Årbok, Naturvitenskap. Rekke* Nr. 5:1–37 (1953).

46. Saxén, L., and S. Toivonen, *Primary Embryonic Induction*, New York: Academic Press (1962).

47. Stefanelli, A., "The Mauthnerian Apparatus in Ichthyopsida; Its Nature and Function and Correlated Problems of Neurohistogenesis," *Quart. Rev. Biol.* 26:17–34 (1951).

48. Takaya, H., "On the Types of Neural Tissue Developed in Connection with Mesodermal Tissues," *Proc. Imp. Acad. Japan* 32:287–292 (1956).

49. ———, "Notochordal Influence upon the Differentiation and Segmentation of Muscle Tissue," *Annot. Zool. Japan* 29: 133–137 (1956).

50. Turing, A. M., "The Chemical Basis of Morphogenesis," *Phil. Trans. Roy. Soc. London Ser. B* 237:37–72 (1952).

51. Waddington, C. H., and E. Deuchar, "Studies on the Mechanism of Meristic Segmentation. I. The Dimensions of Somites," *J. Embryol. Exptl. Morphol.* 1:349–356 (1953).

52. Wedin, B., "Embryonic Segmentations in the Head." M.D. thesis, University of Lund (1955).

53. Weiss, P., "Nervous System (Neurogenesis)," *Analysis of Development*, B. H. Willier, P. Weiss, and V. Hamburger, eds. Philadelphia: Saunders, pp. 346–401 (1955).

54. Woellwarth, C. von, "Die Induktionsstufen des Gehirns," *Arch. Entwicklungsmech. Or.* 145:582–668 (1952).

5

Structure and Mitotic Behavior of the Early Neural Tube

RAY L. WATTERSON[*]

Department of Zoology
University of Illinois
Urbana, Illinois

This report is concerned with the structure and mitotic behavior of the neural tube wall shortly after formation of the neural tube from the neural plate. Its primary purpose is to assemble existing information about these aspects of the early neural tube wall, some of it previously unpublished except in abstract form, and to suggest the developmental significance of these features, especially in chick embryos.

The Concept of Interkinetic Migration

One of the most characteristic features of the neural tube wall in young

[*] Support of the author's investigations by grant B-224-C from the Institute of Neurological Diseases and Blindness of the National Institutes of Health is gratefully acknowledged. I am likewise indebted to Philip Veneziano for assistance with operations, Alex Bartha for preparation of specimens for microscopic study, and Daniel Matulionis for photographic assistance.

vertebrate embryos is the concentration of mitotic figures adjacent to the lumen (Fig. 5.1A). His (33) referred to these mitotic cells as "germinal cells." They were believed to be special stem cells that remained adjacent to the lumen and divided repeatedly to produce daughter cells which migrated out of the germinal zone immediately to become the peripherally located nonmitotic cells. This classical concept is clearly illustrated in highly schematic form in Figure 5.1B. Note the orientation of the mitotic spindle in this illustration. It is so oriented that the outermost daughter cell would literally be squeezed out of the germinal zone at cytokinesis, whereas the innermost daughter cell would tend to remain in this zone where it would continue to function as a stem cell. If this concept of the existence of true germinal cells is correct, the wall of the neural tube from an early stage must be a true stratified epithelium.

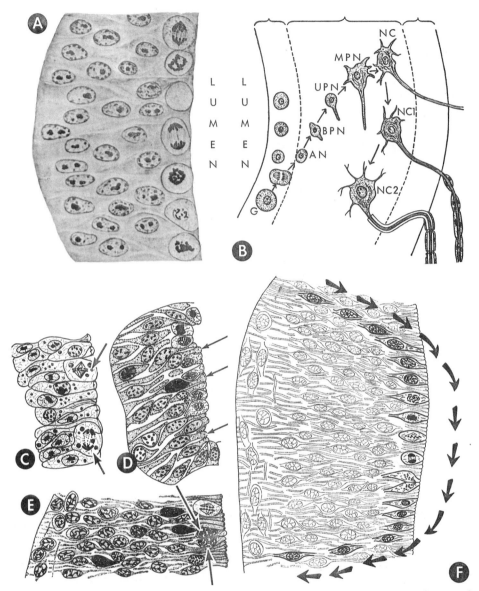

Fig. 5.1 Structure of the neural plate, C, and neural tube wall, A, B, D–F, with special emphasis on the location of mitotic figures. *A.* Part of one wall of the neural tube of a 29-somite chick embryo. (From Hamilton, *Lillie's Development of the Chick*, Fig. 142, courtesy Holt, Rinehart and Winston, 1952.) The wall consists of a pseudostratified epithelium. Mitotic figures occur only in cells adjacent to the lumen. *B.* Highly schematic representation of part of one wall of the neural tube showing fates of the two daughter cells of a so-called germinal cell, G, located adjacent to the lumen. (From Hamilton, Boyd, and Mossman, *Human Embryology—Prenatal Development of Form and Function*, Fig. 236, courtesy W. Heffer and Sons, Ltd.) According to the classical concept, the inner daughter cell remains adjacent to the lumen to function again as a germinal cell, whereas the outer daughter cell escapes from the germinal zone, loses its mitotic capacity and differentiates progressively through apolar, AN, bipolar, BPN, unipolar, UPN, and multipolar, MPN, stages. Neurilemma cells are subsequently

However, careful cytological studies by F. C. Sauer (74, 75) indicated that the wall of the early neural tube in a variety of vertebrates is *not* a true stratified epithelium; rather, it is a pseudostratified epithelium (Fig. 5.1*C*, *D* and *E*) with all cells firmly attached to each other at the lumen by terminal bars (see below). Furthermore, Sauer emphasized that the spindle axis only very rarely lies perpendicular to the lumen as illustrated in Figure 5.1*B*; almost invariably it lies parallel to the lumen, as in Figure 5.1*A* and 5.1*C*, with the consequence that division of each mitotic cell produces two daughter cells lying side by side (Fig. 5.1*F*). Sauer made one other very important observation, namely, that early prophases and late telo-phases, as well as intermitotic stages, could not be identified in the germinal zone adjacent to the lumen. When he searched for these missing stages he found them in nuclei located at some distance from the neural canal. By measurement of the distances between nuclei and the lumen he demonstrated that as nuclei undergo prophase changes they progressively approach the lumen (see arrows in upper part of Fig. 5.1*F*); as they complete telophase and enter interphase stages they migrate away from the neural canal (see arrows in lower part of Fig. 5.1*F*).

On the basis of descriptive studies alone, Sauer therefore arrived at the following conclusions about the structure and mitotic behavior of the early neural tube wall (Fig. 5.1*F*). (1) The

added to the axon, NC1, and a myelin sheath forms still later, NC2. Contrast the orientation of the mitotic spindle with orientation of the spindle in all other illustrations in Fig. 5.1. *C.* Part of the neural plate of an early chick embryo. The exposed surface of the neural plate (future lumen surface) is to the right. Note columnar form of interkinetic cells and rounded form assumed by cells during metaphase and anaphase stages (arrows). All neuroepithelial cells at this stage can divide by mitosis; they always withdraw toward the exposed surface before dividing. *D.* Part of the neural tube wall of a 24-somite toadfish embryo. The lumen is to the right. Arrows indicate three neuroepithelial cells whose entire extent from lumen to outer surface can be seen in this one focal plane. All other neuroepithelial cells likewise extend from lumen to periphery but their entire extent is usually not evident in one focal level. *E.* Part of the alar plate of a 10-mm pig embryo. The lumen is to the right. One mitotic cell can be seen adjacent to the lumen. The arrows indicate two daughter cells which originated by division of a single parent cell; both daughter cells are beginning to lengthen peripherally. The neuroepithelium is now so thick that the cytoplasmic processes extending toward the lumen and toward the surface are very thin and therefore are increasingly difficult to follow throughout their full extent. A mantle layer is just beginning to form at the left. It contains rounded cells which escaped from the neuroepithelium and migrated peripherally. *F.* Diagrammatic representation of the cellular structure of part of the alar plate region of the neural tube wall of a 10-mm pig embryo. Nuclei in various stages of interkinesis and mitosis are shown with dark outlines, as are the cell bodies of the cells concerned. The arrows indicate both the succession of mitotic stages and the to-and-fro migrations of the nuclei and cell bodies of neuroepithelial cells; they move toward the lumen during early prophase changes (top) and away from the lumen during late telophase changes (bottom) and lie adjacent to the lumen during late prophase, metaphase, anaphase, and early telophase stages. There is, of course, no ventrad displacement of nuclei and cell bodies, as might be implied from this diagram. (*C–E* from Figs 3, 4 and 5, F. C. Sauer, *J. Comp. Neurol.* 63:13–23, 1935; *F* modified from Fig. 8, F. C. Sauer, *J. Comp. Neurol.* 62:377–405, 1935, courtesy The Wistar Institute.)

wall consists of a pseudostratified layer of elongated and rounded epithelial cells. (2) All cells in the neural tube wall at this stage are capable of dividing. (3) As one of the elongated cells prepares to divide, its nucleus migrates toward the neural canal and the cell itself begins to round up. (4) Because the cells are firmly attached to one another by terminal bars located at the lumen, the process of rounding up causes the cells to withdraw toward the lumen (peripheral cytoplasmic extensions are progressively withdrawn and presumably disappear completely by the metaphase stage). (5) The rounded cells remain adjacent to the lumen during metaphase, anaphase, and early telophase. (6) Both daughter cells, lying side by side, then begin to elongate peripherally during late telophase stages; their nuclei migrate peripherally as they complete telophase and enter early interphase stages. (7) Both daughter cells therefore become part of the thickening pseudostratified neural epithelium and no daughter cell remains behind adjacent to the lumen to function as a true germinal cell. (8) Dividing cells visible in the germinal zone at any given time are not permanent residents of that zone; rather the population of mitotic cells with most of their cytoplasm present in the germinal zone is changing constantly as cells retract, divide, and extend from this zone to make way for other cells which are moving into it. Although Sauer presented this interpretation in a convincing way, it has been largely ignored in American textbooks and has not gained widespread acceptance, even in research publications (Weiss, 87), presumably because it was based on descriptive evidence alone. Fujita (13)

has recently re-emphasized Sauer's concept of interkinetic migration. Such a migration occurs in other embryonic epithelia, but is not as striking a feature of their development (Sauer, 76, 77; Fujita, 13).

Experimental Proof of the Concept

The Colchicine Method

It would seem that a relatively simple experiment could decide between the classical interpretation and Sauer's interpretation of the mitotic behavior of the wall of the early neural tube (Watterson, Veneziano, and Bartha, 85). One need only establish a mitotic block at the metaphase stage with the aid of a colchicine solution deposited on the surface of the developing embryo *in ovo* at approximately 48 hours of incubation. If the classical interpretation is correct, that is, if a layer of true germinal cells exists at that time adjacent to the lumen of the neural tube (Fig. 5.1*B*), one would expect to find only a single layer of blocked mitoses adjacent to the lumen (Fig. 5.2A) *regardless of the length of time the mitotic block is imposed.* According to this concept, all other cells of the neural tube wall have lost their mitotic capacities once they have left this zone.

But, if Sauer is correct in his interpretation, a single layer of blocked mitoses adjacent to the lumen (Fig. 5.2A) should be encountered only in those embryos exposed to colchicine for a very short time; that is, with a brief exposure to the agent only those few cells approaching metaphase at the time of colchicine application should be arrested in metaphase stages. This initial layer of rounded, turgid cells containing blocked metaphases would presumably remain at the ventricular surface as long as the mitotic block is maintained (Källén, 41) because, according to Sauer, the main cytoplasmic mass of such cells normally extends away from the lumen only in late telophase stages. Colchicine prevents attainment of anaphase and telophase stages in blocked neural tube cells (Woodward and Estes, 90; Källén, 41), thus blocking elongation of postmitotic cells.

As the exposure time to colchicine is increased, other mitotic cells entering prophase stages should attempt to round up and withdraw toward the lumen since colchicine does not interfere with passage of neural tube cells through prophase changes (Woodward and Estes, 90). Cells now entering mitosis would presumably be prevented from withdrawing *all the way* to the lumen because of the presence there of the turgid layer of cells previously blocked by colchicine action; they could only form a layer of blocked

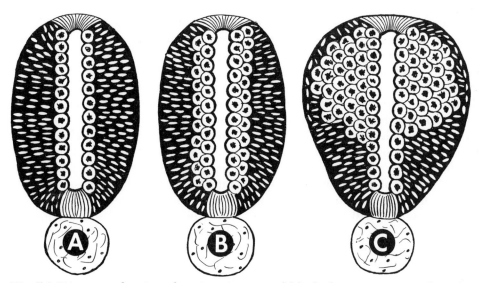

Fig. 5.2 Diagrams showing changing patterns of blocked mitoses *expected* in the neural tube wall with increasing intervals following application of a given amount of colchicine at a given time. White circles with dark center represent cells blocked in metaphase stages by colchicine action. White ovals represent nuclei of neuroepithelial cells in interkinetic stages. *A.* A single layer of colchicine-blocked metaphase stages adjacent to the lumen. Such a condition, according to the classical concept, should exist regardless of the time of exposure to colchicine, but, according to Sauer's interpretation, it should exist only during the first 1–2 hours following exposure to colchicine. *B.* Two layers of colchicine-blocked metaphase stages adjacent to the lumen. Such a condition should not occur, according to the classical concept; it might be expected to occur after 2–4 hours following exposure to colchicine, according to Sauer's interpretation. *C.* Several layers of colchicine-blocked mitoses adjacent to the lumen in the alar plate region, but only a single layer of colchicine-blocked metaphase stages adjacent to the lumen in the basal plate region. Such a condition would be expected, according to Sauer's interpretation, after more than 4 hours following exposure to colchicine (see text). Compare with photomicrographs in Fig. 5.3.

metaphase cells immediately peripheral to the first layer formed. Thus, after several hours of exposure, two to three layers of blocked mitoses should be encountered adjacent to the lumen (Fig. 5.2B), rather than a single layer, as in the case of the classical interpretation.

If colchicine is permitted to act even longer before treated embryos are sacrificed, the number of layers of blocked mitoses bordering the lumen would presumably continue to increase until all cells capable of entering the mitotic cycle had done so. However, the intensity of the reaction to colchicine, as indicated by the number of layers of blocked mitoses accumulating during a given exposure period, might well differ in alar and basal plates as suggested in Figure 5.2C. There is evidence (summarized by Corliss and Robertson, 7) that indicates considerable independence of behavior of these two regions under a variety of conditions.

The results obtained when 1 milliliter or less of a solution containing approximately 1×10^{-5} g of colchicine per milliliter is deposited on the surface of the blastoderm and is allowed to act for increasing periods of time strikingly confirm Sauer's interpretation, although due allowance must be made for the stage variation encountered in embryos incubated 48 hours prior to treatment, as well as for individual variations in the amount of colchicine reaching the cells in question in a given period of time. By 2–3 hours after exposure, several layers of blocked mitoses are usually found adjacent to the lumen (Fig. 5.3A); even with such a brief exposure many layers of blocked mitoses are sometimes present on either side of the lumen, especially in the alar plates (Fig. 5.3B). With longer exposures (4–6 hours) the alar plates typically contain many more layers of blocked mitoses than the basal plates (Fig. 5.3C; see also Fig. A in Overton, 65) and the alar plates tend to bulge into the lumen. Källén (53) has also described many layers of blocked mitoses at the ventricular surface of the mesencephalon of colchicine-treated chick embryos. With still longer exposures (up to $7\frac{1}{2}$ hours) almost all cells of the alar plates are blocked at the metaphase stage, thus revealing their capacity for division (Fig. 5.3D), and the walls of the neural tube become increasingly distorted, especially the alar plate portions (see also Källén, 54, especially his Fig. 4). Paff (67), who was the first to treat 48-hour chick embryos *in ovo* with colchicine by depositing it on the surface of the blastoderm, was so impressed by the large number of blocked mitoses that he was led to postulate that colchicine stimulates cells to pass into mitosis, that is, causes overproduction of neural tube tissue. Some of his illustrations do indeed indicate the presence of excessive amounts of neural tube tissue in colchicine-treated embryos, but they also show that manipulation of the embryos in his experiments caused the neural tube to open secondarily, at least in some of his specimens. Deliberate opening of the previously closed neural tube by slitting the roof plate in otherwise untreated 48-hour chick embryos invariably leads to overproduction of neural tube tissue (Fowler, 12; Watterson, 82). For this and other reasons (Woodward and Estes, 90), Paff's conclusions about the stimulating action of colchicine on early neural tube stages cannot be accepted.

Unfortunately, the correct interpretation of the appearance of histological sections of neural tubes in embryos treated with colchicine is complicated by the fact, demonstrated convincingly by Overton (64), that within an hour after its application colchicine causes a radical shrinkage of the blastoderm, a reduction in the length of the embryo, and formation of conspicuous convolutions in the neural tube (Fig. 5.4A, almost identical with Overton's Fig. 5; see also Fig. B in Overton, 65). It is evident that transverse sections through different levels of such a distorted neural tube would give conflicting pictures of the number of layers of blocked mitoses in a single specimen.

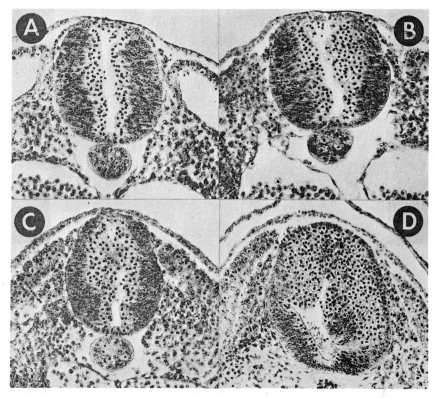

Fig. 5.3 Photomicrographs showing changing patterns of blocked mitoses *obtained* with increasing intervals following application of a given amount of colchicine to chick embryos incubated 48 hours. Compare with expected patterns shown in Fig. 5.2. *A.* 2–3 hours after exposure to colchicine – several layers of blocked mitoses lie adjacent to the lumen. *B.* 2–3 hours after exposure to colchicine – the distribution of the several layers of colchicine-blocked mitoses adjacent to the lumen is less regular than in *A* due, in part, to the exaggeration of neuromeres by colchicine treatment. *C.* 4–6 hours after exposure to colchicine; more colchicine-blocked mitoses lie adjacent to the lumen in the alar plates than in the basal plates. *D.* 7½ hours after exposure to colchicine – almost every neuroepithelial cell in the alar plates has initiated mitosis and has been blocked in metaphase stage by colchicine action. Considerable distortion of the alar plates is evident (see text). Very few colchicine-blocked mitoses are evident in the basal plates.

Careful examination of the distorted neural tubes indicates that the prominent lateral evaginations of the ventricular surface (ventricular furrows) and the less conspicuous bulgings of the outside of the neural tube as well are not distributed at random, but tend to occur at intersomitic levels (Fig. 5.4A; see also the frontal section in Fig. 2 in Källén, 54). Cells lying between the bulges are less affected by colchicine than those lying in the center of the bulges. Similar, though less obvious, spatial relationships are evident in untreated embryos of the same somite stage (Fig. 5.4B), but are much more obvious in younger untreated embryos (Fig. 5.4C); such intersomitic protrusions of the neural tube walls in untreated embryos are the neuromeres (see Bergquist and Källén, 5; Källén, 43, 44, especially

his Fig. 2). According to Källén (40, 41, 46, 47, 56), and Bergquist and Källén (6), neuromeres, as well as pre- and postneuromeres, are simply localized bulges of the neural tube wall caused by local intensifications of proliferation (see also Saetersdal, 73). As noted by Källén (54), colchicine strengthens or emphasizes existing mitotic patterns, and thus accentuates neuromeres and postneuromeres. Neuromery is accentuated in colchicine-treated embryos, in part because more blocked metaphase stages lie adjacent to or close to the lumen within each neuromere or postneuromere than between such structures, as recognized by Källén (40, 54). But this consequence of colchicine action is greatly exaggerated by the shrinkage of the blastoderm and embryo caused by colchicine which, according to Overton

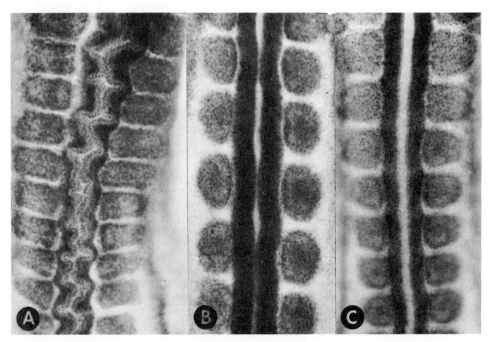

Fig. 5.4 *A.* Exaggerated neuromeres in a 22-somite, colchicine-treated chick embryo. *B.* Neuromeres in normal 22-somite embryo. *C.* Neuromeres in 16-somite chick embryos. Dorsal views of whole mounts.

(64), precedes and is apparently independent of the effect of this agent on the mitotic cycle.

Thus, although the experiments of Watterson, Veneziano, and Bartha (85) with colchicine have been cited as providing the first experimental demonstration of the validity of Sauer's interpretation of the structure and mitotic behavior of the neural epithelium, it is evident that better ways of testing this concept experimentally had to be found. But before discussing the results of more sophisticated methods, it seems desirable to comment briefly on the greater accumulation of blocked mitoses in the alar plates of colchicine-treated embryos, since this result was contrary to expectation.

A greater number of blocked mitoses in the *basal* plates had been anticipated because mitotic density (number of mitotic figures per unit of area of the lining of the central canal) is greater in the basal plates at $2\frac{1}{2}$ days of incubation (Hamburger, 19) and earlier (Corliss and Robertson, 7). According to these investigators, mitotic density in the alar plates exceeds mitotic density in the basal plates only after more than 3 days of incubation, and the same is true of the ratio of mitotic density to mitotic duration, according to Jelínek (39). The fact that more blocked mitoses are found in the *alar* plates of colchicine-treated embryos suggested the possibility that mitotic duration (length of the mitotic cycle) might be less in the alar than in the basal plates at this time. Sauer (74, p. 391) pointed out that ". . . rapid cell multiplication by mitosis might take place with few mitotic figures present at a given time, provided the mitotic stages were passed through rapidly." Similarly, Saetersdal (72, p. 8) stated,

"Presuming an equal duration of the intermitotic periods and a different duration of the mitotic periods in two types of tissues, the largest number of mitotic figures occurs in the tissue with the longest mitotic periods, i.e., in the tissue with the *lowest* proliferative activity." However, according to Jelínek (39) there is no difference in mitotic duration between alar and basal plates of the spinal cord of chick embryos from the 2nd to the 6th day of incubation. Thus it appears that the greater accumulation of blocked mitoses in the alar plates of colchicine-treated embryos simply indicates that many cells of the basal plates, such as somatic motor neuroblasts, begin to differentiate at an early stage (see below) and lose their capacity for proliferation even though they may still be present in the neural epithelium. If so, relative mitotic rates (number of mitotic figures per unit volume of the neural epithelium) might well be greater in alar than in basal plates at $2-2\frac{1}{2}$ days of incubation, especially if the volume of the alar plates at this time is less than the volume of the basal plates. This seems likely from examination of Figure 5 of Corliss and Robertson (7). It seems all the more likely since Hugosson (38) reported that relative mitotic rates are identical in alar and basal plates of spinal cords of older embryos ($5-6\frac{1}{2}$ days) even though mitotic densities are then much greater in the alar plates, according to Hamburger (19) and Corliss and Robertson (7). Thus, observations of the mitotic behavior of the early neural tube wall of embryos treated with colchicine lead to the conclusion that most, if not all, cells of the alar plates are capable of division in embryos incubated $2-2\frac{1}{2}$

days, whereas many cells of the basal plates have lost this capacity at this early stage, even though they are still present in the neural epithelium.

Deoxyribonucleic Acid (DNA) Determinations

M. E. Sauer and Chittenden (78) attempted to demonstrate in a different way the validity of F. C. Sauer's interpretation of the mitotic behavior of the wall of the neural tube of chick embryos. It is now well established that doubling of the DNA content of the nucleus occurs in interphase stages which precede visible prophase changes (Ris, 71). Sauer and Chittenden reasoned that if interphase and very early prophase nuclei lie deep within the neural tube wall at some distance from the lumen (Fig. 5.1F), the mean DNA content of these nuclei should be intermediate between the mean 2n value (53±2.2) obtained in half telophases and the mean 4n value (94±1.7) obtained in metaphase and anaphase stages of the inner portion of the neural tube wall. Their microspectrophotometric measurements of individual nuclei located in the peripheral two-thirds of the wall of the myelencephalon of a 3-day chick embryo stained by the Feulgen technique gave a mean value (69±3.2), which is clearly intermediate between the 2n and 4n values. Moreover, they predicted that nuclei with larger volumes (see upper part of Fig. 5.1F) should, in general, contain larger amounts of DNA than adjacent smaller nuclei, since the larger nuclei are more advanced toward visible prophase changes. Such a positive correlation was found; as nuclear size increases, the amount of DNA per nucleus increases. On the basis of these results

Sauer and Chittenden (78, p. 5) were led to conclude, "Our work . . . no longer leaves room for doubt that the mitotic cycle in the early neural tube involves nuclei at all depths and not just those at the lumen." But an even more convincing proof of the validity of this concept would be the demonstration of nuclear migration by labeling nuclei with tritiated thymidine, which is incorporated into chromosomes of cells preparing for division and is retained by these chromosomes and their progeny.

Labeling DNA with Tritiated Thymidine

M. E. Sauer and Walker (79) deposited 50 μc of thymidine-H^3 (0.05 ml of solution) on the surface of 2½-day chick embryos *in ovo*. Embryos were sacrificed at short intervals and radioautographs were prepared from sections through the brain level of the neural tube. One to two hours after exposure to tritiated thymidine, labeled nuclei were visible only in the outer half to two-thirds of the wall of the neural tube (Fig. 5.5A). Mitotic figures at the lumen were not labeled with such a short exposure time. By 4 hours after addition of thymidine-H^3 (Fig. 5.5B), radioactivity extended throughout the wall, but was not distributed uniformly. A layer of greater intensity was located at the periphery. Mitotic figures at the lumen were radioactive (see arrow). By 8 hours after exposure to tritiated thymidine, strongly radioactive nuclei extended uniformly from periphery to lumen with little change thereafter (Fig. 5.5C). Such results demonstrate strikingly that interphase stages which begin to incorporate tritiated thymidine into newly synthesized DNA are

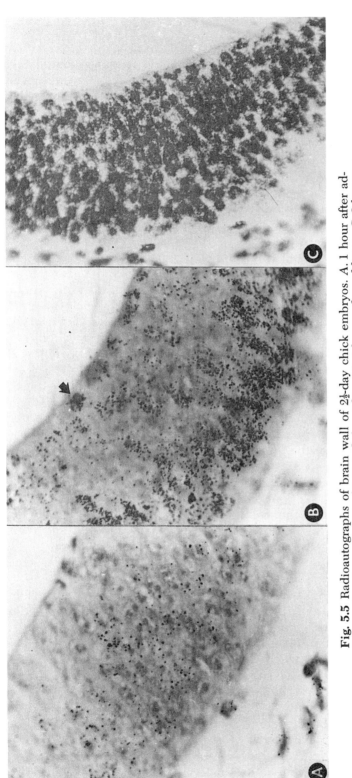

Fig. 5.5 Radioautographs of brain wall of 2½-day chick embryos. *A.* 1 hour after addition of a given amount of tritiated thymidine. *B.* 4 hours after addition. *C.* 8 hours after addition. (From Figs. 1, 2, and 4, Sauer and Walker, *Proc. Soc. Exptl. Biol. Med.* 101:557–560, 1959, courtesy The Society of Experimental Biology and Medicine; originals made available through courtesy of D. Duncan.) Lumen is at upper right in each radioautograph. *A.* Synthesis of DNA as indicated by incorporation of tritiated thymidine begins while nuclei are located in the peripheral half to two-thirds of the neural tube wall. *B.* Labeled nuclei subsequently migrate toward the lumen and take up positions adjacent to the lumen during mitosis (labeled mitotic cell indicated by arrow). *C.* Mitotic capacity of all neuroepithelial cells is indicated by the rather uniform labeling of all nuclei 8 hours after application of thymidine-H³.

located peripherally in the wall of the neural tube (Fig. 5.5A). Partially labeled nuclei then continue to incorporate thymidine-H³ as they continuously migrate toward the lumen, with the result that mitotic figures adjacent to the lumen are then heavily labeled (Fig. 5.5B). By 8 hours, labeled nuclei are migrating both toward the lumen, where they undergo division, and away from it. They again incorporate more thymidine-H³ and repeat the mitotic cycle, as judged by the increased intensity of labeling (Fig. 5.5C). Such results provide especially convincing confirmation of F. C. Sauer's interpretation of the structure and mitotic behavior of the early neural tube wall. The sequence of stages illustrated in Figure 5.5 could occur only if the early neural tube wall is a pseudostratified epithelium and only if the early prophase nuclei, located peripherally, undergo a migration toward the lumen as they prepare to divide, remain adjacent to the lumen as they divide, and then migrate away from the lumen in postmitotic stages.

Cell boundaries stretching from internal to external limiting membranes have been demonstrated by electronmicroscopy in the floor plates of neural tubes of 48-hour chick embryos by Duncan (9). According to the observations of Fujita and Fujita (12a) with the electron microscope, each cell of the matrix layer (neural epithelium) is bounded by a distinct cytoplasmic membrane. But according to the electron microscope studies of Bellairs (2), only the floor plate is one cell thick at this stage; her observations led her to conclude that the ventrolateral part of the neural tube wall at this time is about six cells thick. And yet she stated that occasionally these cells extend as

much as halfway across the wall of the tube. It should be pointed out that cell boundaries have always been difficult to demonstrate in the neural tube wall, both with the light microscope (Hardesty, 24) and with the electron microscope (Duncan, 9), presumably due to fixation difficulties (Sauer, 75). Moreover, in a pseudostratified epithelium, the plane of section might well miss either peripheral or central processes of neuroepithelial cells, especially in the preparation of very thin sections for electronmicroscopy.

Sidman, Miale, and Feder (80) reported almost identical results in the walls of the cerebral vesicles and, with minor variations, elsewhere in the neuraxis of mouse embryos following intravenous injection of thymidine-H³ into pregnant mice at 11 days of gestation. Sidman (79a) concluded that the to-and-fro migration of nuclei in the retina of developing mice is almost identical with the migratory behavior of these nuclei during the mitotic cycle in the neural tube wall. Their results are even more dramatic because in mammals, thymidine-H³ is apparently metabolized rapidly following a single injection and therefore is not available constantly to cells synthesizing DNA, as it is in chick embryos. As a consequence, the movements of cells labeled immediately after exposure to tritiated thymidine are not obscured by movements of cells subsequently labeled, as they are in the chick, shown in Figure 5.5C. (See also Fujita et al., 14c.)

Fujita (14) injected 25 μc of tritiated thymidine into the yolk sac of 1-day and 6-day chick embryos. His observations on the mesencephalic wall and on the alar plates of the spinal cord of embryos treated with thymidine-H³ at

6 days agree closely with those of Sauer and Walker (79). He found that the basal plates of the spinal cord contain very few labeled nuclei even 25 hours after exposure at 6 days of incubation. This observation is in agreement with the very low mitotic density of the basal plates at this time as reported by Hamburger (19) and Corliss and Robertson (7). Fujita's investigation demonstrated that both mitotic time and generation time are very much shorter in the neural tube wall at the younger stage, a conclusion which both Jelínek (39) and Källén (53) had reached earlier from their observations on colchicine-treated embryos. Källén and Valmin (57) deposited a tritiated thymidine solution on the surface of the embryo at 2–10 days of incubation (10 μc added to embryos younger than 8 days, 50 μc to older embryos) and verified and extended the observations of the earlier investigators. They first noted the presence of labeled nuclei in the mantle zone 8 hours after exposure of 4- and 5-day embryos. Essentially similar results were reported more recently in abstract form by Langman and Martin (59) except that escape of labeled cells from the neural epithelium to form the mantle was detected much earlier.

Terminal Bars as Attachment Devices

The mitotic behavior of the walls of the early neural tube as demonstrated above seemingly requires that the cells of the neural epithelium be joined firmly to one another adjacent to the lumen and no place else. According to Sauer (74, 75, 77) they are held together in this region by terminal bars; such structures form a frame around each epithelial cell at its distal extremity. According to the histochemical studies of Puchtler and Leblond (70), terminal bars consist of protein only. Duncan's electron microscope studies (9) revealed that cell boundaries in the form of terminal bars are a prominent feature of the juxtaluminal zone of the neural tube of 48-hour chick embryos (see his Fig. 7). Terminal bars are clearly illustrated by Fujita and Fujita (12a) in neural tubes of 5-day chick embryos, but no such structures are mentioned by Bellairs (2) in her electron microscope studies.

Studies with the electron microscope of terminal bars in other epithelia reveal that they are bipartite structures whose two symmetrical halves are intricate parts of the surfaces of neighboring cells (Fawcett, 10). They have essentially the same fine structure as desmosomes (Yamada, 91) and in transverse sections are indistinguishable from them (10). Hama (18, p. 575) considers terminal bars to be a special type of desmosome. He defines the latter structures as "any specialized attachment body of whatever shape which binds together apposing plasma membranes of cells." Fawcett (11) refers to desmosomes as "attachment devices" and states that there is good evidence that the cells are more firmly adherent at these sites than elsewhere in their contact surfaces. Bennett (see discussion of paper by Puchtler, 69, p. 440) stated that "We can presume bonding forces of unknown nature which hold them firmly together at this point." According to Fawcett (11), the tenacious adhesion of cells at the sites of these surface specializations must be attributed to long-range chemical forces rather than to structural interconnections. Whatever the nature of the bonding forces within the terminal bars, it is especially evident from observations on the neural tubes of colchicine-treated embryos that they must be very powerful. They apparently do not break and release cells from one another even when great numbers of turgid cells have accumulated toward the lumen with sufficient force to distort the walls of the neural tube markedly (see Fig. 5.3, especially 5.3*D*, and Fig. 5.4*A*).

Marked Clustering Tendency of Neural Epithelial Cells

That cells of the early neural epithelium have the capacity to form strong bonding forces with one another, presumably by formation of terminal bars, is also strikingly evident under a variety of experimental conditions which result in the formation of so-called "rosettes" resembling miniature neural tubes in their structure and mitotic behavior.

For example, when a 2-week-old rat or mouse fetus is irradiated with x-rays (Hicks, 29), the first evidence of malformation following necrosis of many "neuroblasts" is the formation of rosettes from the surviving cells (Fig. 5.6*A* and *B*). Hicks (26) noted that the rosette pattern resembled that seen in some retinoblastomas and neuroepitheliomas. Surviving cells in the retina of irradiated fetuses also form rosettes (Hicks, 28, 30; Hicks, D'Amato, and Lowe, 32). When the neuroretina of 7-day chick embryos is dissociated into individual cells, the dispersed cells rapidly aggregate into small clusters containing similar rosettes (Moscona, 63), at least in stationary cultures. Rosette formation is common in the walls of neural tubes of young chick embryos in which the roof plate has been slit in the midsagittal plane (Fowler, 12) as well as in neural tube walls of chick embryos exposed to nitrogen mustard (Watterson, unpublished observations). It is also common in fetal rats and mice whose mothers were given nitrogen mustard or triethylmelamine (Hicks, 27). Rosette formation is also a characteristic phenomenon in the overgrowth of neural tube tissue in brains of chick embryos following extirpation of the cerebellar anlage (Källén, 52, 55) and in pieces of overgrown mesencephalon tissue transplanted to the brain cavity of host embryos (Källén, 51). Similarly, Wilson, Brent, and Jordan (89) described small cell clusters *outside* the neural tube walls of rat embryos irradiated with 100 r at 9 days of gestation which are strikingly similar to rosettes and which arose from neuroepithelial cells originally part of the wall of the neural tube proper (Fig. 5.6*C*). Rosette formation and the formation of other rosettelike structures by the neuroepithelium under a variety of circumstances emphasizes a fundamental property of developing nervous tissue of vertebrate embryos and fetuses, namely its clustering tendency or tendency to form closed vesicles, as pointed out by Hicks (29). (See also Rugh, 71a.)

Mechanism of Rosette Formation

Such information about rosette formation within the walls of the neural tube or neuroretina following some form of injury, as well as the formation of rosettelike "tumors" (Wilson et al., 89), suggests that neuroepithelial cells are strongly polarized, that is, that their presumptive distal ends are different from their presumptive proximal ends. If their original connections to one another at the primary neural canal are disrupted by the experimental conditions imposed, seg-

ments of the neuroepithelium and possibly individual neuroepithelial cells withdraw from the lumen and re-establish bondings with one another at their presumptive distal ends, thereby enclosing *secondary* cavities. (For details, see Hicks, 27, p. 495; 28, pp. 276–277; 30, p. 343; Hicks et al., 31; and Hicks et al., 32, p. 454.) Once a

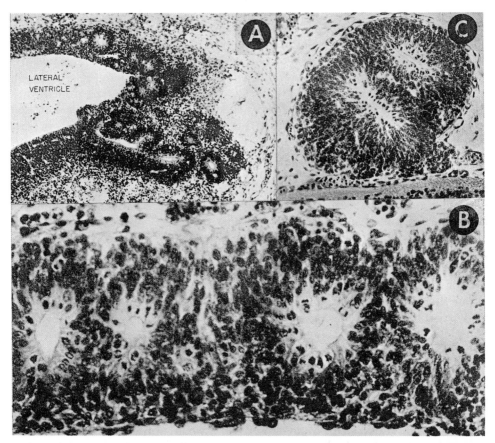

Fig. 5.6 Rosettes and rosettelike structures formed after x-irradiation. *A.* Brain wall of rat fetus, irradiation at about 14 days. (From Fig. 6, Hicks, *J. Cellular Comp. Physiol.* 43 Suppl. 1:151–178, 1954, courtesy The Wistar Press.) *B.* Wall of cerebral vesicle of rat fetus 48 hours after 150 r were given on the 12th day. (From Fig. 2, Hicks, Brown, and D'Amato, *Am. J. Pathol.* 33:459–482, 1957, courtesy The American Association of Pathologists and Bacteriologists.) *C.* "Tumor" adjacent to brain wall of rat fetus irradiated on the 9th day of gestation. (From Fig. 9, Wilson, Brent, and Jordan, *Cancer Res.* 12:222–228, 1952, courtesy The University of Chicago Press.)

rosette has formed, its constituent cells apparently withdraw toward the secondary lumen to undergo metaphase, anaphase, and telophase changes and then extend peripherally again, just as in the normal neural tube wall such migrations occur in relation to the primary lumen of the neural tube. Note the obvious concentration of mitotic figures adjacent to the lumen of each rosette in Figure 5.6. Such behavior suggests that constituent cells of rosettes are only loosely joined to one another and to other cells elsewhere than at their presumptive distal ends.

Whether rosette formation involves the complete disappearance of both halves of the original terminal bars and formation of new terminal bars between the presumptive distal ends of surviving neuroepithelial cells, or whether the halves of the original terminal bars persist and secondarily fall into register as the surfaces of surviving cells move along each other in the establishment of new relationships is not known. Fawcett (11) emphasized that nothing is known about the factors that determine the location of these surface specializations or about the mechanism of their formation except that the formation of a complete terminal bar seems to involve the simultaneous and complimentary specialization of the two apposed surfaces. Overton (66), who examined desmosome alignment in reaggregating cells originating by dissociation of lateral strips of the area pellucida of early chick embryos, found some evidence for persistence and realignment of half desmosomes during the reaggregation process, but she also pointed out that new desmosomes form at the same time under these circumstances and in the same symmetrical fashion as in normal development.

Orientation of Neurons Originating from Rosettes

Of considerable interest is the arrangement of differentiated neurons which arise from the neuroepithelial cells that earlier constituted the walls of rosettes. In the case of irradiated mouse or rat fetuses (Hicks, 27, 29), the resulting neurons of the adult animal retain their bizarre clustered and rosetted architecture. Hicks stated (28, p. 277), ". . . the net result as seen at birth is the formation of a bizarre architectural pattern of neurons and fiber bundles often oriented in discrete or confluent rosettes." According to Hicks, Brown, and D'Amato (31, p. 467), "The mid-brain, medulla, and spinal cord showed deformities characterized by rosettes of neurons and glia . . . ." And in the case of the dissociated chick neuroretinas of Moscona (63) the masses of neuroretinal tissue and nerve fibers subsequently formed are arranged in such a chaotic way that they resemble neuroepitheliomas. Similarly, in the case of retinas of irradiated fetuses, Hicks, D'Amato, and Lowe (32, p. 452) found that "The rosettes were lined with rods and their walls were composed of correspondingly well oriented retina."

The fact emerges from such observations on abnormal situations that neuroepithelial cells bound together in the walls of rosettes during their early development tend to retain their radial arrangement and to remain close together during their subsequent differentiation. Although this leads to an abnormal patterning of nerve cells and fibers in the case of rosettes, the binding together of early neuroepithelial cells by terminal bars under *normal* circumstances may be very important for the following reasons: (1) It imposes a radial orientation upon neuroblasts and neurons during their initial centrifugal migration through the neuroepithelium and into the mantle, and upon axons of primary motor neurons at the time they penetrate the surface of the neural tube. (2) It keeps cells of a given type reasonably close together during the early stages of their migration into the mantle, thus facilitating subsequent aggregation of cells of like types into columns, and nuclei. (3) It exposes cells in different sectors of the neural epithelium to the localized action of factors determining their development. (4) It exposes cells in different sectors of the neuroepithelium to the localized action of factors determining their proliferation patterns.

Migration of Differentiating Neurons from the Neural Epithelium

Although many neuroblasts migrate peripherally from the neural epithelium before any overt differentiation is detectable in them (see Fujita, 14a), the primary motor neuroblasts undergo overt differentiation while they are still present in the neuroepithelium.[1] Thus their lateral migration into

[1] Many observations especially pertinent to this topic are lucidly described and discussed in the following paper which appeared while this book was in press. Lyser, K. M., "Early Differentiation of Motor Neuroblasts in the Chick Embryo as Studied by Electron Microscopy. 1. General Aspects," *Develop. Biol.* 10:433–466 (1964).

the mantle zone can be followed easily with the aid of special silver methods which selectively impregnate neurofibrils (Kershman, 58; Barron, 1). Before the first appearance of discrete neurofibrils, the cytoplasm immediately peripheral to the nuclei of differentiating neuroepithelial cells stains especially darkly with the silver nitrate method of Cajal (Cowdry, 8, Fig. 15b). It is within this darkly stained portion of the cytoplasm (the argentophilic fibrilogenous zone of Held) that the discrete neurofibrils of the axon are first detected. The peripheral portion of the elongated neuroepithelial cell seemingly becomes the axon of the primary motor neuron. Neurofibrils subsequently appear within the cytoplasm on the opposite side of the nucleus, that is, within the portion of the neuroepithelial cell that extends toward the lumen, resulting in the formation of a bipolar neuron. This central process is called a "transient dendrite" by Barron (1). Various stages in the formation of bipolar neurons are evident within the neural epithelium of the spinal cord of the 8-week human embryo illustrated in Figure 5.7.

The release of bipolar cells and visibly undifferentiated neuroblasts from the neuroepithelium enables them to migrate peripherally to establish the mantle zone. It presumably involves either the disappearance of the pre-existing terminal bars which earlier bound them firmly together at the lumen or the failure to form terminal bars following the last mitotic division before onset of their centrifugal migration. According to Barron (1), the transient dendrite tends to be withdrawn as the differentiating neuron moves outward toward the mantle,

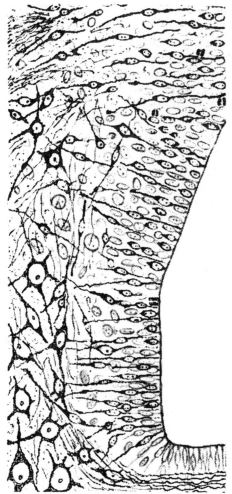

Fig. 5.7 Composite drawing of spinal cord wall of 8-week human embryo. Bielschowsky stain for neurons. Lumen to lower right. (From Fig. 3, Kershman, *Arch. Neurol. Psychiat.* 40:937–967, 1938, courtesy The American Medical Association.)

with the consequence that primary motor neurons in the outer portion of the neuroepithelium tend to be unipolar (Fig. 5.8). According to Hamburger and Levi-Montalcini (21), there occurs a rupture and withdrawal of the central process adhering to the inner limiting membrane at the time of onset of peripheral migration. In either case, it is evident that the developmental sequence in the case of primary motor neurons involves a bipolar stage, followed by a unipolar stage (the persisting process represents the axon), followed in turn by a multipolar stage as definitive dendrites arise (see Fig. 5.1*B* for a highly schematic representation of this sequence). Källén (50) suggested that covert differentiation processes change these cells in such a way that they can no longer divide and lose their connection with the proliferating epithelium. He does not comment on the nature of the connection or the mechanism of release from that connection. Källén (53) and Källén and Valmin (57) merely refer frequently to the *detachment* of migrating cells from the neuroepithelium. Fujita and co-workers (14c) simply state that neuroblasts lose contact with the internal limiting membrane. It is evident that the details of the release mechanism which enables certain neuroepithelial cells to become detached from the others are not known. In older stages, bipolar neurons that differentiated while in the neural epithelium sometimes remain bipolar while migrating into the mantle (Fig. 5.7).

As the cell bodies of the primary motor neurons migrate to the periphery of the neural epithelium (Fig. 5.8*A*) and into the mantle zone (Fig. 5.8*B–D*) they are at first situated at the level of their origin from the epithelium. Thus the basic structure of the neural tube wall is such that differentiating neurons and neuroblasts originating from each sector of the neural epithelium tend to be in rather close proximity to one another, even after they enter the mantle zone, rather than scattered at random. Moreover,

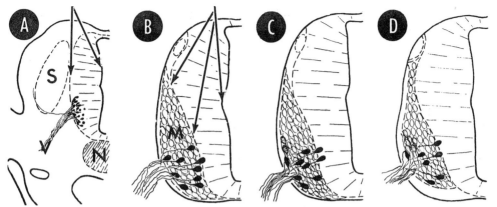

Fig. 5.8 Unipolar form and location of primary motor neurons (black) and secondary motor neurons (stippled) at the brachial level of 3- to 5-day chick embryos. The lumen is to the right in each illustration. Width of the neuroepithelium is indicated by arrows. M, mantle zone, N, notochord, S, somite, V, ventral root. A. Three days of incubation. Cell bodies of primary motor neuroblasts (black) lie ventrolaterally at periphery of neuroepithelium. Their axons constitute the beginnings of the ventral root. A true mantle layer has not formed as yet. B. Four days of incubation. The neuroepithelium has narrowed ventrally through loss of cells to the mantle layer. The cell bodies of the primary motor neuroblasts (black) mostly lie in the mantle zone but tend to retain the same spatial relationships to one another that characterized them before they left the neuroepithelium. C. Four days of incubation. Two secondary motor neuroblasts (stippled) are now differentiating from ventrolateral mantle cells; their axons contribute quantitatively to the ventral root. D. Five days of incubation. Additional secondary motor neuroblasts (stippled) are differentiating from ventrolateral mantle cells and are adding their axons to the ventral root. (From Figs. 1, 2B, 4B and 5A, Barron, *J. Comp. Neurol.* 85:149–169, 1946, courtesy The Wistar Institute.)

Weiss (87, p. 373) has suggested that during their centrifugal migration neurons and neuroblasts "glide along other medullary cells stretching across the neural tube and brain wall," although he has also indicated (86) that they might be guided by "radial fibers deposited by the medullary cells." Such a system of guide lines, by keeping closely together those neurons and neuroblasts emerging from each sector of the neural epithelium, would presumably facilitate aggregation of cells of like kind to form columns and nuclei in the mantle layer.

The axons of the primary motor neurons tend to retain their original radial orientation even when they penetrate the surface of the neural tube, with the consequence that as late as at 4 days of incubation the ventral roots spring from a wide area, dorsoventrally, on the lateral surface of the cord (Fig. 5.8B). Thus it would appear that the basic structure of the neural tube wall at this early stage plays a role in orienting the lengthening axons of the primary neurons perpendicular to the surface of the cord when they penetrate the latter, thereby possibly facilitating penetration. The axons formed by the subsequent differentiation of secondary motor neurons appear to contact and be guided by the primary axons (the process of fasciculation, Weiss, 87); thus the basic orientation of the primary motor axons in turn affects the orientation of axons formed subsequently (Fig. 5.8*C* and *D*).

The preceding observations on the migration of differentiating motor neurons from the neural epithelium suggest the possibility that the neuroblasts in each sector of the neural tube wall may already be determined for different fates in subsequent development, and that this is why it is to the advantage of the developing organism to keep cells originating from a given sector as close to one another as possible after they emerge into the mantle zone. This, in turn, suggests the possibility that the neural epithelium is a mosaic of areas the developmental qualities of which have become specifically restricted at very early stages (see Weiss, 86, and especially 87, pp. 376–379).

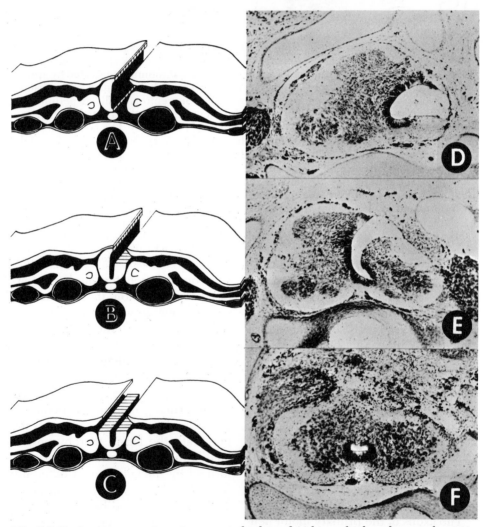

Fig. 5.9 Extirpation experiments on neural tubes of 44-hour chick embryos schematically represented (*A–C*, from Fig. 1, Wenger, *J. Exptl. Zool.* 114:51–86, 1950) and results obtained (*D–F*, from Figs. 4, 5 and 7, respectively, Wenger, *J. Exptl. Zool.* 114: 51–86, 1950, courtesy The Wistar Institute).

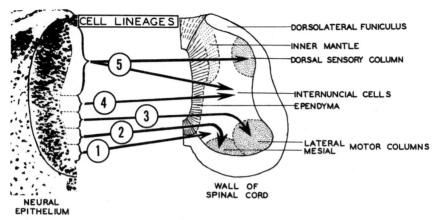

Fig. 5.10 Derivation of groups of neurons characteristic of spinal cord wall (right) from specific sectors of early neural tube wall (left) as revealed by variations in extirpation experiments of Wenger. 1. The ventralmost sector of the basal plate gives rise to the cells between the mesial motor column and the floor plate. 2. The ventrolateral sector of the basal plate gives rise to the mesial motor column (and probably to internuncial cells medial to this column). 3. The lateral sector of the basal plate gives rise to the lateral motor column (and probably to internuncial cells medial to this column). 4. The dorsal sector of the basal plate gives rise to internuncial cells. 5. All sectors of the alar plate apparently contribute both sensory column cells and internuncial cells.

Mosaic Nature of the Early Neural Tube Wall

Wenger (88) provided convincing evidence that *major* sectors of the early neural tube wall develop independently of one another. If she extirpated exactly the right half of the neural tube at 44 hours of incubation (Fig. 5.9*A*), the resulting spinal cord at the operation level was normal as far as the left half was concerned, but the right half was lacking (Fig. 5.9*D*). If she extirpated exactly the right dorsal quarter of the neural tube at 44 hours (Fig. 5.9*B*), the resulting spinal cord at the operation level was normal as far as the left half and right ventral half were concerned, but the right dorsal quarter was lacking (Fig. 5.9*E*). If she successfully removed exactly the dorsal half of the neural

tube (Fig. 5.9*C*), the resulting spinal cord consisted of a normal ventral half only (Fig. 5.9*F*). Rigid mosaic development of each major sector of the early neural tube wall was thus indicated.

A very careful analysis of local areas in which not exactly one-quarter or one-half of the spinal cord has been extirpated likewise enabled Wenger to demonstrate convincingly that rigid mosaic development also characterizes much smaller sectors of the neural epithelium, at least in the basal plates. Each small sector of the basal plate appeared to self-differentiate even though adjacent sectors might be absent. Her results are summarized in Figure 5.10.

Studies of the regenerative capacity of lateral halves of chick (Watterson and Fowler, 83) and amphibian (Holtzer, 37) neural tubes seemingly confirm the mosaic nature of the early neural tube wall (see also Hamburger, 20).[2] Similar results were obtained by Harkmark (25) who studied in chick embryos the migration of cells from the rhombic lip to the olive, pons, nucleus raphe, and some other structures of the gray matter in the medulla. On the basis of experiments in which he produced lesions by electrocautery in various parts of the proliferation center of the rhombic lip he concluded (25, p. 166), "The experimental data . . . show . . . that the proliferation area . . . forms a mosaic where each little region gives rise to its very particular part of the above-mentioned nuclei." On the basis of studies of the differentiation capacity of the neural epithelium of chick embryos transplanted to the coelom of host embryos or isolated in vitro, Källén (50) concluded that premorphological differentiation takes place in the neural epithelium at the same time as the epithelium proliferates.

Determination of Fates of Sectors of the Early Neural Tube Wall

The results of Wenger, Harkmark, and Källén indicate that certain distinctive properties of neurons have already been specified while they or the neuroblasts from which they orig-

[2] The information cited here is seemingly contradicted by Fujita (14b) who claims, on the basis of radioautographic studies following injection of tritiated thymidine, that during the third and fourth days of incubation the alar plates of the chick spinal cord, as well as the basal plates, contribute cells to medial and lateral motor columns. Since the successive positions of labeled cells can usually be followed readily in radioautographs from several animals labeled at the same time and killed at intervals after labeling, this claim cannot be ignored even though no details are given.

inated constituted part of the neuroepithelium (see Fujita, 14a). However, more recent experiments of Steding (81) suggest that the fates of the various sectors of the early neural tube wall are not so rigidly determined that they cannot be modified *if the sectors are brought into contact with different portions of the adjacent mesoderm*. These findings support a prophetic statement of Piatt (68, p. 171), "We shall probably find that inherent factors initiating cell lineage are operative quite early in nervous development but that these factors are plastic and capable of new directions under later exigencies of the environment." Steding removed the ectoderm above the dorsal surface of the neural tube of chick embryos incubated 45–55 hours, stained the dorsal surface with Nile blue sulfate, isolated a length of the stained neural tube, rotated it 180° around its longitudinal axis, and carefully replaced it. Two to three hours after the operation he checked the operated specimens to see whether the original rotation had been retained during healing. As a consequence of this operation, the prospective floor plate came to lie near the dorsal skin, the prospective roof plate near the ventral notochord. In his English summary (81, p. 230) Steding stated, "When nothing was altered in the surrounding mesoderm, the formerly dorsal spinal marrow showed typical ventral characteristics and the formerly ventral spinal marrow, typical dorsal characteristics after several days' incubation. In very successful operations the inversion was almost complete." And in his text he concluded (81, p. 227), "Die dorsal und ventral verschiedene histologische Differenzierung (Histogenese)

. . . ist zum Zeitpunkt der Operation (Stadium 12–14 nach *Hamburger und Hamilton*) noch veränderbar, wenn die Lageverhältnisse des Rückenmarkes geändert werden."

Although Steding's conclusions are stated strongly, the evidence is not as convincing as it would have been had the rotated levels of the neural tube in all his operated specimens centered at wing bud or leg bud levels where the very distinctive lateral motor cells and columns develop. Furthermore, there is reason to question whether the level of the spinal cord illustrated in his Figure 15 actually has participated in the rotation. The characteristics of this specimen are identical with those encountered anterior and posterior to levels where a variety of operations have been performed (Watterson, unpublished observations). Nevertheless, his experiments do demonstrate that at a surprisingly late stage the development of various aspects of the prospective dorsal and ventral halves of the neural tube can be considerably modified when the neural tube is turned upside down and replaced with minor damage to adjacent mesodermal structures. They also suggest the possibility that the factors determining the developmental fates of small sectors of the neural tube wall along the dorsoventral axis reside in the adjacent mesoderm, rather than exclusively within the neural plate itself. Admittedly, such an interpretation is contrary to the conclusion of Holtfreter and Hamburger (36, p. 254) that, as far as the neural plate is concerned, "The elaboration of histological details is left to the *self-organizing capacity* of the neural tissue . . . ."

It is well known that the neural epithelium of neural plate and early neural tube stages responds in highly specific ways to an adjacent notochord or somite. Wherever a notochord contacts the neural plate or early neural tube, even when an extra notochord is present, a floor plate reaction occurs (Fig. 5.11), that is, the wall of the neural tube is thinner directly above the notochords than elsewhere. Wherever a somite contacts the neural plate or early neural tube, even when an extra somite is present, the opposite of a floor plate reaction occurs, namely, a thickening of the neural tube wall (Fig. 5.11). (See Watterson, Goodheart, and Lindberg, 84; and Limborgh, 61, for surveys of the pertinent literature.) It would appear that these effects are accomplished in part by local inhibition of mitosis by the notochord and local stimulation of mitosis by the somite, but other more complex reactions are doubtless involved; at least they are encountered when amphibian tissues are isolated in vitro and are brought together in particular combinations (Holtfreter, 34, 35). Holtfreter and Hamburger (36, p. 254) summarized the relationships: "Thus notochord and somites not only represent the inductor system for the spinal cord

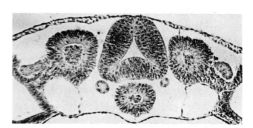

Fig. 5.11 Level of the 17th somites of a 21-somite chick embryo with duplication of anterior end (duplicitas anterior); characteristic triangular shape assumed by neural canal and neural tube when latter lies adjacent to two notochords and three somites.

but they continue to influence the cell distribution within the tube."

Once the floor plate reaction has been initiated, the notochord can be removed and a typical floor plate will develop by self-differentiation (Watterson et al., 84). It appears that floor plate development represents a special type of differentiation of the neuroepithelial cells involved. The extent to which the neural tube wall participates in floor plate differentiation depends on the dimensions of the contact area between notochord and neural tube. This type of determination mechanism seems to be of the "imprinting" type where the extent of the induced area corresponds precisely to the extent of the inducing area, thus resembling determination of the lens (McKeehan, 62).

Whether different sectors of the adjacent somites likewise determine locally the development of the sectors of the neural epithelium in direct contact with them is unknown. That the differences in development between major sectors of the lateral neural tube walls, such as alar and basal plates, may well be determined in this way is suggested by the differentiation pattern of the early somites as described by Hamilton (22). At the time the ventromedian portion of the somites loses its epithelial structure it can be seen that the ventral half of the lateral wall of the neural tube lies adjacent to sclerotome cells, the dorsal half to myotome cells (see Hamilton's Fig. 113). The myotome does not come into close relationship with the ventral neural tube at any time. Even though differentiation of the sclerotome into cartilage is dependent upon stimulation from the ventral neural tube wall (Grobstein and Holtzer, 17; Lash,

Holtzer, and Holtzer, 60), there could well be intrinsic differences in inductive capacities between prospective myotome and prospective sclerotome, independent of capacity for terminal differentiation. If different sectors of the sclerotome determine the development of smaller sectors of the basal plate of the early neural tube wall (Fig. 5.10), it would seem that they must do so while still part of the epithelial wall of the early somite, prior to onset of their migration.

Whether the mechanism of determination of the fates of adjacent sectors of the neural tube wall is by "imprinting" by corresponding sectors of the adjacent mesoderm, or by self-organization of morphogenetic fields within the neural plate, or, more likely, by a combination of the two, it would seem advantageous to keep closely bound together during the processes of determination those few neuroepithelial cells destined for a common developmental fate. This is especially true if the determining influence acts continuously over any appreciable period of time as Steding's results (81) would seem to indicate. (See discussion of Grobstein, 15, about the propagability of differentiated properties in dividing cells.) Furthermore, it would also seem to be advantageous to keep such cells close together during the processes of early differentiation since a variety of experiments have indicated that a given type of differentiation is usually possible only when the mass of cells involved exceeds a certain minimum (see Grobstein, 16). It is suggested that the structure of the early neural tube wall is ideal as far as these requirements are concerned. This structure is also ideal for keeping neurons of a particular type reasonably close together when they migrate into the mantle, thus facilitating their aggregation into functional columns and nuclei, and for orienting the axons of primary motor neurons perpendicular to the surface of the neural tube, possibly facilitating penetration of the latter.

Localized Control of Proliferation of Sectors of the Neural Tube Wall

The fact that the structure of the early neural tube wall keeps neuroepithelial cells from shifting anteroposteriorly or dorsoventrally relative to one another during their proliferative phase may also be very important for facilitating the localized action of the factors determining centers of proliferation in the neural epithelium at any given time. It may also thus determine how many neurons of any given type will be produced. Notwithstanding our ignorance about the nature of the factors involved, it is important to realize, as emphasized by Hamburger and Levi-Montalcini (21, p. 139) that ". . . any discussion of the problems of regional and topographic determination within the cord and the ganglia must include the determination of mitotic patterns which precede, and are basic to, the patterns of differentiation."

That peaks of proliferation occur at different rather sharply restricted levels along the cephalocaudal axis, resulting in a different pattern of localized bulges in the neural tube wall with time (proneuromeres, neuromeres or postneuromeres) has been clearly demonstrated, especially by the Scandinavian investigators (Bergquist, 3; Källén, 48, 54, 56). In the mouse embryo the neural crest portions of the head originate at the levels of the proneuromeres. Källén (42) believes that the factors which stimulate proliferation of proneuromeres also stimulate proliferation of contiguous masses of neural crest as anlagen of head ganglia.

Formation of each successive set of bulges coincides with a period of over-all increase in mitotic activity stimulated in some way, according to Källén (48, 49), by the notochord. How a *general* mitotic stimulus from the notochord at a given time results in *localized* peaks of mitotic activity corresponding to the centers of the subsequent bulges is problematical, although Källén (46, 48, 56) postulates different inherent thresholds of reaction within the neural epithelium to account for this phenomenon and suggests (48) that the threshold patterns may already be established at the time of primary induction. He has also demonstrated that this patterning does not depend on continuity of the neural tube since extirpation of the rostral end or its isolation from the caudal part with the aid of tantalum foil does not interfere with caudal neuromere development. (See also Källén, 46.) Similarly, he has shown that the rhombencephalon transplanted to the ventral surface of a host embryo, together with its mesodermal substratum forms neuromeres (Källén, 49). In 1962 Källén (54) suggested that successive mitotic patterns might result from interactions between a mitotic stimulating factor, probably emanating from notochordal mesoderm, and an antimitotic differentiation promoting factor present within neural epithelium.

That an even more complex localization of peaks of mitosis comes into existence with the formation of migration areas has likewise been demonstrated by these investigators (Bergquist and Källén, 4; Källén, 45, 48, 56). Migration areas are small, sharply circumscribed areas of the neural epithelium of the brain with high central mitotic activity, formed by intersection of longitudinal with transverse (postneuromeric) centers of proliferation. Due to the strong production of cells centrally in each area, the cell density in the migration layer thereby formed is greater in the region adjacent to the center of each migration area than adjacent to the periphery of each such area (Källén, 45). Intensity of proliferation reaches a peak in individual migration areas immediately before formation of a migration layer, then subsides, only to increase again immediately before formation of a second migration layer from the same migration area. In some parts of the nervous system three or even four migration layers may be produced one after the other, resulting in a distinctive stratification of the embryonic neural tube wall, each preceded by a rise in the proliferation activity of the migration areas concerned. Migration layers then subdivide or fuse in characteristic ways to produce specific brain nuclei. The mitotic patterns underlying the morphological patterns of proneuromeres, neuromeres, postneuromeres, migration areas, migration layers, and finally, formation of nuclei, are so constant throughout the vertebrates that they contradict the conclusion reached by Hamburger and Levi-Montalcini (21, p. 137) prior to these detailed studies that "it would seem to be a futile effort to correlate the origins of specific brain centers with special details in proliferative patterns." The degree to which the distribution of mito-

ses in the early neural tube is rigidly patterned in time and space under normal circumstances is truly remarkable! Even before the details were known, Hamburger and Levi-Montalcini (21, p. 139) were led to conclude that "Local conditions extrinsic to prospective mitotic cells, which would *activate cells in groups* [italics mine], would have to be postulated to account for the shifting patterns of proliferation."

That the local conditions involved in determination of the differences in mitotic patterns between alar and basal plates at least (Hamburger, 19; Corliss and Robertson, 7) might reside in the adjacent mesoderm is suggested by results obtained by Steding, described earlier (81). Turning the early neural tube upside down and replacing it caused the half of the neural tube that was formerly ventral in position (the basal plates in particular) to assume a mitotic pattern characteristic of the alar plates of the neural tube in normal position and vice versa. Steding came to the conclusion that the relation of portions of the neural tube wall to their specific mesodermal surroundings determined their specific mitotic patterns. He seemed to consider the determination of mitotic patterns tantamount to determination of differentiation patterns and concluded (81, p. 228), "Aus den beobachteten Entwicklungsvorgängen ist zu schliessen, dass die Histogenese ein von der Proliferation nicht *wesentlich* verschiedener Vorgang ist."

Summary

Information from descriptive studies involving light and electronmicroscopy, colchicine experiments, DNA determinations on individual nuclei in the neural tube wall, and labeling of nuclei with tritiated thymidine is summarized and found to support the conclusion that, until the mantle layer begins to form, the early neural tube wall is a pseudostratified neural epithelium with all cells firmly bound to their neighbors, adjacent to the lumen, by special attachment devices in the form of terminal bars. Because of this structural feature, any neuroepithelial cell (and its nucleus) withdraws toward the lumen and rounds up as it prepares to divide. It then undergoes metaphase, anaphase, and early telophase stages adjacent to the lumen. *Both* daughter cells elongate subsequently to become part of the thickening neuroepithelium; no daughter cell remains behind adjacent to the lumen to function as a true "germinal cell." Mitotic capacity is not restricted to one or two layers of germinal cells adjacent to the lumen, but is a property of almost all the cells of the early neural tube wall at the stages studied, at least in the alar plates. Many neuroepithelial cells in the basal plates appear to lose their proliferative capacity very early as they begin their differentiation into primary motor neurons.

The attachment of neural epithelial cells to one another by terminal bars is very strong and resists disruption. If continuity of the neural epithelium is disrupted under a variety of experimental conditions, the cells reattach to form spherical clusters called "rosettes" which, in section, resemble miniature neural tubes in structure and mitotic behavior. Thus neuroepithelial cells reveal strong grouping tendencies under a variety of circumstances, and force the investigator to concentrate on the development of groups of cells, rather than of individual cells, during formation of the brain and spinal cord. Evidence is assembled and discussed which leads to the conclusion that the firm attachment of neuroepithelial cells to one another at their distal ends is important in normal development for (1) imposing a radial orientation upon both the neuroblasts and neurons, during their initial centrifugal migration through the neuroepithelium and into the mantle, and upon axons of primary motor neurons at the time they penetrate the surface of the neural tube, (2) keeping cells of a given type reasonably close together during the early stages of their migration into the mantle, thus facilitating subsequent aggregation of cells of like types into columns and nuclei, (3) exposing cells in different sectors of the neural epithelium to the localized action of factors determining their developmental fates, and (4) exposing cells in different sectors of the neural epithelium to the localized action of factors determining their proliferation patterns.

Problems associated with the release of neuroepithelial cells from their attachments to one another adjacent to the lumen at the time mantle formation is initiated are discussed briefly.

References

1. Barron, D. H., "Observations on the Early Differentiation of the Motor Neuroblasts in the Spinal Cord of the Chick," *J. Comp. Neurol.* 85:149–169 (1946).
2. Bellairs, R., "The Development of the Nervous System in Chick Embryos,

Studied by Electron Microscopy," *J. Embryol. Exptl. Morphol.* 7:94–115 (1959).

3. Bergquist, H., "The Formation of the Front Part of the Neural Tube," *Experientia* 20:92–93 (1964).

4. ———, and B. Källén, "Studies on the Topography of the Migration Areas in the Vertebrate Brain," *Acta Anat.* 17:353–369 (1953).

5. ———, and ———, "Notes on the Early Histogenesis and Morphogenesis of the Central Nervous System in Vertebrates," *J. Comp. Neurol.* 100:627–660 (1954).

6. ———, and ———, "The Archencephalic Neuromery in *Ambystoma punctatum.* An Experimental Study," *Acta Anat.* 24:208–214 (1955).

7. Corliss, C. E., and G. G. Robertson, "The Pattern of Mitotic Density in the Early Chick Neural Epithelium," *J. Exptl. Zool.* 153:125–140 (1963).

8. Cowdry, E. V., "The Development of the Cytoplasmic Constituents of the Nerve Cells of the Chick. I. Mitochondria and Neurofibrils," *Am. J. Anat.* 15:389–429 (1914).

9. Duncan, D., "Electron Microscope Study of the Embryonic Neural Tube and Notochord," *Texas Rept. Biol. Med.* 15:367–377 (1957).

10. Fawcett, D. W., "Structural Specializations of the Cell Surface," *Frontiers in Cytology*, S. L. Palay, ed. New Haven: Yale University Press, pp. 19–41 (1958).

11. ———, "Intercellular Bridges," *Exptl. Cell Res. Suppl.* 8:174–187 (1961).

12. Fowler, I., "Responses of the Chick Neural Tube in Mechanically Produced spina bifida," *J. Exptl. Zool.* 123:115–152 (1953).

12a. Fujita, H., and S. Fujita, "Electron Microscopic Studies on Neuroblast Differentiation in the Central Nervous System of Domestic Fowl," *Z. Zellforsch. Mikroskop. Anat. Abt. Histochem.* 60:463–478 (1963).

13. Fujita, S., "Mitotic Pattern and Histogenesis of the Central Nervous System," *Nature* 185:702–703 (1960).

14. ———, "Kinetics of Cellular Proliferation," *Exptl. Cell Res.* 28:52–60 (1962).

14a. ———, "The Matrix Cell and Cytogenesis in the Developing Central Nervous System," *J. Comp. Neurol.* 120:37–42 (1963).

14b. ———, "Analysis of Neuron Differentiation in the Central Nervous System by Tritiated Thymidine Autoradiography," *J. Comp. Neurol.* 122:311–327 (1964).

14c. ———, M. Horii, T. Tanimura, and H. Nishimura, "H³-thymidine Autoradiographic Studies on Cytokinetic Responses to X-ray Irradiation and to Thio-TEPA in the Neural Tube of Mouse Embryos," *Anat. Record* 149:37–48 (1964).

15. Grobstein, C., "Differentiation of Vertebrate Cells," *The Cell*, J. Brachet and A. E. Mirsky, eds. New York: Academic Press, vol. I, pp. 437–496 (1959).

16. ———, "Cytodifferentiation and Its Controls," *Science* 143:643–650 (1964).

17. ———, and H. Holtzer, "In vitro Studies of Cartilage Induction in Mouse Somite Mesoderm," *J. Exptl. Zool.* 128:333–358 (1955).

18. Hama, K., "The Fine Structure of the Desmosomes in Frog Mesothelium," *J. Biophys. Biochem. Cytol.* 7:575–578 (1960).

19. Hamburger, V., "The Mitotic Patterns in the Spinal Cord of the Chick Embryo and Their Relation to Histogenetic Processes," *J. Comp. Neurol.* 88:221–284 (1948).

20. ———, "Regeneration in the Central Nervous System of Reptiles and of Birds," *Regeneration in the Central Nervous System*, W. F. Windle, ed. Springfield, Illinois: Charles C Thomas, pp. 47–53 (1955).

21. ———, and R. Levi-Montalcini, "Some Aspects of Neuroembryology," *Genetic Neurology*, P. Weiss, ed. Chicago: University of Chicago Press, pp. 128–160 (1950).

22. Hamilton, H. L., *Lillie's Development of the Chick, An Introduction to Embryology.* New York: Holt, Rinehart and Winston (1952).

23. Hamilton, W. J., J. D. Boyd, and H. W. Mossman, *Human Embryology (Prenatal Development of Form and Function).* Baltimore: Williams and Wilkins (1945).

24. Hardesty, I., "On the Development and Nature of the Neuroglia," *Am. J. Anat.* 3:229–268 (1904).

25. Harkmark, W., "Cell Migrations from the Rhombic Lip to the Inferior Olive, the Nucleus Raphe and the Pons. A

Morphological and Experimental Investigation on Chick Embryos," *J. Comp. Neurol.* 100:115–209 (1954).

26. Hicks, S. P., "Acute Necrosis and Malformation of Developing Mammalian Brain Caused by X-ray," *Proc. Soc. Exptl. Biol. Med.* 75:485–489 (1950).

27. ———, "Some Effects of Ionizing Radiation and Metabolic Inhibition on the Developing Mammalian Nervous System," *J. Pediat.* 40:489–513 (1952).

28. ———, "Developmental Malformations Produced by Radiation. A Timetable of Their Development," *Am. J. Roentgenol. Radium Therapy Nu. Med.* 69:272–293 (1953).

29. ———, "The Effects of Ionizing Radiation, Certain Hormones, and Radiomimetic Drugs on the Developing Nervous System," *J. Cellular Comp. Physiol.* 43, Suppl. 1:151–178 (1954).

30. ———, "Radiation as an Experimental Tool in Mammalian Developmental Neurology," *Physiol. Rev.* 38:337–356 (1958).

31. ———, B. L. Brown, and C. J. D'Amato, "Regeneration and Malformation in the Nervous System, Eye, and Mesenchyme of the Mammalian Embryo after Radiation Injury," *Am. J. Pathol.* 33:459–482 (1957).

32. ———, C. J. D'Amato, and M. J. Lowe, "The Development of the Mammalian Nervous System. I. Malformations of the Brain, Especially the Cerebral Cortex, Induced in Rats by Radiation. II. Some Mechanisms of the Malformations of the Cortex," *J. Comp. Neurol.* 113:435–470 (1959).

33. His, W., "Die Neuroblasten und deren Entstehung im embryonalen Mark," *Archiv Anat. Entwickelungsgeschichte* pp. 249–300 (1889).

34. Holtfreter, J., "Formative Reize in der Embryonalentwicklung der Amphibien, dargestellt an Explantationsversuchen," *Arch. Exptl. Zellforsch.* 15:281–301 (1934).

35. ———, "Gewebeaffinität, ein Mittel der embryonalen Formbildung," *Arch. Exptl. Zellforsch.* 23:169–209 (1939).

36. ———, and V. Hamburger, "Embryogenesis: Progressive Differentiation. Amphibians," *Analysis of Development*, B. H. Willier, P. Weiss and V. Hamburger, eds. Philadelphia: Saunders, pp. 230–296 (1955).

37. Holtzer, H., "Reconstitution of the Urodele Spinal Cord Following Unilateral Ablation. I. Chronology of Neuron Regulation," *J. Exptl. Zool.* 117:523–558 (1951).

38. Hugosson, R., *Morphologic and Experimental Studies on the Development and Significance of the Rhombencephalic Longitudinal Cell Columns.* Lund, Sweden: Håkan Ohlssons Roktryckeri, pp. 1–133 (1957).

39. Jelínek, R., "Proliferace v Centrálním Nervovém Systému Kuřecích Zárodků. I. Doba trvání Mitosy v Germinální Zoně míchy od 2. do 6. Dne Zárodečnécho vývoje," ("Cellular Proliferation in the Central Nervous System of the Chick Embryos. I. Duration of Mitosis in the Germinal Zone of the Spinal Cord from the 2d to the 6th Day of Incubation.") *Cesk. Morfol.* 7:163–173 (1959).

40. Källén, B., "Notes on the Proliferation Processes in the Neuromeres in Vertebrate Embryos," *Acta Soc. Med. Upsalien.* 57:111–118 (1952).

41. ———, "On the Significance of the Neuromeres and Similar Structures in Vertebrate Embryos," *J. Embryol. Exptl. Morphol.* 1:387–392 (1953).

42. ———, "Notes on the Development of the Neural Crest in the Head of *Mus musculus*," *J. Embryol. Exptl. Morphol.* 1:393–398 (1953).

43. ———, "On the Segmentation of the Central Nervous System," *Kgl. Fysiograf. Sällskap. Lund Handl.* 64(18): 1–10 (1954).

44. ———, "Neuromery in Living and Fixed Chick Embryos," *Kgl. Fysiograf. Sällskap. Lund Forh.* 25(9):1–6 (1955).

45. ———, "Notes on the Mode of Formation of Brain Nuclei during Ontogenesis," *Compt. Rend. Assoc. Anat. XLIIe Réunion* pp. 747–756 (1955).

46. ———, "Regulation of Proliferation Processes during Ontogenesis of the Brain," *Progress in Neurobiology*, J. Ariëns Kappers, ed. *Proc. 1st Intern. Meeting Neurobiol.*, New York: Elsevier pp. 353–358 (1956).

47. ———, "Studies on the Mitotic Activity in Chick and Rabbit Brains during Ontogenesis," *Kgl. Fysiograf. Sällskap. Lund Forh.* 26(17):1–14 (1956).

48. ———, "Contribution to the Knowledge of the Regulation of the Prolifera-

tion Processes in the Vertebrate Brain during Ontogenesis," *Acta Anat.* 27: 351–360 (1956).

49. ———, "Experiments on Neuromery in *Ambystoma punctatum* embryos," *J. Embryol. Exptl. Morphol.* 4:66–72 (1956).

50. ———, "Studies on the Differentiation Capacity of Neural Epithelium Cells in Chick Embryos," *Z. Zellforsch. Mikroskop. Anat. Abt. Histochem.* 47:469–480 (1958).

51. ———, "Studies on Experimentally Produced Overgrowth in Chick Embryo Brain, Using Tissue Culture and Transplantation Techniques," *Z. Zellforsch. Mikroskop. Anat. Abt. Histochem.* 50: 361–368 (1959).

52. ———, "Experimental Neoplastic Formation in Embryonic Chick Brains," *J. Embryol. Exptl. Morphol.* 8:20–23 (1960).

53. ———, "Studies on Cell Proliferation in the Brain of Chick Embryos with Special Reference to the Mesencephalon," *Z. Anat. Entwicklungsgeschichte* 122: 388–401 (1961).

54. ———, "Mitotic Patterning in the Central Nervous System of Chick Embryos; Studied by a Colchicine Method," *Z. Anat. Entwicklungsgeschichte* 123:309–319 (1962).

55. ———, "Overgrowth Malformation and Neoplasia in Embryonic Brain," *Confinia Neurol.* 22:40–60 (1962).

56. ———, "Early Morphogenesis and Pattern Formation in the Central Nervous System," *Organogenesis*, R. L. DeHaan and H. Ursprung, eds. New York: Holt, Rinehart and Winston, Chapter 4 (1965).

57. ———, and K. Valmin, "DNA Synthesis in the Embryonic Chick Central Nervous System," *Z. Zellforsch. Mikroskop. Anat. Abt. Histochem.* 60:491–496 (1963).

58. Kershman, J., "The Medulloblast and the Medulloblastoma. A Study of Human Embryos," *Arch. Neurol. Psychiat.* 40: 937–967 (1938).

59. Langman, J., and A. Martin, "Formation of the Three Layers of the Neural Tube in the Chick Embryo, as Shown by Means of Radioautography," *Anat. Record.* 148:304 (1964).

60. Lash, J., S. Holtzer, and H. Holtzer, "An Experimental Analysis of the Development of the Spinal Column. VI. Aspects of Cartilage Induction," *Exptl. Cell Res.* 13:292–303 (1957).

61. Limborgh, J. van, "The Influence of Adjacent Mesodermal Structures upon the Shape of the Neural Tube and Neural Plate in Bird Embryos," *Acta Morphol. Neerl. Scand.* 1:155–166 (1956).

62. McKeehan, M. S., "Cytological Aspects of Embryonic Lens Induction in the Chick," *J. Exptl. Zool.* 117:31–64 (1951).

63. Moscona, A., "Patterns and Mechanisms of Tissue Reconstruction from Dissociated Cells," *Developing Cell Systems and Their Control*, D. Rudnick, ed. New York: Ronald, pp. 45–70 (1960).

64. Overton, J., "Effects of Colchicine on the Early Chick Blastoderm," *J. Exptl. Zool.* 139:329–347 (1958).

65. ———, "Mitotic Pattern in the Chick Pronephric Duct," *J. Embryol. Exptl. Morphol.* 7:275–280 (1959).

66. ———, "Desmosome Development in Normal and Reassociating Cells in the Early Chick Blastoderm," *Develop. Biol.* 4:532–548 (1962).

67. Paff, G. H., "The Action of Colchicine upon the 48-hour Chick Embryo," *Am. J. Anat.* 64:331–349 (1939).

68. Piatt, J., "Differentiation and Growth of Nerve Cells and Fibers," *Genetic Neurology*, P. Weiss, ed. Chicago: University of Chicago Press, pp. 166–173 (1950).

69. Puchtler, H., "Histochemical Analysis of Terminal Bars," *J. Histochem. Cytochem.* 4:439. Abstr. with discussion by Bennett pp. 439–440 (1956).

70. ———, and C. P. Leblond, "Histochemical Analysis of Cell Membranes and Associated Structures as Seen in the Intestinal Epithelium," *Am. J. Anat.* 102:1–32 (1958).

71. Ris, H., "Cell Division," *Analysis of Development*, B. H. Willier, P. Weiss and V. Hamburger, eds. Philadelphia: Saunders, pp. 91–125 (1955).

71a. Rugh, R., "Major Radiobiological Concepts and Effects of Ionizing Radiations on the Embryo and Fetus," *Response of the Nervous System to Ionizing Radiation*, T. J. Haley and R. S. Snider, eds. New York: Academic Press, pp. 3–26 (1962).

72. Saetersdal, T. A. S., "A Critical Review of Quantitative Mitotic Recordings in Animal Tissues with Special Reference to the Central Nervous System," *Arbok Univ. Bergen, Mat.-Nat. Rekke* (10):1–20 (1958).

73. ———, "A Review of Some Recent Studies on Induction and Morphogenesis of the Central Nervous System," *Arbok Univ. Bergen, Mat.-Nat. Ser.* (3):1–20 (1960).

74. Sauer, F. C., "Mitosis in the Neural Tube," *J. Comp. Neurol.* 62:377–405 (1935).

75. ———, "The Cellular Structure of the Neural Tube," *J. Comp. Neurol.* 63:13–23 (1935).

76. ———, "The Interkinetic Migration of Embryonic Epithelial Nuclei," *J. Morphol.* 60:1–11 (1936).

77. ———, "Some Factors in the Morphogenesis of Vertebrate Embryonic Epithelia," *J. Morphol.* 61:563–579 (1937).

78. Sauer, M. E., and A. C. Chittenden, "Deoxyribonucleic Acid Content of Cell Nuclei in the Neural Tube of the Chick Embryo: Evidence for Intermitotic Migration of Nuclei," *Exptl. Cell Res.* 16:1–6 (1959).

79. ———, and B. E. Walker, "Radioautographic Study of Interkinetic Nuclear Migration in the Neural Tube," *Proc. Soc. Exptl. Biol. Med.* 101:557–560 (1959).

79a. Sidman, R. L., "Histogenesis of Mouse Retina Studied with Thymidine-H³," *The Structure of the Eye*, G. K. Smelser, ed. New York: Academic Press, pp. 487–506 (1961).

80. ———, I. L. Miale, and N. Feder, "Cell Proliferation and Migration in the Primitive Ependymal Zone; an Autoradiographic Study of Histogenesis in the Nervous System," *Exptl. Neurol.* 1:322–333 (1959).

81. Steding, G., "Experimente zur Morphogenese des Rückenmarkes. Untersuchungen an Hühnerembryonen (*Gallus gallus*)," *Acta Anat.* 49:199–231 (1962).

82. Watterson, R. L., "Development of the Glycogen Body of the Chick Spinal Cord. IV. Effects of Mechanical Manipulation of the Roof Plate at the Lumbosacral Level," *J. Exptl. Zool.* 125:285–330 (1954).

83. ———, and I. Fowler, "Regulative Development in Lateral Halves of Chick Neural Tubes," *Anat. Record* 117:773–804 (1953).

84. ———, C. R. Goodheart, and G. Lindberg, "The Influence of Adjacent Structures upon the Shape of the Neural Tube and Neural Plate of Chick Embryos," *Anat. Record* 122:539–559 (1955).

85. ———, P. Veneziano, and A. Bartha, "Absence of a True Germinal Zone in Neural Tubes of Young Chick Embryos as Demonstrated by the Colchicine Technique," *Anat. Record* 124:379 (1956).

86. Weiss, P., "An Introduction to Genetic Neurology," *Genetic Neurology*, P. Weiss, ed. Chicago: University of Chicago Press, pp. 1–39 (1950).

87. ———, "Nervous System (Neurogenesis)," *Analysis of Development*, B. H. Willier, P. Weiss and V. Hamburger, eds. Philadelphia: Saunders, pp. 346–401 (1955).

88. Wenger, E. L., "An Experimental Analysis of Relations between Parts of the Brachial Spinal Cord of the Embryonic Chick," *J. Exptl. Zool.* 114:51–86 (1950).

89. Wilson, J. G., R. L. Brent, and H. C. Jordan, "Neoplasia Induced in Rat Embryos by Roentgen Irradiation," *Cancer Res.* 12:222–228 (1952).

90. Woodward, T. M., Jr., and S. B. Estes, "Effect of Colchicine on Mitosis in the Neural Tube of the Forty-eight Hour Chick Embryo," *Anat. Record* 90:51–54 (1944).

91. Yamada, E., "The Fine Structure of the Gall Bladder Epithelium of the Mouse," *J. Biophys. Biochem. Cytol.* 1:445–458 (1955).

6

Embryogenesis of Behavioral Nerve Nets

R. W. SPERRY

Division of Biology
California Institute of Technology
Pasadena, California

The old problem of how all the information required to build a complete organism can be compacted and funneled through the microscopic dimensions of the zygote—and the problem involved in the reading out of all this genetic information, step by step, in development—is encountered in probably its ultimate and most challenging form in the developmental organization of the brain and nervous system, especially in the higher vertebrates. Here, in addition to the many problems of morphogenesis and cytodifferentiation common to other organs and organ systems, formidable enough in themselves, is the more complicated problem of the wiring of this whole system for behavior. Literally billions of individual nerve cell units must each acquire through their arboritic fiber extensions precise patterns of anatomical contact with dozens, and in some cases even hundreds, of other nerve cells—many of which lie at great distances from the parent cell body—thereby posing a truly enormous problem in the patterning of detailed interrelations between individual cells.

For a long time it was believed that the developing embryo avoided the whole problem simply by letting the growth process spin out a random, diffuse, unstructured, essentially equipotential transmission network; a blank slate as it were, leaving behavior, function, practice, experience, learning, and conditioning to mold and shape the fiber pathways into a functionally adaptive communication system. The old saying long prevailed: "Function precedes form in the development of the nervous system."

Many diverse lines of converging evidence reinforced this earlier view well on through the 1930s and into the early '40s. Today, by contrast, most of this supporting evidence has disappeared until now some researchers are taking an almost diametrically opposite stand—to emphasize that the great bulk of the behavioral circuitry of the nervous system, especially in infrahuman vertebrates, is built in. That is, the behavioral networks are organized in advance of their use, by growth and differentiation primarily, with relatively little dependence on function for their orderly patterning. The center of the problem has thus shifted from the province of psychology to that of developmental biology.

On analysis, the problem of the embryogenesis of behavioral nerve nets boils down in large part to questions concerned with the outgrowth and termination of the developing nerve fibers. Particularly critical for the adaptive patterning of functional networks is the matter of selectivity in the guidance and connection of the advancing fiber processes. The present discussion is centered on this selectivity problem to the necessary neglect of other material that would be both pertinent and important in a broader treatment of the subject. How do the thousands of fibers in a peripheral nerve trunk get connected, each to its correct type of end organ and in the proper location, and how do the even more numerous fibers of the central trunk lines manage to find their correct connection zones and the proper individual junctions within each terminal zone? A key concept in the more recent, more genetically oriented outlook on these matters, is that of the chemical differentiation or qualitative specificity of individual nerve cells and fibers and its influence on the formation of fiber pathways and connections. Much of what follows is concerned with the extent to which the cytochemical specificity of the individual nerve cells and fibers determines the kinds of structural linkages that neurons form.

Historical Background

The matter of selectivity in nerve growth has always been rather controversial and has a long history of pros and cons. This in turn has been closely intertwined with related physiological controversy centered around the functional significance of specificity in nerve connections. In the late 1930s when I was first attracted to these problems, the evidence seemed to be almost entirely against cytochemical specificity affecting the kinds of connections nerves form. Many studies of nerve growth and regeneration, both in vivo and in tissue culture, seemed to point to the conclusion that nerve fiber growth and termination are diffuse and indiscriminate.

It was reported, for example, that a skeletal muscle nerve would reinnervate and activate any other muscle as readily as its own muscle; that even sensory nerves would form functional connections with muscles, as would also their dorsal roots. Similarly, motor nerves would reconnect with sense organs, and peripheral nerves reflected into the spinal cord would form functional synapses in the spinal centers. Autonomic nerves would connect with somatic endings and vice versa; and a single motor axon, by successive branching, might innervate three, four, or more different nonsynergic muscles and still activate each independently in its own proper timing. A large number of examples could be cited, and the over-all picture was concluded to be overwhelmingly against any chemical selectivity in nerve growth (Weiss, 78–82).

Electrical selectivity also appeared to have been ruled out along with the chemical, in favor of the mechanical, stereotaxic or contact guidance theory of nerve growth. This seemed adequate, along with various secondary factors like correct timing, differential growth rates, and ultrastructural alignments to explain satisfactorily the total developmental patterning of the brain pathways and connections (Weiss, 82). With appropriate reinterpretations, the mechanical view also appeared to account for earlier examples of supposed chemical and electrical selectivity cited by Cajal and others.

At the same time, and of critical concern for problems of the brain's function as well as its development, strong experimental support had been accumulated during the preceding 15 years for the conclusion that neuronal specificity has its effect, not on the kinds of morphological connections that neurons acquire, but rather on the kinds of signals that they transmit, and to which they selectively respond. Clinical reports as well as experimental observations covering vertebrates from primates to amphibians seemed to show that nerves not only regenerate and connect indiscriminately, but that the kinds of connections they form make little difference to the over-all function.

A series of studies on the surgical disarrangement of nerve-muscle connections in amphibians seemed to indicate that individual limb muscles continue to respond with the same timing, regardless of experimental rearrangements in the pattern of their nerve connections to the spinal limb centers. Each muscle in transplanted supernumerary limbs with deranged innervation would contract in perfect synchrony with its muscle homologue in the original limb (*homologous* or *myotypic* response). This phenome- non, which was found to prevail also in interchanged limbs, in transplanted individual muscles, and even after limb deafferentation and spinal transection (Weiss, 79–81), seemed to contradict the traditional idea of the reflex connection, and the all-or-none conduction principles of neurophysiology. It thus called for a new and different principle for describing selective communication in nerve networks.

The conclusion was being drawn that selective communication in the nervous system must be based, not on selectivity among synaptic connections, as the classical textbook doctrine would have it, but rather upon some kind of qualitative selectivity among the signals carried by different fiber types; that is, some kind of impulse specificity, or "Erregungspecifität," with selective resonance governing the pickup and firing from cell to cell. Schemes of this kind had been suggested earlier by Hering (25), among others, and had been more extensively formalized by Weiss in the resonance principle of nervous function (Weiss 76, 77, 79–81). In the resonance principle, the old telephone switchboard analogy was replaced by a radio broadcasting concept of communication, wherein selective reception and discharge of neurons was held to be independent of specific anatomical connections. The anatomical connections were inferred to be diffuse and nonselective. The issue of signal specificity vs. connection specificity had become critical both from the standpoint of brain function and from that of the developmental patterning of behavioral nerve nets. Its paramount importance was stressed above all others in the nerve growth literature of the 1930's.

In checking over the experimental data underlying the resonance principle and the doctrine of impulse specificity, it occurred to me that an alternative explanation had been overlooked which, if correct, would not only undermine the case for impulse specificity in favor of specific connections, but would at the same time reopen the whole question of chemical selectivity in nerve growth. This alternative explanation was first suggested to Professor Weiss in September 1938. The hypothesis was then outlined more formally during the next two years at the University of Chicago and has since survived a long series of experimental tests.

In brief, the proposal suggested that we completely reverse opinion on the question of chemical selectivity (Sperry 42–53, 55–57). Instead of following the prevailing view that formation of synaptic connections is diffuse and nonselective, it went to the opposite extreme to postulate that the formation and maintenance of synaptic connections take place with great selectivity, and that the whole process is strictly regulated by highly refined and specific chemical affinities between the individual neuronal elements present in any local brain center, neuropile region, or other synaptic zone. It indicated further that earlier attempts to forcibly switch nerve connections in the studies on homologous response in young amphibians had failed to accomplish the effects intended because the synaptic connections started rearranging themselves, in accordance with specific inductive effects in the new periphery and the new pattern of chemical affinities. The end result of the specific growth pressures is the restoration of essentially the same pattern of sensori-neuro-motor reflex linkages that existed at the start. Whether the selective regrowth occurs primarily in the centers or in the periphery is something of an open question at present. Either way the relevant conclusions are the same.

This chemoaffinity interpretation not only offered an explanation of the perplexing 18-year-old problem of homologous response and related phenomena, obviating the concept of impulse specificity, but it also provided the basis for an entire new and attractive hypothesis for the normal developmental patterning of behavioral nerve nets. By incorporating some of the current concepts of experimental embryology such as morphogenetic fields, gradients, and organizer and induction effects, and applying these to the functional wiring of the sensori-neuro-motor system in the chemoaffinity context, it was possible to set up a fairly comprehensive approach to the ontogenetic patterning of behavioral nerve nets. This proved to be much more satisfactory, detailed, and explanatory than any of the ideas previously available, such as neurobiotaxis, disuse atrophy, contact guidance, bioelectric fields, functional trial and error, conditioning, and so on.

Subsequent experimental tests of the hypothesis have been almost uniformly confirmatory. The first promising result came from interchanging motor and sensory nerve relations in 3- to 5-week-old rats (Sperry, 41, 42, 43; Weiss and Sperry, 87). Contrary to expectations and to the voluminous earlier literature, pronounced disfunction effects were obtained. They were exactly the kind that would be expected if selective communication in the nervous system were based on specific nerve connections patterned by growth and subject to little or no rearrangement by re-education. The whole idea of the preceding half-century—that nerve connections are functionally interchangeable—was, I finally concluded (Sperry, 49), simply a myth. The switching of nerve connections to sensory and motor end organs, in man, or any other mammal, produces corresponding distortions of function. This does not apply to the lower vertebrates, particularly to larval salamanders, largely because the embryonic forces for organizing the sensori-neuro-motor hookups remain operative, and are very effective in restoring, in one way or another, the original connection patterns.

More direct tests for selectivity in synaptic formation were undertaken during the next 10 years in lower vertebrates where many central fiber systems were found to be capable of functional regeneration (Sperry, 43–57). Surgical section, scrambling, and transplantation of central fiber tracts and the transplantation of nerve and end organ relations during development led, in all cases, to functional results that supported directly the deduction that the terminal connections of the growing nerve fibers are laid down in a highly selective fashion as postulated; and that these connections are governed by the intrinsic specificity of the advancing fiber tip plus that of the various cellular elements it encounters in its outgrowth.

New Dimensions in Neurospecificity

The initial experiments carried out on the optic nerve disclosed the existence of new orders of refinement in neuronal specificity, so refined as to approach the level of the individual nerve cell and its axon fiber. Even in the resonance principle of Weiss it had seemed unreasonable to imagine a neurospecificity so refined as to provide a different signal quality or specific neuron type for each different direction in visual space—or similarly, for each different point in the cutaneous field. It had been assumed, accordingly, that these directional attributes were probably installed on some other basis (Weiss, 77). Additional dimensions of specification in the population of the optic fibers were later to be inferred with regard to the perception of colors and luminosity and with the different "on-off" fiber unit types described by Hartline (23) and others (Maturana et al., 32) that must presumably be involved in optokinetic responses to moving stripes, in striking at small targets, and in some of the pattern perception tests (Sperry, 55; Arora and Sperry, 3, 5). By the late 1940s the evidence (Sperry, 52, 53; Stone, 67; Sperry and Miner, 66) was sufficient to suggest, as a basic principle, that neuronal specificity and interneuronal affinities operate generally throughout the nervous system with an order of refinement that parallels closely the inherent functional differentiation.

Changing Views

Meantime, with the advent of the chemoaffinity interpretation, the campaign for impulse specificity was promptly abandoned. By 1947 even the strongest opponents of chemical selectivity, swayed increasingly by the above and other evidence (see Holtfreter, 26), had come well around toward a reversal of their earlier position of the 1930s (Weiss, 83). This turnabout of opinion did not come easily after the heavy investment of the preceding two decades against both chemical selectivity on the one hand and fiber connection specificity on the other. It was accomplished in the literature more by verbal subtleties than by any frank acknowledgment of a change or correction of earlier views. As a consequence, the literature since 1939 has become something of a tangled web of ambiguity and forced terminology that is understandably perplexing to the novice not acquainted with the underlying history.

For example, "chemotaxis" and "chemotropism" were first attacked on an antiselectivity basis, but when this no longer seemed wise, the terms were carefully defined (Weiss and Taylor, 88) so as to include the concept of attraction from a distance, and from then on the attack was shifted to the implied distance effects. Instead of chemotaxis and chemotropism, terms like "selective contact guidance," "preferential contact affinities," and the like are used. After the renunciation of Cajal's concept of "selective attraction" it is allowed that there may be selective "proximity" effects in addition to those of direct "contact" (Weiss, 83). "Selective fasciculation" was used initially to describe the tendency of any fiber to follow along those particular preceding fibers that had happened blindly to succeed in achieving a terminal connection, whereas now it is coming to be used more and more to mean the selective segregation in growth of similar fiber types as conceived earlier by Cajal (37, 38). The old terms "stereotropism" and "stereotaxis" mean "guidance through contact with solid surfaces" like contact guidance. But if the aim is to impute distance effects in one's definition of tropisms and taxes,

it is better not to remind the reader of "stereotaxis" or "thigmotaxis."

Specificity in fiber connections was denied for many years as a basis for selective communication in nerve circuits. When the ground started to become shaky on this point, the attack again was not dropped or corrected, but was shifted to decry the notion of absolute invariance in the development of anatomical relations, something that never was much questioned and is largely irrelevant to the issue. The term "resonance" originally used to suggest that muscles respond selectively to specific impulse frequencies even where asynchronous muscles have been innervated by separate branches of the same axon (Weiss, 76, 77), has survived to the present, but only by undergoing repeated metamorphoses of meaning until the original sense is long lost.

Meantime the actual experimental observations showing lack of selectivity in the growth of nerve connections, no longer in accord with the changed outlook, have had to be retracted, contradicted, or strongly qualified (Weiss, 84). The remainder of the findings of the 1930s along this line, including even those indicating a nonselective reinnervation of skeletal muscle by skeletal motor axons, are today open to question and re-examination (see p. 176).

During this same period, when the resonance concept and impulse specificity were being abandoned in developmental biology, the reverse process was going on in electrophysiology, where the general uniformity of nerve action potentials made the postulation of hundreds of thousands of chemically specific fiber types seem a bit difficult to accept. Lettvin and others have argued for years, and correctly so, that the orderliness of the functional recovery in optic nerve experiments and similar ones, does not necessarily prove a selective orderliness in fiber reconnection (Lettvin et al., 30). The optic fibers, it was said, might carry different types of signals or pulse patterns of some sort, which could then be decoded at the central stations even though the central connections were quite randomized. This too was largely abandoned after Gaze reported in 1959 (11–13) that the projected map of the retina on the brain after optic nerve regeneration was the same as before the nerve was cut. This was confirmed within the year by Maturana, Lettvin and co-workers in their own microelectrode studies (Maturana et al., 32). They reported further that they were

able to record separately the several types of fiber terminals pictured in the tectum by Cajal (38) and that each type regenerated selectively to its normal depth and locus in the tectum.

With regard to mapping by electrical methods, however, it has been pointed out (Gaze, 14; Attardi and Sperry, 8) that it is difficult to be certain whether one is recording the topography of the regenerated fibers, or just the more physiologically effective portions thereof; or perhaps not the regenerated fiber system at all but rather the postsynaptic potentials and discharges in the tectal neurons. Further, the course which the regenerated fibers traverse within the amphibian tectum en route to their terminals cannot be traced by the present electrical techniques. Hence the electrical evidence, like the

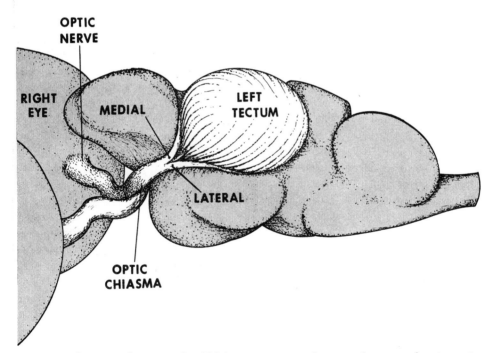

Fig. 6.1 Schematic drawing of goldfish optic system showing division of main optic tract into medial and lateral bundles and their relations with midbrain tectum. (After Attardi and Sperry, *Exptl. Neurol.* 4:262–275, 1961.)

behavioral, is not in itself enough to rule on the question of impulse specificity and signal decoding vs. selective regrowth. What was needed to settle such questions, as pointed out by Gaze (14), was direct histological evidence.

Bodian silver stain studies of optic nerve regeneration have been carried out in fishes in which the optic system in general is more refined and more highly elaborated than in the amphibians (see Fig. 6.1). These results (Attardi and Sperry, 7, 8) provide finally a direct and convincing histological demonstration of strong chemoaffinity effects in regrowth of the optic fibers, not only with respect to the terminal connections that they establish

in the tectum, but also with respect to the central pathways which the fibers take to reach their terminal sites (Fig. 6.2). The selective growth patterns occur, in this case, under conditions where the possibility of alternative mechanical interpretations seems highly remote.

Ever since the early studies of Harrison (22), it has been commonly agreed that nerve fiber growth is universally subject to contact guidance. Nerve fibers have to grow in contact with surfaces and interfaces of some sort; they cannot grow directly across empty liquid or gas spaces. The issue has remained as to whether, in addition, the direction of growth is influ-

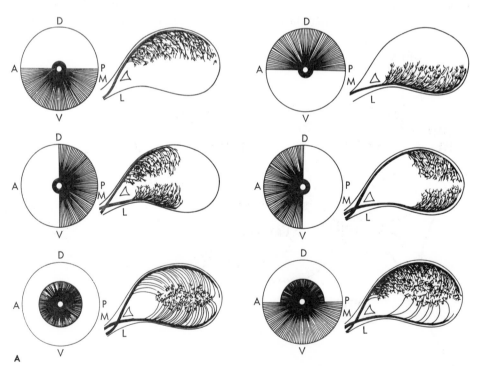

Fig. 6.2 Results of experiments in which the dorsal, ventral, anterior, posterior, or outer peripheral hemiretina is excised, after scrambling of fibers in the optic trunk. (After Attardi and Sperry, *Physiologist* 3:12, 1960; *Exptl. Neurol.* 4:262–275, 1961.) A. Diagrammatic reconstruction of regeneration patterns formed in the optic tracts and tectum by fibers originating from different retinal halves.

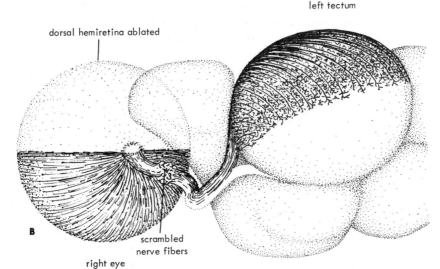

B. Following ablation of the dorsal hemiretina and optic nerve section, regenerating fibers from the ventral retina form synaptic connections only in the dorsal tectum. (After Sperry, *Proc. Natl. Acad. Sci. U.S.* 50:703–710, 1963.)

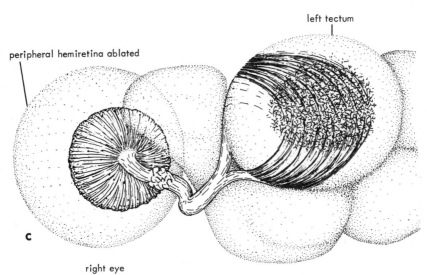

C. Fibers from the center of the retina grow through the denervated peripheral zone of the tectum, but establish synaptic connections when they reach the central tectum. (After Sperry, *Proc. Natl. Acad. Sci. U.S.* 50:703–710, 1963.)

enced also by selective chemical factors (chemotropism) or by electrical factors (galvanotropism), or whether the purely mechanical contact factors (stereotropism) are sufficient, as contended in the mechanical theory. Because the mechanical elements are universally present along with possible chemical factors, it has always been extremely difficult in any given situation to prove the existence of chemical selectivity, especially with the weight of opinion so long against chemical interpretations. In our current experiments, the mechanical conditions are seemingly constant, but fibers from different sectors of the retina show very different growth patterns in the same mechanical matrix.

The availability now of a seemingly unequivocal demonstration of the presence of strong chemical selectivity, in respect to both the course and the termination of the optic nerve fibers, has opened the gates for similar interpretation of many other borderline observations where chemotropic explanations of nerve growth had long appeared possible but had been withheld or were considered suspect because of the dominant long-term bias against anything suggestive of chemotaxis, chemotropism, or neurotropism. In the numerous papers of Hamburger, Piatt, Speidel, Weiss and other students of nerve growth, one can find repeated observations where selective chemical affinities would appear, in retrospect and from the vantage of present evidence, to offer a reasonable and perhaps now the most probable explanation (Hamburger, 20). The problems involved in the directional guidance of a migrating nerve cell would appear to be similar in many respects to those that arise in the advance of the fiber growth tip. The orderly cell migrations described in the beautiful studies of Levi-Montalcini (31) come immediately to mind in this regard.

The Current Thesis

We can turn now to a brief statement of the general working picture as it stands today without dwelling further on the supporting published evidence that can be found in detail in the preceding and later references (see Miner, 33; Sperry, 58–61, 63; Szekely, 71, 72).

It now appears that the complicated nerve fiber circuits of the brain grow, assemble, and organize themselves through the use of intricate chemical codes under genetic control. Early in development the nerve cells, numbering in the billions, acquire, and retain thereafter, individual identification tags, chemical in nature, by which they can be recognized and distinguished one from another.

As the maturing neurons and their long pulse-carrying fibers begin to form functional interconnections to weave the complex communication networks of behavior, the growing fibers become extremely selective about the chemical identity of other cells and fibers with which they will associate. Lasting functional hookups are established only with cells to which the growing fibers find themselves selectively matched by inherent chemical affinities.

The outgrowing fibers are guided by a kind of probing chemical touch system that leads them along exact pathways in an enormously intricate guidance program that involves millions and perhaps billions of different chemically distinct brain cells. By selective chemical preferences the respective nerve fibers are guided correctly to their separate channels at each of the numerous forks or decision points which they encounter as they travel through what is essentially a multiple Y-maze of possible channels (Fig. 6.3).

Each fiber in the brain pathways has its own preference for particular prescribed trails by which it locates and connects with certain other neurons

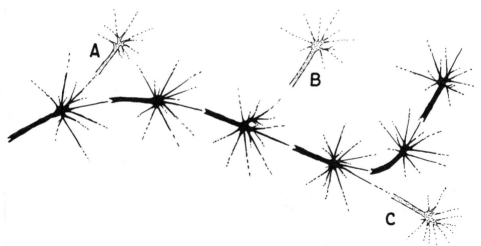

Fig. 6.3 Schematic representation of sequential steps in chemotactic guidance of a growing nerve fiber. Multiple filopodia constantly reach out in front of the advancing fiber tip, testing the environment in all directions. The critical factors determining which filopodia will form the strongest attachments, and thereby direct the route of growth, are apparently chemical. Numerous alternative paths, like those represented at A, B, and C, are open, mechanically feasible, and may even be established temporarily, but fail to survive because of differential selective adhesion.

that have the appropriate cell flavor. The potential pathways and terminal connection zones have their own individual chemical flavors by which each is recognized and distinguished from all others in the same half of the brain and cord. Indications are that right and left halves are chemical mirror maps of one another.

The present scheme provides the basis for a general explanation of how instincts and other inherited components of behavior, of even the most detailed sort, can be ingrown. Limitations in the machinery of growth are largely removed in this view in which the developmental mechanisms are believed to be capable of handling the most highly refined and precise adjustments in the neural networks. In regard to the inheritance of a given behavior pattern, it is no longer so much a question of whether the machinery of growth is

capable of installing it, as to whether the survival rate may be better if the behavior is kept flexible by having it learned in each generation and thus adaptable to external conditions and adjustable to changes. The fact that in any individual the particular constellation of chemical affinities that emerges within the tremendous population of developing neurons happens to yield connection networks that are functionally adaptive goes back to the selection pressures that affect survival throughout evolution. How the process of neurochemical evolution is controlled in ontogeny remains one of the many challenging problems of developmental biology.

It is apparent that our current view, with its emphasis on chemical selectivity, comes closer to the older ideas of Cajal and his contemporaries than to the antichemical, antiselectivity views prevalent in 1940. The course of the selectivity theory, however, has not been so much a return full circle to the earlier position, perhaps, as it has been a hairpin curve or switchback in the upward advance of the field. The stress on physicochemical forces in nerve growth led by Weiss (84) over a period of three decades has been most catalytic and instructive. This whole important aspect of the picture is omitted in the present discussion focused on the selectivity issue. Earlier proponents of chemotaxis and neurotropism had applied these concepts in neurospecificity to the peripheral nervous system principally, mainly to nerve-end-organ relations. Even Cajal had been willing to leave for functional assistance the detailed patterning of the central connections for coordination, perception, sensory local sign, and the like. All of these, in the present interpretation, are believed to fall within the province of growth and differentiation. Although the present scheme allows ample room for learning and memory, it represents a strong swing during the past 25 years toward an increasing recognition of the importance of inheritance in behavior. How far the pendulum may continue to move in this direction remains an open guess.

In no other part of the central nervous system do the cell-to-cell associations have to be installed with greater selectivity and precision than in the sensory pathways and brain centers for vision. Application of our current theory to the human visual system requires that the one million or so fibers that connect eye to brain be individually tagged, each fiber distinguishable according to the latitude and longitude of its point of origin in the retina. We infer that gradients of embryonic dif-

ferentiation, with their axes essentially perpendicular to each other, spread across and through the developing tissues, to impress the required chemical mapping on the embryonic retina and optic centers of the brain. Three of these morphogenetic gradients, superimposed, would be enough for the topographic mapping involved and would give corresponding values for identical points in the retinal fields of each eye and between the retinae and the series of brain centers on each of which the retina is mapped by orderly fiber projections. Nasal-temporal differences at the retina and corresponding right-left cytochemical factors in the centers preserve distinct image paths from each eye with right and left maps in register at each central station, shown in Figure 6.4 (Sperry, 63). The same kinds of processes visualized here with reference to the optic system must go on in all parts of the developing nervous system.

Remaining Problems

The Underlying Chemistry

Rather than review the already published evidence on which the foregoing generalizations are based, it seems more profitable to comment on some of the unsolved problems and the current issues and questions still under investigation. Probably the most obvious question concerns the nature of the biochemistry of the specificity factors that underlie the demonstrated selectivity in nerve growth and other neuroaffinity phenomena. This remains, of course, an open field, practically untouched as yet, with relatively little in the way of evidence to curb creative speculation. The biochemistry in-

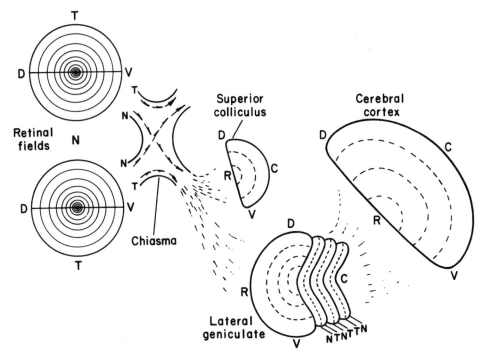

Fig. 6.4 Schematic diagram indicating possible application of chemoaffinity interpretation to genesis of mammalian visual system (see text). Axial labeling of gradients for brain centers is highly tentative because the effective embryonic gradients underlying their topographical differentiation remain uncertain. D–V, dorsoventral gradient; N–T, nasotemporal; R–C, rostrocaudal gradient. (After Sperry, *Proc. Natl. Acad. Sci. U.S.* 50:703–710, 1963.)

volved here is presumably that of cell differentiation carried to extreme refinement within the nerve cell population. Note that three basic axial gradients of differentiation—rostrocaudal, dorsoventral, and radial or mediolateral—would be sufficient to impress a unique chemistry on every single cell of the CNS, and of the entire body for that matter, depending on the steepness of the gradients. As in the differentiation of the organism as a whole, we may presume that many local fields of differentiation and subfields and subgradients are superimposed upon the three primary axial fields. These will be combined presumably with mosaic, frequency distribution and other forms of differentiation involving

suppressive emanation, lateral inhibition, and the like. Differentiation within the CNS may be seen to reflect in more ways than one the differentiation of the total organism in miniature. The chemical problems in principle are presumably of similar nature.

The body and most of its parts are represented in the nerve centers in miniature and in functional perspective, several times over in some instances. For example, the entire body surface in full detail is represented at the spinal and hindbrain levels, again in the thalamus and again in the cerebral cortex. The face, head, and neck, at least, are doubly represented with duplication of right and left sides at thalamic and cortical levels (Fig. 6.5).

Cytochemical differentiation in terms of gradients and fields is basic all through the central nervous system.

Cells close together within a given nucleus or cortical area are similar and those farther apart are increasingly dif-

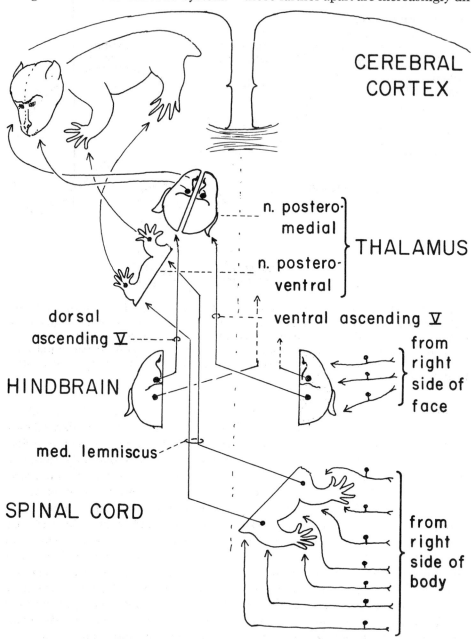

CEREBRAL CORTEX

n. postero-medial

n. postero-ventral

THALAMUS

dorsal ascending Ⅴ

ventral ascending Ⅴ

from right side of face

HINDBRAIN

med. lemniscus

SPINAL CORD

from right side of body

Fig. 6.5 Diagrammatic scheme to show neural representation of body surface in the spinal and hindbrain nuclei, thalamus, and cortex. In neurogenesis, similar differentiation takes place in many other pathways and centers throughout the entire nervous system.

ferent as the separation increases. The tendency for fiber projections from one central field to another to interconnect opposite poles of the two gradients appears so frequently in central nervous organization as to suggest that this affinity between opposites may be a rather direct reflection of the nature of the underlying chemical affinities, a complementarity principle perhaps (Jehle, 27). The dorsal retina, for example, connects to ventral tectum, the lateral somatic thalamus connects to medial cortex, the medial nucleus gracilis projects to lateral thalamus, and so on.

The nature of the gradients and their interrelations via fiber projection systems suggests a chemical basis in which some large molecule or molecular complex or unit has a long range of properties running from one extreme to another with many graded intermediate steps, each one of which is precisely controlled and precisely replicated from within a given cell. The chemical factor is then extended without loss of specificity into all the distant fiber tips of the given neuron (Sperry, 58). As a simplified hypothetical example, imagine a dipole compound molecule made up of units A and P (for anterior and posterior). At the rostral pole there are 99 A units to every one of P and the reverse at the caudal pole with a 50:50 ratio in the center. Once the over-all gradient is established, each unit ratio would become stamped into the differentiation machinery of the neuron and the specific factor transported throughout its arboreal fiber system. As indicated above, most neurons would also be synthesizing additional specifying molecular complexes for the dorsoventral alignment and another for the medio-lateral alignment, plus further nongradient factors like those for color in the retina and for pain and temperature in the cutaneous system.

Though it is entirely possible that the specifying chemical factors become implanted throughout all parts of the nerve cell membrane, it is the soma of the neuron and the axon tips that are especially critical in determining communicative relationships. There are reasons for supposing that the membrane at the fiber tip is specialized not only in the active filopodial flare at the growth tip, but also in the comparatively quiescent synaptic junctions at end organs in the periphery and at end bulbs in the centers. There must be interchange and interaction of cell specificity effects through the fiber tip and soma, including the dendrite system. These effects seem not to be present and frequently are contraindicated along the length of the axon. Insulation of the axon by the myelin sheath is generally thought of in terms of impulse-conduction properties or nutritional processes, or both. The myelin sheath cell complex may also serve an insulating or related effect in reference to the establishment, maintenance, and preservation of chemical specificity.

The specialized cell-to-cell relations that exist in the nervous system, particularly in respect to the long fiber connections between distant cells, offer special analytic advantages for approaching the biochemistry of the morphogenetic field, of induction effects, and of other general features of growth dynamics. The chemical factors involved in the retinal gradients, for example, must be of such nature that they can be extended the full length of the growing axon into the fine probing spiculelike filaments at the advancing fiber tip. They must be present and operating in the active microfilament surface. This would seem to suggest that the chemoaffinity is not dependent on specific patterning of molecular latticework in the surface membrane, for such a pattern would seemingly be difficult to maintain in a rapidly elongating spicule or film. Specificity within individual molecular units, regardless of their interunit patterns, would seem at first sight a more promising hypothesis.

The morphogenetic fields of the nervous system involve populations of contiguous cells as in organogenesis elsewhere. In addition, however, the specific cytochemical properties of the individual units of the field can then be extended and scattered in various ways over long distances and into widespread fiber arborizations. The unit properties are retained in these fiber systems which may themselves become randomly scattered, or rotated, or inverted on one or another axis, or duplicated by axon bifurcation, while the parent cell bodies have to maintain their proper positions in the field. Induction effects also can be mediated through the distant fiber contacts. Whereas, in organogenesis generally, differentiation induced by neighboring elements tends to be local and confined to neighboring cell masses, induction via fiber tip contacts permits distant inductive effects such as that of the integument on the spinal ganglia and dorsal columns (Sperry, 56; Miner and Sperry, 34; Miner, 33).

Innervation of Skeletal Muscle

It is a general impression in the literature that the growth and regeneration of nerves into skeletal muscles is for-

tuitous and nonselective (Weiss, 80; Weiss and Hoag, 86; Bernstein and Guth, 9; Guth, 16). Earlier demonstrations that even sensory fibers will innervate skeletal muscle has been retracted (Weiss and Edds, 85). Whether this nullifies also the conclusions drawn from observations on the mononeuronal reflex arc (Weiss, 78) is not clear. Our own studies emphasize that there is in actuality a great deal of selectivity in the innervation and reinnervation of muscle. We have found a wide variety of selectivity effects in different vertebrates and in different neuromuscular systems (Sperry, 42, 51, 54; Sperry and Deupree, 65; Arora and Sperry, 2, 6). These range from a muscle's complete acceptance of foreign fibers with full functional recovery, to complete rejection of foreign innervation, resulting in atrophy and degeneration of the muscle confronted with foreign nerves (see also Eccles et al., 11). Presumably there are many forms and degrees of neuromuscular selectivity yet to be clarified.

In recent studies (Arora and Sperry, 6) we found that the completely severed oculomotor nerve regenerates selectively in the cichlid fish *Astronotus ocellatus* to restore normal movement of the eyeball. Forcing individual branches of the nerve into the wrong eye muscle by surgical means leads to some reinnervation and weak contraction timed to suit the transplanted nerve but not its new muscle; that is, myotypic response is lacking. We concluded that the chemical specificities involved favor the original reconnections over the abnormal connections. Similar results have just been demonstrated in our laboratory by Mark in studies on reinnervation of the pectoral fin of the same fish. Mark suggests that selective functional recovery in these lower vertebrates is associated with the multiterminal type of innervation. This permits competition of numerous fiber terminals, whereas in the other type of muscle the first fiber to enter, as a rule, captures the muscle and prohibits further competition. In other studies on reinnervation of salamander limbs after nerve cross-union, Mark found so much diffuse sprouting of the manipulated nerves that he decided it was almost impossible to prevent the regenerating fibers from getting back to their original muscles. These recent demonstrations of selectivity in the reinnervation of muscle have caused us to wonder about the claims regarding nonselective reinnervation in the "supernumerary limb" experiments and other early studies. Certainly our own earlier examples of myotypic specification of nerve by muscle (Sperry and Deupree, 65; Arora and Sperry, 2) need now to be rechecked. The critical observation on which the resonance theory of nerve function was founded and supported for over 10 years (Weiss, 76, 77, 79), namely, that a single motor axon can branch into several different asynergic muscles and activate them individually each in its correct timing, also needs to be re-examined in the light of our present knowledge.

In studies of salamander forelimbs transplanted into the opercular region, Hibbard, in our laboratory, has confirmed Detwiler (10a) to the effect that certain muscles of these limbs respond in synchrony with swallowing. The results seem to be an exception to the general rule that the musculature of transplanted limbs must be connected to limb centers in order to function, and that the muscles respond only at the time proper for the given muscle (Weiss, 84). One may tentatively infer that there is some fortuitous chemoaffinity involved between the particular plantar flexor muscles of the forelimb and certain of the nerves of deglutition. In an impressive series of transplantation studies in chicks and salamanders, Szekely and Szentagothai (69–74) obtained a number of results that they found difficult to account for by current theory. In a recent interpretation (Szekely and Szentagothai, 74) they consider a tentative return toward some kind of impulse-specificity scheme reminiscent of the resonance principle of Weiss in which the selective response effects are suggested to be independent of specific fiber connections. Their findings provide new information about the dynamics of neuron specification and the adjustment of nerve-end-organ relations, but it is not as yet clear that they are incompatible with the chemoaffinity-determined fiber connection scheme as outlined above.

Selective Growth in Peripheral Nerves

The demonstration that growing fibers may preferentially enter and follow particular trails to reach their destinations in the central nervous system raises again the question of whether anything of the kind may occur in the regeneration or initial growth within the fiber systems of the peripheral nerves. The evidence in the past has seemed to exclude such selectivity (Weiss and Edds, 85; Guth, 16; Weiss and Hoag, 86; Weiss and Taylor, 88) but the question has been studied thus far only in a very narrow range of conditions and deserves further investigation. There is a great wealth of possibilities for testing; the procedures are simple, and the results come quickly. Incidental observations in a variety of nerve regeneration studies leave this writer with the impression that some selectivity may exist in the regrowth of fibers into degenerated nerve trunks at least on a gross level in the lower vertebrates — as between sensory and motor channels, or between pectoral and pelvic fin nerves. Selectivity on a more refined scale is not excluded.

The course that nerves follow in entering transplanted aneurogenic limbs, as in the experiments of Piatt (35), are strongly suggestive that the general fiber patterns formed in the peripheral nervous system are determined in part at least by chemical affinities. The embryonic formation of the trochlear, as well as of other cranial nerves (Hamburger, 19) is difficult to explain in many cases without assuming selective chemical guidance. It is logical that the addition of any new fibers to peripheral nerves at the later stages of development when the fiber systems are already well formed by preceding nerve outgrowth, would be much more effective if the late-comers were to follow their appropriate channels than if they were obliged to explore at random until the correct end organs were located.

Gradient Plasticity

An apparent deviation from the results of ablating half of the retina in goldfish has been reported recently by Gaze, Jacobson, and Szekely (15). Optic nerves which are composed of a double supply of temporal fibers (obtained by replacing, in embryonic stages, the nasal half retina by a transplanted temporal retina) apparently formed synaptic connections through-

out both halves of the tectum instead of leaving one half uninnervated. Both half retinas were mapped as an orderly single half field but the half field was spread across the whole tectum as if the recipient tectal half field had expanded to include tectal cells labeled originally for nasal retina. It is not inconceivable that the dynamics and biochemistry of the morphogenetic field allow for this kind of plasticity in gradient organization. Before we invest in possible explanations of how a half tectum tagged for nasal fibers can be relabeled for temporal fibers under these conditions, there is an alternative possibility to be ruled out. Hyperplasia and hypertrophy beyond the normal limits are to be expected in the half tectum that receives a double ingrowth of temporal fibers. Conversely, atrophy and hypoplasia are to be expected in the uninnervated half (Kollros, 28). Some shrinkage and swelling accompany denervation and reinnervation of the adult tectum, but the effects are much greater during development. The combination of the resultant atrophy in one half and hypertrophy in the other half might well be responsible for the observed effect obviating the chemical relabeling problem.

CHEMOTROPISM IN REINNERVATION OF OPTIC TECTUM. We are currently trying to test the strength and nature of the selective growth forces in the optic system of fishes, mainly by surgical and histological methods that involve various types of displacement of the central fiber bundles as they approach and enter the optic tectum. When the medial and lateral bundles are cut and crossed at the anterior pole of the tectum shortly beyond the point where they diverge, the crossed bundles regenerate and promptly recross against

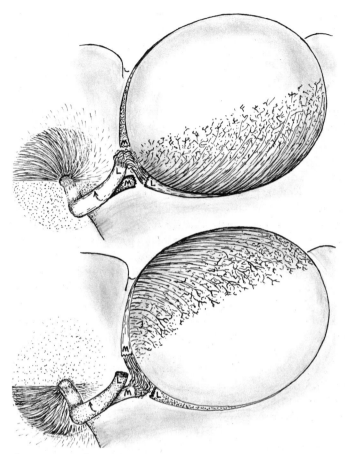

Fig. 6.6 Experiment in which the medial and lateral bundles of the optic nerves are cut and crossed. Regenerating fibers do not enter the tectum indiscriminately or along lines of least resistance, but re-cross to enter their proper channels. (After Arora and Sperry, *Am. Zool.* 2:389, 1962.)

the imposed mechanical biases to re-enter their own proper channels, as shown in Figure 6.6 (Arora and Sperry, 4, 5). In other experiments the lateral bundle is cut long and crossed far up into the emptied channel of the medial bundle. Under these conditions the displaced lateral fibers again avoid connections in the dorsal tectum and manage to get back to the ventral tectum (Arora, 1; Arora and Sperry, 4). They do this, however, not by back-tracking, but by taking a short cut across the dorsal tectum through the parallel layer. In doing so the optic fibers build a heavy fiber system across the equator of the tectum that normally is not present. In highly delicate surgery, Arora has been able to deflect the teased-out posterior fascicle of the lateral bundle across the midline into the medial bundle of the contralateral tectum. Again, the fibers find their way back to the appropriate posteroventral sector of the tectum, but on the contralateral side this time and superimposed on the normal innervation of that side. In part, the lateral fibers mingle with the medial fibers running parallel with them in the parallel layer of the tectum, but they then push onward across the equator to attain their proper posteroventral synaptic zone. Numerous variations of these surgical derangements produce similar and intermediate growth patterns illustrating the same directive tendencies. It is a common and repeated observation that fibers growing through the parallel layer by-pass those regions of the tectum inappropriate for an orderly mapping of the retinotectal projections under conditions where the mechanical opportunities are equal for different fiber types.

Further behavioral indications of the refinement and selectivity of the regeneration process have been obtained in experiments just completed in our laboratory by Limpo. Fish were trained by the jumping technique to discriminate between fine shades of color in the yellow-green, green-blue, and yellow-red ranges in different cases. The thresholds for such discriminations were determined for normal fish and for fish with regenerated optic nerves and found to be of the same order. Also, thresholds tested before optic nerve section and regeneration were not significantly different from those tested on completion of regeneration in the same individuals.

There remain a host of unanswered problems in this field, which we have only begun to investigate. Attempts to study the regrowth of optic axons from smaller and smaller retinal remnants have so far been discouraging for anything smaller than about a third or a fourth of the retinal field. We have been unable, thus far, to obtain satisfactory staining of smaller regenerated fascicles after their entrance into the tectum. The reasons are not clear.

Application to Mammalian Visual System

I have indicated elsewhere how the gradient, chemotactic, and related concepts, based on data from the lower vertebrates, might be useful in explaining the ontogenetic organization of the primate visual system (Sperry, 63). The extensive and refined specification of the optic fibers is most clearly laid out in the lateral geniculate nucleus of man where the visual half field is mapped six times, in layer-cake fashion. Each map is in register with the others, with three layers for each eye and each pair of layers contains different cell types. Just as the optic fibers find their correct terminal zone in the tectum or colliculus, they must similarly find their proper locus on the geniculate surface. Each fiber then dips downward to connect in only one layer, as a rule, and only in the layer appropriate for the eye of origin, by-passing the neurons of other layers.

Presumably all of the refined selectivity that is histologically evident in the lateral geniculate nucleus is retained and more is added in the striate cortex, although in the cortex the different cell types are not so distinctly and visibly segregated. Projection from geniculate to striate cortex seems to involve a slight change in gradient relations in that the cortical units are found to pick up from an elongate field instead of the more circular receptive fields found at the geniculate level (Wiesel and Hubel, 89). The embryogenesis of such a system may be explained tentatively on the assumption that a given cortical unit accepts radiation fiber terminations rather loosely with respect to one or more chemical gradient factors in the fiber system while exercising more strict selectivity for others. The distribution of the loose or sliding affinities would thus reflect the distribution of the cortical unit tilts, and vice versa. The nature of this distribution pattern remains to be worked out, as do the developmental forces that govern it. One would suspect a lateral inhibitory surround effect operating in the differentiation of the various cortical columns to insure a proper distribution of different direction indicators.

Endogenous Physiological Properties

The foregoing discussion of behavioral nerve nets has been concentrated almost entirely on the matter of the patterning of the fiber connections. However, the functional proficiency of the neural circuitry in operation depends not only on the interneuronal contacts and the network diagram, but also on the diverse physiological properties of the various cellular units of which the circuits are composed. The neurons and their fibers act as conductors, but they also appear to serve in a variety of other specialized roles as pacemakers, amplifiers, triggers, tuners, timers, sensors, rectifiers, relays, secretors, and other elements that depend on a correspondingly wide diversification in the endogenous physiological and cytochemical properties. The resting excitatory threshold may be intrinsically high or low, stable or fluctuating in various ways in different cell types (Bullock, 10). The neuron may discharge in bursts or in trains, either of which may vary characteristically to give a wide variety of specific pulse pattern properties (Strumwasser, 68). Neurons may differ also in properties determining their pickup or pulse-pattern detector capacities. In this connection it should be understood that there is nothing in the above discussion intended to be critical of impulse specificity as a factor in central integration except in the particular context in which it was earlier applied

in the resonance explanation of homologous response. It remains entirely possible that pulse specificity plays a significant role in other integrative functions, though at present rather little is known about this in the vertebrate nervous system.

All of the specialized endogenous physiological properties of the various neuron types presumably arise, like the specificities that govern the morphological characteristics and the growth of connections, from cytochemical differentiation of the neuron population during development. They too, like the fiber connection patterns and more gross anatomical features, are thus dependent on genetic control and are, to a large extent, a matter of inheritance.

Functional Shaping of Nerve Circuits

It is obvious that there are endless problems remaining for future analysis in the developmental organization of the nerve circuits of behavior. Some of the problems have special importance because of implications that go far beyond the concerns of organogenesis per se. These perhaps merit some further comment here, even though the experimental evidence is sparse and most aspects are still rather speculative. One area in which more information will have widespread impact concerns the extent to which inheritance influences behavior, particularly in man. The counterpart of this question is the extent to which, and means by which, function shapes and reshapes the behavioral networks. In addition to the practical aspects are implications for theories of memory and learning and of their biological bases. These in turn are hardly separable from problems of perception, motivation, and other higher activities of the nervous system. The recent experiments of Hamburger (21) on the development of behavior in the chick, in which he is collaborating with a psychologist combining psychological and developmental approaches, point to a very promising trend for the future.

It is possible that the unknown changes imposed on the nervous system by learning and experience are distinct and removed from those processes one deals with in development and maturation. It is also possible, and not at all improbable, that the changes imposed by function are similar to, or a direct derivative of developmental features, and perhaps best understood in these terms. There are reasons to think that long-term memory in man could involve a specificity effect in the machinery for late neuron differentiation that gains behavioral expression through either a modification of the cell's fiber contacts or of its intrinsic physiological properties.

An interesting lead is found in the increasing evidence that some nerve cells are subject to disuse atrophy. If not adequately stimulated, these neurons may regress until permanently destroyed. Prisoners kept in "black cells" for several months come out totally blind (Walls, 75). Chimpanzees and other mammals raised in the dark show irreversible degenerative changes in the retina and visual pathways. If the same animals are raised in diffuse light, the atrophic effects are less severe, but apparently those neuronal units activated by edges and contrasts, which are not stimulated in diffuse light, undergo atrophy (Riesen, 39; Wiesel and Hubel, 89). If disuse effects of the same kind obtain farther

centrally among associational neurons of the cortex (see Held and Hein, 24), the result would be more nearly like that of learning. Many elements deeper in the brain centers must discharge only in very special activities, and, if these activities are not exercised — especially during maturational stages when the neurons seem to be particularly dependent on use — the neuron types involved may regress, leaving profound functional deficiencies in the integrative machinery.

One can arbitrarily distinguish use effects that consist of stamping in and preserving neural organization developed in growth, from use effects that add new organization, anatomical or physiological, to the developed system. Despite common impressions to the contrary (especially in psychology) it appears to be mainly the former that has been involved in most of the sensory deprivation studies to date (Sperry, 55). The above distinction tends to break down, however, in the central association areas, where the growth pressures are more diffuse. It is not clear at present to what extent fractional parts of a neuron, like synaptic endings, and separate dendritic branches, spines, or other elements may undergo disuse atrophy, leaving other parts of the same neuron normally functional. The so-called "disuse" effects, described by Cajal (37) from histological studies, appear to be more a reflection of interneuronal trophic dependencies than a dependency on excitation.

Problems relating to the use-dependent properties of nervous elements add up to a whole field in itself, with important ramifications in psychiatry, ethology, and other disciplines concerned with the effects of inheritance and early experience on adult function. It would be no surprise to find that the neural basis of imprinting is a direct evolutionary elaboration of the physiology or biochemistry of the above-mentioned use effects in the neural networks. Furthermore, it remains an open question whether the effects of function – that is, learning and memory – add or subtract any actual fiber structures or synaptic connections to the established morphology. It is possible, though not particularly indicated, that the neural changes implanted by learning and memory are essentially physiological in nature; membrane or other micro or molecular changes could affect excitatory thresh-old, conductance, and resistance to impulse transmission, or endogenous discharge properties all within the already established morphological networks. Between the strictly inherited organization of the behavioral networks and the strictly acquired, we recognize an important intermediate realm of nervous development in which function and growth go on simultaneously with mutual interactions. The anatomical effects of functional influence during these stages may not be large or even visible under the light microscope, but the minute differences may be critical in terms of behavior, especially with reference to human childhood.

References

1. Arora, H. L., "Effect of Forcing a Regenerative Optic Nerve Bundle toward a Foreign Region of the Optic Tectum in Fishes," *Anat. Record* 145:202 (1963).
2. ——, and R. W. Sperry, "Myotypic Respecification of Regenerated Nerve Fibres in Cichlid Fishes," *J. Embryol. Exptl. Morphol.* 5:256–263 (1957).
3. ——, and ——, "Studies on Color Discrimination Following Optic Nerve Regeneration in the Cichlid Fish, *Astronotus ocellatus*," *Anat. Record* 131:529 (1958).
4. ——, and ——, "Optic Nerve Regeneration after Surgical Cross-union of Medial and Lateral Optic Tracts," *Am. Zool.* 2:389 (1962).
5. ——, and ——, "Color Discrimination after Optic Nerve Regeneration in the Fish *Astronotus ocellatus*," *Develop. Biol.* 7:234–243 (1963).
6. ——, and ——, "Selectivity in Regeneration and Reconnection of the Oculomotor Nerve in Cichlid Fishes," *Anat. Record* 148:357 (1964).
7. Attardi, D. G., and R. W. Sperry, "Central Routes Taken by Regenerating Optic Fibers," *Physiologist* 3:12 (1960).
8. ——, and ——, "Preferential Selection of Central Pathways by Regenerat-ing Optic Fibers," *Exptl. Neurol.* 7:46–64 (1963).
9. Bernstein, J. J., and L. Guth, "Nonselectivity in Establishment of Neuromuscular Connections Following Nerve Regeneration in the Rat," *Exptl. Neurol.* 4:262–275 (1961).
10. Bullock, T. H., "Neuron Doctrine and Electrophysiology," *Science* 129:997–1002 (1959).
10a. Detwiler, Samuel A., *Neuroembryology*. London: MacMillan (1936).
11. Eccles, J. C., R. M. Eccles, C. N. Shealy, and W. D. Willis, "Experiments Utilizing Monosynaptic Excitatory Action on Motoneurons for Testing Hypotheses Relating to Specificity of Neuronal Connections," *J. Neurophysiol.* 25:559–580 (1962).
12. Gaze, R. M., "Regeneration of the Optic Nerve in *Xenopus laevis*," *J. Physiol.* 146:40 (1959).
13. ——, "Regeneration of the Optic Nerve in *Xenopus laevis*," *Quart. J. Exptl. Physiol.* 44:290–308 (1959).
14. ——, "Regeneration of the Optic Nerve in Amphibia," *Intern. Rev. Neurobiol.* 2:1–40 (1960).
15. ——, M. Jacobson, and G. Szekely, "The Retino-tectal Projection in *Xenopus*

with Compound Eyes," *J. Physiol.* 165: 484–499 (1963).

16. Guth, L., "Neuromuscular Function after Regeneration of Interrupted Nerve Fibers into Partially Denervated Muscle," *Exptl. Neurol.* 6:129–141 (1962).

17. Hamburger, V., "The Development and Innervation of Transplanted Limb Primordia of Chick Embryos," *J. Exptl. Zool.* 80:347–389 (1939).

18. ———, "Isolation of the Brachial Segments of the Spinal Cord of the Chick Embryo by Means of Tantalum Foil Blocks," *J. Exptl. Zool.* 103:113–142 (1946).

19. ———, "Experimental Analysis of the Dual Origin of the Trigeminal Ganglion in the Chick Embryo," *J. Exptl. Zool.* 148:91–124 (1961).

20. ———, "Specificity in Neurogenesis," *J. Cellular and Comp. Physiol.* Suppl. 1, 60:81–92 (1962).

21. ———, "Some Aspects of the Embryology of Behavior," *Quart. Rev. Biol.* 38: 342–365 (1963).

22. Harrison, R. G., "The Reaction of Embryonic Cells to Solid Structures," *J. Exptl. Zool.* 17:521–544 (1914).

23. Hartline, H. K., "The Response of Single Optic Nerve Fibers of the Vertebrate Eye to Illumination of the Retina," *Am. J. Physiol.* 121:400–415 (1938).

24. Held, R., and A. Hein, "Movement-produced Stimulation in the Development of Visually Guided Behavior," *J. Comp. Physiol. Psychol.* 56:872–876 (1963).

25. Hering, E., *Memory: Lectures on the Specific Energies of the Nervous System.* Chicago: Open Court (1913).

26. Holtfreter, J., "Gewebeaffinität, ein Mittel der Embryonalen Formbildung," *Arch. Exptl. Zellforsch.* 23:169–209 (1939).

27. Jehle, H., "Intermolecular Forces and Biological Specificity," *Proc. N. A. S.* 50: 516–523 (1963).

28. Kollros, J. J., "The Development of the Optic Lobes in the Frog. I. The Effects of Unilateral Enucleation in Embryonic Stages," *J. Exptl. Zool.* 123:153–188 (1953).

29. Lee, F. C., "The Regeneration of Nervous Tissue," *Physiol. Rev.* 9:575–623 (1929).

30. Lettvin, J. L., H. Maturana, W. H. Pitts,

and W. S. McCulloch, "How Seen Movement Appears in the Frog's Optic Nerve," *Federation Proc.* 18:90 (1959).

31. Levi-Montalcini, R., "Events in the Developing Nervous System," *Progress in Brain Research, Growth and Maturation of the Brain,* D. P. Purpura and J. P. Schade, eds. New York: Elsevier, vol. 4 (1964).

32. Maturana, H. R., J. L. Lettvin, W. S. McCulloch, and W. H. Pitts, "Evidence that Cut Optic Nerve Fibers in a Frog Regenerate to Their Proper Places in the Tectum," *Science* 130:1709–1710 (1959).

33. Miner, N., "Integumental Specification of Sensory Fibers in the Development of Cutaneous Local Sign," *J. Comp. Neurol.* 105:161–170 (1956).

34. ———, and R. W. Sperry, "Observations on the Genesis of Cutaneous Local Sign," *Anat. Record* 106:317 (1950).

35. Piatt, J., "Transplantation of Aneurogenic Forelimbs in *Amblystoma punctatum,*" *J. Exptl. Zool.* 91:79–101 (1942).

36. ———, "Experiments on the Decussation and Course of Mauthner's Fibers in *Amblystoma punctatum,*" *J. Comp. Neurol.* 80:335–353 (1944).

37. Ramón y Cajal, S., "Études sur la Neurogenèse de quelques Vertébrés," *Studies on Vertebrate Neurogenesis* (1929). English translation by L. Guth. Springfield, Ill.: Charles C Thomas (1960).

38. ———, "Histologie du Système Nerveux," Madrid: Instituto Ramón y Cajal, vol. II, p. 216 (1955).

39. Reisen, A. H., "Studying Perceptual Development Using the Technique of Sensory Deprivation," *J. Nervous Mental Disease* 132:21–25 (1961).

40. Speidel, C. C., "*In vivo* Studies of Myelinated Nerve Fibers," *International Review of Cytology.* New York: Academic Press, vol. 16, pp. 174–231 (1964).

41. Sperry, R. W., "Functional Results of Muscle Transplantation in the Hind Limb of the Albino Rat," *Anat. Record Suppl.* 75:51 (1939).

42. ———, "The Effect of Crossing Nerves to Antagonistic Muscles in the Hind Limb of the Rat," *J. Comp. Neurol.* 75:1–19 (1941).

43. ———, "Functional Results of Crossing Sensory Nerves in the Rat," *J. Comp. Neur.* 78:59–90 (1943).

44. ———, "Reestablishment of Visuomo-

tor Coordinations by Optic Nerve Regeneration," *Anat. Record* 84:470 (1942).

45. ——, "Visuomotor Coordination in the Newt (*Triturus viridescens*) after Regeneration of the Optic Nerve," *J. Comp. Neurol.* 79:33–55 (1943).

46. ——, "Optic Nerve Regeneration with Return of Vision in Anurans," *J. Neurophysiol.* 7:57–69 (1944).

47. ——, "Centripetal Regeneration of the 8th Cranial Nerve Root with Systematic Restoration of Vestibular Reflexes," *Am. J. Physiol.* 144:735–741 (1945).

48. ——, "Restoration of Vision after Crossing of Optic Nerves and after Contralateral Transplantation of Eye," *J. Neurophysiol.* 8:15–28 (1945).

49. ——, "The Problem of Central Nervous Reorganization after Nerve Regeneration and Muscle Transposition," *Quart. Rev. Biol.* 20:311–369 (1945).

50. ——, "Ontogenetic Development and Maintenance of Compensatory Eye Movements in Complete Absence of the Optic Nerve," *J. Comp. Psych.* 39:321–330 (1946).

51. ——, "Nature of Functional Recovery Following Regeneration of the Oculomotor Nerve in Amphibians," *Anat. Record* 97:293–316 (1947).

52. ——, "Orderly Patterning of Synaptic Associations in Regeneration of Intracentral Fiber Tracts Mediating Visuomotor Coordination," *Anat. Record* 102:63–75 (1948).

53. ——, "Patterning of Central Synapses in Regeneration of the Optic Nerve in Teleosts," *Physiol. Zool.* 21:351–361 (1948).

54. ——, "Myotypic Specificity in Teleost Motoneurons," *J. Comp. Neurol.* 93:277–287 (1950).

55. ——, "Mechanisms of Neural Maturation," *Handbook of Experimental Psychology*, S. S. Stevens, ed. New York: Wiley, pp. 236–280 (1951).

56. ——, "Regulative Factors in the Orderly Growth of Neural Circuits," *Growth Symp.* 10:63–87 (1951).

57. ——, "Developmental Patterning of Neural Circuits," *Chicago Med. School Quart.* 12:66–73 (1951).

58. ——, "Problems in the Biochemical Specification of Neurons," *Biochemistry of the Developing Nervous System*, H.

Waelsch, ed. New York: Academic Press, pp. 74–84 (1955).

59. ——, "Functional Regeneration in the Optic System," *Regeneration in the Central Nervous System*, W. F. Windle, ed. Springfield, Ill.: Charles C Thomas, pp. 66–76 (1955).

60. ——, "Physiological Plasticity and Brain Circuit Theory," *Biological and Biochemical Bases of Behavior*, H. F. Harlow and C. N. Woolsey, eds. Madison, Wis.: University of Wisconsin Press, pp. 401–424 (1958).

61. ——, "Developmental Basis of Behavior," *Behavior and Evolution*, A. Roe and G. G. Simpson, eds. New Haven, Conn.: Yale University Press, pp. 128–139 (1958).

62. ——, "Evidence behind Chemoaffinity Theory of Synaptic Patterning," *Anat. Record* 145:288 (1963).

63. ——, "Chemoaffinity in the Orderly Growth of Nerve Fiber Patterns and Connections," *Proc. Natl. Acad. Sci. U.S.* 50:703–710 (1963).

64. ——, "Recovery of Sight after Transplantation of Eyes and Regeneration of Retina and Optic Nerve," *Proc. Intern. Congr. Tech. Blindness*, L. L. Clark, ed. Vol. II, pp. 87–97 (1963).

65. ——, and N. Deupree, "Functional Recovery Following Alterations in Nerve-Muscle Connections of Fishes," *J. Comp. Neurol.* 106:143–161 (1956).

66. ——, and N. Miner, "Formation within Sensory Nucleus V of Synaptic Associations Mediating Cutaneous Localization," *J. Comp. Neurol.* 90:403–423 (1949).

67. Stone, L. S., "Functional Polarization in Developing and Regenerating Retinae of Transplanted Eyes," *Ann. N. Y. Acad. Sci.* 49:856–865 (1948).

68. Strumwasser, F., "The Demonstration and Manipulation of a Circadian Rhythm in a Single Neuron," *Circadian Clocks*, J. Aschoff, ed. Amsterdam: North Holland Publishing Co., pp. 44–64 (1965).

69. Szekely, G., "Regulationstendenzen in der Ausbildung der "Funktionellen spezifität" der Retinaanlage bei *Triturus vulgaris*," *Arch. Entwicklungsmech. Or.* 150:48–60 (1957).

70. ——, "Functional Specificity of Cranial Sensory Neuroblasts in Urodela,"

Acta Biol. Acad. Sci. Hung. X:107–116 (1959).

71. ——, "The Apparent Corneal Specificity of Sensory Neurons," *J. Embryol. Exptl. Morphol.* 7:375–379 (1959).

72. ——, "Functional Specificity of Spinal Cord Segments in the Control of Limb Movements," *J. Embryol. Exptl. Morphol.* 2:431–444 (1963).

73. ——, and J. Szentagothai, "Experiments with Model Nervous Systems," *Acta Biol.* 12:253–269 (1962).

74. ——, and ——, "Reflex and Behavior Patterns Elicited from Implanted Supernumerary Limbs in the Chick," *J. Embryol. Exptl. Morphol.* 10:140–151 (1962).

75. Walls, G. L., "The Problem of Visual Direction," *Am. J. Optom. Arch. Am. Acad. Optom.* 117:1–101 (1951).

76. Weiss, P. A., "Erregungspecifität und Erregungsresonanz," *Ergeb. Biol.* 3:1–151 (1928).

77. ——, "Das Resonanzprinzip der Nerventätigkeit," *Wien. Klin. Wochenschr.* 39:1–17 (1931).

78. ——, "Motor Effects of Sensory Nerves Experimentally Connected with Muscles," *Anat. Record* 60:437–448 (1934).

78a. ——, "Experimental Innervation of Muscles by the Central Ends of Afferent Nerves (Establishment of a One-neurone Connection between Receptor and Effector Organ), with Functional Tests," *J. Comp. Neurol.* 61:135–174 (1935).

79. ——, "Selectivity Controlling the Central-peripheral Relations in the Nervous System," *Biol. Rev.* 11:494–531 (1936).

80. ——, "Further Experimental Investigations on the Phenomenon of Homologous Response in Transplanted Amphib-ian Limbs. II. Nerve Regeneration and the Innervation of Transplanted Limbs," *J. Comp. Neurol.* 66:481–535 (1937).

81. ——, "The Selective Relation between Centers and Periphery in the Nervous System," *Collect. Net XIII*, no. 2:29–32 (1938).

82. ——, "The Development of the Nervous System (Neurogenesis), Part IV," *Principles of Development.* New York: Holt, Rinehart and Winston, pp. 491–557 (1939).

83. ——, "The Problem of Specificity in Growth and Development," *Yale J. Biol. Med.* 19:235–278 (1947).

84. ——, "Nervous System (*Neurogenesis*)," *Analysis of Development*, B. H. Willier, P. H. Weiss, and V. Hamburger, eds. Philadelphia: Saunders, pp. 346–401 (1955).

85. ——, and M. Edds, "Sensory-motor Nerve Crosses in the Rat," *J. Neurophysiol.* 8:173–194 (1945).

86. ——, and A. Hoag, "Competitive Reinnervation of Rat Muscles by Their Own and Foreign Nerves," *J. Neurophysiol.* 9:413–418 (1946).

87. ——, and R. W. Sperry, "Unmodifiability of Muscular Coordination in the Rat, Demonstrated by Muscle Transposition and Nerve Crossing," *Amer. J. Physiol.* 129:492 (1940).

88. ——, and A. C. Taylor, "Further Experimental Evidence against Neurotropism in Nerve Regeneration," *J. Exptl. Zool.* 95:233–257 (1944).

89. Wiesel, T. N., and P. H. Hubel, "Single-cell Responses in Striate Cortex of Kittens Deprived of Vision in One Eye," *J. Neurophysiol.* 26:1003–1017 (1963).

90. Young, J. Z., "The Functional Repair of Nervous Tissue," *Physiol. Rev.* 22:318–374 (1942).

7

The Action of Nerve Growth Factor on Sensory and Sympathetic Cells

RITA LEVI-MONTALCINI AND PIETRO U. ANGELETTI*

Department of Zoology
Washington University
St. Louis, Missouri

The early discovery of a nerve growth-promoting agent released by fragments of some mouse tumors in tissue culture (Levi-Montalcini, 15; Levi-Montalcini et al., 25) led to the isolation and purification of the nerve growth factor (NGF). The biological properties of this factor have been extensively studied and described in recent years (Levi-Montalcini and Cohen, 23; Levi-Montalcini and Angeletti, 20; Levi-Montalcini, 18). The NGF acts directly on the receptive nerve cells, namely the sensory cells, during an early phase of their life cycle, and on the sympathetic cells throughout all their life. The in vitro effect consists of the production of a dense halo of nerve fibers by explanted

ganglia; the halo is apparent after only 6 hours of incubation. The growth effect is elicited by NGF at a concentration of 10^{-9} M. Evidence has been given that NGF plays an essential role in the growth and maintenance of the receptive cells. When dissociated sensory or sympathetic neuroblasts are cultured in minimum essential medium, their survival is strictly conditioned to the presence of NGF (Levi-Montalcini and Angeletti, 21). The in vivo effect of this growth factor was investigated in the chick embryo as well as in newborn and adult mammals. In the chick embryo it calls forth a striking hypertrophic and hyperplastic response in sensory and sympathetic ganglia and hyperinnervation of the viscera (Levi-Montalcini and Hamburger, 24). In newborn and adult mammals the effect is restricted to the sympathetic ganglia. Newborn mice injected daily with NGF (10 μg/g body weight) show at the end of the first

* The work described in this paper was supported by grants from the National Institute of Neurological Diseases and Blindness, Public Health Service (NB-01602, NB-03777), the National Science Foundation (GB-1862), and Merck, Sharp and Dohme Research Laboratories.

187

week of treatment a volume increase of ten times that of controls. The over-all effect is due to increase in cell number and cell size. Adult mammals respond to NGF with marked hypertrophy of the same cells (Levi-Montalcini and Booker, 22).

The nerve growth factor is a protein. Its molecular weight has been estimated to be of the order of 44,000. Its biological activity is heat labile, is destroyed by proteolytic enzymes, and is unstable to acid pH but resistant to alkaline pH. It is endowed with antigenic properties and when injected into rabbits with Freund's adjuvant, induces the production of specific antibodies (AS) (Cohen, 6). Injection of AS into newborn mammals results in the almost total atrophy of the sympathetic ganglia. The destruction of the sympathetic cells is permanent. The effects cited have been described in detail in previous publications (Levi-Montalcini and Angeletti, 19; Levi-Montalcini, 17).

The growth effect elicited by NGF on responsive nerve cells has now been investigated at the metabolic level. The results of these studies will be dealt with in the following sections.

NGF Effect on Glucose Metabolism

It was demonstrated that NGF, to be effective, needs a source of energy which may be supplied by glucose or mannose. Total deprivation of carbohydrates from the medium results in a lack of fiber outgrowth from explanted ganglia. When labeled glucose is added to the culture medium, the growth effect is accompanied by increased oxidation of glucose to CO_2. This increased glucose oxidation is not prevented by glycolytic inhibitors such as fluoride. These results suggested the existence of a direct oxidative pathway in the responsive nerve cells (Cohen, 5). Experiments were performed to study the effect of NGF on the utilization of glucose by nerve cells. The relative yields of $C^{14}O_2$ from glucose-1-C^{14} and glucose-6-C^{14} were investigated in sensory and sympathetic ganglia incubated in Warburg flasks with and without NGF (Angeletti et al., 2). In all these experiments, carried out for a 3-hour period, there was a marked increase in the oxidation of 1-C-glucose and only slight increase in the yield of CO_2 from 6-C-glucose. These experiments, performed at first with intact ganglia, were then repeated with a suspension of cells obtained after trypsinization of the ganglia (Table 7.1). In a second set of experiments the in vivo effect of NGF on glucose utilization was studied. The NGF was injected in newborn mice 12 to 24 hours before sacrifice. The ganglia were then dissected out and incubated in a Warburg flask with labeled glucose. Here again, the oxidation of glucose-1-C^{14} was significantly increased, thus suggesting an influence of NGF on the hexosemonophosphate pathway. Control experiments with different nervous tissue known not to be responsive to NGF did not show any change in glucose metabolism. Since it is generally believed that the oxidation of 6-C-glucose reflects mainly the activity of the glycolytic pathway, while the oxidation of 1-C-glucose is due to the activity of both this pathway and of the hexosemonophosphate shunt (Horecker, 12), we tested in our experimental material the effect of glycolytic inhibitors on glucose oxidation. Addition of NaF to the medium at a concentration of $10^{-2} M$ causes a strong inhibition of the utilization of 6-C-glucose, but only a slight inhibition of 1-C-glucose (Fig. 7.1). These findings are in line with previous observations on sensory ganglia explanted in semisolid medium, where the addition of fluoride, while inhibiting the growth of fibroblasts, would enhance the nerve fiber outgrowth elicited by NGF (Cohen, 5).

NGF Effect on Lipid Bio-synthesis in Sensory and Sympathetic Ganglia

The effect of the NGF on lipid synthesis was investigated by studying the incorporation of labeled acetate into lipids by sympathetic and sensory ganglia explanted in vitro and incubated in the presence or absence of NGF (Angeletti et al., 1). Pools of contralateral sensory ganglia from 8-day chick embryos, or pools of six superior cervical ganglia from newborn mice were incubated in Maximow dishes

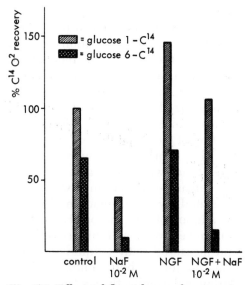

Fig. 7.1 Effect of fluoride on glucose oxidation to CO_2 by sensory ganglia incubated with and without NGF. (Reproduced from Angeletti et al., *Biochim. Biophys. Acta* 90:445–450, 1964.)

containing 1 ml of Eagle medium added with $1\text{-}C^{14}$-acetate (1 μc/ml). The incubation was carried out for various lengths of time in a CO_2-conditioned

TABLE 7.1   Metabolism of $1\text{-}C^{14}$- and $6\text{-}C^{14}$-glucose to CO_2 by Cell Suspensions from Sympathetic Ganglia, Sensory Ganglia, Brain, and Medulla of Chick Embryos[a]

SUSPENSION	MEDIUM	$C^{14}O_2$ FROM $1\text{-}C^{14}$-GLUCOSE	$C^{14}O_2$ FROM $6\text{-}C^{14}$-GLUCOSE	$1\text{-}C^{14}$-GLUCOSE/ $6\text{-}C^{14}$-GLUCOSE
Sympathetic cells	Control	1464	1008	1.4
	+ NGF	1870	1050	1.8
	Control	882	624	1.4
	+ NGF	1140	700	1.6
	Control	720	460	1.5
	+ NGF	1098	510	2.0
Sensory cells	Control	3120	2350	1.4
	+ NGF	3870	2170	1.8
	Control	2640	1594	1.6
	+ NGF	3300	1440	2.3
	Control	1945	1660	1.2
	+ NGF	2625	1840	1.5
Medulla cells	Control	1134	794	1.4
	+ NGF	1082	720	1.5
Brain cells	Control	1236	770	2.1
	+ NGF	1128	680	1.95

[a] Incubation 3 hours, temperature 37° C.

incubator at 37° C. The NGF extracted and purified with the usual procedure was added at concentration of 0.05 μg/ml. At the end of the incubation, the ganglia were removed and washed several times with cold acetate, then homogenized in 0.5 ml of a chloroform–ethanol mixture (2 : 1) for the extraction of the total lipids (Folch et al., 8). The homogenates were washed three times with saline and each time the ethanol–chloroform extract was separated by centrifugation. Finally, an aliquot of the radioactive extract was mixed with a liquid scintillator and measured with a liquid scintillation counter. In both control and experimental ganglia, the acetate-C^{14} was actively incorporated into total lipid and the rates of incorporation were found to be linear within the first hours. The addition of NGF to the medium greatly increased the rate of acetate incorporation in both sympathetic and sensory ganglia. It was significantly increased after 2 hours of incubation, and at the fourth hour it was more than 50 percent above the control values (Fig. 7.2, Table 7.2). In all these experiments the NGF concentration in the medium was 0.05 μg/ml. In tissue culture of explanted ganglia this dose calls forth a dense halo of nerve fiber outgrowth within 6–8 hours after the

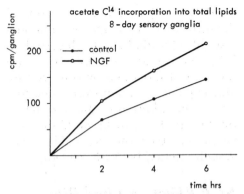

Fig. 7.2 NGF effect on acetate-C^{14} incorporation into total lipids of 8-day sensory ganglia. Experimental conditions as described in the text. (Reproduced from Angeletti et al., *Biochim. Biophys. Acta* 84:778–781, 1964.)

beginning of incubation. As reported elsewhere, with higher concentrations of NGF (10–100 times higher) the nerve fiber outgrowth does not take place (Levi-Montalcini, 16); the reason for this lack of effect is still unexplained. Experiments on acetate incorporation performed with different doses of NGF show that the rate of incorporation of labeled acetate into mixed lipids increases only at an optimal concentration of NGF (0.1–0.05 μg/ml). Lower or higher doses have no effect. The mechanism whereby the stimulation of lipid biosynthesis in ganglia treated with NGF takes place

TABLE 7.2   Incorporation of Acetate-C^{14} into Lipids by Superior Cervical Ganglia of Newborn Mice (2-day-old). Pool of 4 Ganglia Incubated in Eagle Medium plus Acetate-C^{14} (1 μc/ml)[a]

EXPERIMENT	TIME (HRS.)	RADIOACTIVITY INTO LIPID EXTRACT CPM
Control	4	1440
Exper.		2460
Control	4	1920
Exper.		2670
Control	6	2520
Exper.		3900

[a] Reproduced from Angeletti et al., *Biochem. Biophys. Acta* 90:445, 1964.

is a matter for further investigation. In this connection, it is of interest that NGF increases glucose utilization through a direct oxidative pathway, which according to some reports is activated in certain tissues during lipogenesis (Glock, McLean, and Whitehead, 10). Furthermore, it has been demonstrated that TPNH is a necessary co-factor in the reductive synthesis of fatty acids (Lynen, 26). It is attractive, in view of these findings, to consider the two metabolic changes induced by NGF in nerve cells as reciprocally correlated. To investigate this point further, the effect of a strong oxidizing agent such as methylene blue on both acetate incorporation and glucose metabolism was investigated in our experimental system. It was possible to show that methylene blue increases glucose metabolism through the hexose shunt by serving as hydrogen acceptor oxidizing TPNH formed by triphosphopyridine nucleotide (TPN). If TPNH is required for fatty acid synthesis, then the oxidation of TPNH by methylene blue should decrease the rate of lipid synthesis. In some preliminary experiments, in fact, addition of methylene blue (10^{-4} M) to the incubation medium effectively reduces acetate incorporation in control and experimental ganglia, while the oxidation of glucose-C^{14} is enhanced.

NGF Effect on Protein Synthesis

This effect was investigated by studying the incorporation rate of labeled amino acids into protein by sympathetic and embryonic sensory ganglia (Angeletti et al., 3). The ganglia were incubated in basal Eagle medium supplemented with L-leucine-C^{14} and L-threonine-C^{14}. The NGF was added to the medium at an effective concentra-

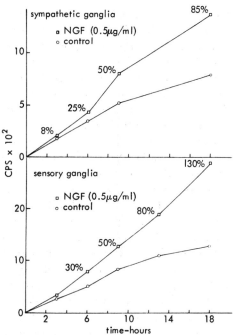

Fig. 7.3 NGF effect on amino acid incorporation (L-leucine-C^{14} and L-threonine-C^{14}) by sensory and sympathetic ganglia incubated in basal Eagle medium. (Reproduced from Angeletti et al., *Biochim. Biophys. Acta* 95:111–120, 1965.)

tion of 0.05 μg/ml. The rate of incorporation was found to be linear during the first 6–8 hours. The addition of NGF stimulated an incorporation of labeled amino acids into protein which was more than 30 percent above control values after 6 hours of incubation. The results are shown in Figure 7.3. In some experiments, the NGF was injected into newborn mice (30 μg/g of body weight) 12 hours before sacrifice. The superior cervical ganglia were then rapidly removed and incubated in the radioactive medium. Also in these circumstances there was marked stimulation of isotope incorporation into ganglia from NGF-treated mice. Control experiments carried out with other tissues (brain, spinal cord, sensory ganglia from 14-day chick embryos) showed no effect of the nerve growth factor on incorporation of amino acid.

The possibility that the increased rate of amino acid incorporation into protein might be due to the effect of the NGF on amino acid transport across the membrane was next explored. There is, in fact, evidence that some hormones (growth hormone and insulin in muscle, estrogen in uterus) produce a parallel increase of intracellular amino acid concentration and of amino acid incorporation into protein (Manchester and Young, 27; Mueller et al., 28). In our system the problem was investigated by studying the effect of NGF on the accumulation of a non-metabolized amino acid (α-aminoisobutyric acid) in sensory and sympathetic ganglia in vitro. The ganglia were incubated in Krebs Ringer buffer and in Eagle medium containing α-aminoisobutyric acid-1-C^{14}; the NGF was added at concentrations ranging from 0.5 to 0.05 μg/ml. Incubation was carried out for various lengths of time,

then the ganglia were quickly removed, washed three times in saline solution, and finally homogenized in cold trichloroacetic acid. The radioactivity was then counted on trichloroacetic acid extracts and in samples of the incubation media. Parallel experiments were performed with leucine-C^{14} to check the NGF effect on amino acid incorporation into protein. As can be seen from Figure 7.4, the NGF had no effect on accumulation of α-amino-isobutyric acid within the ganglia, whereas it effectively increased the incorporation of leucine into protein. At variance with other hormonal effects, then, NGF does not seem to influence primarily the mechanism of membrane transport. Therefore, the stimulation of protein synthesis in the ganglia cannot be attributed to an increased availability of intracellular substrate.

The effect of NGF on intracellular protein turnover was investigated by measuring the rate of disappearance of

SUPERIOR CERVICAL GANGLIA

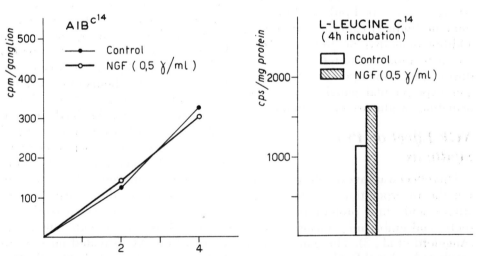

Fig. 7.4 NGF effect on α-aminoisobutyric acid-C^{14} accumulation into superior cervical ganglia and on L-leucine-C^{14} incorporation into proteins of the same ganglia. Experimental conditions as described in the text.

radioactivity in ganglia preincubated in hot medium for a short time and transferred to a cold medium with or without addition of a chaser. It appears that increase in protein synthesis under NGF stimulation is accompanied by an increase in protein turnover.

Effect of NGF on RNA Synthesis

When sensory ganglia are incubated in Eagle medium containing uridine-H^3, the NGF results in a marked increase of uridine incorporation (Toschi et al., 30). Five hours later, the incorporation of uridine into the treated ganglia exceeds that of control ganglia by more than 100 percent. Figure 7.5 shows the relative amount of protein

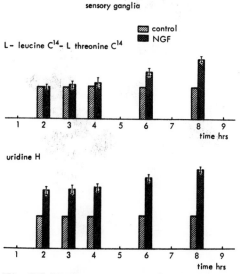

Fig. 7.5 Time sequences of NGF-stimulated acceleration of protein (top) and RNA (bottom) synthesis in 8-day chick embryo sensory ganglia. Incubation in Eagle basal medium added with L-leucine-C^{14}, L-threonine-C^{14} (2 μc/ml), or with uridine-H^3 (10 μc/ml). Results expressed as percent of the control values. (Reproduced from Angeletti et al., *Biochim. Biophys. Acta* 95:111–120, 1965.)

and RNA labeled in sensory ganglia incubated with or without NGF. The rise in uridine-H^3 labeling of RNA in the treated ganglia precedes the increase in amino acid incorporation.

In order to gain more information on stimulation by the NGF on RNA synthesis, pulse-labeling experiments were performed for various lengths of time. In a typical experiment, sensory ganglia were incubated for 4 hours with NGF and then exposed to uridine-H^3 for 60 minutes. The RNA was then extracted and analyzed by sucrose gradient. Preliminary data indicate that rapidly labeled RNA is rather heterogenous with a predominance of heavy components. Radioautographic controls demonstrate that the nuclei of nerve cells treated with NGF are much more heavily labeled than nuclei of control cells (Fig. 7.6).

Effects of Specific Metabolic Inhibitors

The possibility that NGF stimulates protein synthesis by regulating the rate of an RNA functionally similar to the messenger-RNA described in bacterial systems was explored by using some specific metabolic inhibitors. Puromycin, known to inhibit protein synthesis at the ribosomal level, added to the culture medium at a concentration of 20 μg/ml, suppressed amino acid incorporation in both control and experimental ganglia. Uridine incorporation, however, was only slightly reduced (to 70 percent of normal values). Under these conditions, the NGF stimulation of RNA synthesis was still clearly evident. After 6 hours of incubation in presence of the inhibitor, the ratio of radioactivity incorporated into treated ganglia and controls was 2:1.

In order to test whether or not complete suppression of protein synthesis would prevent the NGF effect on RNA synthesis, puromycin (40 μg/ml) was added to the medium 30 minutes before the addition of NGF; the ganglia were incubated for 4 hours and then exposed for 60 minutes to labeled uridine. The results of these experiments are shown in Figure 7.7 which indicates that: (1) Inhibition of protein synthesis at the ribosomal level does not prevent the NGF effect on the synthesis of RNA. (2) This effect is not mediated by *de novo* synthesis of some protein molecules in the cell.

Actinomycin-D, a powerful inhibitor of DNA-primed RNA synthesis, at a concentration of 1 μg/ml in our system, was found to reduce uridine incorporation to 10–15 percent of normal values in both control and experimental ganglia. Protein synthesis was only slightly inhibited in both control and experimental ganglia but the NGF stimulation of amino acid incorporation was completely abolished (Fig. 7.8). These findings give support to the hypothesis that the primary action of NGF is at the nuclear level, at a step which involves new synthesis of DNA-primed RNA.

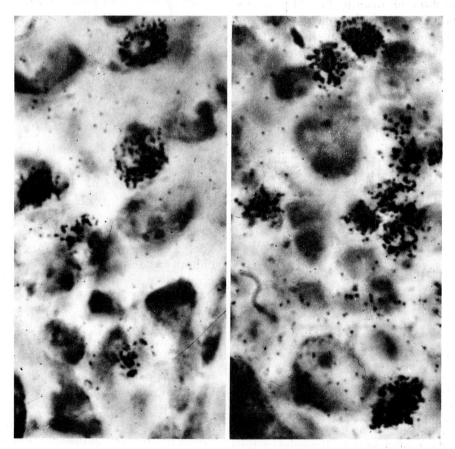

Fig. 7.6 Radioautography of 8-day sensory ganglia incubated for 2 hours in Eagle medium added with uridine-H³ (1 μc/ml) and NGF (0.05 μg/ml).

Additional evidence was gained in experiments where sensory ganglia were incubated with or without NGF for a 4-hour period and then transferred to a medium with radioactive amino acids containing actinomycin-D for 4 more hours. Under these conditions, there was a clear-cut stimulation of amino acid incorporation into treated ganglia. A conceivable explanation of these results is that preincubation with NGF would call forth an increased synthesis of RNA which, in turn, is reflected in a stimulation of protein synthesis.

Discussion

An attempt is made in the present paper to correlate the nerve growth effect, investigated in the past mainly at

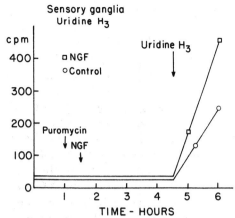

Fig. 7.7 Effect of puromycin (40 μg/ml) on the NGF stimulation of uridine incorporation in sensory ganglia. The inhibitor was added to the medium 30 minutes before the addition of NGF (0.05 μg/ml). Uridine-H[3] added at arrow. (Reproduced from Angeletti et al., *Biochim. Biophys. Acta* 95:111–120, 1965.)

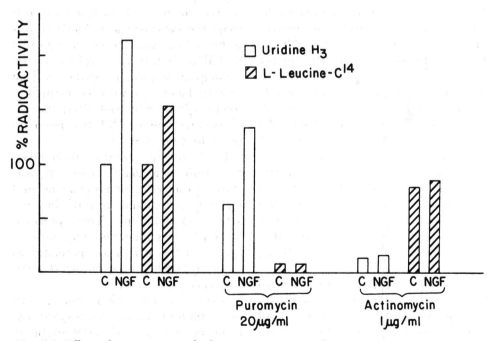

Fig. 7.8 Effect of puromycin and of actinomycin on uridine-H[3] and on L-leucine-C[14] incorporation by 8-day sensory ganglia incubated in Eagle medium with and without NGF. Results expressed as percent of control values. (Reproduced from Angeletti et al., *Biochim. Biophys. Acta* 95:111–120, 1965.)

a morphological level, with measurable effects on various metabolic pathways. The analysis of these effects and of their temporal sequence is a prerequisite to an understanding of its mechanism of action. The data gathered so far, although not complete, allow some considerations of the metabolic changes induced by the NGF, and suggest some working hypotheses amenable to experimental testing.

We shall first consider the NGF effect on protein metabolism in receptive nerve cells, since the problem of protein synthesis holds a key position in any attempt to explain growth and its regulation.

Evidence has been presented that the addition of very minute amounts of NGF to sensory or sympathetic ganglia cultured in liquid media increases the incorporation of amino acids into protein and apparently also increases the rate of protein turnover. The experiments on α-aminoisobutyric acid transport in our system indicate that the initial step in protein synthesis, the transfer of amino acids from extracellular to intracellular compartments, is not affected by the NGF, thus ruling out a primary NGF effect on amino acid transport across the cell membrane. Pertinent in this connection are the recent observations that the kinetics of incorporation of amino acids into protein are not dependent upon the rate at which amino acids enter the intracellular pool (Kipnis et al., 14; Segal, 29).

The experiments reported herein have not answered the question as to the specific site in the machinery of protein synthesis at which the NGF action is exerted. However, if one compares the lag preceding the increase in the rate of amino acid incorporation to the immediate stimulation in RNA synthesis, it would appear that NGF stimulates the production of an essential component of the cell synthetic system (m-RNA) rather than activating pre-existing cell components. Experiments with specific inhibitors lend support to this hypothesis. Actinomycin-D, in fact known to inhibit DNA-primed RNA synthesis, entirely abolishes the NGF effect on amino acid incorporation. Puromycin on the other hand, although suppressing protein synthesis, does not prevent the initial NGF stimulation of RNA synthesis.

The above considerations are obviously in the frame of currently accepted models suggested for the genetic control of protein synthesis in bacteria (Jacob and Monod, 13). Although definite evidence is still lacking that the rapidly synthesized RNA in the nucleus of mammalian cells plays the same role as in bacteria, it is difficult to escape the conclusion that this RNA is directly involved in the regulation of protein synthesis. That growth factors as well as some hormones might act by controlling the rate of synthesis of m-RNA has been repeatedly proposed.

Ecdysone, the hormone produced by the prothoracic gland in insects, was shown to activate certain gene loci and elicit the appearance of puffs in large salivary chromosomes. These puffs exhibit a high synthetic activity with respect to RNA, which seems related to enhanced protein biosynthesis (Clever and Karlson, 4; Gall, 9).

Insulin, besides other effects, stimulates both RNA and protein synthesis. It has been suggested that it might act by controlling the synthesis of some messenger-RNA (Wool and Munro, 31). Recently, however, it has been shown that the insulin effect on protein synthesis can be dissociated from its effect on RNA synthesis, since actinomycin-D abolishes the latter, leaving the former unaffected (Eboué-Bouis et al., 7).

The sequence of RNA and protein synthesis during early estrogen action has been the object of several investigations. It has been shown that many of the responses of the uterus to estrogen, including the striking increase of RNA synthesis, are blocked by prior puromycin treatment (Mueller et al., 28; Hamilton, 11). The hypothesis has been advanced that the primary effect of estrogen might be an increased synthesis of RNA polymerase (28). At variance with these findings, the stimulation of RNA synthesis by NGF in the responsive nerve cells is apparently not dependent upon a previous stimulation of protein synthesis.

In suggesting the stimulation of nuclear RNA synthesis as the site of action of NGF, we leave unanswered the question of how this stimulation takes place. Since the NGF is normally present in responsive nerve cells and has proved to be essential to their survival, it can be inferred that it is part of a basic growth control mechanism of these cells.

When, under experimental conditions, larger concentrations of the NGF are suddenly made available to these cells, they are brought to an excited state in which all anabolic processes are stimulated to their maximal rate. The increased rate of protein and lipid synthesis, as well as the enhanced carbohydrate utilization, reflects this shift in cell homeostasis, which ultimately results in the remarkable cellular overgrowth which we have described.

References

1. Angeletti, P. U., A. Liuzzi, and R. Levi-Montalcini, "Stimulation of Lipid Synthesis in Sensory and Sympathetic Ganglia by a Specific Nerve Growth Factor," *Biochim. Biophys. Acta* 84:778–781 (1964).
2. ——, ——, ——, and D. Gandini-Attardi, "Effect of a Nerve Growth Factor on Glucose Metabolism by Sympathetic and Sensory Nerve Cells," *Biochim. Biophys. Acta* 90:445–450 (1964).
3. ——, D. Gandini-Attardi, G. Toschi, M. L. Salvi, and R. Levi-Montalcini, "Metabolic Aspects of the NGF Effect on Sympathetic and Sensory Ganglia: Protein and RNA Synthesis," *Biochim. Biophys. Acta* 95:111–120 (1965).
4. Clever, U., and P. Karlson, "Induktion von Puff-veränderungen in den Speicheldrüsenchromosomen von Chironomus tentans durch Ecdyson," *Exptl. Cell. Res.* 20:623–626 (1960).
5. Cohen, S., "Purification and Metabolic Effects of a Nerve-growth-promoting Protein from Snake Venom," *J. Biol. Chem.* 234:1129–1137 (1959).
6. ——, "Purification of a Nerve-growth-promoting Protein from the Mouse Salivary Gland and Its Neurocytotoxic Antiserum," *Proc. Natl. Acad. Sci. U. S.* 46:302–311 (1960).
7. Eboué-Bouis, D., A. M. Chambaut, P. Volfin, and H. Clauser, "Action of Insulin on the Isolated Rat Diaphragm in the Presence of Actinomycin-D and Puromycin," *Nature* 199:1183–1184 (1963).
8. Folch, J., M. Lees, and G. H. Sloane Stanley, "A Simple Method for the Isolation and Purification of Total Lipides from Animal Tissues," *J. Biol. Chem.* 226:497–509 (1957).
9. Gall, J. G., "Chromosomes and Cytodifferentiation," *Cytodifferentiation and Macromolecular Synthesis*, M. Locke, ed. New York: Academic Press, pp. 119–143 (1963).
10. Glock, G. E., P. McLean, and J. K. Whitehead, "Pathways of Glucose Utilization in the Mammary Gland of the Rat," *Biochim. Biophys. Acta* 19:546–547 (1956).
11. Hamilton, T. H., "Sequences of RNA

and Protein Synthesis during Early Estrogen Action," *Proc. Natl. Acad. Sci. U. S.* 51:83–89 (1964).

12. Horecker, B. L., "Interdependent Pathways of Carbohydrate Metabolism," *The Harvey Lectures*. New York: Academic Press, vol. 57, pp. 35–61 (1962).

13. Jacob, F., and J. Monod, "Genetic Regulatory Mechanisms in the Synthesis of Proteins," *J. Mol. Biol.* 3:318–356 (1961).

14. Kipnis, D. M., E. Reiss, and E. Helmreich, "Functional Heterogeneity of the Intracellular Amino Acid Pool in Mammalian Cells," *Biochim. Biophys. Acta* 51:519–524 (1961).

15. Levi-Montalcini, R., "Effects of Mouse Tumor Transplantation on the Nervous System," *Ann. N. Y. Acad. Sci.* 55:330–343 (1952).

16. ——, "Chemical Stimulation of Nerve Growth," *A Symposium on the Chemical Basis of Development*, W. D. McElroy and B. Glass, eds. Baltimore: The Johns Hopkins Press, pp. 645–665 (1958).

17. ——, "Analysis of a Specific Nerve Growth Factor and of Its Antiserum," *Sci. Rept. Ist. Super. Sanita* 2:345–368 (1962).

18. ——, "Growth Control of Nerve Cells by a Protein Factor and Its Antiserum," *Science* 143:105–110 (1964).

19. ——, and P. U. Angeletti, "Biological Properties of a Nerve Growth Promoting Protein and Its Antiserum," *Regional Neurochemistry*. London: Pergamon Press, pp. 362–377 (1960).

20. ——, and ——, "Growth Control of the Sympathetic System by a Specific Protein Factor," *Quart. Rev. Biol.* 36:99–108 (1961).

21. ——, and ——, "Essential Role of the Nerve Growth Factor in the Survival and Maintenance of Dissociated Sensory and Sympathetic Embryonic Nerve Cells *in vitro*," *Develop. Biol.* 7:653–659 (1963).

22. ——, and B. Booker, "Excessive Growth of the Sympathetic Ganglia Evoked by a Protein Isolated from Mouse Salivary Glands," *Proc. Natl. Acad. Sci. U. S.* 46:373–384 (1960).

23. ——, and S. Cohen, "Effects of the Extract of the Mouse Submaxillary Salivary Glands on the Sympathetic System of Mammals," *Ann. N. Y. Acad. Sci.* 85:324–341 (1960).

24. ——, and V. Hamburger, "A Diffusible Agent of Mouse Sarcoma, Producing Hyperplasia of Sympathetic Ganglia and Hyperneurotization of Viscera in the Chick Embryo," *J. Exptl. Zool.* 123:233–288 (1953).

25. ——, H. Meyer, and V. Hamburger, "*In vitro* Experiments on the Effect of Mouse Sarcomas 180 and 37 on the Spinal and Sympathetic Ganglia of the Chick Embryo," *Cancer Res.* 14:49–57 (1954).

26. Lynen, F., "Participation of Acyl-CoA in Carbon Chain Biosynthesis," *J. Cellular Comp. Physiol.* 54:33–43 (1959).

27. Manchester, K. L., and F. G. Young, "The Effect of Insulin on Incorporation of Amino Acids into Protein of Normal Rat Diaphragm *in vitro*," *Biochem. J.* 70:353–358 (1958).

28. Mueller, G. C., J. Gorski, and Y. Aizawa, "The Role of Protein Synthesis in Early Estrogen Action," *Proc. Natl. Acad. Sci. U. S.* 47:164–169 (1961).

29. Segal, S., "Hormones, Amino Acid Transport and Protein Synthesis," *Nature* 203:17–19 (1964).

30. Toschi, G., D. Attardi-Gandini, and P. U. Angeletti, "Effect of a Specific Neuronal Growth Factor on RNA Metabolism by Sensory Ganglia from Chick Embryo," *Biochem. Biophys. Res. Commun.* 16:111–115 (1964).

31. Wool, J. G., and A. I. Munro, "An Influence of Insulin on the Synthesis of a Rapidly Labeled RNA by Isolated Rat Diaphragm," *Proc. Natl. Acad. Sci.* 50:918–923 (1963).

8

Cell Associations and Organogenesis in the Nervous System of Insects

VINCENT B. WIGGLESWORTH

Department of Zoology
University of Cambridge
Cambridge, England

In the developing embryo of the insect a neural groove forms along the midventral line shortly before the appearance of the stomodaeal and proctodaeal invaginations (Fig. 8.1). On each side of this groove a neural ridge develops and later gives rise to the paired nerve strands. The ectoderm in the region of the neural groove becomes two-layered; the outer layer is composed of ordinary ectodermal cells and the inner layer is composed of large nerve cells, or neuroblasts. At the same time, other cells separate from the ectoderm in the midventral line— that is, from the roof of the neural groove—to form a median nerve strand, the subsequent fate of which is controversial.

The neuroblasts in the lateral ridges proceed to divide repeatedly at right angles to the surface, so that each gives rise to a column of daughter cells, the future ganglion cells, more or less perpendicular to the ectoderm. When the germ band undergoes segmentation, the lateral nerve cords become constricted metamerically into segmental divisions which develop into the ganglia. Exaggeration of these changes at the anterior extremity of the embryo leads to the formation of the ganglia of the brain.

The ganglion cells give out axon processes, which extend from one ganglionic mass to the next to form the connectives, or which interlace in the dorsal region of the ganglia to form the neuropile. The dorsal limit of the neuropile is at first in direct contact with the yolk. Later it becomes covered by nerve cells and finally the whole system becomes invested by perineurium cells overlaid by a fibrous membrane, the neural lamella. The embryonic origin of this investing system is still a

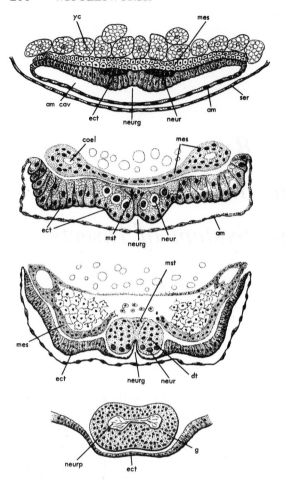

Fig. 8.1 Semi-diagrammatic cross sections of a generalized insect embryo showing four successive stages in the differentiation of an abdominal ganglion. am, amnion; am cav, amniotic cavity; coel, coelomic cavity; dt, daughter cells of the neuroblasts, which will become ganglion cells; ect, ectoderm; g, ganglion cells; mes, mesoderm; mst, median nerve strand; neur, neuroblasts; neurg, neural groove; neurp, neuropile; ser, serosa; yc, yolk cells. (Modified from Johannsen and Butt, *Embryology of Insects and Myriapods*, McGraw-Hill, 1941.)

subject of dispute (Johannsen and Butt, 3; Gouin, 2).

It is not my intention to present a detailed comparative account of these developmental processes, nor an analysis of the conflicting views that have been put forward about the source and movements of the different cellular components during embryonic development. I propose to deal with two matters only: (1) the differentiation and development of sensilla during postembryonic life; and (2) the organization of cells within the central nervous system, with special reference to the relations between neurones and glia.

Methods

The observations to be described have almost all been made with the light microscope. During recent years much has been learned about the fine structure of the insect nervous system by the use of the electron microscope, but there are many features of the system that are too large to be visible by this means. From the top of the Empire State Building it is easy to recognize the layout of the avenues and streets of New York City. But if one were furnished with a series of sections through New York City which could be examined only by means of a hand lens, it would be virtually impossible to recognize the existence of avenues and streets. Indeed, it would require an observant and industrious worker to recognize the important features of even a single building. On the other hand, the light microscopist must constantly use the findings of electronmicroscopy as a background for his thinking.

Fixation and Staining: The Osmium–Ethyl Gallate Method

By far the greater part of light microscopy has been done on tissues hardened with acid fixatives. As was shown by my teacher William Bate Hardy during the last century, and as has been amply confirmed by the electron microscope, the disruption of the cytoplasm by fixatives of this type is such as to make the examination of its structure a complete waste of time, even with the light microscope. From this same time it has been recognized that osmium tetroxide will give excellent preservation of cytoplasmic structure, but its slow rate of penetration, combined with the failure of the tissues to take up the common histological stains after osmium fixation, has greatly restricted its use for purposes of general histology.

Osmium tetroxide has two effects on living tissues: (1) It leads instantly to the polymerization and hardening of unsaturated lipids, with the simultaneous reduction and binding of the osmium. (2) The osmium tetroxide is reduced by free amino, imino, and sulfhydryl groups in protein. The reduced osmium becomes bound, or at least insoluble, at the site of the reaction, but it will still react with ethyl gallate to give an intense blue-black coloration.

In this way the reduced osmium can be visualized for the light microscope. And since a large part of the image obtained with the electron microscope is produced by the scattering of electrons by bound osmium, the cellular picture that results is closely similar to a low-power electronmicrograph (Wigglesworth, 10).

The most abundant reactive groups in the living cell are usually the ethylenic double bonds in the lipids. To a large extent, the resulting picture can be described as a microscopy based on lipids. It reveals lipid droplets, plasma and nuclear membranes, nucleoli, mitochondria and Golgi bodies, myelin, and so on (Wigglesworth, 10). It also stains concentrations of proteins that are rich in basic groups, notably the hemaglobin in the erythrocytes (containing histidine), connective tissue (containing proline), and neurosecretory deposits (containing cysteine). The strongly basic histones that are concentrated in the chromosomes and in the ribosomes fail to react. That is because their reactive groups are masked by combination with the phosphoric acid residues in the nucleic acids. If the living cells are exposed to weak acids ($0.001\ M$ acetic acid, or saturated carbon dioxide), the histones can be unmasked and caused to react with osmium. In this way it is possible to obtain good nuclear staining in tissues in which there is also good cytoplasmic fixation—a result that has not been obtainable in the past (Wigglesworth, 19).

These methods have been applied to the nervous system of insects in two ways: (1) The isolated integument is fixed and stained and is then examined as a whole mount from the inner surface. It is easy to work on such material with the oil immersion objective. (2) The ganglia are fixed with buffered osmium tetroxide, stained in bulk with ethyl gallate, embedded in agar and ester wax, and sections cut on a film of water on a cover slip at 0.5–2 μ (Wigglesworth, 14).

Postembryonic Development of Sense Organs

The sense organs of insects are, for the most part, made up of independent sensilla. Each sensillum is furnished with its own sense cell, or group of sense cells, which are located peripherally in close association with the epidermis. These sense cells are generally accepted as being primary sense cells with axons running directly to the central nervous system. In the course of postembryonic development, new sensilla are differentiated from the ordinary epidermal cells. They represent one of several potential lines of development that are latent within the epidermal cell. In this respect the epidermal cell is an embryonic cell and its developmental potentialities provide a model of embryogenesis that is accessible to experimental study (Wigglesworth, 15, 18).

Determination of Sensilla

In the blood-sucking bug *Rhodnius*, apart from remaining as an ordinary member of the epidermis, the epidermal cell may develop into a pair of oenocytes (special secretory cells concerned in the formation of the new cuticle), a four-celled dermal gland (which secretes the protective cement

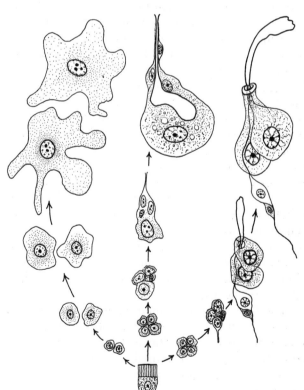

Fig. 8.2 Three lines of differentiation in the epidermal cells of *Rhodnius* during postembryonic development. Left: Oenocytes. Middle: Dermal gland. Right: Tactile sensillum.

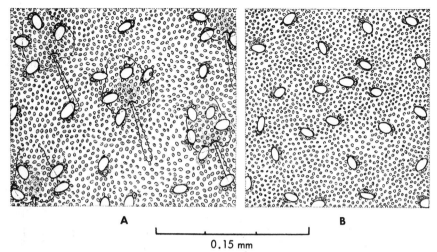

Fig. 8.3 Integument of *Rhodnius* viewed from the inner surface. *A*. Normal integument showing distribution of sensory hairs and distended dermal glands. *B*. At the first molt after the repair of a burn; only dermal glands have been regenerated.

over the surface of the new cuticle), or a four-celled sensillum, shown in Figure 8.2 (Wigglesworth, 15).

There are various factors concerned in this process of determination. An obvious one is the mutual separation of the existing sensilla. Each sensillum clearly exerts an inhibitory influence which prevents the appearance of a new sensillum in its immediate vicinity. It was suggested many years ago that some essential factor may be required to activate that part of the gene system in the epidermal cell that will lead to sensillum formation and that existing sensilla during their renewed development at molting drain off this factor from a surrounding zone and thus prevent the emergence of new sensilla for a certain distance around them (Wigglesworth, 8). At each molt, new sensilla appear at those points where the existing sensilla are most widely separated.

After an area of the epidermis has been killed by burning, the new epi-

dermis formed during repair does not give rise to any sensilla at the following molt (they appear only at the molt after that). But it does give rise to dermal glands, which are much more numerous and less widely spaced than the sensilla (Fig. 8.3). It was therefore suggested that perhaps the same factor may be required for the determination of dermal glands as for sensilla, but at a lower concentration or in smaller quantity (Wigglesworth, 9).

Differentiation and Development of the Sensilla

The earliest stage in the differentiation of a tactile hair that is detectable in *Rhodnius* is when there are four apparently similar cells with small nuclei (Fig. 8.2). In the course of a few days, two of these cells become very large and provide the trichogen cell that forms the hair and the tormogen cell that forms the socket; one cell becomes the sense cell that gives off a dendrite that is attached to the base of

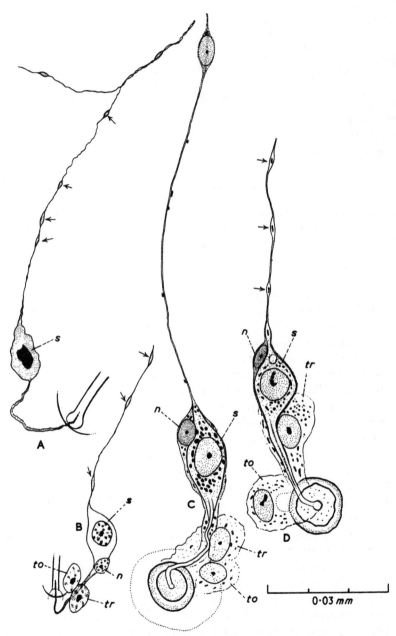

Fig. 8.4 Sensilla on the abdomen of *Rhodnius* drawn from whole mounts. A. Tactile hair (methylene blue stain). *B*. Tactile hair (Romanes's silver method stain). *C.,D.* Campaniform organs (osmium–ethyl gallate stain). n, neurilemma cell; s, sense cell; to, tormogen cell; tr, trichogen cell. Arrows indicate fusiform enlargements of the sensory axon; in *D* these contain mitochondria.

the hair, and an axon that grows inward. The axon continues to grow until it meets the axon from another sensillum and it accompanies this through the basement membrane to join a sensory nerve, which it follows to the central nervous system. The fourth cell, the neurilemma cell, has a small darkly staining nucleus; it is closely applied to the sense cell (Wigglesworth, 9).

It was shown by Clever (1) that in the wings of *Galleria* the formation of the sensory bristle by the trichogen cell requires the presence of the sense cell. The sense cell can be selectively killed by the injection of methylene blue into the living insect, and then the bristle fails to develop.

Preparations of sensilla stained with osmium and ethyl gallate are in some respects more informative. They show that the sense cells contain numerous mitochondria and that the fusiform dilatations of the fine axons, which can commonly be seen in methylene blue or silver-stained preparations, are indeed enlargements of the axon at points where a mitochondrion is present, shown in Figure 8.4D (Wigglesworth, 12). These mitochondria have presumably passed along the axon from the cell body. The axon resembles a snake that has swallowed a frog.

Neurilemma Cells and Schwann Cells

One feature observable in the osmium–ethyl gallate preparations is that the cytoplasm from the neurilemma cell spreads as a thin sheath containing mitochondria over the entire surface of the sense cell (Fig. 8.4 C). This sheath can be traced a short distance in the opposite direction along the axon and the presence of occasional mitochondria adherent to the surface of the axon probably indicates that the sheath accompanies the axon throughout its length (Wigglesworth, 12).

It was inferred from these observations that the sense cell and its axon are completely ensheathed and insulated by the neurilemma. That has been borne out by the study of insect nerves with the electron microscope. It has been shown by Osborne (6) that the dendrites of sense cells supplying the stretch receptors are completely ensheathed and only the extreme tip of the dendrite, where it ends in the substance of the connective tissue strand,

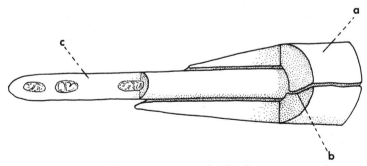

Fig. 8.5 Schematic figure of the termination of a dendrite in a stretch receptor of *Periplaneta*. a, Schwann cells; b, mesaxon; c, freely exposed tip of the dendrite with mitochondria. (After Osborne, *J. Ins. Physiol.* 9:237–245, 1963.)

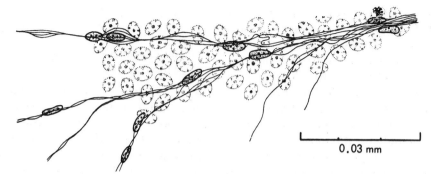

Fig. 8.6 Axons between the epidermis and basement membrane in *Rhodnius* coming together to form a small nerve, showing numerous elongated Schwann cell nuclei.

is freely exposed (Fig. 8.5). It is suggested that the effective stimulus is the compression of this exposed ending by tension on the stretch receptor (Osborne, 6).

The neurilemma cell is probably to be regarded as a Schwann cell. If the sensory axons are traced inward as they form small nerves, first between the epidermal cells and the basement membrane, and later in the body cavity, occasional Schwann cells, with just the same staining properties as the neurilemma cells, are to be seen among them (Fig. 8.6). In the larger nerves, Schwann cell nuclei are conspicuous both at the surface and deep in the interior. Their cytoplasm insinuates itself between the axons and insulates them from one another, as in Figure 8.7 (Wigglesworth, 12).

Transverse sections of the nerves as they approach the central nervous system show that the slender sensory axons, after traversing the entire length of a limb or of the abdomen, show the same local dilations containing mitochondria. One of the sensory axons will have a diameter of about 0.45 μ; where it contains a mitochondrion, the diameter is approximately doubled to 0.95 μ. These mitochondria have trav-

eled a long way from their peripheral sense cells (Wigglesworth, 12).

The question of what may be the source and origin of the Schwann cells in the remote peripheral nerves arises. Apart from the neurilemma cell of the sensillum, there is no evidence that they come from the epidermis. A study of the olfactory organ that develops in the pupa of the cabbage butterfly *Pieris rapae* was undertaken by Kim (4) from this point of view. He found, first of all, that a string of connective tissue cells, or hemocytes, is established as a framework extending from the nervous system to the palp. Then glial cells come down the connective tissue strand from the central nervous system, forming a pathway up which the nerve fibers from the sense cells of the palp can grow. It has recently been shown by Schoeller (7) that the development of innervated sensilla in the antennal rudiment of the blowfly *Calliphora* is dependent on the outgrowth of a nerve from the central nervous system and that a nerve from the abdominal ganglia is just as effective as a nerve from the brain. She supposes the outgrowth to be a motor nerve which exerts some undefined influence on differentiation. But it may be that, as in *Pieris*, the outgrowth is merely one of connective tissue and Schwann cells which provides a pathway for the ingrowing sensory axons.

Regeneration of Sensory Nerves

If the axons of sensory nerves are interrupted, as they run below the epidermal cells, by touching the cuticle of the body wall with a heated wire, it is possible to study the changes in the components of the sensillum during regeneration. Within a day or so after axon section the sense cells and their nuclei enlarge considerably and the cytoplasm comes to contain granules staining darkly with hematoxylin, presumably indicating increased formation of ribonucleic acid (Wigglesworth, 9). As seen after osmium – ethyl gallate staining, the nucleolus is much enlarged, the mitochondria are greatly increased in number and are streaming out into a dilated axon process, shown in Figure 8.8 (Wigglesworth, 12).

The outgrowing axon continues to extend, as in normal development, until it encounters another axon which it then accompanies. This may lead to a

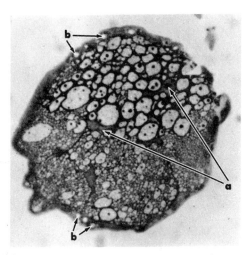

Fig. 8.7 Transverse section of nerve from a leg in *Rhodnius* shortly before entering the thoracic ganglion. Above: The large motor axons. Below: Mainly fine sensory axons. a, nuclei of Schwann cells; b, tracheal branches immediately below the neural lamella.

nerve and so to the central nervous system. But there is often much confusion in the regenerating tissues. The outgrowing axon may wander around until it makes contact with itself. It may then continue to grow indefinitely, forming a circular nerve which never gains connection with the central gan-

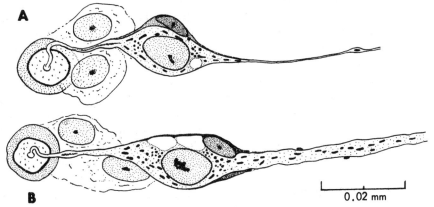

Fig. 8.8 Campaniform sensilla on the abdomen of *Rhodnius*. A. Normal uninjured structure. B. 4 days after the axon had been interrupted by burning.

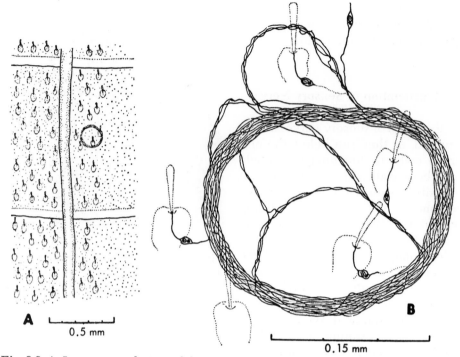

A └─────────────┘
     0.5 mm

0.15 mm

Fig. 8.9 *A.* Low-powered view of the integument of 4th-stage larva of *Rhodnius* after an extensive burn in the 3rd stage. The burned area lies to the right and is devoid of plaques and hairs. A small circular nerve lies just inside the unburned area. *B.* Detail of the circular nerve, showing the cell bodies from which it is derived.

glia, shown in Figure 8.9 (Wigglesworth, 9).

This attraction of the growing axon for another axon with which it remains in close association is a striking phenomenon. It probably reflects the tendency of Schwann cells not only to spread themselves indefinitely over the surface of the neurones, but to hold closely to one another. We shall see evidence of this same property within the central nervous system.

Histology of the Central Nervous System

Almost the whole of the extensive literature on the microscopic anatomy of the central nervous system in insects is concerned with the course of nerve tracks. Much less attention has been paid to the mutual relations between the cells—what might be regarded as the straight histology of the system. The osmium–ethyl gallate method has proved very informative in filling this gap, particularly when the conclusions are supplemented by electron microscope studies.

The most striking feature of the ganglia when prepared in this way is the intense staining of the central neuropile, as contrasted with the overlying ganglion cells. The axons, large and small, are almost completely unstained and appear as colorless threads with deeply staining mitochondria scattered along them, shown in Figures 8.10 and

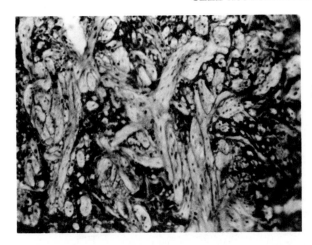

Fig. 8.10 Section (0.85 μ) of the neuropile in *Rhodnius* in a region with many large axons and dendrites showing mitochondria. Dark glial cytoplasm between also contains mitochondria.

8.14A (Wigglesworth, 13). There are differences in detail in different insects, particularly in respect to the glial cells, but the one constant feature is the ubiquity of the glial cytoplasm, which everywhere surrounds the cell bodies of the neurones and their axons and dendrites. Clearly, the glial system is of great physiological importance in the ganglia and nerves. I propose to consider the glial cells and other components of the nervous system under a series of functional headings.

Nutrition

The organs of insects are nearly all made up of single sheets of cells or quite small aggregations. The nerve ganglia are almost the only solid structures. They may be 3–4 mm³ or more in volume. They are enclosed in a fibrous collagenous sheath (the neural lamella) which may be 2 μ thick. They are penetrated by air-containing tracheae which provide for their respiratory needs, but there is no circulatory system within the ganglion and all nutrients and all waste products must be translocated from cell to cell (Wigglesworth, 16).

It is clear that the glial cells must play an essential part in nutrition. In most early figures of the glial cells, notably those of Cajal, they are pictured as spidery structures, rather like neurones giving out branching dendrites in every direction. It is obvious, however, from osmium–ethyl gallate preparations and from electronmicrographs, that their outgrowths are, in fact, flattened sheaths, continuous everywhere over the surface of the neurones and their processes.

It is convenient to regard the perineurium cells below the neural lamella as a specialized type of glial cell (Fig. 8.11, gl 1). In the cockroach *Periplaneta* these take up and store large quantities of glycogen, which serve as a nutritive reserve for the ganglion (Wigglesworth, 16).

A second type of glial cell resembles the Schwann cell of vertebrates; it provides a thick myelin sheath for a lateral group of motor axons (Fig. 8.11, gl 2). These are present in both *Rhodnius* (Wigglesworth, 13) and *Periplaneta* (Wigglesworth, 17).

In *Rhodnius*, a third type of glial cell is a giant cell with nucleus about 30 μ in length and with cytoplasm of indefinite extent, rich in mitochondria and

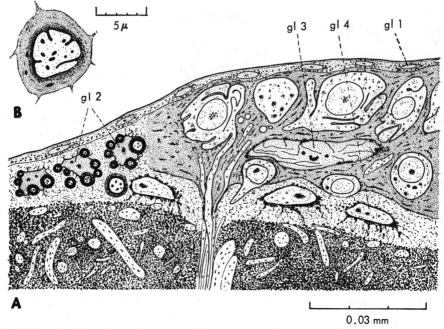

Fig. 8.11 A. Section through margin of thoracic ganglion in *Rhodnius* to show types of glial cell. gl 1, perineurium cells with neural lamella externally; gl 2, glial cell nuclei producing the myelin sheath for the lateral motor axons; gl 3, giant glial nucleus with invaginated membrane; gl 4, glial nuclei with cytoplasm investing the nerve fibers of the neuropile. *B*. Detail of myelinated motor axon with mitochondria and invaginations of the sheath.

other inclusions, spreading widely between the cell bodies in the cortex of the ganglion, shown in Figure 8.11, gl 3 (Wigglesworth, 13). In *Periplaneta*, giant cells of this kind are not present; their place is taken by a large number of cells of more moderate dimensions, shown in Figure 8.12,c (Wigglesworth, 16). But in both insects the plasma membrane of the larger ganglion cell is deeply invaginated so that extensions of the glia may reach almost to the nucleus. These glial extensions often contain mitochondria which properly belong to the glial cells (Fig. 8.13*B*). It is interesting that in the giant glial cells of *Rhodnius* similar invaginations are present in the large nucleus, as shown in Figure 8.11, gl 3

(Wigglesworth, 13). This system of invaginations, the so-called trophospongium of Holmgren, is clearly concerned in the nutrition of the large ganglion cells. They too accumulate glycogen, particularly in the axon cone (Wigglesworth, 16). In *Periplaneta*, these glial cells contain extensive intracellular cavities, which have been called the "glial lacunar system" Fig. 8.12,e), whose function is unclear (Wigglesworth, 16).

A fourth type of glial cell forms an investing sheath around the central neuropile (Fig. 8.11, gl 4). In *Rhodnius*, the nuclei of these cells are large (5–15 μ), but they appear at first sight to have almost no cytoplasm; there is only a thin covering of deeply staining

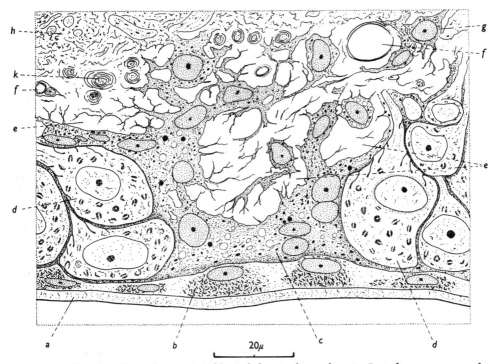

Fig. 8.12 Section through margin of last abdominal ganglion in *Periplaneta*. a, neural lamella; b, perineurium cells with massed mitochondria; c, outer glial cells investing the large ganglion cells; d, large ganglion cell with Golgi bodies; e, glial lacunar system with glial cell filaments; f, tracheae between ganglion cells and neuropile; g, inner glial cells applied to neuropile; h, neuropile; k, axons with concentric sheaths.

cytoplasm applied to the nucleus. But if a large number of these cells are studied, it becomes apparent that they have a very extensive cytoplasm extending far into the neuropile. It is, indeed, the staining of the plasma membranes and mitochondria and other inclusions of this extensive cytoplasm that is responsible for the intense staining of the neuropile. This has been amply confirmed with the electron microscope. The cytoplasmic extensions of this type 4 glial cell bear the same relation to the dendrites of the neuropile as the cytoplasm of the type 3 cell does to the cell bodies.

Nutrients can reach the neurons only by passage through the cytoplasm of these various glial cells. It is reasonable to suppose that they are being actively transported.

Energy Supply

It is generally supposed that the power supply of living tissues is provided by the mitochondria. Mitochondria are very evident in the perineurium cells, where they form great clumps between the deposits of glycogen (Fig. 8.12,b). They are plentiful also throughout the glial cytoplasm, even where this is invaginated into the body of the large ganglion cells (Fig. 8.13*B*) and throughout the neuropile.

Mitochondria are plentiful also in the cell body of the ganglion cell and can be seen passing into the axon. Presumably they originate within the cell body and are carried into the axon by the stream of axoplasm. In the large motor neurones in the thorax of *Rhodnius* the axon is at first relatively thin. But in the neuropile it enlarges to 4–5 μ. These large motor axons form two groups: a medial group in which the axons retain their thickness unchanged as they run out to the motor nerves (Fig. 8.13A, ma), and a lateral group (Fig. 8.13A, la), in which the axons show an abrupt funnellike constriction to a diameter of 1–1.5 μ as they leave the neuropile. This constriction is thickly myelinated, but it comes to an end as the nerve leaves the ganglion,

and the diameter increases again to 4 or 5 μ. It is interesting to note that at the point of constriction the axoplasm is always filled with a great quantity of globular mitochondria (Fig. 8.13A). It appears to represent a point of congestion as the mitochondria move down the axon (Wigglesworth, 13). More recently, a similar congestion of mitochondria has been produced experimentally by artificially damming mature myelinated vertebrate nerves (P. Weiss, personal communication).

The mitochondria farther down the motor nerves often occur in pairs, as though they had recently divided and occasionally they occur in chains (like bacteria) 20 μ in length, containing as

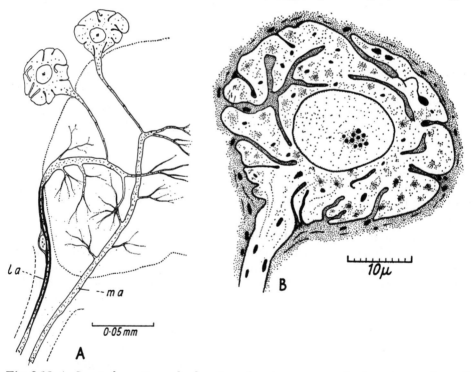

Fig. 8.13 *A.* Semischematic scale drawing of motor neurones in thoracic ganglion of *Rhodnius*. la, lateral motor axon with constricted myelinated segment; note accumulation of mitochondria above the constriction. ma, medial motor axon. The dotted lines mark the boundaries of the nerve and of the neuropile. *B.* Detail of motor ganglion cell, surrounded by glial cytoplasm, showing deep invaginations of the plasma membrane.

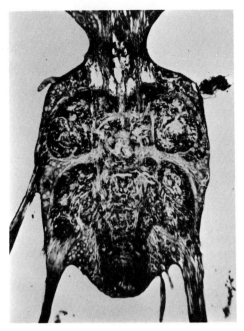 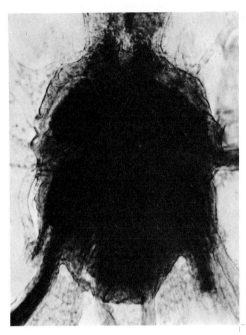

A   B

Fig. 8.14 *A.* Horizontal section of the fused meso- and metathoracic and abdominal ganglia in *Rhodnius* showing the darkly staining neuropile and unstained axons (osmium–ethyl gallate stain). *B.* Whole mount of ganglion showing cholinesterase confined to neuropile and nerve tracts (5-bromoindoxylacetate stain).

many as 25 mitochondria, which diminish progressively in size toward the extremities of the chain and appear to be incompletely separated from one another. These appearances give the impression that mitochondria may be multiplying in the axons themselves. Mitochondria occur also in dilatations of fine dendrites deep in the neuropile.

Oxygen Supply

In insects, in general, the richness of the tracheal supply runs parallel with the intensity of metabolism in the different tissues. It is not surprising that the perineurium cells, with their abundant mitochondria and their evident importance in metabolism, receive a plentiful supply of tracheoles. But the large ganglion cells are almost devoid of tracheal supply, although they have to secrete and maintain their long axons. There is a richer supply to the nerve tracts and the nerves (Fig. 8.7,b), but the richest tracheal supply is directed to the ring of glial cells around the neuropile and to the neuropile itself. This supports the conclusion that the glial system penetrating from the periphery throughout the neuropile is actively engaged in metabolism.

Cholinesterase

It has long been known that the ganglia of insects are exceptionally rich in acetylcholine. They also contain cholinesterase and other esterases. It has been shown that cholinesterase in the ganglia of *Rhodnius* is confined to the neuropile (Fig. 8.14*B*), if cholinesterase is defined as an enzyme hydrolyzing 5-bromoindoxyl acetate, but completely inhibited by $10^{-4} M$ eserine. The axons are completely negative in this test; the enzyme is interaxonal. It is most active in regions staining most deeply with osmium and ethyl gallate. These are the regions where the axons are finest and the interaxonal glial material most abundant (Wigglesworth, 11).

These dark-staining areas have been regarded (admittedly, without definite evidence) as the main synaptic regions, and it has therefore been supposed that cholinesterase is associated mainly with the synapses of the neuropile. It is always present, though less active, in the interaxonal glial substance of the intraganglionic nerve tracts and in the peripheral nerves. It is absent from the ganglion cells and from the neuromuscular junctions. The control of cholinesterase is clearly another function of the glial cells (Wigglesworth, 11).

Organization of Large Axons

The axons coming from the large ganglion cells in *Rhodnius* commonly have a ropelike appearance, as though composed of multiple strands, each about half a micron thick. Within the cell body, the strands spread out fanwise and become lost in the cytoplasm (Wigglesworth, 13). These fine strands correspond to the neurofibrils often described by histologists in fresh and silver-stained material. These strands have been studied in some detail in the ganglia of *Periplaneta* (Wigglesworth, 17).

The last abdominal ganglion in *Periplaneta* is the point of origin of giant axons which run the whole length of the nerve cord. Where the most massive of these axons (15–20 μ thick) cross over in the last abdominal ganglion, they are clearly made up of multiple colorless strands, about 0.5 μ thick, with mitochondria between (Fig. 8.15).

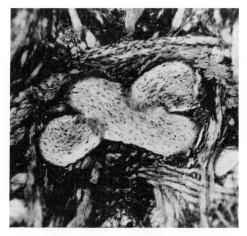

Fig. 8.15 Giant axons (about 20 μ diameter) crossing in the midline of the last abdominal segment in *Periplaneta*, showing neurofibrils and mitochondria.

All the large axons show this ropelike structure. Where they fan out into the cytoplasm of the large ganglion cells, the dark-staining material of the dictyosomes (Golgi bodies) can be seen applied to the individual strands (Fig. 8.17*B,C*). Wormlike colorless strands of the same dimensions can be seen in the cytoplasm of the ganglion cells (Fig. 8.16) and colorless strands of the same type can be detected running from the annular or horseshoelike dictyosomes, shown in Figure 8.17*A* (Wigglesworth, 17).

On the basis of these observations, it has been suggested that the dictyosomes provide the matrix for the individual neurofibrils which unite at the axon cone to form the axon (Fig. 8.18). Unfortunately these neurofibrils have no membranous walls which would

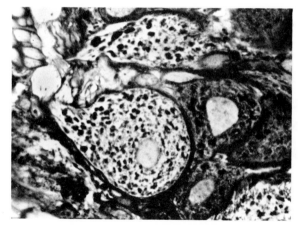

Fig. 8.16 Pale and dark ganglion cells in *Periplaneta* (osmium–ethyl gallate stain). The dark cell right of center shows pale wormlike canals (neurofibrils?) in the cytoplasm; the pale cell left of center shows dictyosomes oriented toward the axon.

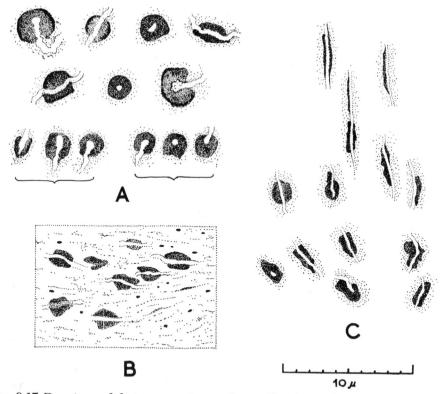

Fig. 8.17 Drawings of dictyosomes in ganglion cells of *Periplaneta* (osmium–ethyl gallate stain). They show the relation of the colorless neurofibrils to the darkly stained dictyosomes. The bracketed groups in *A* show single dictyosomes seen at three levels of focus. *B* shows a group of dictyosomes in the axon cone; the axon lies to the right. In *C*, the elongated dictyosomes above were in the axon cone of the cell; those below in the body of the cell.

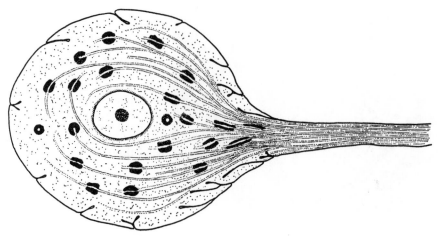

Fig. 8.18 Schematic drawing of ganglion cell showing glial invaginations and the suggested relation between dictyosomes and neurofibrils. (The "neurofibrils" of the light microscopist are not to be confused with the 100 A tubular "neurofilaments" seen with the electron microscope. There will be fifty or more neurofilaments in the cross section of one neurofibril.)

make them visible in the electron microscope. The large axon of a neurosecretory cell in the preoptic nucleus of the cod has been shown by Lederis (5) to have just the same ropelike structure when examined in section with the electron microscope, but no clear-cut boundaries to the structures responsible can be seen.

Summary

The differentiation and development of the peripheral sense organs and their subsequent union with the central nervous system provide a simple model of embryogenesis in the nervous system.

The insulation of the neurones at all levels (ganglion cell bodies, central dendrites, axons, and peripheral sense cells) is provided by ubiquitous glial and neurilemmal sheaths.

Evidence is described for a continuous outflow of substance from the cell bodies to the axons, including the passage of mitochondria. The universal investment of the neurones of the central nervous system by glial cytoplasm and its invagination into the large ganglion cells represents a specialized nutritional system.

Evidence (at present incomplete) that the oxygen supply to the ganglion is concentrated upon the glial cytoplasm is discussed. It is suggested that the glia may be undertaking some of the chief energy-consuming processes on behalf of the neurones.

In general, it would seem that, whereas the neurones are responsible for maintaining and operating the nervous system of communication, the glial cells are largely responsible for the physiological welfare of the neurones (nutrition, oxygen and energy supply, cholinesterase). There must be a very efficient system for the transportation of material by the glial cytoplasm. The neurosecretory system is not considered.

References

1. Clever, U., "Der Einfluss der Sinneszellen auf die Borstenentwicklung bei *Galleria mellonella*" L. *Arch. Entwicklungs mech. Or.* 151:137–159 (1960).

2. Gouin, F. J., "Morphologie und Entwicklungsgeschichte der Myriapoden und Insekten," *Fortschr. Zool.* 14:86–114 (1962).

3. Johannsen, O. A., and F. H. Butt, *Embryology of Insects and Myriapods.* New York: McGraw-Hill (1941).

4. Kim, Chang-Whan, "Development of the Chordotonal Organ, Olfactory Organ and Their Nerves in the Labial Palp in *Pieris napae* L," *Bull. Dept. Biol. Korea Univ.* 3:1–8 (1961).

5. Lederis, K., "Ultrastructure of the Hypothalamo-Neurohypophysial System in Teleost Fishes and Isolation of Hormone-containing Granules from Neurohypophysis of the Cod (*Gadus morrhua*)," *Z. Zellforsch.* 58:192–213 (1962).

6. Osborne, M. P., "An Electron Microscope Study of an Abdominal Stretch Receptor of the Cockroach," *J. Ins. Physiol.* 9:237–245 (1963).

7. Schoeller, J., "Recherches Descriptives et Expérimentales sur la céphalogenèse de *Calliphora erythrocephala* (Meigen) au Cours des Développements Embryonnaires et Postembryonnaires," *Arch. Zool. Exptl. Gen.* 103:1–216 (1956).

8. Wigglesworth, V. B., "Local and General Factors in the Development of Pattern in *Rhodnius prolixus* (Hemiptera)," *J. Exptl. Biol.* 17:180–200 (1940).

9. ——, "The Origin of the Sensory Neurones in an Insect *Rhodnius prolixus* (Hemiptera)," *Quart. J. Microscop. Sci.* 94:93–112 (1953).

10. ——, "The Use of Osmium in the Fixation and Staining of Tissues," *Proc. Roy. Soc. London Ser. B,* 147:185–99 (1957).

11. ——, "The Distribution of Esterase In the Nervous System and Other Tissues of the Insect *Rhodnius prolixus*," *Quart. J. Microscop. Sci.* 99:441–450 (1958).

12. ——, "The Histology of the Nervous System of an Insect, *Rhodnius prolixus* (Hemiptera). I. The Peripheral Nervous System," *Quart. J. Microscop. Sci.* 100: 285–298 (1959).

13. ——, "The Histology of the Nervous System of an Insect, *Rhodnius prolixus* (Hemiptera). II. The Central Ganglia," *Quart. J. Microscop. Sci.* 100:299–313 (1959).

14. ——, "A Simple Method for Cutting Sections in the 0.5 to 1μ Range, and for Sections of Chitin," *Quart. J. Microscop. Sci.* 100:315–320 (1959).

15. ——, *The Control of Growth and Form.* Ithaca, N.Y.: Cornell University Press (1959).

16. ——, "The Nutrition of the Central Nervous System in the Cockroach *Periplaneta americana* L. The Role of Perineurium and Glial Cells in the Mobilization of Reserves," *J. Exptl. Biol.* 37:500–512 (1960).

17. ——, "Axon Structure and the Dictyosomes (Golgi bodies) in the Neurones of the Cockroach, *Periplaneta americana*," *Quart. J. Microscop. Sci.* 101:381–388 (1960).

18. ——, "The Epidermal Cell," *The Cell and the Organism*, J. A. Ramsay and V. B. Wigglesworth, eds. London: Cambridge University Press, pp. 127–143 (1961).

19. ——, "The Union of Protein and Nucleic Acid in the Living Cell and Its Demonstration by Osmium Staining," *Quart. J. Microscop. Sci.* 105:113–122 (1964).

9

The Eye

ALFRED J. COULOMBRE

Laboratory of Neuroanatomical Sciences
National Institute of Neurological Diseases and Blindness
National Institutes of Health
Bethesda, Maryland

During the development of the vertebrate eye a large number of tissues (Fig. 9.1) assemble in such a manner that their size, shape, orientation, and relative positions meet the precise geometrical tolerances required by the optical function of this organ. The cells which make up these tissues are contributed by the ectoderm and mesoderm. They become highly specialized to fulfill the diverse functional requirements of the eye. For example, both the cellular and extracellular portions of the dioptric media (cornea, lens, vitreous body) become highly transparent. The intrinsic musculature of the eye (protractor lentis, retractor lentis or ciliary musculature) is appropriately oriented and attached to alter the position or shape of the lens and to focus the visual image in the plane of the retina. The outer tips of the visual cells are specialized to transform the light energy of these images into coded trains of nerve impulses. The neural retina, which is a peripherally developed portion of the central nervous system, develops a cytoarchitectural organization, enabling it to reorganize the output of the visual cells into a form suitable for transmission to the brain. It is important that the eye maintain constant shape during visual function. The scleral and corneal cells construct an outer eye wall which maintains its shape in the face of intraocular pressure and the pull of the extrinsic muscles.

Tissues are marshaled into the eye during development by a complex, but orderly, chain of interactions. Enough of the individual steps in the sequence are now known so that it is possible to construct a flow sheet (Fig. 9.2) that approximates the terminal steps in this chain of dependent events. While this morphogenetic flow sheet is necessarily incomplete and oversimplified, it will be of help as we explore the complex interactions among the tissues that build the eye. It also provides a rational basis for predicting and understanding the abnormalities which re-

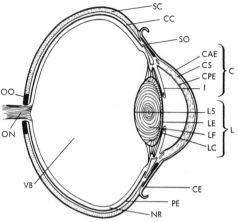

Fig. 9.1 Diagram of an axial section of the typical vertebrate eye. This is a composite of ocular features drawn from several vertebrate groups showing the relationships between the major structures in the eye. C, cornea; CAE, corneal anterior epithelium; CC, choroid coat; CE, conjunctival epithelium; CPE, corneal posterior epithelium; CS, corneal stroma; I, iris; L, lens; LC, lens capsule; LE, lens epithelium; LF, lens fibers; LS, lens suture; NR, neural retina; OO, os opticus; ON, optic nerve; PE, pigmented epithelium; SC, scleral cartilage; SO, scleral ossicle; VB, vitreous body.

sult if the chain is disturbed at one step or another. In developing the theme of ocular morphogenesis, the restrictions of space make it necessary to limit attention to the interactions among retina, lens, cornea, and sclera.

Retina

Each eye is represented early in development by an ectodermal region in the anterior blastodisc which will form part of the primitive diencephalic wall, as in Figure 9.3 (Woerdeman, 268; Adelmann, 2, 3; Mangold, 139, 140, 141; Alderman, 7; Nieuwkoop et al., 171; Jacobson, 106). Under the influence of the underlying archenteron roof and mesoderm this region becomes re-

stricted to the lateral retinal fields (Adelmann, 3, 4, 5; Mangold, 138, 141; Alderman, 7, 8; Mikami, 157; von Woellwarth, 267; Waechter, 252). The presumptive retina of these retinal fields is destined to play a dominant role in directing the step-by-step construction of the developing eye.

At, or shortly before, the time when the neural folds begin to meet in the midline, the presumptive retina begins to evaginate from the lateral diencephalic walls to form blind outpocketings, the optic vesicles (Fig. 9.3). While the mechanisms underlying evagination are not clearly understood, the regional pattern of mitosis and growth may, in part, be responsible. Following closure of the anterior neuropore, fluid accumulates in the brain ventricles (Weiss, 261; Coulombre and Coulombre, 41). Since the cavities of the optic vesicles are confluent with the ventricles, the pressure of the accumulating fluid contributes to the expansion of the vesicles (Chanturishvili, 33; Lopashov, 135).

The subsequent development of the vesicles depends on a complex of interactions with surrounding tissues. For instance, the immediately adjacent mesenchyme must be present for normal development (Holtfreter, 93; Lopashov, 135). Another necessary interaction occurs between the laterally expanding optic vesicles and the surface ectoderm (presumptive lens). When these tissues fail to contact one another, the tip of the optic vesicle (presumptive neural retina) tends to form pigmented epithelium instead of neural retina (Mikami, 156; Lopashov, 135). This interaction may be necessary before the neural retina can differentiate (Dragamirow, 63, 64, 66). Following contact, the optic vesicle in-

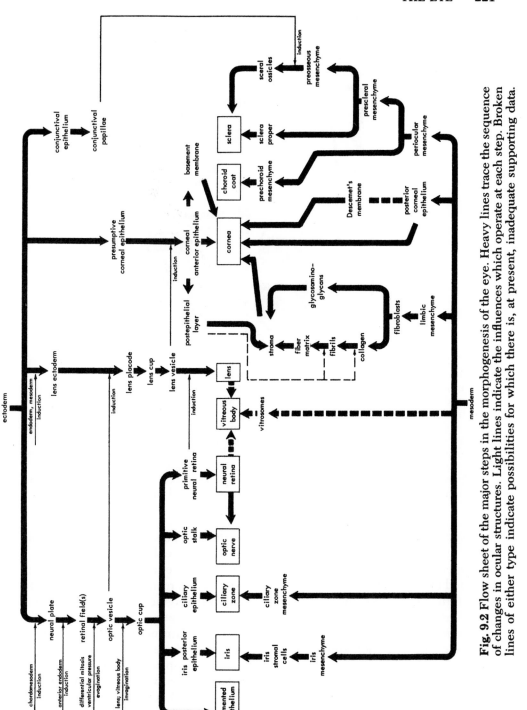

Fig. 9.2 Flow sheet of the major steps in the morphogenesis of the eye. Heavy lines trace the sequence of changes in ocular structures. Light lines indicate the influences which operate at each step. Broken lines of either type indicate possibilities for which there is, at present, inadequate supporting data.

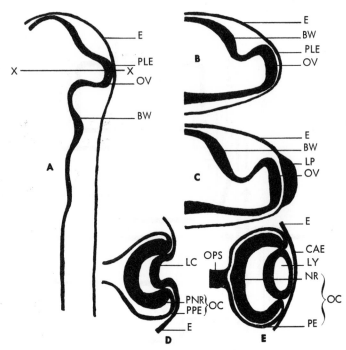

Fig. 9.3 Diagram of the steps in the development of the optic cup, lens, and cornea. A. Dorsal aspect of the embryo at the stage at which the optic vesicle makes contact with the overlying ectoderm. B. Transverse section through the level X-X at the same stage as that represented in A. C. Transverse section at the same level following induction of the lens placode by the tip of the optic vesicle. D. Invagination of the optic cup and optic vesicle. E. Separation of the lens vesicle from the surface, and reunion of the surface ectoderm to form the presumptive anterior corneal epithelium. BW, brain wall; CAE, corneal anterior epithelium; E, ectoderm; LC, lens cup; LP, lens placode; LY, lens vesicle; NR, neural retina; OC, optic cup; OPS, optic stalk; OV, optic vesicle; PE, pigmented epithelium; PLE, presumptive lens epithelium; PNR, presumptive neural retina; PPE, presumptive pigmented epithelium.

vaginates at its tip so that the vesicle cavity is obliterated and an optic cup is formed (Fig. 9.3). The cup remains attached to the brain by the optic stalk. Cup formation occurs normally only when the vesicle retains intimate contact with the invaginating lens (Lopashov and Stroeva, 136). Initially, both the outer and the inner walls of the cup are a single cell in thickness. The outer wall, which will form the pigmented portion of the retina, remains a simple, low, cuboidal epithelium throughout life. The inner wall, which will form

the neural portion of the retina, becomes many cells thick.

For a time during early development, the presumptive neural retina can form pigmented epithelium and the presumptive pigmented epithelium can form neural retina. This can be demonstrated by reversing these layers, or by placing them in otherwise suitable environments (Dragamirow, 63, 64, 65, 67; Alexander, 9; Dorris, 61; Neifach, 166; Orts Llorca and Genis-Galvez, 177; Stroeva, 237). Both the otic vesicle (Dragamirow, 62) and the nasal placode (Holtfreter, 92; Ikeda, 102, 103), neither of which is normally in contact with the optic cup, can induce a secondary neural retina in the pigmented epithelium.

The polarity of the neural retina becomes fixed early in its development. Its nasotemporal axis (tested by rotating the embryonic eye at different stages and subsequently testing visual function) becomes fixed before its dorsoventral axis (Sperry, 224, 225; Stone, 228, 231; Szekely, 239, 240). Thereafter the radial polarity of the neural retina (tested by radially reversing patches of retina at different developmental stages) becomes fixed (Eakin, 70). The pigmented epithelium and the lens may determine the radial polarity.

The choroid fissure, which is a linear opening through the wall of the optic cup, extending from the cup margin to the optic stalk, usually develops ventrally (Fig. 9.3). Embryonic eyes which are experimentally rotated 180° at different stages in development show that the location of the choroid fissure is dictated by the immediate tissue environment of the developing eye. The location of the fissure only gradually becomes fixed with respect to the eye (Sato, 201; Woerdeman, 269; Barden, 19, 20).

Following invagination of the optic cup, mitosis contributes to the increase in both the thickness and the area of the developing neural retina. During early stages in development, metaphase figures are confined to the margin of the optic cup and to the outer surface of the neural retina abutting the obliterated ventricular space of the optic vesicle. Radioautographic analysis of embryonic retinas labeled with tritiated thymidine demonstrates that immature retinal cells migrate to the outer surface as they divide, and that the daughter cells then migrate back to take up appropriate stations in the retinal layers which are differentiating internally (Sidman, 211). This mechanism of increase in the thickness of the neural retina is similar to that seen in other regions of the brain wall (DaCosta, 53). The gradual increase in thickness and cytoarchitectural complexity of the neural retina is attended by waves of cell death (Glücksman, 79, 80). The significance of this phenomenon is not known, but it seems probable that the deletion of cells is not random and that it is in some way related to the orderly establishment of the definitive neuronal network.

The innermost layers of the retina differentiate first, and the rods and cones in the outermost layer last. Furthermore, the neural retina in the deepest portion of the optic cup is always more advanced than that at the margin of the cup. Thus, mitotic activity ceases first at the back of the cup and persists longest at its margin. It is generally assumed that persistent mitotic activity at the margin of the cup accounts for the increase in area of the neural retina. Although the neural retina may initially require the influence of other tissues to initiate its differentiation, once it has begun to grow, its increase in thickness and in area appears to be independent of any specific influence of the surrounding ocular tissues (Coulombre, 37; Coulombre and Coulombre, 46). At first, cells of the neural retina are morphologically indistinguishable from one another (Fig. 9.4). Glial cells (Müller's fibers) are among the first retinal cells to differentiate (Nakayama, 162). Müller's fibers (which will eventually intimately envelop the neurons of the retina) are each connected by cytoplasmic processes with both surfaces of the neural retina. The end feet of these processes abut in continuous mosaics at the retinal surfaces to form the internal and external "limiting membranes." Ganglion cells, which form the innermost layer of neurons in the retina, are the next cells to differentiate. They enlarge and send out centrally directed axons which course in parallel array between the ganglion cell layer and the internal limiting membrane. The axons then grow into the optic stalk (Fig. 9.3) to form the optic nerve. The peripherally directed dendritic processes of the ganglion cells synapse in the adjacent, cell-free, inner plexiform layer with axonal processes from more superficial layers of neurons. In many species the synapses of the inner plexiform layer are arranged in discrete mats which lie parallel to one another and to the eye wall; these mats appear sequentially during development (Coulombre, 36; Shen et al., 210). As the inner plexiform layer develops, the neuroblasts just external to it organize as the inner nuclear layer. The inner nuclear layer contains at least three types of neurons: the amacrine cells, which lie toward the inner surface; bipolar cells, which have cell bodies that share the central stratum of the layer with the cell bodies of Müller's fibers; and horizontal cells, which are externally situated. The axons of the amacrine and bipolar cells synapse with ganglion cell dendrites in the inner plexiform layer. The cells in the outermost layer of the neural retina (the outer nuclear layer) begin to differentiate at about the time mitosis ceases locally. As these neuroblasts differentiate, their axons synapse with the dendrites of the bipolar cells in the subja-

cent, cell-free, outer plexiform layer. In some species two types of visual cell nuclei become separately stratified within the outer nuclear layer. These nuclear strata correspond to the differentiation into rods or cones externally (Brockoff, 26).

The light-sensitive rods and cones develop at the outer poles of the cells of the outer nuclear layer (Fig. 9.4). They are the last elements of the neural retina to differentiate. Comparative and cytogenetic studies of the rods and cones have been summarized by a number of workers (Detwiler, 59; Rochon-Duvigneaud, 195; Walls, 258; Wolff, 270). Each visual cell produces a single cytoplasmic bud at its distal end. Each bud protrudes through a pore in the external limiting membrane and is destined to form either a rod or a cone. These buds first form the inner segments of the rods and cones, and it is from them, at later stages, that the outer segments will arise. Several specialized cell organelles develop in the inner segment: myoid, elipsoid, paraboloid, and oil droplet. The complement of organelles which is present in the inner segments of the rods or cones varies with the species (Detwiler, 59; Prince, 186). The myoid is a contractile region in the basal portion of the inner segment which, in the adults of many species, appropriately positions the photosensitive elements relative to the pigmented epithelium during photomechanical adjustments to different light intensities (Detwiler, 59). This region is rich in acetylcholinesterase (Shen et al., 210; Yoshido, 272). The ellipsoid or lentiform body, which appears shortly after the inner segment begins to form (Lewis, 128; Carasso, 30), is a tightly packed aggregation of mitochondria and conse-

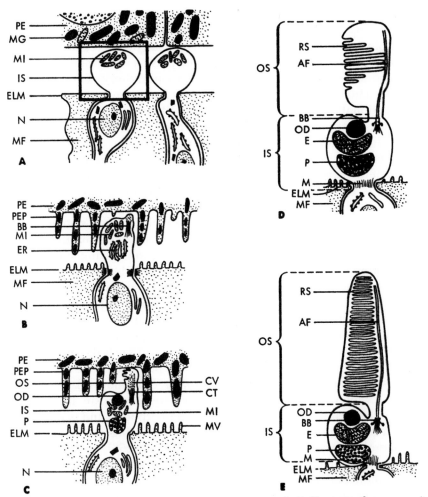

Fig. 9.4 Schematic diagram of rod and cone cytogenesis. *A–E* illustrate the successive stages in the maturation of the cone. AF, axial filament; BB, basal body; CT, ciliary tubules; CV, ciliary vesicles; E, ellipsoid; ELM, external limiting membrane; ER, endoplasmic reticulum; IS, inner segment; M, myoid; MF, Müller's fiber; MG, melanin granule; MI, mitochondrion; MV, microvillus; N, nucleus; OD, oil droplet; OS, outer segment; P, paraboloid; PE, pigmented epithelium; PEP, pigmented epithelial process; RS, rod sac.

quently shows high succinic dehydrogenase activity (Hellström, 90). The paraboloid, which appears late in development (Saxén, 202; Rebollo, 189), is a dense collection of glycogen granules. This organelle is foreshadowed by a local concentration of granular endoplasmic reticulum with cisternae that gradually become engorged with glycogen granules ranging in diameter in thin sections from 150 A to 250 A (Carasso, 32). The oil droplets, which are usually confined to the cones, are spherical globules of carotenoids such as astacene, xanthophyll, and galloxanthin (Wald and Zussman, 256, 257); they appear late in development (Coulombre, 36) between the mitochondria of the ellipsoid and the tip of the inner segment (Carasso, 30). In some forms (for example, some reptiles and birds) which have colored oil droplets, each cone concentrates only one type of carotenoid. This calls attention to possible functional differences among cones which otherwise appear morphologically similar. Situated as they are at the junction of the inner and outer segments of the cones, the oil droplets may serve as focusing lenses and, in those species with colored droplets, as optical filters.

Another organelle, the diplosome, migrates into the inner segment early in its development (Tokuyasu and Yamada, 246). The outer centriole of the diplosome (basal body) elaborates a cilium which participates in the development of the outer segments of the rods and cones (De Robertis, 56; Carasso, 31; Tokuyasu and Yamada, 246, 247). These cilia are homologues of the motile cilia which line the ependymal surface of the primitive brain ventricles. Each cilium produces nine pairs of peripheral ciliary tubules, but no central filaments. The peripheral doublets lengthen and collectively form the axial filament of the outer segment. When the axial filament is 1.0 to 1.5 μ long, it becomes enveloped in a club-shaped cytoplasmic bud (primitive outer segment) which develops at the distal tip of the inner segment. Minute rows of vesicles (ciliary vesicles) extend from the tip of the ciliary tubules to the apex of the developing outer segment. At the points where ciliary vesicles contact the plasma membrane, the cell surface folds inward to form large, irregular sacs. These rods or cone sacs become flattened in a plane perpendicular to the long axis of the outer segment and become stacked in the man-

ner of a stack of coins. As this stack grows, the outer segment elongates. Each sac preserves its connection with the plasma membrane by a hollow stalk at its periphery. This connection persists for some time, perhaps throughout life in some forms. Thus the cavity of each sac is continuous with the outer surface of the cell. The suspicion is strong that the ciliary vesicles elicit the rod sac infoldings. In abnormally developing rods, ciliary vesicles sometimes impinge on the plasma membrane of the inner segment. When this occurs, sacs develop from the point of contact, suggesting not only that the ciliary vesicles bring about the infolding, but also that the plasma membrane of the inner segment, which does not normally form sacs, is capable of responding to the stimulus.

The rod sac is the presumed location of the photosensitive pigment (porphyropsin or rhodopsin). In some amphibians, porphyropsin is present before metamorphosis and is replaced by rhodopsin during metamorphosis (Wald, 255; Wilt, 266). In rods the photopigment is present as soon as rod sacs begin to form, as evidenced by the simultaneous development of light-avoiding reactions and of the electroretinogram (ERG) (Detwiler, 58; Parry, 180), and by the first detection of visual purple when the outer segments begin to develop (Tansley, 241). In predominantly cone retinas, however, the outer segments begin to develop some time before the ERG can be demonstrated (Garcia-Austt, 75; Rebollo, 189; Kramisheva, 117).

The outer wall of the optic cup remains a simple, low, cuboidal epithelium which develops into the pigmented epithelium of the retina posteriorly, and the basal layer of the ciliary and iris epithelia anteriorly. The differentiation of the pigmented epithelium depends on a number of cooperating factors. Mechanical tension appears to be essential for the early differentiation of this layer, both in vivo and in vitro (Boterenbrood, 25; Lopashov, 135). The close proximity of ectomesenchyme or mesodermal mesenchyme to the outer surface of the cup supplies a necessary stimulus (Lopashov, 135). The proximity of the neural retina to the inner surface of the pigmented epithelium represses the tendency of the pigmented epithelium to form neural retina. Even modest separation of the two layers of the retina early in development results in the formation of neural retina from the pigmented epithelium (Alexander, 9; Dorris, 61; Lopashov, 134; Reinbold, 191; Dabaghian, 51; Stroeva, 237; Orts Llorca and Genis-Galvez, 177). In some urodeles this relationship continues throughout life (Wachs, 251; Stone, 229, 230; Reyer, 193; Stone and Steinitz, 234; Hasegawa, 89).

In response to these cues, and perhaps to other influences from its neighboring tissues, the pigmented epithelium undergoes a complex differentiation. An initial moderate accumulation of glycogen granules in the cytoplasm disappears as the cells differentiate (Janosky and Wenger, 109). During differentiation, melanin granules, which develop in the epithelium in most diurnal species, appear concomitantly with the first detectable tyrosinase activity (Harrison, 88). The granules arise in the Golgi apparatus (Güttes, 82, 83). Albino animals have nonpigmented granules which correspond in size, number, location, and time of appearance with the melanin granules of pigmented forms (Güttes, 82; Koecke,

116). Each granule arises as a sac whose wall is 70 A thick; within each sac small vesicles accumulate and merge to form spirally arranged lamellae. Melanin is deposited on these lamellae (Moyer, 159).

Each pigmented epithelial cell gives rise to numerous, long, fine cytoplasmic processes over its inner surface. These interdigitate with the outer segments of the rods and cones which arise simultaneously. The two layers of the retina are thus locked together ending a period when they are free to slide over one another as they pursue their separate patterns of growth (Coulombre et al., 49). The processes secrete a nonsulfated mucopolysaccharide which coats the outer segments of the rods and cones (Zimmerman and Eastham, 273). In many species melanin granules migrate into or out of these processes from the cell body in photomechanical response to changing light conditions. The pigmented epithelium is also important as an avenue of exchange between the choroid vascular bed outside it and the neural retina internally. This importance is underscored by the fact that submammalian forms (excepting the eel) have avascular retinae (Prince, 186). The fine structure of the mature pigmented epithelium is suggestive of its transport function (Yamada et al., 271; Porter and Yamada, 185).

Lens

Initially, most regions of the primitive embryonic ectoderm are competent to form lens (Mangold, 138). However, this competence rapidly becomes confined to that region overlying the optic vesicle or the optic cup. The ectoderm is influenced in the lens direction by successive interactions with the underlying endoderm of the foregut and with portions of the presumptive heart mesoderm (Mangold, 138; Holtfreter, 92; Liedke, 132, 133; ten Cate, 242; Jacobson, 105). In some species, these influences are of sufficient force and duration to initiate the differentiation of lens tissue from ectoderm (Spemann, 223; Balinsky, 16). More usually, they lower the threshold of the ectoderm to induction by the optic vesicle. It is the tip of the optic vesicle (presumptive neural retina) which plays the final role in inducing lens from overlying ectoderm, and in aligning the lens precisely with the rest of the eye (Spemann, 221, 222; Lewis, 129, 131; Alexander, 9; van Deth, 57; McKeehan, 148). It is not yet known whether induction of the lens by endoderm, mesoderm, and optic vesicle all involve the same mechanisms. However, the alternative or sequential action of several inducing tissues on the same target tissue decreases the probability that lens formation would be aborted by accidents during the early phases of induction. In addition to the tissues which normally induce lens, this structure can also be induced and sustained in competent ectoderm in experimental confrontations by embryonic otic vesicle (Dragamirow, 62), and by guinea pig thymus (Toivonen, 244, 245). The several inductors are even differentially responsive to environmental conditions. For example, lens induction by mesoderm in amphibians proceeds more rapidly at lower temperatures than does induction by the optic vesicle (ten Cate, 242).

The terminal inductive interaction requires proximity, but not necessarily contact, between the optic vesicle and the ectoderm. A periodic acid Schiff

(PAS) positive zone several micra in thickness develops between these two layers of cells before and during the inductive period in the chick embryo. This acellular layer arises in the region of fusion of the basement membranes of the ectoderm and the optic vesicle (O'Rahilly and Meyer, 175; Hunt, 96; Weiss and Jackson, 263). This barrier poses no difficulty because the inductive influence can be mediated across sheets of material experimentally interposed between the tip of the optic vesicle and the overlying ectoderm (McKeehan, 151).

While the nature of the inductive influence remains unknown, there are indications that substances may be transferred from the presumptive neural retina to the overlying ectoderm during induction. There is a progressive loss in cytoplasmic basophilia in cells at the tip of the optic vesicle during early induction, and a concomitant gain in cytoplasmic basophilia in the cells of the overlying ectoderm (McKeehan, 150). Similarly, ribosomal concentration (estimated from electron micrographs) decreases in the cytoplasm of the cells of the presumptive neural retina at the same time that it is increasing in the lens ectoderm (Hunt, 96). Concurrently, electron-dense masses appear in the extracellular material separating the two layers of cells. There is more direct evidence that some substances may be transferred from the presumptive neural retina to the presumptive lens cells (Sirlin and Brahma, 213). When unlabeled competent ectoderm was experimentally confronted with optic vesicles which had been labeled with DL-3-phenyl (alanine-2-C^{14}), it was demonstrated radioautographically that the label appeared specifically in that area of the ectoderm destined to form lens. These studies do not indicate which substance or substances are transferred, which substances are involved in induction, or the ultimate nature of the inductive interaction, but they may point the way.

Also open to question is the duration of this influence. When the lens is removed to a neutral environment (coelom) at different stages of development, it has been shown that it only gradually becomes independent of the optic cup (McKeehan, 149). This prolonged dependence was suggested as early as 1907 (LeCron, 125). The optic cup continues to influence the lens throughout an appreciable period of its normal development in the chick embryo (Coulombre and Coulombre, 46). This influence is present even in the adult in some salamanders (Stone, 232). A prolonged period of inductive interaction not only increases the probability that lens induction will occur successfully in the face of accidental interference, but provides a mechanism for continuously adjusting the size, shape, position and orientation of the lens to that of the retina.

During the early stages of the inductive process, the ectodermal cells immediately overlying the tip of the optic vesicle elongate perpendicularly to the body surface to form a thickened disc (lens placode). During this elongation, intercellular spaces are obliterated by the close approximation of adjacent cell membranes (Hunt, 96). The change in cell shape is accomplished without change in cell volume (McKeehan, 148). The number of cells, however, continues to increase during this period. Toward the end of lens placode formation, acidophilic fibrils appear in the apices of the lens placode cells

(Langman, 122). At about this time, the placode invaginates to form the lens cup. This invagination is independent of the concomitant invagination of the underlying optic vesicle, and is probably due to forces operating within the lens ectoderm. During invagination, basophilic granules increase in number in the basal cytoplasm of the lens cells (Langman, 122). As the lens cup deepens, its opening (lens pore) becomes progressively constricted until its lips meet and fuse, cutting off the lens vesicle internally and re-establishing continuity in the overlying ectoderm (presumptive corneal epithelium). As a consequence the lens becomes completely invested with the basement membrane which had underlaid the placode. This membrane is the precursor of the lens capsule (O'Rahilly and Meyer, 176). Closure of the lens pore is attended by, and possibly accomplished by, a local and temporarily restricted wave of cell death. Following closure of the lens pore, the cells at the back of the lens vesicle continue to elongate, under the influence of the neural retina, to form the lens fibers. As the fibers grow, the cavity of the vesicle is obliterated. The lens cells toward the ectoderm, which do not elongate further, form the lens epithelium.

The continued influence of the retina is also necessary for the normal growth of the lens, and probably for the appropriate orientation of the lens relative to the optic axis. This growth dependence was demonstrated by removal of the neural retina in amphibians (Le Cron, 125). When the iris of the salamander was reversed front-to-back and the attached lens subsequently removed, a lens regenerating from the dorsal margin of the iris was

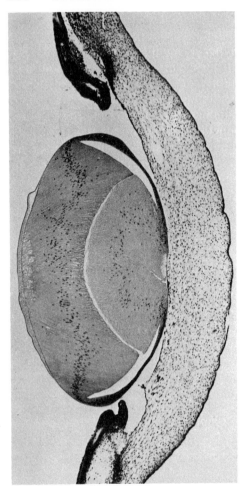

Fig. 9.5 Axial section of an 11-day chick embryonic lens that had been surgically reversed at 5 days of incubation so that the epithelium faced the vitreous body. The former epithelial cells have elongated to form new fibers, and the polarity of the equatorial zone has become reversed so that it now adds epithelial cells toward the cornea and fibers to the edge of the new fiber mass posteriorly.

oriented appropriately to the eye and not to the reversed iris (Stone, 232). This continuing influence has also been demonstrated during normal development in the eye of the chick embryo by surgically reversing the lens at 5 days of incubation so that its epi-

thelium faces the vitreous body (Coulombre and Coulombre, 50). The epithelial cells which have been turned toward the retina immediately begin to elongate and form lens fibers (Fig. 9.5). The original group of lens fibers, now situated beneath the cornea, stops growing. The polarity of the equator becomes reversed so that fibers are now added to the surface of the newly forming fiber mass on the vitreal side, while epithelial cells are added on the corneal side to reconstitute a new, appropriately positioned, but incomplete lens epithelium. If two 5-day lenses are introduced in several different orientations into a lensectomized 5-day eye, those epithelial cells in each lens which lie on the neural retinal side of the plane through the rim of the optic cup elongate to form lens fibers (Unpublished results, author's laboratory). The sheet of epithelial cells on the corneal side of this plane becomes extended by mitosis to cover the corneal faces of the lenses, and the size and shape of the combined lenses gradually adjust toward values which are normal for a single lens at the age of the host. Whatever the ultimate basis of this phenomenon, it clearly provides a mechanism for continually adjusting the geometric alignment of the lens to that of the rest of the optical system of the eye during development.

The zone of transition between the lens epithelium and the lens fiber mass occurs near the lens equator just opposite the ciliary processes. Near this juncture, the cells of the epithelium have larger nuclei, more prominent nucleoli, a higher concentration of cytoplasmic RNA, more numerous mitochondria, and an increased height. It is in this stage in their development, and at this place, that these cells probably begin the active synthesis of the proteins of the gamma group (Papaconstantinou and Resnick, 178; Papaconstantinou, Resnick, and Saito, 179). The increased height of the cells at the equator is often (notably among the Sauropsida) sufficient to produce an equatorial thickening in the epithelium (ringwulst, annulus, or annular pad). As cells rotate through the equatorial region, they take their places on the surface of the growing fiber mass. They elongate rapidly toward the poles of the lens where they meet with other fibers in planes of junction called sutures (Rabl, 187). The patterns formed by the lens sutures vary from single planes to many radiating planes of conjuncture. The suture pattern and the orientation of the suture planes with respect to the eye are constant in a given species and become determined at a specific time in development (Woerdeman, 269). At any one time the number of cells in the lens is a function of the original number of cells in the lens primordium, the history of mitosis in the tissue, the loss of cells either by cell death or by emigration of cells, and the increase in cell number attributable to immigration. The number of cells in the original lens population is determined by the area of contact between the tip of the optic vesicle and the overlying ectoderm (Rotmann, 197, 198; McKeehan, 148; Balinsky, 17). It is, however, improbable that the size of this initial population of lens cells is a decisive factor in the subsequent size of the lens. Lens tissue remains highly responsive to factors which assure that it will increase in size at a rate appropriate to the geometry of the remainder of the eye. As the lens vesicle forms, and its posterior cells elongate to form lens fibers, the

sheet of cuboidal lens epithelial cells which faces the cornea continues to show mitotic activity. This generates additional cells which serve not only to increase the area of the epithelium as the lens grows, but also, by differentiation into lens fibers at the equator, to increase the number of cells in the posteriorly situated fiber mass.

As each fiber grows, its nucleus becomes positioned at about the center of the fiber. As a consequence, a plane of cell nuclei, convex outward, is formed across the lens fiber mass. This is called the lens bow, which is continuous at the equator with the plane formed by the nuclei of the lens epithelium. Since newer fibers are always deposited superficially, the oldest fibers in the lens come to lie centrally and are referred to collectively as the lens nucleus. In time the cell nuclei of this region become pycnotic and finally disappear. Since pycnotic nuclei are seen only at the center of the lens, it appears that cell death occurs either exclusively or predominantly at this location. It is usually assumed, although no definitive information exists concerning this point, that the dead fibers at the center of the lens are not broken down and removed, but remain in place. If this is true, then cell death, in the usual sense of dissolution and removal, would not contribute to the change in lens volume. The complete envelopment of the lens in a dense fibrous capsule seems to preclude the possibility that lens cell number is modified by the migration of cells into or out of the lens cell pool.

Thus the size and shape of the lens must ultimately be controlled by factors which control the number, size, and shape of the lens cells. These regulatory factors are of two types: retinal factors necessary not only for the growth of the lens, but also for the orientation of lens fibers within the lens; and lens-inhibitory factors possibly arising from the lens (Stone, 233). By comparing lens volume and retinal area in the untreated eyes of several species of amphibian embryos, as well as in eyes that resulted from heteroplastic combination of lens and eyecup precursors, it was shown that both the basic size and the rate of increase in lens size show a strong correlation with the surface area of the developing retina (Balinsky, 17).

Phases of lens development other than its morphogenesis cannot be covered here. However, recent reviews of this extensive literature are available as follows: biochemistry (Pirie and van Heynengen, 181); immunochemistry (Zwaan, 274); and regeneration (Reyer, 194).

Cornea

The vertebrate cornea contains three types of cells, nerve fibers, and a remarkably small number of extracellular components (Rochon-Duvigneaud, 195; Thomas, 243; Polyak, 183; Wolff, 270; Dejean et al., 55; Duke-Elder, 68; and Walls, 258). This modest list of constituents is assembled in time and space in such a manner that the cornea develops a large number of strikingly different functional characteristics (avascularity, tensile strength, deturgescence, a tissue-specific population of ions, regenerative capacity, a characteristic interference pattern in polarized light, an appropriate refractive index, a precisely controlled curvature that contributes importantly to its refracting power, and transparency). Simultaneous development of such diverse properties sets strict limits on the manner and sequence in which the corneal components can be compatibly assembled during development. Descriptive and experimental studies of how the cornea is actually assembled have been extensively reviewed for a number of vertebrate species (Mangold, 138; Mann, 142, 143, 144; Redslob, 190; Twitty, 248; Pirie and van Heyningen, 181; Meyer and O'Rahilly, 154; O'Rahilly and Meyer, 175, 176; Lopashov and Stroeva, 136, 137; and Coulombre, 39, 40).

The anterior epithelium, the first corneal structure to form, arises from ectoderm. Competence to form corneal epithelium is widespread in the early embryonic ectoderm (amphibians: Lewis, 130; Dürken, 69; Fischel, 71, 72; Groll, 81; Adelmann, 1; Popov, 184; Reyer, 192; Ignatieva, 98, 99; chick embryo: Neifach, 165, 167). Despite this, the cornea normally arises only over the embryonic eye, and is of a size, shape, and orientation appropriate to the eye (Lewis, 130; Fischel, 71; Lazarev, 123; Neifach, 165; Reyer, 192). This alignment is achieved and maintained because the corneal anterior epithelium is induced by the lens and the optic cup (amphibians: Spemann, 221; Lewis, 129, 130; chick embryo: Amprino, 10; Neifach, 165, 167). While the eye cup alone is sufficient to induce corneal anterior epithelium from ectoderm in amphibians, it is not capable of supporting its full development. It is the lens that is principally responsible for the induction and maintenance of the cornea. The eye gradually loses its ability to induce cornea as development proceeds (Bedniakova, 21, 22; Ignatieva, 100, 101; Beliaeva, 23).

The corneal anterior epithelium also becomes progressively more independent of its inductor (amphibians: Lewis, 130; Dürken, 69; Fischel, 72; Groll, 81; Beliaeva, 23; birds: Neifach, 168; Bytinski-Salz, 28; Coulombre and Coulombre, 46; mammals: Stroeva, 236). Anuran tadpoles and some teleosts have an external cornea that is continuous with the skin, and which is separated by a space from an internal cornea that is continuous with the sclera. In anurans these layers fuse at metamorphosis (Harms, 86; Popov, 184) under the influence of thyroxine (Kaltenbach, 110). Until this fusion occurs, the external cornea reverts to skin when the subjacent eye is removed (Lewis, 130; Dürken, 69; Fischel, 72; Groll, 81; Beliaeva, 23). In some fish the two corneal layers remain separate throughout life and the external cornea is dependent upon the eye, even in the adult.

The corneal anterior epithelium increases both in thickness and in area by mitosis in its basal layer. This mitosis, which continues throughout life to replace cells lost by desquamation at the surface, cycles diurnally from a maximum at night to a minimum during the day (cat: Fortuyn-van Leyden, 73, 74; frog: Meyer, 153; mouse: Vasama and Vasama, 250). Diurnal cycling appears to be under endocrine control (Sigelman et al., 212; Scheving and Chiakulas, 203, 204), but it is not yet known when cycling commences during embryonic development. Although mitotic activity supports the normal growth of the corneal anterior epithelium, it cannot effect regeneration of this layer in vivo until after the 10th day of incubation in the chick embryo (Weiss and Matoltsy, 264).

A PAS+ basement membrane which contains lipid and reticulin and which stains orthochromatically with tolu-

idine blue underlies the anterior epithelium of the cornea (Calmettes et al., 29) from the earliest stages of its development (Offret and Haye, 174; O'Rahilly and Meyer, 176). It regenerates with the epithelium following corneal wounding (Busacca, 27). In the newborn mouse it is about 600 A thick and contains cross-banded fibrils (Sheldon, 209).

The space between the lens vesicle and the overlying presumptive anterior epithelium of the cornea contains acellular material ("anhistic mass," Kessler, 111; "anterior vitreous body," v. Lenhossék, 126; "mesostroma," Studnicka, 238). In the chick embryo an acellular directional membrane appears in this space beneath and parallel to the presumptive anterior epithelium of the cornea (Knape, 115; Laguesse, 119, 120; Redslob, 190; O'Rahilly and Meyer, 175). Another acellular stratum, the postepithelial layer, is deposited between the anterior epithelium and the directional membrane (birds: Kessler, 111; Ladijenski, 118; Laguesse, 121; Hagedoorn, 85; O'Rahilly and Meyer, 175; mammals: Rabl, 187; Levi, 127; Mann, 143; Medvedeva, 152); the stroma will form in this stratum. It is along the posterior surface of the directional membrane that mesenchyme cells from the limbic region migrate to form the simple, low, cuboidal posterior epithelium ("endothelium") of the cornea (Seefelder and Wolfrum, 207; Knape, 115; Laguesse, 121; Hagedoorn, 84; Redslob, 190; Streeter, 235; Stocker, 227; O'Rahilly and Meyer, 175). As the endothelium increases in area, its cells continue to divide (von Sallmann et al., 200). Eventually mitotic activity ceases (Ballowitz, 18; Nagano, 161; Cogan, 34; Binder and Binder, 24; Mills and Donn, 158; von

Sallmann, 199) and resumes only when the posterior epithelium is wounded (Binder and Binder, 24; Mills and Donn, 158; von Sallmann et al., 200). The posterior epithelium, as well as the anterior epithelium, assumes an important role in keeping the stroma deturgesced (Davson, 54; Harris, 87).

Descemet's membrane arises under the influence of the posterior epithelium. In the chick embryo it appears on the 10th day of incubation as acellular islands of material between the posterior epithelium and the stroma (Jakus, 108). These isolates thicken and fuse laterally to form a continuous sheet composed of parallel lamellae in the plane of the cornea. The lamellae are separated from one another by about 170 A. In the plane of each lamella there is a regular hexagonal array of electron-dense nodes with an internode distance of 1070 A. Filaments 100 A in diameter connect each node with its six neighbors. The principal constituent of the membrane appears to be a form of collagen (Dohlman and Balazs, 60). Following wounding of the posterior cornea, Descemet's membrane is regenerated, but only after the posterior epithelium is reconstituted (Collins, 35; Ranvier, 188).

The postepithelial layer is probably synthesized by the anterior epithelium (Laguesse, 119, 120; Levi, 127; Mann, 142; Migazzo, 155; Neifach, 169). During the early acellular phase of its existence, the postepithelial layer thickens progressively (Migazzo, 155). Since the stroma develops within it, its structure is of some interest. It contains extremely fine fibrils, which are deposited at its outer surface beneath the anterior epithelium. They are disposed in lamellae parallel to the overlying epithelium (Ladijenski, 118; La-

guesse, 119, 120; Neüschuler, 170; Redslob, 190; Watzka, 259; Iasvoin, 97). The fibrils of adjacent lamellae form an orthogonal ply, do not interlace, and may represent in miniature the collagenous pattern of the adult stroma that develops after the invasion of fibroblasts (Ladijenski, 118).

The postepithelial layer becomes invaded by fibroblasts from the mesenchyme of the limbic area (Redslob, 190). They enter the posterior lamellae first (Meyer and O'Rahilly, 154), and quickly, under the influence of the postepithelial layer (Attardi, 14), become differentiated cytologically from the cells at the limbus (Rones, 196). Cell number increases in the developing stroma, not only by continued migration from the limbus, but also as a result of mitoses of cells already in the stroma. While cell division ceases at a point in development which varies with the species (the pool of stromal cells stabilizes at about 16 days of incubation in the chick embryo: Herrmann, 91), the ability to divide is never lost and, following wounding, can be reactivated by proteolytic release of a factor from the injured anterior epithelium (Weimar, 260). The stromal fibroblasts synthesize collagen and glycosaminoglycans.

Collagen fibers begin to appear in the stroma as soon as it is invaded by fibroblasts (Ladijenski, 118; Laguesse, 119, 120; Levi, 127; Neüschuler, 170; Rones, 196; Neifach, 168; Ghiani and Bergamini, 77, 78). Precursors of the collagen are synthesized in the endoplasmic reticulum of the fibroblasts and are released into the extracellular space where they polymerize (Schwarz, 206). The fibrils which form have a small diameter from the outset (rat: 250–300 A, Jakus, 107; man: 300–350 A, Schwarz,

205), and have a crossband macroperiod of about 640 A (van den Hooff, 95). These collagen fibrils, unlike their counterparts in other connective tissues, do not become coarse, but retain essentially the same diameter throughout life. As the stromal fibroblasts become inactive, their nucleoli decrease in size and the cells are referred to as stromal corpuscles. When they are reactivated during healing of stromal wounds, the fibrils of collagen are no longer of uniform diameter, but exhibit the range of size seen in other connective tissues. Such scars are not transparent. Aside from calling attention to the possible importance of uniform fibril diameter for the development of transparency, this observation also suggests that the uniform dimensions of the stromal fibrils are imposed by the extracellular environment (postepithelial layer), and not by the fibroblasts. Once the extracellular matrix is destroyed or disrupted, it is not reestablished and collagen, which polymerizes in the gap, is randomly disposed.

The definitive lamellae of collagen are deposited in sequence, beginning in the deepest (and oldest) stratum of the postepithelial layer (Meyer and O'Rahilly, 154; Coulombre and Coulombre, 45). Those strata of the stroma toward the anterior epithelium tend to be devoid of cells during development. While this acellular layer disappears by adulthood in most species, it persists as Bowman's membrane in such forms as primates.

There are two fundamental types of fiber arrangement in vertebrate stromas (Fig. 9.6). In mammals the fibrils are aggregated as broad, straplike fibers lying in the plane of the cornea and crossing each other with apparent randomness (Polack, 182). In submammalian forms, the fibrils become aggregated into sheets or lamellae, which lie in the plane of the cornea and extend to the limbus at all points (Coulombre and Coulombre, 45; Polack, 182). The fibrils in each lamella are roughly at right angles to those in adjacent lamellae. There is, however, a systematic, clockwise, angular shift in this orthogonal ply between the outer and inner surface of the stroma in the chick embryo. The shift becomes less pronounced as the deeper strata are approached. This angular shift is in the same direction in both right and left eyes, and is, consequently, asymmetric around the body midplane. Progressive thickening of the lamellae, which is always more advanced in the deeper layers (Smelser and Ozanics, 216; Coulombre and Coulombre, 45), eventually permits identification of individual layers at relatively low powers of magnification (Neüschuler, 170; Snesarev, 220; Meyer and O'Rahilly, 154).

The manner in which collagen fibrils are disposed in the stromal space accounts for several important corneal properties. The characteristic interference pattern that is seen when the cornea is viewed between crossed polarizers must rest upon the geometry of this matrix (Stanworth, 226; Naylor, 163, 164; Kikkawa, 112, 113, 114; Coulombre and Coulombre, 45). Both the mammalian and the submammalian patterns provide for a uniform tensile strength in the corneal plane and stabilize corneal shape in the presence of considerable intraocular pressure. The fibrillar matrix may also provide the physical basis for corneal transparency (see below).

In addition to collagen, the fibroblasts also probably produce the gly-

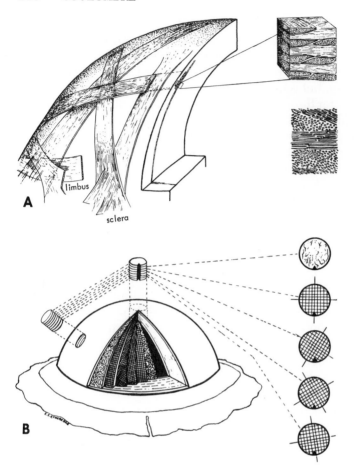

Fig. 9.6 A. Diagrammatic representation of the disposition of collagen in the mammalian stroma. (From Polack, *Am. J. Ophthalmal.* 51, no. 5, part II, 1051–1056, 1961.) B. Diagrammatic representation of the disposition of collagen in the submammalian vertebrate stroma. (From Coulombre and Coulombre, pp. 405–420 in *The Structure of the Eye*, G. K. Smelser, ed. Academic Press, 1961.)

cosaminoglycans (mucopolysaccharides) (Jackson, 104; Schwarz, 206) which are deposited in the interfibrillar space. Of the three glycosaminoglycans that have been identified (chondroitin-4-sulfate, chondroitin, and keratan sulfate), keratan sulfate is characteristic of the cornea and is rarely found elsewhere in the body. Glycosaminoglycans, particularly keratan sulfate, increase in amount as development proceeds (Smits, 219; Anseth, 12). The deposition of glycosaminoglycans in the extracellular compartment of the stroma accounts for its metachromasia. During early development, PAS positivity (O'Rahilly and Meyer, 176) and faint metachromasia (Smelser and

Ozanics, 217) are widespread in the stroma. As development proceeds, intense metachromasia appears in the deepest and oldest strata of the stroma and in time spreads toward the anterior epithelium (chick embryo: van Walbeek et al., 254; van den Hooff, 94; Ghiani and Bergamini, 77; Coulombre and Coulombre, 42; human, guinea pig, rat, mouse, and rabbit: Aurell and Holmgren, 15; human: Gemolotto and Patrone, 76; rat: Alagna, 6; Seo, 208; rabbit: Smelser and Ozanics, 215, 216, 217, 218). Glycosaminoglycans also account for the considerable water-binding capacity of the stroma (Ashton, 13; van Walbeek, 253), alter its refractive index, influence its electrolyte ecology, and prevent its vascularization (Ashton, 13). Since the blood vessels present in the limbic region fail to invade the stroma from the earliest stages of development, the conditions which prevent vascularization must develop early.

The cornea becomes progressively thicker and more opaque during early development, but eventually increases in transparency, slowly in the rabbit (Smelser and Ozanics, 215, 218), and more abruptly in the chick embryo (van den Hooff, 94; Coulombre and Coulombre, 42). Concurrently, the cornea loses water rapidly and becomes thinner under thyroid influence (Coulombre and Coulombre, 44, 47). Adult levels of hydration and transparency are achieved simultaneously.

Two physical bases have been suggested for corneal transparency. The uniform refractive index hypothesis (summarized by Maurice, 147) holds that when the interfibrillar space becomes filled with a substance having the same refractive index as the fibrils, the stroma becomes transparent. The alternative, or lattice, hypothesis (Maurice, 145, 146, 147) suggests that a regular array of fibrils will interfere destructively with a light beam in all directions except that of its propagation, provided that the fibrils have small diameters relative to the wavelengths of light, are uniform in diameter, and spaced in a regular parallel array with an interfibrillar distance that is small relative to the wavelengths of light traversing the system. The disposition of the fibrils in the adult stroma meets all of these requirements. The progressive dehydration of the cornea during development is compatible with both theories of transparency. On the one hand, loss of water from the interfibrillar compartment would increase the refractive index of substances contained in this space in the direction of the refractive index of collagen. On the other hand, dehydration of the stroma would bring collagenous fibrils closer together in space and permit the establishment of the regular array required by the lattice hypothesis.

Change in corneal thickness as development proceeds is contributed to in several ways. The anterior epithelium thickens progressively by the deposition of additional cell strata. The thickness of the stroma is increased from the outset by the deposition of additional lamellae underneath the anterior epithelium. Following the invasion of fibroblasts and the deposition of collagen, these lamellae increase in thickness rapidly. Later, during the phase of rapid dehydration, the stroma undergoes a marked decrease in thickness. In the chick embryo, collagen continues to be synthesized within the individual lamellae beyond 19 days of incubation (Herrmann, 91), when adult levels of hydration and transparency have been achieved (Coulombre and Coulombre, 42). In most species the cornea is remarkably uniform in thickness over its entire area, although in some forms, including man, the cornea is thinner at its center than toward the limbus.

In the adult, the cornea has a greater curvature (smaller radius of curvature) than the remainder of the globe. The refractive power of the cornea is a function of its curvature and of the difference in refractive index across it. In land vertebrates it separates media of widely different refractive index and its curvature is thus important in determining its high refracting power. For this reason, the mechanisms which control the shaping of the cornea during development deserve attention (van Alphen, 249). Mechanical forces appear to play a dominant role (Neifach, 169; Coulombre, 37, 38; Coulombre and Coulombre, 43). The motive power for expansion of the eye wall as a whole arises from tangential forces generated in the eye wall by the accumulation of vitreous substance internally. The shaping of the differential corneal curvature is accomplished by the differentiation in the limbic area of structurally strong materials such as cartilage in submammalian eyes (Coulombre and Coulombre, 42) and collagen in mammalian eyes (Smelser and Ozanics, 218). The appearance of these structured elements at the limbus in an otherwise soft and yielding eye wall results in differential expansion of the wall into a highly curved cornea anteriorly and a sclera of lesser curvature posteriorly. When pressure is prevented from building up inside the eye during development, no differential corneal curvature develops.

The tangential forces generated in the eye wall by the accumulation of vitreous substance in the vitreous cavity appear to be essential, but not sufficient, for the normal increase in corneal area. The increase in corneal diameter can continue for a considerable period of the life span (Norrby, 172). We do not, at the present time, have a satisfactory explanation of how this increase in diameter is brought about within the stromal context.

Sclera

The adult sclera of some vertebrates, notably snakes and mammals, is entirely collagenous. Collagenous sclerae contain fibrils of widely varying diameters which are much less regularly disposed than those of the corneal stroma. In contrast to the transparent corneal stroma, the adjacent sclera reflects most of the incident light and is white.

Most submammalian species possess a true ocular skeleton (Fig. 9.7). A typical ocular skeleton consists of a thin-walled cup of hyaline cartilage enclosing the posterior segment of the globus oculi and a ring of intramembranous bones in the edge of the sclera at its junction with the cornea. In some species of birds there is, in addition, a ring of bone surrounding the head of the optic nerve (Gemminger's ossicle).

Ossicles of intramembranous origin number up to 18 in each eye, depending on the species. They are trapezoidally shaped and overlap one another to form a ring between the edge of the scleral cartilage and the limbus. While the scleral ossicles of the primitive teleosts resemble those of higher vertebrate forms in their development and structure, those of the elasmobranchs and modern teleosts are somewhat different. Elasmobranch "ossicles" are really hyaline cartilage, although they tend to calcify with age. The ossicles of the modern teleosts number one or two in each eye. They develop endochondrally in the medial and lateral regions of the scleral cartilage.

The intramembranous scleral ossicles are first foreshadowed in the conjunctiva by the development of a ring of papilliform thickenings which correspond in number and position to the membrane bones which will subsequently develop in the underlying mesenchyme (sparrow: Slonaker, 214; Sauropsida: Dabelow, 52; chicken: Nussbaum, 173; Dabelow, 52; Murray, 160; Coulombre et al., 48). In the chick embryo the conjunctival papillae appear during the 8th day of incubation.

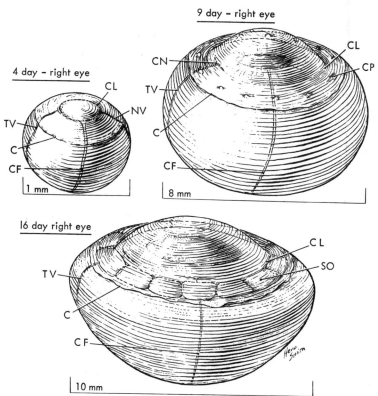

Fig. 9.7 This diagram illustrates the spatial and developmental relationships of the structures associated with the ocular skeleton of the chicken. C, cut edge of conjunctiva; CF, choroid fissure; CL, corneal limbus; CN, bifurcation of the temporal vessel; CP, conjunctival papilla; NV, nasal vessel; SO, scleral ossicle; TV, temporal vessel.

They usually number 14. They are transient structures which begin to disappear on the 12th day just as the ossicles are beginning to ossify in the underlying mesenchyme. During its existence each papilla undergoes a characteristic series of changes, including striking alterations in shape and extensive cell death. During these changes, PAS and Feulgen-positive granules, as well as basement membranelike strands are liberated from the papillae into the underlying preosseous mesenchyme. Surgical removal of a papilla before a critical stage in its maturation results in the absence of the ossicle that would have underlain

it. Once removed, the papilla does not regenerate. The number of papillae and ossicles which form is less if the growth rate of the eye is subnormal between the 4th and the 8th day of incubation (Coulombre et al., 48). The growing ossicles inhibit each other in zones of overlap. This is one of the factors involved in shaping these bones.

The scleral cartilage develops in the mesenchyme that condenses around the expanding optic cup. In the chick embryo this mesenchyme is determined as cartilage as early as the 4th day of incubation, although it does not differentiate into hyaline cartilage until the 7th or 8th day of incubation

(Weiss and Amprino, 262). While the inductor of the scleral cartilage remains unknown, the ability of the neural tube to induce vertebral cartilage (Lash, 124) suggests that the neural retina or pigmented epithelium, both of neural origin, may serve as inductors. The scleral cartilage (excepting foramina for nerves and vessels) corresponds precisely in area with the underlying pigmented epithelium of the retina. Once their fate has been determined, the cells of the precartilagenous scleral mesenchyme will form flat plates of cartilage in tissue culture, even after they have been disaggregated and reaggregated. In contrast, similarly treated mesenchyme from the bone rudiments of the limb of the chick embryo form rods of cartilage (Weiss and Moscona, 265). Once the cartilage has begun to differentiate, its thickness, shape, and the arrangement of its cells are greatly influenced by mechanical factors (Weiss and Amprino, 262; Amprino and Pansa, 11). These mechanical forces are generated in the developing sclera by the expanding vitreous body (Coulombre and Coulombre, 45), the accumulation of which is under the control of the lens (Coulombre and Coulombre, 46). The skeletal elements and collagen of the sclera not only become tailored to the developing eye, but also, by locally altering the tensile strength of the wall as they differentiate, contribute to the shaping of the eye. Thus, they account for the development of the corneal curvature anteriorly, as well as the marked departure of the posterior segment from spherical shape in so many submammalian eyes.

Summary

It is tempting to liken the interactions which occur among the ocular tissues during development to a conference. The neural retina appears to play the role of chairman and to marshal the interactions among the participants in such a way that their geometric relationships become suitable for optical function. All of the participating tissues seem to have been identified. A good deal is known concerning which tissues convey information, which tissues respond to this information, what information is being transferred, and the timetable according to which these exchanges are made. Despite our increasingly detailed knowledge of these aspects of ocular morphogenesis, we have no specific information on the mechanisms by which one tissue of the eye influences another. One of the most important and significant undertakings in the period ahead will be to determine the language in which this morphogenetic conference is being conducted.

References

1. Adelmann, H. B., "The Formation of Lenses from the Margin of the Optic Cup in Eyes Implanted in the Belly Wall of *Triton* and the Possibility of the Formation of Lenses from Belly Ectoderm," *Arch. Entwicklungsmech. Or.* 113:704–723 (1928).

2. ———, "Experimental Studies on the Development of the Eye. II. The Eye Forming Potencies of the Median Portions of the Urodelan Neural Plate (*Triton taeniatus* and *Amblystoma punctatum*)," *J. Exptl. Zool.* 54:219–317 (1929).

3. ———, "Experimental Studies on the

Development of the Eye. III. The Effect of Substrate on the Heterotopic Development of Median and Lateral Strips of the Anterior End of the Neural Plate of *Amblystoma*," *J. Exptl. Zool.* 57:223–281 (1930).

4. ———, "Problem of Cyclopia," *Quart. Rev. Biol.* 11:161–182; 284–304 (1936).

5. ———, "Experimental Studies on the Development of the Eye. IV. The Effect of the Partial and Complete Excision of the Prechordal Substrate on the Development of the Eyes of *Amblystoma punctatum*," *J. Exptl. Zool.* 75:199–227 (1937).

6. Alagna, G., "Ricerche Sperimentali sul Mucoide Corneale. Nota 1. Suo Compartamento in Rapporta all' età," *Arch. Ottalmol.* 58:259–271 (1954).

7. Alderman, A. L., "The Determination of the Eye in the Anuran, *Hyla regilla*," *J. Exptl. Zool.* 70:205–232 (1935).

8. ———, "A Factor Influencing the Bilaterality of the Eye Rudiment in *Hyla regilla*," *Anat. Record* 72:297–302 (1938).

9. Alexander, L. E., "An Experimental Study of the Role of Optic Cup and Overlying Ectoderm in Lens Formation in the Chick Embryo," *J. Exptl. Zool.* 75:41–73 (1937).

10. Amprino, R., "Ricerche Sperimentale sulla Morfogenese del Cristallino nell' Embrione di Pollo. Induzione e Rigenerazione," *Arch. Entwicklungsmech. Or.* 144:71–80 (1949).

11. ———, and E. Pansa, "Ricerche Sulla Differenziazione e sull' Accrescimento della Cartilagine in Condizioni Meccaniche Sperimentalmente Modificate," *Arch. Entwicklungsmech. Or.* 148:179–194 (1955).

12. Anseth, A., "Glycosaminoglycans in the Developing Corneal Stroma," *Exptl. Eye Res.* 1:116–121 (1961).

13. Ashton, N., "Corneal Vascularization," *The Transparency of the Cornea*, S. Duke-Elder and E. S. Perkins, eds. Springfield, Ill.: Charles C Thomas, pp. 131–148 (1960).

14. Attardi, G., "La Coltivazione *in vitro* di Cellule Fisse Corneali di Embrione di Pollo," *Arch. Ital. Anat. Embriol.* 59:38–56 (1954).

15. Aurell, G., and H. Holmgren, "On the Metachromatic Staining of the Corneal Tissue and Some Observations on Its Transparency," *Acta Ophthalmol.* 31:1–27 (1953).

16. Balinsky, B. I., "On the Eye Cup-Lens Correlation in Some South African Amphibians," *Experientia* 7:180–181 (1951).

17. ———, "On the Factors Determining the Size of the Lens Rudiment in Amphibian Embryos," *J. Exptl. Zool.* 135(2): 255–299 (1957).

18. Ballowitz, E., "Ueber das Epithel der Membrana Elastica Posterior des Auges, seine Kerne und eine Merkwürdige Struktur seiner grossen Zellsphären," *Arch. Mikroskop. Anat. Entwicklungsgeschichte* 56:230–291 (1900).

19. Barden, R. B., "The Origin and Development of Chromatophores of the Amphibian Eye," *J. Exptl. Zool.* 90:475–519 (1942).

20. ———, "Changes in the Pigmentation of the Iris in Metamorphosing Amphibian Larvae," *J. Exptl. Zool.* 92:171–197 (1943).

21. Bednyakova, T. A., "Changes in Embryonic Skin Transplanted to the Site of the Cornea in Adult Rats," *Dokl. Akad. Nauk SSSR* 99:1103–1106 (1954).

22. ———, "Changes in Embryonic Skin Transplanted to the Site of the Cornea in Adult Rabbits," *Dokl. Akad. Nauk SSSR* 100:1195–1198 (1955). *Excerpta Med. Sec. XII*, 10:453 Abstr. (1956).

23. Beliaeva, T. G., "Replacement of an Open Defect in the Rabbit Cornea by Embryonic Skin," *Dokl. Akad. Nauk SSSR* 100:179–182 (1955).

24. Binder, R. F., and H. F. Binder, "Regenerative Processes in the Endothelium of the Cornea," *A.M.A. Arch Ophthalmol.* 57:11–13 (1957).

25. Boterenbrood, E. C., "Organization in Aggregates of Anterior Neural Plate Cells of *Triturus alpestris*," *Koninkl. Ned. Akad. Wetenschap. Proc. Ser. C* 61:470–481 (1958).

26. Brockhoff, V., "Zur Entwicklung der Sehzellen und zur Frage der Kernsekretion in der Retina," *Anat. Anz. Suppl.* 104:162–166 (1957).

27. Busacca, M. A., "La Membrane Basale de l'Épithélium Cornéen," *Bull. Soc. Ophtalmol. France* 62: 133–134 (1949).

28. Bytinski-Salz, H., "Chromatophore Studies. VII. The Behavior of Bombina

Melanophores during the Epidermisation of the Cornea," *Embryologia* 6:67–83 (1961).

29. Calmettes, L., F. Déodati, H. Planel, and P. Bec, "Etude Histologique et Histochemique de l'Épithélium Antérieur de la Cornée et de Ses Basales," *Arch. Ophtalmol. Paris* 16:481–506 (1956).

30. Carasso, N., "Ultrastructure de Cellules Visuelles de Larves d'Amphibiens," *Compt. Rend. Acad. Sci.* 247:527–531 (1958).

31. ——, "Etude au Microscope Éléctronique de la Morphogenèse du Segment Externe des Cellules Visuelles Chez le Pleurodèle," *Compt. Rend. Acad. Sci.* 248:3058–3060 (1959).

32. ——, "Role de l'Ergastoplasme dans l'Élaboration du Glycogène au cours de la Formation du Paraboloide des Cellules Visuelles," *Compt. Rend. Acad. Sci.* 250: 600–602 (1960).

33. Chanturishvili, P. S., "Evidence Concerning the Question of Causality and of Wolffian Regeneration," *Soobshch. Akad. Nauk Gruz.* 3:261–268 (1942).

34. Cogan, D. G., "Applied Anatomy and Physiology of the Cornea," *Trans. Am. Acad. Ophthalmol. Otolaryngol.* 55:329–359 (1951).

35. Collins, E. T. "The Development of the Posterior Elastic Lamina of the Cornea or Membrane of Descemet," *Roy.' Ophthalmol. Hosp. Rep.* 14:305–311 (1897).

36. Coulombre, A. J., "Correlations of Structural and Biochemical Changes in the Developing Retina of the Chick," *Am. J. Anat.* 96:153–189 (1955).

37. ——, "The Role of Intraocular Pressure in the Development of the Chick Eye. I. Control of Eye Size," *J. Exptl. Zool.* 133: 211–225 (1956).

38. ——, "The Role of Intraocular Pressure in the Development of the Chick Eye. II. Control of Corneal Size," *A.M.A. Arch. Ophthalmol.* 57:250–253 (1957).

39. ——, "Cytology of the Developing Eye," *International Review of Cytology*, G. Bourne, ed. New York: Academic Press, vol. 11, pp. 161–194 (1961).

40. ——, "Problems in Corneal Morphogenesis," *Advances in Morphogenesis*, M. Abercrombie and J. Brachet, eds. New York: Academic Press, vol. 4, pp. 81–109 (1965).

41. ——, and J. L. Coulombre, "The Role of Mechanical Factors in Brain Morphogenesis," *Anat. Record* 130:289–290 (1958).

42. ——, and ——, "Corneal Development. I. Corneal Transparency," *J. Cellular Comp. Physiol.* 51:1–12 (1958).

43. ——, and ——, "The Role of Intraocular Pressure in the Development of the Chick Eye. IV. Corneal Curvature," *A.M.A. Arch. Ophthalmol.* 59: 502–506 (1958).

44. ——, and ——, "Control of the Development of Corneal Transparency by Pituitary Grafts," *Anat. Record* 133:264–265 (1959).

45. ——, and ——, "The Development of the Structural and Optical Properties of the Cornea," *The Structure of the Eye*, G. K. Smelser, ed. New York: Academic Press, pp. 405–420 (1961).

46. ——, and ——, "Lens Development. I. Role of the Lens in Eye Growth," *J. Exptl. Zool.* 156:39–47 (1964).

47. ——, and ——, "Corneal Development. III. Role of the Thyroid in Dehydration and the Development of Transparency," *Exptl. Eye Res.* 3:105–114 (1964).

48. ——, ——, and Hasmukh Mehta, "The Skeleton of the Eye. I. Conjunctival Papillae and Scleral Ossicles," *Develop. Biol.* 5:382–401 (1962).

49. ——, ——, and S. N. Steinberg, "The Role of Intraocular Pressure in the Development of the Chick Eye. V. Pigmented Epithelium," *Invest. Ophthalmol.* 2:83–89 (1963).

50. ——, and ——, "Lens Development. Fiber Elongation and Lens Orientation," *Science* 142:1489–1490 (1963).

51. Dabaghian, N. V., "Regulative Properties of the Eye in the Embryos of Acipenseridae," *Dokl. Akad. Nauk SSSR* 125:938–940 (1959).

52. Dabelow, A., "Der Scleralring der Sauropsiden, sein Phylogentischer Ursprung und seine Ontogenetische Entwicklung," *Z. Morphol. Anthropol.* 26:305–332 (1927).

53. Da Costa, A. C., "Sur Quelques Faits Cytologiques de l'Histogénèse de la Rétine," *Acta Anat.* 4:79–86 (1947).

54. Davson, H., "The Hydration of the Cornea," *Biochem. J.* 59:24–28 (1955).

55. Dejean, C., G. Leplat and F. Hervouët,

L'Embryologie de l'Oeil et Sa Tératologie. Paris: Masson et Cie (1958).

56. De Robertis, E., "Morphogenesis of the Retinal Rods. An Electron Microscope Study," *J. Biophys. Biochem. Cytol. Suppl.* 2:209–218 (1956).

57. Deth, J. H. M. G. van, "Induction et Régénération du Cristallin Chez l'Embryon de la Poule," *Acta Neerl. Morphol.* 3:151–169 (1940).

58. Detwiler, S. R., "Experimental Observations upon the Developing Retina," *J. Comp. Neurol.* 55:473–492 (1932).

59. ———, *Vertebrate Photoreceptors.* New York: Macmillan (1943).

60. Dohlman, C. H., and E. A. Balazs, "Chemical Studies on Descemet's Membrane of the Bovine Cornea," *Arch. Biochem.* 57:445–457 (1955).

61. Dorris, F., "Differentiation of the Chick Eye *in vitro*," *J. Exptl. Zool.* 78:385–415 (1938).

62. Dragamirow, N. I., "Ueber die Faktoren der Embryonalen Entwicklung der Linse bei Amphibien," *Arch. Entwicklungsmech. Or.* 116:633–668 (1929).

63. ———, "Über die Entwicklung des Augenbechers aus Transplantierten Stückchen des Embryonalen Tapetums," *Arch. Entwicklungsmech. Or.* 126:636–662 (1932).

64. ———, "Über die Koordination des Teilprozesses in der Embryonalen Morphogenese des Augenbechers," *Arch. Entwicklungsmech. Or.* 129:552–560 (1933).

65. ———, "Ueber die Determination der Augenbecherblätter bei *Triton taeniatus*," *Arch. Entwicklungsmech. Or.* 131:540–542 (1934).

66. ———, "Die Determination des Augenkeimes bei Amphibien," *Tr. Inst. Zool. Biol. Akad. Nauk Ukr. SSSR* 8:25–149 (1935).

67. ———, "Über Induktion sekundärer Retina im Transplantierten Augenbecher bei *Triton* und *Pelobates*," *Arch. Entwicklungsmech. Or.* 134:716–737 (1936).

68. Duke-Elder, S., "System of Ophthalmology. II. The Anatomy of the Visual System," St. Louis: C. V. Mosby, Co. (1961).

69. Dürken, B., "Ueber einseitige Augenextirpation bei jungen Froschlarven. Ein Beitrag zur Kenntness der Echten Entwicklungs Korrelationen," *Z. Wiss.*

Zool. Abt. A 105:192–242 (1913).

70. Eakin, R., "Determination and Regulation of Polarity in the Retina of *Hyla regilla*," *Univ. Calif. Publ. Zool.* 51:245–287 (1947).

71. Fischel, A., "Ueber Rücklaufige Entwicklung. I. Die Rückbildung der Transplantierten," *Arch. Entwicklungsmech. Or.* 42:1–71 (1917).

72. ———, "Ueber den Einfluss des Auges auf die Entwicklung und Erhaltung der Hornhaut," *Klin. Mbl. Augenheilk* 62:1–5 (1919).

73. Fortuyn-van Leyden, C. E., "Some Observations on Periodic Nuclear Division in the Cat," *Proc. Koninkl. Ned. Akad. Wetenschap.* 19:38 (1917).

74. ———, "Day and Night Period in Nuclear Divisions," *Proc. Koninkl. Ned. Akad. Wetenschap.* 29:979–988 (1926).

75. Garcia-Austt, E., "Aparicion y Desarrollo del ERG del Embrion de Pallo," *Trabajo de Adscripcion de Fisiologia, Facultad de Medicina, Montevideo* (1953).

76. Gemolotto, G., and C. Patrone, "Rilievi Isto-chimici Sulla Distribuzione del Mucopolisaccaride nella Cornea e nella Sclera dell'Occhio Umano nelle Diverse Età," *Giorn. Ital. Oftalmol.* 8:42–52 (1955).

77. Ghiani, P., and G. Bergamini, "Aspetti della Evoluzione Fisiomorfologica della Cornea. Osservazioni Istochimiche in Embrione di Pollo," *Atti Accad. Ligure Sci. Lettere Genoa* 14:298–301 (1958).

78. ———, and ———, "Modificazioni Sperimentale nella Morfogenesi della Cornea. Richerche in Embrione di Pollo," *Atti Accad. Ligure Sci. Lettere Genoa* 14:403–408 (1958).

79. Glücksmann, A., "Development and Differentiation of Tadpole Eye," *Brit. J. Ophthalmol.* 24:153–178 (1940).

80. ———, "Cell Deaths in Normal Vertebrate Ontogeny," *Biol. Rev. Cambridge Phil. Soc.* 26:59–86 (1951).

81. Groll, O., "Über Transplantation von Rückenhaut an Stelle der Conjunctiva bei Larven von *Rana fusca* (Rösel)," *Arch. Entwicklungsmech. Or.* 100:385–429 (1923).

82. Güttes, E., "Die Herkunft des Augenpigments beim Kaninchen-Embryo," *Z. Zellforsch. Mikroskop. Anat. Abt. Histochem.* 39:168–202 (1953).

83. ——, "Über die Beinflussung du Pigmentgenese im Auge des Hühnerembryos durch Röntgenstrahlen und über die Herkunft du Pigmentgranula," *Z. Zellforsch. Mikroskop. Anat.* 39:260–275 (1953).

84. Hagedoorn, A., "The Early Development of the Endothelium of Descemet's Membrane, the Cornea and the Anterior Chamber of the Eye," *Brit. J. Ophthalmol.* 12:479–495 (1928).

85. ——, "Beitrag zur Entwicklungsgeschichte des Auges," *Arch. Augenheilk* 102:33–110, 393–433 (1930).

86. Harms, W., "Brillen bei Amphibienlarven," *Zool. Anz.* 56:136–142 (1923).

87. Harris, J. E., "The Physiologic Control of Corneal Hydration," *Am. J. Ophthalmol.* 44: no. 5, part II: 262–280 (1957).

88. Harrison, J. R., "*In vitro* Analysis of Differentiation of Retinal Pigment in the Developing Chick Embryo," *J. Exptl. Zool.* 118:209–242 (1951).

89. Hasegawa, M., "Restitution of the Eye after Removal of the Retina and Lens in the Newt, *Triturus pyrrhogaster*," *Embryologia* 4:1–32 (1958).

90. Hellström, B. E., "Experimental Approach to the Pathogenesis of Retrolental Fibroplasia. IX. The Histochemical Localization of Succinic Dehydrogenase in the Retina of Normal and Oxygen-Exposed Animals," *Acta Pathol. Microbiol. Scand.* 39:8–14 (1956).

91. Hermann, H., "Some Problems of Protein Formation in the Sclera and Cornea of the Chick Embryo," *A Symposium on the Chemical Basis of Development*, W. D. McElroy and B. Glass, eds. Baltimore: The Johns Hopkins Press, pp. 329–338 (1958).

92. Holtfreter, J., "Morphologische Beinflussung von Urodelenektoderm bei xenoplastischer Transplantation," *Arch. Entwicklungsmech. Or.* 133:367–426 (1935).

93. ——, "Gewebeaffinität, ein Mittel der embryonalen Formbildung," *Arch. Exptl. Zellforsch.* 23:169–209 (1939).

94. Hooff, A. van den, "De Doorzichtigheid van de Cornea," *Ned. Tijdschr. Geneesk.* 95:2491–2494 (1951).

95. ——, "Electronenmicroscopisch Onderzoek ten Behoeve van Cytologie en Histologie," Thesis, University of Amsterdam, Excelsior, The Hague (1957).

96. Hunt, H. H., "A Study of the Fine Structure of the Optic Vesicle and Lens Placode of the Chick Embryo during Induction," *Develop. Biol.* 3:175–209 (1961).

97. Iasvoin, G. V., "Development of Cornea in Chick." (In Russian). *Arkh. Anat. Gistol. i Embriol.* 21:31–44 (1939). *Biol. Abstr.* 14:10570 (1940).

98. Ignatieva, G. M., "Histological Change of Skin Transplanted into the Eye in Tailless Amphibians." (In Russian). *Dokl. Akad. Nauk SSSR* 81:701–704 (1951). *Ophthalmic Lit.* 5:6028 Abstr. (1951).

99. ——, "Formation of the Cornea in the Tadpole from the Skin of *Triton taeniatus* Larvae." (In Russian). *Dokl. Akad. Nauk SSSR* 82:167–170 (1952).

100. ——, "Restoration of the Cornea in Anuran Amphibians after Its Partial and Total Ablation." (In Russian). *Dokl. Akad. Nauk SSSR* 100:187–190 (1955).

101. ——, "Replacement of the Cornea of Adult Amphibia by Larval Skin." (In Russian). *Dokl. Akad. Nauk SSSR* 100: 385–388 (1955). *Excerpta Med. Sec. XII*, 10:454 Abstr. (1956).

102. Ikeda, Y., "Ueber die Bildung Akzessorischer Retina aus dem Tapetum bei Hynobius," *Arch. Entwicklungsmech. Or.* 136:676–680 (1937).

103. ——, "Ueber die Wechselseitigen Beziehungen der Sinnesorgane Untereinander in ihrer Normalen und Experimentell Bedingten Entwicklung," *Arb. Anat. Inst. Japan Univ. Sendai* 21:1–44 (1938).

104. Jackson, S. F., "Cytoplasmic Granules in Fibrogenic Cells," *Nature* 175:39–40 (1955).

105. Jacobson, A. G., "The Roles of Neural and Nonneural Tissues in Lens Induction," *J. Exptl. Zool.* 139 (3):525–557 (1958).

106. Jacobson, C. O., "The Localization of the Presumptive Cerebral Regions in the Neural Plate of the Axolotl Larva," *J. Embryol. Exptl. Morphol.* 7:1–21 (1959).

107. Jakus, M. A., "Studies on the Cornea. I. The Fine Structure of the Rat Cornea," *Am. J. Ophthalmol.* 38, no. 1, part II: 40–53 (1954).

108. ——, "Studies on the Cornea. II. The Fine Structure of Descemet's Membrane," *J. Biophys. Biochem. Cytol. Suppl.* 2:243–252 (1956).

109. Janosky, I. D., and B. S. Wenger, "A Histochemical Study of Glycogen Distribution in the Developing Nervous System of *Amblystoma*," *J. Comp. Neurol.* 105:127–150 (1956).

110. Kaltenbach, J., "Local Action of Thyroxin on Amphibian Metamorphosis. I. Development of Eyelids, Nictitating Membrane, Cornea and Extrinsic Ocular Muscles in *Rana pipiens* Larvae Affected by Thyroxin-Cholesterol Implants," *J. Exptl. Zool.* 122:41–51 (1953).

111. Kessler, L., "Zur Entwicklung des Auges der Wirbeltiere," Leipzig: F. C. W. Vogel (1877).

112. Kikkawa, Y., "Elastic Double System and Selective Permeability to Cations in the Stroma of the Rabbit Cornea," *Japan J. Physiol.* 6:300–312 (1956).

113. ——, "Light Scattering Studies of the Rabbit Cornea," (In Japanese). *J. Clin. Ophthalmol. Tokyo* 13:1409–1421 (1959).

114. ——, "Light Scattering Studies of the Rabbit Cornea," *Japan J. Physiol.* 10:292–302 (1960).

115. Knape, E. V., "Über die Entwicklung der Hornhaut des Hühnchens," *Anat. Anz.* 34:417–424 (1909).

116. Koecke, H. U., "Die Differenzierung der Melanoblasten zu Melanocyten und die Bildung des Melanins *in vivo* beim Entenembryo (Khaki Campbell)," *Z. Zellforsch. Mikroskop. Anat.* 50:238–274 (1959).

117. Kramisheva, V. N., "Development of the Retina in the Groundling." (In Russian). *Dokl. Akad. Nauk SSSR* 109:1219–1221 (1956). *Intern. Abstr. Biol. Sci.* 14:1853 Abstr. (1959).

118. Ladijenski, V. de, "Sur l'Évolution de la Structure Fibrillaire de la Cornée Chez l'Embryon de Poule," *Compt. Rend. Soc. Biol.* 78:307–308 (1915).

119. Laguesse, E., "Les Lamilles Primitives de la Cornée du Poulet Sont, comme le Corps Vitré, d'Origine Mésostromale Ectodermique," *Compt. Rend. Soc. Biol.* 89:543–546 (1923).

120. ——, "Chondriome et Développement des Fibrilles dans la Cornée," *Compt. Rend. Soc. Biol.* 89:871–873 (1923).

121. ——, "Développement de la Cornée Chez le Poulet; Rôle du Mésostroma; Son Importance Générale; les Membranes Basales," *Arch. Anat. Microscop.* 22:216–265 (1926).

122. Langman, J., "Appearance of Antigens during Development of the Lens," *J. Embryol. Exptl. Morphol.* 7 (2):264–274 (1959).

123. Lasarev, N. I., "On the Source of the Morphogenic Influence in the Process of Induction of the Cornea," *Dokl. Akad. Nauk SSSR* 53:483–486 (1946).

124. Lash, J., "Tissue Interaction and Specific Metabolic Responses: Chondrogenic Induction and Differentiation," *Cytodifferentiation and Macromolecular Synthesis*, M. Locke, ed. New York: Academic Press, pp. 235–260 (1963).

125. Le Cron, W. L., "Experiments on the Origin and Differentiation of the Lens in *Amblystoma*," *Am. J. Anat.* 6:245–257 (1907).

126. Lenhossek, M. von, "Die Entwicklung und Bedeutung der Zonulafasern, nach Untersuchungen am Hühnchen," *Arch. Mikroskop. Anat.* 77:280–310 (1911).

127. Levi, G., "Le Développement de la Cornée Chez les Amniotes," *Compt. Rend. Assoc. Anat. 21ᵉ Réunion Liège* pp. 358–369 (1926).

128. Lewis, M. R., "Mitochondria in the Visual Cells of the Fowl," *Anat. Record* 25:110–111 Abstr. (1923).

129. Lewis, W. H., "Experimental Studies on the Development of the Eye in Amphibia. I. On the Origin of the Lens in *Rana palustris*," *Am. J. Anat.* 3:505–536 (1904).

130. ——, "Experimental Studies on the Development of the Eye in Amphibia. II. On the Cornea," *J. Exptl. Zool.* 2:431–446 (1905).

131. ——, "Experiments on the Origin and Differentiation of the Optic Vesicle in Amphibia," *Am. J. Anat.* 7:259–277 (1907).

132. Liedke, K. B., "Lens Competence in *Amblystoma punctatum*," *J. Exptl. Zool.* 117:573–591 (1951).

133. ——, "Studies on Lens Induction in *Amblystoma punctatum*," *J. Exptl. Zool.* 117:353–379 (1955).

134. Lopashov, G. V., "On the Significance of Different Processes in the Restoration of Amphibian Eyes," *Dokl. Akad. Nauk SSSR* 69:865–868 (1949).

135. ——, *Developmental Mechanisms*

of *Vertebrate Eye Rudiments*, translated by Jean Medawar. New York: Pergamon Press (1963).

136. ——, and O. G. Stroeva, "Morphogenesis of the Vertebrate Eye," *Advances in Morphogenesis*, M. Abercrombie and J. Brachet, eds. New York: Academic Press, vol. 1, pp. 331–377 (1961).

137. ——, and ——, *Development of the Eye in the Light of Experimental Investigations*. Monograph. Moscow: USSR Academy of Sciences Press (1963).

138. Mangold, O., "Das Determinationsproblem. III. Das Wirbeltierauge in der Entwicklung und Regeneration," *Ergeb. Biol.* 7:193–403 (1931).

139. ——, "Isolationsversuche zur Analyse der Entwicklung bestimmter kopforgan," *Naturwissenschaften* 21:394–397 (1933).

140. ——, "Entwicklung und Differenzierung der Präsumptiven Epidermis und ihres Unterlagernden Entomesoderms aus der Neurula von *Triton alpestris* als isolat," *Arch. Entwicklungsmech. Or.* 147:131–170 (1954).

141. ——, "Experimente zur Entwicklungsphysiologie des Urodelenkopfes," *Verhandl. Anat. Ges.* 54:3–53 (1957).

142. Mann, I. C., "Development of the Cornea," *Trans. Ophthalmol. Soc. United Kingdom* 51:63–88 (1931).

143. ——, *Development of the Human Eye*. New York: Grune & Stratton (1950).

144. ——, *Developmental Abnormalities of the Eye*. Philadelphia: J. B. Lippincott (1957).

145. Maurice, D. M., "The Structure and Transparency of the Cornea," *J. Physiol. London* 136:263–286 (1957).

146. ——, "The Physics of Corneal Transparency," *The Transparency of the Cornea*, S. Duke-Elder and E. S. Perkins, eds. Springfield, Ill.: Charles C Thomas, pp. 41–50 (1960).

147. ——, "The Cornea and Sclera," *The Eye, Vegetative Physiology and Biochemistry*, H. Davson, ed. New York: Academic Press, vol. 1, pp. 289–368 (1962).

148. McKeehan, M. S., "Cytological Aspects of Embryonic Lens Induction in the Chick," *J. Exptl. Zool.* 117:31–64 (1951).

149. —— "A Quantitative Study of Self-Differentiation of Transplanted Lens Primordia in the Chick," *J. Exptl. Zool.* 126:157–176 (1954).

150. ——, "The Relative Ribonucleic Acid Content of Lens and Retina during Lens Induction in the Chick, *Am. J. Anat.* 99:131–155 (1956).

151. ——, "Induction of Portions of the Chick Lens without Contact with the Optic Cup," *Anat. Record* 132:297–305 (1958).

152. Medvedeva, I. M., "A Comparative-Embryological Study of the Mammalian Eye." Thesis, Moscow State University (1955).

153. Meyer, M., "Über den Tages rythmus und die relative Dauer der Zellteilungen im Epithel der Spälarven ausseren Cornea von *Rana temporaria*," *Z. Zellforsch. Mikroskop. Anat.* 40:228–256 (1954).

154. Meyer, D. B., and R. O'Rahilly, "The Development of the Cornea in the Chick," *J. Embryol. Exptl. Morphol.* 7: 303–315 (1959).

155. Migazzo, C., "Origine del Mesostroma della Cornea nell'Embrione di Pollo," *Boll. Soc. Ital. Biol. Sper.* 7:698–700 (1932).

156. Mikami, Y., "Lens Induction in the Urodelan *Triturus* with Special Reference to the Free Formation of the Lens," *Mem. Coll. Sci. Univ. Kyoto. Ser. B* 15: 134–157 (1939).

157. ——, "Experimental Studies on the Development of the Eye in Urodele, *Triturus pyrrhogaster* (Boie)," *Japan J. Zool.* 9:303–319 (1941).

158. Mills, N. L., and A. Donn, "Incorporation of Tritium-Labeled Thymidine by Rabbit Corneal Endothelium," *A.M.A. Arch. Ophthalmol.* 64:443–446 (1960).

159. Moyer, F., "Electron Microscope Observations on the Origin, Development and Genetic Control of Melanin Granules in the Mouse Eye," *The Structure of the Eye*, G. Smelser, ed. New York: Academic Press, pp. 469–486 (1961).

160. Murray, P. D. F., "The Development of the Conjunctival Papillae and of the Scleral Bones in the Embryo Chick," *J. Anat.* 77:225–240 (1943).

161. Nagano, "Untersuchungen zur Pathologie des Hornhautendothels," *Arch. Augenheilk* 76:26–68 (1914).

162. Nakayama, K., "Histochemical Studies on the Human Fetal Retina in the Course of Development (2 nucleic

acids)," *J. Clin. Ophthalmol. Tokyo* 11: 1024–1032 (1957).

163. Naylor, E. J., "Polarized Light Studies of Corneal Structure," *Brit. J. Ophthalmol.* 37:77–84 (1953).

164. ———, "The Structure of the Cornea as Revealed by Polarized Light," *Quart. J. Microscop. Sci.* 94:83–88 (1953).

165. Neifach, A. A., "Investigation of the Role of the Optic Rudiment in the Development of the Cornea in the Chick." (In Russian). *Dokl. Akad. Nauk SSSR* 75: 141–144 (1950).

166. ———, "The Development of the Chick Eye on the Chorioallantois," *Dokl. Akad. Nauk SSSR* 81:949–952 (1951).

167. ———, "Zavisimost' Razvitija Rogovicy ot Okružajuščih ee Častej Zarodyša," *Dokl. Akad. Nauk. SSSR* 85:937–940 (1952).

168. ———, "Transplantation of the Cornea at Various Stages of Development in Chorio-allantois." (In Russian). *Dokl. Akad. Nauk SSSR* 85:1177–1180 (1952). *Ophthalmic. Lit.* 6:3924 Abstr. (1952).

169. ———, "The Role of Some Form-producing Relations between the Different Parts of the Growing Cornea." (In Russian). *Dokl. Akad. Nauk SSSR* 85:1411–1414 (1952). *Ophthalmic. Lit.* 6:3925 Abstr. (1952).

170. Neüschuler, I., "Sul Differenziamento della Cornea nell'Embrione di Pollo," *Mon. Zool. Ital.* 42:289–297 (1931).

171. Nieuwkoop, P. D., I. Oikawa, and J. Boddingius, "The Anterior Transverse Neural Fold in Amphibians," *Arch. Neerl. Zool.* 13, Suppl. 1:167–184 (1958).

172. Norrby, Å., "On the Growth of the Crystalline Lens, the Eyeball and the Cornea in the Rat, and a Tentative Comparison with These Factors in *Homo*," *Acta Ophthalmol.* Suppl. 49:1–42 (1958).

173. Nussbaum, M., "Zur Ruckbildung Embryonaler Anlagen," *Arch. Mikroskop. Anat.* 57:676–705 (1901).

174. Offret, G., and C. Haye, "La Membrane Basali de l'Épithélium Cornéen," *Arch. Ophtalmol. Paris* 19:126–159 (1959).

175. O'Rahilly, R., and D. B. Meyer, "The Early Development of the Eye in the Chick, *Gallus domesticus* (Stages 8 to 25)," *Acta Anat.* 36:20–58 (1959).

176. ———, and ———, "The Periodic Acid-Schiff Reaction in the Cornea of the Developing Chick," *Z. Anat. Entwicklungsgeschichte* 121:351–368 (1960).

177. Orts-Llorca, F., and J. M. Genis-Galvez, "Experimental Production of Retinal Septa in the Chick Embryo. Differentiation of Pigment Epithelium into Neural Retina," *Acta Anat.* 42:31–70 (1960).

178. Papaconstantinou, J., and R. A. Resnik, "Characterization of the Lens Proteins," *Ann. Report Director, Dept. Embryol. Carnegie Inst. Wash.* 378–379 (1960).

179. ———, ———, and E. Saito, "Biochemistry of Bovine Lens Proteins. I. Isolation and Characterization of Adult α-Crystallins," *Biochim. Biophys. Acta* 60:205 (1962).

180. Parry, H. B., "Degenerations of the Dog Retina. I. Structure and Development of the Retina of the Normal Dog," *Brit. J. Ophthalmol.* 37:385–404 (1953).

181. Pirie, A., and R. van Heyningen, *Biochemistry of the Eye.* Oxford: Blackwell Scientific Publications (1956).

182. Polack, F. M., "Morphology of the Cornea. I. Study with Silver Stains," *Am. J. Ophthalmol.* 51, no. 5, part II:1051–1056 (1961).

183. Polyak, S. L., *The Vertebrate Visual System.* Chicago: University of Chicago Press (1957).

184. Popov, V. V., "Studies on the Morphogenesis of the Cornea in Anura,"*Arb. Staatsuniv. Gorky* 8:24–87 (1938).

185. Porter, K., and E. Yamada, "Studies on the Endoplasmic Reticulum. V. Its Form and Differentiation in Pigment Epithelial Cells of the Frog Retina," *J. Biophys. Biochem. Cytol.* 8:181 (1960).

186. Prince, J., *Comparative Anatomy of the Eye.* Springfield, Ill.: Charles C Thomas (1956).

187. Rabl, C., "Über den Bau und die Entwicklung der Linse," *Z. Wiss. Zool. Abt. A* 63:496–572; 65:257; 67:1–138 (1898–1900).

188. Ranvier, L., "Recherches Expérimentales sur le Mécanism de la Cicatrisation des Plaies de la Cornée," *Arch. Anat. Microscop. Morphol. Exptl.* 2:177–188 (1898).

189. Rebollo, M. A., "Some Aspects of the Histogenesis of the Retina," *Acta Neurol. Latinoam.* 1:142–147 (1955).

190. Redslob, E., "Le Développement de la Cornée," *Arch. Anat. Histol.*

248 COULOMBRE

Embryol. Strasbourg 19:135–229 (1935).
191. Reinbold, R., "Régulation de l'Oeil et Régénération du Cristallin chez l'Embryon de Poulet Opéré en Culture *in vitro*," *Arch. Anat. Microscop. Morphol. Exptl.* 47:341–357 (1958).
192. Reyer, R. W., "An Experimental Study of Lens Regeneration in *Triturus viridescens viridescens*. II. Lens Development from the Dorsal Iris in the Absence of the Embryonic Lens," *J. Exptl. Zool.* 113:317–353 (1950).
193. ———, "Lens Regeneration from Homoplastic and Heteroplastic Implants of Dorsal Iris into the Eye Chamber of *Triturus viridescens* and *Amblystoma punctatum*," *J. Exptl. Zool.* 133:145–189 (1956).
194. ———, "Regeneration in the Amphibian Eye," *Regeneration*, D. Rudnick, ed. New York: Ronald Press Co., pp. 211–265 (1962).
195. Rochon-Duvigneaud, A., *Les Yeux et la Vision des Vertébrés*. Paris: Masson et Cie (1943).
196. Rones, B., "Development of the Human Cornea," *A.M.A. Arch. Ophthalmol.* 8:568–575 (1932).
197. Rotmann, E., "Der Anteil von Induktor und reagierendem Gewebe an der Entwicklung der Amphibienlinse," *Arch. Entwicklungsmech. Or.* 139:1–49 (1939).
198. ———, "Über den Auslösungscharakter des Induktionsreizes bei der Linsenentwicklung. Versuche mit Experimentell verkleinerten bzw. vergrösserten Augenbechern bei *Triton taeniatus*," *Biol. Zentr.* 62:154–170 (1942).
199. Sallmann, L. von, "Experimental Studies of Some Ocular Effects of Alphachymotrypsin," *Trans. Am. Acad. Ophthalmol.* 4:25–32 (1960).
200. ———, L. L. Caravaggio, and P. Grimes, "Studies on the Corneal Endothelium of the Rabbit. I. Cell Division and Growth," *Am. J. Ophthalmol.* 51:955–969 (1961).
201. Sato, T., "Über die Determination des Fetalen Augenspalts bei *Triton taeniatus*," *Arch. Entwicklungsmech. Or.* 128:342–377 (1933).
202. Saxén, L., "The Glycogen Inclusion of the Visual Cells and Its Hypothetical Role in the Photomechanical Responses. Histochemical Investigation during Frog Ontogenesis," *Acta Anat.* 25:319–330 (1955).
203. Scheving, L. E., and J. J. Chiakulas, "The Effect of Hypophysectomy on the Daily Rhythmic Character of the Mitotic Rate in Larval Corneal Epithelium," *Anat. Record* 139:271–272 Abstr. (1961).
204. ———, and ———, "Effect of Hypophysectomy on the 24-hour Mitotic Rhythm of Corneal Epithelium in Urodele Larvae," *J. Exptl. Zool.* 194:39–43 (1962).
205. Schwarz, W., "Electronenmikroskopische Untersuchungen über die Differenzierung der Cornea – und Sklerafibrillen des Menschen," *Z. Zellforsch. Mikroskop. Anat.* 38:78–86 (1953).
206. ———, "Electron Microscopical Studies of the Fibrillogenesis in the Human Cornea," *The Structure of the Eye*, G. Smelser, ed. New York: Academic Press, pp. 393–404 (1961).
207. Seefelder, R., and W. Wolfrum, "Zur Entwicklung der vorderen Kammer und des Kammerwinkels beim Menschen, nebst Bemerkungen über ihre Entstehung bei Tieren," *Arch. Ophthalmol.* 63:430–451 (1906).
208. Seo, S., "Changes in the Reaction of Tissues to Periodic Acid Schiff's Stain during the Development of the White Rat," *Kyushu J. Med. Sci.* 5:169–182 (1955).
209. Sheldon, H., "An Electron Microscope Study of the Epithelium in the Normal Mature and Immature Mouse Cornea," *J. Biophys. Biochem. Cytol.* 2:253–262 (1956).
210. Shen, S. -C., P. C. Greenfield, and E. J. Boell, "Localization of Acetylcholinesterase in Chick Retina during Histogenesis," *J. Comp. Neurol.* 106:433–461 (1956).
211. Sidman, R., "Histogenesis of Mouse Retina Studied with Thymidine-H^3," *The Structure of the Eye*, G. Smelser, ed. New York: Academic Press, pp. 487–506 (1961).
212. Sigelman, S., C. H. Dohlman, and J. S. Friedenwald, "Mitotic and Wound Healing Activities in the Rat Corneal Epithelium. Influence of Various Hormones and Endocrine Glands," *A.M.A. Arch. Ophthalmol.* 52:751 (1954).
213. Sirlin, J. L., and S. K. Brahma, "Studies on Embryonic Induction Using Ra-

dioactive Tracers. II. The Mobilization of Protein Components during Induction of the Lens," *Develop. Biol.* 1:234–246 (1959).

214. Slonaker, J. R., "The Development of the Eye and Its Accessory Parts in the English Sparrow (*Passer domesticus*)," *J. Morphol.* 35:263–357 (1921).

215. Smelser, G. K., and V. Ozanics, "Studies on the Differentiation of the Cornea and Sclera of the Rabbit," *Anat. Record* 124:362 Abstr. (1956).

216. ——, and ——, "Distribution of Radioactive Sulfate in the Developing Eye," *Am. J. Ophthalmol.* 44, no. 4, part II:102–110 (1957).

217. ——, and ——, "Morphologic and Functional Development of the Cornea," *Am. J. Ophthalmol.* 47:100–101 Abstr. (1959).

218. ——, and ——, "Morphological and Functional Development of the Cornea," *The Transparency of the Cornea*, S. Duke-Elder and E. S. Perkins, eds. Springfield, Ill.: Charles C Thomas, pp. 23–40 (1960).

219. Smits, G., "Quantitative Interrelationships of the Chief Components of Some Connective Tissues during Foetal and Postnatal Development in Cattle," *Biochim. Biophys. Acta* 25:542–548 (1957).

220. Snesarev, P., "On the Construction of Cornea in the Light of Dynamics of Intermediary Fibrillar Substance." (In Russian). *Arkh. Anat. Gistol. i Embriol.* 21:209–240 (1939). *Biol. Abstr.* 14:10583 (1940).

221. Spemann, H., "Ueber Korrelationen in der Entwicklung des Auges," *Verhandl. Anat. Ges. Bonn* 61–79 (1901).

222. ——, "Über Linsbildung nach Experimenteller Entfernung der primären Linsenbildungzellen," *Zool. Anz.* 28: 419–432 (1905).

223. ——, "Zur Entwicklung des Wirbeltierauges," *Zool. Jahrb.* 32:1–98 (1912).

224. Sperry, R. W., "Optic Nerve Regeneration with Return of Vision in Anurans," *J. Neurophysiol.* 7:57–70 (1944).

225. ——, "Restoration of Vision after Crossing of Optic Nerves and after Contralateral Transplantation of Eye," *J. Neurophysiol.* 8:15–28 (1945).

226. Stanworth, A., "Effect of Intraocular Pressure on the Polarization Optics of the Cornea," *Acta 16th Concilium Ophthalmol. Britannia* pp. 1368–1376 (1950).

227. Stocker, F. W., "The Endothelium of the Cornea and Its Clinical Implications," *Trans. Am. Ophthalmol. Soc.* 51: 669 (1953).

228. Stone, L. S., "Functional Polarization in Developing and Regenerating Retinae of Transplanted Eyes," *Ann. N. Y. Acad. Sci.* 49:856–865 (1948).

229. ——, "Neural Retina Degeneration Followed by Regeneration from Surviving Retinal Pigment Cells in Grafted Adult Salamander Eyes," *Anat. Record* 106:89–109 (1950).

230. ——, "The Role of Retinal Pigment Cells in Regenerating Neural Retinae of Adult Salamander Eyes," *J. Exptl. Zool.* 113:9–13 (1950).

231. ——, "Normal and Reversed Vision in Transplanted Eyes," *A.M.A. Arch. Ophthalmol.* 49:28–35 (1953).

232. ——, "Further Experiments on Lens Regeneration in Eyes of the Adult Newt *Triturus v. viridescens*," *Anat. Record* 120:599–623 (1954).

233. ——, "Regeneration of the Retina, Iris, and Lens," *Regeneration in Vertebrates*, C. S. Thornton, ed. Chicago, Ill.: University of Chicago Press, pp. 3–14 (1959).

234. ——, and H. Steinitz, "Regeneration of Neural Retina and Lens from Retina Pigment Cell Grafts in Adult Newts," *J. Exptl. Zool.* 135(2):301–318 (1957).

235. Streeter, G. L., "Developmental Horizons in Human Embryos," *Contrib. Embryol. Carnegie Inst. Wash. Publ.* 592, 34: 165–196 (1951).

236. Stroeva, O. G., "Study of the Regenerative Ability of the Retina in Adult Frogs (Bombina) and Rats," *Izv. Acad. Nauk SSSR Biol. Nauki* no. 5:76–84 (1956).

237. ——, "Experimental Analysis of the Eye Morphogenesis in Mammals," *J. Embryol. Exptl. Morphol.* 8:349–368 (1960).

238. Studnicka, F. K., "Das Mesenchym und das Mesostroma der Froschlarven und deren Produkte," *Anat. Anz.* 40:33–62 (1911).

239. Székely, G., "Zur Ausbildung der lokalen funktionellen Spezifität der Ret-

ina," *Acta Biol. Acad. Sci. Hung.* 5:157–167 (1954).

240. ——, "Regulationstendenzen in der Ausbildung der 'Funktionellen Spezifität' der Retinaanlage bei *Triturus vulgaris*," *Arch. Entwicklungsmech. Or.* 150:48–60 (1957).

241. Tansley, K., "Factors Affecting the Development and Regeneration of Visual Purple in the Mammalian Retina," *Proc. Roy. Soc. London Ser. B* 114:79–103 (1933).

242. ten Cate, G., "The Intrinsic Development of Amphibian Embryos." Dissertation. Amsterdam: North Holland Publishing Co. (1953).

243. Thomas, C. I., *The Cornea.* Springfield, Ill.: Charles C Thomas (1955).

244. Toivonen, S., "Ueber die Leistungsspezifität der abnormen Induktoren im Implantaversuch bei *Triton*," *Ann. Acad. Sci. Fennicae Ser. A*, 45:3–150 (1940).

245. ——, "Zur Frage der Induktion selbständiger Linsen durch abnorme Induktoren im Implantatversuch bei Triton," *Ann. Zool. Soc. Vanamo* 11:1–28 (1945).

246. Tokuyasu, K., and E. Yamada, "The Fine Structure of the Retina Studied with the Electron Microscope. IV. Morphogenesis of Outer Segments of Retinal Rods," *J. Biophys. Biochem. Cytol.* 6:225–230 (1959).

247. ——, and ——, "The Fine Structure of the Retina. V. Abnormal Retinal Rods and Their Morphogenesis," *J. Biophys. Biochem. Cytol.* 7:187–190 (1960).

248. Twitty, V. C., "Eye," *Analysis of Development*, B. H. Willier, P. Weiss and V. Hamburger, eds. Philadelphia: Saunders pp. 403–414 (1955).

249. van Alphen, G., "On Emmetropia and Ametropia," *Ophthalmologica* Suppl. 142:1–92 (1961).

250. Vasama, Raimo, and Ritva Vasama, "On the Diurnal Cycle of Mitotic Activity in the Corneal Epithelium of Mice," *Acta Anat.* 33:230–237 (1958).

251. Wachs, H., "Restitution des Auges nach Extirpation von Retina und Linse bei *Tritonen*," *Arch. Entwicklungsmech. Or.* 46:328–390 (1920).

252. Waechter, H., "Die Inductionsfähigkeit der Gehirnplatte bei Urodelen und ihr medianlaterales Gefälle," *Arch. Entwicklungsmech. Or.* 146:201–274 (1953).

253. Walbeek, K. van, "Turgescence and Swelling Pressure," *The Transparency of the Cornea*, S. Duke-Elder and E. S. Perkins, eds. Springfield, Ill.: Charles C Thomas, pp. 51–66 (1960).

254. Walbeek, K. van, H. Neumann, J. E. Winkelman, J. H. C. Ruyter, and A. van den Hooff, "Nadere onderzoekinten over het Bindeveefsel van het Hoornvlies," *Koninkl. Vlaam. Acad. Gen. Belg.* 12:226–238 (1950).

255. Wald, G., "The Significance of Vertebrate Metamorphosis," *Science* 128:1481–1490 (1958).

256. ——, and H. Zussman, "Carotenoids of the Chicken Retina," *Nature* 140:197 (1937).

257. ——, and ——, "Carotenoids of the Chicken Retina," *J. Biol. Chem.* 122:449–460 (1938).

258. Walls, G., *The Vertebrate Eye and Its Adaptive Radiation.* New York: Hafner Publishing Co. (1963).

259. Watzka, M., "Über die Entwicklung der Cornea und der Linsenkapsel des Hühnchens," *Z. Anat. Entwicklungsgeschichte.* 104:424–439 (1935).

260. Weimar, V., "Healing Processes in the Cornea," *The Transparency of the Cornea*, S. Duke-Elder and E. S. Perkins, eds. Springfield, Ill.: Charles C Thomas, pp. 111–124 (1960).

261. Weiss, P., "Secretory Activity of the Inner Layer of the Embryonic Midbrain of the Chick, as Revealed by Tissue Culture," *Anat. Record* 58:299–302 (1934).

262. ——, and R. Amprino, "The Effect of Mechanical Stress on the Differentiation of Scleral Cartilage *in vitro* and in the Embryo," *Growth* 4:245–258 (1940).

263. ——, and S. Fitton-Jackson, "Fine Structural Changes Associated with Lens Determination in the Avian Embryo," *Develop. Biol.* 3(4):532–554 (1961).

264. ——, and A. G. Matoltsy, "Wound Healing in Chick Embryos *in vivo* and *in vitro*," *Develop. Biol.* 1:302–326 (1959).

265. ——, and A. Moscona, "Type-specific Morphogenesis of Cartilages Developed from Dissociated Limb and Scleral Mesenchyme *in vitro*," *J. Embryol. Exptl. Morphol.* 6:238–246 (1958).

266. Wilt, F. H., "The Differentiation of Visual Pigments in Metamorphosing Larvae of *Rana catesbiana*," *Develop. Biol.* 1:199–233 (1959).

267. Woellwarth, C. von, "Die Induktions-

stuffen des Gehirns," *Arch. Entwick-lungsmech. Or.* 145:582–668 (1952).

268. Woerdeman, M. W., "Experimentelle Untersuchungen über Lage und Bau der augenbildenden Bizerke in der Medullarplatte beim Axolotl," *Arch. Entwicklungsmech. Or.* 116:220–241 (1929).

269. ———, "Ueber die Determination der Augenlinsenstruktur bei Amphibien," *Z. Mikroskop. Anat. Forsch.* 36:600–606 (1934).

270. Wolff, E., *The Anatomy of the Eye and Orbit.* New York: McGraw-Hill (1958).

271. Yamada, E., K. Tokuyasu, and S. Iwaki, "The Fine Structure of Retina Studied with Electron Microscope. II. Pigment Epithelium and Capillary of the Choriocapillary Layer," *J. Electronmicroscop.* 6:42 (1958).

272. Yoshida, M., "Acetylcholine-hydrolyzing Enzyme in the Isolated Inner and Outer Segments of the Receptor Cell of Frog Retina," *Japan J. Physiol.* 8:155–159 (1958).

273. Zimmerman, L. E., and A. B. Eastham, "Acid Mucopolysaccharide in the Retinal Pigment Epithelium and Visual Cell Layer of the Developing Mouse Eye," *Am. J. Ophthalmol.* 47, no. 1, part II:488–499 (1959).

274. Zwaan, J., "Immunochemical Analysis of the Eye Lens during Development," *Lab. Anat. and Embryol.* Univ. of Amsterdam, Rototype, Amsterdam (1963).

SECTION III The Limb

The kind

10

Aspects of Limb Morphogenesis in the Chicken

RODOLFO AMPRINO

Institute of Human Anatomy
University of Bari
Bari, Italy

Several accounts of the development of limbs of tetrapod vertebrates have been published in recent years. Most of the descriptive and experimental data available have been reviewed and discussed, and forms such an extensive literature that it cannot be reported in detail here. This article, therefore, will be limited to selected basic aspects of limb morphogenesis in the chick embryo, particularly mechanisms of growth and individuation of territories, regulative processes, and the morphogenetic relationships between ectoderm and mesoderm of the limb bud.

Early Phases of Limb Formation

The position of the prospective limb areas lateral to the anterior and posterior part of the rhomboidal sinus was first determined by Wolff (74, 75), by means of localized x-irradiation of 9- to 13-somite chick embryos. The limb areas undergo displacement in a cranial and lateral direction until the 14-somite stage. By means of intracoelomic grafts of mapped regions of early chick embryos, Rudnick (58) showed the capacity for autonomous development of the wing territory at the presomitic or late cephalic fold stage, and of the hindlimb area at the 6-somite stage. The grafted territories developed according to their characteristic laterality and type. She also demonstrated that the wing territory lies slightly posterior to the region indicated by Wolff.

Chaube's (29) experiments, in which she marked both the ectoderm and mesoderm in the areas surrounding the sinus, in 2- to 16-somite embryos, indicated that no displacement of the ectoderm, relative to the mesoderm, takes place up to the 20- to 27-somite stage. The prospective mesoderm of the wing apparently attains its definitive position at the 2-somite stage. Enlargement of the prospective limb areas occurs uniformly and simultaneously in both cell layers. The limb-forming territories are at first close together, lateral to the posterior region of the sinus behind the primitive node. Later, they are shifted more cranially. At the 9- to 13-somite stage, the location of the limb areas is similar to that observed by Rudnick (58), whereas at 12- to 15-somites they lie more anteriorly than described by Rudnick, in a position which corresponds to Wolff's description (75).

From the results of grafts of the prospective wing territory, Chaube concluded that the craniocaudal (anteroposterior, ap) axis becomes determined at the 5-somite stage, and the dorsoventral (dv) axis at 13 somites. This sequence of determinations is similar for both the wing of the chick and the anterior limb of the urodele; in both species the fixation of the ap axis takes place earlier than the dv axis. It is suggested that the ap polarity may be determined as the limb mesoderm is segregated and localized during gastrulation. However, the dorsoventral axis in the chick limb becomes fixed relatively earlier than in amphibians.

The limb-forming areas of the chick embryo do not become morphologically distinguishable until stage 14. The anlage of the wing is indicated by a slight condensation of mesoderm at Hamburger-Hamilton stage 15 (39) and by a thickened ridge at stage 16 (Hamburger, 38). At stage 17 both limbs are distinct swellings. Rapid growth and gradual changes in shape (Fig. 10.1A) and structure of the limb rudiment soon occur. A thickening of the ectoderm covering the free edge of the mesodermal outgrowth appears

(Fig. 10.1B) and becomes more prominent with time in all amniotes.

In the chick the ectodermal thickening covers the entire free border of the bud initially, but undergoes a gradual reduction cranially and caudally during elongation of the bud. In mammals the ectodermal thickening forms during a comparatively later period. In the mouse and the mole, for example, it first appears in the caudal sector of the distal border of the digital plate rudiment at 10 to 10½ days, and extends rapidly in a cranial direction until it covers the whole distal border between 10½ and 11 days (Milaire, 53; Chapter 11). At this stage, precartilaginous blastemas have already differentiated in the stylozeugopod and in the region of ray IV of the metapod (Milaire, 53). In the human embryo (O'Rahilly et al., 56), the ectodermal thickening differentiates earlier in the cranial sector of the distal border of limb bud and extends in a caudal direction.

According to Milaire (53), cytochemical characteristics of the apical ridge proper, such as accumulation of cytoplasmic RNA and positive reaction for phosphatases, are detectable at an even earlier stage, in the comparatively thick ectoderm of the ventral face of the bud (9½ to 10 days in mouse and mole embryos). The thickening of the ventral ectoderm of the limb bud has also been observed in the human embryo (Blechschmidt, 23), as well as in various reptiles (Milaire, 52). In the chick, the ectoderm appears thicker and more basophilic in the ventral than in the dorsal aspect of the bud, at stages in which the apical thickening has already formed. The phosphatase reaction is more intense in the ectoderm of the distal border (Milaire, 53).

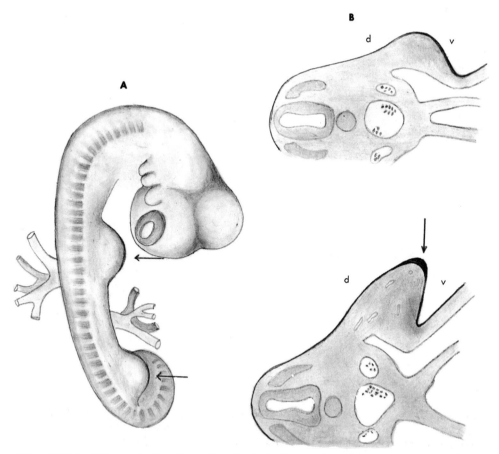

Fig. 10.1 *A.* Schematic drawing of a chick embryo, stage 21. Limb buds (arrows) appear as prominent swelling on the body wall. *B.* Cross sections of chick embryos, stage 17 (top) and stage 19 (bottom) at the wing bud level. Differences in thickness of the ectoderm between ventral, v, and dorsal, d, face of the wing bud. Arrow points to the apical ridge.

During limb elongation, characteristic asymmetries become more apparent along each axis and the bud is invaded by blood vessels (Barasa, 18).

Mechanism of Growth of the Limb Bud

All the proximodistal levels of the limb may develop from the early bud or its precursor when it is heterotopically transplanted to the coelomic cavity or chorioallantoic membrane. The early primordium of the limb thus con-tains all the materials and all the potencies for its independent development.

It had long been supposed that formation of the autopod precedes that of more proximal limb segments. Saunders (60), however, offered the first clear evidence that only the prospective stylopod is "individuated" (Waddington, 72) in the bud of the 3-day chick embryo. Individuation of the zeugopod takes place at the beginning of the 4th day, distal to the stylo-

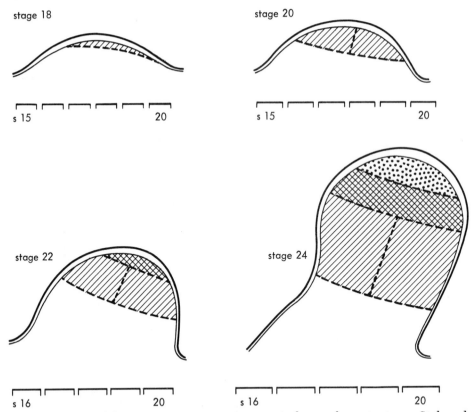

Fig. 10.2 Maps of the prospective wing segments in four embryonic stages. Stylopod: arm (blank). Zeugopod: forearm and carpus (hatched area). Autopod: metacarpus (crosshatched area), and proximal phalanges (dotted area). The apical ridge of the ectoderm and the regional somites are indicated.

pod. Still later, the rudiment of the autopod appears in the apical region of the elongating bud (Fig. 10.2). According to Saunders, the segregation of the prospective limb segments takes place in the distal region of the growing bud beneath the thickened ectoderm (apical ridge). A similar pattern of individuation has been traced in the chick hindlimb bud (Hampé, 40, 41). In the amphibian embryo, *Xenopus laevis*, individuation of the limb segments appears to be identical to that shown in the chick by Saunders (Tschumi, 70). A few experimental observations of Smith (quoted by Zwil-

ling, 83) in *Cricetus* suggest that the various limb territories appear at the apex of the bud in proximodistal sequence in mammalian embryos as well.

The mechanisms underlying this pattern of individuation are poorly understood. Minute carbon particles inserted in the distalmost layers of the bud mesoderm, beneath the ectodermal apical ridge, are later found in more proximal regions; moreover, the less developed the bud when marked, the more proximal the position of the mark later (Saunders, 60; Amprino and Camosso, 5; Hampé, 41). This evi-

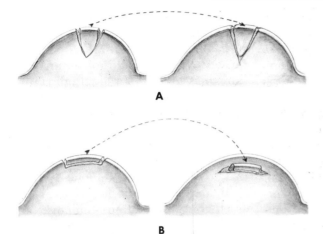

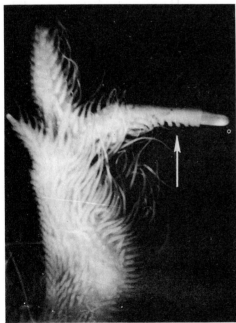

Fig. 10.3 A. Graft to the wing bud (right) of a wedge-shaped isolate from a hindlimb bud. B. Graft to the wing bud (right) of a thin distal layer of apical mesoderm and overlying thickened ectoderm from a hindlimb bud. C. Toe (arrow) developed on the wing distally, from the graft shown in B.

give rise to the more distal territories are of unknown origin. Carbon particles inserted in the subepithelial mesoderm near the base of the bud, in stage 18 to 21 embryos, maintain their subepithelial position, although they move distally. However, such displacement does not bring the labeled layer to the apex proper (Amprino and Camosso, 5). Hence, proximodistal sliding of the subectodermal mesoderm, as suggested by Blechschmidt (24) for the human embryo, could not account for the individuation of the apical territories.

Another possibility not excluded by such marking experiments is that individual cells or small groups of cells may move distally from relatively proximal regions of the bud to the apex without displacement of the carbon marks. There are two experiments which tend to argue against this idea: (1) If a wedge-shaped sector taken from the leg bud is inserted into a proximodistal groove in the wing bud (Fig. 10.3A), the wing develops a full set of skeletal parts, while the graft material gives rise to one toe. This result is obtained whether the operation is

dence seems to support the idea that the mesoderm which was originally distal is gradually displaced and separated from the apical ridge region as other mesodermal territories are formed at the tip.

These mesodermal cells which assemble beneath the apical ridge to performed at stage 18 or 20, that is, before individuation of the autopodal structures (Amprino and Camosso, 14). (2) If a thin strip of apical mesoderm and overlying thickened ectoderm from the leg bud is grafted to the dorsal aspect of the wing bud apex (Fig. 10.3B), a normal wing develops, containing at its distal tip additional skeletal structures of the foot (Fig. 10.3C). The number and proximodistal level of the foot parts which form are determined by the stage of the donor bud and the thickness of the mesodermal strip taken for the graft.

Thus the mesodermal cells destined to form the distalmost parts appear to be located in the apical region, even before any detectable individuation of the territories to which they will give rise. These cells may lie initially in a thin marginal layer at the tip of the adjacent, previously individuated territory. The insertion of carbon particles into such a layer would be practically impossible. Proliferation of these cells would give rise to a "newly individuated territory" with a new distal layer, which would then represent the matrix for a successively more distal part of the limb bud.

The gradual elongation of the limb bud and the individuation of mesodermal territories in an ordered temporal sequence from the base toward the apex of the bud requires (1) more rapid proximodistal growth than craniocaudal and dorsoventral, and (2) a comparatively higher rate of proliferation in the distal than in the proximal mesoderm of the bud during the period of territory individuation. Both these requirements are fulfilled during limb bud elongation. The distance between two marks inserted in the mesoderm along the proximodistal axis of the bud increases more rapidly than that between marks arranged along the craniocaudal or dorsoventral axis. This indicates that the rate of interstitial growth is higher in a longitudinal direction. Furthermore, a higher percentage of mitoses has been found in the apical portion of the bud than in the rest of the bud mesoderm (Camosso et al., 26). It must be stressed, however, that no discrete region endowed with a particularly high mitotic activity, such as a highly proliferating center or layer, has been found in the mesoderm subjacent to the apical ridge; rather, mitotic activity shows a steady, though not uniform, decrease in distoproximal direction (although see Hay, Chapter 13).

The distribution of mitoses is nearly uniform in the dorsal and ventral epidermis of the bud in the rat embryo (Hinrichsen, 44). In the chick, mitoses are comparatively more numerous along a narrow band on the ventral face of the bud close to its base. However, they appear evenly distributed in the rest of the limb bud ectoderm. In the apical ridge, mitoses are rare and numerous cells undergo nuclear pyknosis between stages 19 and 24 (Glücksmann, 32, 33; Camosso et al., 26).

It has not been established whether given portions of the mesoderm are covered by the same area of ectoderm throughout development, or if a shift between the two components gradually occurs. The latter alternative appears more probable, however, since ectodermal growth is nearly uniform, while growth of the mesoderm takes place chiefly along the proximodistal axis, and is relatively greater in the distal regions. According to Tschumi (70), carbon particles laid on the ectoderm in *Xenopus* embryos maintain their original distance from the distal border

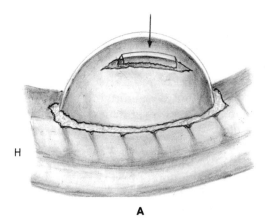

H

A

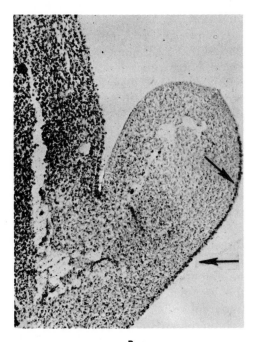

B

Fig. 10.4 *A.* Wing bud removed from donor embryo treated with thymidine-H³ and grafted to the trunk of a normal host, H. Apical mesoderm and overlying ectoderm, isolated from a normal bud, have been grafted to the radioactive bud (arrow). *B.* Radioautograph of a cross section of the unlabeled apical material grafted to the radioactive bud, 30 hours after implantation. The labeled ectoderm of the implantation bed (arrows) has spread dorsally over a great part of the apical implant.

of the bud, while marks introduced into the underlying mesoderm gradually acquire a more proximal position. Similarly, carbon particles placed on the dorsal ectoderm of the bud near its base, in stage 18–21 chick embryos, gradually move toward the distal border. Apparently the epidermis of the bud slides distalward, and contributes new cells to the region of the apical ridge. The proximodistal gliding of the bud epidermis is evidenced also by the following experiment. A limb bud excised from a donor embryo labeled with thymidine-H³ may be implanted into the trunk of a normal host embryo. Apical material from an unlabeled donor can then be implanted (Fig. 10.4) on the dorsal surface of this graft. Continuity between the labeled and unlabeled graft epidermis is soon established. Under these circumstances, the radioactive epidermis slides over the surface of the implanted apex, gradually reducing the extent of bud surface covered with the unlabeled epithelium.

Searls and Zwilling (67) have recently offered additional evidence showing that the epidermis of the limb bud faces contributes to the formation of the apical thickening when the ridge regenerates after surgical removal or degeneration. In this case, the new ridge forms "from adjacent ectoderm which moves under the old ridge" (Searls and Zwilling, 67, p. 52).

Growth of the ridge proper is related to at least two factors, (1) the relatively poor proliferative activity of its cells, and (2) the slow gliding of ectoderm over the adjacent surfaces of the bud proximodistally (Amprino and Camosso, 5). The characteristic manner of growth of the ridge seems to determine its tendency to change its radius of curvature and to lift off the mesoderm. This tendency of the ridge may be demonstrated experimentally if the thickened ectoderm and a thin strip of the subjacent mesoderm of the bud apex are grafted to the dorsal aspect of a host bud. The graft soon grows into a cone-shaped outgrowth lifting off the surrounding limb. Similar grafts of nonapical material do not form cone structures, but simply spread.

Regulative Processes

DEFECT EXPERIMENTS.   Contrary to the view that the chick limb territory or bud behaves like a mosaic system (Spurling, 68; Murray and Huxley, 54; Murray and Selby, 55; Hunt, 45; Warren, 73; Chambers, 28), the production of duplicate limb parts by Rudnick (58, 59) demonstrated the remarkable plasticity of the early bud, at least up to 60–70 hours of incubation. Other investigators have shown that the bud can produce supernumerary segments (Wolff and Kahn, 77), and exhibits marked regulative ability (Wolff and Hampé, 76; Amprino and Camosso, 3, 6, 7, 12; Hampé, 41; Hansborough, 42).

Recent experiments by Barasa (19) have shown that a normal wing could form even if 85–90 percent of the limb bud ectoderm and mesoderm was excised at stages 18–21. This operation left only a part of the mesoderm of the bud base and a thin marginal strip of mesoderm covered by the apical ectoderm. The maps of the prospective territories of the intact wing bud show that only material for the stylopod and a part of the zeugopod was removed in the operation mentioned; the prospective girdle and the mesoderm for the distal zeugopod and the autopod were preserved.

An even greater regulative capacity was observed by Zwilling (80) by grafting to the flank a thin distal portion of the limb bud. Development of a complete limb ensued. Camosso and I (7, 8) were unable to confirm this result. The wing bud apex grafted to the host trunk did not develop wing parts of a more proximal level than those represented as prospective material in the graft.

ADDITION OF TISSUE.   The processes of regulation of excess material introduced into the limb bud have also been investigated, though less thoroughly than the regulation of deficiencies.

Hampé (41) and Kieny (46) have reported that a harmonious limb can develop from a complex formed by the whole donor bud grafted to the tip of a host bud from which the apex has been removed. In our own experience with such composite buds, (Amprino and Camosso, 14) the integration of the excess material appears to be poor; nearly all the prospective territories of the composite bud develop according to their original fate. Only parts of homologous territories which come to lie in direct contact with one another are integrated. If other territories intervene, no integration seems to take place, though a part of the excess tissue may undergo reduced development. Integration of an entire segment of the limb is rarely attained, even under more favorable conditions such as the introduction of the prospective stylopod of a donor bud within the stylopod of the host bud. Good integration may be observed when a wedge-shaped sector is excised from the intermediary region of a donor bud and inserted into a host bud of the same type (Fig. 10.5A). The homologous territories of the donor and host are thus brought into register along the various levels of the bud in a proximodistal di-

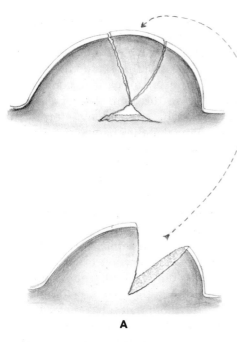

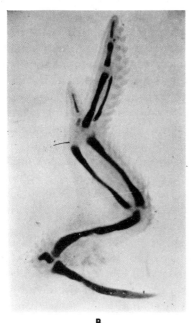

Fig. 10.5 A. Large wedge-shaped sector (arrow), isolated from a donor wing bud (bottom), and implanted into a host wing bud. B. Normal wing developed from the composite wing bud.

rection. A normal limb develops in the majority of such cases (Fig. 10.5B). However, such grafts contain much less than one-third of the prospective zeugopod and nearly one-third of the material from which the autopod of the donor limb would arise. If a graft of about the same size and prospective fate is excised from a donor bud of a type different than that of the host (for example, leg material grafted to the wing bud), regulation as a rule does not occur.

Formation of a harmonious limb from excess grafted material depends not only on processes of regulation, such as adjustments in proliferation rates and changes in the fate of parts of the mesoderm, it may also involve reduction in size or rate of growth of the donor or host material at the implantation site. This may be a consequence of abnormal mechanical stresses, temporary vascular disorders, and so on. In a recent paper, Kieny (49) confirmed that excess territories undergo only limited regulation.

MECHANISMS OF REGULATION. Wolff and Hampé (76) and Zwilling (83) assumed that the apical ridge plays as important a role in the regulation of defects as it does in normal limb development. However, Hampé (41, p. 440) observed that at least the "régulation intermédiaire" described by Wolff and Hampé (76) can occur in the absence of the ectodermal thickening. This is in agreement with results of experiments (Amprino and Camosso, 4) showing that a complete wing can develop after removal of the greater part of the apical ridge and a relatively thick layer of subjacent mesoderm. Apparently the presence of all or even most of the ridge is not essential for regulation to take place.

In this laboratory, Barasa (Unpublished observations) has attempted a histological analysis of the course of regulation in embryos from which the central portion (30–40 percent) of the wing bud was excised. Embryos were fixed and serial sections made at closely spaced time intervals after the operation. Mitotic activity and numbers of pyknotic nuclei were determined. He found that the initial wound closed within 6–20 hours, depending on the stage at which the operation was performed. The closure does not depend on early proliferation and migration of mesodermal cells into the wound, but rather on collapse or contraction of the bud components preserved around the operative gap. Shortly afterward, the bud became revascularized. The number of pyknotic nuclei increased rapidly after operation, reaching a maximum at about 14 hours. They then began decreasing at a stage before a full vascular network had re-formed. Mitotic activity decreased for the first 6–8 hours after operation, and then began to increase to a level almost three times control values, by 24–26 hours. The greatest compensatory growth occurred in the pre- and postaxial tissue adjacent to the wound and in the territories proximal to the wound. Proliferation of apical material appeared to be involved more with continued outgrowth of the bud distally than with the regulative processes.

Morphogenetic Relationships between Limb Bud Ectoderm and Mesoderm

Since the pioneering researches on the causality of limb development it has been debated whether the first in-dications of limb development appear in the ectoderm or the mesoderm of these areas and which one of the layers is the seat of limb developmental factors. The results of early experimental analyses on the limb disc of the amphibian embryo were long interpreted as showing that the characteristic properties of limb development are inherent to mesoderm (Harrison, 43, Rotmann, 57). Then, Balinsky (15, 16) deduced from his experiments of induction of heterotopic limbs that the limb-forming properties are not limited to the normal limb areas. Various stimuli exerted on any portion of the somatopleure of the flank of triton embryos lying between the limb territories may elicit development of a heterotopic limb, possibly by activating factors which are normally present in the mesoderm of the region mentioned. Balinsky suggested that both mesenchyme and epithelium take an active part in the development of an induced as well as a normal limb. The activity of the prospective limb mesoderm would change the overlying ectoderm into a specific limb epidermis; this change represents a biological reaction of the epithelial component. The influences received by the ectoderm would be reflected upon the subjacent mesoderm as return activities, *Rückwirkungen*, responsible for the morphogenetic processes of the mesoderm in successive developmental stages (Balinsky, 16, 17).

Early investigations on the amphibian embryo had been focused on the possible active role of the whole ectoderm of the limb disc. Steiner was the first to study the consequences on limb development of the destruction of only the thickened ectodermal band which covers the distal border of the limb bud in *Rana fusca* and *Triton taeniatus* in comparatively late stages of limb bud morphogenesis. According to Steiner (69), the thickened apical ectoderm does influence the development of the limb bud. More recently, Tschumi (70, 71) maintained that the distally thickened epidermis of the limb bud in *Xenopus* displays a growth-promoting activity on the subjacent mesoderm by controlling the development of the marginal vein and of the capillary system connected with it. This pattern of blood vessels would in turn promote the multiplication of the apical mesenchymal cells.

During the past 20 years, much experimental work has been directed to the study of the ectoderm-mesoderm interrelations in limb morphogenesis in the avian embryo. An increasing body of evidence has accumulated which indicates the active and indispensable participation of the ectoderm in limb development. Recent review articles report a great part of the research accomplished in this field (Zwilling, 83; Levi-Montalcini and Angeletti, 51; Amprino, 1; Milaire, 53; Koecke, 50; DeHaan and Ebert, 30). The conclusions drawn by these authors reflect the general agreement reached on certain essential aspects of limb development, and the persisting uncertainty concerning the role played by the ectoderm, especially by its thickened portion which is morphologically more prominent in birds (Saunders' apical ridge) than in amphibians.

Two different hypotheses have been formulated recently to account for the development of limbs in tetrapod vertebrates. In both hypotheses the main importance is attributed to the mesoderm as the site of the primary essen-tial potencies for limb development. One group of authors (Zwilling, Saunders, Hampé, Tschumi, Milaire, Goetinck, and Abbott) considers the thickened portion of the apical ectoderm as a structure endowed with a mesoderm-dependent inductor activity. The other group (Amprino and Camosso, Barasa, Bell and co-workers, Koecke) denies the inductor role of the apical ridge, and attributes the major formative role to the mesoderm instead. Both hypotheses will be presented and discussed in the light of the information available. For greater details, the reader is referred to the accounts by Zwilling (83), Amprino (1), and Koecke (50).

Two Theories of Limb Morphogenesis

THE SAUNDERS-ZWILLING MODEL. According to the Saunders-Zwilling scheme of limb development, the mesoderm, the first of the two primitive components of the limb district to be activated, induces the formation of the apical ridge in the overlying ectoderm. The appearance of this thickened band represents the chief morphological indication that the ectoderm has acquired an active role in the distal outgrowth of the bud. The persistence of the apical ridge as an active influence on continued elaboration of distal limb elements depends upon a factor (maintenance factor), which is present in a part of the limb mesoderm, distributed asymmetrically, and transmissible in a proximodistal direction (Fig. 10.6). The varying thickness of the apical ridge along the ap axis of the bud is an index of the distribution and concentration of the maintenance factor in the mesoderm, and of the outgrowth inductor activity of the ridge itself. Once the mesoderm for the various

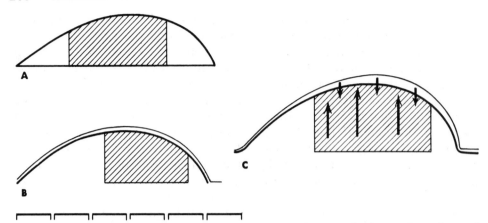

Fig. 10.6 Distribution of the maintenance factor in the wing bud mesoderm (striped area), according to Zwilling (*A*) and Saunders et al. (*B*). *C*. Schematic representation of reciprocal interactions between limb bud mesoderm and ectoderm, and vice versa, according to the Saunders-Zwilling theory. The activity of the mesodermal factor on the ridge is indicated by the lower arrows. The outgrowth activity exerted on the mesoderm by the activated and thickened apical ridge is represented by the upper arrows.

proximodistal levels of the limb bud has been laid down, further development unfolds independently of the ridge activity.

This scheme of limb development rests on two series of experimental data (Zwilling, 83) which show that the apical ridge is essential for limb development and that a mesodermal factor exists and plays a special role upon the ectoderm. The major evidence in favor of the inductor role of the ridge can be listed as follows: (1) Failure of development of the distal limb structures as a consequence of the removal of the apical ridge (Saunders, 60). Only the prospective territories of the proximal limb levels, which are individuated at the time of the operation, undergo development. The more distal territories, whose segregation takes place in relatively late stages in the intact limb, fail to form. Removal of the ridge suppresses the segregation of the mesoderm for the future distal parts of the limb. (2) Development of toes from isolates of

mesoderm of the prospective thigh region, grafted to the apex of the wing bud beneath, and in close contact with the apical ridge (Saunders et al., 62, 64, 65). The graft maintains its limb-type characteristic and the change of the regional character of morphological differentiation must depend on the inductor activity of the ridge. (3) Development of foot structures from the proximal stump of the hindlimb bud whose amputation surface has been covered with an ectodermal cap isolated from the apex of another limb bud, as shown in Figure 10.7A (Hampé, 41). Distal structures develop from mesoderm of the prospective zeugopod under the influence of the thickened band of the apical cap of ectoderm. (4) Development of two sets of digital structures when one apical cap of ectoderm is arranged on each of the opposite surfaces of the denuded limb bud mesoderm (Zwilling, 80). Outgrowth from the original tip of the bud stops and two new outgrowths develop in direct as-

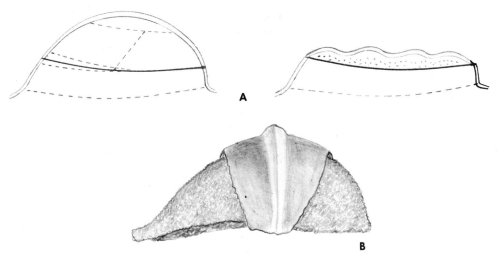

Fig. 10.7 A. Hampé's experiment (41): ectodermal cap, isolated from donor limb bud, implanted on the amputation surface of the host bud (right). At the left, the prospective segments of the host limb bud and the plane of amputation are indicated. B. Zwilling's experiment (79): leg bud mesoderm covered with ectodermal cap rotated 90°.

sociation with the two grafted ridges. (5) Changes of the asymmetry of the distal part of the limb after 90° reorientation of the apical ectodermal cap (Fig. 10.7B). All of the outgrowth takes place at right angles to the original long axis of the mesoderm and the apical cap appears to be the determining component of the changes of the axis relations (Zwilling, 79). (6) Failure of development of distal limb elements from denuded limb mesoderm covered by nonlimb ectoderm (Zwilling, 78). (7) Formation of recognizable limb structures frequently complete with digits from 7–12 small fragments (0.1–0.2 mm) of limb bud mesoderm picked at random, placed in an ectodermal jacket isolated from another limb bud, then grown as flank grafts or on chorioallantoic membrane (Zwilling, 82, 83, 84).

The main evidence which, according to Zwilling (83), support the existence and activity of the maintenance factor are the following: (1) Flattening of the apical ridge and defects of distal growth when a thin sheet of mica is introduced between the apical ridge and the apical mesoderm and kept there for $1\frac{1}{2}$ hour or more (Saunders, 61). (2) Failure of nonlimb mesoderm, stuffed into an ectodermal jacket that is isolated from a limb bud, to give rise to limb structures. If a fragment of limb mesoderm is introduced into the ectodermal jacket beneath the ridge, the latter maintains its thickened structure locally and an elongated outgrowth forms (Zwilling, 82). (3) Strict topographical correspondence between the local thickness of the ridge, and bulges or irregularities of the mesoderm outgrowth responsible for the asymmetries characteristic for a given limb type. The ridge thickness seems always to conform to the pattern expected of the mesoderm. This has been shown in limb bud ectoderm rotated 180° in relation to the mesoderm, in wing bud ectoderm placed on leg bud mesoderm and vice versa (Zwilling, 78, 79). Moreover, when the thickest regions from two to three ridges are placed in tandem along the distal edge of one limb mesoderm they do not remain thick but fuse to form a single ridge with a typically normal configuration, and a normal limb develops (Zwilling, 80). When the ectodermal cap of a genetically normal embryo is combined with mesoderm of a polydactylous limb bud, the ridge maintains its thickened configuration in its preaxial portion — where flattening normally occurs — and accessory distal structures form as in the polydactylous controls (Zwilling and Hansborough, 85). Finally, if the ectoderm, isolated from the wing bud of genetically normal embryos, is combined with the mesoderm of a "wingless" limb bud, the ectodermal ridge regresses as it does in the wingless phenotype, and no distal parts develop from the wingless mesoderm. The mesodermal factor is assumed to be produced only in the early stages of wing bud outgrowth in the wingless mutant; thereafter, the thickened structure of the ridge cannot be maintained (Zwilling, 81).

THE OPPOSITION VIEW.   In the opinion of the other group of authors, the experimental results available on limb morphogenesis are not sufficient to prove the inductor activity of the apical ridge. The crucial demonstration of such a role of the thickened limb bud ectoderm is still wanting. According to Amprino and his associates, the results of all the experiments published so far are compatible with the working hypothesis that all developmental factors reside in the mesoderm of the limb district and govern its outgrowth, the gradual individuation of the territories, and the determination and differentia-tion of the latter according to a given temporal sequence in proximodistal direction. The limb bud ectoderm is indispensable for limb development. It represents a biological boundary which isolates the bud mesoderm as a closed system that communicates with the rest of the embryonic body through the bud base only. Moreover, the ectoderm possesses a characteristic growth pattern which is to some extent related to, and dependent upon the growth pattern of the underlying mesoderm; thus it can exert a sort of modeling role on the mesoderm and favor the gradual changes in shape of the bud apex during limb elongation.

Distal limb outgrowth depends on the differential growth of the various parts of the bud mesoderm, not on the existence, beneath the ridge, of a strip of apical mesoderm endowed with a particularly high proliferative activity, as would be expected if the ridge had an outgrowth inductor activity (Amprino, 1). The growth rate of the mesoderm varies along the main axes of the limb bud; it is higher in the distal compared to the proximal, in the postaxial than in the preaxial territories (Camosso et al., 26). The proliferation of the mesoderm, uniformly intense in the early bud, is gradually reduced in the proximal regions in parallel with the onset of differentiation, which progresses from the base toward the apex of the limb bud.

The growth of each territory which has been individuated predominates along the proximodistal axis of the bud. The latter modality of growth accounts for the progressive elongation of the bud, while the differential growth at the various proximodistal levels of the bud mesoderm is responsible for the "distal outgrowth" of the limb bud.

All the developmental processes undergone by the territories of the limb seem to be governed by influences which propagate gradually from the limb bud base to adjacent, more and more distal bud levels. In fact, if a thin distal portion of the bud apex, isolated from the bud, is grafted heterotopically when it is not yet capable of autonomous development, its growth and developmental fate appear to depend on the new connections established with the mesoderm of the implantation site, which may exert influences on the grafted mesoderm of the bud apex. The apical material, when grafted to the trunk, undergoes poor growth; it tends to flatten and does not form the skeletal structures which it would have developed in situ. The same material, implanted to the dorsal aspect of the apex of the limb bud of the same or of different type, undergoes an intense growth, and digits develop. A relatively thick portion of the apex, isolated from the limb bud, would presumably contain a part of mesoderm already determined. This material, if grafted to the trunk, gives rise to the full set of structures which would have formed in situ (Amprino and Camosso, 8).

Changes of the growth rate and of the developmental pattern of the limb mesoderm take place also in the 180° ap-reoriented apex of the wing bud. After reorientation, new topographical relations are in fact established between proximal territories (in the stump) and distal territories of the apex, preaxially and postaxially. Duplication of the hand occurs under these conditions (Amprino and Camosso, 6, 7; Saunders et al., 66).

All these facts suggest the existence of a control exerted by the mesoderm of the implantation site on the growth rate as well as on the developmental fate of adjacent more distal territories of the mesoderm. In these experiments, the grafts contained apical mesoderm and the overlying apical ridge of ectoderm. Therefore, the results might be interpreted as evidence for the existence and activity of a varying amount of maintenance factor in the mesoderm of the graft and of the implantation site, which could activate the apical ridge (Zwilling, 83). However, rise of the mitotic rate and change of the developmental fate of the transplanted mesoderm take place also under experimental conditions in which the ridge cannot possibly be held responsible for outgrowth of the bud mesoderm. Such is the case for the development of toes from isolates of the prospective thigh mesoderm grafted to the wing bud apex not in contact with the apical ridge, in embryos of stages 24–26 (Amprino and Amprino Bonetti, 2). Such is also the case for the development of one or two digits from the material of the preaxial border of the zeugopod and stylopod of the hindlimb bud transplanted to the dorsal surface of the apex of the leg or wing bud, in embryos of stages 24–26 (Amprino and Camosso, 10, 11, 13). The mesoderm of the graft is not skeletogenous in situ, and does not give rise to digits when implanted onto the flank. The ectoderm covering the mesoderm of the preaxial border does not have a thickened structure, and does not undergo any detectable thickening when grafted with the subjacent strip of mesoderm to the limb apex.

Comparing the Two Theories of Limb Morphogenesis

The two hypotheses on limb morphogenesis reported in the previous section show large areas of agreement, in that both imply that the mesoderm is the first of the two components of the limb district to be activated, that some sort of "influences" gradually propagate in a proximodistal direction in the bud mesoderm, and that individuation, determination, and differentiation of limb segments take place according to a given spatiotemporal sequence starting from the bud base and dependent on properties inherent to the mesoderm. The area of disagreement is in the role played by the bud ectoderm, particularly by the apical ridge. Apical outgrowth of the mesoderm depends either on an inductor activity of the apical ridge or, alternatively, is an expression of the inherent growth pattern of the mesoderm, independent of any induction exerted by the apical ectoderm.

It has been stressed (Amprino, 1) that much descriptive and experimental data argues against the assumption that outgrowth of the limb bud depends on an outgrowth inductor activity of the ectodermal ridge. For example, a significant part of limb bud outgrowth and territory individuation seems to take place before formation of the apical ridge, independently of its activity, in the embryos of some mammals (Milaire, 53). Furthermore, according to the Saunders-Zwilling hypothesis, the preaxial portion of the limb mesoderm in the chick embryo does not produce maintenance factor; however, the ridge, whose formation would depend on the polarized transmission of the maintenance factor, develops in the preaxial portion of the bud also, although it undergoes a gradual reduction there, from stage 21 on. This part of the limb mesoderm, which lacks maintenance factor, should not be capable of preserving the thickened

structure and inductor activity of the ridge, which in turn would be responsible for the outgrowth of the underlying mesoderm. But, when the central, thickened portion of the ridge and a thin layer of subjacent mesoderm, isolated from the distal edge of a leg bud, are implanted on the preaxial region of the wing bud, the grafted ridge does not flatten, and a typical toe develops; the host wing also forms all its normal skeletal constituents (Amprino and Camosso, unpublished observations). The same material grafted to the flank does not form a toe, indicating that the graft is not capable of autonomous development at implantation time. Therefore, either the preaxial region of the normal limb bud does produce maintenance factor, or else formation of the extra digit does not depend on the inductor activity of the ridge. According to Amprino and Camosso's hypothesis, it is the mesoderm of the host bud that influences directly the growth and differentiation of the adjacent mesoderm of the graft.

In the Saunders-Zwilling theory, the distribution of the mesodermal factor along the anteroposterior axis of the bud is the condition which determines the craniocaudal length of the ridge and its local thickness, and, subsequently, the number and arrangement of the developing limb structures. In polydactylous mutants (Zwilling and Hansborough, 85), the mesodermal factor is assumed to be produced in the preaxial region of the bud mesoderm; preaxial extra digits develop in these mutants. If the ectoderm isolated from the limb bud of a genetically normal embryo is combined with polydactylous limb mesoderm, the preaxial sector of the ridge increases in thickness and acquires outgrowth inductor ability, and supernumerary preaxial digits develop under these conditions. The extension of the production of maintenance factor to the preaxial mesoderm would be the factor which determines indirectly the development of excess preaxial digits (Zwilling and Hansborough, 85). However, formation of digits in excess does not take place when the craniocaudal extent of the mesoderm and of the overlying ectodermal ridge are experimentally increased in a normal bud. This can be done by introducing a fairly large wedge-shaped sector, isolated from the intermediate part of a donor wing bud, into a proximodistal cleft of a host wing bud from which no material is removed (Fig. 10.5B). The resulting bud is about one-third larger craniocaudally and its thickened ridge is one-third longer than normal. This large bud attains a normal size within 40–48 hours and a typically normal wing develops in over 80 percent of the cases (Amprino and Camosso, 14). The donor wing bud (Fig. 10.5A), which lacks one-third of its thickened ridge and a corresponding portion of the mesoderm, undergoes a quicker growth than a normal bud and often forms a normal wing. Thus, the ap extent of the mesoderm which is assumed to produce maintenance factor, and the ap extent of the apical ridge, seem not to be instrumental in the development of a normal limb.

According to the Saunders-Zwilling theory, definite topographical and physiological relations exist between the mesoderm, which produces maintenance factor, and the various sectors of the overlying ridge, which respond to the stimuli exerted by the factor. The cranial and the caudal halves of the ridge would, in turn, promote outgrowth of the corresponding part of the subjacent mesoderm. Outgrowth

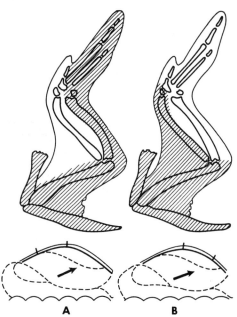

Fig. 10.8 Consequences of the removal of the cranial (A) or of the caudal (B) half of the apical ridge of ectoderm (lower schemes) on the development of the wing bud. Wing parts which form are shaded. (Redrawn from Saunders, *J. Exptl. Zool.* 108:363–403, 1948.)

and development of distal structures occur only in the region of the bud apex which is covered by the ridge as shown in Figure 10.8 (Saunders, 60; Zwilling and Hansborough, 85). However, the limb, and in particular a full set of digits, develops from limb mesoderm associated with only a very limited preaxial sector of the ridge. When the wing bud is divided into two parts according to an oblique plane and the caudodistal portion is dorsoventrally reoriented (Fig. 10.9), the arm, the forearm, and a complete hand develop from the cranioproximal part of the bud which is covered by thickened ectoderm in a small portion of its preaxial edge (Camosso, 25).

One essential aspect of the Saunders-Zwilling theory has not been proved so far. If the outgrowth of the meso-

A

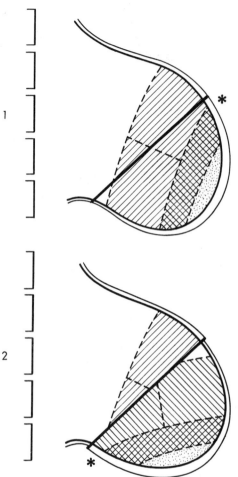

B

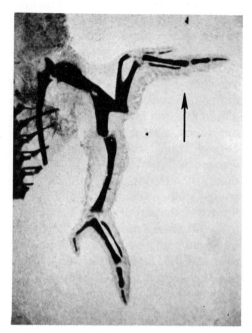

Fig. 10.9 A. Distribution of the prospective territories of the mesoderm, before (1) and after (2) anteroposterior and dorsoventral reorientation of the distocaudal portion of the wing bud (stage 23). *B.* Twinned wing developed from the recombined bud. The arrow indicates the wing formed from the cranioproximal part of the bud (Camosso's experiment, see text).

derm is stimulated by the inductor activity of the apical ridge and the thickness of the latter is an index of its activity, which depends in turn on the distribution and concentration of the maintenance factor propagated from the subjacent mesoderm, *thickening of the ridge should take place before the burst of outgrowth of the underlying mesoderm,* in normal limb development and under experimental conditions. However, this is not the case, as indicated by the following observation. After ap reorientation of the wing bud apex, a duplicate hand forms (Amprino

and Camosso, 7, 12; Saunders et al., 66). Under these conditions, Saunders and Gasseling (63) described a "definite thickening in the postaxial (originally preaxial) portion of the ridge within 24 to 36 hours in most cases which developed subsequently supernumerary digits." Formation of the latter would depend on the thickening and subsequent increase of the inductor activity of the corresponding part of the ridge, which is influenced by the new distribution of the maintenance factor in the wing bud after apex reorientation (Fig. 10.10A). A study of

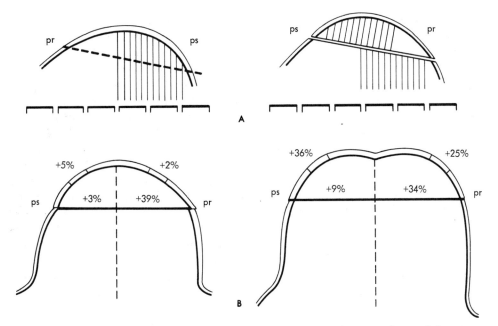

Fig. 10.10 A. Redistribution of the maintenance factor in the mesoderm of the wing bud (shaded area) after apdv-reorientation of the bud apex, according to Saunders et al. (66). B. Diagrams of the changes in thickness of the ectodermal ridge and in the rate of proliferation of the apical mesoderm 13–18 (left) and 34–38 hours (right) after apdv-reorientation of the wing bud apex. The thickness of the preaxial, pr, and of the postaxial, ps, part of the reoriented ridge is expressed as percent increment over the thickness of corresponding sectors of the ridge in control wing buds fixed at the time of the operation. The values for proliferation of the mesoderm in the reorientated apex are expressed as percent increment of the mitotic rate over that of corresponding regions of the apex of the normally growing contralateral wing bud. (Averages from a series of five cases.) (Camosso's experiment, see text.)

the distribution and number of mitoses in the ectoderm and mesoderm of the ap reoriented apex carried out in this laboratory (Camosso and Racanelli, 27; unpublished observations), shows that the caudal, (originally preaxial) sector of the ridge increases a few micra in thickness (5–7 percent) within 24 hours (Fig. 10.10B). By 34–36 hours after apex reorientation—when a deformation of the bud outline as a consequence of the outgrowth of the apical mesoderm is apparent—the caudal sector of the ridge has undergone an increment of 25–30 percent in thickness in comparison to its original condition.

However, the mitotic index of the caudal (originally preaxial) portion of the apical mesoderm is increased by approximately 40 percent within 13–18 hours after apex reorientation. A decrease of the proliferation of this mesoderm occurs from the 30th–34th hour. Thus, the "reactive" proliferation of the apical mesoderm—which is the preparatory step for the duplication of the bud apex—precedes by a significant interval of time the histologically detectable changes in thickness of the overlying ridge. Therefore, this augmented mesodermal mitosis cannot be a consequence of a thickening or increased activity of the ridge. It must be emphasized in this connection that the number of mitoses of the epithelial cells of the ridge proper does not increase in the sector which undergoes thickening. In fact, the latter event is mainly due to proximodistal sliding of the epidermis of the bud faces. It appears, therefore, that the mesodermal stimuli which indirectly determine changes in thickness of the ridge exert their influence on large areas of the thin epidermis of the bud faces, not directly on the ridge proper.

As mentioned earlier, the main experimental data which have been advanced as evidence of the inductor activity of the apical ridge *do not necessarily prove* the existence of this activity, while they can be explained satisfactorily in line with the view held by Amprino and Camosso.

For example, from the arrest of limb bud outgrowth following removal of the ridge (Saunders, 60) it cannot be deduced that the structure removed plays an outgrowth inductor role on the mesoderm (Amprino, 1). The arrest of limb development may depend on other factors—namely, the disruption of the growth pattern of the mesoderm following alterations of the local homeostasis which occur when the mesoderm is exposed abruptly to abnormal environmental conditions. These alterations are shown by the high number of pyknotic cells, the early and lasting depression of mitotic activity (Amprino and Camosso, 4, 8; Camosso et al., 26), and the secondary vascular deficiences (Barasa, 18) in the uncovered mesoderm. The damage appears to be more severe and the restoration of the injured mesoderm poorer when the cell population of the limb district affected is small and the exposed terri-

tory (Amprino and Camosso, 8) is not yet differentiated. The apical territories are built of very thin layers of mesodermal cells when they arise in the course of limb bud outgrowth, and their differentiation commences in a comparatively later period than that of the proximal districts of the bud. Thus, it is not surprising that the alterations of the exposed mesoderm are more severe in the distal than in the proximal regions. Besides, the apical mesoderm is the material from which more and more distal limb parts arise. When this source of new territories is severely impaired, further segregation of distal parts is hampered and outgrowth of the bud is necessarily arrested (Amprino, 1).

It has been mentioned already that toes develop from isolates of mesoderm of the prospective thigh region grafted to the wing bud apex, not only when the transplant is inserted in contact with the apical ridge (Saunders et al., 62, 64, 65), but also when it is separated from the ridge by intervening mesoderm of the wing host bud (Amprino and Amprino Bonetti, 2). Formation of toes from the grafted thigh mesoderm takes place even when the operation is performed in embryos of stages 25–26, a period in which, according to Saunders and co-workers (62), the apical territories are capable of autonomous development independently of the outgrowth inductor activity of the ridge. Hence, outgrowth and changes of the developmental fate of the grafted thigh mesoderm should be attributed to direct organogenetic influences of the surrounding mesoderm of the wing apex, not to the inductor activity of the ridge.

Development of distal structures from the mesoderm of the proximal stump of the limb bud covered with an ectodermal cap isolated from another limb bud, as shown in Figure 10.7A,B (Hampé, 41), does not necessarily prove that the thickened portion of the ectodermal cap exerts an outgrowth inductor activity on the mesoderm of the preserved zeugopod of the limb bud stump. In fact, formation of one or two digits from the mesoderm of the zeugopod has been observed under conditions in which this mesoderm has no relations with any thickened part of the limb ectoderm (Amprino and Camosso, 7, 11, 12, 13). Hampé's results may simply be due to the regulative tendency of the bud deprived of a part of its mesoderm. In this regard, it is known that the proximal territories may regulate the loss of more distal ones, while it has not been proved conclusively that distal territories may regulate the loss of proximal regions. In Hampé's experiment, the mesoderm of the limb bud stump proliferates and fills in the ectodermal cap, which covers the amputation surface. The cap, by growing as a keel-shaped compartment in a proximodistal direction, provides a suitable cover for the protection and modeling of the mesodermal mass (Amprino, 1).

This modeling capacity of the ectodermal cap is shown even better by Zwilling's experiment (79), in which change of the asymmetry of the distal part of the limb occurs after 90° reorientation of the apical ectoderm (Fig. 10.7B). Under these experimental conditions, the new orientation of the bud apex cannot be attributed to inductor activity of the ridge. In fact, according to the Saunders-Zwilling scheme, activity of the ridge is maintained by the continuous and polarized transmission of the mesodermal factor, which is distributed along the ap axis of the mesoderm. If the interactions between mesoderm and overlying ectoderm did occur as suggested by the scheme mentioned, the ridge, which has been arranged at right angles to the plane of transmission of the maintenance factor, could be reached by the factor over a very limited portion of its length. Hence, the ridge should flatten and a new ridge along the ap axis of the bud should be induced by the maintenance factor. But these expected changes do not occur. The 90° reoriented ridge persists and the growing apical cap is progressively filled with apical mesoderm, which apparently adjusts itself to the anatomical configuration of the cap.

If this mechanical modeling role of the apical cap represents a sufficient explanation of the shift in orientation of the bud outgrowth in the experimental conditions mentioned, (which cannot be explained in line with the Saunders-Zwilling scheme) the same explanation should be valid in the other case of formation of two distal outgrowths in association with two apical caps of ectoderm grafted to the opposite surfaces of the denuded limb bud mesoderm (Zwilling, 80).

The formation of recognizable limb structures from parts of the limb mesoderm reduced to small fragments or dissociated into a cell suspension and introduced into limb ectoderm (Zwilling, 82, 83, 84), may again be the result of the regulative activity of the early limb bud. It has been stressed elsewhere (Amprino, 1, p. 118) that the result of this experiment cannot be explained satisfactorily in line with the Saunders-Zwilling hypothesis. In this connection, it must be emphasized that fragments of limb bud mesoderm implanted beneath the somatopleure of the flank in early chick embryos, that is, in association with nonlimb ectoderm, can form full limbs (Kieny, 47, 48). Moreover, definite digits develop from ectoderm isolated from the tail tip (chick embryos at stages 21 to 22), stuffed with fragments of limb mesoderm, and grown as grafts on the limb bud or the chorioallantoic membrane (Zwilling, 84). In the latter case, a quite typical ridge was found in the ectoderm of the grafts in sections made several days after transplantation. It must be proved, however, that the ridge forms before the burst of outgrowth of the mesoderm, otherwise the postulated causal relationship between the two events remains hypothetical.

More or less the same considerations apply when discussing the interpretation of another series of experiments directed at the problem of the capacity of self-development of the limb bud mesoderm isolated from the ectoderm by means of ultrasonation or versene treatment, and transplanted to the flank or the coelomic cavity (Bell et al., 20, 21, 22; Dubey, 31). From a recent contribution by Goetinck and Abbott (35), it appears very unlikely that a limb may develop from its mesodermal component alone. As has been stressed previously, the presence of the ectoderm is necessary for limb development. Goetinck and Abbott have shown that epithelial residues, accidentally left on the surface of the limb mesoderm denuded of its ectodermal cover, may be sufficient for the regeneration of a complete epidermal sheet. It remains undecided how long a time is required for the restoration of the entire limb epidermis, and what temporal relations exist between formation of the new ridge and mesodermal outgrowth.

Gene-dependent Anomalies of Limb Morphogenesis

The interrelations between ectoderm and mesoderm in limb development have also been investigated in mutants affecting the limb skeleton. From descriptive studies, mainly on mammalian embryos, it appears that most of the mutants involve the apical ridge of ectoderm to some extent. However, according to Grüneberg (37, p. 234) "there is no *prima facie* case that the dimension (and thus presumably the functional state) of the apical ectodermal ridge is either cause or effect of changed growth processes."

In recent years, interesting experiments have been carried out in chick embryo mutants. Combination experiments of polydactylous limb ectoderm with normal limb mesoderm and vice versa, have shown that the genetic defect affects the mesoderm only (Zwilling and Hansborough, 85). Analogous experiments carried out by Zwilling (81) on "wingless" chick embryos lead that author to conclude that the mesoderm is affected in this mutation, although a normal wing does not develop from combinations of normal limb mesoderm with "wingless" ectoderm.

Other mutants (talpid[2], eudiplopodia) were experimentally tested more recently by Goetinck and Abbott (35, 36). In talpid[2] the genetic defect appears to be inherent to limb mesoderm, in eudiplopod to the ectoderm. In the eudiplopod phenotype, a secondary ridge forms in the ectoderm of the hindlimb bud, dorsal and proximal to the normal apical ridge (stages 22–24). A variable number of supernumerary toes develop dorsal to the normal digital set. From combination experiments of eudiplopod ectoderm with genetically normal, or scaleless mesoderm and vice versa, it appears that development of extra digits is causally related to the formation of a secondary ectodermal thickening. According to Goetinck (34), the eudiplopod phenotype is very similar to the duplications obtained by Zwilling (79) with the implantation of one apical cap of ectoderm on each side of the isolated limb bud mesoderm. Goetinck offers an interpretation of the mechanism of extra digit formation in eudiplopod which fits in the scheme of limb development hypothesized by Saunders and Zwilling. However, the development of excess toes associated with the formation of a secondary ridge in the eudiplopod limb appears compatible as well with the thesis that the ridge may favor outgrowth of the limb mesoderm simply by providing a keel-shaped compartment endowed with a peculiar growth pattern.

Goetinck (34) suggests also that in the eudiplopod mutant a genetic factor could render the dorsal ectoderm of the limb bud "competent" to the activity of Zwilling's mesodermal factor, for the formation of the secondary ridge. This assumption would imply that only the narrow band of ectoderm which covers the distal edge of the normal limb bud is competent to form apical ridge, or, alternatively, that the bud ectoderm loses its original competence once the ridge has differentiated. However, independently of the hypothetical role exerted by the mesodermal factor in eliciting formation of the ecto-

dermal ridge, it is known that the ectoderm of the faces of the limb bud contributes to the formation of the ridge and to its maintenance as a thickened structure throughout limb bud outgrowth, as it does also in the special case of ridge regeneration. Besides, formation of a typical ridge has been observed in nonlimb ectoderm associated with limb mesoderm. This seems to prove that the cells not only of the limb ectoderm but also of foreign epidermis are normally competent to change their morphological and histochemical characters into those of the cells of the ridge proper.

Summary

A short account is given of the early localization and determination of the limb-forming areas, of their gradual displacements, and of the time of fixation of the various axes of the future limbs. The morphological changes undergone by the limb district and by each of its two primitive components, from the early somitic stages to the formation of a distinctly elongated limb bud, are briefly described.

The main descriptive and experimental data on the mechanisms of growth and elongation of the limb bud, and of segregation of the mesodermal territories for the future limb segments are presented. A gradual shift of the topographical relations between ectoderm and the subjacent mesoderm, depending on proximodistal sliding of the ectoderm during limb bud elongation, seems to occur in the chick embryo.

As to the regulative ability, the limb bud shows a remarkable tendency to compensate for the removal of rather large parts, even in relatively advanced stages. The integration of excess limb territories appears comparatively more limited. Information concerning the mechanisms of regulation is too scanty to offer any conclusions on this aspect of the limb district properties.

The problem of the morphogenetic factors in limb development and of the role played by the limb bud primitive components, ectoderm and mesoderm respectively, is still unsolved. Two theories advanced recently to account for limb development are presented and discussed on the basis of the numerous experimental data available. The mesoderm appears to be the primary seat of limb developmental potencies. Individuation, determination, and differentiation of the limb territories in a definite temporal sequence and according to a proximodistal pattern, seem to be expression of inherent properties of the mesoderm. The interpretation of the role played by the ectoderm is uncertain. Apparently limb ectoderm does not behave in a merely passive manner. However, it is not yet conclusively established whether the thickened region of the ectoderm (apical ridge) exerts a mesoderm-dependent inductor activity on the outgrowth of the apical mesoderm, or the ectoderm of the apex favors elongation and modeling of the bud tip on account of its peculiar and gradually changing anatomical configuration, which in turn depends on the growth pattern that is characteristic of the limb ectoderm itself.

References

1. Amprino, R., "Aspetti della Morfogenesi delle Estremità nei Vertebrati," *Mon. Zool. Ital.* Suppl. 70–71:7–130 (1962–1963).
2. ——, and D. Amprino Bonetti, "Effect of the Implantation Site on the Development of Grafted Limb Bud Mesoderm in Chick Embryos," *Nature* 204:298 (1964).
3. ——, and M. Camosso, "Ricerche Sperimentali sulla Morfogenesi degli Arti nel Pollo," *J. Exptl. Zool.* 129:453–493 (1955).
4. ——, and ——, "Le Rôle Morphogénétique de la Crête Ectodermique Apicale du Bourgeon des Membres de l'Embryon de Poulet," *Compt. Rend. Assoc. Anat.* 42:197–203 (1955).
5. ——, and ——, "Analisi Sperimentale dello Sviluppo dell'ala nell'Embrione di Pollo," *Arch. Entwicklungsmech. Or.* 150:509–541 (1958).
6. ——, and ——, "Experimental Observations on Influences Exerted by the Proximal over the Distal Territories of the Extremities," *Experientia* 14:241–243 (1959).
7. ——, and ——, "Observations sur les Duplications Expérimentales de la Partie Distale de l'Ébauche de l'Aile chez l'Embryon de Poulet," *Arch. Anat. Microscop. Morphol. Exptl.* 48:261–305 (1959).
8. ——, and ——, "On the Role of the Apical Ridge in the Development of Chick Embryo Limb Bud," *Acta Anat.* 38:280–288 (1959).
9. ——, and ——, "Résultats de Greffes Réciproques de Parties de l'Ébauche de l'Aile et du Membre Pelvien dans l'Embryon de Poulet," *Anat. Anz.* 109:150–152 (1960–1961).
10. ——, and ——, "Greffes Hétérotopiques d'Ectoderme et Mésenchyme Marginal de l'Ébauche des Extrémités. Etude Histologique," *Compt. Rend. Assoc. Anat.* 47:62–68 (1961).
11. ——, and ——, "Development of Digits from the Proximal Pre-axial Material of the Wing and Hindlimb Bud in Chick Embryos," *Experientia* 17:92–93 (1961).
12. ——, and ——, "Effects of Exchanging the Ap-reoriented Apex between Wing and Hind-limb Bud," *Acta Embryol. Morphol. Exptl.* 6:241–259 (1963).
13. ——, and ——, "Developmental

Fate of Heterotopically Grafted Proximal Pre-axial Material of the Chick Embryo Limb Bud," *Acta Anat.* In press (1965).

14. ——, and ——, "La Régulation d'Excédents de l'Ébauche de Membres du Poulet," *Arch. Anat. Microscop. Morphol. Exptl.* In press (1965).

15. Balinsky, B. I., "Ueber die Mesodermverschiebungen bei der Extremitäteninduktion," *Arch. Entwicklungsmech. Or.* 116:604–632 (1929).

16. ——, "Zur Dynamik der Extremitätenknospenbildung," *Arch. Entwicklungsmech. Or.* 123:565–648 (1931).

17. ——, "A New Theory of Limb Induction," *Proc. Natl. Acad. Sci. U. S.* 42:781–785 (1956).

18. Barasa, A., "Conseguenze dell'Ablazione della Cresta Ectodermica Apicale sullo Sviluppo dell'Abbozzo dell'ala nell'Embrione di Pollo," *Riv. Biol.* 52:257–292 (1950).

19. ——, "On the Regulative Capacity of the Chick Embryo Limb Bud," *Experientia.* 20:443 (1964).

20. Bell, E., M. A. Kaighn, and L. M. Fessenden, "The Role of Mesodermal and Ectodermal Components in the Development of the Chick Limb," *Develop. Biol.* 1:101–124 (1959).

21. ——, J. W. Saunders, Jr., and E. Zwilling, "Limb Development in the Absence of Ectodermal Ridge," *Nature* 184:1736–1737 (1959).

22. ——, M. T. Gasseling, and J. W. Saunders, Jr., "On the Role of the Ectoderm in Limb Development," *Develop. Biol.* 4:177–196 (1962).

23. Blechschmidt, E. von, "Mechanische Genwirkungen," "Musterschmidt" KG. Göttingen (1948).

24. ——, "Entwicklungsfunktionelle Untersuchungen am Bewegungsapparat," *Acta Anat.* 27:62–88 (1956).

25. Camosso, M., "Produzione di Estese Duplicazioni nell'ala dell'Embrione di Pollo," *Mon. Zool. Ital.* Suppl. 72. In press (1965).

26. ——, V. Jacobelli, and N. Pappalettera, "Ricerche Descrittive e Sperimentali sull'Organogenesi dell'Abbozzo dell'ala dell'Embrione di Pollo," *Riv. Biol.* 52:323–357 (1960).

27. ——, and A. Racanelli, "Comportamento della Cresta Apicale dell'ala dell

Embrione di Pollo in Condizioni Sperimentali," *Mon. Zool. Ital.* XXII Suppl. 70 (1962).

28. Chambers, H. S., "Regional Potencies in the Hindlimb of the 72-hour Chick," *Anat. Record* 67:60 (1937).

29. Chaube, S., "On Axiation and Symmetry in Transplanted Wing of the Chick," *J. Exptl. Zool.* 140:29–77 (1959).

30. DeHaan, R. L., and J. D. Ebert, "Morphogenesis," *Ann. Rev. Physiol.* 26:15–46 (1964).

31. Dubey, P. N., "Role of Mesoderm in the Morphogenesis of Chick Limb," *J. Anat. Soc. India* 11:24–28 (1962).

32. Glücksmann, A., "Ueber die Entwicklung der Amniotenextremitäten und ihre Homologie mit den Flossen," *Z. Anat.* 102:498–520 (1934).

33. ——, "Cell Deaths in Normal Vertebrate Ontogeny." *Biol. Rev.* 26:59–86 (1951).

34. Goetinck, P. F., "Studies on Avian Limb Morphogenesis. II. Experiments with the Polydactylous Mutant, *Eudiplopodia*," *Develop. Biol.* 10:71–91 (1964).

35. ——, and U. K. Abbott, "Tissue Interaction in the Scaleless Mutant and the Use of Scaleless as an Ectodermal Marker in Studies of Normal Limb Differentiation," *J. Exptl. Zool.* 154:7–19 (1963).

36. ——, and ——, "Studies in Limb Morphogenesis. I. Experiments with the Polydactylous Mutant, Talpid²," *J. Exptl. Zool.* 155:161–170 (1964).

37. Grüneberg, H., *The Pathology of Development. A Study of Inherited Skeletal Disorders in Animals.* Wiley (1963).

38. Hamburger, V., "Morphogenetic and Axial Differentiation of Transplanted Limb Primordia of 2-day Chick Embryos," *J. Exptl. Zool.* 77:379–400 (1938).

39. ——, and H. L. Hamilton, "A Series of Normal Stages in the Development of the Chick Embryo," *J. Morphol.* 88:49–92 (1951).

40. Hampé, A., "Sur la Topographie des Ébauches présomptives du Membre Postérieur du Poulet," *Compt. Rend. Acad. Sci.* 243:970–973 (1956).

41. ——, "Contribution à l'Étude du Développement et de la Régulation des Déficiences et des Excédents dans la Patte de l'Embryon de Poulet," *Arch. Anat.*

Microscop. Morphol. Exptl. 48:345–478 (1959).

42. Hansborough, L. A., "Regulation in the Wing of the Chick Embryo," *Anat. Record* 120:698 (1954).

43. Harrison, R. G., "Experiments on the development of the Fore Limb of *Amblystoma*, a Self-differentiating Equipotential System," *J. Exptl. Zool.* 25:413–462 (1918).

44. Hinrichsen, K., "Die Bedeutung der epithelialen Randleiste für die Extremitätenentwicklung. *Z. Anat.* 119:350–364 (1956).

45. Hunt, E. A., "The Differentiation of Chick Limb Buds in Chorioallantoic Grafts, with Special References to the Muscles," *J. Exptl. Zool.* 62:57–91 (1932).

46. Kieny, M., "Sur la Constitution du Membre Chimère Produit par l'Association d'un Bourgeon d'Aile et d'un Bourgeon de Patte chez l'Embryon de Poulet," *Compt. Rend. Soc. Biol.* 153:1508–1512 (1959).

47. ———, "Rôle du Mésoderme dans le Développement du Bourgeon de Membre chez l'Embryon de Poulet," *Compt. Rend. Acad. Sci.* 249:1571–1573 (1959).

48. ———, "Rôle Inducteur du Mésoderme dans la Différentiation Précoce du Bourgeon de Membre chez l'Embryon de Poulet," *J. Embryol. Exptl. Morphol.* 8:457–467 (1960).

49. ———, "Régulation des Excédents et des Déficiences du Bourgeon d'Aile de l'Embryon de Poulet," *Arch. Anat. Microscop. Morphol. Exptl.* 53:29–44 (1964).

50. Koecke, H. V. "Entwicklungsphysiologie der Vögel," *Fortschr. Zool.* 16:395–468 (1963).

51. Levi-Montalcini, R., and P. V. Angeletti, "Growth and Differentiation," *Ann. Rev. Physiol.* 24:11–56 (1962).

52. Milaire, J., "Contribution à la Connaissance Morphologique et Cytochimique des Bourgeons de Membres chez Quelques Reptiles," *Arch. Biol.* 68:429–512 (1957).

53. ———, "Etude Morphologique et Cytochimique du Développement des Membres chez la Souris et chez la Taupe," *Arch. Biol.* 74:129–317 (1963).

54. Murray, P. D. F., and J. S. Huxley, "Self-differentiation in the Grafted Limb-bud of the Chick," *J. Anat.* 59:379–384 (1925).

55. ———, and D. Selby, "Grafts of Longitudinal Halves of Limb-buds of the Four-day Chick," *Australian J. Exptl. Biol. Med. Sci.* 5:181–188 (1928).

56. O'Rahilly, R., E. Gardner, and D. J. Gray, "The Ectodermal Thickening and Ridge in the Limbs of Staged Human Embryos," *J. Embryol. Exptl. Morphol.* 4:254–264 (1956).

57. Rotmann, E., "Die Rolle des Ektoderms und Mesoderms bei der Formbildung der Kiemen und Extremitäten von *Triton*," *Arch. Entwicklungsmech. Or.* 124:747–794 (1931).

58. Rudnick, D., "Limb-forming Potencies of the Chick Blastoderm, Including Notes on Associated Trunk Structures," *Trans. Conn. Acad. Arts Sci.* 36:353–377 (1945).

59. ———, "Regulation and Localization in the Hind-limb Bud of the Chick Embryo," *Anat. Record* 67:60 (1946).

60. Saunders, J. W., Jr., "The Proximo-distal Sequence of Origin of the Parts of the Chick Wing and the Role of the Ectoderm," *J. Exptl. Zool.* 108:363–403 (1948).

61. ———, "An Analysis of the Role of the Apical Ridge of Ectoderm in the Development of the Limb Bud in the Chick," *Anat. Record* 105:567 (1949).

62. ———, J. M. Cairns, and M. T. Gasseling, "The Role of the Apical Ridge of Ectoderm in the Differentiation of the Morphological Structure and Inductive Specificity of Limb Parts in the Chick," *J. Morphol.* 101:57–87 (1957).

63. ———, and M. T. Gasseling, "Transfilter Propagation of Apical Ectoderm Maintenance Factor in the Chick Embryo Wing Bud," *Develop. Biol.* 7:64–78 (1963).

64. ———, ———, and J. M. Cairns, "Effect of Implantation Site on the Development of an Implant in the Chick Embryo," *Nature* 175:673–674 (1955).

65. ———, ———, and ———, "The Differentiation of Prospective Thigh Mesoderm Grafted beneath the Apical Ectodermal Ridge of the Wing Bud in Chick Embryo," *Develop. Biol.* 1:281–301 (1959).

66. ———, ———, and S. M. D. Gfeller, "Interactions of Ectoderm and Mesoderm in the Origin of Axial Relationships in the

Wing of the Fowl," *J. Exptl. Zool.* 137: 39–74 (1958).

67. Searls, R. L., and E. Zwilling, "Regeneration of the Apical Ectodermal Ridge of the Chick Embryo Limb Bud," *Develop. Biol.* 9:38–55 (1964).

68. Spurling, R. G., "The Effect of Extirpation of the Posterior Limb Bud on the Development of the Limb and Pelvic Girdle in Chick Embryos," *Anat. Record* 26:41–56 (1923).

69. Steiner, K., "Entwicklungsmechanische Untersuchungen über die Bedeutung des ektodermalen Epithels der Extremitätenknospe von Amphibienlarven," *Arch. Entwicklungsmech. Or.* 113: 1–11 (1928).

70. Tschumi, P. A., "Die Bedeutung der Epidermisleiste für die Entwicklung der Beine von *Xenopus laevis* Daud," *Rev. Suisse Zool.* 63:707–716 (1956).

71. ———, "The Growth of the Hind-limb Bud of *Xenopus laevis* and Its Dependence upon Epidermis," *J. Anat.* 91:149–173 (1957).

72. Waddington, C. H., *Principles of Embryology.* London: G. Allen, (1956).

73. Warren, A. E., "Experimental Studies on the Development of the Wing in the Embryo of *Gallus domesticus*," *Am. J. Anat.* 54:449–485 (1934).

74. Wolff, Et., "Production Expérimentale et Déterminisme d'une Monstruosité Inconnue: la Symélie Antérieure," *Compt. Rend. Acad. Sci.* 119:1673–1675 (1934).

75. ———, "Les Bases de la Tératogénèse Expérimentale des Vertébrés Amniotes d'après les Résultats de Méthodes Directes," *Arch. Anat. Histol. Embryol.* 22: 1–382 (1936).

76. ———, and A. Hampé, "Sur la Régulation de la Patte du Poulet Après Résection d'un Segment Intermédiaire du Bourgeon de Patte," *Compt. Rend. Soc. Biol.* 148:154–156 (1954).

77. ———, and J. Kahn, "Production Expérimentale de la Polydactylie chez l'Embryon d'Oiseau," *Compt. Rend. Acad. Sci.* 224:1583–1584 (1947).

78. Zwilling, E., "Ectoderm-Mesoderm Relationship in the Development of the Chick Embryo Limb Bud," *J. Exptl. Zool.* 128:423–441 (1955).

79. ———, "Interaction between Limb-Bud Ectoderm and Mesoderm in the Chick Embryo. I. Axis Establishment. *J. Exptl. Zool.* 132:157–171 (1956).

80. ———, "Interaction between Limb-bud Ectoderm and Mesoderm in the Chick Embryo. II. Experimental Limb Duplication," *J. Exptl. Zool.* 132:173–187 (1956).

81. ———, "Interaction between Limb-bud Ectoderm and Mesoderm in the Chick Embryo. IV. Experiments with a Wingless Mutant," *J. Exptl. Zool.* 132: 241–253 (1956).

82. ———, "Genetic Mechanism in Limb Development," *Cold Spring Harbor Symp. Quant. Biol.* XXI:349–354 (1956).

83. ———, "Limb Morphogenesis," I. *Advances in Morphogenesis.* New York: Academic Press pp. 301–330 (1961).

84. ———, "Development of Fragmented and Dissociated Limb-bud Mesoderm," *Develop. Biol.* 9:20–37 (1964).

85. ———, and L. A. Hansborough, "Interaction between Limb-bud Ectoderm and Mesoderm in the Chick Embryo. III. Experiments with Polydactylous Limbs," *J. Exptl. Zool.* 132:219–239 (1956).

11

Aspects of Limb Morphogenesis in Mammals

J. MILAIRE

Laboratoire d'Anatomie et d'Embryologie humaines
de l'Université Libre de Bruxelles
Bruxelles, Belgium

In all amniote vertebrates, the first demonstrable limb rudiments appear as localized swellings of the dorsal somatic mesoderm which raise the adjacent trunk ectoderm into smooth hillocks. These early limb buds soon project beyond the body wall of the embryo and begin their lengthwise outgrowth. In the present article, recent work on limb morphogenesis in mammals will be reviewed, including material previously published by the author (Milaire, 1–8).

Let us begin by summarizing the structural changes that take place during the growth and organization of the precartilaginous limb mesoderm in the embryonic mouse hindlimb bud. These changes are shown in Figures 11.1–11.14, all of which illustrate preparations stained with the Unna-Brachet technique for RNA.

Growth and Organization of the Limb

Early Cartilage Formation

Figure 11.1 shows a transverse section of a 10-day hindlimb bud in situ. At this stage, the whole limb mesoderm is derived from the dorsal somatopleure, which has recovered a thin epithelial appearance. Except in a small proximal area located at the junction of the limb bud and the axial embryonic structures, most of the undifferentiated limb mesoderm is compact and very basophilic. Study of later stages has shown that the presumptive skeletal mesoderm lies in the center of this basophilic cell mass, as well as in its marginal portion which is responsible for its further proliferation. The outer mesoderm, that which lies under the dorsal and ventral surfaces of the

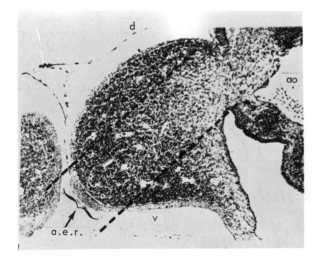

Figs. 11.1–11.14 are sections of mouse hindlimb buds at different stages stained with Unna-Brachet's technique for demonstration of RNA, after fixation with Serra's fluid. Fig. 11.1 Transverse section of the right hindlimb bud in situ on the 10th day. The area between the two dashed lines contains all the presumptive material for the limb skeleton. d, dorsal; ao, dorsal aorta; a.e.r., apical ectodermal ridge; v, ventral.

Fig. 11.2 Tangential section through a 10-day right hindlimb bud showing the asymmetrical distribution of the basophilic mesoderm. pre., preaxial; mvs, marginal venous sinus; art., artery; post., postaxial.

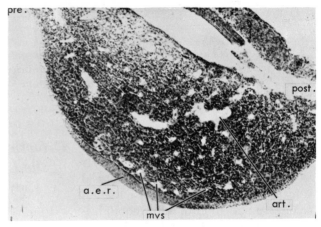

bud, will give rise to the soft tissues such as the muscles, tendons, and connective tissue. At this stage, the limb ectoderm is generally thicker than that of the dorsal surface of the embryo, with a maximal thickness all along the marginal border of the bud. This thicker marginal ectoderm will transform into a crestlike and transitory structure—the apical ectodermal ridge.

The best way to follow the further growth and organization of the presumptive skeletal mesoderm is to study limb buds in "tangential" sections, that is, sections oriented parallel to the ventral surface of the bud and passing through the a.e.r. (Figs. 11.2–11.14).

At the 10-day stage, such a section (Fig. 11.2) shows that the amount of basophilic mesoderm is greater in the postaxial (or caudal) half of the bud than in the preaxial (or cephalic) half. A similar asymmetry is present in the apical ectoderm, which is thicker postaxially.

Several limb buds collected at short intervals during the first half of the 11th day *in utero* (Figs. 11.3, 11.4, and 11.5) show the gradual condensation of the mesoderm in a proximo-postaxial area. This early organization represents the primary femoral blastema. Changes occur at the same time in the vascular pattern of the mesoderm. One of the

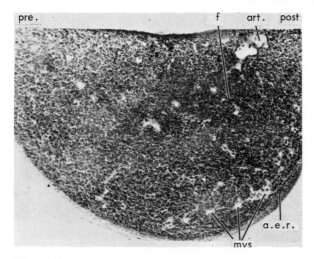

Fig. 11.3

Figs. 11.3–11.5 Tangential sections through three right hindlimb buds collected during the first half of the 11th day *in utero*. Note the condensation of the femoral blastema and the entrance of the main artery caudal to the limb bud axis. f, femur precartilage.

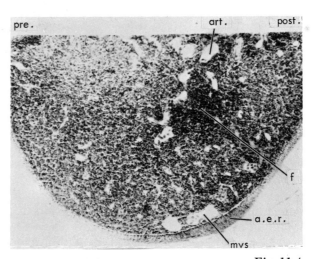

Fig. 11.4

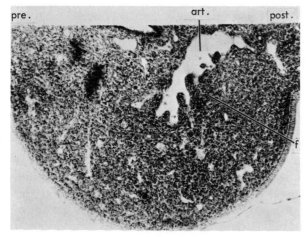

Fig. 11.5

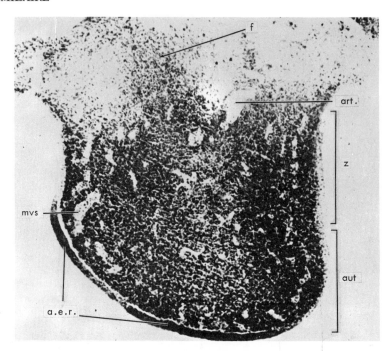

Fig. 11.6 Tangential section through a right hindlimb bud reaching the middle of the 11th day *in utero*. First demonstrable distinction between the limb skeletal segments. aut, autopod; z, zeugopod; f, femur; mvs, marginal venous sinus.

five small arteries which supplies the $9\frac{1}{2}$-day limb bud becomes predominant at the early 10-day stage. This vessel enters the mesoderm caudal to the limb bud axis and divides into numerous terminal branches (Fig. 11.5). It represents the later femoral artery. Simultaneously, a great number of venous lacunae are formed in the marginal mesoderm underlying the a.e.r. These peripheral vessels will later form an important (but transitory) marginal venous system which will drain most of the blood to the cardinal vein.

When the embryo reaches the middle of its 11th day *in utero*, the hindlimb bud becomes longer than it is wide. This important proximodistal outgrowth carries the a.e.r. distalward so that this structure no longer covers the entire marginal border of the bud, but only its distal third (Fig. 11.6). The

proximal two-thirds of the mesoderm are now covered by a normal two-layered ectoderm similar to that of the dorsal or ventral surface. Other changes have simultaneously taken place in the mesoderm itself, establishing differences between its proximal and distal parts. In the proximal "stump" the femoral precartilage becomes individuated, while more distally, the presumptive mesoderm of the zeugopod (tibia + peroneus) has condensed and forms a common precartilaginous plate. In the distal third of the limb bud, the mesoderm is still undifferentiated and forms a thick and very basophilic marginal layer underlying the a.e.r. This mesoderm represents the presumptive material of the distal limb segment (the autopod) which is normally more abundant postaxially. This mesodermal asymmetry modifies the general outline of the early footplate producing a postaxial projection and a flat preaxial part. At this stage also, the main artery runs around the postaxial side of the femoral precartilage before entering the axial part of the more distal zeugopodial plate. This vessel then divides into numerous radiating branches which run distalward through the undifferentiated mesoderm of the footplate. The marginal venous system is still an irregular network of anastomotic veins underlying the a.e.r.

A few hours later, between 11½-day and 12-day embryo, the differences described above between the proximal, two-part stump and the distal footplate become very clear (Fig. 11.7). The proximal precartilages of the stylopod (femur) and of the zeugopod (tibia + peroneus) are now highly condensed and retain their previous relationships with the main artery. At later stages, these three skeletal blastemata progressively chondrify, reaching the cartilaginous state between the 13th and the 14th day *in utero*.

During the same period, the distal presumptive mesoderm of the autopod begins to grow and become organized in a proximodistal and caudocephalic direction. As a result of these simultaneous gradients of morphogenesis, the different precartilaginous masses of mesoderm condense successively from the tarsal element to the distal phalanx in each digital ray, while at the same level along the proximodistal axis they appear successively from the fifth ray to the first. This sequence of morphogenesis in the distal limb segment is shown in Figures 11.7–11.10, in which are represented successive stages of the hindlimb bud from the 11th to the 12th day *in utero*.

At the 12-day stage (Fig. 11.10), the preskeletal mesoderm of the footplate

appears as a series of five precartilaginous columns converging at their proximal ends into a uniform and compact mass of cells which establishes the junction with the zeugopod. At its distal end, each of these radiating precartilages is still continuous with the thick layer of marginal mesoderm from which it has originated. At this stage, each precartilaginous column includes the material for the tarsal (cuneiform or cuboid) element, the metatarsal element, and the proximal part of the first phalanx. Thus, two important aspects remain to be considered in our description of limb morphogenesis: (1) How does the chondrification progress in the distal limb segment? (2) What are the final steps leading to the individuation of the toes?

Chondrification of the Distal Limb

As in the more proximal segments, the chondrification of the footplate progresses in a proximodistal direction. However, the caudocephalic gradient, observed during the period of growth and organization of the undifferentiated mesoderm, no longer exists in the later transformation of mesoderm into cartilage. The three proximal elements of the tarsus (talus, calcaneum, and naviculare) begin chondrifying at the 13th day in the compact mass of mesoderm lying between the zeugopod and the more distal radiating precartilages of the autopod. As shown in Figure 11.12 (14th day) and Figures 11.13 and 11.14 (15th day), each of these elements reaches the cartilaginous state very quickly. The more distal tarsal as well as metatarsal precartilages of each toe then differentiate successively in the corresponding radiating column of mesoderm. There, chondrification begins earlier in the three medial rays than in the two outer ones.

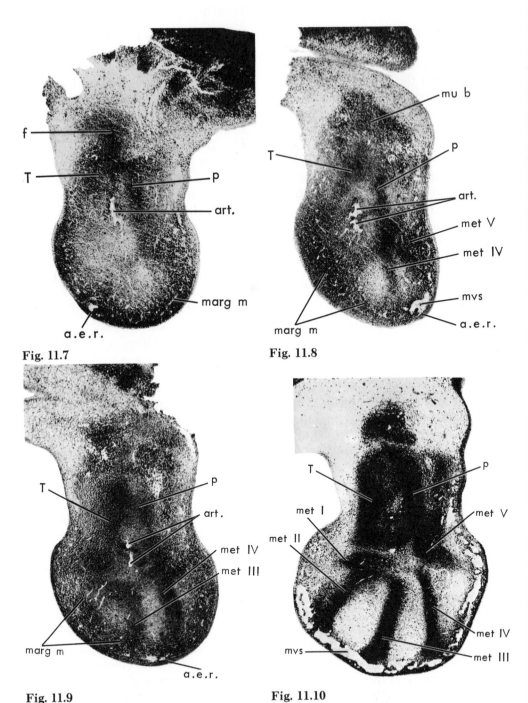

Fig. 11.7

Fig. 11.8

Fig. 11.9

Fig. 11.10

Figs. 11.7–11.10 Tangential section through right hindlimb buds collected at intervals between 11- and 12-day stages. Demonstration of the topographical gradients which appear during the development of the autopod. T, tibia precartilage; marg m, marginal mesoderm; p, peroneus precartilage; met I–V, 1st to 5th metatarsal precartilages; mu b, muscular blastema.

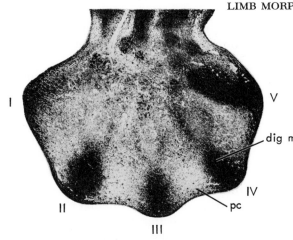

Fig. 11.11 Tangential section of the footplate of a 13-day left hindlimb bud. The section goes through the distal basophilic part of the radiating columns (where the digital mesoderm is proliferating). Numerous pycnotic cells can be seen in the interdigital areas. pc, pycnotic cells; dig m, digital mesoderm.

Individuation of Digits

As will be described later in greater detail, the formation of digits proceeds by two different kinds of morphogenetic activities. The first is the maintenance of five limited growing centers at the distal tip of each mesodermal ray of the footplate. These centers represent the only parts of the marginal mesoderm in which the cells continue to divide actively (Fig. 11.11). The resulting new material is progressively laid down in a proximodistal direction and gives rise to the distal phalanges. It must be mentioned here that the overlying a.e.r. regains the structural appearance of a normal two-layered ectoderm as early as the middle of the 13th day *in utero*, that is, at the very beginning of digital outgrowth. The marginal venous system is simultaneously broken down and replaced by a series of deep veins running parallel to the arteries. The second morphogenetic process taking part in the individuation of digits is a regional degeneration occurring in each interdigital area of the marginal mesoderm. The first dying cells are demonstrable close to the marginal ectoderm at the early 12-day stage. At later stages, more and more pycnotic cells appear until the

entire interdigital area has become necrotic. At the 14-day stage, the ectoderm covering the dorsal and ventral surfaces of the interdigital areas sinks into the degenerating mesoderm separating the proximal phalanges of the adjacent digits.

Apart from some minor variations, the structural changes demonstrable during the organogenesis of the limb skeleton of the mouse have been found to be similar to those of other mammalian embryos such as the rat and mole. Moreover, most of these changes are also similar to those occurring in the forelimb buds of the same species. Our present knowledge of the fine morphological changes occurring in the developing chick limb buds remains incomplete, despite the tremendous amount of interesting data which have been obtained for this species by experimental methods (see Amprino, Chapter 10).

The Role of the Ectoderm

Comments on the Chick Limb

As emphasized in Amprino's report (Chapter 10), many of the experiments performed on chick embryos which

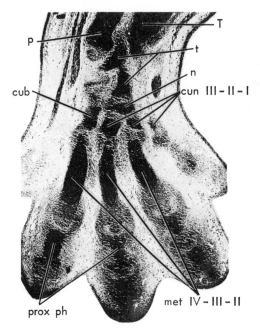

Fig. 11.12 Tangential section of the foot-plate of a 14-day left hindlimb bud. Pre-cartilaginous elements of the autopod. cub, cuboid precartilage; prox ph, proximal phalanx precartilage; cun I–III, 1st to 3rd cuneiform precartilages; n, naviculare precartilage; t, talus precartilage.

been removed, suggests that the ultrasound may exert a stimulating action on the mesoderm cells.

In the absence of further evidence we may consider that this physical treatment acts at the molecular level to release some mesodermal properties which would normally be switched on by ectodermal factors. On the other hand, the lack of early regeneration of the apical ectoderm has been considered in many experimental conditions as evidence that the ectoderm is not involved in the observed regenerative properties of the mesoderm. Recent results obtained by Searls and Zwilling (12) have shed new light on this matter. They show clearly that a new ectodermal ridge may regenerate after the original one has undergone degenera-

might be considered as convincing evidence for a morphogenetic role of the ectoderm may also be interpreted in other ways, depending on whether or not one admits such an ectodermal contribution. However, there are a large number of experimental results which are highly suggestive of a morphogenetic role for the apical ectoderm, while there is only one piece of evidence arguing against such an ectodermal activity: that is the fact that a grafted limb bud mesoderm can develop normally after its ectodermal jacket has been removed by the use of ultrasound. The fact that after the action of versene or trypsin the same ectoderm-free mesoderm always fails to develop, provided all the ectoderm has

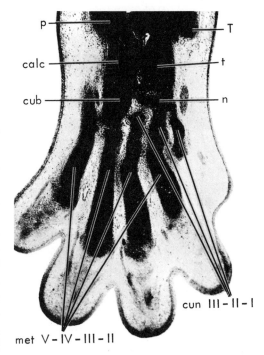

Fig. 11.13 Tangential section of the foot-plate of a 15-day left hindlimb bud. Cartilages of the tarsus and the metatarsus. calc, calcaneum precartilage.

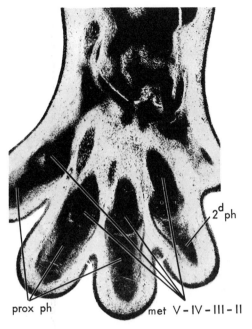

Fig. 11.14 Tangential section of the footplate of a 15-day left hindlimb bud. More distal cartilages of the toes. 2^dph, 2nd phalanx precartilage.

tion or has been completely removed, provided the ectoderm remains in close association with the limb bud mesoderm. It is therefore evident that in the interpretation of their further experimental results, all investigators will have to pay constant attention to the precise behavior of the remaining operated ectoderm.

Another assumption, that the amniotic fluid exerts a noxious action on the ectoderm-free mesoderm, is doubtful. Although my doubt is mostly intuitive, common sense leads me to believe that the embryo's own environment must provide it with the best physical and chemical conditions for its normal development. From a more objective point of view, this impression is supported by the result of an experiment performed by Saunders (11). In this ex-periment, an ectoderm-free limb bud is grafted onto the stump of another limb bud, with a single ectodermal ridge grafted onto its distal border. In such conditions, the complete recovery of the ectoderm, from the initial host stump to the distal border of the graft, takes 24 hours. Despite this exposure to the amniotic fluid, the grafted meso-derm forms a normal limb bud.

Finally, it must be pointed out that most of Amprino's objections to the mesodermal maintenance factor pos-tulated by Zwilling are valid. Although the existence of the apical ectodermal ridge maintenance factor has been clearly demonstrated in recent experi-ments performed by Zwilling (14), the limited information on its spatial dis-tribution, its mode of action, and its regulative abilities is not sufficient to provide an adequate explanation for all experimental or genetic modifications of limb morphogenesis.

The Mammalian Limb

Our own information about limb de-velopment refers almost exclusively to mammalian limb buds. This material has been studied from three different points of view. In a first group of studies (Table 11.1), various chemical substances or enzymatic activities have been cytochemically located in the de-veloping normal limb buds of rat, mouse, and mole embryos. Other prep-arations of the same kind have been made in a few reptiles and also in the chick embryo, but they remain in-complete. In each species the cyto-chemical changes have been studied parallel with the morphological ones. In a second group of studies (Table 11.2), the same cytochemical tech-niques have been applied to abnormal limb buds of mutant mice. Four muta-

TABLE 11.1   Cytochemical Studies of Normal Limb Buds

SPECIES	METABOLITES OR ENZYMES DEMONSTRATED
Rat (1956)	RNA, glycogen, mucopolysaccharides, alkaline phosphatase
Reptiles (1957) (*Emys, Pseudemys*) (*Chamaeleo, Mabuia*)	RNA, glycogen, mucopolysaccharides
Mouse and mole (1963)	RNA, glycogen, mucopolysaccharides, alkaline phosphatase, acid phosphatase
Mouse (1964) Detailed study of the autopod	RNA, glycogen, mucopolysaccharides, alkaline phosphatase, acid phosphatase ATP, UTP, CTP, ITP ⎫ ADP ⎬ -phosphohydrolase AMP, IMP ⎭ *Partial information about:*
Guinea pig Chick	RNA, glycogen, mucopolysaccharides alkaline phosphatase

tions have been studied so far, each of them having its main action upon the distal limb segment. Our third source of information is a recent experimental analysis in which Mulnard and I (Table 11.3) studied the behavior of the early mouse limb bud explanted in vitro, either intact or separated into its two components by the use of trypsin or versene. Our conclusions will be presented as a series of five propositions, each of them dealing with a particular aspect of the problem.

PROPOSITION 1. *The first demonstrable activities of limb morphogenesis take place in the mesoderm.* At a particular stage, a dorsal area of the somatic mesoderm starts proliferating all along the trunk region of the embryo. The resulting mesodermal mass raises the ectoderm and forms a lengthened swelling termed "Wolff's crest" (Fig. 11.15). Shortly after this, the growth of the mesoderm continues at each end of the crest where it gives rise to the limb buds themselves, while the intermediate part is progressively included into the body wall of the embryo. The causal factors underlying these activities are unknown. The ectoderm is apparently not involved, for

at these early stages it is still thin and does not show any cytochemical peculiarity. Recent experimental results obtained by Murillo-Ferrol (10) on the chick embryo suggest that the somites may exert a very early morphogenetic influence on the more ventral presumptive limb mesoderm. It must be said that at these early stages mouse limb bud mesoderm is unable to grow or chondrify when explanted in vitro without its ectodermal covering.

PROPOSITION 2. *The presumptive limb segments in mammals are successively individuated in a proximodistal sequence.* This agrees with what has been demonstrated in chick and *Xenopus* embryos. It has been shown by studying the topographical evolution of the various cytochemical changes occurring at later stages during the transformation of mesoderm into precartilage. It can also be observed that, at least in the case of the distal limb segment, the mesoderm which makes up the progressively more distal areas arises from active cell proliferation taking place under the apical ectoderm. There is no evidence for movement of mesoderm from proximal areas to more distal ones.

TABLE 11.2   Cytochemical Studies of Mutant Mouse Limb Buds

MUTATION	SYMBOL	METABOLITES AND ENZYMES DEMONSTRATED
Oligosyndactylism (1962)	Os/+	RNA, glycogen, mucopolysaccharides, alkaline phosphatase, acid phosphatase
Syndactylism (1964)	sm/sm	RNA, glycogen, mucopolysaccharides alkaline phosphatase
Brachypodism (1964)	Bp/Bp	acid phosphatase
Dominant hemimelia (1964)	Dh/+	ATP, CTP, ITP, UTP ADP ⎫-phosphohydrolase AMP, IMP

PROPOSITION 3. *An early segregation occurs in the undifferentiated growing mesoderm between the presumptive material of the soft tissues and that of the skeletal blastemata.* Contrary to the classical conception, presumptive muscle condenses in a thick cellular layer underlying the dorsal and ventral ectoderm, while the cartilaginous elements condense in the central part of the bud (Fig. 11.16). From the moment of its early individuation, the outer mesodermal mantle is thicker ventrally, and this early dorsoventral asymmetry heralds the later predominance of the flexor musculature over the extensor. At subsequent stages the myogenic mesoderm undergoes an active movement, bringing it close to the central precartilaginous masses. It finally cleaves into several morphological units. Although we do not intend, in such a short account, to deal with this particular aspect of limb morphogenesis (see Milaire, 7), it may be said that some observations strongly suggest that the early individuation of the myogenic mesoderm requires a morphogenetic influence from the overlying ectoderm, that is, the ectodermal mantle excluding the apical area.

PROPOSITION 4. *Changes occur in the structure and metabolic properties of the ectoderm from the early beginning of limb bud outgrowth until the* presumptive digital mesoderm has been laid down. These changes show a significant correlation with the activities of the underlying mesoderm. In some cases such correlations suggest that the ectodermal changes are the result of mesodermal influences, while in other cases the mesodermal activities seem to depend on ectodermal influences. A few examples of

TABLE 11.3   Experiments Performed to Study the Behavior of the Early Mouse Limb Bud, Explanted in vitro

PRETREATMENT OF THE EXPLANTS	DIFFERENT KINDS OF CULTURES PERFORMED
None	Intact limb bud
Action of trypsin (3%, 5 min)	Intact or recombined
Action of versene (0.1%, 45 min)	Intact or recombined
Ectoderm isolated by versene Mesoderm isolated by trypsin	Crossed reassociations

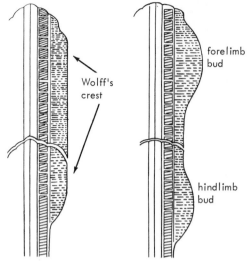

Fig. 11.15 The external appearance of the lateral wall of a mammalian embryo just before the outgrowth of the limb buds (left) and at the early beginning of limb morphogenesis (right).

these two modalities will be presented (Fig. 11.17).

Morphologically, the ectodermal changes include the growth of each basal ectodermal cell, while the peridermal cells undergo a transformation, thickening and creeping deep into the basal layer, to come into close contact with the basement membrane. Cytochemically, the thickened areas of the ectoderm show an increase in RNA content in the basal cytoplasmic columns which lie close to the basement membrane. In addition, all cells show a significant rise in various dephosphorylating enzyme activities.

Whatever the stage considered, these ectodermal changes are limited to those limb bud areas where the outer mesoderm is still undifferentiated. The whole ectodermal covering is active at very early stages; this activity later becomes confined to the apicoventral area and still later to the apical ectodermal ridge where it reaches its maxi-

mal intensity. The same ectodermal properties are maintained finally at the tip of each digital bud, the last regions where the proliferating activities of the outer mesoderm still give rise to new material for the most distal limb parts. The ectodermal changes are of the same kind wherever they take place, but their degree of importance shows local and chronological variations correlated with the activities occurring in the underlying mesoderm.

A series of examples will show that there are at least three circumstances in which the ectodermal changes appear as the result of earlier modifications occurring in the mesoderm.

The amount of primary mesoderm laid down by proliferation in the somatopleure is higher in the ventral part of the bud than more dorsally (Fig. 11.18). As a consequence, the later ectodermal changes predominate on the ventral aspect of the limb bud. Shortly after, all the cytochemical properties acquired by the ectoderm show a significant increase in a limited apicoventral area which later will thicken to form the apical ridge. This local increase is probably the result of stronger mesodermal influences exerted by the marginal mesoderm.

Although the early limb bud mesoderm is equally distributed between the pre- and postaxial halves of the bud, special enzymatic and vascular conditions prevail in the postaxial area. At later stages, a similar caudocephalic asymmetry appears in the apicoventral area of the ectoderm, as if it had been determined by mesodermal factors. The morphological transformation of this part of the ectoderm into a ridge-like structure starts at the postaxial extremity of the marginal border whence it gradually spreads preaxially. When

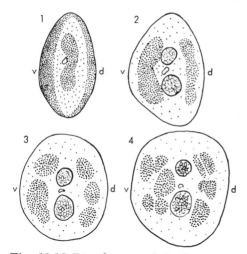

Fig. 11.16 Distribution of the basophilic and compact mesoderm in cross sections through the zeugopod of the mouse hindlimb bud at four successive developmental stages. 1. 11 days. The basophilic mesoderm forms an outer mantle underlying the ectoderm and a compact mass in the center of the bud. The former represents the presumptive material of the muscles and tendons; it is thicker ventrally. The latter is the early preskeletal blastema. 2. 11½ days. The outer, premuscular mesoderm has lost its contact with the ectoderm while the central skeletal mass of cells has divided into two precartilages, one preaxial (the tibia) and one postaxial (the peroneus). 3. 12 days. While the central precartilages are chondrifying, the premuscular material cleaves into several smaller blastemata. 4. 13 days. Some of the premuscular blastemata undergo a secondary cleavage, so that most of the definitive muscles can be identified. v, ventral; d, dorsal.

sity of the enzymatic reactions gradually decrease in a caudocephalic direction, as an evident consequence of degenerative phenomena appearing in this part of the ridge. The caudocephalic gradient of structural individuation of the ectodermal ridge is thus followed by the development of a true functional asymmetry in this structure. These observations strongly support the assumption of a maintenance influence exerted by the mesoderm on the apical ectodermal ridge.

In addition, the developmental abnormalities recently observed in mutant embryos heterozygous for oligosyndactylism are in good agreement with this idea (Fig. 11.19). In these limb buds, the preaxial part of the ectodermal ridge undergoes more marked

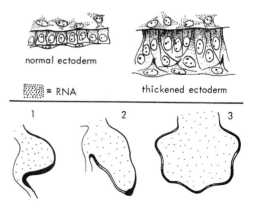

topographical evolution of the cytochemical
properties in the ectoderm

Fig. 11.17 The top drawings show the morphological changes occurring in the thickening ectoderm as well as the increase of RNA close to the basement membrane. The bottom drawings show the different regions in which an ectodermal thickening can be observed during development. In 1 (9 days) and 2 (10½ days) the hindlimb bud is shown in situ in a transverse section. In 3 (12¼ days) the distal part of the limb bud is sectioned parallel to the plane of the footplate. The cytochemically active parts of the ectoderm are shown in black.

the whole ectodermal ridge has formed, it retains the cytochemical properties already present before its morphological transformation. However, important quantitative changes have occurred all along the structure. All reactions remain strong in the postaxial half of the ridge where all cells look quite healthy. In the preaxial portion, the amount of RNA and the inten-

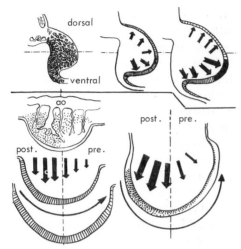

Fig. 11.18 Correlated changes postulated in the mesoderm and the ectoderm of the developing mammalian limb bud. The three top drawings show the relationships during the early outgrowing period. The bottom drawings depict the development of a caudocephalic gradient preceding morphogenesis of the autopod (see text).

degeneration than in the normal condition. Unpublished data have shown that such ectodermal changes are preceded by the occurrence of extensive degeneration in the preaxial mesoderm. The primary action of the mutant gene may thus be located in the mesoderm, whose maintenance is thus weakened.

In two other abnormal genetic conditions, however, intrinsic changes occur in the preaxial part of the ectodermal ridge without any apparent previous modification in the underlying mesoderm. In the case of syndactylism, the gene affects the morphological reactivity of the marginal ectoderm to the normal influence exerted by the mesoderm. It is, however, surprising to observe that the resulting hypertrophic transformation of the ridge is limited to its preaxial part only. The fact that

the postaxial part is preserved is probably the consequence of stronger influences exerted by the postaxial mesoderm. In dominant hemimelia, the preaxial ectodermal ridge is not affected by cell pycnosis which would hurt it slightly in normal conditions. As a consequence, all of its metabolic properties show a significant increase. The last two examples show that, in spite of its close dependence on the underlying mesoderm, the apical ectodermal ridge has intrinsic and genetically controlled morphogenetic properties.

The early events of digital outgrowth provide a third significant example in which ectodermal changes appear as the direct consequence of earlier modifications occurring in the mesoderm (Fig. 11.20). From the beginning of limb development to the footplate stage, the mesodermal maintenance factor, though unequally distributed between the pre- and postaxial halves

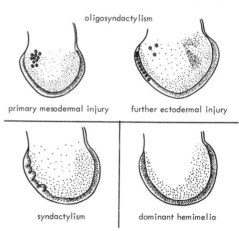

Fig. 11.19 Three mutant conditions in the mouse leading to different injuries in the preaxial part of the presumptive autopod. On each of these tangential sections of the footplate, the preaxial border is on the left side of the picture (see text). Large dots, pycnotic cells; small dots, RNA.

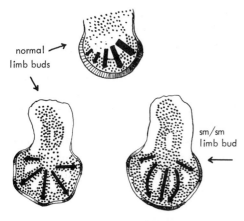

normal
limb buds

sm/sm
limb bud

late breaking – up of the mesodermal
a.e.r. maintenance factor

Fig. 11.20 Changes occurring in the presumed ectoderm-mesoderm interactions during the development of digits in the mouse hindlimb bud. The arrows on the top drawing symbolize the uninterrupted distribution of the mesodermal maintenance factor. At this 11-day stage the growing mesoderm underlying the a.e.r. may be considered as the presumptive material for the basipod and the metapod. Below, left (12-day stage), the changes occurring in the cytochemical properties of the apical ectoderm suggest a breaking up of the mesodermal maintenance factor into five limited digital areas (arrows). The drawing below, right, shows how the above hypothesis can be useful for the interpretation of the abnormal events occurring in the sm/sm limb buds (see text). Small dots, basophilic growing mesoderm; full black, cytochemically active parts of the ectoderm; arrows, presumed mesodermal maintenance factor.

of the limb bud, exerts its influence on the whole ectodermal ridge. Soon after the mesoderm has organized itself into five radiating blastemata, important changes occur in the ectodermal ridge. Its metabolic activities seem to break up into five limited digital areas. Whereas the whole ectodermal ridge gradually thins out and loses its former cytochemical asymmetries, the earlier metabolic properties are maintained

only at the distal tip of each radiating precartilage, while they shade off in the intermediate zones affected by new degenerative phenomena. These events suggest that the five radiating precartilaginous blastemata are the only parts of the mesoderm which retain their ability to maintain the ectodermal ridge in a functional state. The morphogenetic deviations occurring in limb buds affected by recessive syndactylism provide a clear demonstration of this. In this mutant, the transitory hypertrophy of the ectodermal ridge hampers the proximodistal expansion of the mesoderm and forces the radiating blastemata to converge at their distal extremity. As a result of a similar convergence of the maintenance influences exerted by each blastema, the metabolic properties of the ectoderm are maintained in an excessive portion of the overlying ectodermal ridge (Fig. 11.20).

The second part of our proposition may be restated as follows: The activities of the undifferentiated limb bud mesoderm are controlled by ectodermal influences. Our in vitro experiments with the mouse limb bud show that, up to early in the 11th day, the explanted limb bud mesoderm is unable to grow and differentiate without being associated with limb bud ectoderm including the basement membrane. In many circumstances, the cytochemical observations made on normal limb buds show that the growing activities of the undifferentiated mesoderm undergo chronological and topographical variations which are correlated with earlier changes occurring in the overlying ectoderm. Two significant examples have been chosen to illustrate such correlative activities. In the first one (Fig. 11.21), the early foot-

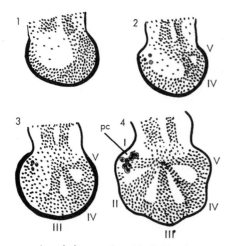

caudocephalic growth and individuation
of the metapod mesoderm

Fig. 11.21 Four successive stages of development of the autopod as observed on
sections tangential to the volar plane of
the footplate of the mouse hindlimb bud.
1. 10½ days. 2. 11 days. 3. 11½ days 4. 12
days. Small dots, basophilic growing mesoderm; large dots, pycnotic cells, pc.

plate mesoderm can be seen to grow
and differentiate according to a typical
caudocephalic gradient, as a result of
the functional asymmetries which previously appeared in the ectodermal
ridge. In other words, the marginal
mesoderm starts growing postaxially
and its proliferation then progresses toward the preaxial border of the bud.
Later, the resulting mesoderm condenses in five radiating blastemata
which appear one after the other from
the fifth to the first. In addition, the
more preaxial mesoderm underlying
the weakest part of the ectodermal
ridge forms the smallest blastema and
also shows extensive degeneration.
The second example (Fig. 11.22) shows
how the distal limb bud mesoderm behaves after the metabolic activities of
the apical ectoderm have broken up
into five digital regions. Because of the

maintenance of functional asymmetries
in the overlying ectoderm, the presumptive digital mesoderm proliferates
actively and further organizes itself in
a proximodistal direction. In the interdigital areas, where the ectoderm has
lost its previous properties, the mesoderm stops growing and undergoes cell
pycnosis. This degeneration first affects
the cells which lie in close contact with
the ectoderm and then spreads to more
and more proximal regions of the interdigital area.

Finally, there are at least two genetically abnormal conditions in which the

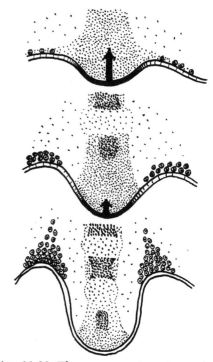

Fig. 11.22 Three successive stages (top
to bottom) of the development of a mammalian digital bud and of the two neighboring interdigital areas (see text). Small
dots, basophilic mesoderm; large dots,
pycnotic cells; full black, cytochemically
differentiated areas of the ectoderm;
arrows, presumed ectodermal influence on
the underlying mesoderm.

growing activities of the mesoderm are modified as a result of earlier genetic ectodermal changes. The first can be observed in dominant hemimelia, where the preaxial hyperactivity of the ectodermal ridge is followed by an excessive growth of the underlying mesoderm with the final formation of an extra phalanx in the first toe. The second condition deals with the last morphogenetic events leading to recessive syndactylism. Here, the whole undifferentiated mesoderm, which underlies the extensive portion of the active marginal ectoderm, undergoes a typical transformation into digital material. As a consequence of the absence of interdigital involution, the resulting digital structures show what has been called a primary process of fusion.

It may be concluded, from what has been said about the fourth proposition, that the early events of limb morphogenesis in mammals appear as an uninterrupted series of interactions between the ectoderm and the mesoderm. This interpretation is in agreement with the reciprocal activities demonstrated by Saunders, Zwilling, and other investigators of the chick embryo. However, two qualifications must be made. The precise chronological correlations between the developmental features occurring respectively in the mesoderm and the ectoderm show that, as a morphological entity, the mammalian ectodermal ridge is only concerned with the formation of the distal limb segment. Consequently, the presumptive mesoderm of the more proximal limb territories must have originated under the influence of the apicoventral ectoderm before the latter had thickened into a ridgelike structure. This means that morphogenetic properties may be evinced by the ectoderm even if it does not show the morphological appearance of the ectodermal ridge. If this concept can be applied to the experiments performed on the chick embryo it suggests that the absence of morphological regeneration of the ectodermal ridge does not necessarily exclude functional regeneration of its morphogenetic properties in the healing ectoderm. It should therefore be interesting to study the cytochemical changes occurring in the experimental limb buds.

Secondly, it is quite evident that, if we consider the morphogenetic role of the ectoderm as a nonspecific stimulation of mesodermal growth, the problem of the regional determination of the mesoderm still remains open. These more specific aspects of limb morphogenesis might be the result of intrinsic mesodermal factors such as those postulated by Amprino, although there is no evidence to support this assumption. This latter point of view, however, is not incompatible with our former interpretation of the ectodermal role. Indeed, we may assume that the mesodermal influence responsible for the maintenance of the apical ectoderm has the same topographical pattern as that which acts directly on the new distal mesoderm originating under the nonspecific stimulation of the ectodermal ridge. Such dissociation between the factors which respectively entail the growth and the regional determination of the mesoderm has already been suggested by Tschumi (13).

PROPOSITION 5. *Although the morphogenetic factors which have been demonstrated so far in the mesoderm and ectoderm of early limb buds have considerably improved our understanding of limb morphogenesis, they still remain insufficient to explain the complete and normal development of a limb.* This conclusion has been drawn from recent observations on brachypod limb buds, a mutation responsible for severe skeletal disturbances in the distal limb segment. In this case, all the primary morphogenetic events of limb development undergo their normal sequence. The first genetic defect affects late mesodermal activities lead-ing to the formation of precartilage. It modifies the early processes of cellular organization as well as the ability of the chondroblasts to synthetize the mucoproteins of the fundamental cartilaginous substance. Later genetic factors are thus still required to insure the final organization of the mesoderm. We may hope that further studies of other mutant conditions will help to clarify this matter.

References

1. Milaire, J., "Etude Morphologique et Cytochimique des Bourgeons de Membres chez le Rat," *Compt. Rend. Soc. Biol.*, 148:2040–2043 (1955).

2. ——, "Contribution à l'Étude Morphologique et Cytochimique des Bourgeons de Membres chez le Rat," *Arch. Biol.* 67:297–391 (1956).

3. ——, "Contribution à la Connaissance Morphologique et Cytochimique des Bourgeons de Membres chez Quelques Reptiles," *Arch. Biol.* 69:429–572 (1957).

4. ——, "Le Rôle de la Cape Apicale dans la Formation des Membres des Vertébrés," *Ann. Soc. Roy. Zool. Belg.* 91:129–145 (1961).

5. ——, "Histochemical Aspects of Limb Morphogenesis in Vertebrates," *Advan. Morphogenesis* 2:183–209 (1962).

6. ——, "Détection Histochimique de Modifications des Ébauches dans les Membres en Formation chez la Souris Oligosyndactyle," *Bull. Classe Sci. Acad. Roy. Belg.* 48:505–528 (1962).

7. ——, "Etude Morphologique et Cytochimique du Développement des Membres chez la Souris et chez la Taupe," *Arch. Biol.* 74:129–317 (1963).

8. ——, "Etude Morphogénétique de Trois Malformations Congénitales de l'Autopode chez la Souris (Syndactylisme – Brachipodisme – Hémimélie Dominante) par des Méthodes Cytochimiques," *Acad. Roy. Belg. Classe Sci. Mem. Collection in 8°.* In press. (1965).

9. Mulnard, J., and J. Milaire, "Analyse Expérimentale de la Chondrogénèse dans le Bourgeon de Membre de la Souris," *Compt. Rend. Acad. Sci.* 258:6525–6526 (1964).

10. Murillo-Ferrol, N. L., "Analisis Experimental de la Participacion del Mesoblasto Paraaxial sobre la Morfogenesis de los Miembros en el Embrion de las Aves," *Ann. Desarrollo* 11:63–76 (1963).

11. Saunders, J. W., "The Differentiation of Prospective Thigh Mesoderm Grafted beneath the Apical Ectodermal Ridge of the Wing Bud in the Chick Embryo," *Develop. Biol.* I:281–301 (1959).

12. Searls, R. L., and E. Zwilling, "Regeneration of the Apical Ectodermal Ridge of the Chick Limb Bud," *Develop. Biol.* 9:38–55 (1964).

13. Tschumi, P. A., "Form und Musterbildung bei der Tetrapodenextremität," *Rev. Suisse Zool.* 69:239–254 (1962).

14. Zwilling, E., "Development of Fragmental and of Dissociated Limb Bud Mesoderm," *Develop. Biol.* 9:20–37 (1964).

12

The Morphogenesis of Joints

BENJAMIN C. MOFFETT, JR.[*]
Department of Orthodontics
School of Dentistry
University of Washington
Seattle, Washington

Joints are classified anatomically into three categories—fibrous, cartilaginous, and synovial—indicating the type of tissue found between the ends of the bones or within the joint (Fig. 12.1). Fibrous joints include: sutures, the junctions between the bones of the cranium; syndesmoses, such as the interosseous membrane joining the radius and ulna; and gomphoses or the joints between the teeth and alveolar bone in the jaws. Cartilaginous joints include epiphyseal plates or the remnants of the original cartilage model which serve as centers for growth, and joints like the intervertebral disc and pubic symphysis. Synovial joints are the most movable, and are provided with a lubricating or synovial fluid, as in the joints of the limbs.

Most of the studies on the morphogenesis of joints have concentrated on the embryology of synovial joints, usually of the limbs (see citations by O'Rahilly, 18). The review to be given here will focus as much as possible on the joints which are seldom studied or which represent modifications of the usual developmental pattern. It will also include available information on postnatal development.

Fibrous Joints

The development of sutural joints has been described by Pritchard and co-workers (21). They distinguished two main types: facial sutures, in which the bones grow toward each other through loose mesenchymal tissue; and the sutures of the cranial vault in which the bones approach each other through a preformed fibrous membrane. In both types, as the bones meet each other, the sutural ligament differentiates into five intervening layers and two uniting layers. During fetal life, the suture

[*] The author's investigations on the temporomandibular joint and joints of the clavicle were supported by Public Health Service research grant A-5694. Photomicrographs were prepared by the Armed Forces Institute of Pathology and by the Department of Embryology, Carnegie Institution of Washington.

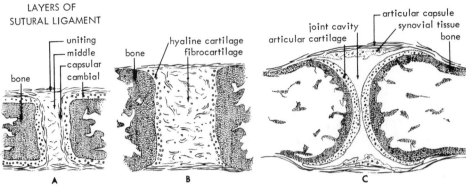

LAYERS OF
SUTURAL LIGAMENT

Fig. 12.1 Three types of joints: *A.* Fibrous joint (suture) showing the five layers of a sutural ligament. *B.* Cartilaginous joint (pubic symphysis). *C.* Synovial joint (finger).

serves as the site of marginal extension of the adjoining bones by means of marked proliferative activity in its cambial layers. The cambial layers are continuous with and identical to the cellular or proliferative layers of the periosteum on the nonsutural surfaces of the bones. In adults the bone edges show no signs of growth and the cambial layers are reduced to a single row of flattened cells. Several sutures show cartilage at the margins of the bones or in the sutural tissue itself during the period of growth. This is most commonly seen in the sagittal and midpalatal sutures.

The layering of the sutural ligament parallels the early differentiation seen in synovial joints. The five intervening layers of the suture correspond to the three-layered interzone of the synovial joint; the uniting layers appear homologous with the fibrous capsule. The location of sutures is determined by the meeting of the adjacent bones and is altered by any deviation in bone growth. After bone growth is completed, the sutural ligament may be replaced by bone, forming a synostosis (Fig. 12.2). The time at which this happens is not constant enough for this phenomenon to serve as a reliable indicator of age.

Little information is available concerning the development of other fibrous joints. Baume (6) states that the fibers in the periodontal joints which attach the teeth to the jaws are derived from the connective tissue fibers of the primitive dental sac. In addition to sup-

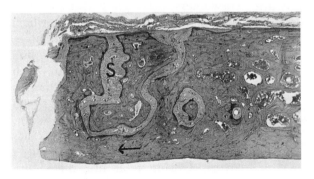

Fig. 12.2 Cranial suture, *S*, with serrated pattern. In this adult specimen the suture is being converted to a synostosis on its inner surface (see arrow). ×7⅓ (Courtesy Armed Forces Institute of Pathology.)

porting the teeth, the periodontal ligaments might play a role in tooth eruption. The location of these joints changes during growth due to the differential in growth rate between the teeth and surrounding bone (Sicher and Weinmann, 25). This shift in location is made possible by means of remodeling activity in the adjacent bone. The periodontal joints occasionally develop areas of fibrocartilage in the ligament and sometimes form a bony ankylosis, as in the sutural joints (Bauer, 5; and Parker et al., 19).

Cartilaginous Joints

Included in the category of cartilaginous joints is a group of temporary joints in which the cartilage is replaced by bone after growth is completed. Examples are the epiphyseal growth plates in the bones of the limbs (Fig. 12.3). The ends of these bones develop ossification centers called epiphyses. They are connected to the shaft or diaphysis of the bone by a remnant of the original cartilage model which persists until growth ceases. The bone is increased in length mainly by means of proliferative activity in this plate of

cartilage. The time at which these epiphyseal plates break down and become replaced by bone is constant enough for each bone for the phenomenon to be used as an indicator of age. The age at which epiphyseal fusion occurs in each bone is given in Lockhart's textbook (13, pp. 142–143).

An example of a permanent cartilaginous joint is the intervertebral disc (Fig. 12.4). It consists of a pad of fibrocartilage between the bodies of adjacent vertebrae. The center of the pad contains a gelatinous mass, the nucleus pulposus. This is surrounded by a fibrocartilaginous envelope, the annulus fibrosus. The morphogenesis of this joint is described by Peacock (20). Cells of the notochord persist in the area between two developing vertebral bodies and form the nucleus pulposus. Mesenchymal cells in the anlage of the disc become fibroblastic and form the annulus fibrosus around the periphery.

At birth the nucleus pulposus has been invaded by strands of fibrocartilage, cartilage cells are numerous, and notochordal cells inconspicuous. This process of invasion continues throughout life, until in the senile disc, notochordal cells are almost impossible to

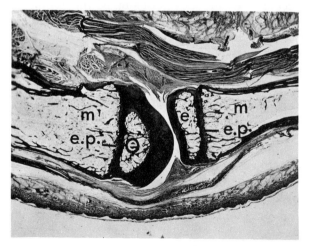

Fig. 12.3 Epiphyseal growth plates, e.p., in finger joint. When the growth plate is obliterated, the epiphysis, e, fuses with the metaphysis, m, and epiphyseal growth is ended. ×5½ (Courtesy Armed Forces Institute of Pathology.)

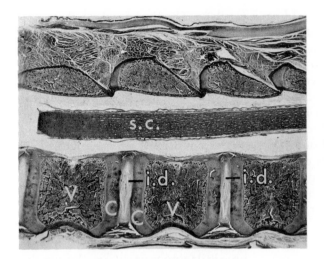

Fig. 12.4 Intervertebral discs, i.d., of a goat vertebral column, longitudinal section. This is a young specimen with growth cartilage, C, still present on the vertebral bodies, V.; s.c., spinal cord. ×2 (Courtesy Armed Forces Institute of Pathology.)

find and the mucoid material is largely replaced by fibrocartilage. During life the water content of the nucleus pulposus decreases from 90 percent at birth to 70 percent in old age.

Another cartilaginous joint is the pubic symphysis. Although little is known about its prenatal development, a number of postnatal changes have been described. Putschar (22) observed that the articular tissue of the pubic symphysis proliferates excessively with each pregnancy, the excess material being shed into a small joint space at the end of pregnancy. Todd (26, 27) has described in detail the changes occurring in the bone of the pubic symphysis in postnatal life. These changes in contour are so regular they can be used as an indication of the individual's age between 18 and 50 years.

Synovial Joints

The development of synovial joints has been reviewed by Gardner (10), based mainly on the joints of the limbs. After the limb buds appear, a blastema or condensation of cells develops along the longitudinal axis (Fig. 12.5). This blastema segments in the regions where joints will develop. Once this happens the components of the joint develop rapidly, so that by the end of embryonic life (7 weeks in the human) the joints resemble those of the adult. The synovial tissue is derived from the extrablastemal mesenchyme around the ends of the bones. The articular cartilage represents remnants of the cartilage model of the bone (Fig. 12.6). Differentiation proceeds directly from the anlage to the specific, adult form of the joint.

These generalizations do not apply to the development of the temporomandibular joint or jaw joint, which is also a synovial joint. It develops relatively late in embryonic life, compared to the large joints of the extremities. During the 7th prenatal week the jaw joint lacks such components as the condylar growth cartilage, joint cavities, synovial tissue, and articular capsule. The manner in which the joint develops differs from that of most synovial joints (Moffett, 15). The temporal bone and mandible arise from separate blastemata which do not lie in contact with each other.

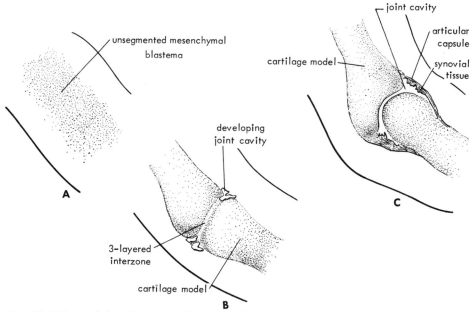

Fig. 12.5 Typical development of a synovial joint: *A.* Mesenchymal blastema prior to its segmentation into a joint. *B.* The blastema has differentiated into cartilage models of the bones, the joint cavity is developing peripherally. *C.* A synovial cavity has appeared between the two cartilage models. It is enclosed by a fibrous joint capsule lined with synovial tissue.

During the 12th week of gestation a growth cartilage appears in the condyle of the mandible and functions like the epiphyseal growth plate in a long bone, except that the mandibular condyle does not develop an ossification center or epiphysis. By the 16th week, growth of the condyle has brought the mandible into contact with the temporal bone. The mesenchyme which originally separated the two bones has now become modified into synovial cavities and articular tissue (Fig. 12.7). In this way the articular surfaces of the temporomandibular joint gain a covering of fibrous connective tissue which changes gradually during postnatal life into fibrocartilage. In other synovial joints, excluding those of the clavicle, the articular tissue is hyaline cartilage derived from the cartilage model of the bone.

The temporomandibular joint contains a complete articular disc which divides the joint space into separate synovial cavities. The lateral part of the disc develops from a condensation of mesenchyme extending between the masseter and lateral pterygoid muscles and passing posteriorly over the condyle. The medial part of the disc appears to be derived from an extension of the lateral pterygoid tendon, which also runs over the mandibular condyle and inserts with the lateral part on the posterior end of Meckel's cartilage, which is differentiating into the malleus. Thus, the disc does not develop directly into its specific definitive form. Instead, the disc maintains its attachment to the malleus during most of fetal life. It does not transfer to its final definitive attachment on the posterior part of the joint capsule until the Glaserian

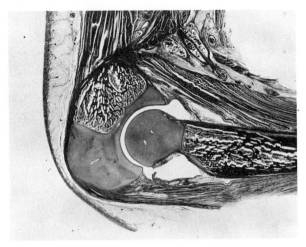

Fig. 12.6 Elbow joint in a human fetus. The articular surfaces are formed by the cartilage model of the bones. ×13⅓ (Courtesy Armed Forces Institute of Pathology.)

fissure closes at 22 weeks. When this happens, the portion of Meckel's cartilage running from the mandible to the cranium degenerates into the sphenomandibular ligament.

At birth the temporomandibular joint lacks its adult contours. The articular tubercle or the convex part of the temporal bone with which the condyle articulates does not complete its development until the twelfth year of life. Histologically, the contours of both the temporal bone and the mandibular condyle show evidence of remodeling activity during the entire lifetime of the

individual. This is a characteristic seen in all of the weight-bearing or loaded joints and is a morphological adaptation to the mechanical stimuli associated with function.

The joints of the clavicle resemble the temporomandibular joint in their development and histology. Like the mandible, the clavicle develops from a mesenchymal blastema through intramembranous ossification. Cartilage growth centers appear secondarily at both ends of the clavicle and add to the length of the bone by endochondral ossification. The articulations which re-

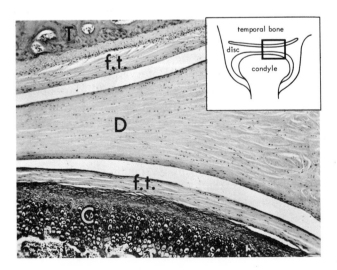

Fig. 12.7 Fibrous articular tissue, f.t., on surfaces of temporomandibular joint in a young monkey. T, temporal bone; D, disc; C, condyle. ×53 (Courtesy Armed Forces Institute of Pathology.)

sult medially with the sternum and laterally with the acromion process likewise have articular surfaces consisting of fibrous connective tissue and also contain articular discs which appear to have a developmental association with adjacent muscle tendons or their extension. For example, in human embryos of 20–80 mm crown-rump length, there appears to be a continuity between the clavicular head of the sternocleidomastoid muscle and the articular disc of the sternoclavicular joint (Fig. 12.8). Although this continuity between the muscle attachment and the disc is not maintained in the adult, one is led to believe that the sternoclavicular joint and its disc develop in a manner similar to that seen in the temporomandibular joint, namely, by the impingement of an embryonic muscle tendon as it passes between two bones where they articulate with each other. Evidence from comparative anatomy also supports this concept in that many mammals have only a rudimentary clavicle embedded in the raphe of a sheet of

muscle and without an articulation at either end of the clavicle. In other species the clavicle is larger and establishes contact with the skeleton medially or laterally or at both ends, as in man. Even at the lateral end of the clavicle there is evidence of a muscle tendon becoming incorporated into the acromioclavicular joint. In some human embryos the insertion of the pectoralis minor muscle extends from the coracoid process of the scapula to the lateral end of the clavicle as the coracoclavicular ligament (Fig. 12.9). In the embryonic stage of development this extension appears continuous with the anlage of the disc in the acromioclavicular joint.

It is probable that other synovial joints will show features in their development similar to those described.

Theories of Synovial Joint Cavitation

The mechanism of formation of synovial joint cavities has not been fully

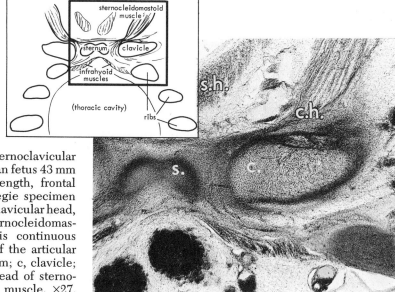

Fig. 12.8 Sternoclavicular joint in a human fetus 43 mm crown-rump length, frontal section, Carnegie specimen No. 886. The clavicular head, c.h., of the sternocleidomastoid muscle is continuous with anlage of the articular disc. s, sternum; c, clavicle; s.h., sternal head of sternocleidomastoid muscle. ×27.

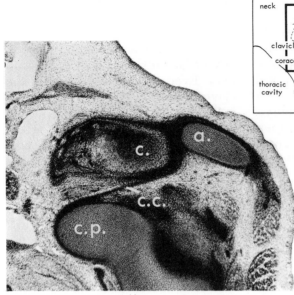

Fig. 12.9 Acromioclavicular joint in a human fetus 25.5 mm crown-rump length, sagittal section, Carnegie specimen No. 2779. The coracoclavicular ligament, c.c., runs from the coracoid process, c.p., to the joint between the acromion, a, and clavicle, c. ×27.

explained. Experiments by Fell and Canti (9) on chick embryo knee joints dissected free of muscle and grown in tissue culture show that growth pressures from the adjacent cartilage models of the bones play a role in causing the articular surfaces to form. It appears from Drachman and Coulombre's (8) study on curarized chick embryos that once the articular surfaces have developed, movement of the joint is necessary to prevent secondary fusion of the articular surfaces.

Does the process of cavitation result from an enzymatic liquefaction of intercellular mucopolysaccharides? Andersen (2) has found acid mucopolysaccharides in the intermediate layer of the interzone prior to the development of the joint cavity. As the cavity forms, the intermediate layer becomes incorporated into the adjacent chondrogenous blastema. There is no evidence, direct or otherwise, that the synovial cavity results from the enzymatic liquefaction of the interzone.

Work by Saunders and co-workers (24) suggests that the synovial cavity might result from the death of cells in that region rather than from a specific metabolic activity such as the secretion of a depolymerizing enzyme. They describe the presence of fields of cellular death in avian limb morphogenesis which appear responsible for the shaping of the limb. The onset of cellular death seems to be under genetic control. Moreover, the size of the area involved can be influenced by hormonal administration. Histological and electron microscopic studies of joint cavitation should be made to test the validity of this hypothesis.

Postnatal Development of Synovial Joints

The genetic control of joint form establishes itself during prenatal life. Superimposed on this, and acting postnatally, is the influence of function, which can alter the chemical composition and contours of joints and even produce a new joint or pseudoarthrosis (Fig. 12.10) where none was intended.

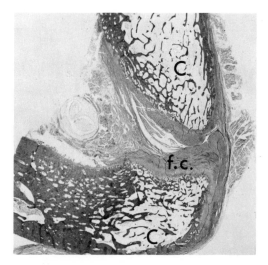

Fig. 12.10 Pseudoarthrosis in a human clavicle resulting from a nonunited fracture. The articular surfaces of the new joint are covered with fibrocartilage, f.c.; C, clavicle. ×2 (Courtesy Armed Forces Institute of Pathology.)

Matthews (14) has shown that the chondroitin sulfate content of articular cartilage is higher in weight-bearing joints than in those which are not weight-bearing. Similar differences can be demonstrated within a joint, the larger amounts of chondroitin being found in the areas subjected to pressure. That this is related to function is shown by Akeson and co-workers (1) who found that the chondroitin sulfate content of articular cartilage decreases considerably after the limb has been inactivated by denervation. Additional evidence of morphological response to function is seen in the temporomandibular joint which, at birth, has fibrous connective tissue instead of cartilage on its articular surfaces. In the areas of the joint which are subjected to loading or compression during function this fibrous tissue is converted to fibrocartilage. Such a conversion is seen wherever fibrous connective tissue is subjected to repeated pressure.

The increased production of chondroitin sulfate under the stimulus of loading is accompanied by other signs of metabolic activity in the articular tissue of all synovial joints. The cartilage cells undergo mitotic activity,

forming clones of cells, and the articular cartilage increases in thickness (Saaf, 23; Crelin and Southwick, 7). If the proliferative activity continues, other changes occur in the subchondral tissue. The calcified zone in the basal layer of articular cartilage widens and then becomes invaded by blood vessels from the underlying bone. Resorption cavities appear in the calcified zone and osteoblasts begin forming bone in the resorbed areas. The net result of these changes is that the articular surface advances toward the joint cavity because of cartilage proliferation. The subchondral bone advances also, tending to restore the cartilage to its original thickness. By this mechanism, an articular cartilage adds as much as 25 mm to the length of the femur during the first 15 years of life (Johnson, 11).

This cellular activity continues in the articular cartilage even after growth has ceased. When it is localized to only a part of the joint surface, the result is a change in the articular contour (Fig. 12.11). This sequence of events is called articular remodeling. The pattern and frequency of articular remodeling in the temporomandibular joint

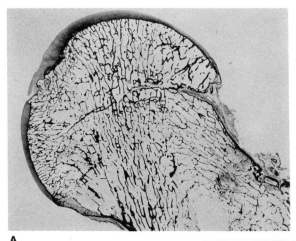

A

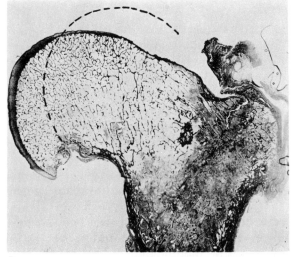

B

Fig. 12.11 *A.* Normal articular contour on head of femur. ×1⅓ *B.* Contour of head of femur altered by articular remodeling. Broken line indicates the normal contour and location of the articular surface. ×1 (Courtesy Armed Forces Institute of Pathology.)

have been described by Moffett and co-workers (16).

Articular remodeling includes more than a reshaping of the joint contours. The internal architecture of the subchondral bone is also changed. One finds that in the weight-bearing areas of a joint the underlying bone consists of many generations of osteone systems which have replaced the original lamellar bone in response to mechanical stress. An osteone is a histological unit of bone consisting of concentric lamellae of bone laid down around a vascular channel. Osteones are not ran-

domly oriented in bone but are lined up in groups or systems oriented with lines of mechanical stress. The non-weight-bearing regions show a smaller amount of osteone replacement.

When the remodeling activity becomes excessive, the articular cartilage begins to undergo destructive changes: excessive shedding of the surface layers, fibrillation, and gross loss of cartilage. Cystic changes occur eventually in the subchondral bone and the picture becomes that of degenerative arthritis.

The hypothesis that degenerative arthritis results from excessive articular remodeling, which in turn is the result of mechanical stimuli associated with function, implies that the degenerative process might be controlled by redistributing or altering the mechanical loading of a joint. Clinical application of this concept is already being made for the treatment of advanced arthritis in the hip joint. An osteotomy is performed which alters the angulation of the head of the femur (King and Dooley, 12). This procedure produces radiographic and clinical signs that the arthritic process has been arrested and even reversed.

Barnett and co-workers describe numerous examples of postnatal development in joints (3, pp. 133–137). These involve alterations in the shape and angulation of the joints of the ribs as the thorax changes its shape and proportions. Mention has already been made of the changing contours of the temporomandibular joint associated with the eruption of teeth and later with the loss of dentition. Spinal curvatures develop in the vertebral column during the first two years of life. All the joints of the leg are altered as changes occur in the angulation of the femur and as the extremity becomes extended from its flexed position in the fetus.

Murray (17) cites a variety of evidence, experimental and circumstantial, indicating that the structural arrangement of bone is modified by the mechanical stresses applied to it. The mechanism of this action is not known. Bassett and Becker (4) cite studies which indicate that bioelectric direct-current fields influence cellular activity. Their own experiments on dissected long bones from animal limbs show that mechanical stress does generate an electrical potential in bone. The amplitude of the potential is de-pendent on the rate and amount of bony deformation; the polarity is determined by the direction of bending —the compressed area becoming negative. This potential does not depend on the presence of viable cells. It does not appear when the bone has been decalcified. Whether such potentials can be demonstrated in vivo and if so, whether they play a role in articular remodeling is not known.

Other problems still to be investigated include studies on the postnatal development of joints from the point of view of their remodeling activity: where in a specific joint is remodeling activity concentrated; how can this activity be facilitated to provide better repair of injured joints; under what circumstances does articular remodeling become a degenerative process; and to what extent can the degenerative changes of joints be controlled or prevented through the application of findings on articular remodeling.

It is becoming increasingly evident that joints continue their morphogenesis during the entire lifetime of the individual, contributing by means of cellular mechanisms to the growth in length of bones, altering the contours of joints to provide a better adaptation to function, and eventually undergoing a transition into degenerative arthritis. When viewed in these aspects, joints take on increased importance in skeletal development and physiology. They can no longer be regarded as mechanically inert discontinuities in bone.

Summary

Joints are classified anatomically into three categories: fibrous, cartilaginous, and synovial. Most of the studies on the morphogenesis of joints have concentrated on the embryology of synovial joints, usually of the limbs. The present review focuses on joints seldom studied and on those which represent modifications of the usual developmental pattern. Information on postnatal development is included.

Examples of joints in each category are reviewed briefly: cranial and facial sutures for fibrous joints; epiphyseal growth plates, intervertebral disc, and pubic symphysis for cartilaginous joints; temporomandibular and clavicular joints for synovial joints. Factors influencing the embryonic formation of synovial cavities are discussed.

The form of a joint is established genetically in prenatal life but is altered increasingly by function during the postnatal period. Alterations in the contour of joints and in the architecture of the bone and cartilage constitute articular remodeling. When this remodeling process becomes excessive, the articular cartilage shows destructive changes and the picture becomes that of degenerative arthritis. Examples of postnatal articular remodeling are cited in the joints of the ribs, the temporomandibular and vertebral joints. The manner in which mechanical stresses are translated into remodeling activity is not known. The role played by remodeling in bone growth, adaptation of joints to function, and in the development of degenerative arthritis requires a greater emphasis on studies of postnatal development of joints.

References

1. Akeson, W. H., L. E. Eichelberger, and M. Roma, "Biochemical Studies of Articular Cartilage. II. Values Following the Denervation of an Extremity," *J. Bone Joint Surg.* 39A:153–162 (1957).

2. Andersen, H., "Histochemical Studies of the Development of the Human Hip Joint," *Acta Anat.* 48:258–292 (1962).

3. Barnett, C. H., D. V. Davies, and M. A. MacConaill, *Synovial Joints. Their Structure and Mechanics.* Springfield, Ill.: Charles C Thomas, pp. 133–137 (1961).

4. Bassett, C. A. L., and R. O. Becker, "Generation of Electric Potentials by Bone in Response to Mechanical Stress," *Science* 137:1063–64 (1962).

5. Bauer, W. H., "Effect of a Faultily Constructed Partial Denture on a Tooth and Its Supporting Tissue with Special Reference to Formation of Fibrocartilage in the Periodontal Membrane as Result of Disturbed Healing Caused by Abnormal Stresses," *Oral Surg. Oral Med. Oral Pathol.* 27:640–665 (1941).

6. Baume, L. J., "Tooth and Investing Bone: A Developmental Entity," *Oral Surg. Oral Med. Oral Pathol.* 9:736–741 (1956).

7. Crelin, E. S., and W. O. Southwick, "Mitosis of Chondrocytes Induced in the Knee Joint Articular Cartilage of Adult Rabbits," *Yale J. Biol. Med.* 33:243–245 (1960).

8. Drachman, D. B., and A. J. Coulombre, "Experimental Clubfoot and Arthrogryposis Multiplex Congenita," *Lancet* 7255: 523–526 (1962).

9. Fell, H. B., and R. G. Canti, "Experiments on the Development *in vitro* of the Avian Knee Joint," *Proc. Roy. Soc. London Ser. B* 116:316–351 (1934).

10. Gardner, E., "Development of Joints," *Amer. Acad. Orthopedic Surgeons Instructional Course Lectures* 9:149–155 (1952).

11. Johnson, L. C., "Kinetics of Osteoarthritis," *Lab. Invest.* 8:1223–1238 (1959).

12. King, T., and B. J. Dooley, "Observations on the Late Results of the McMurray Osteotomy for Osteoarthritis of the Hip," *J. Bone Joint Surg.* 44B:595–601 (1962).

13. Lockhart, R. D., G. F. Hamilton, and F. W. Fyfe, *Anatomy of the Human Body.* Philadelphia: J. B. Lippincott, pp. 142–143 (1959).

14. Matthews, B. F., "Collagen/Chondroitin Sulphate Ratio of Human Articular Cartilage Related to Function," *Brit. Med. J.* 2:1295 (1952).

15. Moffett, B. C., "The Prenatal Development of the Human Temporomandibular Joint," *Carnegie Inst. Wash. Publ. 611, Contrib. Embryol.* 36:19–28 (1957).

16. ———, L. C. Johnson, J. B. McCabe, and H. C. Askew, "Articular Remodeling in the Adult Human Temporomandibular Joint," *Am. J. Anat.* 115:119–142 (1964).

17. Murray, P. D. F., *Bones: A Study of the Development and Structure of the Vertebrate Skeleton.* New York: Cambridge University Press, (1936).

18. O'Rahilly, R., "The Development of Joints," *Irish J. Med. Science* Ser. 6, 382:456–461 (1957).

19. Parker, W. S., H. E. Frisbe, and T. S. Grant, "The Experimental Production of Dental Ankylosis," *Angle Orthodontist* 34:103–107 (1964).

20. Peacock, A., "Observations on the Prenatal Development of the Intervertebral Disc in Man," *J. Anat.* 85:260–274 (1951).

21. Pritchard, J. J., J. H. Scott, and F. G. Girgis, "The Structure and Development of Cranial and Facial Sutures," *J. Anat.* 90:73–86 (1956).

22. Putschar, W., *Entwicklung, Wachstum und Pathologie der Beckenverbindungen des Menschen.* Jena, Germany: Gustav Fischer Verlagsbuchhandlung (1931).

23. Saaf, J., "Effects of Exercise on Adult Articular Cartilage," *Acta Orthopaed. Scand. Suppl.* 7:1–186 (1950).

24. Saunders, J. W., Jr., M. T. Gasseling, and L. C. Saunders, "Cellular Death in Morphogenesis of the Avian Wing," *Develop. Biol.* 5:147–178 (1962).

25. Sicher, H., and J. P. Weinmann, "Bone Growth and Physiologic Tooth Movement," *Oral Surg. Oral Med. Oral Pathol.* 30:109–132 (1944).

26. Todd, T. W., "Age Changes in the Pubic Bone. I. The Male White Pubis," *Am. J. Phys. Anthropol.* 3:285–334 (1920).

27. ———, "Age Changes in the Pubic Bone. II. The Pubis of the Male Negro-White Hybrid. III. The Pubis of the White Female. IV. The Pubis of the Female Negro-White Hybrid," *Am. J. Phys. Anthropol.* 4:1–70 (1921).

13

Metabolic Patterns
in Limb Development and Regeneration

ELIZABETH D. HAY*

Department of Anatomy
Harvard Medical School
Boston, Massachusetts

The present era has witnessed an unusual degree of interest in nucleic acid synthesis and protein metabolism in developing systems. Bacteria and isolated fractions of cells have been studied to best advantage, for it is difficult to approach the intact cell as a whole unit, and almost impossible to measure, with biochemical techniques, the metabolic parameters of a developing system of cells mixed in origin and fate. Yet, it is extremely important to take into account the complex metabolism and fine structure of differentiating vertebrate cells before dogmatically concluding that general principles derived from the study of growing unicellular organisms will be applicable to the process of vertebrate organogenesis. In this chapter, recent radioauto-graphic studies of protein, nucleic acid, and mucopolysaccharide synthesis in the developing amphibian limb will be reviewed from this point of view and the changing structure of the cells will be stressed.

In order to limit the chapter to a reasonable length without being unduly superficial, the greatest share of attention will be given to only one of the tissues of the limb, cartilage. Brief reference will be made to myogenesis, and the description of nucleic acid metabolism will deal with the limb as a whole. The developmental phenomena described are similar in embryonic and regenerating limbs, for they occur in the period during which the growing blastema or limb bud is transformed into the definitive appendage. The actual origin of the mesenchymal cells of the limb blastema is, of course, different in the two cases; the embryonic limb mesenchyme arises from "undif-

* The original research reported in this paper was supported by grant HD 00143-06 from the United States Public Health Service.

ferentiated" mesoderm (see Amprino, Chapter 10) whereas the mesenchymatous cells of the regenerating amphibian limb arise from the formed tissues of the limb stump by a process of dedifferentiation (Butler, 1; Thornton, 41; Hay, 15). During the subsequent period of growth and differentiation, however, the regenerating limb is remarkably similar to the embryonic limb in its structure and metabolic activities. It is with this latter stage of limb development that we shall be primarily concerned here.

Structure of the Limb during Growth and Differentiation

After the cells that will comprise the inner, mesenchymal core of the presumptive limb have proliferated to form a blastema, the developing appendage assumes the shape of a cone. The inner cells are relatively undifferentiated in appearance in this phase of rapid growth. The epithelium covering the distal region of the limb bud or blastema is thickened. It has the appearance of an apical cap or ridge in the embryonic appendage (Chapter 11). During limb regeneration, the apical epithelium is at first more like a thickened wound epidermis with basal invaginations that penetrate the underlying tissue. In the cone stage of development, however, the distal epithelium resembles the embryonic apical cap in its appearance (Rose, 37; Singer and Salpeter, 40).

Subsequently, the mesenchymal inner cells that will form the cartilaginous skeleton of the limb aggregate along the midline, beginning in the proximal area of the blastema, and the limb takes the shape of a paddle. The apical epithelium thins out and as-

sumes a very close contact with the tips of the developing phalanges. In the finger bud stage, the cartilages of the limb take on their definitive form. Cartilage matrix is secreted and the cells pass through a coordinated cycle of structural and metabolic changes, which involves the acquisition of hypertrophied organelles and is followed by tissue differentiation and cessation of growth. Muscle develops next to the cartilaginous skeleton and here again, differentiation proceeds in a proximodistal direction. The vessels, nerves, and connective tissues which will characterize the fully formed limb now assume their definitive positions.

In the following section, patterns of DNA and RNA synthesis in the cone, paddle, and finger bud stages of development will be described and the histological features referred to above will be illustrated. We will then consider in more detail the cycle of structural change which occurs in chondrocytes and myocytes and, finally, the structural sequence in chondrocytes will be related to the metabolic events which occur during the synthesis of cartilage matrix.

Nucleic Acid Synthesis in Relation to Growth and Differentiation

One might assume, since the histological differentiation and determination of the parts of the limb proceeds in a proximodistal direction (Saunders, 39; Zwilling, 46), that cell proliferation would be greatest in the most distal region of the limb. On the contrary, Chalkley (4) found, in a very careful study of mitotic indices, that the peak of proliferative activity is just proximal to the tip of regenerating salamander

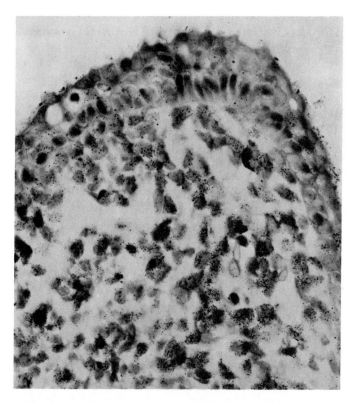

Fig. 13.1 Radioautograph of a regenerating salamander limb in the cone stage of development, showing the pattern of DNA synthesis in the early limb bud. The animal (a 40-mm *Amblystoma opacum* larva) received an intraperitoneal injection of 0.05 μc of thymidine-H³ 1 hour before the limb was fixed in Bouin's fluid. The tissue was embedded in paraffin, sectioned, and coated with Kodak NTB-3 emulsion. After a 3-week exposure, the radioautograph was developed and the underlying tissue stained through the emulsion with aniline blue and acid fuchsin. The cytoplasm of the mesenchymal cells is not clearly revealed by this staining technique. There are silver grains over most of the nuclei of the mesenchymal cells, indicating that these cells were actively synthesizing DNA at the time of administration of the isotope. The distal cells are not as intensely labeled as the proximal cells. The apical epithelium is not significantly labeled. Epithelial cells located more proximally divide and move distally as the limb grows. ×265.

limbs at all stages, and Milaire (27, 28) and others reported much the same pattern in embryonic limbs. Radioautographic studies with tritiated thymidine as a precursor of DNA demonstrate this distal to proximal gradient of cell reproduction in an even more striking fashion (Hay and Fischman, 18). There is little, if any, DNA synthesis in the apical cap epithelium or the distal epithelium overlying the tips of the cartilaginous phalanges. The distal epithelium is, in fact, maintained by cells derived from proximal epithelium which may complete their mitoses as they migrate distally (18). These observations, made initially in studies of regenerating adult salamander forelimbs, have now been extended to larval salamander limbs (Fig. 13.1).

During the paddle stage of development, those proximal mesenchymal cells that form precartilage are at first the most actively proliferating cells in the blastema. As development proceeds, however, differentiating cartilage cells gradually cease to synthesize DNA. By the finger bud stage, it is clear that most of the DNA synthesis is along the lateral edges of the presumptive long bones and on the periphery of the presumptive carpals (Fig. 13.2). Only occasional cartilage cells in the interior synthesize DNA and divide. The inverse correlation between DNA synthesis and specific protein synthesis in cartilage has recently been substantiated by double-isotope radioautography (Trelstad, 42). In differentiating muscle, DNA replication also ceases. Whatever the physiological significance of the phenomenon may be (Grobstein, 13; Holtzer, 20), it is clear that the developing chondrocytes, myocytes, and certain other cell types show relatively little cell division at the time that specific differentiated cell products are being actively produced.

Approximately 50 percent of the mesenchymal cells of the blastema at the cone stage are synthesizing DNA, as judged by thymidine incorporation in regenerating larval salamander limbs fixed 1 hour after injection of tritiated thymidine. Almost all of the cells are synthesizing RNA, as judged by tritiated uridine incorporation in limbs fixed 1–4 hours after the animal received the radioisotope (Figs. 13.3 and 13.5). Controls done with similar material fixed in formalin and treated with ribonuclease demonstrate that most of the labeled uridine is incorporated into RNA in regenerating salamander

limbs (Hay, 17). Yamada and Karasaki (44) reached a similar conclusion in studies of regenerating lens. Thus, it seems reasonable to conclude that some of the growing cells are synthesizing both RNA and DNA. Interestingly enough the apical cap epithelium incorporates uridine (Fig. 13.3), although it fails to incorporate thymidine (Fig. 13.1).

In the paddle and finger bud stages of development, again, essentially all of the cells of the mesenchymatous blastema and the overlying epithelium actively incorporate tritiated uridine. The nuclei of differentiating chondroblasts in the process of forming cytoplasmic organelles seemed more heavily labeled than the relatively undifferentiated precartilage cells. There is some incorporation of uridine into mature muscle, and epithelium seems to continue to synthesize RNA indefinitely. The chondrocyte synthesizes very little RNA during the phase of most active matrix formation (Fig. 13.4). This is the period in which the cytoplasm contains abundant ribosomes, presumably engaged in synthesis of specific matrix proteins (Revel and Hay, 35). It seems likely, then, that the mature cells are using some of the "old" RNA, synthesized in the preceding precartilage period, to produce new proteins in the later stages of development. Protein synthesis can occur in the absence of RNA synthesis (Prescott, 32).

The question of RNA turnover in an intact vertebrate system can be investigated with radioautographic techniques by fixing the material, not at the short intervals described above, but at daily intervals after treatment with an RNA precursor. The isotope should be

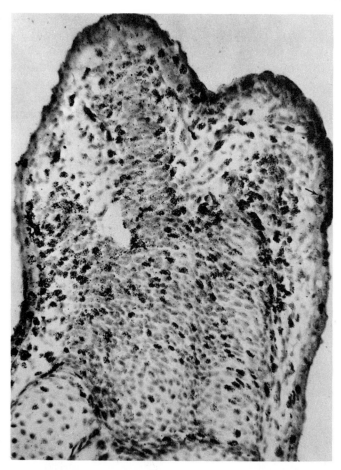

Fig. 13.2 Radioautograph of a regenerating *Amblystoma* limb in the finger bud stage of development. The tissue was fixed an hour after the animal received thymidine-H³ and was processed as described in the caption for Fig. 13.1. The distal epithelium and underlying blastema are similar to that of the 7-day regenerate (Fig. 13.1) in that they fail to incorporate significant amounts of thymidine-H³. The bulk of the blastema, however, has differentiated into cartilage at 14 days postamputation and there is a shift in the pattern of DNA synthesis within the limb. The young cartilage cells along the periphery of the developing bones continue to synthesize DNA and divide, but the more differentiated centrally located cells gradually cease proliferating. Muscle cells and fibroblasts also stop synthesizing DNA as they differentiate, but the highly specialized Leydig cells of the skin of the larva continue to divide (arrow). ×145.

administered as a "pulse," if possible; that is, the amount given should be small enough to be completely utilized within a few hours. Leblond and Amano (24) found that in differentiated mammalian liver cells, significant radioactivity remained in the cytoplasm for at least 10 days after a pulse dose of tritiated cytidine, a finding consistent with recent reports that liver RNA is not turned over nearly as rapidly as bacterial RNA (Revel and Hiatt, 36).

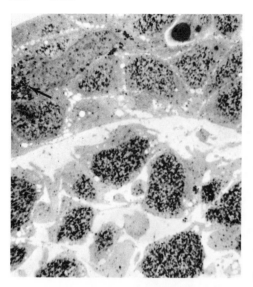

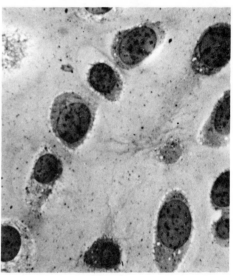

43) were injected with tritiated uridine, and the limbs fixed at hourly intervals and at 1, 3, 6, and 12 days postinjection. In the first few hours, the label was found primarily over nuclei and nucleoli of chondroblasts, and then gradually increased in the cytoplasm as the cells transformed into chondrocytes (Fig. 13.6). The label has completely disappeared from nucleoli by 3 days, yet continues to accumulate in the cytoplasm for 6 days after the initial

Fig. 13.3 Radioautograph of a regenerating *Amblystoma* limb in the cone stage, showing incorporation of uridine-H³ into nuclei of apical epithelium and distal mesenchymal cells. This limb was fixed in osmium tetroxide 4 hours after intraperitoneal injection of the isotope (10 μc), then washed 1 hour in water and embedded in epon resin for thin sectioning. A fine-grained radioautographic emulsion (Ilford L-4) was used to coat the section. Because the section and film of emulsion are each < 1 μ in thickness, radioautographic resolution is improved. The basophilic cytoplasm of the cells is well fixed here and is stained with toluidine blue, a basic dye. The arrow points to a cluster of pigment granules in a melanocyte whose nucleus lies to the right of the arrow. ×800.

Leblond and Amano detected labeled RNA in chromatin and nucleoli first, but the cytoplasm became radioactive within a short time. They suggested that the cytoplasmic RNA originated in the nucleolus rather than the chromatin.

In the experiment illustrated here (Figs. 13.6–13.8), salamander embryos with forelimbs in the early finger bud stage of development (Harrison stage

Fig. 13.4 Radioautograph of part of the unamputated proximal skeleton (humerus) in the same limb illustrated in Fig. 13.3. The cartilage cells of the "old" skeleton are fully differentiated and are engaged in producing extracellular matrix in a salamander larva of this age. Interestingly enough, the chondrocytes do not incorporate very much uridine-H³. The few grains over the nuclei may indicate continuing synthesis of small amounts of ribonucleic acid. The cell has acquired its complement of ribosomes, and nucleoli are no longer prominent. When a cartilage at this stage is amputated, the cells revert to the mesenchymal type (Fig. 13.3). Nuclei enlarge and nucleoli become prominent again (Fig. 13.5) as RNA turnover increases. ×800.

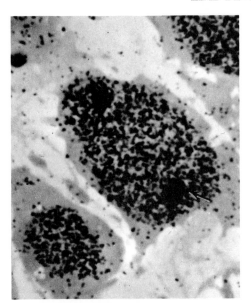

Fig. 13.5 High-magnification light micrograph of a mesenchymal cell from the regenerate illustrated in Fig. 13.3. In limbs fixed 1–4 hours after administration of uridine-H³, the label is located over the chromatin and nucleoli of the cells. A few scattered grains can be seen over the cytoplasm at this time, but the majority of the RNA is synthesized in the nucleus and subsequently (1–6 days later) appears in the cytoplasm. The silver grains in the emulsion over the nucleolus at 4 hours are so numerous that they obscure the underlying nucleoplasm (arrow). ×2200.

become apparent shortly, the peak of RNA synthesis occurs at the time when the granular endoplasmic reticulum is enlarging in the chondrocyte cytoplasm. It is tempting to conclude, therefore, that much of the RNA synthesized in the earlier period becomes part of the ribonucleoprotein associated with the reticulum. Whereas the radioautographic studies do not permit exact identification of the type of RNA synthesized, they do suggest that the pattern of RNA metabolism in the differentiating vertebrate cell

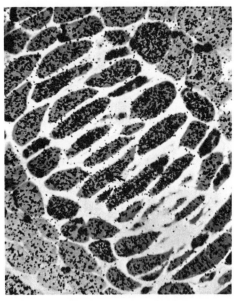

Fig. 13.6 Radioautograph of a developing long bone (radius) of an embryonic *Amblystoma* limb in the finger bud stage of development (Harrison stage 43). The embryo was given 0.001 ml (1 μc) of a solution of uridine-H³ by slow injection into the pericardial cavity through a minute glass needle. The limb illustrated was fixed in osmium tetroxide 20 hours after the injection and processed as that in Fig. 13.3. The label is found primarily over the nucleolus (arrow) and chromatin of the cells. There is, in fact, very little cytoplasm present at this early stage of cartilage development. ×750.

administration of tritiated uridine (Figs. 13.7–13.8). It is difficult to believe, then, that all of the label appearing in the cytoplasm has arisen from the nucleoli. Labeled material decreases in amount in nuclear chromatin over the entire period. Twelve days after administration of tritiated uridine, chondrocyte cytoplasm is still radioactive. The turnover pattern of RNA thus is consistent with the conclusion reached earlier that maturing chondrocytes retain much of the RNA synthesized in the earlier stage. As will

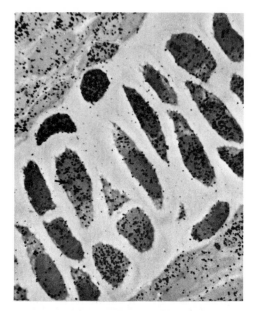

large vesicular nuclei, moderately prominent nucleoli, and relatively little cytoplasm for the most part (Hay, 14; Godman and Porter, 11; Fitton-Jackson, 21). When the cells aggregate to form the anlagen of the cartilages, there is at first little change in these structural features. The cells, however, are now in very close contact. In many regions the space between the cell membranes is less than 100 A, as reported also by Lesseps (25) in studies of the aggregation of chick cells, and in some areas the contact is reminis-

Fig. 13.7 Light micrograph at the same magnification as Fig. 13.6, illustrating the location of label in the developing long bone (radius) several days later. The embryo was injected at the same stage and in the same way as in Fig. 13.6, but the limb was fixed 6 days after the brief "pulse" exposure to uridine-H³. The embryo has advanced to Harrison stage 46. The chondrocytes now have abundant cytoplasm and the ergastoplasm is significantly radioactive. It probably contains labeled RNA that was assembled in part or *in toto* in the nucleus of chondrocytes at the earlier stage (Fig. 13.6). The cell indicated at the arrow is shown at higher magnification in Fig. 13.8. ×750.

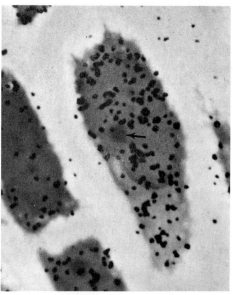

Fig. 13.8 High-magnification light micrograph of one of the cartilage cells shown in Fig. 13.7. Radioactive uridine disappears from the nucleolus (arrow) within 3 days after the initial "pulse" treatment at stage 43. Label subsequently appears in the cytoplasm of the chondrocytes of the radius, and indeed most of their cytoplasm is formed between 3 days (Harrison stage 44–45) and 6 days (stage 46) after administration of the isotope. It is difficult to believe, then, that the cytoplasmic label depicted arose from the nucleous. More likely, it came from the nucleus proper. ×2200.

differs from that in both the proliferating mesenchymal cell and the unicellular organism.

Fine Structure of Differentiating Cartilage and Muscle Cells

The growing mesenchymal cells of the embryonic limb bud and regenerating larval salamander limb have very

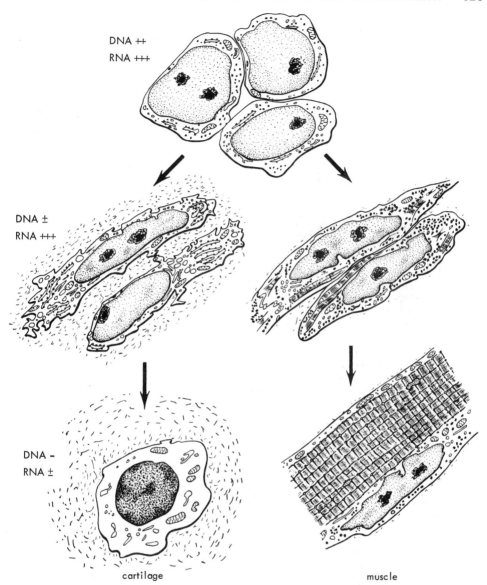

DNA ++
RNA +++

DNA ±
RNA +++

DNA −
RNA ±

cartilage   muscle

Fig. 13.9 Diagram illustrating the changes in fine structure of mesenchymal cells as they aggregate within the limb blastema (top) and differentiate into cartilage (on the left) and muscle (on the right). In cartilage, the newly formed differentiated products are destined for the extracellular compartment. They are synthesized and secreted by the granular endoplasmic reticulum and Golgi complex. In muscle, the differentiated proteins (myofibrils) are intracellular in location. They seem to be synthesized by free ribosomes in the cytoplasm without the intervention of the granular endoplasmic reticulum. The muscle cell contains only a few profiles of granular reticulum and has a smaller Golgi apparatus than the cartilage cell. It later acquires a special kind of smooth-surfaced reticulum. Also depicted in the diagram are the relative amounts of DNA and RNA synthesized by the cells in the developmental stages illustrated.

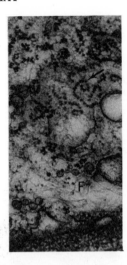

Fig. 13.10 Electronmicrograph of a small portion of the cytoplasm of a developing cartilage cell, showing a tangentially sectioned cisterna of the endoplasmic reticulum at the arrow. Ribonucleoprotein granules attached to the reticulum tend to be arranged in geometric patterns. They may form rows or whorls of 30 or more contiguous ribosomes. Part of the nucleus appears at the bottom of the figure and, above it, a few of the tonofilaments, F, which sometimes occur in the cytoplasm of connective tissue cells. × 38,250.

cent of the tight junctions described by Farquhar and Palade (7). The cytoplasm contains mitochondria, small amounts of granular endoplasmic reticulum, free ribonucleoprotein granules or ribosomes, and a rather diffuse juxtanuclear Golgi apparatus represented by small vesicles and numerous smooth-surfaced lamellae. In the nucleus, the chromatin, for the most part, is highly dispersed, but there are a few dense clumps of chromatin along the nuclear envelope.

In the young cartilage cells which have begun to secrete extracellular matrix, the granular endoplasmic reticulum increases markedly in amount. Secretory vacuoles of moderate to large size appear in the Golgi apparatus (Fig. 13.9). The cells elongate perpendicularly to the long axis of the limb. The nuclei now are somewhat flattened, rather than round in shape as in earlier stages, and nucleoli seem to be somewhat more prominent. This is the stage of most active RNA synthesis in chromatin and nucleoli and, it will be recalled, DNA synthesis has all but ceased by this time. Cytoplasmic ribosomes are increasing in number throughout the phase of organelle differentiation. These granules are, for the most part, associated with the reticulum, forming whorls and other patterns which can best be seen in regions where the membranes of the cisternae are sectioned tangentially (arrow, Fig. 13.10).

Interestingly enough, although the cells become separated by the newly formed cartilage matrix, they retain contact with one another by means of long cytoplasmic processes. As the cartilage cell reaches maturity, the cytoplasm swells, presumably due to hydration of the cytoplasmic ground substance, and dense clumps of heterochromatin appear throughout the nucleus. Nucleoli are small and difficult to distinguish from the clumped chromatin. The chondrocyte is now surrounded by abundant matrix and has entered a quiescent metabolic phase.

It seems clear that the development of the hypertrophied granular endoplasmic reticulum and Golgi apparatus by the cartilage cell is during the most active phase related to synthesis and secretion of the matrix. By comparison, these organelles are relatively undifferentiated in developing muscle cells (Figs. 13.9, 13.11, 13.12). The mesenchymal cells that will form the muscle anlage aggregate in much the same way as the precartilage cells (Hay, 15, 16), but the myoblasts remain in close contact, for the differentiated products produced are primarily intracellular in location (MYO, Fig. 13.12). Nuclei are large and vesicular, and nucleoli are prominent, as ribosomes accumulate in the cytoplasm. The ribosomes tend to aggregate in clumps and rows (arrows, Fig. 13.11), which in earlier stages are closely associated with developing thin filaments (Hay, 15). These ribosomes are free in the cytoplasm, rather than attached to the reticulum. The small amount of endoplasmic reticulum which characterizes developing muscle cells resembles the Golgi vesicles and is probably the precursor of the smooth-surfaced sarcoplasmic reticulum. In the next section, we will examine the evidence that the granular reticulum and Golgi complex of the cartilage cell are actually involved in secretion of extracellular matrix.

Localization of Metabolic Activities in the Cytoplasmic Organelles of Chondrocytes

Direct evidence for the participation of the cytoplasmic organelles of the chrondrocyte in formation of the proteinaceous and carbohydrate products that will subsequently make up the matrix can be obtained by radioautographic studies using appropriate radioactive precursors. To explore the pattern of protein synthesis in developing cartilage, we chose the radioactive amino acid, tritiated proline; the abundant collagen of the matrix contains 25 percent proline and its derivative, hydroxyproline. Forty percent of the dry weight of cartilage matrix is collagen

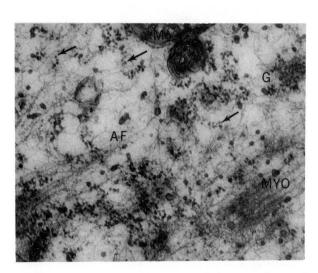

Fig. 13.11 Electronmicrograph of a small portion of the cytoplasm of a developing muscle cell. The ribosomes are arranged in single or double rows (arrows) which are often contiguous with developing thin filaments, AF. They also form large clumps of granules, G. The thin filaments may be the precursors of both the actin and the myosin filaments of the formed myofibril. Ribosomes are not usually associated with thick filaments and the thick filaments (myosin) are usually found only in partly assembled myofibrils, MYO. Part of a mitochondrion appears at M. × 38,250.

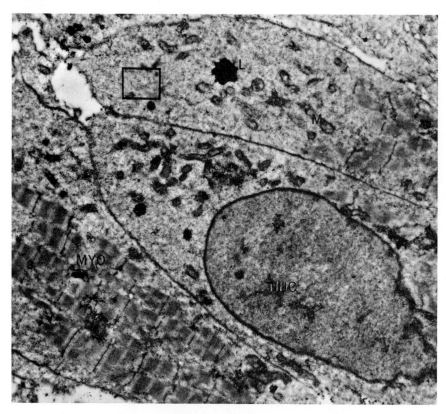

Fig. 13.12 Electronmicrograph at lower magnification, showing in the rectangle the approximate area illustrated in Fig. 13.11. Parts of three developing muscle cells and the nucleus, NUC, of one cell are included in the picture. Formed myofibrils occur in some areas of the cytoplasm, MYO, whereas in other areas "free" ribonucleoprotein granules and diffuse filaments fill the cytoplasm (rectangle). The diffuse, newly synthesized filaments are apparently assembled into myofibrils at a later stage. A lipid droplet appears at L and a mitochondrion at M. Figures 13.10–13.12 are from a regenerating *Amblystoma* limb 17 days after amputation. × 5900.

and over 90 percent of the proline in cartilage has been reported to be in collagen (Malawista and Schubert, 26; Eastoe, 5). It seems reasonable to assume, then, that the principal pathway of secretory activity delineated by tritiated proline in cartilage is that of collagen. Chondromucoproteins might be labeled (Fitton-Jackson, 21) and some of the proline will go into nuclear proteins. In muscle, considerably less tritiated proline is incorporated than in cartilage, and this label seems confined to

myofibrils and nuclear material. In the experiments, which were done in collaboration with Dr. Jean-Paul Revel, tritiated proline was injected into salamander larvae when their regenerating limbs were in the finger bud stage. The limbs were fixed 10 minutes, 15 minutes, 30 minutes, and at hourly and daily intervals thereafter (35).

Within 15 minutes after the administration of tritiated proline, the nucleus and cytoplasm of the cartilage cell contain labeled proline-rich material.

The nuclear radioactivity was greatest in blastema and precartilage cells and gradually disappeared over the course of 3 weeks. There was no indication that intranuclear precursors were involved in collagen synthesis directly. Indeed, nuclei of the cells whose cytoplasm was most actively engaged in protein synthesis had a low level of tritiated proline incorporation. At 15 minutes the marked radioactivity in such cells is confined to the basophilic regions of the cytoplasm. At 30 minutes, much of the newly synthesized radioactive material has moved into the Golgi zone and the material is secreted into the extracellular matrix 1–4 hours later. Thus, the sequence of amino acid incorporation and protein secretion by chondrocytes is similar to that observed in the pancreatic acinar cells (Caro and Palade, 3; Warshawski, et al., 43). Three weeks later, much of the labeled material is still present in the matrix, more or less equidistant from the cells.

It is now possible to analyze radioautographs of thin sections in the electron microscope by using extremely thin layers of emulsion to coat the preparation (Caro, 2; Revel and Hay, 34). In the electron microscope, each developed silver grain is resolved as a tangled skein of metallic silver instead of one small dot (Figs. 13.13 and 13.14). Electronmicrographs reveal that the label is associated with the cisternae of the reticulum 15–30 minutes after injection of tritiated proline (Fig. 13.13). Occasionally, dilated ergastoplasmic sacs can be found which contain labeled product within the confines of the cisternae (Revel and Hay, 35). The radioautographic data thus are compatible with the theory that proteins destined for the extracellular compartment are synthesized in association with the ribosomes of the ergastoplasm and soon thereafter are segregated in the membrane-bounded compartment of the reticulum. When the labeled secretory product appears in the Golgi zone 20–30 minutes after the injection of the precursor, it seems to be sequestered within the large Golgi vacuoles (Fig. 13.14). It is conceivable that the product is transported to the vacuoles via a "bucket brigade" of small vesicles which originate from the reticulum (Revel and Hay, 35; Zeigel and Dalton, 45; Palade, et al., 29). Label is rarely detected over the smooth-surfaced Golgi lamellae and thus it seems unlikely that the proteinaceous product passes through them in this cell type. Extrusion of the labeled product probably takes place by fusion of the limiting membrane of the vacuole with the cell membrane. It is possible to assemble a series of electron images to support this concept, as shown in Figure 13.15 (35).

There is no evidence from radioautographic studies to support the hypothesis that collagen is extruded directly from the ectoplasm of connective tissue cells, as Porter (31) and others have suggested. It is possible that the cell membrane is of importance in directing early fibrillogenesis (31), but radioautographic data would indicate that collagen and other matrix proteins often traverse considerable distances before polymerizing in cartilage (Fig. 13.16) and in other connective tissues (Ross and Benditt, 38; Hay and Revel, 19). Thus, the extracellular environment within the matrix itself must be of importance in determining the pattern of precipitation of the components secreted by the cells (see review by Fitton-Jackson, 21). Unlike the free-living bacteria, the chondrocytes

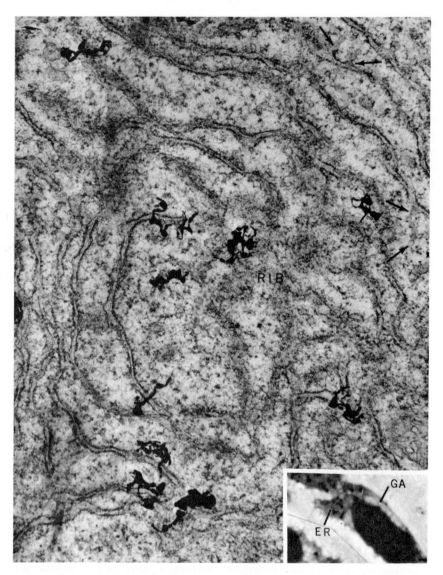

Fig. 13.13 Electronmicrograph showing part of the ergastoplasm (granular endoplasmic reticulum) in a chondrocyte 30 minutes after the larval salamander received an intraperitoneal injection of proline-H³. The limb had been regenerating for 12 days and was in the finger bud stage. It was processed for radioautography as in Fig. 13.3, except that the thin (0.1 μ) section was put on a grid for examination in the electron microscope. Each silver grain in the emulsion overlying the section is resolved as a tangled skein of metal. The newly synthesized radioactive product is associated with the cisternae of the endoplasmic reticulum. Cisternae are cut obliquely at RIB, showing the ribosomes to better advantage. A mitochondrion appears at M. Smooth-surfaced vesicles which seem to bud off the reticulum (arrows) may transport the product to the Golgi complex. At 15 minutes, the product is located entirely in the ergastoplasm (ER, inset) and none is as yet present in the Golgi apparatus (GA, inset). × 32,000. The inset is a light micrograph. × 1600 (From Revel and Hay, Z. *Zellforsch.* 61:110–144, 1963.)

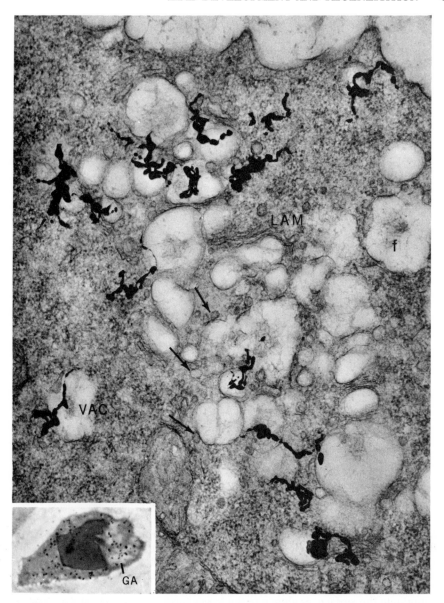

Fig. 13.14 Electronmicrograph showing part of the Golgi complex in a chondrocyte 30 minutes after the larval salamander received an injection of proline-H³. At this time, some of the labeled proteinaceous product synthesized in the ergastoplasm has moved into the Golgi apparatus, also illustrated in the inset, GA, at the light microscopic level. The electron microscope reveals that the labeled product is localized within the secretory vacuoles, VAC, of the centrosphere. It does not appear to be associated with the Golgi lamellae, LAM. Rather, it would seem as if small vesicles (arrows) fuse directly with the vacuoles to discharge the protein into them. The product within the Golgi vacuole now has a filamentous, f, character not unlike that of the extracellular matrix itself. × 35,200. The inset is a light micrograph. × 1600 (From Revel and Hay, Z. *Zellforsch.* 61:110–144, 1963.)

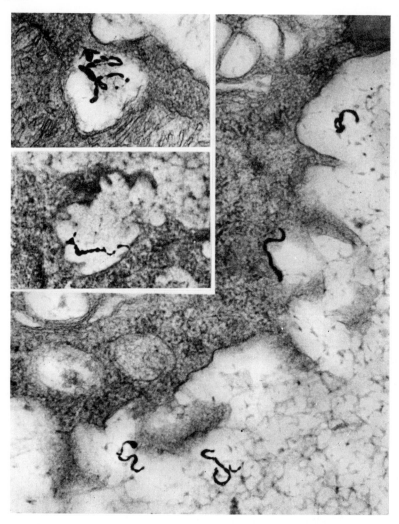

Fig. 13.15 The product within the Golgi vacuole is probably exteriorized by fusion of the membrane of the vacuole with the plasmalemma. A series of images to support this theory can be assembled from radioautographs of sections of chondrocytes, 30 or more minutes after the animal received proline-H³. Vacuoles appear to move toward the cell membrane (top left). Two or more vacuoles may fuse with each other before opening onto the surface, as shown in the lower inset. The surface of the chondrocyte is highly excavated during the period of secretion. These excavations, as shown in the larger micrograph, probably represent stages in the fusion of vacuoles with the cell membrane, a process that might be thought of as reverse "pinocytosis." × 45,000 (From Revel and Hay, Z. *Zellforsch.* 61:110–114, 1963.)

create a relatively stable extracellular milieu through which they exert an effect on each other and on the metabolic activities of the tissue as a whole.

The fact that most of the labeled proteinaceous secretory products pass through the Golgi zone of the cells is interesting. Most investigators are agreed that the Golgi apparatus is in-

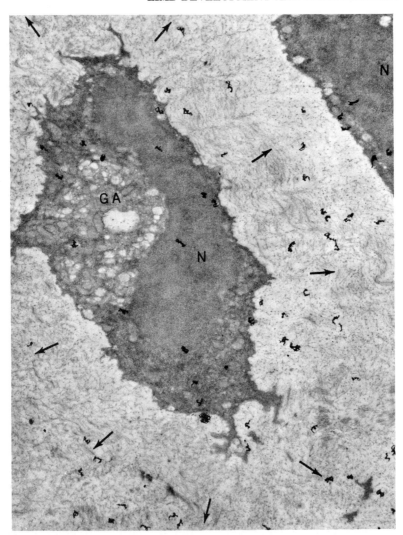

Fig. 13.16 Electronmicrograph of a small area of cartilage 2 hours after the animal received proline-H³. The isotope was circulating for a short time only and this "pulse" has now moved through the cell and out into the matrix. The newly synthesized proteins diffuse through the matrix (arrows) and may accumulate some distance from the cells. The radioactivity remaining in the nucleus, N, and cytoplasm at this time is probably associated with structural intracellular protein. The Golgi apparatus is now essentially devoid of label, GA × 8000 (From Revel and Hay, Z. *Zellforsch.* 61:110–114, 1963.)

volved in secretion, yet there is a paucity of substantiated information as to its actual role in the cell. Situated as it is, in close relation to the juxtanuclear centrioles, the Golgi zone has earned the name centrosphere. Perhaps with some justification, the term implies that the Golgi complex might have a function of some importance in directing the over-all metabolism of the cytoplasm. The organelle seems clearly implicated in cytoplasmic membrane turnover, for pinocytosis vesicles originating from the cell surface seem to pass into it, and secretory vacuoles pass out of it to reach the cell membrane (see review by Fawcett, 9). It is possible that the Golgi lamellae participate in the membrane synthesis required for such turnover (Revel and Hay, 35; Goldberg and Green, 12). Moreover, several enzymes have been localized near or in the smooth-surfaced membranes of the Golgi complex (Essner and Novikoff, 6).

Jenning and Florey (22) suggested from radioautographic studies of goblet cells that the Golgi region might be involved in sulfation of mucoproteins. It is interesting to note that in cartilage cells the morphological appearance of the secretory product within the Golgi vacuoles is quite different from the product within the reticulum. Indeed, it now resembles the extracellular matrix and, for the first time, gives a positive reaction to colloidal metal stains for acid mucopolysaccharide (Revel, 33; Peterson and Leblond, 30). Recently, Godman and Lane (10) demonstrated in a radioautographic study that sulfation of the mucopolysaccharide seems to occur for the most part in the Golgi complex in developing cartilage, a finding which we have confirmed.

Karrer (23) suggested that membranes associated with or derived from the Golgi complex might be involved in polysaccharide anabolism. Indeed, the smooth-surfaced membranes of the Golgi complex are always well developed in cells which make mucopolysaccharides, such as spermatids (Fawcett, 8). Peterson and Leblond (30) and Revel (33) have recently explored the possibility that polysaccharides are synthesized within the Golgi complex. Revel treated tissues from newborn

mice with a brief pulse dose of tritiated glucose and fixed the cartilages of the tail and limb at 15 minutes, 30 minutes, and hourly intervals thereafter. At 15 minutes, tritiated glucose had been incorporated into the Golgi zone, presumably largely into the Golgi vacuoles, and at 2 hours, the product had been secreted into the matrix.

The available evidence thus would lead us to believe that the enigmatic juxtanuclear complex may serve as a center for the synthesis of nonprotein secretory products by enzymes located on or within its membrane-bounded compartments. It seems likely, moreover, that the Golgi complex not only directs and coordinates the process of secretion but also that it has an overall role of even greater importance in the membrane metabolism of differentiating cells. The Golgi apparatus, particularly the smooth-surfaced lamellae, occurs to some extent in nonsecretory cells and its function in these cells may be essential to development.

Concluding Remarks

Figure 13.17 is a diagram which summarizes some of the diverse data on nuclear and cytoplasmic function in differentiating cartilage cells presented in this chapter. The undifferentiated mesenchymal cells that comprise the growing blastema of the developing limb are synthesizing RNA and DNA, but are making relatively few specific proteins, such as collagen. These are the cells destined to differentiate into the diverse tissue types that will be represented by muscle, cartilage, and other connective tissues of the formed limb (Fig. 13.9). During the period of limb outgrowth, the cells destined to become chondrocytes aggregate in the

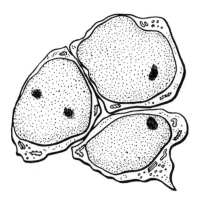

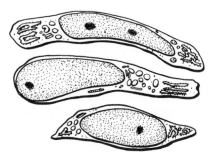

DNA synthesis ++
RNA synthesis +++
collagen synthesis ±
acid mucopolysaccharide –

DNA synthesis ±
RNA synthesis +++
collagen synthesis ++
acid mucopolysaccharide ++

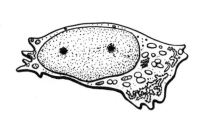

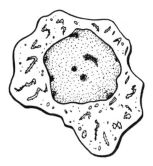

DNA synthesis –
RNA synthesis ±
collagen synthesis +++
acid mucopolysaccharide +++

DNA synthesis –
RNA synthesis ±
collagen synthesis ±
acid mucopolysaccharide +

Fig. 13.17 Diagram summarizing the metabolic events that occur in cartilage cells during various stages of differentiation. The figures are intended only to be relative. They do not imply, for example, that every cell is initially synthesizing DNA (top left) or that the only protein secreted into the matrix is collagen (top right). The relative amount of collagen synthesis is estimated from studies using proline-H^3 as a precursor, and mucopolysaccharide synthesis is estimated from studies using glucose-H^3. DNA and RNA synthesis were judged on the basis of thymidine and uridine incorporation. The diagram illustrates well the progressive change in nucleocytoplasmic ratio as differentiation proceeds. It has been drawn to scale, using camera lucida drawings to estimate cell size. As the cytoplasm of the chondrocyte becomes more abundant and more active in the synthesis of matrix, the nucleus decreases in size and gradually turns off its metabolic activities. Finally, the whole cell reaches a relatively quiescent phase and remains so for the life of the cartilage, unless the tissue is stimulated to regenerate.

proximal limb bud at a stage which roughly corresponds to the time of determination of the proximal parts. Presumptive muscle cells then aggregate along the skeletal anlage. Such cells have large nuclei and relatively little cytoplasm and they are still actively synthesizing DNA.

When the cells begin to synthesize specific proteins and carbohydrates, DNA synthesis and cell division decrease (Fig. 13.17, upper right) and the cytoplasmic organelles hypertrophy. The granular endoplasmic reticulum in cartilage cells is involved in the synthesis of proteins destined for the matrix, and the Golgi apparatus seems to play a role in the formation of mucopolysaccharides which, together with the proteins, accumulate in secretory vacuoles that subsequently discharge the product into the matrix. In muscle cells, however, the granular reticulum and Golgi vacuoles are not well developed (Fig. 13.9). Clumps and rows of free ribosomes seem to be directly involved in the synthesis of the proteinaceous myofilaments.

At the peak of development of the cytoplasmic organelles, the nucleus of the chondrocyte decreases its synthesis of RNA and nuclear proteins (Fig. 13.17, lower left). Yet in other tissues, such as muscle, RNA synthesis may continue after cytoplasmic differentiation has ensued. The cartilage cell seems to embark on a path of senescence from the moment it traps itself within the matrix. From a teleological point of view, it would seem that the nucleus of the chondrocyte learns early when enough RNA has been produced to sustain the cell through the subsequent period of protein synthesis. It is as if, in a sense, the cell responds to the environment which it is helping to produce before the matrix achieves its definitive size. The fact that the chondrocyte can be activated to divide and its progeny to redifferentiate when the skeleton is injured, attests to the subtle interactions which must continue between this cell and its environment. It is difficult to imagine the kind of feedback mechanisms that might explain the fact that these cells faithfully reproduce, in this environment, exactly the right amount of cartilage in just the right form, every time a vertebrate limb develops.

With the risk of being redundant, I would like to express my doubt that understanding the lives of freely living organisms such as bacteria will answer such problems as these. My colleagues have called attention to the complexity of tissue interactions in the multicellular organism elsewhere in this volume. I would like to emphasize the enormous array of intermediate organelles interposed between the chromosome and the ultimate expression of the message in a vertebrate cell; the possible control of cytoplasmic metabolism by a membranous centrosphere which contains no RNA; the well-ordered extracellular environment which seems to be fashioned in part by physicochemical factors that operate some distance from the cell; the seemingly long life of the RNA of the cytoplasm and the partitioning of nucleic acid anabolism within a membrane-bounded nuclear compartment.

It does not seem likely, either, that studies of the metabolism and fine structure of differentiating cells will, in themselves, completely answer these questions. But a fuller description of morphogenesis at this level is imperative if we are to plan future experiments in embryology which will explain the actual cell mechanisms that are involved in organogenesis.

References

1. Butler, E. G., "The Effects of X-radiation on the Regeneration of the Forelimbs of *Amblystoma Larvae*," *J. Exptl. Zool.* 65: 271–315 (1933).

2. Caro, L. G., "Electron Microscopic Radioautography of Thin Sections: the Golgi Zone as a Site of Protein Concentration in Pancreatic Acinar Cells," *J. Biophys. Biochem. Cytol.* 10:37–45 (1961).

3. ——, and G. E. Palade, "Protein Synthesis, Storage, and Discharge in the Pancreatic Exocrine Cell. An Autoradiographic Study," *J. Cell Biol.* 20:473–495 (1964).

4. Chalkley, D. T., "A Quantitative Histological Analysis of Forelimb Regeneration in *Triturus viridescens*," *J. Morphol.* 94:21–70 (1954).

5. Eastoe, J. E., *Biochemist's Handbook*, C. Long, ed. Princeton, N.J.: Van Nostrand, pp. 724–726 (1961).

6. Essner, E., and A. B. Novikoff, "Cytological Studies on Two Functional Hepatomas. Interrelations of Endoplasmic Reticulum, Golgi Apparatus and Lysosomes," *J. Cell Biol.* 15:289–312 (1962).

7. Farquhar, M. G., and G. E. Palade, "Junctional Complexes in Various Epithelia. *J. Cell Biol.* 17:375–412 (1963).

8. Fawcett, D. W., "Changes in the Fine Structure of the Cytoplasmic Organelles during Differentiation," *Developmental Cytology*, D. Rudnick, ed. New York: Ronald (1959).

9. ——, "Physiologically Significant Specializations of the Cell Surface," *Circulation* 26:1105–1125 (1962).

10. Godman, G. C., and N. Lane, "On the Site of Sulfation in the Chondrocyte," *J. Cell Biol.* 21:353–366 (1964).

11. ——, and K. R. Porter, "Chondrogenesis, Studies with the Electron Microscope," *J. Biophys. Biochem. Cytol.* 8: 719–760 (1960).

12. Goldberg, B., and H. Green, "An Analysis of Collagen Secretion by Established Mouse Fibroblast Lines," *J. Cell Biol.* 22:227–258 (1964).

13. Grobstein, C., "Cytodifferentiation and Its Controls," *Science* 143:643–650 (1964).

14. Hay, E. D., "The Fine Structure of Blastema Cells and Differentiating Cartilage Cells in Regenerating Limbs of *Amblystoma Larvae*," *J. Biophys. Biochem. Cytol.* 4:583–592 (1958).

15. ——, "Cytological Studies of Dedifferentiation and Differentiation in Regenerating Amphibian Limbs," *Regeneration*, D. Rudnick, ed. New York: Ronald (1962).

16. ——, "The Fine Structure of Differentiating Muscle in the Salamander Tail," *Z. Zellforsch.* 59:6–34 (1963).

17. ——, Unpublished observations (1964).

18. ——, and D. A. Fischman, "Origin of the Blastema in Regenerating Limbs of the Newt *Triturus viridescens*," *Develop. Biol.* 3:26–59 (1961).

19. ——, and J. P. Revel, "Autoradiographic Studies of the Origin of the Basement Lamella in *Amblystoma*," *Develop. Biol.* 7:152–168 (1963).

20. Holtzer, H., "Mitosis and Cell Transformations," *General Physiology of Cell Specialization*, D. Mazia and A. Tyler, eds. New York: McGraw-Hill (1963).

21. Jackson, S. Fitton-, "Connective Tissue Cells," *The Cell*, J. Brachet and A. E. Mirsky, eds. New York: Academic Press, vol. 6 (1964).

22. Jenning, M. A., and H. W. Florey, "Autoradiographic Observations on the Mucous Cells of the Stomach and Intestine," *Quart. J. Exptl. Physiol.* 41:131–152 (1956).

23. Karrer, H. E., "Electron-microscopic Observations on Developing Chick Embryo Liver. The Golgi Complex and Its Possible Role in the Formation of Glycogen," *J. Ultrastruct. Res.* 4:149–165 (1960).

24. Leblond, C. P., and N. Amano, "Synthetic Activity in the Nucleolus as Compared to That in the Rest of the Cell," *J. Histochem. Cytochem.* 10:162–174 (1962).

25. Lesseps, R. J., "Cell Surface Projections: Their Role in Aggregation of Embryonic Chick Cells as Revealed by Electron Microscopy," *J. Exptl. Zool.* 153: 171–182 (1963).

26. Malawista, I., and M. Schubert, "Chondromucoprotein; New Extraction Method and Alkaline-degradation," *J. Biol. Chem.* 230:535–544 (1958).

27. Milaire, J., "Histochemical Aspects of Limb Morphogenesis in Vertebrates," *Advances in Morphogenesis*, M. Abercrombie and J. Brachet, eds. New York: Academic Press, vol. 2 (1962).

28. ———, "Étude Morphologique et Cytochimique de Développement des Membres chez la Souris et chez la Taupe," *Arch. Biol.* 74:129–317 (1963).

29. Palade, G. E., P. Siekevitz, and L. G. Caro, "Structure, Chemistry and Function of the Pancreatic Exocrine Cell," *The Exocrine Pancreas*, A. V. S. de Reuck and M. P. Cameron, eds. Boston: Little, Brown & Co., (1961).

30. Peterson, M., and C. P. Leblond, "Synthesis of Complex Carbohydrates in the Golgi Region, as Shown by Radioautography after Injection of Labeled Glucose," *J. Cell Biol.* 21:143–148 (1964).

31. Porter, K. R., "Cell Fine Structure and Biosynthesis of Intercellular Macromolecules," *Biophys. J.* 4:167–196 (1964).

32. Prescott, D. M., "The Normal Cell Cycle," *Synchrony in Cell Division and Growth*, E. Zeuthen, ed. New York: Interscience Publishers (1964).

33. Revel, J. P., "A Stain for the Ultrastructural Localization of Acid Mucopolysaccharides," *J. Micros.* 3:535–544 (1964).

34. ———, and E. D. Hay, "Autoradiographic Localization of DNA Synthesis in a Specific Ultrastructural Component of the Interphase Nucleus," *Exptl. Cell Res.* 25:474–480 (1961).

35. ———, and ———, "An Autoradiographic and Electron Microscopic Study of Collagen Synthesis in Differentiating Cartilage," *Z. Zellforsch.* 61:110–144 (1963).

36. Revel, M., and H. H. Hiatt, "The Stability of Liver Messenger RNA," *Proc. Natl. Acad. Sci. U. S.* 51:810–818 (1964).

37. Rose, S. M., "The Effect of NaCl in Stimulating Regeneration of Frogs," *J. Morphol.* 77:119–139 (1945).

38. Ross, R., and E. P. Benditt, "Wound Healing and Collagen Formation. III. A Quantitative Radioautographic Study of the Utilization of Proline H^3 in Wounds from Normal and Scorbutic Guinea Pigs," *J. Cell Biol.* 15:99–108 (1962).

39. Saunders, J. W., "The Proximo-distal Sequence of Origin of the Parts of the Chick Wing and the Role of the Ectoderm," *J. Exptl. Zool.* 108:363–403 (1948).

40. Singer, M., and M. Salpeter, "The Role of the Wound Epithelium in Vertebrate Regeneration," *Growth in Living Systems*, M. X. Zarrow, ed. New York: Basic Books, Inc. (1961).

41. Thornton, C. S., "The Histogenesis of Muscle in the Regenerating Forelimb of Larval *Amblystoma punctatum*," *J. Morphol.* 62:17–47 (1938).

42. Trelstad, R., "High Resolution Double-isotope Autoradiography," *Exptl. Cell Res.* In press (1965).

43. Warshawski, H., C. P. Leblond, and B. Droz, "Synthesis and Migration of Proteins in the Cells of the Exocrine Pancreas as Revealed by Specific Activity Determination from Radioautographs," *J. Cell Biol.* 16:1–23 (1963).

44. Yamada, T., and S. Karasaki, "Nuclear RNA Synthesis in Newt Iris Cells Engaged in Regenerative Transformation into Lens Cells," *Develop. Biol.* 7:595–604 (1963).

45. Zeigel, R. F., and A. J. Dalton, "Speculations Based on the Morphology of the Golgi System in Several Types of Protein Secreting Cells," *J. Cell Biol.* 15:45–54 (1962).

46. Zwilling, E., "Limb Morphogenesis," *Advances in Morphogenesis*, M. Abercrombie and J. Brachet, eds. New York: Academic Press, vol. 1 (1961).

14

Aspects of Cytodifferentiation of Skeletal Muscle

IRWIN R. KONIGSBERG

Department of Embryology
Carnegie Institution of Washington
Baltimore, Maryland

This volume has been organized around the theme of the development of organs and organ systems. Even a cursory examination of the table of contents, however, will inform the reader that the concept of what constitutes an organ has been interpreted rather broadly. I believe that this breadth of interpretation may be symptomatic of the intuitive knowledge, which many of us share, that any narrower interpretation would be anachronistic. When descriptive studies dominated the attention of most embryologists, and even after experimental morphology had come of age, the pervading preoccupation was with the fascinating panoply of differences in developmental mechanics from organ to organ, tissue to tissue, and cell to cell. What unifying principles *were* framed had to be couched in language which described rather than defined. Thus communication between embryologists and other members of the scientific community was slow and difficult.

Where once the examination of development, organ by organ, had the utility of making the inventory of descriptive differences more manageable, today we are looking for explanations rather than descriptions. We are looking for the common denominators of developmental processes which cut across all of the artificial barriers which by now have served their heuristic purpose. We are looking for these common denominators at all of the levels of organization of living matter, molecular, cellular, and higher levels.

If we choose to study a particular cell, tissue, or organ, it is usually because we see some unique property in that particular material which makes it better suited than another to an investigation of some broader aspect of development. Two characteristic features of skeletal muscle are its functional associations with nerve and the direct relationship of its primary physiological function, contraction, to a small number of well-characterized proteins. The nerve-muscle association has been used to advantage to study the mechanisms directing the formation of pattern in development and the specificity of cell-cell interactions. These questions are dealt with elsewhere in this volume (Sperry, Chapter 6 and Trinkaus, Chapter 3) and will not be discussed here.

Developmental biology is the search for an understanding of how structure arises in biological systems, it being assumed as axiomatic that structure and function are inexorably linked. In skeletal muscle this relationship need not be assumed; it is nowhere more clearly obvious. It is obvious at any level of organization one chooses to examine — from the organismic to the molecular. Not only can the molecular components of the microscopic contractile elements be identified, but recently certain of these structures have been reproduced outside of the cell. When cellular organelles can be synthesized in the laboratory, there is reason to hope that we may soon know how this is accomplished in the cell.

Survey of Muscle Development

A detailed account of the comparative histogenesis of muscle cells would obviously exceed the space restrictions imposed. Neither can any single chapter in any of the standard texts be recommended. Two relatively recent publications contain good descriptive accounts of histogenesis in the somite (Holtzer, Marshall, and Finck, 34) and in the hindlimb (Kitiyakara, 39) of the chick embryo. Both accounts stress the high degree of asynchrony of cytodifferentiation. At progressively later stages, the proportion of differentiated cells increases. However, for a considerable period of time, cells corresponding to a variety of developmental stages can be observed in close association. The temporal sequence of the course of cytodifferentiation also differs in different muscle-forming regions. For example, Kitiyakara states that by the 5th to 6th day of development, although the somites have already formed longitudinal columns of differentiated fibers, the limb buds are only beginning to show islands of myogenesis. Straus and Rawles (69) point out that, in fact, a gradient of myogenic differentiation exists starting dorsally in the somites, traversing the lateral mesoderm in a dorsoventral direction, and finally involves the limb musculature. It is this directionally graded participation in myogenic differentiation, they consider, which led earlier workers to believe that all of the body musculature was derived from somite cells which migrated ventrally.

In a carefully executed series of carbon-marking and extirpation experiments, these investigators (69) were able to demonstrate that lateral and trunk musculature, in the chick, are in fact not of somitic origin, but develop in situ from the mesoderm of the lateral plate. There is, of course, good experimental evidence that the musculature of the appendages in all orders above fishes is purely of lateral plate origin (see Boyd, 7). It is difficult to imagine that myogenic potency is restricted only to the limb-forming areas of the lateral plate in all orders except birds. However, a contribution of lateral plate mesoderm to the abdominal and lateral body musculature is not thought to be universal (Detwiler, 13; Liedke, 47).

The sequence of cytological changes typical of skeletal muscle involves several stages which can be distinguished at the level of resolution of the light microscope. The first gross change distinguishing the presumptive myoblast from neighboring mesenchymal cells is an elongation of the cell, giving it a spindle-shaped appearance. In the somite, such cells continue to elongate in the anterior-posterior axis, reaching lengths of approximately 400 micra. The first myofibrils are laid down in such nondividing mononucleated myoblasts (Stockdale and Holtzer, 68). Subsequently, such cells fuse to form multinucleate syncytia. In the limb musculature, such extremely elongate cells are not generally observed. This may be due to the lack of the precise orientation found in somitic muscle or may indicate that the short spindle-shaped cells fuse sooner to form the syncytial fiber.

Although embryonic skeletal muscle will differentiate in the absence of peripheral nerves (Harrison, 23; Lewis and Lewis, 46; Hamburger, 22, and others), there is evidence that the growth of somitic muscle is stimulated by the adjacent spinal cord (Muchmore, 55; Holtzer and Detwiler, 31, 32). Muchmore (56, 57) has suggested that the influence is nonspecific.

Embryology is hardly noted for either the precision or the parsimony of its specialized terminology. In this respect the literature on myogenesis is not exceptional. The terms "multinucleated myoblast," "myotube," "sacroblast," "syncytioblast," and "myocytic strap" have all been applied to the early syncytium. The term "myotube" is, if nothing else, a picturesque description of such syncytia in which the disposition of the darkly staining myofibrillae in close association to the sarcolemma give these cells, in cross section, a tubular appearance.

While the myofibrils in the myotube are increasing both in number, by addition of fibrils laterally, as well as in length, the nuclei are centrally located. As the myofibrils fill the central portion of the sarcoplasm, the nuclei are displaced to a position just beneath the sarcolemma, their definitive location.

The "Myoblast"

Boyd (7) has discussed recently the nomenclature of myogenesis and in particular the ambiguity of the term "myoblast." There are no universally acceptable criteria for determining when a cell has first become committed to myogenesis. The difficulty, however, is not simply one of semantics. It involves, rather, the fundamental problem of cellular differentiation. We do not know by what mechanisms the cell becomes committed to one or another alternative developmental pathway, and when we can detect the first cell-type specific structures we know that it has already happened. There seems no alternative, at present, but to continue to use the term "myoblast" as an operational definition. Nevertheless, newer approaches to cytological investigation have permitted operational definitions of greater precision.

Fluorescent antibody techniques have considerably narrowed the gap between cytological morphology and the identification of the molecular components of microscopic structure. The use of these techniques in the study of myogenesis (Holtzer, Marshall, and Finck, 34; Engel and Horvath, 17; Emmart, Kominz, and Miquel, 15) has revealed the presence of myofibrils in earlier stages than were previously

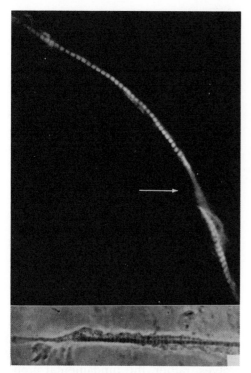

Fig. 14.1 High-magnification fluorescence photomicrograph of a part of a myofibril in an isolated stage 23 myoblast stained with fluorescent antimyosin. Fibril extended the entire length of the cell (over 400 μ). Arrow indicates position of the nucleus which is obscuring the detail of the fibril in this region. (From Holtzer, Marshall, and Finck, *J. Biophys. Biochem. Cytol.* 3:705–724, 1957.) The photographs here reproduced from printed halftone copy show a loss of detail, and the quality of the results is not representative of the originals.

a stage in which the cell is committed to myogenesis but is not synthesizing contractile proteins? Although we now know that the contractile proteins are present before they are organized into a myofibril which is recognizable at the level of the light microscope, the question, nevertheless, is still valid. In an earlier era, embryologists recognized a period in development when a cell could be demonstrated to have at least a bias toward a particular pathway of differentiation, although by the techniques then available, no cytological evidence of such bias was discernible. Certainly, under the scrutiny of techniques of higher resolution, this period is shrinking.

An obvious paradox exists in defining a myoblast solely on the basis of the presence of a structure or molecule characteristic of the differentiated cell. It begs the question of the absence of a truly "covert" phase of differentiation. In a study of the fine structure of developing muscle cells in the salamander embryo, Hay (25) has described several characteristics of what are presumably myoblasts. The location of these cells adjacent to unequivocally identifiable early muscle cells suggests that they are myoblasts. More conclusive is the fact that, in some of these cells at least, myofilaments can be identified. Such cells are characterized by an abundance of ribonucleoprotein granules (presumably ribosomes), the vast majority of which are found free in the cytoplasm, rather than in association with endoplasmic reticulum. Variable amounts of endoplasmic reticulum are present, but usually in the form of smooth-surfaced vesicles. On the other hand, in the mesenchymal cells, which Hay can identify by electronmicroscopic radioautography (Chapter 13),

demonstrable (Fig. 14.1). Holtzer, Marshall, and Finck (34) for their purposes designated only those cells containing myofibrils which stained with fluorescent labeled antimyosin as myoblasts. They reserved the term "presumptive myoblast" for those cells in the same area which could not be positively identified by their criterion. Further, they raise the cogent question: Is there

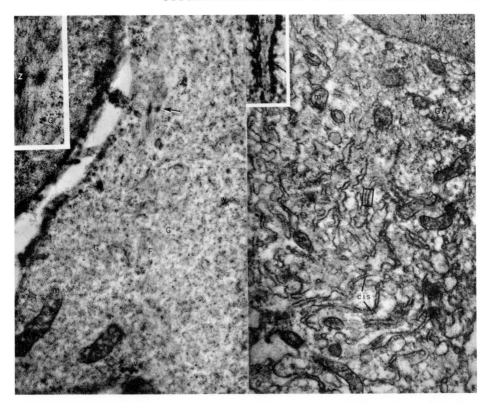

Fig. 14.2 Comparison of the fine structure of a myoblast (left) compared to a mesenchymal cell (right). Arrow in the photomicrograph on the left indicates an aggregation of myofilaments and associated Z-band material (see inset). The mesenchymal cell at the right contains a highly developed granular endoplasmic reticulum (see inset) in contrast to the myoblast in which the ribonucleoprotein granules are free in the cytoplasm. G, ribonucleoprotein granules; Z, Z-band material; F, isolated myofilaments; W, wisps of membranous material (in myoblast); GA, Golgi apparatus; m, mitochondria; N, nucleus; cis, cisternae; v, "vesicles" possibly associated with cell membrane. (From Hay, Z. *Zellforsch. Mikroskop. Anat. Abt. Histochem.* 59:6–34, 1963.)

the ribonucleoprotein granules are attached to a limiting membrane (granular reticulum). She suggests that the association of granules with endoplasmic reticulum may be a general characteristic of cells whose cell-specific products are deposited extracellularly (that is, collagen) in contrast to those in which it is retained (that is, myosin). Admittedly, the strength of the identification rests on those cases in which both myofilaments and the character-

istic distribution of ribonucleoprotein granules were found coexistent in the same cell. It does provide, however, a cytological criterion for identifying myoblasts which may precede the formation of myofilaments and perhaps the synthesis of the contractile proteins (Fig. 14.2).

In still another manner, it has been possible to identify myoblasts by criteria peculiar to the embryonic cell itself. During a study of the development

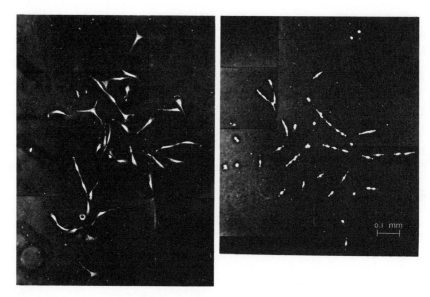

Fig. 14.3 Colonies which have formed by the mitotic division of single trypsin-dissociated cells derived from embryonic chick muscle. Living cells were photographed using phase optics, 4 days after the single cells were plated. The colony on the right is a colony of myoblasts (note the bipolar shape of the individual members). The colony on the left, in which cell shape is more variable, is a colony of "fibroblast like" cells. The apparent differences in cell size is due most probably to the more accentuated flattening of the "fibroblast like" cell. (From Konigsberg, *Scientific American,* vol. 211, (2) p. 63, 1964.)

of colonies of differentiated muscle in vitro from single embryonic skeletal muscle cells, Konigsberg (42) found that the progenitors of the muscle colony could be distinguished from fibroblastlike cells. The former are spindle-shaped cells not unlike the early presumptive myoblasts seen in vivo (Fig. 14.3). An exceedingly high proportion of the colonies which developed from such cells differentiated into colonies containing cross-striated myotubes.

Origin of Multinuclearity

Unique to skeletal muscle among the contractile cells of the vertebrate body is the syncytial character of its cells. Smooth muscle is of course composed of single cellular units. Cardiac muscle, once thought to be syncytial, has relatively recently been shown to be composed of single closely associated cells. The intercalated discs have been demonstrated to be the cell membranes separating adjacent cellular units (see DeHaan, Chapter 16). However, the electronmicroscopic evidence supports the older view that the skeletal muscle cell is an elongated multinuclear fiber.

Although its multinuclear nature has never seriously been questioned, a lively controversy has surrounded the question of the origin of multinuclearity in skeletal muscle cells. One view held that this cell was a true syncytium which, as Haeckel originally defined the term, arose by the fusion of many separate cells. Alternatively, and with at least equal vigor, it has been maintained that the presence of multiple nuclei within a common cytoplasm resulted from repeated nuclear division in the absence of cytokinesis. Since mitotic figures are rarely reported in multinuclear skeletal muscle cells, the later hypothesis requires the additional assumption that direct nuclear division can and does occur. The proponents of this latter hypothesis have based their conclusions entirely upon the types of nuclear configurations which can be observed in fixed, stained material. Nuclei bearing clefts or deformed into "dumbbell" shapes have been interpreted to represent stages in the process of "amitotic" division.

Suggestive as these configurations may be, without following the process to completion, one cannot be satisfied with the validity of the interpretation. Indeed, one such sequence of nuclear deformations in a muscle cell in vitro was followed with time-lapse cinematography by Cooper and Konigsberg (10). During the period of observation, several nuclear changes (that is, cleft formation, "dumbbell" deformation) were observed to be reversible (see also Stockdale and Holtzer, 68). The evidence for amitotic nuclear replication is at the very best only suggestive.

Interest in the origin of the multinuclearity of muscle cells was revived recently, largely through the stimulus of Holtzer and his associates (30). A variety of experimental approaches have been applied in various laboratories. The weight of the evidence leaves little room for doubt that skeletal muscle fibers are true syncytia formed by cellular fusion.

The most thoroughly documented argument in favor of the fusion hypothesis is based on the absence of a correlation between DNA synthesis and the development of multinuclearity. If the number of nuclei within a cell were to increase by any form of nuclear replication, it would have to be preceded by DNA synthesis. Therefore, during the period of the development of multinuclearity one would expect to be able to detect such synthesis in the nuclei of the developing fiber. One type of measurement which has been made is the microspectrophotometric determination of Feulgen-DNA per nucleus. Such measurements have been made on both regenerating mouse muscle (Lash, Holtzer, and Swift, 45) and on chick skeletal muscle cultured in explant (Firket, 19; Bassleer, 3), or as a monolayer (Strehler, Konigsberg, and Kelley, 70). These studies indicate that in the surrounding mononucleated cells (in vivo as well as in vitro) the distribution of DNA values is bimodal corresponding to the $2n$ and $4n$ values. In the developing multinuclear cells, however, a single peak of DNA values corresponding to the $2n$ value is observed. Since DNA doubling cannot be detected in any of the syncytial nuclei, it is unlikely that nuclear replication occurs within the developing fiber. [It is of interest to note that, in a similar study applied to the human placenta, Galton (20) concludes that the syncytiotrophoblast forms by cellular coalescence.] Studies using radioautographic techniques to detect the incorporation of isotopically labeled DNA precursors also support this conclusion. Relatively short exposures to the precursor (tritiated thymidine) do not label syncytial nuclei, although substantial numbers of the mononucleated cells are labeled. With longer periods of time, either in the continued presence of precursor or during a "chase" period following a pulse of labeled precursor, labeled nuclei appear within the syncytia (Firket, 19; Stockdale and Holtzer, 68; Bintliff and Walker, 6; Zhinkin and Andreeva, 79; Bassleer, 3). In an interesting extension of this approach, Kityakara and Angevine (40) concluded that in the postnatal growth of the limb musculature of the mouse, elongation occurs through addition by fusion of cells primarily at the end of existing fibers.

These workers counted labeled nuclei along the length of the gracilis muscle in neonatal mice sacrificed at different time intervals after a single injection of tritiated thymidine. In animals killed within 1–4 hours after injection, most of the labeled subsarcolemmal nuclei are found in the terminal zones of the muscle. At progressively later periods, two peaks of labeling are found near the belly of the muscle. Although the muscle has grown appreciably longer, the distance between these peaks remains approximately the same and roughly corresponds to the length of the muscle at the time of injection.

The postnatal growth of muscle in both human (Montgomery, 54) and rat (Enesco and Puddy, 16) has also been shown to involve an increase in nuclei per multinucleated muscle fiber. MacConnachie, Enesco, and Leblond (50) have recently described mitoses within the basement membrane of muscle fibers in the young postnatal rat. Many of these mitotic figures (in colchicine arrest) are surrounded by cytoplasm which is distinct in appearance from the cytoplasm of the fiber proper. They suggest that these mitoses may represent dividing satellite cells (see Mauro, 52).

Although the nature of this strongest evidence supports fusion by precluding either mitosis or "amitosis" within the developing fiber itself, the process of fusion of muscle cells in vitro has, in fact, been recorded cinematographically (Cappers, 9; Cooper and Konigsberg, 10; Bassleer, 3).

Fine structural details suggestive at least of cellular fusion have been described by Hay (25) and by Shafiq (66). Both of these investigators call attention to areas containing strings of vesicles traversing what are apparently newly formed myotubes which may be the remnants of the old limiting cell membranes.

If nuclear replication is not a concomitant process in the formation of multinuclear muscle fibers, then the inhibition of DNA synthesis should not prevent the formation of such elements. Using the nitrogen mustard, methyl-bis(β-chlorethyl)amine, Konigsberg, McElwain, Tootle, and Herrmann (44) were able to demonstrate that the inhibition of DNA synthesis does not block the development of multinuclearity. Bassleer, Collignon, and Matagne-Dhoossche (4), using another radiomimetic drug, Myleran, have drawn similar conclusions. Also Rinaldini (63) has pointed out that in monolayer cultures of skeletal muscle cells in media which normally do not support cell multiplication, multinucleated fibers may form within 24 hours. Such cells, when dispersed in complete media, will divide with a generation time of 24 hours, reaching a stationary phase (within 2 to 4 days, depending on the inoculum size used). However, multinuclear cell formation which also occurs rapidly in such cultures can be correlated roughly with the attainment of the stationary phase (Konigsberg, 41). Thus it may well be that cellular fusion in culture occurs *only* when conditions will not support cellular multiplication of at least particular members of the population.

With the formation of multinucleate fibers, a number of seemingly abrupt changes occur. These changes are most readily observed in cultured muscle, although they have been described in vivo as well. The following are included in these changes: (1) Intense basophilia appears, presumably as RNA (Kityakara, 39; Lash, Holtzer, and Swift, 45). (2) Large numbers of mitochondria and mitochondrial enzymes appear. The latter have been demonstrated histochemically (Cooper and Konigsberg, 10; Konigsberg, 41) and immunologically (Emmart, Kominz, and Miquel, 15). (3) Related probably to this increase in mitochondria, the multinucleated fiber can be destroyed by concentrations of antimycin A (an inhibitor of oxidative phosphorylation) which do not effect the proliferating mononucleated myoblast (Konigsberg, 43). (4) Creatine-phosphokinase activity can first be detected at about the time that multinucleated cells form in culture (Reporter, Konigsberg, and Strehler, 61).

Proliferation and Specific Protein Synthesis

Most pertinent to the problem of the cytodifferentiation of skeletal muscle is the rapid accumulation of contractile proteins in the multinucleated fiber. There is good evidence, however, that the accumulation of contractile proteins is not related to multinuclearity per se. Stockdale and Holtzer (68) suggest rather that the appearance of myofibrils is related to the nonproliferative state of the syncytium. In those mononucleated myoblasts (for example, in early somites) which have ceased proliferating, well developed myofibrils can be demonstrated (Holtzer, Marshall, and Finck, 34; Stockdale and Holtzer, 68). The latter authors suggest that "the synthesis of DNA and the

synthesis of contractile proteins may be mutually exclusive events." (One should note, however, that they specifically caution against assuming an irreversible commitment to one or the other activity.)

Though never clearly defined or rigorously investigated, the premise that in some way differentiation and cell proliferation are incompatible events has enjoyed popularity among students of development for many years. It is clear that the accumulation, at least of detectable quantities of muscle-specific proteins, occurs only after cell division has ceased (Stockdale and Holtzer, 68).

This accumulation of cell-type specific proteins at a particular phase in the developmental history of a cell could reflect either (1) the initiation of synthesis of the particular proteins, (2) an increased rate of synthesis, or (3) stabilization of the protein (for example, sequestering it in a more stable configuration such as a myofibril). Current speculation seems to revolve principally around the possibility that stability of messenger-RNA is a characteristic of the nonproliferating cell. This is an extrapolation from the situation in the reticulocyte, in which it has been convincingly demonstrated that hemoglobin is synthesized on a polysome which has a long half-life. Scott and Bell (65), on the basis of a study of the stability of polysomes in a variety of embryonic tissues after treatment with actinomycin-D, suggest that stable polysomes are characteristic only of those cell types in which the attainment of the definitive differentiated state involves cell death (that is, the reticulocyte, the lens fiber cell, and the cells of the avian feather). Among the tissues tested in which they could not demonstrate long-lived polysomes, they list developing muscle. On the other hand, Yaffee and Feldman (78) find, in monolayers of neonatal mouse muscle in vitro, differential survival of myotubes in cultures treated with actinomycin-D just before myotube formation. They interpret this as indicative of differences in messenger half-life in myotubes as compared to myoblasts. A similar differential survival was noted by Konigsberg, McElwain, Tootle, and Herrmann (44) with high concentrations of nitrogen mustard. This agent inhibits DNA synthesis specifically only at lower concentrations. At those high levels which destroy mononucleated cells preferentially, we found that the over-all rate of protein synthesis was also inhibited. Continued synthesis of myosin for 18 hours following the administration of actinomycin-D has been reported by Strohman, Cerwinsky, and Holmes (71). They believe this implicates the presence of messenger-RNA in a stable form. In view of the accumulating evidence which suggests that the effects of actinomycin-D may not be as sharply defined as once thought (see, for example, Revel, Hiatt, and Revel, 62; Kennell, 38), it would be of considerable value to be able to determine the half-life of messenger-RNA by an independent method.

Detection of Contractile Proteins

Any attempt to correlate the initiation of synthesis with cessation of proliferation, or any other event in a cell's developmental history, involves establishing the time when the protein is first synthesized. Synthesis, however, is generally equated with detection of the product. Only rarely has synthesis actually been studied in terms of the rate of incorporation of radioactive precursor into a specific protein of an embryonic tissue. [See, however, the work of Herrmann and his associates (28) and Strohman, Cerwinsky, and Holmes (71)].

Several of the properties of the contractile proteins myosin and actin and of the conjugate actomyosin have been used as assays for these proteins. Csapo and Herrmann (11) made use of the viscometric change of myosin and actomyosin in the presence of ATP as an assay. Measurements of myosin-adenosine triphosphatase activity have been also employed as an assay procedure by several investigators (Herrmann, Nicholas and Vosgian, 26; Robinson, 64; de Villafranca, 12; Maruyama, 51; Love, 48, 49; Nass, 58; and Deuchar, 14). Myosin adenosine triphosphatase can be distinguished from other enzymes with similar activity only at the pH optimum of the myosin enzyme and in the presence of calcium rather than magnesium as the activating ion. Quantitative extraction and chromatographic procedures have also been used (Love, 49; Herrmann, 28; Baril, Love, and Herrmann, 2) to measure the amounts of myosin in embryonic chick muscle. Not all of these investigations were addressed to the problem of detecting the earliest evidence of myosin synthesis, but rather to other questions—for example, the factors which regulate the rates of protein synthesis in embryonic tissues and the identity or lack of identity between myosin in adult and embryonic tissues.

This latter question is still unresolved. It has been suggested that the properties of embryonic myosin differ from those of the protein isolated from adult animals (reviewed recently by

Nass, 58). This premise has been questioned on immunological grounds (Holtzer, Marshall, and Finck, 34; Holtzer, 30). One cannot rule out the possibility that the immunological properties may be similar, although certain physical properties might differ between embryonic and adult myosin. However, this question cannot be resolved until more confidence can be placed in the purity of the myosin prepared from embryonic tissues. In the one study in which preparative procedures were exhaustively studied and controlled, it was demonstrated that by the criteria of solubility, chromatographic behavior, electrophoretic properties (see also Goffart-Louis, 21), ATP sensitivity, and adenosine triphosphatase activity, embryonic (14-day chick) myosin did not differ from the adult protein (Love, 49). A more recent report from the same laboratory describes a difference in chromatographic behavior with muscle preparations from younger (11-day chick) embryos (Baril, Love, and Herrmann, 2). These investigators demonstrate, however, that the anomalous behavior is due to bound RNA which can be enzymatically removed.

The First Molecule

The ability to detect small quantities of a particular protein will depend upon the precision and sensitivity of the technique employed. This was clearly demonstrated by Holtzer, Marshall, and Finck (34). They could rank four different cytological procedures in order of their sensitivity, showing that in somite cells in which myofibrils could not be demonstrated by one technique, they could be detected by the next, more sensitive, procedure. Thus, the establishment of the earliest time

that myosin can be detected will have meaning only within the context of the assay technique used. There is no assurance that a more sensitive technique could not "turn the clock" still further back. In fact, one might question whether the "earliest time" has any meaning other than a relative one. It is not possible to prove that an entity does not exist (every theologian understands this), only that it does exist. Fortunately, an understanding of developmental phenomena does not depend entirely upon the construction of timetables.

Of the techniques presently available for detecting contractile proteins or the aggregates of such proteins, the two which seem to offer the requisite sensitivity for studying the earliest phases of cytodifferentiation are immunochemical and electronmicroscopical techniques.

Both precipitin tests (Ogawa, 59) and fluorescent antibody techniques (Holtzer, Marshall, and Finck, 34; Engel and Horvath, 17; Emmart, Kominz, and Miquel, 15) have been applied to study the development of skeletal muscle. The use of fluorescent antibodies has the advantage of permitting the localization of reactive groups at the cellular level. This advantage was fully exploited by Holtzer, Marshall, and Finck in their investigation of the development of somitic muscle. Cross-striated myofibrils were first observed in stage 16 to 17 embryos in mononucleated elongated myofibrils (at a time when they could not be detected in iron-hematoxylin stained somite cells). Somewhat earlier, only a delicate filament, without cross-striation, was observed. The authors speculated that a less organized state may immediately precede the definitive sarcomere pattern, although they considered also that other techniques might resolve the striated pattern in even this first filament.

The sensitivity of fluorescent-antibody staining does not permit the resolution of stages of lesser organization than the fibril itself (such as filaments). This was observed also in the work of Engel and Horvath (17) on cultured embryonic chick muscle. On the other hand, Emmart, Kominz, and Miquel (15), also dealing with cultured muscle cells, describe granular staining with fluorescent antimyosin in cells which they classify on these grounds as early myoblasts.

Formation of the First Myofibril

With the improvements in the technical aspects of electronmicroscopy, a few studies have appeared in which the prefibril stages of fibrillogenesis have been observed (Hay, 24, 25; Bergman, 5; Shafiq, 66; Heuson-Stiennon, 29; Allen and Pepe, 1). There is general agreement that the earliest myofibril is preceded by a stage in which the myofibrillar filaments exist within the cell in a disordered state. Hay (25), for example, describes two types of filaments found in myoblasts but not in mesenchymal cells in the developing salamander tail. Thick filaments, in both her sectioned material as well as those shown in the other investigations, are clearly myosin (A band) filaments, by virtue of their 100 A diameter and characteristic lateral projections (Fig. 14.7). The thin filaments are not so readily identified. Allen and Pepe (1) also observed these two types of filaments in sections of developing chick somite cells. Moreover, they have identified the thin

Fig. 14.4 Electronmicrograph of longitudinal section through several myofibrils in a muscle fiber from an adult rabbit. Compare to diagrams in Fig. 14.5 (Courtesy of H. E. Huxley.)

filaments in negatively stained extracts of somite cells of the same stage. In such preparations they could demonstrate beaded thin filaments, identical in fine structural detail to F-actin filaments or to I-band filaments isolated from adult muscle.

The developing chick somite can be more precisely staged than the material used in the other investigations. It may be for this reason that Allen and Pepe (1) were able to detect a short period of approximately 16–21 hours during which time, although increasingly larger numbers of thin filaments were observed, thick filaments could not be demonstrated. It would be somewhat premature to conclude from this data that the synthesis of the two contractile proteins is initiated sequentially. One cannot as yet entirely exclude the possibility that the indi-

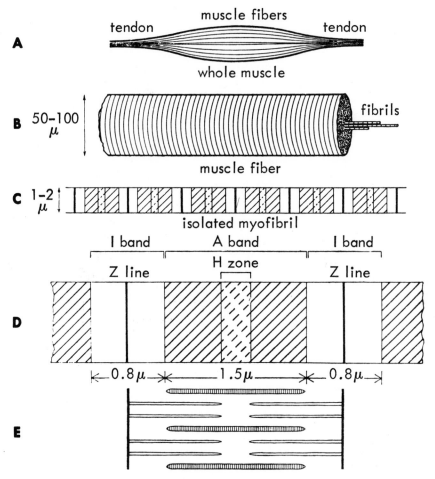

Fig. 14.5 Structure of muscle showing the relationship of the contractile elements to the cell and to the organ. A. An individual (anatomical) muscle is composed of many muscle fibers (multinucleate differentiated cell) B. Each fiber contains numerous cross-striated myofibrils. C. A single myofibril is subdivided along its length into a repetitive pattern of lines and bands of different optical density. D. A single unit of the repeat (a sarcomere) in a muscle at rest length is diagrammed, giving the nomenclature and dimensions of the subdivisions of the sarcomeric pattern, E. The pattern is produced by the arrangements of two kinds of protein filaments, a thick filament (100 A diameter) which consists of myosin, and a thin filament (50 A diameter) attached to the Z line, containing actin and probably another muscle protein. (See also Fig. 14.6.) (From Huxley and Hanson, p. 184 in *Structure and Function of Muscle*, vol. 1, G. Bourne, ed. Academic Press, 1960, and Huxley and Hanson, *Scientific American* 199(5) 71, 1958.)

vidual molecules are present for some time before they form the aggregated myofilament. It is of interest, however, that Ogawa (59), using a precipitin test, reported that he could obtain a positive test for actin reactive groups some 24 hours before he could demonstrate myosin groups in extracts of whole chick embryos. His assay would presumably detect the free molecules as well as the filamentous aggregates.

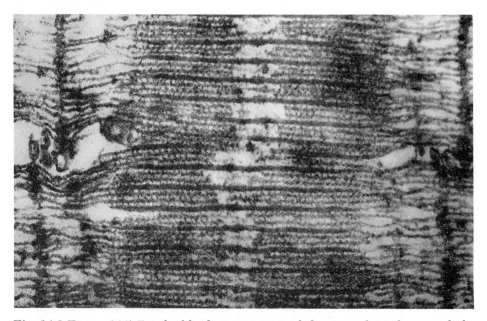

Fig. 14.6 Figure 14.5 *E* is highly diagrammatic and does not show the cross links between the two types of filaments. These can be seen between the thick and thin filaments in this electronmicrograph of a longitudinal section through a single sarcomere in each of two adjacent myofibrils. In frontal sections through a myofibril each thick filament can be observed to be surrounded by six thin filaments. Depending upon the plane of a longitudinal section, the thick filaments will be separated by two thin filaments (as shown) or by only one thin filament. (From Huxley and Hanson, pp. 183–227 in *Structure and Function of Muscle*, vol. 1, G. Bourne, ed. Academic Press, 1960.)

After the myofilaments are formed, they are ordered into a myofibril whose sarcomeric subdivisions, although discernible at the fine structural level, are not apparent to light microscopy. The stages in the formation of this primitive fibril are described differently by Hay (25) and by Allen and Pepe (1). Hay observed that at the time myofilaments are discernible some of them may be associated with an electron-dense material which she tentatively identified as Z-band material. Shafiq (66) observed similar configurations in developing insect flight muscle and Heuson-Stiennon (29) in fetal rat muscle. Hay suggests that "the initial stage of myofibril formation may in some cases consist of a coalescence of clumps of myofilaments and Z-bands." Such a mechanism, she points out, might explain many of the earlier interpretations of light microscopic observations suggesting the coalescence of granules, threads, and so on to form fibrils.

Allen and Pepe (1) on the other hand, believe that small aggregates of thick and thin filaments become aligned to form "loosely connected, nonstriated myofibrils." Before any evidence of Z-band material can be seen, the myofibrils are segmented by a system of encircling tubules spaced at intervals of 1.5 μ along the length of the fibril. (This interval corresponds to the length of a myosin filament.) At later stages, dense Z-lines form at the level of these tubules and only then can the subdivisions of the sarcomere be seen distinctly. These investigators suggest that only after the formation of a Z-band to which the thin filaments can be anchored can discrete I and A bands form.

The details of these two different sets of observations are difficult to reconcile. Irrespective of the differences in the mechanism of fibril construction which each suggests, they clarify two points. First, whether the early fibril appears homogeneous because of the lack of precise ordering of sarcomere lengths as Hay suggests (Fig. 14.8), or appears homogeneous because of complete overlap of thick and thin filaments, as Allen and Pepe (1) suggest, the primitive fibril contains both of the major contractile proteins, actin and myosin. Indeed, knowing as we do now (Huxley and Hanson, 36) how myosin and actin filaments interact, it is difficult to imagine how a fibril could be maintained in any other fashion. Secondly, it seems gratuitous to assume any longer that the fibril need be assembled on some supramolecular template or surface.

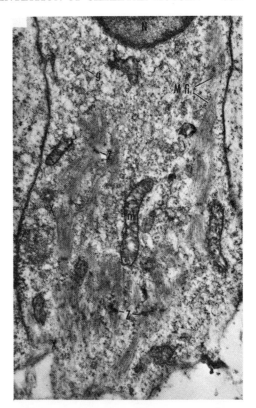

Fig. 14.7 Developing muscle cell (regenerating salamander limb). At this magnification the largest myofilaments, M fi, can be identified. Forming Z bands (Z) can also be distinguished. N, nucleus; m, mitochondria; g, free ribonucleoprotein granules; x, unknown body; Z, Z bands; I, I band. (From Hay, p. 198, in *Regeneration*, D. Rudnick, ed., The Ronald Press Co., © 1962.)

The Protein-Forming Apparatus

Before the mechanism of protein synthesis was elaborated in as much detail as it is currently understood, the possibility was entertained that the myofibril was organized on a higher order template such as the sarcolemma or an earlier formed fibril. These conclusions are natural extensions of the fact that the first fibrils are found in close association with the sarcolemma and that they increase in number by the lateral addition of new myofibrils and form initially a subsarcolemmal sheath within the myotube. It had also been suggested that the myofibril itself may participate in the synthesis of the contractile proteins (Holtzer, 30; Winnick and Winnick, 77). The polysome concept of protein assembly renders the scant evidence which has been marshaled in support of this hypothesis even less compelling today. Purified myosin does indeed contain ribonucleic acid which can only be dissoci-

Fig. 14.8 Electron photomicrograph of a portion of an early muscle fiber (myotube) showing "primitive" myofibrils. Compare this to the myofibrils of adult muscle cells (Fig. 14.4). Z, Z bands; MF, thick filaments; F, thin filaments; A, A band; I, I band; cm, cell membrane; x, unknown body; er, smooth endoplasmic reticulum; Pb, lead precipitate from the stain. (From Hay, *Z. Zellforsch. Mikroskop. Anat. Abt. Histochem.* 59:6–34, 1963.)

ated by rather rigorous treatment (Perry and Zydowo, 60; Mihalyi, Laki, and Knoller, 53; Baril, Love, and Herrmann, 2). It has been suggested that this ribonucleic acid, if functional, might account for Velick's (72) observation that the two trypsin dissociable fragments of myosin (heavy and light meromyosin) are synthesized and turn over at different rates since the nucleic

acid is associated with the more rapidly synthesized fragment (Mueller and Perry, 57a). There is no evidence, as yet, that the nucleic acid is more than a strongly adsorbed artifact formed during the isolation of myosin from muscle tissue (see also Baril et al., 2).

The issue of the role of the myofibril in protein synthesis cannot be definitively resolved at present. However, several lines of investigation have demonstrated in developing muscle cells those components of the protein-synthesizing apparatus which are currently regarded as universal in all types of cells.

Both Hay (25) and Bergman (5) have called attention to the abundance of free ribonucleoprotein particles in the cytoplasm of the myoblast. These are found in close association with the myofilaments, and Hay points out that such particles are frequently arranged in rows. The suggestion is made that these are ribosomes associated with the synthesis of the filament proteins. Since the first demonstration of the existence of the multiple ribosomal structure, the polysome, and its role in protein synthesis (Warner, Rich, and Hall, 74; Warner, Knopf and Rich, 75; Slayter, Warner, Rich, and Hall, 67; Wettstein, Staehlin, and Noll, 76), several investigators have reported the presence of structures suggestive of polysomes in developing muscle. Waddington and Perry (73) reported helically arranged ribosomes in tail somite cells of *R. pipiens* embryos. They felt, however, that they appeared to involve "too many ribosomes to correspond to the polyribosomes thought to be the functional units in the synthesis of hemoglobin." More recently, Heuson-Stiennon (29) has described similar helically arranged ribosomes apparently held together by a filament of about 15 A in diameter. These chains contain generally from seven to ten ribosomes and may be associated in some cases with endoplasmic reticulum, with myofilaments, or apparently may be free in the cytoplasm (Fig. 14.9).

These multiple ribosomal structures, observed with the electron microscope, can be identified only by analogy to studies in which the ribosomal monomers have been at least demonstrated to be both held together by RNA and to be active in amino acid incorporation (Warner, Knopf, and Rich, 75). Although similar studies have not as yet been reported for embryonic muscle, Breuer, Davies, and Florini (8) have examined such correlations in cell-free preparations of adult rat skeletal muscle. Their isolated ribosome fractions contain a spectrum of multiple ribosome structures in which the most rapidly sedimenting fractions have the highest specific activity after labeling in an in vitro protein-synthesizing system. Using appropriate enzymatic treatments, they show also that the integrity of the polysomal structure is maintained by RNA and not by DNA, protein, or lipid, and they examine treated preparations by both sucrose density and electronmicrographic techniques. Their most striking finding is the extremely long chain lengths of some of these polysomes (60–100 monomers per chain). Based on alternative assumptions of the structure (that is, extended or coiled) of the associated messenger-RNA, they speculate that a protein of the size of the myosin subunit could be accommodated by an m-RNA molecule large enough to form a polysome containing 60–70 monomers.

Admittedly these calculations, while

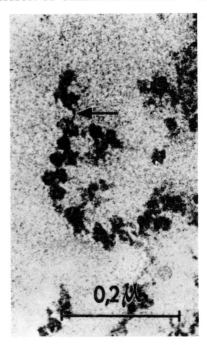

Fig. 14.9 Multiple ribosome structure (polysome) in the cytoplasm of a myoblast of a rat embryo (16–17 days). A thin strand (15-20 A in diameter uniting the ribosomes is clearly visible, arrow). (From Heuson-Stiennon, *J. Microscop.* 3:229–232, 1964.)

suggestive, fall short of constituting evidence that such polysomes are actually those involved in myosin synthesis. In developing muscle cells, similar large polysomes can be observed both in ultrathin sections and in negatively stained extracts, but only after the thick (myosin) filaments can be observed (Allen and Pepe, 1). During the brief period preceding this stage when thin filaments alone can be detected, only free ribosomes or small polysomes (3–8 monomers) are observed.

Molecular Cytology

Current research into the cytodifferentiation of muscle is thus bringing us closer to the chain of molecular events which occur in the construction of a cell with contractile properties. The information, to be sure, is still largely at a descriptive level rather than mechanistic. However, by describing developmental events in molecular terms, a firmer foundation has been laid for an inquiry into the mechanisms which specify and regulate the acquisition of that spectrum of molecules characterizing the skeletal muscle cell. No satisfactory explanation of differentiation can stop at this level. This spectrum of molecules is ordered into the supramolecular complexes and organelles which comprise the cell-type specific cytoarchitecture of the cell and define its physiology.

The anatomy of this progression from molecule to organelle and the relationship of the cytological structure to physiological function is better understood in the muscle cell than in any other type of cell (see Huxley and Hanson, 36). The structure of the contractile unit, the myofibril, has been more thoroughly dissected than any other subcellular structure.

A single sarcomere, which is the unit of length between successive Z lines, is constructed of an ordered series of thin filaments attached to each lattice-like Z band. The distal portions of both groups of thin filaments interdigitate with a single array of thick filaments in the middle of the sarcomere (Fig. 14.1). Huxley and Hanson have proposed that contraction is effected by the thin filaments sliding along the thick filaments, thereby drawing the Z bands closer together (36). It has also been established that actin is restricted to the I-band region, which contains the thin filaments, and myosin to the A band containing the thick filaments (Huxley

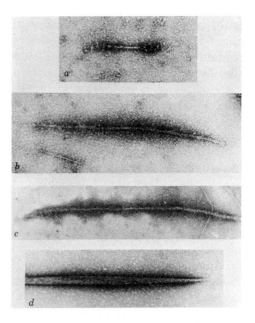

Fig. 14.10 Synthetic myosin filaments formed by lowering the ionic strength of solutions of pure myosin. *a.* about 0.6 μ in length. *b.* 1.5 μ in length. Note that projections are absent from the central region. *c.* A thick filament mechanically separated from the myofibrils of muscle. This "natural" filament is also devoid of projections in the central region. *d.* Filament formed from L-meromyosin. The projections, which are attributed to the H-meromyosin component of myosin, are absent. (From Huxley, p. 263 in *The General Physiology of Cell Specialization* D. Mazia and A. Tyler, eds. McGraw-Hill, 1963.)

and Hanson, 37; Holtzer, et al., 34).

More recently, the anatomy of these two types of filaments has been examined further by mechanically disrupting isolated myofibrils and comparing, by negative staining, the natural filaments with synthetic filaments prepared from pure protein solutions (Huxley, 35). The naturally occurring thick filament and the synthetic filaments which are formed (by aggregation) when the ionic strength of solutions of pure myosin is lowered are so similar (Fig. 14.10) that one is compelled to conclude that the structure of the filament is a reflection of the properties of the myosin molecule itself. Both the natural and synthetic myosin filaments bear numerous regularly spaced short lateral projections, except in the central (H zone) region of the filament. The development of the myosin myofilaments in solution can be deduced by comparing progressively larger aggregates. The smallest aggregates consist of two to eight myosin molecules in which aggregation has occurred "tail to tail." The individual myosin molecule consists of a globular head (the H-meromyosin end) and an extended tail region (Zobel and Carlson, 80; Huxley, 35). It is apparently this initial "tail to tail" aggregation which establishes the central region free of lateral projections (namely, globular heads). As the aggregate grows in both directions from this central region, molecules are added with the tail region overlapping the tail of the preceding molecule having its globular head projecting laterally from the axis of the filament. It is these laterally projecting globular heads which form the reversible cross-linkage between thick and thin filaments. Cross-linkage can, in fact, be demonstrated to occur in solution between I filaments and myosin or H-meromyosin.

From studies of the reversible denaturation of protein, it has been inferred that the secondary and tertiary structure may be determined by the primary amino acid sequence (Epstein, Goldberger, and Anfinsen, 18). Huxley's (35) analysis takes us a step beyond to the level of cytological structure and demonstrates the remarkable degree to which such structures can be reconstructed from their protein components. One cannot ignore the strong implication that such higher-order structure is also ultimately referable to the primary sequence of amino acids in the constituent proteins.

The wondrously complex myofibril may be a spontaneously formed structure whose ordering is a function of the properties of the myofilaments, which in turn reflect the properties of the molecules of which they are the aggregates or copolymers.

References

1. Allen, E. R., and F. A. Pepe, "Ultrastructure of Developing Muscle Cells in the Chick Embryo," *Am. J. Anat.* 116: 115–148 (1965).
2. Baril, E. F., D. S. Love, and H. Herrmann, "Chromatography of Ribonuclease-treated Myosin Extracts from Early Embryonic Chick Muscle," *Science* 146:413–414 (1964).
3. Bassleer, R., "Etude de l'Augmentation du Nombre de Noyaux dans des Bourgeons Musculaires Cultivés *in vitro*. Observations sur le Vivant, Dosages Cytophotométriques et Histoautoradiographies," *Z. Entwicklungsgeschichte* 123:184–205 (1962).
4. ———, P. Collignon, and Fr. Matagne-Dhoossche, "Effets Cytologiques du Myleran sur le Muscle Strié de l'Embryon de Poulet *in ovo* et de la Queue d'Axolotl en Régénération. *Arch. Biol.* 74:79–94 (1963).
5. Bergman, R. A., "Observations on the Morphogenesis of Rat Skeletal Muscle," *Bull. Johns Hopkins Hosp.* 110:187–201 (1962).
6. Bintliff, S., and B. E. Walker, "Radioautographic Study of Skeletal Muscle Regeneration," *Am. J. Anat.* 106:233–245 (1960).
7. Boyd, J. D., "Development of Striated Muscle," *Structure and Function of Mus-*

cle, G. H. Bourne, ed. New York: Academic Press, vol. I, pp. 63–85 (1960).

8. Breuer, C. B., M. C. Davies, and J. R. Florini, "Amino Acid Incorporation into Protein by Cell-Free Preparations from Rat Skeletal Muscle. II. Preparation and Properties of Muscle Ribosomes and Polysomes," *Biochemistry* 3:1713–1719 (1964).

9. Capers, C. R., "Multinucleation of Skeletal Muscle *in vitro*," *J. Biophys. Biochem. Cytol.* 7:559–566 (1960).

10. Cooper, W. G., and I. R. Konigsberg, "Dynamics of Myogenesis *in vitro*," *Anat. Record* 140:195–206 (1961).

11. Csapo, A., and H. Herrmann, "Quantitative Changes in Contractile Proteins of Chick Skeletal Muscle during and after Embryonic Development," *Am. J. Physiol.* 165:701–710 (1951).

12. de Villafranca, G., "Adenosinetriphosphatase Activity in Developing Rat Muscle," *J. Exptl. Zool.* 127:367–388 (1954).

13. Detwiler, S. R., "Experiments on the Origin of the Ventrolateral Trunk Musculature in the Urodele (*Amblystoma*)," *J. Exptl. Zool.* 129:45–76 (1955).

14. Deuchar, E. M., "Adenosine Triphosphatase Activity in Early Somite Tissue of the Chick Embryo," *J. Embryol. Exptl. Morphol.* 8:251–258 (1960).

15. Emmart, E. W., D. R. Kominz, and J. Miquel, "The Localization and Distribution of Glyceraldehyde-3-phosphate Dehydrogenase in Myoblasts and Developing Muscle Fibers Growing in Culture," *Histochem. Cytochem.* 11:207–217 (1963).

16. Enesco, M., and D. Puddy, "Increase in the Number of Nuclei and Weight in Skeletal Muscle of Rats of Various Ages," *Am. J. Anat.* 114:235–244 (1964).

17. Engel, W. K., and B. Horvath, "Myofibril Formation in Cultured Skeletal Muscle Cells Studied with Antimyosin Fluorescent Antibody," *J. Exptl. Zool.* 144:209–223 (1960).

18. Epstein, C. J., R. F. Goldberger, and C. B. Anfinsen, "The Genetic Control of Tertiary Protein Structure: Studies with Model Systems. *Cold Spring Harbor Symp. Quant. Biol.* 28:439–449 (1963).

19. Firket, H., "Recherches sur la Synthèse des Acides Désoxyribonucléiques et la Préparation à la Mitose dans des Cellules Cultivées *in vitro* (Etude Cytophotométrique et Autoradiographique)," *Arch. Biol.* 69:1–166 (1958).

20. Galton, M., "DNA Content of Placental Nuclei," *J. Cell Biol.* 13:183–191 (1962).

21. Goffart-Louis, P., "Étude Électrophorétique de la Composition Protéinique des Muscles de Foetus de Bovidé. Isolement et Proprietes de Certains Constituants," *Arch. Intern. Physiol. Biochem.* 67:427–460 (1959).

22. Hamburger, V., "Experimentelle Beitrage zur Entwicklungsphysiologie der Nervenbahmen in der Froshextremität," *Arch. Entwicklungsmech. Or.* 119:47–99 (1929).

23. Harrison, R. G., "An Experimental Study of the Relation of the Nervous System to the Developing Musculature in the Embryo of the Frog," *Am. J. Anat.* 3:197–220 (1904).

24. Hay, E. D., "Cytological Studies of Dedifferentiation and Differentiation in Regenerating Amphibian Limbs," *Regeneration*, D. Rudnick, ed. New York: Ronald (1962).

25. ――――, "The Fine Structure of Differentiating Muscle in the Salamander Tail," *Z. Zellforsch. Mikroskop. Anat. Abt. Histochem.* 59:6–34 (1963).

26. Herrmann, H., J. S. Nicholas, and M. E. Vosgian, "Liberation of Inorganic Phosphate from Adenosine Triphosphate by Fractions Derived from Developing Rat Muscle," *Proc. Soc. Exptl. Med.* 72:454–457 (1949).

27. ――――, L. Lerman, and B. N. White, "Uptake of Glycine-1-^{14}C into the Actomyosin and Collagen Fractions of Developing Chick Muscle," *Biochim. Biophys. Acta* 27:161–164 (1958).

28. ――――, "Quantitative Studies of Protein Synthesis in Some Embryonic Tissues," *Cytodifferentiation and Macromolecular Synthesis* M. Locke, ed. New York: Academic Press, pp. 85–118 (1963).

29. Heuson-Stiennon, J.-A., "Intervention de Polysomes dans la Synthèse des Myofilaments du Muscle Embryonnaire du Rat," *J. Microscop.* 3:229–232 (1964).

30. Holtzer, H., "Aspects of Chondrogenesis and Myogenesis," *Synthesis of Molecular and Cellular Structure* D. Rudnick, ed. New York: Ronald (1961).

31. ――――, and S. R. Detwiler, "Induction

of Skeletogenous Cells," *J. Exptl. Zool.* 123:335–370 (1953).

32. ——, and S. R. Detwiler, "The Dependence of Somitic Differentiation on the Neural Axis," *Anat. Record* 118:390 (1954).

33. ——, J. Lash, and S. Holtzer, "The Enhancement of Somitic Muscle Maturation by the Embryonic Spinal Cord," *Biol. Bull.* 111:303–304 (1956).

34. ——, J. M. Marshall, and H. Finck, "An Analysis of Myogenesis by the Use of Fluorescent Antimyosin," *J. Biophys. Biochem. Cytol.* 3:705–724 (1957).

35. Huxley, H. E., "Electron Microscope Studies of the Structure of Natural and Synthetic Protein Filaments from Striated Muscle," *J. Mol. Biol.* 7:281–308 (1963).

36. ——, and J. Hanson, "The Molecular Basis of Contraction in Cross-striated Muscles," *Structure and Function of Muscle* G. H. Bourne, ed. New York: Academic Press, vol. I, pp. 183–227 (1960).

37. ——, and ——, "Quantitative Studies on the Structure of Cross-striated Myofibrils. I. Investigations by Interference Microscopy," *Biochim. Biophys. Acta* 23:229–249 (1957).

38. Kennell, D., "Persistence of Messenger RNA Activity in *Bacillus megaterium* with Actinomycin," *J. Mol. Biol.* 9:789–800 (1964).

39. Kitiyakara, A., "The Development of Non-myotomic Muscles of the Chick Embryo," *Anat. Record* 133:35–45 (1959).

40. ——, and D. M. Angevine, "A Study of the Pattern of Postembryonic Growth of *M. Gracilis* in Mice," *Develop. Biol.* 8:322–340 (1963).

41. Konigsberg, I. R., "Some Aspects of Myogenesis *in vitro*," *Circulation* 24:447–457 (1961).

42. ——, "Clonal Analysis of Myogenesis," *Science* 140:1273–1284 (1963).

43. ——, *Ann. Rept. Dir. Dept. Embryol., Carnegie Inst.* Wash., Year Book 63:517 (1964).

44. ——, N. McElvain, M. Tootle, and H. Herrmann, "The Dissociability of Deoxyribonucleic Acid Synthesis from the Development of Multinuclearity of Muscle Cells in Culture," *J. Biophys. Biochem. Cytol.* 8:333–343 (1960).

45. Lash, J. W., H. Holtzer, and H. Swift, "Regeneration of Mature Skeletal Muscle," *Anat. Record* 128:679–693 (1957).

46. Lewis, W. H., and M. Lewis, "Behavior of Cross-striated Muscle in Tissue Culture," *Am. J. Anat.* 22:169–194 (1917).

47. Liedke, K. B., "Experiments on the Development of the Trunk Muscles in Anura (*Rana pipiens*)," *Anat. Record* 131:97–117 (1958).

48. Love, D. S., "Preparation and Purification of Embryonic Chick Myosin," *Federation Proc.* 19:256 (1960).

49. ——, "Isolation and Characterization of L-myosin from Chick Embryo Muscle." Thesis, University of Colorado (1961).

50. MacConnachie, H. F., M. Enesco, and C. P. Leblond, "The Mode of Increase in the Number of Skeletal Muscle Nuclei in the Postnatal Rat," *Am. J. Anat.* 114:245–253 (1964).

51. Maruyama, K., "Interaction between ATP and Actomyosins from Honeybee Muscles during Pupal Development," *Z. Vergleich. Physiol.* 40:451–453 (1957).

52. Mauro, A., "Satellite Cell of Skeletal Muscle Fibers," *J. Biophys. Biochem. Cytol.* 9:493–495 (1961).

53. Mihalyi, E., K. Laki, and M. I. Knoller, "Nucleic Acid and Nucleotide Content of Myosin Preparations," *Arch. Biochem. Biophys.* 68:130–143 (1957).

54. Montgomery, R. D., "Growth of Human Striated Muscle," *Nature* 195:194–195 (1962).

55. Muchmore, W. B., "Differentiation of the Trunk Mesoderm in *Amblystoma maculatum*," *J. Exptl. Zool.* 118:137–186 (1951).

56. ——, "Differentiation of the Trunk Mesoderm in *Amblystoma maculatum*. II. Relation of the Size of Presumptive Somite Explants to Subsequent Differentiation," *J. Exptl. Zool.* 134:293–314 (1957).

57. ——, "The Influence of Embryonic Neural Tissues on Differentiation of Striated Muscle in *Ambystoma*," *J. Exptl. Zool.* 139:181–188 (1958).

57a. Mueller, H., and S. V. Perry, "The Chromatography of the Meromyosins on Diethylaminoethylcellulose." *Biochem. J.* 80:217–223 (1961).

58. Nass, M. M. K., "Developmental

Changes in Frog Actomyosin Characteristics," *Develop. Biol.* 4:289–320 (1962).

59. Ogawa, Y., "Synthesis of Skeletal Muscle Proteins in Early Embryos and Regenerating Tissue of Chick and *Triturus*," *Exptl. Cell Res.* 26:269–274 (1962).

60. Perry, S. V., and M. Zydowo, "Ribonucleoprotein of Skeletal Muscle and Its Relation to the Myofibril," *Biochem. J.* 72:682–690 (1959).

61. Reporter, M. C., I. R. Konigsberg, and B. L. Strehler, "Kinetics of Accumulation of Creatine Phosphokinase Activity in Developing Embryonic Skeletal Muscle *in vivo* and in Monolayer Culture," *Exptl. Cell Res.* 30:410–417 (1963).

62. Revel, M., H. H. Hiatt, and J.-P. Revel, "Actinomycin D: an Effect on Rat Liver Homogenates Unrelated to Its Action on RNA Synthesis," *Science* 146:1311–1313 (1964).

63. Rinaldini, L. M., "An Improved Method for the Isolation and Quantitative Cultivation of Embryonic Cells," *Exptl. Cell Res.* 16:477–505 (1959).

64. Robinson, D. S., "A Study of the Adenosine Triphosphatase Activity of Developing Chick Muscle," *Biochem. J.* 52:633–637 (1952).

65. Scott, R. B., and E. Bell, "Protein Synthesis During Development: Control through Messenger RNA," *Science* 145:711–713 (1964).

66. Shafiq, S. A., "Electron Microscopic Studies on the Indirect Flight Muscles of *Drosophila melanogaster*. II. Differentiating Myofibrils," *J. Cell Biol.* 17:363–373 (1963).

67. Slayter, H. S., J. R. Warner, A. Rich, and C. E. Hall, "The Visualization of Polyribosomal Structure," *J. Mol. Biol.* 7:652–657 (1963).

68. Stockdale, F. E., and H. Holtzer, "DNA Synthesis and Myogenesis," *Exptl. Cell Res.* 24:508–520 (1961).

69. Straus, W. L., Jr., and M. E. Rawles, "An Experimental Study of the Origin of the Trunk Musculature and Ribs in the Chick," *Am. J. Anat.* 92:471–510 (1953).

70. Strehler, B. L., I. R. Konigsberg, and J. E. T. Kelley, "Ploidy of Myotube Nuclei Developing *in vitro* as Determined with a Recording Double Beam Microspectrophotometer," *Exptl. Cell Res.* 32:232–241 (1963).

71. Strohman, R. C., E. W. Cerwinsky, and D. W. Holmes, "Protein Synthesis in Developing Muscle: Incorporation of C^{14}-leucine into Protein by Muscle Minces," *Exptl. Cell Res.* 35:617–628 (1964).

72. Velick, S., "The Metabolism of Myosin, the Meromyosins, Actin, and Tropomyosin in the Rabbit," *Biochim. Biophys. Acta* 20:228–236 (1956).

73. Waddington, C. H., and M. M. Perry, "Helical Arrangement of Ribosomes in Differentiating Muscle Cells," *Exptl. Cell Res.* 30:599–600 (1963).

74. Warner, J. R., A. Rich, and C. E. Hall, "Electron Microscope Studies of Ribosomal Clusters Synthesizing Hemoglobin," *Science* 138:1399–1403 (1962).

75. ———, P. M. Knopf, and A. Rich, "A Multiple Ribosomal Structure in Protein Synthesis," *Proc. Natl. Acad. Sci. U. S.* 49:122–129 (1963).

76. Wettstein, F. O., T. Staehlin, and H. Noll, "Ribosomal Aggregate Engaged in Protein Synthesis: Characteristics of the Ergosome," *Nature* 197:430–435 (1963).

77. Winnick, R. E., and T. Winnick, "Protein Synthesis in Skeletal Muscle, with Emphasis on Myofibrils," *J. Biol. Chem.* 235:2657–2661 (1960).

78. Yaffee, D., and M. Feldman, "The Effect of Actinomycin D on Heart and Thigh Muscle Cells Grown *in vitro*," *Develop. Biol.* 9:347–366 (1964).

79. Zhinkin, L. N., and L. F. Andreeva, "DNA Synthesis and Nuclear Reproduction during Embryonic Development and Regeneration of Muscle Tissue," *J. Embryol. Exptl. Morphol.* 11:353–367 (1963).

80. Zobel, C. R., and F. D. Carlson, "An Electron Microscopic Investigation of Myosin and Some of Its Aggregates," *J. Mol. Biol.* 7:78–89 (1963).

SECTION IV **The Skin**

15

The Skin

Eugene Bell

Department of Biology
Massachusetts Institute of Technology
Cambridge, Massachusetts

This discussion will be concerned primarily with some problems of development which have been probed through the use of skin tissues. Previous reviews on development of skin have appeared (Rawles, 62, 63). The present paper will not consider development, breakdown, or regeneration of basement membranes or lamellae. These subjects have been discussed by Edds (32) and Gross (43). Nor will this review allude to the role of epidermis in limb development or regeneration, topics which have been surveyed by Zwilling (90), Singer and Salpeter (81), Rose (68), and Goss (42). Attention will be directed mainly to avian skin and to developing feathers; some recent unpublished work of the author and his colleagues will be included.

Induction

That tissue interactions are in part responsible for the progress of embryonic differentiation is now considered axiomatic. Skin follows the rule, and in particular, epidermis exhibits well-documented dependencies on mesenchyme for its specific path of maturation. In addition, evidence has accumulated that early during development the skin of the domestic chick undergoes a change ascribed to humoral factors which permits it to differentiate, even when cultured in partly (Sengel, 77) or completely defined medium (Bell, 10). Before $5\frac{1}{2}$ days no explanted skins differentiate in vitro, but after 6 days virtually all do. The induction may begin earlier than $5\frac{1}{2}$ days since a fragment of $4\frac{3}{4}$-day skin implanted into the flank of a 3-day host will make feathers before the skin of the host does. If induction began at $5\frac{1}{2}$ days the donor skin would have had to wait $2\frac{1}{2}$ days for the stimulus from the host. But it does not; instead, it differentiates according to its own clock as though sufficient exposure to an embryonic environment of any age provided conditions necessary for feather formation. It is apparent from this experiment that skin is committed very early to its specialized future.

After the humoral "induction," differentiation depends upon dermal-epidermal interactions, (Sengel, 77, 78, 79; Wessells, 86). Recently Rawles (64) examined in detail interactions leading to the formation of scale, feather, beak, and spur.

Tissue layers were dissociated in cold 1 percent trypsin and ingeniously grafted to the chorioallantoic membrane. Dermis of diverse origins acquired inductive capacity at different stages of embryonic development. For example, the capacity of dermis from tarsometatarsus to elicit scale formation in overlying foreign epidermis was first observed at 13 days, while dermis from the spur region of the tarsometatarsus induced a spur scale in nonspur epidermis at 9 days. Dermis from the middorsum was strongly inductive over a long period. Between 5 and $8\frac{1}{2}$ days it was able to induce feathers in epidermis.

In studying epidermal competence, Rawles found that $8\frac{1}{2}$-day back epidermis does not alter its course of differentiation, but makes feathers when presented with 13-day tarsometatarsus dermis. In contrast, 5 to $8\frac{1}{2}$-day dermis from the beak induces a perfect beak in the same back epidermis. Thus, as late as $8\frac{1}{2}$ days, when germs are already well developed, the feather commitment is still reversible and epidermis can be remolded to produce an alternate structure.

Failure of epidermis to respond to dermis in a scaleless mutant (Abbott and Asmundson, 1) has been studied by Sengel and Abbott (80). The combination of mutant dermis with normal epidermis resulted in formation of sensible structures, but mutant epidermis was unable to cooperate with normal dermis in the morphogenesis of either feathers or scales. The results of experiments by Gomot (40, 41) show

that ectoderm of the uropygial gland requires the specific action of underlying mesoderm for its differentiation, and that mesoderm from other sources cannot induce gland formation.

Saunders (69), Cairns and Saunders (23), Saunders and Gasseling (71), have demonstrated that feather tract specificity is determined by the mesoderm. Saunders (70) has shown that when prospective leg mesoderm was applied to epidermis of the future wing, feathers, scales, and claws characteristic of the leg were induced in the wing tissue.

Further evidence that mesoderm plays the key role in directing skin differentiation comes from experiments by McLoughlin (52) in which mesenchyme from gizzard, proventriculus, heart, and limb were combined with limb bud epidermis in vitro. Each kind of mesoderm exerted a characteristic effect on the limb bud epidermis with which it was associated.

Epidermis alone from 5-day chick embryo can keratinize in vitro, but fails to grow, becomes partly necrotic, and loses its skinlike organization (McLoughlin, 53). Epidermis from 12-day skin was unable to survive on plasma clot as an organized tissue (Dodson, 31). Frozen, killed dermis or a collagen gel were found to be suitable substitutes for native dermis. The ability of 11-day chick shank epidermal cells to incorporate tritiated thymidine and to maintain their morphology depends upon contact with dermis (Wessells, 87) or other suitable substrates, plus an "active fraction" from embryo juice (Wessells, 89).

Accumulated evidence leads to the conclusion that through some mode of interaction the early differentiation of epidermis is decided by the subjacent dermis. By what route the dermis acts, whether directly by transmission of a gene activator which itself communicates with epidermal cell chromosomes, or circuitously through the machinery of the epidermal cell, remains to be shown. This is a question which is asked about many inductive interactions. The skin is an excellent tissue in which to study the question because epidermis is able to respond uniquely to each of a number of different derma. Production of beak, feather, scale, or mucous can be directed by use of the appropriate dermis. The principal limitation on biochemical manipulation is the labor involved in collection of material.

Ontogeny of Proteins

Eventually it may be possible to describe nearly completely the course of differentiation of a cell or tissue by determining the sequence of appearance of the proteins which distinguish it from other cells or tissues. Methods for doing this have not yet been perfected. The immunological method of looking at proteins has limited resolving power; nonetheless, it can give information about at least some new proteins. Ben-Or and Bell (16) have studied the appearance of new proteins in skin and feathers of the developing chick in relation to other embryonic events. They found that three new antigens were detectable (by double diffusion in agar) in 6-day skins or immediately after the humoral induction, when all skins can differentiate autonomously on completely defined medium (Bell, 11). It has not been determined yet whether the newly acquired capacity to differentiate in vitro depends upon the new proteins which appear at 6 days. Two of the antigens were stage specific, meaning that they were found

in other tissues as well as in the skin, and one was skin specific. At 11 to 12 days, two additional stage-specific antigens were found. At 13 days a second skin-specific antigen was detected. None of the antigens was identified.

Proteins of epidermis and its derivatives are still only poorly characterized (Mercer, 56; Lundgren and Ward, 48; and Matoltsy, 51). The feather has a distinct β-keratin diffraction pattern, as distinguished from hair or mammalian skin, which have α patterns. It is not known how many proteins are responsible for the patterns, or how many proteins make up what is generically called keratin.

In the feather, the adult pattern for β-keratin is first detected at about 14 days of incubation (Bell and Thathachari, 15). Components of the adult pattern, among them the 35 A equatorial reflection, are seen as early as 10 to 11 days. A new reflection appears at 12 days and the final 24 A meridional reflection between 13 and 14 days. It is possible that lipid acts to stabilize the developing macromolecular protein complex until fibers are cross-linked through S—S bonds which can first be demonstrated histochemically at 14 days (Bell and Thatachari, 15). There are good reasons for suggesting that extensive cross-linking of existing protein through S—S bond formation occurs when feather cells begin to synthesize a new protein late on the 13th day.

The feather at 13 days still has a low sulfur content. It contains about 2.5 percent cystine, in contrast with the completed down feather which has about 7 percent cystine. Nonetheless a fibrillar protein can be extracted from the 13-day feather by mild procedures (Malt, Bell, and Meyer, 49; Bell, Malt, and Stewart, 12).

Synthesis of a new protein on the

13th day can be correlated with the beginning of an increase in sulfur content of the feather. A feather-specific protein was detected immunologically on the 13th day (Ben-Or and Bell, 16). Also late on the 13th day, a population of polysomes which had been quiescent for at least 4 days is activated and makes new protein (Humphreys, Penman, and Bell, 44). It is not known yet how many proteins are made on the polysomes activated on the 13th day.

It is plausible to suggest that deposition of structural feather proteins occurs in at least two steps. Feather cells accumulate a low-sulfur fibrillar protein during the period of maximum growth and morphogenesis. After the latter is essentially completed and growth tapers off, a sulfur-rich protein begins to be added. It cross-links with pre-existing fibrillar protein with which it keratinizes to form the hard feather.

Further evidence to support this interpretation comes from tracer studies in which it has been shown that incorporation of radioactive cystine into protein begins to increase sharply at about 14 days (Fig. 15.7). Before that time there is little change in the amino acid composition of the epidermis or the feather (Bell, 10).

In studies on the hair it has been proposed that sulfur-containing amino acids are added to preformed protein in the final phase of keratinization (Mercer, 55), but this idea has been shown to be less likely than *de novo* synthesis of a cystine-containing protein (DeBersaques and Rothman, 30).

Growth of Skin

Studies of growth of skin or its derivatives have been conducted primarily in adult tissues and these will be given only the briefest consideration here. Hair growth has been studied by Chase and his colleagues (24, 25, 26) and also by Argyris and co-workers (2–5). An extensive review is presented by Montagna (57). Rates of proliferation in skin are related to renewal requirements in different tissues, (Medawar, 54; Leblond and Walker, 46). Differential rates in various parts of the skin have been reported. For example, follicles in the growth phase of the hair growth cycle have a much higher mitotic rate than cells of the surrounding epidermis. A theory of hormonal control of mitotic activities in the skin and in other organs has been proposed by Bullough (19) who provides evidence from some of his own papers (Bullough and Laurence, 20, 21).

Evidence for the existence of two populations of cells which differ in their behavior during the cell division cycle has been presented by Gelfant (39) who studied cell divisions initiated by plucking hair or wounding mouse skin. One population has a relatively short G_2 period (the period between DNA synthesis and mitosis) of only a few hours; the other remains in the G_2 period for as long as 2 days. Hence, cells of the germinal layers are physiologically non-homogeneous.

Coincident with the first sign of mesenchymal condensations in chick skin, which mark the sites of future feathers, is an abrupt change in mitotic activity. There are no divisions in cells which form the condensation nor are there divisions in the basal cells of the overlying epidermis, where they were previously distributed, as judged in radioautographs of tissue treated with thymidine-H^3 (Wessells, 88). As soon as the initial condensation is completed,

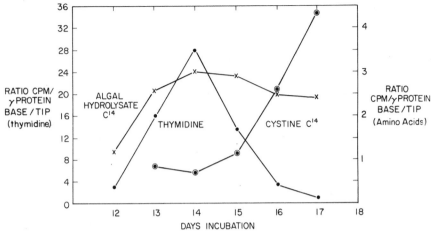

Fig. 15.1 Incorporation in vivo of C¹⁴-labeled amino acids into protein, and thymidine into DNA at various stages of feather development. Twelve-day feathers were cut into two parts after incubation with isotope and older feathers were cut into three parts to give base, middle, and tip. Each point represents a ratio of specific activities of base/tip. The specific activity of the base was in all cases greater than that in the feather tip.

cells of the epidermis overlying it, as well as cells of the condensed mesenchyme itself, begin to divide at a more rapid rate than those in surrounding nonfeather skin tissues.

Elongation of the feather during embryogenesis has been measured by Watterson (83). Maximum growth was found to occur between 13 to 14 days of incubation. It is possible to study growth of the feather from day to day biochemically by comparing ratios of specific activities of feather parts (Bell, 9). Isotopes were injected into the upper yolk sac or into a chorioallantoic vein 2 hours before the embryo was removed and its feathers plucked. After removal, feathers were cut into three parts and cpm/gamma of protein was determined, comparing the base of the feather with the tip, and middle with tip, among feathers 12 to 17 days of age. Three different isotopes were used. The first was algal hydrolysate in which all amino acids are present and labeled.

The second was cystine, and the third thymidine. Results are shown in Fig. 15.1. Incorporation of all amino acids into protein, which probably reflects general protein synthesis, reaches a peak at 14 days and declines slightly thereafter. Similarly, incorporation of thymidine into DNA reaches a peak at 14 days and declines sharply thereafter. It is only at 14 days that incorporation of cystine into protein begins to increase. It reaches a maximum at 17 days. Hence, it is only when cell divisions begin to decline and morphogenesis is essentially done that synthesis of cystine-rich protein is accelerated in the developing feather.

Control of Protein Synthesis

Control of protein synthesis in the differentiating cell at the level of messenger RNA has been discussed by Scott and Bell (75, 76). They suggested that there are at least two ways by which differentiating cells can make large amounts of one or a few characteristic proteins. The first is to make the specific proteins through the continued synthesis of short-lived messenger-RNA. The second is through the repeated use of limited amounts of the long-lived messenger-RNA.

The appearance of stable polysomes during development of chick skin and feathers has been studied by Bell and his associates (Bell, 11; Humphreys et al., 44; Bell et al., 11a). In the feather, stable polysomes (those which persist after treatment of feathers with 60 γ/ml actinomycin-D) on which protein is synthesized can be detected for the first time late on the 13th day. There is present in feather cells between 9 and 13 days a 4-ribosome-polysome peak which is actinomycin and ribonuclease insensitive. No protein synthesis is associated with it. The polysome profiles of untreated skins or feathers remain unchanged between $5\frac{1}{2}$ days to 15 days of incubation. Before 14 days of development, the 4-ribosome-polysome peak strikingly predominated. After 13 days, the 5- and 6-ribosome-polysome peaks increased until by 15 days they were the same height as that of the 4-ribosome-polysome peak (Figs. 15.2 and 15.3). The untreated profile is characteristic of chick skin and feathers and was not observed in other chick tissues studied (Scott and Bell, 75). After 12 hours in actinomycin-D the polysome profile from 9-day skin and 11- and 13-day feathers consisted of only a sharp peak in the 4-ribosome polysome region. This peak persisted until the tissue began to disintegrate at about 18 hours (9-day skin) or beyond 24 hours (11- and 13-day feathers). The persistent peak did not incorporate labeled precursor into protein, even when the

tissue was incubated with isotopes for 20 minutes. The ratio of optical density at 260 mμ to 280 mμ in the persistent peak was 1.9, which is the same as that for the single ribosome peak. The RNA of the persistent peak sedimented in a sucrose gradient exactly like the RNA of single ribosomes. It was concluded that this persistent peak therefore represents a multiple ribosomal aggregate. Thus stable polysomes in developing skin and feathers are quiescent to the 13th day of incubation. They appear to accumulate in the developing feather for use after morphogenesis is completed. Late on the 13th day of development, and thereafter, radioactive amino acids are incorporated into the polysomes, which remain intact after incubation in actinomycin-D for 24 hours or longer. It appears therefore that maturation of the down feather is completed by the rapid deposition of structural protein between 13 and 17 days of incubation. During feather growth and morphogenesis, feather cells are preparing for this final step by producing and storing 4-ribosomal aggregates as nonfunctional polysomes whose messenger-RNA is specifically protected against ribonuclease activity. When morphogenesis is almost completed at 13 days, this store of polysomes appears to be activated to produce the proteins necessary for maturation. These proteins are then made on message which has a long half-life (greater than 30 hours).

Recently, Bell and co-workers (11a) have shown in electronmicrographs that inactive, ribonuclease-insensitive stable polysomes from 12-day feathers are arranged in the form of tight, symmetrical squares, whereas active ones of the same value from 14-day feathers are strung out in chains. At the same

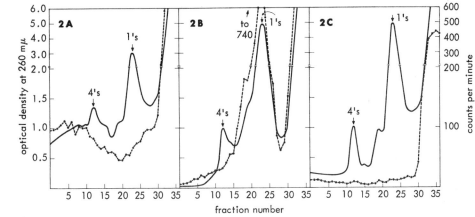

Fig. 15.2

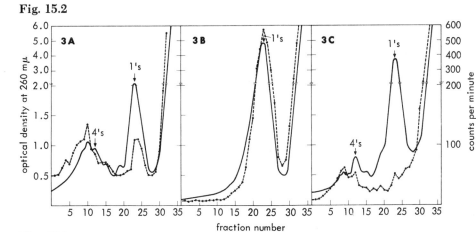

Fig. 15.3

Figs. 15.2 and 15.3 Polysome profiles from zone sedimentation of radioactive amino acid-labeled cytoplasmic extracts centrifuged 24,000 rpm for 3 hours at 8°C on a 15–30 percent sucrose gradient. Solid line is optical density at 260 mμ. Broken line is trichloroacetic acid precipitable counts per minute. **Fig. 15.2.** Extracts from early 13-day feathers. **Fig. 15.3.** Extracts from 15-day feathers. A. Freshly isolated tissue. B. Extract A after treatment with 1 ribonuclease at 4°C for 30 min. C. Tissue treated with actinomycin-D for 24 hours.

time that the 4-ribosome polysomes are activated, there appear two additional stable polysome peaks of 5 and 6 ribosomes respectively. They also are dispersed by ribonuclease and are associated with nascent protein. This may be taken as evidence that a number of proteins are made on stable message.

Consistent with the foregoing account would be a set of controls which would be expected to operate in the regulation of protein synthesis. Sometime early in development, possibly at the time of induction, genes would be activated to produce messenger-RNA for the nonfunctional aggregates. After synthesis the message might become associated with a repressor. In the cytoplasm the repressed or specifically protected message would complex with 4 ribosomes and remain quiescent until late 13 days. At that time the polysomal aggregate would be activated and stabilized to function over the period necessary for completion of specialized protein synthesis.

Effects of Various Substances on Skin Growth and Development

Growth-stimulating and metaplastic substances may prove potent tools in the analysis of gene activation in differentiating tissues; a brief account of their effects on skin is included.

A heat-stable protein has been isolated from the submaxillary gland of the male mouse which, when injected into the newborn mouse or rat, results in precocious opening of eyelids, in increase of epidermal keratinization, and in stimulation of epidermal growth (Cohen, 27; Cohen and Elliott, 29). The protein, which has a molecular weight of approximately 15,000 and an unusual amino acid composition devoid of lysine and phenylalanine, also exerts a stimulatory effect on growth of chick skin in vitro (Cohen, 28).

The metaplastic effect of vitamin A on the skin is now well known (Fell and Mellanby, 53; Pelc and Fell, 60; and Fell, 33). The manner in which vitamin A switches germinal skin cells from a course leading to keratinization, to the production of mucus or cilia, is still obscure. Recently, Lucy (47) has explored the action of vitamin A on the membranous components of various cells.

Evidence has been presented that estrogens and androgens stimulate mitotic activity in skin, while epinephrine nor-epinephrine and glucocorticoids have an inhibitory effect on cell division. It is of interest that while the latter hormones supress mitotic activity in superficial epidermis, they exert virtually no effect on hair follicles which are mitotically active (Bullough, 19). It has been reported recently that application of cortisone to chick embryos *in ovo* resulted in inhibition of both feathers and scale formation (Moscona and Karnofsky, 59).

Keratin; Keratinization and Fine Structure

Problems relating to the synthesis and structure of keratin and to keratinization have been published in two symposia (Butcher and Sognnaes, 22; Montagna, 58). Recent papers by Lundgren and Ward (48), and Rogers and Filshie (66) also review the subject.

Bell (10) has reported the amino acid composition of embryonic skin and feathers of various ages. As late as 13 days of incubation the amino acid composition of the feather is still not characteristic of the 1-day-hatched down feather. The 13-day feather has a cystine content of 2.6 percent while that of the 1-day feather is 7 percent. Also, the cystine content of a fibrillar protein from buffered extracts of whole 13-day feathers is surprisingly low (1.6%, Malt and Bell, 49a), yet it is almost identical to the cystine content of "prekeratin" isolated from cow's nose (Matoltsy, 50a). The composition of representative keratins has been reported by Ward and Lungdren (82), and Lundgren and Ward (48). It is apparent that striking differences exist among the various epidermal derivatives such as wool, hair, horn, quill, feather, and epidermis. Parts of the feather have been analyzed for amino acid composition (Schroeder and Kay, 74) and differences were observed when barbs, calamus, and rachis were compared. It is clear from variations in composition of epidermal structures and from differences observed in extracts from them, that the epidermis and its derivatives are made up of many different proteins. In wool at least two components are present. One is a low-sulfur fibrillar protein (MW = 100,000), the other is an amorphous protein which has a high sulfur content (MW = 20,000) (Rogers, 66). Approximately 24 bands are observed when the supernatant from a homogenate of 13-day feather spun at 50,000 rpm in the Model L ultracentrifuge is fractionated by electrophoresis on acrylamide gel (Reeder, work in progress).

It must be concluded that epidermal structures contain a number of proteins which are loosely referred to as keratins. During development or growth these proteins are cross-linked covalently through disulfide bridges. The process is referred to as keratinization, and is one which probably occurs in a number of steps. A first step may involve the synthesis and organization of fibrillar components into tonofilaments (Fitton-Jackson and Fell, 36). Where these are laid down, a number of investigators have observed RNA particles free in the cytoplasm. Rhodin and Reith (65) have observed this in the newborn rat and the adult mouse. Kischer (45) made similar observations in the developing feather. There is still no agreement on the role of keratohyalin granules which are observed in some tissues but not in others. It has been suggested (Brody, 17, 18) that keratohyalin granules are the immediate precursors of keratin and form by fusion of tonofilaments. Keratohyalin granules have been isolated and shown to contain neither sulfide nor disulfide bonds (Matoltsy, 50). This finding was confirmed by Barrnett and Sognnaes (7),

who concluded that keratohyalin granules have nothing to do with keratinization. It has been proposed elsewhere in this paper that a final step in keratinization may be the synthesis of an amorphous protein which binds fibrillar components into a fixed network.

Studies on the fine structure of wool have suggested, at least tentatively, a 9-protofibril structure surrounding two centrally situated protofibrils (Rogers and Filshie, 64). Bundles of fibrils embedded in a matrix have been observed in the feather (Filshie and Rogers, 35). The microfibrils are of the order of 30 A in diameter and their center-to-center separation is about 35 A. The prominent 34 or 35 A equatorial reflection in the feather is probably due to the microfibrils, whose separation is of the same dimension.

Patterns from x-ray diffraction studies probably reflect the macromolecular organization of a number of proteins. A variety of structures have been proposed for feather keratin (Bear and Rugo, 8; Pauling and Corey, 60; Fraser and MacRae, 37; Astbury and Beighton, 6; and Schor and Krim, 72, 73).

Differentiation of Dissociated and of Cultured Skin Cells

Embryonic skin cells have been used in studies concerned with the relationship of cell differentiation to cell division, and related problems of cell selection in vitro, of loss of the differentiated state in vitro, and of the capacity of cells of different embryonic ages to cohere. Weiss and James (84) found that dissociated chick skin cells were able to reorganize into primitive feather germs. Reorganized skin underwent at least some keratinization. In contrast, skin cells exposed for brief periods to vitamin A failed to organize into feather primordia and did not keratinize. Instead, they underwent mucous metaplasia.

Weiss and Taylor (85) reported that associated skin cells from chick embryos grown on the chorioallantoic membrane were able to make well-structured feathers. This was confirmed by Bell and Schuler (13) and Bell, Schuler, and Merrill (14), who studied the capacity of skin cells cultured for different periods to engage in morphogenesis and to synthesize skin proteins. Rapidly dividing skin cells performed as well as those which underwent no division. The critical factor responsible for the loss of capacity to differentiate appeared to be not the number of divisions which preceded the challenge but the length of time which the cells were kept in vitro.

Experiments have been performed by Garber and Moscona (38) with mixed chick and mouse embryonic skin cells. They report the development of keratinized sheets of chimeric skin, but hair follicles and primordial sebaceous glands consisted of mouse cells only. Feather formation in chimeric aggregates appeared to be completely inhibited.

Summary

In studies on development of skin and its derivatives, questions axial to an understanding of differentiation have been raised. It is not known how cell and tissue interactions, hormones or growth substances, result in gene activation, which might itself generate positive feedback to activate the genome further. Knowledge about the proteins of skin is primitive; only little is known about the sequence of their appearance or their character. New proteins detected immunologically have not yet been described adequately. How proteins are arranged into organelles (tonofibrils, keratohyalin granules) which may play a role in keratinization has been the subject of a number of studies. X-ray diffraction data on skin and its derivatives must be due to the organized arrangements of many, rather than one, protein and hence describe heterogeneous complexes. Although synthesis of some proteins begins when growth and morphogenesis is terminating, it is likely that synthesis of other skin-specific proteins occurs early and continues throughout development. Whereas processes of cell division and cell differentiation sometimes seem antagonistic, at other times they appear to occur simultaneously. Some controls of protein synthesis in the skin operate at the level of the gene while others probably exist at the level of m-RNA. Knowledge of how skin differentiates is still basically limited, but a many-pronged attack on the problem is increasing information.

References

1. Abbott, U. K., and V. S. Asmundson, "Scaleless, an Inherited Ectodermal Defect in the Domestic Fowl," *J. Heredity* 48:63–70 (1957).

2. Argyris, T. S., and B. F. Argyris, "Stimulation of Hair Growth during Skin Regeneration," *Develop. Biol.* 1:269–280 (1959).

3. ———, and ———, "Factors Affecting the Stimulation of Hair Growth during Wound Healing," *Anat. Record* 142:139–145 (1962).

4. ———, and ———, "Differential Response of Skin Epithelium to Growth-promoting Effects of Subcutaneously Transplanted Tumor," *Cancer Res.* 22:73–77 (1962).

5. ——, and M. E. Trimble, "On the Mechanism of Hair Growth Stimulation in Wound Healing," *Develop. Biol.* 9: 230–254 (1964).

6. Astbury, W. T., and E. Beighton, "Structure of Feather Keratin," *Nature* 191:171 (1961).

7. Barrnett, R. J., and R. Sognnaes, "Histochemical Distribution of Protein-found Sulfhydryl and Disulfide Groups in Vertebrate Keratins. *Fundamentals of Keratinization*, E. Butcher and R. Sognnaes, eds. Washington, D.C.: Am. Assoc. Advan. Sci., pp. 27–43 (1962).

8. Bear, R. S., and H. J. Rugo, "The Results of X-ray Diffraction Studies on Keratin Fibers," *Trans. N.Y. Acad. Sci.* 53:637 (1951).

9. Bell, E., Unpublished observations.

10. ——, "The Induction of Differentiation and the Response to the Inducer," *Cancer Res.* 24:28–34 (1964).

11. ——, "Protein Synthesis in Differentiating Chick Skin," *Symp. Metabolic Control Mechanisms in Animal Cells*, W. Rutter, ed., *Natl. Cancer Inst. Monograph* 13, Washington, D.C.: U.S. Government Printing Office, vol. 1 (1964).

11a. Bell, E., T. Humphreys, H. S. Slayter, and C. E. Hall, "Geometry of Inactive and Active Polysomes of the Developing Down Feather," *Science* (In press)

12. ——, R. A. Malt, and G. Stewart, "Note on Feather Keratin," *Biology of Keratinization*, W. Montagna, ed. New York: Academic Press (1964).

13. ——, and M. Schuler, "Studies on the Development of Chick Skin," *Abst. 13th Ann. Meeting Tissue Culture Assoc.* Washington, D.C. page 39 (1962).

14. ——, ——, and C. Merrill, "Feather Formation and Synthesis of Keratin by Primary Skin Cells and by Skin Cells Grown *in vitro*," *The Epidermis*, W. Montagna and W. C. Lobitz, Jr., eds. New York: Academic Press (1964).

15. ——, and Y. T. Thathachari, "Development of Feather Keratin during Embryogenesis of the Chick," *J. Cell Biol.* 16:215–223 (1963).

16. Ben-Or, S., and E. Bell, "Skin Antigens in the Chick Embryo in Relation to Other Developmental Events," *Develop. Biol.* (In press) (1965).

17. Brody, I., "An Ultrastructural Study on the Role of the Keratohyalin Granules in the Keratinization Process," *J. Ultrastruct. Res.* 3:84–104 (1959).

18. ——, "Different Staining Methods for the Electron Microscopic Elucidation of the Tonofibrillar Differentiation in Normal Epidermis," *The Epidermis*, W. Montagna and W. C. Lobitz, Jr., eds. New York: Academic Press (1964).

19. Bullough, W. S., "Control of Mitotic Activity in Adult Mammalian Tissues," *Biol. Rev.* 37:307–342 (1962).

20. ——, and E. B. Laurence, "The Mitotic Activity of the Follicle," *The Biology of Hair Growth*, W. Montagna and R. A. Ellis, eds. New York: Academic Press, pp. 171–187 (1958).

21. ——, and ——, "Control of Mitotic Activity in Mouse Skin: Dermis and Hypodermis," *Exptl. Cell Res.* 21:394–405 (1960).

22. Butcher, E. O., and R. F. Sognnaes, *Fundamentals of Keratinization*. Washington, D.C.: Am. Assoc. Advan. Sci. (1962).

23. Cairns, J. M., and J. W. Saunders, "The Influence of Embryonic Mesoderm on the Regional Specification of Epidermal Derivatives in the Chick," *J. Exptl. Zool.* 127:221–248 (1954).

24. Chase, H. B., "Physical Factors which Influence the Growth of Hair," *The Biology of Hair Growth*, W. Montagna and R. A. Ellis, eds. New York: Academic Press, pp. 435–439 (1958).

25. ——, and G. Eaton, "The Growth of Hair Follicles in Waves," *Ann. N.Y. Acad. Sci.* 83:365–368 (1959).

26. ——, H. Rauch, and V. W. Smith, "Critical Stages of Hair Development and Pigmentation in the Mouse," *Physiol. Zool.* 24:1–8 (1951).

27. Cohen, S., "Isolation of a Mouse Submaxillary Gland Protein Accelerating Incisor Eruption and Eyelid Opening in the Newborn Animal," *J. Biol. Chem.* 237:1555–1562 (1962).

28. ——, "Isolation and Biological Effects of an Epidermal Growth-stimulating Protein," *Symp. Metabolic Control Mechanisms in Animals Cells*, W. Rutter, ed. *Natl. Cancer Inst. Monograph* 13:13–21, Washington, D.C.: U.S. Government Printing Office (1964).

29. ——, and G. A. Elliott, "The Stimulation of Epidermal Keratinization by a Protein Isolated from the Submaxillary

Gland of the Mouse," *J. Invest. Dermatol.* 40:1–5 (1963).

30. DeBersaques, J., and S. Rothman, "Mechanism of Keratin Formation," *Nature* 193:147–148 (1962).

31. Dodson, J. W., "On the Nature of Tissue Interactions in Embryonic Skin," *Exptl. Cell Res.* 31:233–235 (1963).

32. Edds, M. V., "Chemical and Morphological Differentiation of the Basement Lamella," *Synthesis of Molecular and Cellular Structure*, D. Rudnick, ed. New York: Ronald, pp. 111–138 (1961).

33. Fell, H. B., "Changes in Synthesis Induced in Organ Cultures," *Synthesis of Molecular and Cellular Structure*, D. Rudnick, ed. New York: Ronald, pp. 139–160 (1961).

34. ———, and E. Mellanby, "Metaplasia Produced in Cultures of Chick Ectoderm by High Vitamin A," *J. Physiol.* 119:470–488 (1953).

35. Filshie, B. K., and G. E. Rogers, "An Electron-Microscope Study of the Fine Structure of Feather Keratin," *J. Cell Biol.* 13:1–12 (1962).

36. Fitton-Jackson, S., and H. B. Fell, "Epidermal Fine Structure in Embryonic Chicken Skin during Atypical Differentiation Induced by Vitamin A in Culture," *Develop. Biol.* 7:394–419 (1963).

37. Fraser, R. D. B., and T. P. MacRae, "Molecular Organization in Feather Keratin," *J. Mol. Biol.* 1:387 (1959).

38. Garber, B., and A. A. Moscona, "Aggregation *in vivo* of Dissociated Cells. I. Reconstruction of Skin on the Chorioallantoic Membrane from Suspensions of Embryonic Chick and Mouse Skin Cells," *J. Exptl. Zool.* 155:179–202 (1964).

39. Gelfant, S., "A New Theory on the Mechanism of Cell Division," *Cell Growth and Cell Division*, R. J. C. Harris, ed. New York: Academic Press, vol. 2, pp. 229–259 (1963).

40. Gomot, L., "Interaction Ectoderme-Mesoderme dans la Formation des Invaginations Uropygiennes des Oiseaux," *J. Embryol. Exptl. Morphol.* 6:162–170 (1958).

41. ———, "Contribution a l'Etude du Developpement Embryonnaire de la Glande Uropygienne chez le Canard," *Arch. Anat. Microscop. Morphol. Exptl.* 48:63–141 (1959).

42. Goss, R. J., "The Role of Skin in Antler Regeneration," *Advances in Biology of Skin*, W. Montagna, ed. Oxford: Pergamon Press, vol. 5, pp. 194–207 (1964).

43. Gross, J., "Studies on the Biology of Connective Tissues: Remodeling of Collagen in Metamorphosis," *Medicine* 43:291–303 (1964).

44. Humphreys, T., S. Penman, and E. Bell, "The Appearance of Stable Polysomes during the Development of Chick Down Feathers," *Biochem. Biophys. Res. Comm.* 17:618–623 (1964).

45. Kischer, C. W., "Fine Structure of the Developing Down Feather," *J. Ultrastruct. Res.* 8:503–527 (1963).

46. Leblond, C. P., and B. E. Walker, "Renewal of Cell Populations," *Physiol. Rev.* 36:255–276 (1956).

47. Lucy, J. A., "Membrane Permeability and the Control of Cellular Function," *Metabolic Control Mechanisms in Animal Cells*, W. Rutter, ed. *Natl. Cancer Inst. Monograph* 13:93–107. Washington, D.C.: U.S. Government Printing Office, (1964).

48. Lundgren, H. P., and W. H. Ward, "The Keratins," *Ultrastructure of Protein Fibers*, R. Borasky, ed. New York: Academic Press, pp. 39–122 (1963).

49. Malt, R. A., E. Bell, and H. Meyer, "Studies on Proteins Extracted from Embryonic Chick Feathers," *Proc. 7th Meeting Biophys.* p. MA5 (1963).

49a. Malt, R. A., and E. Bell, "Feather Proteins during Embryonic Development," *Nature* 205:1081–1083 (1965).

50. Matoltsy, A. G., "Mechanism of Keratinization," *Fundamentals of Keratinization*, E. Butcher and R. Sognnaes, eds. Washington, D.C.: Am. Assoc. Advan. Sci., pp. 1–25 (1962).

50a. Matoltsy, A. G., "Amino-acid Composition of Prekeratin," *Nature* 204:380–381 (1964).

51. ———, "Soluble Proteins in Different Levels of the Epidermis," *J. Invest. Dermatol.* 42:11–114 (1964).

52. McLoughlin, C. B., "The Importance of Mesenchymal Factors in the Differentiation of Chick Epidermis. II. Modification of Epidermal Differentiation by Contact with Different Types of Mesenchyme," *J. Embryol. and Exptl. Morphol.* 9:385–409 (1961).

53. ———, "The Importance of Mesen-

chymal Factors in the Differentiation of Chick Epidermis. I. The Differentiation in Culture of the Isolated Epidermis of the Embryonic Chick and Its Response to Excess Vitamin A," *J. Embryol. and Exptl. Morphol.* 9:370–384, (1961).

54. Medawar, P. B., "Micro-anatomy of Mammalian Epidermis," *Quart. J. Microscop. Sci.* 94:481–506 (1953).

55. Mercer, E. H., "Electron Microscopy in the Biosynthesis of Fibers," *The Biology of Hair Growth*, W. Montagna and R. A. Ellis, eds. New York: Academic Press, pp. 91–133 (1958).

56. ———, *Keratin and Keratinization.* New York: Pergamon Press (1961).

57. Montagna, W., *The Structure and Function of Skin*, 2d edition. New York: Academic Press, (1962).

58. ———, and W. C. Lobitz, Jr., eds. *The Epidermis*, New York: Academic Press. (1964).

59. Moscona, M. H., and D. A. Karnofsky, "Cortisone Induced Modifications in the Development of the Chick Embryo," *Endocrinology* 66:533–549 (1960).

60. Pauling, L., and R. B. Corey, "The Structure of Feather Rachis Keratin," *Proc. Natl. Acad. Sci. U.S.* 37:261 (1951).

61. Pelc, S. R., and H. B. Fell, "The Effect of Excess Vitamin A on the Uptake of Labelled Compounds by Embryonic Skin in Organ Culture," *Exptl. Cell Res.* 19:99–113 (1960).

62. Rawles, M. E., "Skin and Its Derivatives," *Analysis of Development*, B. Willier, P. Weiss and V. Hamburger, eds. Philadelphia: Saunders, (1954).

63. ———, "The Integumentary System," *Biology and Comparative Physiology of Birds*, A. J. Marshall, ed. New York: Academic Press, vol. 1, pp. 189–240 (1960).

64. ———, "Tissue Interactions in Scale and Feather Development as Studied in Dermal-Epidermal Recombination," *J. Embryol. Exptl. Morphol.* 11:765–789 (1963).

65. Rhodin, J., and E. Reith, "Ultrastructure of Keratin in Oral Mucosa, Skin, Esophagus, Claw and Hair," *Fundamentals of Keratinization*, E. Butcher, and R. Sognnaes, eds. Washington, D.C.: Am. Assoc. Advan. Sci., pp. 61–94 (1962).

66. Rogers, G. E., "Structural and Biochemical Features of the Hair Follicle,"

The Epidermis, W. Montagna and W. C. Lobitz, Jr., eds. New York: Academic Press (1964).

67. ———, and B. K. Filshie, "Some Aspects of the Ultrastructure of β-Keratin, Bacterial Flagella, and Feather Keratin," *Ultrastructure of Protein Fibers*, R. Borasky, ed. New York: Academic Press, pp. 123–138 (1963).

68. Rose, S. M., "Tissue-arc Control of Regeneration in the Amphibian Limb," *Regeneration*, D. Rudnick, ed. New York: Ronald, pp. 153–176 (1962).

69. Saunders, J. W., "The Role of the Mesoderm in Organizing the Regional Specificity of Epidermal Derivatives in the Skin of the Chick," *Anat. Record* 111:450 (1951).

70. ———, "Inductive Specificity in the Origin of Integumentary Derivatives in Fowl," *A Symposium on the Chemical Basis of Development*, W. D. McElroy and B. Glass, eds. Baltimore: Johns Hopkins Press, pp. 239–254 (1958).

71. Saunders, J. E., Jr., and M. T. Gasseling, "The Origin of Pattern and Feather Germ Tract Specificity," *J. Exptl. Zool.* 135(3):503–527 (1957).

72. Schor, R., and S. Krimm, "Studies on the Structure of Feather Keratin. I. X-ray Diffraction Studies and Other Experimental Data," *Biophys. J.* 1:467 (1961).

73. ———, and ———, "Studies on the Structure of Feather Keratin. II. A β-helix Model for the Structure of Feather Keratin," *Biophys. J.* 1:489 (1961).

74. Schroeder, W. A., and L. M. Kay, "The Amino Acid Composition of Certain Morphologically Distinct Parts of White Turkey Feathers; and of Goose Feather Barbs and Goose Down," *J. Am. Chem. Soc.* 77:3901 (1955).

75. Scott, R. B., and E. Bell, "Protein Synthesis during Development: Control through Messenger RNA," *Science* 145:711–714 (1964).

76. ———, and ———, "Messenger RNA Utilization during Chick Lens Development," *Science* (1964).

77. Sengel, P., "Analyse Experimentale de Development *in vitro* des Germes Plumaires de l'Embryon de Poulet," *Experientia* 13:177 (1957).

78. ———, "Recherches Experimentales sur la Differenciation des Germes Pluamires et du Pigment de la Peau de l'Em-

bryon de Poulet en Culture *in vitro*," *Ann. Sci Nat. Zool.* 20:432–514 (1958).

79. ——, "The Determination of the Differentiation of the Skin and the Cutaneous Appendages of the Chick Embryo," *The Epidermis*, W. Montagna and W. C. Lobitz, Jr., eds. New York: Academic Press (1964).

80. ——, and U. K. Abbott, "*In vitro* Studies with the Scaleless Mutant: Interactions during Feather and Scale Differentiation," *J. Heredity* 54:255–262 (1963).

81. Singer, M., and M. M. Salpeter, "The Presence of a Mitosis Inhibitor in the Serum and Liver of Adult Rats," *Canad. J. Biochem. Physiol.*, 36:855–859 (1961).

82. Ward, W., and H. P. Lundgren, "The Formation, Composition and Properties of the Keratins," *Advan. Protein Chem.* 9:243–297 (1954).

83. Watterson, R. L., "The Morphogenesis of Down Feathers with Special Reference to the Developmental History of Melanophores," *Physiol. Zool.* 15:234–259 (1942).

84. Weiss, P., and R. James, "Skin Metaplasis *in vitro* Induced by Brief Exposure to Vitamin A," *Exptl. Cell Res. Suppl.* 3: 381–394 (1955).

85. ——, and A. C. Taylor, "Reconstitution of Complete Organs from Single Cell Suspensions of Chick Embryos in Advanced Stages of Differentiation," *Proc. Natl. Acad. Sci. U.S.* 46:1177–1185 (1960).

86. Wessells, N. K., "Tissue Interactions during Skin Histodifferentiation," *Develop. Biol.* 4:87–107 (1962).

87. ——, "Effects of Extra-epithelial Factors on the Incorporation of Thymidine by Embryonic Epidermis," *Exptl. Cell Res.* 30:36–55 (1963).

88. ——, "Tissue Interactions and Cytodifferentiation," *J. Exptl. Zool.* 157:139–152 (1964).

89. ——, "Substrate and Nutrient Effects upon Epidermal Basal Cell Orientation and Proliferation," *Proc. Natl. Acad. Sci. U.S.* 52:252–259 (1964).

90. Zwilling, E., "Limb Morphogenesis," *Advances in Morphogenesis*, M. Abercrombie and J. Brachet, eds. New York: Academic Press, pp. 301–330 (1961).

SECTION V **The Viscera**

16

Morphogenesis of the Vertebrate Heart

ROBERT L. DeHAAN

Department of Embryology
Carnegie Institution of Washington
Baltimore, Maryland

In this analysis of the development of the vertebrate heart, I shall attempt to integrate three areas of the literature: the older studies of descriptive developmental anatomy, performed largely on human and other mammalian embryos; more recent works in which techniques of experimental embryology have been used to analyze processes of cardiac morphogenesis, mainly with chick, rat, and amphibian material; and, finally, studies of cardiac histodifferentiation done within the last decade with the electron microscope.

The component processes of cardiogenesis in forms as divergent as the chick, frog, and man are not, of course, identical. They are, however, sufficiently similar that critical comparisons may provide meaningful insights. For purposes of reference in the ensuing discussion, embryonic age or stage of heart development will be related, where possible, to the condition in the human embryo. Embryos will be staged in accordance with the Streeter "Horizons" (Heuser and Corner, 64; Streeter, 135), and the Hamburger-Hamilton series of normal chick stages (Hamburger and Hamilton, 57).

Origins

Early Localization

In certain invertebrates (for example, the tunicates, annelid worms, and mollusks), some degree of specific localization of organ- or tissue-forming capacity exists even in the fertilized egg. Definite organogenetic potencies appear to be distributed to the early cleavage blastomeres in characteristic "mosaic" fashion (Weber, 145). Clement (25), for example, has localized heart-forming capacity in the derivatives of a single cell, "4d," of the early cleavage stage of the marine snail *Ilyanassa*. In vertebrates, however, determination of specific regions to produce specific types of tissue does not occur until after many cell divisions. Nonetheless, long before recognizable cardiac tissue can be observed, masses of apparently undifferentiated mesoderm can be identified as presumptive heart material by their ability to differentiate into heart muscle when explanted from the embryo.

In all vertebrate embryos studied, the first localization of cells with heart-forming capacity occurs at about the time of onset of gastrulation. In amphibian embryos, the position of the prospective heart material has been identified by tracing the fate of vitally stained regions (Vogt, 142), and by extirpation and transplantation procedures. The approximate locations of the heart-forming mesoderm in urodele embryos at successive stages are shown in Figure 16.1. During early gastrulation, presumptive cardiac material turns in through the lateral lips of the blastopore, and is located transiently as a pair of laterally placed regions, one on each side of the blastopore lip. If one of these regions is dissected out and cultured in a simple salt solution, it may differentiate into an S-shaped, rhythmically pulsating tube, which is clearly heartlike (Bacon, 3).

As seen in Figure 16.1, the paired nature of the cardiac primordia is maintained into the late neurula stage, during which time the presumptive heart tissue migrates anteriorly with the edge of the mesodermal mantle to sites which border the mesoderm-free ventral region of the embryo (Fig. 16.1D). At the end of neurulation, the free edges of the mesoderm mantle gradually converge toward the midline (Wilens, 149), thicken, and give rise to a small number of loose mesenchymal cells in contact with the endoderm (Fig. 16.2). The thickened borders of the left and right mesoderm mantles soon fuse in the ventral midline to

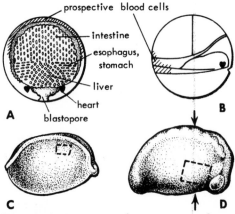

Fig. 16.1 Location of prospective heart material in *Ambystoma*. A. Organ-forming areas mapped on the ventral portion of an opened gastrula, dorsal view. B. Gastrula, left lateral view. C. Neurula, stage 15, right lateral view. D. Tail bud, stage 22, right lateral view. Heart-forming areas are outlined on C and D with broken lines. (Redrawn after W. M. Copenhaver, p. 441 in *Analysis of Development*, B. H. Willier, P. A. Weiss, and W. Hamburger, eds. W. B. Saunders, 1955.)

form a longitudinal trough of prospective myocardium. The loose mesenchymal cells which were liberated accumulate in the myocardial trough as a longitudinal strand, which eventually hollows out to form a thin-walled tube of endocardium.

In the birds and mammals, the early developmental stages and organization of the germ layers are carried out in a disc-shaped rather than a spherical embryo. Nonetheless, the mode of organization of the heart-forming material exhibits basic similarities. Just as in the amphibian, heart-forming capacity in the chick embryo is not well localized or easily identifiable in "blastular" or prestreak stages (Fig. 16.3A). Olivo (97) found that pulsating, but poorly organized, heart muscle would develop in tissue cultures of all peripheral regions from prestreak blastodiscs, though not in similar cultures of the remaining central area. Butler (17) and Spratt (130) also found heart-forming capacity widespread in prestreak blastoderms, and did not report even the degree of restriction observed by Olivo.

The thickening in the posterior half of the embryo which forms the initial primitive streak is brought about by movement of cells of the epiblast toward the posterior midline (Spratt and Haas, 132), (Hamburger-Hamilton stage 2). With these movements, heart-forming capacity is restricted to the posterior half of the embryo, in a region of epiblast of the anterior end of the forming primitive streak, shown in Figure 16.3*B* and 16.3*C* (Spratt, 130; Rudnick, 116). As epiblast cells migrate toward and through the elongating primitive groove to form the layer of mesoderm, primordial heart cells are at one period concentrated about Hensen's node, as in Figure 16.3*D* (Rudnick, 117; Mulherkar, 95). At the median primitive streak stages (H-H stage 3), for example, only a very limited area can form cardiac muscle in vitro or in grafts, with the center of heart-forming capacity being just lateral to, or in the node itself. The presumptive cardiac cells soon move through the primitive groove, join the mesoderm, and begin to move laterally away. By the definitive primitive streak stage (H-H stage 4–4+), these cells are taking up positions in two paired regions lateral to, but still near, Hensen's node (Fig. 16.3*E*). At this stage, Hensen's node is approximately equivalent to the blastopore lip in the amphibian gastrula, and the paired precardiac regions have similar relative positions (compare Fig. 16.1*AB* and Fig. 16.3*E*).

As gastrulatory movements continue,

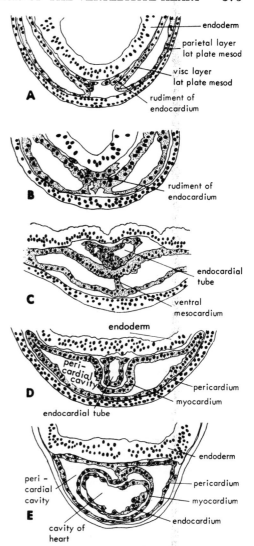

Fig. 16.2 Formation of primitive heart tube in amphibians. Transverse sections at level of arrows in Fig. 16.1*D* at progressively later stages. (After Balinsky, p. 316 in *Introduction to Embryology*, W. B. Saunders, 1960.)

early notochordal cells fan out forward from the node, where they condense into the head-process. The precardiac mesoderm moves rostrolaterally with the leading edges of the lateral plate and becomes localized in two fairly

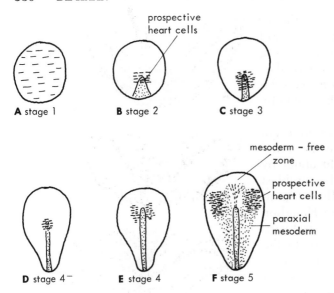

A stage 1   **B** stage 2   **C** stage 3

prospective
heart cells

mesoderm - free
zone

prospective
heart cells

paraxial
mesoderm

D stage 4⁻   **E** stage 4   **F** stage 5

Fig. 16.3 Progressive localization of heart-forming cells (horizontal hatching) in the chick. (Redrawn after Rudnick, *J. Exptl. Zool.* 79:399–425, 1935, and Rawles, *Physiol. Zool.* 16:22–42, 1943.)

well-defined areas, now termed the cardiac primordia. The position and extent of these regions in the head-process stage chick embryo has been mapped with some degree of precision (Fig. 16.3F) by explanting fragments of the blastoderm to the chorioallantoic membrane of 8–9-day host embryos, and determining which fragments can form heart tissue (Rawles, 111). Precise mapping experiments have not yet been performed on mammalian presomite embryos; however, the paired nature of the cardiac primordia in the mammal has long been recognized (Hensen, 62). If fusion of the lateral regions is prevented by experimental intervention, each primordium is capable of developing into an independently beating tubular heart, resulting in a double-hearted or "cardia bifida" embryo (for review, see DeHaan, 30).

Biochemical Differentiation

The capacity of tissue fragments to self-differentiate into cardiac tissue suggests that the component cells already differ in some way at a submicroscopic level from their neighbors, and that this difference of chemistry or molecular structure is associated with the fact that these cells produce heart muscle rather than blood, bone, or some other mesodermal derivative. Just such differences in biochemical properties have been reported. It has been shown, for example, that immunologically reactive groups of cardiac myosin are restricted to two bilateral regions of the embryo at the head-process stage which match Rawles' heart-forming areas (Ebert, 44; Ebert et al., 45). Moreover, preheart cells in the head-process embryo have nutritional requirements different from the rest of the embryo (Spratt, 131), and appear to be characterized by a largely glycolytic metabolism. There are several lines of evidence supporting this latter idea. Heart muscle in the early embryo is highly resistant to anoxia (Burrows, 16). It is also low in succinoxidase (Sippel, 125) and cytochrome oxidase (Leslie and Yarnell, 78) activity. Moreover, Spratt (131) reported that oxidative inhibitors such as cyanide, iodoacetate, or low oxygen tension, used at levels sufficient to block differentiation of nervous tissue, had little effect on the formation or function of the heart in explanted chick embryos. In contrast, cardiogenesis was specifically inhibited by fluoride, an inhibitor of glycolysis. However, both fluoride and antimycin A, an oxidative inhibitor which blocks electron transport in the cytochrome chain, produced well-defined areas of cell necrosis which were limited to the paired heart primordia (Duffey and Ebert, 42), when applied to the ventral surface of head-process stage embryos in culture (McKenzie and Ebert, 89). Reporter and Ebert (112) have recently shown that the antimycin A effect may be blocked by a mitochondrial extract.

Cells of the lateral heart-forming regions also become rich in glycogen early in their differentiation. Chiquoine (23) was able to localize an area of splanchnic mesoderm on each side of the primitive streak in the mouse embryo of 8 days' gestation, which was composed of cells containing numerous granules staining darkly with periodic-acid Schiff reagent. This reaction was abolished after incubation of the sections in diastase. Surrounding mesenchyme was devoid of such granules. Further, heart tissue remains rich in glycogen throughout its embryonic development (Allen, 2; Chiquoine, 23; and McCallion and Wong, 88).

Inductive Relations

There is evidence that in amphibians the heart-forming regions are determined in their cardiogenic potency by interactions with neighboring tissues (Chuang and Tseng, 24; Jacobson, 70; Mangold, 86). As noted earlier, the cells that in the normal course of de-

velopment will become heart are located as paired regions of the inner marginal zone of the urodele blastula (Fig. 16.1). They are part of the lateral leading edge of the mesoderm mantle that begins to migrate anteriorly as the surface mesoderm invaginates around the lateral lips of the blastopore. The prospective heart mesoderm thus comes into contact with presumptive foregut endoderm at the earliest gastrula stage and the two tissues move together to the anterior position attained in the neurula. During this period, the heart mesoderm is subjected to a continual positive inductive influence from the endoderm. During the same period the anterior neural plate material exerts a repressive effect on heart formation. The evidence for this is quite clear. Balinsky (7) and Nieuwkoop (96) demonstrated that extirpation of the entire endoderm from neurulae results in absence of a heart. Moreover, fragments of precardiac mesoderm explanted from urodele embryos at gastrula or early neurula stages into salt solution produce beating heart tissue only rarely. However, if the explant also included some anterior lateral endoderm, vigorously beating, well-formed hearts developed in every case (24, 70). Endoderm from other regions exhibited a similar trophic effect, though weaker (Mangold, 87). In contrast, precardiac mesoderm from early neurulae never produces heart tissue when combined with neural plate, whether endoderm is included or not. From late neurulae, such explants produce heart tissue in the presence of endoderm, but not without it. Only precardiac mesoderm from tail bud embryos can self-differentiate into heart tissue irrespective of the presence of endoderm or neural plate (Jacobson, 71). This is because mesoderm from early neurulae is not fully determined in the direction of heart formation. Therefore, when removed from contact with its associated endoderm and explanted, it rarely forms heart. If explanted with endoderm, it of course does so. If explanted with neural plate, the repressive effects of the neural factor outweigh the inductive influence of the endoderm, and no heart tissue forms. Only if mesoderm and endoderm remain in contact into the tail bud stage (stages 24–26) is the preheart mesoderm sufficiently well determined to proceed with differentiation of functional heart tissue without continued association with endoderm, and despite the presence of neural tissue.

Evidence for inductive influences on the precardiac mesoderm of birds and mammals is much less satisfactory. A study by Waddington (143) is frequently cited as demonstrating that a heart can develop in the absence of endoderm in the avian embryo. Waddington removed the entire area pellucida "endoderm" (hypoblast) from mid-streak and late-streak embryos, and cultured the remaining epiblast on plasma clots overnight. Neural plate, somites, and notochord developed in these cultures, but "no really satisfactory hearts" formed. In a second series, epiblasts from two embryos were apposed with their ventral (that is, mesodermal) surfaces in contact and allowed to develop. Again, neural and mesodermal structures were formed, but in seven out of eight such pairs, no heart tissue appeared. In one culture a beating heart was reported. Waddington (143, p. 193) concludes that "this shows that a heart can develop in the absence of endoderm." However, these results

seem much more reasonably to indicate that removal of the hypoblast from primitive-streak embryos prevents heart formation in the majority of cases.

Extensive experiments by Dalton (28) permit a similar conclusion. He transplanted transverse strips of embryos including, or just posterior to, Hensen's node onto the chorioallantoic membrane of 9-day hosts. Some of the explants consisted of epiblast only, others included all three germ layers. Donor embryos lacking hypoblast ranged from stage 2 to stage 5. The study included several hundred explants. Heart formation was common in mid- to late-streak transplants which included endoderm. In no case did a heart form from epiblast alone. In only two transplants of epiblast from initial primitive streak stages (H-H stage 2–3), which included the anterior tip of the forming streak, did heart tissue develop.

Recently Orts-Llorca (100) reported that extirpation of the "endoderm" overlying the presumptive heart mesoderm from stage 4–6 embryos prevented heart formation on the operated side. This investigator also concluded that the necessary inducer tissue was removed. In his experiments, the donor embryo was cultured, but the explanted tissue was discarded.

I have performed similar operations (36) in which both the donor embryo and explanted tissue fragments were maintained in culture. In confirmation of the results of Orts-Llorca and his predecessors, heart tissue never developed on the operated side in the donor embryo. However, 38 of the 53 cultured hypoblast explants developed masses of beating heart tissue. Clearly, in such operations, the layer which peels off the embryo is not endoderm alone, but splanchnopleure, that is, endoderm plus its tightly adherent splanchnic mesoderm. Thus, the reason that primitive streak epiblast does not form heart tissue is apparently not because of the lack of the presumed inducer, but because the heart-forming mesoderm itself has been removed with the endoderm.

From these studies on the avian embryo, we can derive only the unsatisfying conclusion that none of the experiments reported has tested critically the hypothesis that endoderm exerts an inductive influence on the precardiac mesoderm. There are no relevant experiments on mammalian embryos.

Early Morphogenetic Movements

The head-process stage chick (stage 5) or mammalian embryo (human horizon VIII to IX) may be characterized as a roughly flat plate of cells in which the three germ layers are clearly delimited, with the precardiac material located anteriorly in the "wings" of the lateral plate mesoderm (Fig. 16.3F). Continued cardiogenesis during the period of early somite formation (H-H stage 5–8; horizon IX and X) depends upon a complex of four types of morphogenetic movements, occurring simultaneously in different components of the system, which result in the convergence of the two lateral primordia into the ventral midline. These are: (1) folding movements of the endoderm to form the crescentic pouch of the anterior intestinal portal (AIP) and early shallow foregut; (2) formation of the amniocardiac vesicles (ACV) by separation of the splanchnic and somatic mesoderm; (3) rapid anteromesiad mi-

gration of splanchnic precardiac mesoderm; and (4) ventrad emigration of cells from the splanchnic mesoderm to form the hemangioblast layer.

Folding Movements of the Endoderm

The endodermal movements are of great importance because it is this cohesive layer with which precardiac mesodermal cells are in contact in these early stages, and which they use as a substratum for their own migratory activity (DeHaan, 36). The movements that occur in the endoderm of the chick during early formation of the foregut have been carefully studied by Bellairs (10). She classifies them broadly as two-dimensional movements, which take place more or less in the original plane of the endoderm, and three-dimensional movements of the layer rostral and lateral to the presumptive roof of the foregut. These are oblique, backwardly directed foldings which tend to swing the tissues destined to form the floor of the foregut medioventrally. Thus the crescent-shaped pocket of endoderm is formed, which is the early shallow foregut, and anterior intestinal portal. These oblique movements take place at progressively posterior and more lateral levels, as development proceeds, and in this way the ventral closure of the foregut gradually spreads backward. The analogous process has been examined in embryos of the duck (Yoshida, 154), guinea pig (Yoshinaga, 155), and human (Davis, 29).

Formation of Amniocardiac Vesicles

At the same time another process of primary importance in cardiogenesis occurs. This is the formation of the em-

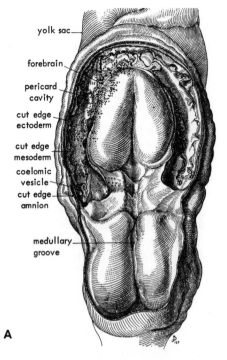

yolk sac

forebrain

pericard
cavity

cut edge
ectoderm

cut edge
mesoderm

coelomic
vesicle

cut edge
amnion

medullary
groove

A

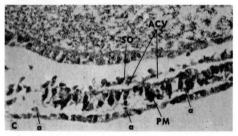

bryonic coelom or amniocardiac vesicles, with concomitant differentiation of splanchnic mesoderm. The lateral plate mesoderm at the head-process stage is not a cohesive layer of cells, as are the ectoderm and endoderm, but is instead a compact meshwork of stellate mesenchymal cells. As the head fold and foregut begin to form, the mesoderm in the region of the cardiac primordia shows a looser arrangement, with the interstices between individual cells becoming larger and more distinct. Presumably, some differentiation of the cell surfaces occurs at this time, so that they become less adhesive toward one another (see Trinkaus, Chapter 3). Soon, a narrow cleavage appears in the mesoderm, separating a dorsal layer (the somatic mesoderm) from a ventral one (the splanchnic mesoderm). The coelomic cavity, which in this region forms the early pericardial cavity or amniocardiac vesicles, thus originates from multiple foci of cell separation which gradually grow rostrad and fuse to produce a horseshoe-shaped space (Fig. 16.4). This process was first described in the rabbit embryo by Van der Stricht (141) in 1895, and has been studied in detail in the chick (Sabin, 121), duck (154), and many other mammals (see 29 for review).

The cleavage which separates the splanchnic and somatic mesoderm is of special interest because all of the pri-

Fig. 16.4 Formation of the amniocardiac vesicles and early coelom. *A.* Human embryo (Carnegie collection #5080, horizon IX) just before the first somite pair is formed, showing the pericardial cavity as a horseshoe-shaped space. The positions of angioblasts, as determined from a reconstruction of the embryo, are indicated by black dots. (After Davis, *Carnegie Contrib. Embryol.* 19:245–284, 1927.) *B.* Cross section through the left lateral cardiogenic plate of a stage 8 chick embryo, at the level shown by arrows in the inset. ×60 E, ectoderm; PM, precardiac mesoderm; EN, endoderm; VM, vitelline membrane. *C.* Enlargement of the region within the box in *B.* The somatic, SO, and splanchnic precardiac mesoderm, PM, are separated by the cleft of the early coelomic cavity, ACV. Angioblasts, a, migrating ventrally form contacts with the endoderm. ×300.

mordial cardiac cells migrate ventrally before the split occurs, and are found, after the ACV are formed, in the splanchnic layer. It is for this reason that Mollier (93) termed the crescentic layer of thickened splanchnic mesoderm the "cardiogenic plate."

One of the major differences in development of the heart in the bird and mammal concerns the time at which this horseshoe-shaped space is formed. In the chick and duck, separate lateral amniocardiac vesicles make their appearance at the stage of 1–3 somites. They extend forward to meet in the midline under the foregut by the stage of 6–7 somites, but fuse to form a single pericardial cavity only after rupture of the ventral mesocardium, beginning at about the 9-somite stage. In contrast, in the human (Davis, 29; Heuser, 63) and other mammals (see Goss, 53), lateral ACV form earlier and remain separate only briefly. Immediately after their formation, the cavities expand in a craniomesial direction, meeting in the midline even before the first pair of somites has fully formed (Fig. 16.4A). At this stage the head fold and early foregut have not yet folded under. Therefore, the central part of the pericardial coelom lies rostral to the end of the notochord for a brief period.

Cell Migration in the Splanchnic Mesoderm

Even before the coelomic space develops, the precardiac mesodermal reticulum is distributed in an inhomogeneous fashion, as a loose meshwork of stellate mesenchyme, within which lie small clusters of more tightly packed cells. Analysis of these regions with the aid of time-lapse cinematography has shown that the clusters migrate actively, and independently of each other, from their initial positions in the lateral heart primordia into the forming tubular heart (DeHaan, 34, 35). Whether the nonaggregated mesenchyme cells migrate with the precardiac clusters, and what contribution, if any, they make to the forming heart, is not yet known.

The shape and position of the masses of precardiac mesoderm are illustrated in Figure 16.5. This is a series of photographs taken of a single chick embryo during its development in culture, from stage 5 to stage 10+, when the embryo has 11 pairs of somites, and a beating tubular heart. Each photograph is an enlargement of an individual frame taken at regular intervals from one of the time-lapse films, viewing the embryo from its ventral surface. In this series, approximately 300 frames, or 1 hour of development, elapsed between each picture shown. In Figure 16.6, tracings of these photographs have been rendered on which the parts of the embryo have been labeled. (For a complete description of techniques and other details, see DeHaan, 33, 35.)

At stage 5 the regions of the thickened mesoderm (LHFR, RHFR) are broad and rather diffuse; however, they match nicely the areas shown to have heart-forming capacity as explants (Rawles, 111; DeHaan, 32). If the movements of individual clusters are traced on film through subsequent stages, it is noted that for the first few hours, during stages 5–6, the direction of migration of a given cluster may bear no relation to its later "goal" at the AIP. Clusters move at different speeds and in different directions from their neighbors. Some clusters move completely away from the heart-form-

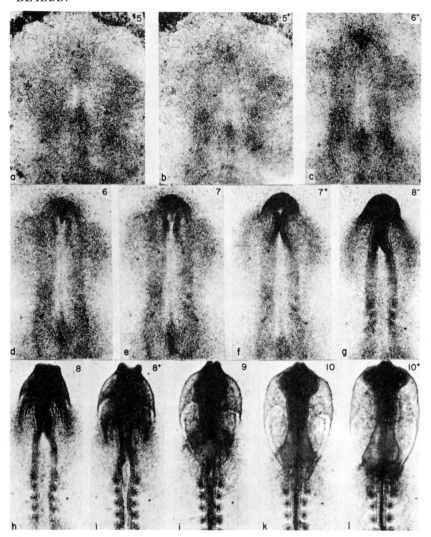

Fig. 16.5 Photographs from a time-lapse film showing sequential stages of a single chick embryo developing in culture. Ventral view. ×25 (From DeHaan, *Acta Embryol. Morphol. Exptl.* 6:26–38, 1963.)

ing regions, to take up positions in the head mesenchyme or extraembryonic vasculature.

With development through stages 6 and 7, the anterior medial border of each mass of heart-forming cells extends forward and mesiad, forming the crescent of cardiogenic material which arcs rostral to the prechordal plate (PCP). (Human horizon IX; see 33 for discussion of the cardiogenic plate in birds and mammals.) At this time a pattern of organization of the clusters within the crescent emerges, relating their position with their later differentiation. When the movements of 20 or

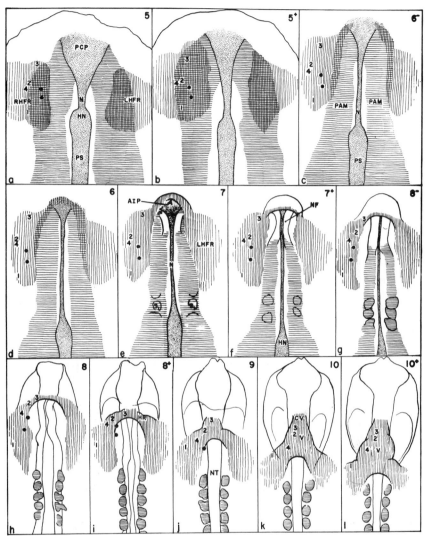

Fig. 16.6 Tracings of photographs shown in Fig. 16.5. Paraxial mesoderm, PAM, and its derivative somites, S, are shown with horizontal hatching; the primitive streak, PS, notochord, N, and prechordal plate, PCP, are stippled; cardiac mesoderm in the left and right heart-forming regions, LHFR and RHFR, the heart rudiments, HR, and the primitive tubular heart are drawn with vertical hatching. Folded and tubular structures such as the anterior intestinal portal, AIP, neural folds, NF, neural tube, NT, and heart are outlined heavily, as are the somites. The parts of the heart shown are the conoventricular region, CV, and the ventricle, V. The numbers 1–4 in the right heart-forming region represent the positions of four specific cell clusters. The two closed circles represent particles of iron oxide adhering to the endoderm. The number in the upper right corner of each panel refers to the Hamburger-Hamilton stage. (From DeHaan, *Acta Embryol. Morphol. Exptl.* 6:26–38, 1963.)

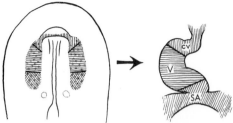

Fig. 16.7 Embryonic fate of clusters of cardiogenic mesoderm. cv, conoventricular tissue; V, ventricle; SA, atrial and sinoatrial tissue. Sinoatrial material at this stage is also represented by the bilateral areas of undifferentiated mesoderm at the posterior end of the heart. (From DeHaan, *Ann. N. Y. Acad. Sci.*, 1965.)

There are at least three lines of evidence indicating that these oriented movements of the mesoderm clusters involve contact of the clusters with the intact endodermal substratum.

1. The embryonic endoderm may be treated, at stage 6 or 7, with a solution of sodium citrate. This denudes the endodermal layer, leaving the mesoderm and ectoderm relatively intact, but unable to undergo further cell migrations (DeHaan, 33). After such treatment, mesoderm cells within the crescent

more clusters within one heart-forming region are traced on film, it is seen that those that occupy positions in the most rostral regions of the crescent at stage 6 enter the heart rudiments early, and form parts of the heart at its conoventricular end. Clusters in the posterolateral limbs of the crescent enter the heart progressively later, contributing to the ventricle and sinoatrial tissue. Thus, the clusters become arranged in a stable configuration, such that the position of each cluster relative to its neighbors is maintained from stage 6 until the cluster enters the forming heart, each cluster joining the heart rudiment in order of its place along an anteroposterior axis (Fig. 16.7).

The change in migratory behavior which takes place as the cardiogenic plate is established is dramatic. Where previously the movements of the clusters were randomly oriented and unrelated to each other, at stages 6–7 the mesoderm appears to be subjected to an orienting influence by the endoderm, which causes the clusters to move up the cardiogenic crescent in smoothly curved, parallel paths toward the forming anterior intestinal portal.

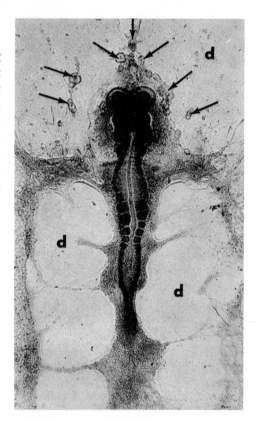

Fig. 16.8 Chick embryo incubated 40 hours, treated at stage 6+ with 40 mM sodium citrate solution. Each arrow indicates a pulsating vesicle or mass of heart tissue. The large clear regions, d, have been denuded of endoderm by the treatment. ×35 (From DeHaan, *Acta Embryol. Morphol. Exptl.* 6:26–38, 1963.)

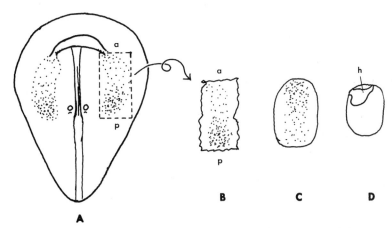

Fig. 16.9 Diagrammatic representation of an experiment in which (A) a rectangle of endoderm with its adherent precardiac mesoderm is explanted from a stage 7 embryo to the surface of a nutrient agar culture medium. B. Immediately after explanation, the density of prospective heart cells is greatest near the posterior, p, end (as indicated with stippling). C. After 12 hours, the presumptive heart tissue has migrated in an anterior, a, direction. D. By the end of 24 hours in culture, it has differentiated into a pulsating vesicle of heart tissue, h, at the anterior edge of the explant.

condense into small masses which, within 24 hours, differentiate into spontaneously beating heart tissue, still arrayed in their crescentic arrangement around the abortive medullary plate (Fig. 16.8).

2. As noted above, the endoderm overlying one or both limbs of the crescent can be peeled off. When this operation is performed, the adherent splanchnic mesoderm comes off with the explant, leaving behind the intact ectoderm plus some or all of the somatic mesoderm. If the explant of endoderm-mesoderm is spread flat on a semisolid nutrient medium and cultured for 24 hours, the mesoderm first migrates to the anteriormost edge of the fragment, and then differentiates into spontaneously beating heart tissue (Fig. 16.9). Similar explants transferred to a plastic substratum, which disrupts the original organization of the endoderm, exhibit no anterior migration of the mesoderm (DeHaan, 36).

3. According to current hypotheses

concerning the control of cell movements, orienting information may be provided to migratory cells by the substratum upon which they move (see DeHaan, 34; DeHaan and Ebert, 39). The embryonic endoderm, up to stage 5, is composed of squamous endothelial cells having irregular polygonal shapes. At about stage 6, cells in a band running anteroposteriorly through each precardiac area begin to decrease in lateral dimension and elongate in a direction parallel to the embryonic axis, to form spindle-shaped or lunate columnar cells. This band of oriented endoderm cells extends forward and mesiad in the form of a crescent, establishing a "path" in precisely the appropriate place and at the correct time to provide the required orienting influence for the migrating mesoderm clusters. It is tempting to postulate that the precardiac mesoderm in vivo is influenced by the oriented lines of cell junctions, which become aligned with the alteration in cell shape, or by gradients of differential adhesiveness developing in the endoderm (DeHaan, 35, 36).

Formation of the Angioblast Layer

As the cardiogenic plate develops, the first histological evidence of distinguishable precardiac cells can be seen with the formation of "angioblasts" in the region of the original amniocardiac vesicles. These cells migrate individually and in small clusters out of the mesoderm to form a third loose layer in the narrow meso-endodermal space. Termed the "vascular layer of Pander" by Sabin (120), it gives rise to the endocardium of the heart. In more posterior regions this layer produces the blood islands, from which in turn will develop the endothelium of the rest of the vasculature, erythroblasts, and blood plasma. Thus, the endocardium arises in continuity with the blood vessels of the pellucid area, and is not different from them.

These angioblasts collect into delicate strands and clusters, closely applied to the underlying endoderm (Sabin, 121). Their strong attachment to the endoderm apparently retards their rostral migration relative to the rapidly moving clusters of splanchnic mesoderm, as shown by the following experiment.

A small fragment of the cardiogenic crescent consisting of a rectangle of splanchnic mesoderm, angioblasts, and endoderm, may be removed and replaced with homologous tissue from a donor embryo of the same age, which has been labeled with tritiated thymidine. The implant heals in, and contributes in normal fashion to the host heart and foregut (Rosenquist and DeHaan, unpublished observations).

When the heart develops, after further incubation, the position of the labeled cells can be determined radioautographically. For example, if a fragment in the middle of the cardiogenic plate is implanted, a region of myocardium in the belly of the ventricle may show the label 24–30 hours later. Labeled cells in the endocardium are not found in the same region, however, but more posteriorly, in the atrial or sinus tissue.

In Figure 16.4 the spatial relations between the ACV, the splanchnic mesoderm, and the angioblasts are illustrated. By sprouting of original cell clusters and continuous addition of new angioblasts from the mesoderm, a network of solid cell bands soon forms. The strands of angioblasts become hollowed out, again by cell separation, to form irregular, narrow tubules. These tubules represent the rudimentary endocardium of the primitive tubular heart.

Formation of the Primitive Tubular Heart

As the splanchnic mesoderm migrates anteromesially, and leaves its contact with the folding endoderm, it thickens markedly and swings down in a ventral direction to form the paired epimyocardial troughs. These are first visible in most forms at the stage of 3–4 somites (beginning of horizon X). From this structure will later develop the bulk of the muscular wall of the heart (myocardium), its thin outer peritoneal covering (epicardium), and the inner lining of the pericardium. Figure 16.10 diagrams four stages in the development of the chick heart, from its paired angioblastic rudiments to the primitive tubular heart. Figure 16.11 illustrates x-sections through equivalent stages of

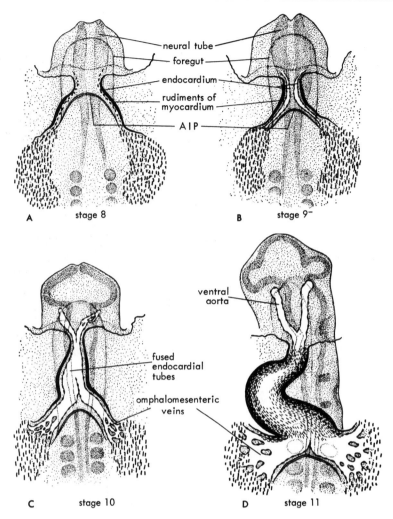

neural tube
foregut
endocardium
rudiments of myocardium
AIP

A   stage 8   B   stage 9⁻

ventral aorta

fused endocardial tubes

omphalomesenteric veins

C   stage 10   D   stage 11

Fig. 16.10 Fusion of the primitive tubular heart from paired angioblastic rudiments, in a chick embryo viewed from the ventral side. Undifferentiated precardiac mesoderm is indicated with vertical hatching.

human embryos, while in Figure 16. 12A and 16.12B are represented drawings of reconstructions of pericardial regions of two early-somite human embryos with the ventral myocardial wall dissected to expose the two parallel channels of endocardium. At the 4-somite stage, the myocardium still shows traces of its origin from two tubes.

At the 7–8 somite stage (H-H stage 9)

the endothelial tubes fuse, first in the conotruncal region, and then progressively caudally in the ventricle. In the human, this fusion becomes complete at about 8 somites, with the atria still paired. Thus at its first appearance, the primitive heart consists of a presumptive conotruncal (bulbotruncal) region trailing off into the ventral aortic roots, and the anterior portion of the ventri-

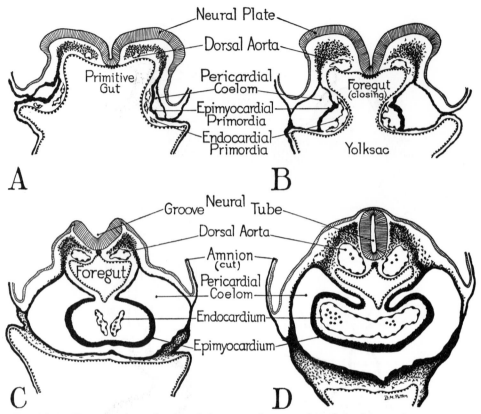

Fig. 16.11 Four stages in fusion of the paired primordia of the human heart as seen in cross section. *A.* 2 somites. *B.* 4 somites. *C.* 7–8 somites. *D.* 10 somites. (From Patten, pp. 24–92 in *Pathology of the Heart*, S. E. Gould, ed. Charles C Thomas, 1960.)

cle. The paired halves of the posterior ventricle and primitive atrium are still widespread over the arch of the AIP (Fig. 16.12*B*). The endocardium of these regions fuses insensibly into the omphalomesenteric, or vitelline, veins.

Since the embryonic body was at first open ventrally, lying spread out on the surface of the yolk sac, the folding under of the lateral margins of the embryonic disc brings the ventrolateral walls of the body into their definitive position (Fig. 16.11). Thus the embryo is closed ventrally, and structures which arose as separate halves are established in the midline.

Folding off of the embryonic body continues with concomitant progress in the closure of the foregut. The paired endocardial tubes are brought into closer proximity and finally in the same process the epimyocardial layers swing together ventrally and mesially, completely enveloping the endocardium, while the initially separate right and left coelomic spaces become confluent to form the median pericardial cavity (Fig. 16.11*C,D*). Dorsally, the right and left epimyocardial layers become contiguous, but do not fuse immediately. They persist for a time as a double-layered supporting membrane,

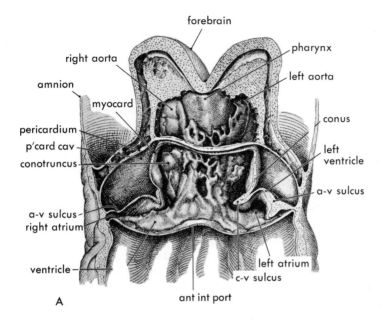

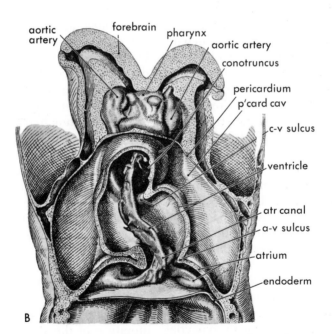

Fig. 16.12 Two stages in the formation of the human heart during horizon x, showing the ventral myocardial wall dissected to expose the endocardium. *A.* Carnegie Embryo 3709, 4 somites. ×50. *B.* Carnegie Embryo 391, 8 somites. ×50. (After Davis, *Carnegie Contrib. Embryol.* 19:245–254, 1957.)

the dorsal mesocardium. In this manner, the primitive heart is established as a nearly straight tube-within-a-tube, suspended mesially in the anterior coelom (horizon x).

Histogenesis

The histogenesis of cardiac tissue may be considered as starting with the differentiation of the endothelial angioblasts from the splanchnic mesoderm, and the thickening of the splanchnic mesoderm itself as it differentiates into the myocardium and epimyocardial mantle.

The space between the endocardium and myocardium soon becomes filled by a thick gelatinous layer, termed the "cardiac jelly" by Davis (29). This material has been shown to contain aldehydic, acid mucopolysaccharides (Ortiz, 99), and to lose its metachromatic staining properties after treatment with hyaluronidase (Barry, 5). Cells from both the endocardial and myocardial layers migrate into this mucoprotein matrix to establish the loose reticulum of stellate cells characteristic of the early tubular heart (Patten, Kramer, and Barry, 108).

A substantial older literature on the histodifferentiation of heart muscle exists (see Patten, 106; Davis, 29; Streeter, 135 for reviews). However, much of it suffers from the limitations of the light microscope and the fixation techniques generally employed for light microscopy. Therefore, it is not surprising that conflicting theories should have arisen concerning such questions as the cellular or syncytial nature of heart tissue, the nature of intercalated discs, the mechanisms of fibrillogenesis, the nature of myofibrils and their striations, and the structure

and relationships of the sarcolemma and other membranous structures. In the past two decades, since the introduction of electron microscopy to the study of heart muscle (Beams et al., 9; Hall, Jakus, and Schmitt, 56) most of these controversies have been resolved.

The Cellular Nature of Heart Tissue

Early histologists considered heart muscle as cellular in structure, and interpreted the intercalated discs as junctional zones of apposed cell membranes, which stained heavily as a result of intercellular cement substance. For example, Eberth (46), to whom the first detailed description of the intercalated disc is usually attributed, regarded the discs as intercellular structures both because of their histologic appearance and strong reaction to silver nitrate (known to stain cell membranes), and also because of the tendency of macerated heart muscle to fragment along the discs (Yokoyama et al., 153). Later, Ranvier (110) also described mammalian myocardium as composed of individual rhomboidal branching cells.

It was not until after the turn of the century that Heidenhain (61) and Godlewski (52) enunciated clearly the hypothesis that the heart was syncytial in nature. These workers felt that the discs represented either contraction artifacts or the sites of sarcomere differentiation (see below).

The controversy over syncytium versus cells recurred periodically in the literature of the first half of this century, as some microscopists continued to make observations corroborating the earlier cell view (Werner, 148; Lewis, 80). However, most investigators dur-

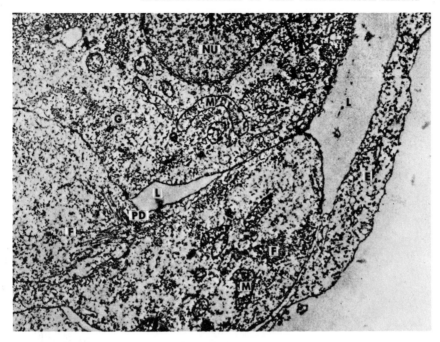

Fig. 16.13 Electronmicrograph of a 10-day-old embryonic mouse ventricle. The thin endothelial lining, E, of the lumen is separated from the myocardial cells by lacunae, L, which penetrate between all of the cells. Sparse mitochondria, M, Golgi and granular components, G, can be seen. Scattered foci of developing filaments, F, variously oriented, occur in many cells. Such filaments are frequently associated with zones of intercellular contact, forming primitive intercalated discs, PD. ×8437 (From Challice and Edwards, pp. 44–73 in *The Specialized Tissues of the Heart*, A. P. de Carvalho, W. C. de Mello, B. F. Hoffman, eds. Elsevier, 1961.)

ing this period tended to accept the syncytial hypothesis. This was strengthened by early physiological studies of cardiac conduction which were interpreted on the basis of protoplasmic continuity between heart fibers (see DeHaan, 31, for review).

Since the application of modern techniques of electronmicroscopy and tissue culture, however, the idea that the heart is syncytial has been shown repeatedly and without exception to be false. Numerous electron microscopists, using ever more sophisticated techniques, have found that the intercalated disc does consist of a pair of apposed cell membranes, covered with electron-dense granules. The myofibrils do not cross the intercalated discs, nor is there other evidence for any kind of protoplasmic continuity across the membranes. Each elongate cell of a myocardial fiber is consistently observed to be surrounded by an intact plasma membrane, as diagrammed in Figure 16.16 (Fawcett and Selby, 47; Jamieson and Palade, 72; Sjöstrand and Andersson-Cedergren, 126; Stenger and Spiro, 133).

Published electronmicrographs of embryonic hearts of chicks, rabbits, and mice have not been of the same high resolution as is common for those of adult tissues. Early embryonic tis-

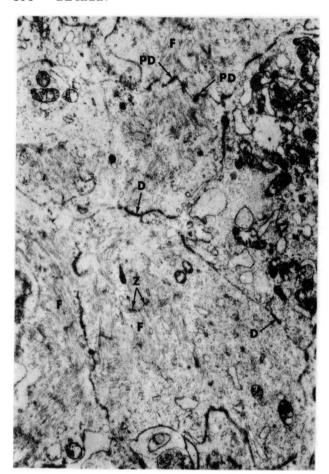

Fig. 16.14 Electronmicrograph of myoblasts of 14-somite chick embryo myocardium. Primitive desmosomes, D, form between the closely apposed cells. Bundles of myofilaments, F, in association with dense regions of Z-band material are scattered throughout the cytoplasm. ×9000 (From Olivo, Laschi, and Lucchi, *Lo Sperimentale* 114:69–78, 1964.)

sue is so watery and loosely organized as to be difficult to fix and highly susceptible to disruption during embedding in plastic. Nonetheless, numerous previously controversial points have been clarified. For example, it has been confirmed that, just as in the adult, embryonic heart tissue exhibits no evidence of syncytial structure at any time in development.

In the early tubular heart the endocardium is composed of a single layer of flattened, granulated cells. The myocardium is only two to three cells thick, comprised of irregularly polygonal or spindle-shaped myoblasts. The cytoplasm of these cells is distinctly watery in appearance, containing large amounts of granular material (presumably RNA and glycogen), randomly dispersed mitochondria, and vesicular components of the sarcoplasmic reticulum. Wide, irregular interstitial spaces separate the loosely organized cells (Fig. 16.13).

By light microscopy, intercalated discs were not demonstrable during embryonic or early fetal life (Witte, 150), although it had been reported that they appeared and became progressively more distinct after birth (Jordan and Steele, 74) or after prolonged cultivation of heart explants in tissue culture (Hogue, 68). However,

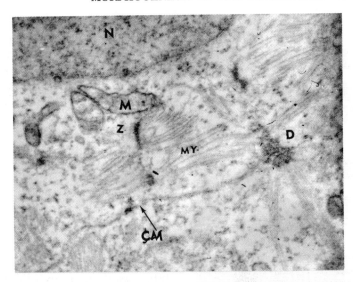

Fig. 16.15 Electronmicrograph of two myoblasts of an embryonic rabbit heart, 10 days after coitus. Two closely apposed cells are seen. Myofilaments, MY, associated with Z bands, Z, are scattered in the cytoplasm. Where these converge on the cell membrane, M, an intercalated disc, D, forms. ×16800 (From Muir, *J. Biophys. Biochem. Cytol.* 3:193–202, 1957.) The photographs here reproduced from printed halftone copy inevitably show a loss of detail, and the quality of the results is not representative of the originals.

electronmicrographs of even very early heart have shown that such structures do indeed exist (29- to 33-hour chick, Wainrach and Sotello, 144; Olivo et al., 97a; 10-day mouse, Challice and Edwards, 21; 10-day rabbit, Muir, 94). Where neighboring cells are in contact, their apposed membranes may be thickened in discrete localized areas by aggregates of electron-dense granules. If these are not associated with fibrillar material, they form typical desmosomes (Fig. 16.14). In other regions, similar structures may appear in association with tufts of myofibrils (Fig. 16.15). These have been referred to as primitive intercalated discs, or protodiscs (21, 94).

During subsequent days, the myocardium thickens by mitotic activity. The cells become elongated and oriented into chains, and pack together

more closely. More desmosomes form along the lateral walls, and intercalated discs may be seen where a pair of cell membranes transect bundles of myofibrils at the abutting ends of cells.

The early disc may pass obliquely across the myofibrillar axis. Gradually, however, each disc becomes oriented at right angles to the fibrils, and develops the highly plicated structure characteristic of the adult. These developmental changes are shown schematically in Figure 16.16.

Despite their nonsyncytial morphology, both embryonic and adult heart exhibit conductile properties which can largely be accounted for by classical core-conductor theory (Crill et al., 26; Hoffman and Cranefield, 67). This has given rise to the concept of the cardiac fiber as a "functional syncytium." Either the intercalated discs represent

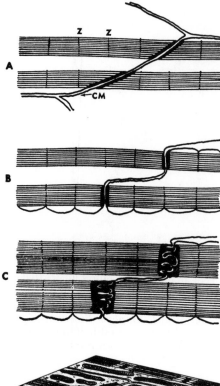

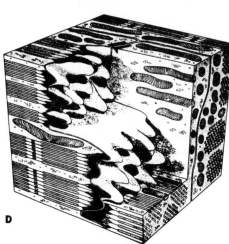

Fig. 16.16 Formation of the intercalated disc. Schematic representation of the disc in (A) embryo, (B) late fetus, (C) adult. (From Muir, *J. Biophys. Biochem. Cytol.*, 3:193–202, 1957.) (D). A three-dimensional representation showing the fingerlike plications of the adult disc. (From Sjöstrand and Andersson-Cedergren, pp. 421–445 in *Structure and Function of Muscle*, G. H. Bourne, ed. Academic Press, 1960.)

areas of reduced membrane resistance to ion flow (Dewey and Barr, 41; Loewenstein and Kanno, 83; Rhodin et al., 113; Van der Kloot and Dane, 140; Weidman, 146) or else, despite their high ohmic resistance (Thompson, 139) they exhibit a specialized synapselike chemical transmission of an impulse from one membrane to the other (Sperelakis and Lehmkuhl, 127).

Fibrillogenesis

The clearest and probably most accurate analysis of fibril formation in differentiating myoblasts is that of Hay (60), based upon excellent electronmicrographs of differentiating amphibian skeletal muscle (see Konigsberg, Chapter 14). It is remarkable that, owing to the similarity of ultrastructure of heart and skeletal muscle (Spiro and Sonnenblick, 127a), none of the observations made on developing avian or mammalian heart cells conflict in any way with her interpretation.

The earliest hearts studied with the electron microscope are those of the 7-somite chick (Olivo et al., 97a) the 10-day rabbit (Muir, 94), and the 10-day mouse (Challice and Edwards, 21). Myoblasts in this primitive heart tissue already contain concentrations of granular material and loose myofilaments. Within a few hours, some myofilaments are grouped into short, thin bundles, usually in association with one or more transverse dense regions of Z material (Fig. 16.15). In other areas, loose filaments remain scattered in the cytoplasm.

As condensations of Z substance become denser and more frequent, Z bands may commonly be seen as centers from which several bundles of myofilaments arise in irregular radial patterns (Fig. 16.14). This arrangement has suggested to several authors that the Z bands may be the site of growth or deposition of myofibrillar material (Challice and Edwards, 21; Fawcett and Selby, 47; Meyer and Queiroga, 92; Wainrach and Sotelo, 144), an idea dating back at least to the turn of the century (Heidenhain, 61). Grimley and Edwards (54) have commented upon the structural continuity and similarity between Z bands and intercalated discs, suggesting that these structures may be involved in sarcomere formation. Support for this idea comes from a recent analysis by Franzini-Armstrong and Porter (49), who postulate that the Z disc is a modified membrane structure, homologous with the desmosome and intercalated disc.

The controversy in the early literature over the time of initial appearance of striated fibrils has been largely settled with the introduction of more sophisticated techniques. Using neutral osmic acid as a fixative, Lewis (79) was the first to demonstrate cross-striated fibrils in the 10-somite chick heart. More recently, Baud (8) observed birefrigent myofibrils in the 8- to 9-somite chick heart, and Olivo and co-workers (97a) have shown scattered myofilaments in electronmicrographs of 7-somite chick heart cells (Fig. 16.14). Holtzer and co-workers (69) using fluorescent antisera reported cross-striated fibrils in cardiac rudiments of 26-hour chicks. By at least 36 hours of incubation, some cells in chick heart can be seen in electronmicrographs to contain wavy bundles of parallel myofilaments, divided into sarcomeres by well-defined Z bands (Hibbs, 65). Lindner (82) has seen such structures in the 9-somite embryo, in cells at the right side of the primitive ventricle.

Recalling that spontaneous contractions begin in the chick heart at 9 to 10 somites, on the right side of the ventricle (Patten and Kramer, 107), it seems safe to conclude that scattered myofilaments form very early and striated myofibrils then differentiate in certain heart cells shortly before, or just at the time that they begin pulsating. This conclusion is supported by the observations of Rumery and associates (118) on cultured heart cells isolated from 48-hour chick embryos. They were able to watch striated fibrils forming, using polarizing and phase optics, and reported that contractions were never seen in a cell until such fibrils were present.

Subsequent fibrillogenesis consists of continued synthesis of new filament bundles and their increasingly orderly alignment, with Z bands coming into register (Fig. 16.17). It should be emphasized, however, that histodifferentiation in the heart is not at all regular or completely progressive. At any stage, some cells are much more advanced than others (cf. Figs. 16.14 and 16.17). Even as late as 9 days in the chick (Weissenfels, 147) or 18 days in the rabbit (Muir, 94), poorly differentiated myoblasts are still present with primitive myofibrillar bundles indistinguishable from those in early tubular hearts.

In the earliest hearts, as the Z bands appear, loose tubular and vesicular components of the sarcoplastic reticulum may be seen. As soon as myofilament bundles become aligned, and distinct sarcomeres form (by 30 to 40 hours in the chick), vesicles of the reticulum may already be seen in association with the Z bands, forming a primitive transverse tubular system. By about 45 hours of incubation, longitudinal canaliculi

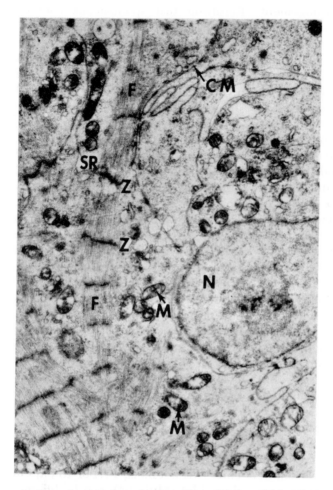

Fig. 16.17 Electronmicrograph of a myoblast of 14-somite chick embryo myocardium, showing well-formed sarcomeres and aligned myofilament bundles, F. Sarcoplasmic reticulum, SR, may be seen in association with Z bands. CM, cell membrane; M, mitochondria; N, nucleus. ×9000 (From Olivo, Laschi, and Lucchi, *Lo Sperimentale* 114:69–78, 1964.)

may be observed on both sides of the myofibrillar bundles (Wainrach and Sotelo, 144). Moreover, there is apparently no longitudinal growth of filaments between Z bands. The sarcomere length, established in the early myoblast, remains constant throughout development (94). Thus, by the time the heart has developed as a four-chambered organ and septation is well under way, its fibrillar structure is similar to that in the adult, and its general histology differs only by being somewhat less compact and regular.

The complex fibrous architecture of the embryonic heart has been examined by several investigators (Shaner, 122; MacCallum, 84; Taussig, 137). However, nothing is known of the mechanisms of fiber formation or orientation, and even at the descriptive level, interpretations vary widely (Mall, 85; Thomas, 138; Brecher and Galletti, 12).

Mitotic Activity

The growth rate of the heart was first studied systematically throughout the course of development by Olivo and Slavich (98). These workers showed

TABLE 16.1   Mitotic Activity in the Embryonic Chick Heart[a]

Days of Incubation	Ventricular Myocardium	Atrial Myocardium	Ventricular Septal Myocardium	Endocardium of Conus and AV Canal
1½	1.50			
2	2.65	2.15		2.30
3	2.75	2.20		2.10
4	3.15	2.30	0.60	2.15
5	2.80	1.65	0.75	1.75
6	2.00	1.05	0.75	1.00
7	2.00	1.15	1.10	1.00
8	1.90	1.30	1.60	0.95
9	1.95	1.50	1.50	0.95
10	1.85	1.35	1.80	
11	1.40	1.20	1.60	0.90
12	1.25	1.10	1.20	
14	1.10	1.25	1.10	0.55
16	0.85	1.25	0.80	
20	0.40	0.40	0.40	0.45

[a]Compiled from Grohmann, Z. *Zellforsch.* 55:104–122, 1961.

that the mitotic index (M.I. = number of mitotic figures per 100 cells counted) is high in the forming tubular heart on the second day of incubation, and that this value gradually falls off to very low levels just before hatching. They were unable to find evidence of any mitosis at all in the heart of young chickens 10 days posthatching.

These results have been confirmed and extended in a more detailed study by Grohmann (55), from which Table 16.1 has been compiled. Grohmann did separate counts on the ventricular and atrial myocardium, as well as that of the ventricular septum, and on the endocardium and endocardial cushions of the bulbus region and AV canal. The M.I. of the 36-hour ventricle is 1.5. This value rises rapidly to a peak of 3.15 in the ventricular myocardium of the 4-day heart, and then falls gradually to a M.I. of 0.4 just before hatching. A similar pattern is to be seen in the atrial myocardium, although the mitotic peak at 4 days is not so marked. In contrast, the M.I. in the ventricular septum re-

mains low during the first week of incubation, increasing only gradually until it reaches the same level as the rest of the ventricle.

Grohmann emphasized the striking differences in M.I. in the different parts and tissues of the heart. For example, during the first 12 days of development, the M.I. of ventricular myocardium is notably higher than that of the atrial tissue. However, during the second half of the incubation period, the atrial mitotic rate remains high until shortly before hatching, whereas ventricular proliferation falls to low levels rapidly. Moreover, a significant difference exists between the walls of the left and right ventricle, especially between 10 and 16 days, during which time cells in the left ventricle are dividing more rapidly than in the right. In contrast, between 5 and 10 days of incubation, cells in the wall of the right atrium are proliferating significantly faster than those in the left.

During the first week, mitotic activity is about equal in the myocardium and endocardium of the atria. However, endocardial proliferation is much more retarded from 8 to 16 days, even in the endocardial cushions of the AV canal, as compared with the myocardium (see below). A direct comparison of myocardial and endocardial activity in the ventricle was, unfortunately, not made.

The gradual reduction in M.I. throughout development suggests that mitotic restraints or controls are progressively imposed on the cells as each part of the heart completes its morphogenesis. This idea is consistent with the well-established fact that the fully formed heart is composed of a population of stable, nondividing cells (Leblond et al., 75; Sparagen et al., 129; Pelc, 109). The postembryonic heart grows simply by an increase in fiber diameter (Shipley et al., 123). Even the heart undergoing hypertrophy shows no evidence of cell division or an increased number of fibers. It, too, enlarges by an increase in diameter of fiber, resulting, apparently, from synthesis of new myofibrils within each cell (Richter and Kellner, 114).

The mechanisms underlying mitotic control are largely unknown (Bullough, 14). However, the restraints on cells must be extrinsic, since cells liberated from mitotically inactive tissues generally begin dividing rapidly within a short time after being placed in vitro. For example, cells emigrating from explanted fragments of chick ventricle exhibit a M.I. of 1.5–2.0 after 30–40 hours of culture, irrespective of the age of the donor embryo (Chaytor, 22; Lefford, 76). Thus 7- to 9-day ventricle which, according to Table 16.1, has an in vivo M.I. of approximately 2, exhibits the same rate of division in vitro. Ventricular cells from a 20-day donor divide equally rapidly in culture, despite the fact that 20-day heart in vivo has a M.I. of only 0.4.

Chaytor and others have suggested that the restraint upon cell division in the intact tissue may be in the form of inhibitor substances. Inasmuch as critical evidence for or against such an idea is lacking it should be accepted with caution. It is difficult to understand how any general mitotic inhibitor could produce the highly localized differential growth rates in the heart, reported above by Grohmann.

Myocardial cells seen in situ during the embryonic period are usually uninucleate. However, cells with two nuclei are not uncommonly found in cultures of disaggregated embryonic chick heart (DeHaan, unpublished observations). Moreover, in the rabbit (Muir, 94), and apparently in the mouse (Challice and Edwards, 21), heart cells with two or more nuclei may be seen after parturition. This suggests that despite the low M.I., some cells may undergo nuclear divisions which are not followed by cytokinesis (see Konigsberg, Chapter 14).

The observed decrease in mitotic activity must be viewed against the background of other progressive changes taking place in the heart. We noted above, for example, that the initial loose reticular arrangement of cells in the early heart changes with age as the cells become more densely packed. Cells emigrate from cultured fragments of early heart much more readily than from similar fragments taken from 16- to 20-day donors (Medawar, 91; Lefford, 76), apparently because of the greater areas of intercellular contact, or more durable adhesive relations established between neighbors during the course of histodifferentiation. Abercrombie (1) has suggested that cells in strong adhesive contact with their neighbors may be restrained in their mitotic activity.

Histodifferentiation

The mature heart is not composed of a homogeneous population of myocardial cells. From the mesoderm of the paired heart-forming regions in the prestreak embryo, several different cell types differentiate (Patten, 106).

Fetal and adult endocardium is composed of the endocardial endothelium and the subendothelial connective tissue, which includes fibroelastic and collagenous mesenchyme, and smooth muscle. All of these cell types are commonly described as differentiating from the embryonic angioblast layer, on the basis of classical descriptive studies (Tandler, 136; Davis, 29). Experimental evidence is lacking.

From the thickened embryonic epimyocardium are derived, in similar fashion, the mesothelial layer of the epicardium, the myocardial fibrous connective tissue and collagenous framework of the heart, the cardiac muscle which makes up the bulk of the organ, and the various components of the sinoventricular conducting system. Again, the exact origin or mode of differentiation of any of these cell types has not been critically investigated.

It is well known that the heart is spontaneously active, and that its beat normally originates in the specialized tissues of the sinoatrial node. It is also commonly accepted, however, that myocardium and conductive tissue are basically similar, differing only in degree in their various properties. Nonetheless, evidence has been accumulating in recent years that this is not true — that cells of the myocardium, like skeletal muscle, are normally quiescent until stimulated by an extrinsic source. It is only the components of the sinoventricular conduction tissue, and some specialized fibers in the atria (Paes de Carvalho et al., 101) that have the capacity to generate their own bioelectric potentials. The evidence for this contention stems largely from three sources (DeHaan, 31, 38):

1. It is usually possible to identify known pacemaker regions histologically as those giving rise to pacemaker prepotentials.

2. Fragments of adult heart tissue which do not contain cells of the conduction system, identified histologically, are quiescent.

3. Individual cells dissociated from embryonic hearts with trypsin and isolated in tissue culture do not all beat spontaneously. In 1955 Cavanaugh (20) disaggregated hearts of 5-day chick embryos into a cell suspension and found that when these cells had settled and attached to the bottom of a culture dish only about 9 percent of them were pulsating. After a few days, however, when the cells had spread and made contacts with their neighbors, as many as 50 percent were contracting rhythmically. There is now ample evidence that this change reflected the conduction of pacemaker potentials from cells of the original 9 percent that were beating, to many myocardial cells capable of contracting in response to such a stimulus, but incapable of initiating their own beat (see below).

This evidence suggests that the myocardium is composed of nonpacemaker, contractile cells. Presumably, during cardiac development, a population of cells capable of generating their own pacemaker potentials differentiates, and develops into the sinoventricular

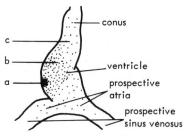

Fig. 16.18 Stage 10 chick heart at the time of initiation of spontaneous beat (ventral view). The first contractions can be observed in the darkly shaded area, a. From there the beat spreads gradually along the right border of the heart and across the ventricle to include region b (lighter stippling). The pulsations finally extend over the whole of the ventricle, to include area c. (Redrawn from Johnstone, *Bull. Johns Hopkins Hosp.* 36:299–311, 1925.)

conduction system. The development of this system has been reviewed elsewhere (DeHaan, 31; Patten, 105).

The Onset of Function

The heart begins to contract as soon as the primitive ventricle has formed. In the chick embryo, where precise observations have been made, the beat begins at the 10-somite stage (Sabin, 120; Johnstone, 73; Patten and Kramer, 107). Contraction is initiated in the myocardium at the posterior end of the ventricle, along its right margin (Fig. 16.18). Similar observations are, of course, lacking for the human embryo; however, in other mammals, contractions begin even earlier. In the rat (Goss, 53) and rabbit (Dwinnell, 43), pulsations are first seen at the 3- to 4-somite stage, even before fusion of the ventricular rudiments has been completed. On the basis of its structure, it seems probable that the human heart also begins its pulsation at these early somite stages (early in horizon x).

The sequential nature of the fusion of the cardiac primordia in a cephalocaudal direction determines the manner in which the initiation of the beat is established. In its earliest stages of activity the ventricle initiates its own beat. Later the atrial region is added on caudally, and finally, the sinus venosus is formed caudal to the atrium. As each new region differentiates, it brings tissues with different physiological properties to the heart, and the functional character of the entire organ shows correlated changes. This was early demonstrated by surface electrograms of embryonic hearts (Bogue, 11; Hoff et al., 66). More recently, with intracellular electrodes, the shape and characteristics of the action potentials recorded from cells in ventricular, atrial, or sinoatrial tissues have been shown to be distinctly different (Fingl et al., 48; Meda and Ferroni, 90; for complete discussion see Lieberman, 81). Moreover, it has long been known that these various regions differ in their intrinsic pulsation rate.

The Rate Gradient

When the heart begins contracting at stage 10, it starts with an irregular spasmodic beat, but soon develops a rhythmic slow rate of 30–40 beats per minute. Gradually, as more posterior regions of the heart differentiate, the rate increases. By the time the belly of the ventricle has formed and a distinct AV sulcus is observable, the heart rate may have increased to 80–90 beats per minute. By the middle of the third day of development, after the atria and sinoatrial tissue have differentiated (H-H stage 15–16), the heart normally beats 110–120 times a minute.

If the heart at this later stage, beating, say, 120 times a minute, is cut transversely into three fragments, the sinoatrial piece continues to beat at the same rate, whereas the ventricular fragment slows down perhaps to 90 beats per minute. The conoventricular part may stop altogether, or maintain its rhythm at a slow rate of 30–40 beats per minute. This result led Barry (4) to postulate a continuous anteroposterior gradient of rhythmicity in the heart, such that any fragment of myocardium beats more slowly than those posterior, and more rapidly than those anterior to it. Since the spontaneous beat of heart tissue depends upon stimulation of myocardial cells by pacemaker cells, the inherent differences of rate must reside in these pacemaker cells. That such rate differences are in fact a property of individual cells, rather than larger regions of tissue, was shown by Cavanaugh (20) in her disaggregation experiments. She found that cells isolated from the atria beat faster, on the average, than those from the ventricle. Under these conditions, each beating cell necessarily determined its own rate.

This gradient of rhythmicity is apparently built into the cardiogenic mesoderm in the early embryo, well before the heart itself forms. The stage 6–7 chick embryo can be cut into fragments containing either the anterior, middle, or posterior portion of the cardiogenic crescent (Fig. 16.7), which are destined to form respectively, the conoventricular, ventricular, and sinoatrial parts of the heart. Such fragments isolated in culture medium differentiate into vesicles containing masses of heart tissue. When their rate of spontaneous beating was counted, it was found that the anterior fragments produced heart tissue which averaged 36 beats per minute. The middle pieces beat on the average of 65 times a min-

ute whereas the rates of the vesicles derived from the posterior fragments ranged around 115 beats per minute (DeHaan, 32). These results indicate that each region of the cardiogenic crescent contains prepacemaker cells which differentiate membrane properties different from those in other regions.

Differentiation of Pacemaker Function

The concept that a region with a high intrinsic rate acts as pacemaker for the rest of the heart was set forth by Gaskell (51), and confirmed in convincing fashion by Paff (102). The latter cultured two fragments of embryonic chick heart with different spontaneous rates, close together in a single plasma clot. As the growth zones around each fragment overlapped, forming a bridge of tissue between them, both pieces took on the rate of the initially faster one. Thus, that area of the heart which at a given stage has the highest intrinsic rate of pulsation apparently contains the cells which are acting as pacemaker for the entire heart. This accounts for Barry's finding (4) that after transection, each portion of the heart slowed down to a rate corresponding to an earlier stage, with the exception of the most posterior region. It also explains an observation by Johnstone (73). After noting the position of the cells in which the first contractions were initiated in the 10-somite chick heart, he found that ligating the heart posterior to that point had no effect on heart rate. At that stage, the conoventricular region must be acting as its own pacemaker, since no heart tissue with a higher rate has yet differentiated posterior to it.

It is clear, however, that it is not the position in the heart of a given group of cells which determines its intrinsic rate. If the region which is acting as pacemaker is transplanted to a new site, it continues to drive the heart at its original rate, even though this may entail a reversal of the normal peristaltic contraction wave (Paff, 103; Rijlant, 115). Thus we see that at each stage in the development of the tubular heart, cells at the posterior, or venous end act as pacemaker, resulting in a continuous cephalocaudal movement of pacemaker function (Patten, 105). There is not "a" pacemaker in the early heart, but a succession of pacemaker zones, each holding its dominance for only a brief period. As new regions are formed caudally each in turn takes over the pacemaker function. The last such region is the embryonic sinus venosus, from which the definitive, adult pacemaker is derived.

Pacemaker Cells in Tissue Culture

Many observations pertinent to the differentiation of heart tissue have been made on cells in vitro. It was reported by Burrows (16) more than half a century ago that cells emigrating from explants of chick heart continue to beat when completely isolated, and maintain characteristic different rates. As noted above, this has been confirmed by more recent workers (Lewis, 20; Cavanaugh, 80). Furthermore, it has long been known that rapidly beating individual cells can act as pacemakers, influencing their slower neighbors to take on a faster rate when random movements bring them into contact (Garofolini, 50). When trypsin-dissociated heart cells are plated in a culture dish, those that beat initially do so with their different intrinsic rates. After a few days however, when the cells

have spread and multiplied to form a reticular monolayer, each cell makes contact with several neighbors by means of long protoplasmic extensions. At this time large areas of the cell sheet may be beating in synchrony in response to one cell or a small group of cells which act as pacemaker (Harary and Farley, 58: DeHaan, 38). Using differential temperature gradients, Harary and Farley (59) have confirmed that it is the fastest cell or cells that act as pacemaker for the entire cell sheet. A cell which is caused to beat rapidly by warming always acts as pacemaker for its cooler — and therefore slower — neighbors.

Simple physical contact between two cells is not sufficient for the conduction of an impulse. Sperelakis and Lehmkuhl found that a beating cell pushed mechanically into contact with a slower or quiescent neighbor did not influence the latter's activity (127). This suggests (as noted above) that in the area of intercellular contact the plasma membranes of apposed cells must be specialized for conduction of the impulse.

The proportion of spontaneously active cells in the total cell population of the embryonic heart has been variously estimated in cell cultures as from 2 percent (52) to 80–90 percent (77). Cavanaugh (20) reported about 9 percent spontaneously beating cells; Wollenberger (150a) obtained 1–50 percent. Unfortunately, none of these counts is meaningful since the effects of culture conditions were not taken into account. The report of 80–90 percent beating cells by Lehmkuhl and Sperelakis was derived from cells cultured at such a high density as to make it exceedingly probable that some of those active cells were nonpacemakers which were being driven by spontaneous neighbors (DeHaan, 38). The other two estimates are probably unrealistically low. Recent studies have indicated (DeHaan and Kormann, in preparation) that the percentage of spontaneously active cells derived from an embryonic heart at any given age can be made to vary from about 5 percent to 50 percent in a reproducible way, by changing the components of the culture medium. Not unexpectedly, the ionic composition (especially the potassium concentration) of the medium is a key factor in the control of pacemaker activity (Cunningham et al., 27). A suspension of cells from a 7-day chick heart, plated in a medium containing 4 mEq/l of potassium, exhibits 20–25 percent spontaneously active cells after 24 hours in culture. If potassium is increased to 8 mEq/l, only 10–15 percent are active, whereas reducing the potassium concentration to 1 mEq/l permits 40–50 percent of the cultured cells to beat. Thus far we have been unable to find conditions which permit more than 50 percent of the cells dissociated from a 7-day heart to beat.

Other factors, such as cardiac glycosides (Wollenberger and Halle, 151; DeHaan, 37), and RNA inhibitors (Cahn, 19; Yaffe and Feldman, 152), are also known to increase the rhythmicity of heart cells in culture. However, these effects have not been studied systematically.

Another problem in estimating the percentage of pacemaker cells in the heart from the activity of cell cultures is the probable effect of the dissociation procedures employed. Wollenberger (150a) has reported that trypsinization of embryonic chick heart disrupts myofibrillar structure. Thus, some spontaneously active cells in a culture may not be beating visibly because of a nonfunctional intracellular contractile mechanism. Further, Holtzman and Agin (69a) have shown that prolonged trypsinization of frog muscle fibers reduces their resting potential almost to zero. A similar effect on heart muscle would preclude pacemaker activity. Either of these effects of trypsin would produce low estimates of the number of spontaneously active cells in a culture. On the other hand, treatment of skeletal muscle fibers with trypsin for moderate periods elicited spontaneous contractions in many cases (69a). Thus, some of the spontaneous activity of cells in culture could result from trypsin-induced alterations of their plasma membranes.

Curvature and the Formation of Chambers

With continued growth in length of the tubular heart (horizon X and XI), its curvature becomes progressively more marked (Fig. 16.19). It is sometimes stated that the folding of the heart into an S-shape is caused by its rapid growth within the less-rapidly growing pericardial space (Patten, 104; Van Mierop, 141a). This probably is an oversimplified view, considering the complexity and constancy of that curvature. Moreover, we have already noted that the organ undergoes fairly normal curvature, in amphibians, even when isolated from the body and allowed to grow in culture (Bacon, 3).

Similar isolation experiments have been performed on the early chick heart in an attempt to analyze the causes of ventricular curvature. Butler (18) excised the ventricular tube from embryos at the stage of 9 to 16 somites.

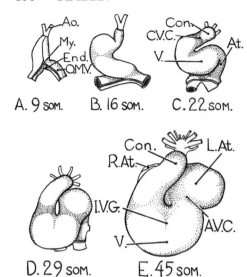

A. 9 SOM.   B. 16 SOM.   C. 22 SOM.

D. 29 SOM.   E. 45 SOM.

Fig. 16.19 Curvature of the heart. In the chick the stages illustrated would be at about (A) 36 hours, (B) 46 hours, (C) 52 hours, (D) 62 hours, and (E) 3½ to 4 days. Equivalent stages would occur during the first 4 weeks of development in the human. At, L and R, left and right atrium; Ao., ventral aortic root; A.V.C., atrioventricular constriction; Con., conus arteriosus; C.V.C., conoventricular constriction; End., endocardial tube; I.V.G., interventricular groove; O.M.V., omphalomesenteric vein; My., cut edge of myocardium; V, ventricle. (Redrawn from Patten, *Am. J. Anat.*, 30: 373–397, 1922.)

These were cultured in hanging-drop preparation for 24 hours. In all cases, the tube curved into a C-shape, similar to that formed in situ, with the primary dorsal surface forming the concavity of the curve. By making careful measurements of the primary dorsal and ventral surfaces of the heart tube before and after the period of culture, it could be shown that the primary ventral surface increases from 13 to 34 percent in length, while the primary dorsal surface actually decreases from 21 to 40 percent of its initial length. Thus the curvature of the heart results from dif-

ferential change in the length of the two sides of the heart tube. Butler was also able to demonstrate that the reason the heart bulges to the right is that torsion of the heart tube during the period from 9 to 11 somites brings the primary ventral surface of the ventricular region to the right side.

It was noted above that differential growth in various regions of the early heart is an important factor in continuing cardiac development. Shortly after the atrial primordia fuse in the midline, the right and left atrial regions begin enlarging. Similarly, as the ventricular loop is carried ventrolaterally to the right, and then caudally (Fig. 16.19 B–D), it too grows rapidly to form a bulging chamber. A region of less enlargement between the two primitive chambers forms the atrioventricular constriction. A conoventricular constriction divides the ventricle from the early conus in like manner.

Examination of the changing shape of the lumen of heart illustrates this differential growth. Figure 16.20 shows models of the atrial and ventricular endocardial cavities of human hearts of embryos through the 9–10 mm stage (horizons XI to XVI, 24 to 33 days of gestation). In Figure 16.21 are shown drawings made from similar models of the endocardial cavity of the venous end of hearts of human embryos from 10–30 somites, all shown at the same magnification. The tremendous swelling of the atria, and the superimposition of the sinus venosus on the vitelline plexus, are notable.

As the atria swell and the sinus venosus is formed, anterior and posterior cardinal plexuses flow together bilaterally, to form right and left common cardinal veins (Fig. 16.21), emptying into the sinus. By this time (early in hori-

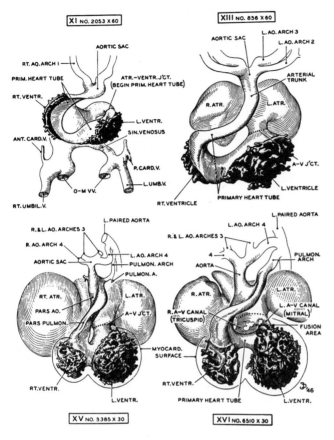

Fig. 16.20 Drawings of models of the human atrial and ventricular lumina (ventral view). Only endothelium is shown. The two trabeculated areas on the frontal border of the heart tube at horizon XI can be seen to enlarge into the left and right ventricular pouches at horizon XVI. XI and XIII, ×60; XV and XVI, ×30 (From Streeter, Embryology Reprint, *Carnegie Inst. Wash.* vol. 11, 1951.)

zon XII, H-H stage 12) circulation is established as a strong, pulsatile, unidirectional flow. The hemodynamic force of this circulating blood is another factor which is said to be important in molding the heart into its definitive shape.

Flow-molding of the Heart

In 1923, Alexander Spitzer (128) elaborated his "phylogenetic theory" of cardiac development, in which one of his basic assumptions was the formative effect of blood pressure and pulsatile fluid flow on the cavity of the heart. He described in great detail, in a largely teleological fashion, how these forces could bring about the changes in shape and internal structure of the

heart seen during its morphogenesis. A decade later a similar idea was used by Bremer (13) in a much more scientific attempt to explain the location of the sites of septum formation in the embryonic chick heart. Decisive experiments to test this concept have proved difficult to devise and execute; however, results in the literature have generally been either inconclusive or negative. Many of the changes which Spitzer and others (for example, DeVries and Saunders, 40) have attributed to the eroding force of blood flow, are probably initiated in the embryonic heart at a time before circulation is established (Stephan, 134). We saw earlier that in the amphibian and chick heart the initial curvature can occur

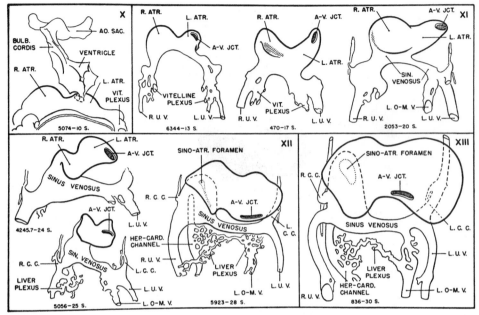

Fig. 16.21 Drawings of models of the venous end of the human heart, viewed from the front. Horizon X to XIII. All enlarged to the same scale, ×50. A-V. JCT, atrioventricular junction; L.C.C., left common cardinal vein; R.C.C., right common cardinal vein; L.U.V., left umbilical vein; R.U.V., right umbilical vein; L.O.M.V., left omphalomesenteric vein. (From Streeter, Embryology Reprint, *Carnegie Inst. Wash.*, vol. 11, 1951.)

even when the organ develops completely isolated from a blood stream (Bacon, 3; Butler, 18). However, experiments performed in recent years to study the effects of surgically altering the venous inflow to the embryonic heart have produced malformations which do appear to be related to the direction and force of the blood flow (Rychter, 119; Simons, 124). Much more work in this field is needed.

Division of the Heart

Examination of Figure 16.20 emphasizes the modifications which have occurred in the different regions of the heart tube by the end of the first month of development. The most striking specialization of the heart tube at this stage is the outgrowth of endothelial diverticulae which occur at two sharply defined areas peripherally on the edge of the tube. In these two areas (Fig. 16.20, horizons XI and XIII) the endothelium opens outward in the form of two trabeculated pouches which are the primordia of the right and left ventricles. The tube has become bent and shows local dilatations and constrictions. Its internal structure is just beginning to presage its division into separate right and left sides. However, at this stage it has not yet altered its primitive method of functioning. The blood enters the heart posteriorly, via the sinus venosus, passes through the atria into the single ventricle, from which it is pumped out through the conus and truncus as an undivided stream, just as was the case at an earlier stage when the heart was a simple straight tube.

During the second month of development in the human (H-H stages 17–27), the single tubular heart is converted into a double pump system, arranged in parallel so that oxygenated blood from the lungs, and systemic venous blood can later be handled separately. This is accomplished by three major morphogenetic events, all spatially interdependent, and all occurring more or less simultaneously. These are: (1) division and torsion of the conotruncal canal to form separate pulmonary and aortic trunks, (2) division of the AV canal into separate left and right channels, (3) formation of the interatrial and interventricular septa.

Unfortunately, the timing of specific morphogenetic events during these latter phases (horizons XIX to XXII) has not been determined as exactly, using reconstructions of carefully staged embryos, as is true for cardiac development during the first five weeks (Streeter, 135). Furthermore, almost nothing is known of the causal mechanisms involved in any of these processes, since experimental investigations of cardiac development during these later phases are lacking. Such cellular activities as mitosis, migration, adhesion, and deadhesion, which may fairly safely be inferred to play important roles in these processes on the basis of descriptive studies, can at present only lie in the realm of experimentally approachable questions (Barry, 6).

In this brief chapter, we have not considered it appropriate to examine further details of cardiac development. Molding of the valves, formation of the papillary muscles, the important changes which take place in the sinus region, entrance and development of the pulmonary veins, formation of the coronary system; these and many other crucial aspects in the differentiation of the mature heart have been ignored, out of lack of information, or lack of space, or both.

Summary

The first localization of cells with heart-forming capacity occurs in vertebrate embryos at about the time of onset of gastrulation. The precardiac mesoderm soon becomes localized into paired primordia. At the earliest stages at which these areas of mesoderm become determined to form heart, the cells already show evidence of biochemical differentiation from their neighbors, exhibiting distinctive immunologic, enzymologic, and metabolic characteristics. There is evidence that in amphibians the heart-forming regions are determined in their cardiogenic potency by a balance of interactions with the endoderm and ectoderm. Critical experiments indicating such interactions in amniote embryos are lacking.

The clusters of precardiac mesoderm that make up the heart-forming regions come together in the ventral midline by a combination of morphogenetic movements which include: the folding movements of the endodermal substratum to which they adhere; the separation of the somatic, splanchnic, and hemangioblast layers as the amniocardiac vesicles and endothelium are established; and autonomous migration of the mesoderm clusters on the endoderm. These migratory activities are apparently directed by adhesive relationships between the mesoderm and endoderm. As the splanchnic mesoderm migrates anteromesially and swings down ventrally, it thickens and lifts off the endoderm to form the paired epimyocardial troughs, within which delicate endocardial tubes develop. These paired structures then fuse in the midline, first in the conotruncal region, and then progressively caudally, to form the primitive tubular heart.

The developing myocardium is soon converted into a compact tissue as desmosomal contacts are established between closely apposed cells. As fibrillogenesis begins, those desmosomes associated with tufts of forming myofibrils are termed primitive intercalated discs. Myoblasts of the earliest hearts studied (7-somite chick; 10-day mouse) contain concentrations of granular material and scattered loose myofilaments. These myofilaments become grouped into short, thin bundles, usually associated with dense regions of Z band, which is probably a membrane structure. This suggests that the Z bands may be the site of growth or deposition of myofibrillar material.

Although scattered loose myofilaments form very early, these become organized as striated myofibrils only shortly before, or just at the time the heart first begins pulsating, and then only in certain cells. Until late in the course of histodifferentiation many cells remain in a highly primitive state while neighboring tissues become well organized.

Mitotic activity varies greatly in different parts and tissues of the forming heart, but is generally high in early phases of development and gradually declines to zero as embryogenesis is completed.

Among the cell types which differentiate from the cardiogenic mesoderm are endothelial, fibroelastic, smooth muscle, and collagenous cells, as well as the myocardium and conductive tissue. The conductive system apparently derives from a limited population of pacemaker cells which alone are capable of generating their own bioelectric potentials, and therefore of stimulating the myocardium. Ordinary myocardial cells are apparently normally nonspontaneous.

Prepacemaker cells are localized with their respective regions of presumptive heart mesoderm in the cardiogenic crescent of the early somite embryo. At this stage they are already coded for the spontaneous rate of pulsation appropriate for the part of the heart in which they will later differentiate. The heart begins to beat as soon as a sufficient level of histodifferentiation is attained (in the chick at 9–10 somites). Its rhythm is at first slow. As pacemaker cells differentiate in progressively more anterior regions, they manifest gradually increasing rates of firing, and thereby supersede more anterior regions in their pacemaker function. Thus there is not a single pacemaker in the early heart, but a succession of pacemaker zones, each holding its dominance for only a brief period until the definitive sinoatrial node differentiates. Studies of pacemaker cells in tissue culture indicate that the activity of these cells can be controlled by varying the components of the culture medium.

The primitive tubular heart becomes looped and divided into the four-chambered structure characteristic of the adult organ as a result of such cellular activities as differential mitosis, migration, adhesion, de-adhesion and cell death. Whether the hemodynamic effects of fluid pressure and pulsatile blood flow also have significant roles in cardiac morphogenesis has not been established by critical experiments.

References

1. Abercrombie, M., "The Control of Growth and the Cell Surface," *Lect. Sci. Basis Med.* 8:19–31 (1958).

2. Allen, H. J., "Glycogen in the Chick Embryo," *Biol. Bull.* 36:63–70 (1919).

3. Bacon, R. L., "Self-differentiation and Induction in the Heart of *Amblystoma*," *J. Exptl. Zool.* 98:87–121 (1945).

4. Barry, A., "Intrinsic Pulsation Rates of Fragments of Embryonic Chick Heart," *J. Exptl. Zool.* 91:119–130 (1942).

5. ——, "The Distribution of Metachromasia in the Heart of the Embryonic Chick," *Anat. Record* 109:363–364 (1951).

6. ——, "Developmental Processes Involved in Cardiogenesis," *Congenital Heart Disease*, A. D. Bass and G. K. Moe, eds. Washington, D. C.: Am. Assoc. Advan. Sci. pp. 11–19 (1960).

7. Balinsky, B. I., "Experiments on Total Extirpation of the Whole Endoderm in *Triton* Embryos," *Compt. J. Rend. Acad. Sci. USSR* 23:196–198 (1939).

8. Baud, Ch. A., "Les Premiers Stades de la Differenciation Submicroscopique du Cytoplasme dans les Cellules Embryonnaires," *Fine Structure of Cells, International Union of Biological Sciences Symp.* Ser. B no. 21. Groningen, Netherlands: P. Noordhoff, N. V. pp. 214–221 (1955).

9. Beams, H. W., T. C. Evans, C. D. Janney, and W. W. Baker, "Electron Microscope Studies on the Structure of Cardiac Muscle," *Anat. Record* 105:59–81 (1949).

10. Bellairs, R., "Studies on the Development of the Foregut in the Chick Blastoderm. II. The Morphogenetic Movements," *J. Embryol. Exptl. Morphol.* 1: 369–385 (1953).

11. Bogue, J. Y., "The Electrocardiogram of the Developing Chick," *J. Exptl. Biol.* 10:286–292 (1933).

12. Brecher, G. A., and P. M. Galletti, "Functional Anatomy of Cardiac Pumping," *Handbook of Physiology, Sec. 2: Circulation.* Washington, D. C.: American Physiological Society 2:759–798 (1963).

13. Bremer, J. L., "The Presence and Influence of Two Spiral Streams in the Heart of the Chick Embryo," *Am. J. Anat.* 49:409–440 (1932).

14. Bullough, W. S., "The Control of Mitotic Activity in Adult Mammalian Tissues," *Biol. Rev.* 37:307–342 (1962).

15. Burrows, M. T., "Rhythmical Activity of Isolated Heart Muscle Cells *in vitro*," *Science* 36:90–92 (1912).

16. ——, "The Reserve Energy of an Actively Growing Embryonic Tissue," *Proc. Soc. Exptl. Biol. Med.* 18:133–136 (1921).

17. Butler, E., "The Developmental Capacity of Regions of the Unincubated Chick Blastoderm as Tested in Chorioallantoic Grafts," *J. Exptl. Zool.* 70:357–389 (1935).

18. Butler, J. K., "An Experimental Analysis of Cardiac Loop Formation in the Chick." M. A. Thesis, University of Texas (1952).

19. Cahn, R. D., "Developmental Changes in Embryonic Enzyme Patterns: the Effect of Oxidative Substrates of Lactic Dehydrogenase in Beating Chick Embryonic Cell Cultures," *Develop. Biol.* 9: 327–346 (1964).

20. Cavanaugh, M. W., "Pulsation, Migration and Division in Dissociated Chick Embryo Heart Cells *in vitro*," *J. Exptl. Zool.* 128:573–589 (1955).

21. Challice, C. E., and G. A. Edwards, "On the Micromorphology of the Developing Ventricular Muscle," *The Specialized Tissues of the Heart*, A. Paes de Carvalho, W. C. de Mello, B. F. Hoffman, eds. Amsterdam: Elsevier, pp. 44–73 (1961).

22. Chaytor, D. E. B., "Mitotic Index *in vitro* of Embryonic Heart Fibroblasts of Different Donor Ages," *Exptl. Cell Res.* 28:212–213 (1962).

23. Chiquoine, A. D., "The Distribution of Polysaccharides during Gastrulation and Embryogenesis in the Mouse Embryo," *Anat. Record* 129:495–515 (1957).

24. Chuang, H. H., and M. P. Tseng, "An Experimental Analysis of the Determination and Differentiation of the Mesodermal Structures of Neurula in Urodeles," *Scientia Sinica (Peking)* 6:669–708 (1957).

25. Clement, A. C., "Development of Ily-

anassa Following Removal of the D Macromere at Successive Cleavage Stages," *J. Exptl. Zool.* 149:193–216 (1962).

26. Crill, W. E., R. E. Rumery, and J. W. Woodbury, "Effects of Membrane Current on Transmembrane Potentials of Cultured Chick Embryo Heart Cells," *Am. J. Physiol.* 197:733–735 (1959).

27. Cunningham, A. W. B., K. Kleutch, and W. Herbst, "Effect of Supernatant Potassium-level on Cardiac Activity in Quantitative Tissue Culture," *Nature* 186: 241–242 (1960).

28. Dalton, A. J., "The Potencies of Portions of Young Chick Blastoderms as Tested in Chorio-allantoic Grafts," *J. Exptl. Zool.* 71:17–52 (1935).

29. Davis, C. L., "Development of the Human Heart from Its First Appearance to the Stage Found in Embryos of Twenty Paired Somites. *Carnegie Contrib. Embryol.* 19:245–284 (1927).

30. DeHaan, R. L., "*Cardia bifida* and the Development of Pacemaker Function in the Early Chick Heart," *Develop. Biol.* 1: 586–602, (1959).

31. ——, "Differentiation of the Atrioventricular Conducting System of the Heart," *Circulation* 24:458–470 (1961).

32. ——, "Regional Organization of Prepacemaker Cells in the Cardiac Primordia of the Early Chick Embryo," *J. Embryol. Exptl. Morphol.* 11:65–76 (1963).

33. ——, "Organization of the Cardiogenic Plate in the Early Chick Embryo," *Acta Embryol. Morphol. Exptl.* 6:26–38 (1963).

34. ——, "Oriented Cell Movements in Embryogenesis," *Biological Organization at the Cellular and Supercellular Level*, R. H. C. Harris, ed. New York: Academic Press, pp. 147–164 (1963).

35. ——, "Migration Patterns of the Precardiac Mesoderm in the Early Chick Embryo," *Exptl. Cell Res.* 29:544–560 (1963).

36. ——, "Cell Interactions and Oriented Movements during Development," *J. Exptl. Zool.* 157:127–138 (1964).

37. ——, "Morphogenetic Movements in Cardiogenesis," *Report of the Director, Dept. Embryol.* Washington, D. C.: Carnegie Inst. Wash., Year Book 63: 525–535 (1964).

38. ——, "Development of Pacemaker Tissue in the Embryonic Heart," *Ann. N. Y. Acad. Sci.* (1965).

39. ——, and J. D. Ebert, "Morphogenesis," *Ann. Rev. Physiol.* 26:15–46 (1964).

40. DeVries, P. A., and J. B. de C. M. Saunders, "Development of the Ventricles and Spiral Outflow Tract in the Human Heart," *Carnegie Contrib. Embryol.* 37: 87–114 (1962).

41. Dewey, M. M., and L. Barr, "A Study of the Structure and Distribution of the Nexus," *J. Cell Biol.* 23:553–585 (1964).

42. Duffey, L. M., and J. D. Ebert, "Metabolic Characteristics of the Heart-forming Areas of the Early Chick Embryo," *J. Embryol. Exptl. Morphol.* 5:324–339 (1957).

43. Dwinnell, L. A., "Physiological Contraction of Double Hearts in Rabbit Embryos," *Proc. Soc. Exptl. Biol. Med.* 42: 264–267 (1939).

44. Ebert, J. D., "Analysis of the Synthesis and Distribution of the Contractile Protein, Myosin, in the Development of the Heart," *Proc. Natl. Acad. Sci. U. S.* 39: 333 (1953).

45. ——, R. A. Tolman, A. M. Mun, and J. F. Albright, "The Molecular Basis of the First Heart Beats," *Ann. N. Y. Acad. Sci.* 60, no. 7:968–985 (1955).

46. Eberth, C. J., "Die Elemente der quergestreiften Muskeln," *Arch. Pathol. Anat. Physiol.* 37:100–124 (1866).

47. Fawcett, D. W., and C. C. Selby, "Observations on the Fine Structure of the Turtle Atrium," *J. Biophys. Biochem. Cytol.* 4:63–72 (1958).

48. Fingl, E., L. A. Woodbury, and H. H. Hecht, "Effects of Innervation and Drugs on Direct Membrane Potentials of Embryonic Chick Myocardium," *J. Pharmacol. Exptl. Therap.* 104:103–114 (1952).

49. Franzini-Armstrong, C., and K. R. Porter, "The Z-disc of Skeletal Muscle Fibrils," *Z. Zellforsch.* 61:661–672 (1964).

50. Garofolini, L., "Rhythmical Contractions of Single Heart Muscle Cells in Tissue Culture *in vitro*," *J. Physiol. London* 63:V (1927).

51. Gaskell, W., "The Contraction of Cardiac Muscle," *Textbook of Physiology*, E. A. Schäfer, ed. 2:169–227 (1900).

52. Godlewski, E., "Die Entwicklung des Skelet- und Herz-muskelgewebes der

Säugethiere," *Arch. Mikroskop. Anat.* 60: 111–156 (1902).

53. Goss, C. M., "Development of the Median Coordinated Ventricle from the Lateral Hearts in Rat Embryos with Three to Six Somites," *Anat. Record* 112:761–796 (1952).

54. Grimley, P. M., and G. A. Edwards, "The Ultrastructure of Cardiac Desmosomes in the Toad and Their Relationship to the Intercalated Disc," *J. Biophys. Biochem. Cytol.* 8:305–318 (1960).

55. Grohmann, D., "Mitotische Wachstumintensität des Embryonalen und Fetalen Hünchenherzens und ihre Bedeutung für Entstehung von Herzmissbildungen," *Z. Zellforsch.* 55:104–122 (1961).

56. Hall, C. E., M. A. Jakus, and F. O. Schmitt, "The Structure of Certain Muscle Fibrils as Revealed by the Use of Electron Stains," *J. Appl. Phys.* 16:459–465 (1945).

57. Hamburger, V., and H. L. Hamilton, "A Series of Normal Stages in the Development of the Chick Embryo," *J. Morphol.* 88:49–92 (1951).

58. Harary, I., and B. Farley, "*In vitro* Studies on Single Beating Rat Heart Cells. I. Growth and Organization," *Exptl. Cell Res.* 29:451–465 (1963).

59. ———, and ———, "*In vitro* Studies on Single Beating Heart Cells. II. Intercellular Communication," *Exptl. Cell Res.* 29:466–474 (1963).

60. Hay, E. D., "The Fine Structure of Differentiating Muscle in the Salamander Tail," *Z. Zellforsch.* 59:6–34 (1963).

61. Heidenhain, M., "Ueber die Structur des menschlichen Herzmuskels," *Anat. Anz.* 20:33–78 (1901).

62. Hensen, V., "Beobachten über die Befruchtung und Entwicklung des Kaninchens und Meerschweinchens," *Z. Anat. Entwicklungsgeschichte* 1:353–423 (1876).

63. Heuser, C. H., "A Pre-somite Human Embryo with a Definite Chorda Canal," *Carnegie Contrib. Embryol.* 23:251–267 (1932).

64. ———, and G. W. Corner, "Developmental Horizons in Human Embryos. Description of Age Group X, 4 to 12 Somites," *Carnegie Contrib. Embryol.* 36: 29–39 (1957).

65. Hibbs, R. G., "Electron Microscopy of Developing Cardiac Muscle in Chick Embryo," *Am. J. Anat.* 99:17–51 (1956).

66. Hoff, E. C., T. C. Kramer, D. Dubois, and B. M. Patten, "The Development of the Electrocardiogram of the Embryonic Heart," *Am. Heart J.* 17:470–488 (1939).

67. Hoffman, B. F., and P. F. Cranefield, *Electrophysiology of the Heart.* New York: McGraw-Hill (1960).

68. Hogue, M. J., "Intercalated Discs in Tissue Culture," *Anat. Record* 99:157–162 (1947).

69. Holtzer, H., J. Abbot, and M. W. Cavanaugh, "Some Properties of Embryonic Cardiac Myoblasts," *Exptl. Cell Res.* 16: 595–601 (1959).

69a. Holtzman, D. and D. Agin, "Effect of Trypsin on Resting Potential of Frog Muscle," *Nature* 205:911–912 (1965).

70. Jacobson, A. G., "Influences of Ectoderm and Endoderm on Heart Differentiation in the Newt," *Develop. Biol.* 2: 138–154 (1960).

71. ———, "Heart Determination in the Newt," *J. Exptl. Zool.* 146:139–151 (1961).

72. Jamieson, J. D., and G. E. Palade, "Specific Granules in Atrial Muscle Cells," *J. Cell Biol.* 23:151–172 (1964).

73. Johnstone, P. N., "Studies on the Physiological Anatomy of the Embryonic Heart. II. An Inquiry into the Development of the Heart Beat in Chick Embryos, Including the Development of Irritability to Electrical Stimulation," *Bull. Johns Hopkins Hosp.* 36:299–311 (1925).

74. Jordan, H. E., and K. B. Steele, "A Comparative Microscopic Study of the Intercalated Discs of Vertebrate Heart Muscle," *Am. J. Anat.* 13:151–173 (1912).

75. Leblond, C. P., B. Messier, and B. Kopriwa, "Thymidine-H³ as a Tool for the Investigation of the Renewal of Cell Populations," *Lab. Invest.* 8:296–308 (1959).

76. Lefford, F., "The Effect of Donor Age on the Emigration of Cells from Chick Embryo Explants *in vitro,*" *Exptl. Cell Res.* 35:557–571 (1964).

77. Lehmkuhl, D., and N. Sperelakis, "Transmembrane Potentials of Trypsin-dispersed Chick Heart Cells Cultured *in vitro,*" *Am. J. Physiol.* 205:1213–1220 (1963).

78. Leslie, I., and M. Yarnell, "Succinic

Dehydrogenase and Cytochrome Oxidase Activities in Cell Cultures," *J. Biochem. Biophys. Cytol.* 7:265–272 (1960).

79. Lewis, M. R., "Development of Cross-Striations in the Heart Muscle of the Chick Embryo," *Bull. Johns Hopkins Hosp.* 30:176–181 (1919).

80. Lewis, W. H., "The Cultivation of Embryonic Heart Muscle," *Carnegie Contrib. Embryol.* 18:1–32 (1926).

81. Lieberman, M., "An Electrophysiological Study of the Embryonic Chick Heart." Ph.D. Thesis, Dept. Physiology, State University of New York, Downstate Medical Center (1964).

82. Lindner, E., "Myofibrils in the Early Development of Chick Embryo Hearts as Observed with the Electron Microscope," *Anat. Record* 136:234 (1960).

83. Loewenstein, W. R., and Y. Kanno, "Studies on an Epithelial (Gland) Cell Junction. I. Modifications of Surface Membrane Permeability," *J. Cell Biol.* 22:565–586 (1964).

84. MacCallum, J. B., "On the Muscular Architecture and Growth of the Ventricles of the Heart," *Johns Hopkins Hosp. Rep.* 9:307–335 (1900).

85. Mall, F. P., "On the Muscular Architecture of the Ventricles of the Human Heart," *Am. J. Anat.* 11:211–266 (1911).

86. Mangold, O., "Entwicklung und Differenzierung der präsumptiven Epidermis und ihres unterlagernden Entomesoderms aus der Neurula von Triton alpestris als Isolat," *Arch. Entwicklungsmech. Or.* 147:131–170 (1954).

87. ———, "Zur Analyse der Induktionsleistung des Entoderms der Neurula von Urodelen," *Naturwissenschaften* 44:289–290 (1957).

88. McCallion, D. J., and W. T. Wong, "A Study of the Localization and Distribution of Glycogen in Early Stages of the Chick Embryo," *Canad. J. Zool.* 34:63–67 (1956).

89. McKenzie, J., and J. D. Ebert, "The Inhibitory Action of Antimycin A in the Early Chick Embryo," *J. Exptl. Embryol. Morphol.* 8:314–320 (1960).

90. Meda, E., and A. Ferroni, "Early Functional Differentiation of Heart Muscle Cells," *Experientia* 15:427–428 (1959).

91. Medawar, P. B., "The Growth, Growth Energy and Ageing of the Chicken's Heart," *Proc. Roy. Soc. London Ser. B* 129:332–355 (1940).

92. Meyer, H., and L. T. Queiroga, "Electron Microscopic Study of the Developing Heart Muscle Cell in Thin Sections of Chick-embryo Tissue Cultures," *The Specialized Tissues of the Heart*, A. Paes de Carvalho, W. C. de Mello and B. F. Hoffman, eds. Amsterdam: Elsevier, pp. 76–79 (1961).

93. Mollier, S., "Die erste Anlage des Herzens bei den Wirbeltieren," *Handbuch der Vergleichenden und experimentellen Entwickelungslehre der Wirbeltiere*, O. Hertwig, ed. Jena, Germany: Gustav Fisher Uerlangsbuchhandlung, vol. 1, pp. 1019–1051 (1906).

94. Muir, Alan, R., "An Electron Microscope Study of the Embryology of the Intercalated Disc in the Heart of the Rabbit," *J. Biophys. Biochem. Cytol.* 3:193–202 (1957).

95. Mulherkar, L., "Induction by Regions Lateral to the Streak in the Chick," *J. Exptl. Embryol. Morphol.* 6:1–14 (1958).

96. Nieuwkoop, P. D., "Experimental Investigations on the Origin and Determination of the Germ Cells, and on the Development of the Lateral Plates and Germ Ridges in Urodeles," *Arch. Neerl. Zool.* 8:1–205 (1947).

97. Olivo, O. M., "Précoce Détermination de l'Ébauche du Coeur dans l'Embryon de Poulet et Sa Différenciation Histologique et Physiologique *in vitro*," *Compt. Rend. Assoc. Anat. Prague* 23:357–374 (1928).

97a. ———, R. Laschi, and M. L. Lucchi, "Genesi delle Miofibrille del Cuore Embrionale di Pollo Osservate al Microscopio Elettronico e Inizio dell'Attivita Contrattile," *Lo Sperimentale* 114:69–78 (1964).

98. ———, and E. Slavich, "Ricerche sulla Velocita dell'Accrescimento delle Cellule e Degli Organi," *Arch. Entwicklungsmech. Or.* 121:96–110 (1930).

99. Ortiz, E. C., "Estudio Histoquimico de la Gelatina Cardiaca en el Embrion de Pollo," *Arch. Inst. Cardiol. Mex.* 28:244–262 (1958).

100. Orts-Llorca, F., "Influence of the Endoderm on Heart Differentiation during the Early Stages of Development of the Chicken Embryo," *Arch. Entwicklungsmech.* 154:533–551 (1963).

101. Paes de Carvalho, A., DeMello, W. C., and B. F. Hoffman, "Electrophysiological Evidence for Specialized Fiber Types in

Rabbit Atrium," *Am. J. Physiol.* 196:483–488 (1959).

102. Paff, G. H., "Conclusive Evidence for Sino-atrial Dominance in Isolated 48-hour Embryonic Chick Hearts Cultivated *in vitro*," *Anat. Record* 63:203–210 (1935).

103. ——, "Transplantation of Sino-atrium to Conus in the Embryonic Heart *in vitro*," *Am. J. Physiol.* 117:313–317 (1936).

104. Patten, B. M., "Formation of the Cardiac Loop in the Chick," *Am. J. Anat.* 30:373–397 (1922).

105. ——, "The Development of the Sinoventricular Conduction System," *Mich. Univ. Med. Bull.* 22:1–21 (1956).

106. ——, "The Development of the Heart," *Pathology of the Heart*, 2d edition, S. E. Gould, ed. Springfield, Ill.: Charles C Thomas, pp. 24–92 (1960).

107. ——, and T. C. Kramer, "The Initiation of Contraction in the Embryonic Chick Heart," *Am. J. Anat.* 53:349–375 (1933).

108. ——, ——, and A. Barry, "Valvular Action in the Embryonic Chick Heart by Localized Apposition of Endocardial Masses," *Anat. Record* 102:299–312 (1948).

109. Pelc, S. R., "Labelling of DNA and Cell Division in So-called Non-dividing Tissues," *J. Cell Biol.* 22:21–28 (1964).

110. Ranvier, L., *Traite Technique d'Histologie*, 2d edition, Paris: F. Savy (1889).

111. Rawles, M. E., "The Heart-forming Areas of the Early Chick Blastoderm," *Physiol. Zool.* 16:22–42 (1943).

112. Reporter, M. C., and J. D. Ebert, *Report of the Director, Dept. Embryol., Carnegie Inst. Wash.*, Year Book 63:521–525 (1964).

113. Rhodin, J. A. G., P. del Missier, and L. C. Reid, "The Structure of the Specialized Impulse-conducting System of the Steer Heart," *Circulation* 24:349–367 (1961).

114. Richter, G. W., and A. Kellner, "Hypertrophy of the Human Heart at the Level of Fine Structure," *J. Cell Biol.* 18:195–206 (1963).

115. Rijlant, P., "Contribution a l'Etude de l'Automatisme et de la Conduction dans le Coeur – Ablation et Greffe Intercardiaque du Noeud de Keith-Flack (sinus) chez la Chevre, le Mouton, le Chat et le Lapin. Greffes Heterogenes du Noeud de Keith-Flack Chez le Chien, la Chevre et le Mouton," *Bull. Acad. Roy. Med. Belg.* Ser. 5, 7:161–200 (1927).

116. Rudnick, D., "Differentiation in Culture of Pieces of Early Chick Blastoderm. II. Short Primitive Streak Stages," *J. Exptl. Zool.* 79:399–425 (1938).

117. ——, "Teleosts and Birds," *Analysis of Development*, B. H. Willier, P. A. Weiss, and V. Hamburger, eds. Philadelphia: Saunders, pp. 297–314 (1955).

118. Rumery, R. E., R. J. Blandau, and P. W. Hagey, "Observations of Living Myocardial Cells from Cultured 48-hour Chick Hearts," *Anat. Record* 141:253–262 (1961).

119. Rychter, Z., "Experimental Morphology of the Aortic Arches and the Heart Loop in Chick Embryos," *Advan. in Morphogenesis* 2:333–371 (1962).

120. Sabin, F. R., "Origin and Development of the Primitive Vessels of the Chick and of the Pig," *Carnegie Contrib. Embryol.* 6:61–124 (1917).

121. ——, "Studies on the Origin of Blood-vessels and of Red Blood-corpuscles as Seen in the Living Blastoderm of Chicks during the Second Day of Incubation," *Carnegie Contrib. Embryol.* 9:213–264 (1920).

122. Shaner, R. F., "The Development of the Muscular Architecture of the Ventricles of the Pig's Heart, with a Review of the Adult Heart and a Note on Two Abnormal Mammalian Hearts," *Anat. Record* 39:1–35 (1928).

123. Shipley, R. A., L. J. Shipley, and J. T. Wearn, "The Capillary Supply in Normal and Hypertrophied Hearts of Rabbits," *J. Exptl. Med.* 65:29–42 (1937).

124. Simons, J. R., "Pulmonary Return as an Agent in the Final Development of the Atrium in *Rana temporaria*," *J. Embryol. Exptl. Morphol.* 5:250–255 (1957).

125. Sippel, T. O., "Growth of Succinoxidase Activity in Hearts of Rat and Chick Embryos," *J. Exptl. Zool.* 126:205–221 (1954).

126. Sjöstrand, F. S., and E. Andersson-Cedergren, "Intercalated Discs of Heart Muscle," *Structure and Function of Muscle*, G. H. Bourne, ed. New York: Academic Press, vol. I, pp. 421–445 (1960).

127. Sperelakis, N., and D. Lehmkuhl, "Effect of Current on Transmembrane Potentials in Cultured Chick Heart Cells," *J. Gen. Physiol.* 47:895–927 (1964).

127a. Spiro, D., and E. H. Sonnenblick, "Comparison of the Ultrastructural Basis of the Contractile Process in Heart and Skeletal Muscle," *Circulation Res.* Suppl. 2:14–37 (1964).

128. Spitzer, A., *The Architecture of Normal and Malformed Hearts. A Phylogenetic Theory of Their Development*, translated by M. Lev and A. Vass. Springfield, Ill.: Charles C Thomas (1951).

129. Sparagen, S. C., V. P. Bond, and L. K. Dahl, "DNA Synthesizing Cells in Rabbit Heart Tissue after Cholesterol Feeding," *Circulation Res.* 11:982–986 (1962).

130. Spratt, N. T., "Location of Organ-specific Regions and Their Relationship to the Development of the Primitive Streak in the Early Chick Blastoderm," *J. Exptl. Zool.* 89:69–101 (1942).

131. ———, "Nutritional Requirements of the Early Chick Embryo. II. Differential Nutrient Requirements for Morphogenesis and Differentiation of Heart and Brain," *J. Exptl. Zool.* 114:375–402 (1950).

132. ———, and H. Haas, "Morphogenetic Movements in the Lower Surface of the Unincubated and Early Chick Blastoderm," *J. Exptl. Zool.* 144:139–158 (1960).

133. Stenger, R. J., and D. Spiro, "The Ultrastructure of Mammalian Cardiac Muscle," *J. Biophys. Biochem. Cytol.* 9:325–351 (1961).

134. Stephan, F., "La Morphogenese du Coeur Chez le Poulet aprés Resection des Territoires Posterieurs de Son Ébauche Gauche," *Compt. Rend. Soc. Biol.* 152:139–141 (1958).

135. Streeter, G. L., "Development Horizons in Human Embryos, Age Groups XI to XXIII," Embryology Reprint, *Carnegie Inst. Wash.* vol. 11 (1951).

136. Tandler, J., "The Development of the Heart," *Manual of Human Embryology*, F. Keibel and F. P. Mall, eds. Philadelphia: Lippincott, 2:534–570 (1912).

137. Taussig, H. B., "The Anatomy of the Heart in Two Cases of *situs transversus*," *Bull. Johns Hopkins Hosp.* 39:199–202 (1926).

138. Thomas, C. E., "The Muscular Architecture of the Ventricles of Hog and Dog Hearts," *Am. J. Anat.* 101:17–58 (1957).

139. Thompson, T. E., "The Properties of Bimolecular Phospholipid Membranes," *Cellular Membranes in Development*, M. Locke, ed. New York: Academic Press, pp. 83–96 (1964).

140. Van der Kloot, W. G., and B. Dane, "Conduction of the Action Potential in the Frog Ventricle," *Science* 146:74–75 (1964).

141. Van der Stricht, O., "La Première Apparition de la Cavité Coelomique dans l'Aire Embryonnaire du Lapin," *Compt. Rend. Soc. Biol. Ser. 10*, 12:207–211 (1895).

141a. Van Mierop, L. H. S., R. D. Alley, H. W. Kausel, and A. Stranahan, "Pathogenesis of Transposition Complexes. I. Embryology of the Ventricles and Great Arteries," *Am. J. Cardiol.* 12:216–225 (1963).

142. Vogt, W., "Gesteltungsanalyse am Amphibienkeim mit örtlicher Vitalfärbung," *Arch. Entwicklungsmech. Or.* 120:384–706 (1929).

143. Waddington, C. H., "Experiments on the Development of Chick and Duck Embryos Cultivated *in vitro*," *Phil. Trans. Royal Soc. London Ser. B* 221:179–230 (1932).

144. Wainrach, S., and J. R. Sotelo, "Electron Microscope Study of the Developing Chick Embryo Heart," *Z. Zellforsch.* 55:622–634 (1961).

145. Weber, R., "Submicroscopical and Biochemical Characteristics of Morphodynamic Units in Spirally Cleaving Eggs," *Symp. Germ Cells Develop.*, Inst. Intern. Embryol. and Fondazione A. Baselli, pp. 225–254 (1961).

146. Weidmann, S., "The Electrical Constants of Purkinje Fibers," *J. Physiol.* 118:348–360 (1952).

147. Weissenfels, N., "Der Einfluss der Gewebezüchtung auf die Morphologie der Hühnerherzmyoblasten. IV. Über Differenzierungs- und Abbauvorgänge an den Muskelelementen," *Protoplasma* 55:99–113 (1962).

148. Werner, Marie, "Besteht die Herzmuskulatur der Säugetiere aus allseits scharf begrenzten Zellen oder nicht?" *Arch. Mikroskop. Anat.* 75:101–149 (1910).

149. Wilens, S., "The Migration of Heart Mesoderm and Associated Areas in *Amblystoma punctatum*," *J. Exptl. Zool.* 129:576–606 (1955).

150. Witte, L., "Histogenesis of the Heart

Muscle of the Pig in Relation to the Appearance and Development of the Intercalated Discs," *Am. J. Anat.* 25:333–347 (1919).

150a. Wollenberger, A., "Rhythmic and Arrhythmic Contractile Activity of Single Myocardial Cells Cultured *in vitro*," *Circulation Res.*, Suppl. 2:184–201 (1964).

151. ——, and W. Halle, "Specificity of the Effects of Cardiac Glycosides on the Rhythmic Contraction of Single Cultured Cardiac Muscle Cells," *Nature* 188: 1114–1115 (1960).

152. Yaffe, D., and M. Feldman, "The Effect of Antinomycin D on Heart and Thigh Muscle Cells Grown *in vitro*," *Develop. Biol.* 9:347–366 (1964).

153. Yokoyama, H. O., R. B. Jennings, and W. B. Wartman, "Intercalated Discs of Dog Myocardium," *Exptl. Cell Res.* 23: 29–44 (1961).

154. Yoshida, T., "Fusion of the Cardiac Anlagen in the Duck, *Anas*," *Arb. Med. Univ. Okayama* 3:61–91 (1932).

155. Yoshinaga, T., "A Contribution to the Early Development of the Heart in Mammalia, with Special Reference to the Guinea Pig," *Anat. Record* 21:239–308 (1921).

17

Development and Regeneration
of the Liver

Y. Croisille and N. M. Le Douarin

*Laboratoire d'Embryologie Expérimentale
du Collège de France
et du Centre National de la Recherche Scientifique
Nogent-sur-Marne, France*

Early work on liver development, at the turn of the century, was essentially descriptive (Felix, 73; Brouha, 18; Choronshitzky, 30). More recent studies have led to greater precision without modifying the general lines of the classical descriptions (Lipp, 140; Elias, 68; Kingsbury et al., 120). The subject of the gross development of the liver has been repeatedly analyzed and reviewed, but apparently little attention has been paid to the problem of early hepatic organogenesis in vertebrates. It is for that reason that one of us (Le Douarin) decided to explore the inductive mechanisms intervening during early differentiation of the hepatic cells. The results of that study will be presented in detail in the first section of the present review. The second section will be concerned largely with recent studies of the development of different components of the liver cell

as seen with the electron microscope. In a third section, some biochemical changes accompanying liver development will be described. Finally, the structural, functional, and biochemical changes accompanying the regeneration of the liver will be reviewed and the problems of the specific control of liver growth and of the initial stimulus to regeneration discussed.

Before centering attention on the first section, it should be recalled that in amniotes the primary hepatic rudiment is an endodermal evagination of the floor of the foregut which extends forward into the mesenchyme of the septum transversum. In contact with the ductus venosus the hepatic primordium divides into two parts: a cranial and ventral part, and a caudal dorsal part. In the chick embryo the primary diverticulum appears at the 20- to 22-somite stage. In the mesenchyme of the

421

septum transversum the secondary hepatic primordia enlarge and form a cylindrical envelope around the ductus venosus which disappears as it is fragmented by the hepatic cords which invade it. Now the right and left lobes of the liver develop. The lower part of the cranial bud gives rise to the hepato-enteric duct, whereas the basal part of the caudal bud develops into the hepatocystic duct and gall bladder. In mammals the hepatic cords are usually formed by the cranial part of the primary diverticulum, the caudal part giving rise to the biliary ducts.

Early Embryological Mechanisms of Liver Differentiation

It is in the chick embryo that Le Douarin (126–133) decided to investigate the mechanisms intervening during early hepatic organogenesis. Attention has been focused on the following questions: (1) the distribution of hepatic histogenetic potencies at stages preceding the appearance of the first hepatic primordium, (2) the role of the different regions of the presumptive hepatic area during histogenesis of the liver, (3) the inductive mechanisms underlying the transformation of the undifferentiated endoderm into hepatic endoderm.

Hepatic Histogenetic Potencies

Since the work of Rudnick (181) and of Rawles (174) the localization of the liver-forming areas at early developmental stages of the chick has been well established. Liver potency occurs in close association with heart potency. At the primitive streak stage the prospective cardiohepatic areas are located in the anterior part of the blastoderm. At the head-process stage, cardiohepatic potency is concentrated in two bilateral areas, one on each side of Hensen's node. At the 9- to 15-somite stage, the greatest part of the hepatic areas remains located bilaterally, but in the anterior part of the embryo these areas merge on the medioventral line in the floor of the foregut and cardiac fold. The latter localizations have been established by the use of localized radio destruction and marking

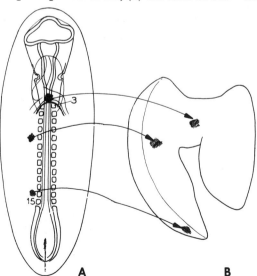

Fig. 17.1 Carbon particle marking of the chick embryo liver. A. 15-somite-stage embryo (ventral view). Three marks are inserted in the tissues, one in the cardiac fold, the two others at two different levels of the right lateral area. B. At the 8th day of incubation the marks are found in the median part and in the right lobe of the liver. (Le Douarin, *Bull. Biol. Fr. Belg.* 98(4):543–583; 98(5):589–676, 1964.)

A   B

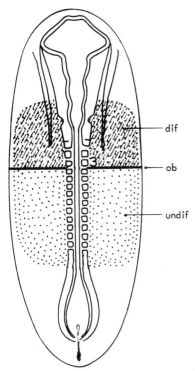

dif

ob

undif

Fig. 17.2 13-somite-stage embryo in which transverse obstacles have been placed at the level of the 3rd somite. Liver differentiates, dif, only ahead of the obstacles, ob. (Le Douarin, *Bull. Biol. Fr. Belg.* 98(4): 543–583; 98(5):589–676, 1964.)

with carbon particles as shown in Figure 17.1 (Le Douarin, 127, 128, 131, 133).

At the head-process stage, histogenetic potencies are homogeneously distributed in the whole presumptive hepatic area (174), each part of that area being capable of forming liver when transplanted to the chorioallantoic membrane. The situation is different at the 9- to 15-somite stage (131, 133). Certain regions belonging to the hepatic presumptive area do not undergo hepatic histogenesis when transplanted to the coelom of a host embryo. This is the case with the lateral parts; these areas take part in the genesis of

hepatic tissue only if they are in association with the cardiac fold. Only the latter region is capable of forming liver by autodifferentiation.

One can thus draw the conclusion that at the stage preceding the appearance of the liver buds, the presumptive hepatic area is more extensive than the region capable of forming liver by self-differentiation. The foregoing observations raise the problem of the role played by the different parts of the hepatic area during liver organogenesis.

In ovo Isolation of the Lateral Hepatic Areas

If the presumptive hepatic area is divided by a transverse slit into which a mechanical obstacle (a fragment of shell membrane) is inserted, liver differentiates only in the anterior part ahead of the obstacles, as shown in Figure 17.2 (123, 131, 133). The same result can be obtained by removing a rectangular portion of the lateral embryonic area at a level extending from the third to sixth somite. The posterior part of the hepatic area, located behind the obstacles or cut, does not differentiate into liver tissue. These results corroborate previous findings obtained by coelomic grafting experiments which showed that the posterior part of the hepatic area does not differentiate into liver when it is isolated from the anterior part comprising the cardiac fold.

The posterior lateral hepatic area, behind the obstacles, develops into two loose mesenchymal cell masses which are limited by a thickened coelomic epithelium. The location of these mesenchymal cell masses is the same as that of the right and left lobes of the liver (Fig. 17.3) in intact 5-day-old embryo (Brouha, 18). The mesenchymal cells are arranged in strands separated only by blood sinusoids (Fig. 17.4). Thus, behind the obstacles, the mes-

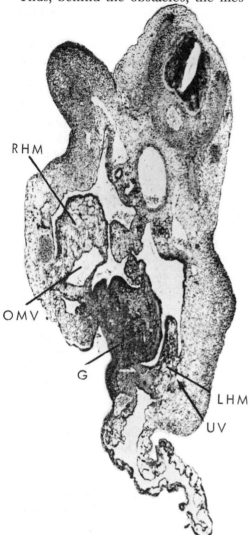

RHM

OMV

G

LHM

UV

Fig. 17.3 Transverse section of a 5-day-old embryo in the part located behind the obstacles. The gizzard, G, remained open ventrally. In the coelomic cavity there are two mesenchymal masses, RHM, and LHM (right and left hepatic mesenchyme), which surround the omphalomesenteric vein, OMV, on the right, and the umbilical vein, UV, on the left side. (Le Douarin, *Bull. Biol. Fr. Belg.* 98(4):543–583; 98(5):589–676, 1964.)

enchymal part of the hepatic lobes has developed, but it is devoid of epithelial cords.

In the anterior part of the embryo, ahead of the obstacles, the hepatic endodermal buds appear at the level of the anterior intestinal portal at the same time as during normal development (20–22-somite stage). The glandular cords formed by these buds invade the mesenchyme of the septum transversum.

From these results it can be concluded that at late stages preceding the appearance of the hepatic buds, the presumptive hepatic area is no more homogenous than it was at presomite stages. The endodermal part is localized in the anterior intestinal portal at the angle formed by the reflection of the endoderm (Fig. 17.5). The mesodermal area is more widespread. It is not only localized in the cardiac fold but in two lateral regions extending to about the 15th somite. Only the region containing both the endodermal primordium and mesenchyme can differentiate into liver tissue when experimentally isolated.

The mesenchymal part provides a matrix into which the endodermal epithelial cords proliferate. At the time the endodermal buds appear, the hepatic mesenchyme is not yet individualized in the region behind the cardiac fold. It is invaded by the hepatic cells during its formation, while closure of the preumbilical intestine is accomplished. Thus, at no time during its organogenesis does the liver consist of an individualized mesenchymal primordium and a still undifferentiated epithelial primordium, as is the rule for most other organs of mixed origin (lung, pancreas, metanephros).

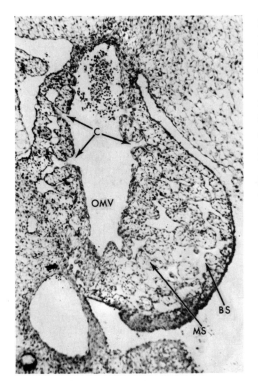

Fig. 17.4 Structure of the hepatic mesenchyme (right lobe). Between the mesenchymal strands, MS, one observes wide blood sinusoids, BS, which are largely communicating, C, with the omphalomesenteric vein, OMV. (Le Douarin, *Bull. Biol. Fr. Belg.* 98(4):543–583; 98(5):589–676, 1964.)

Role of the Mesenchyme during Differentiation of Hepatocytes

Two questions will be raised: Does the hepatic mesenchyme exert a morphogenetic action upon the endoderm? If so, is the action specific?

At the 20- to 22-somite stage the primary hepatic bud appears at the angle formed by the reflection of the endoderm of the anterior intestinal portal. It is formed by epithelial cells not yet differentiated into hepatocytes. If that endodermal primordium is separated by trypsinization from the underlying

mesenchyme (Fig. 17.6*B*), it cannot express its hepatogenic potencies when cultivated in vitro or grafted into the coelom of a host embryo (Le Douarin, 133). Isolated in vitro according to the method of Wolff and Haffen (212), the endodermal bud, deprived of mesenchyme, degenerates rapidly. If it is grafted into the coelom of a host embryo, the endoderm loses its epithelial aspect and gives rise to little masses of undifferentiated cells.

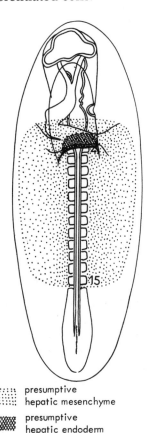

:::::: presumptive
:::::: hepatic mesenchyme

▩ presumptive
▩ hepatic endoderm

Fig. 17.5 Distribution of the hepatic endodermal and mesodermal areas in the 15-somite-stage embryo. The presumptive hepatic endoderm is localized in the anterior intestinal portal. (Le Douarin, *Bull. Biol. Fr. Belg.* 98(4):543–583; 98(5):589–676, 1964.)

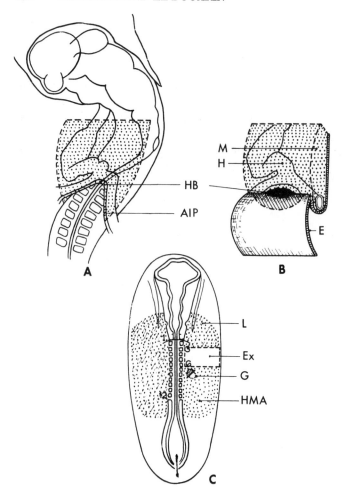

Fig. 17.6 Experimental schema of the *in ovo* association of the hepatic endodermal buds with homologous mesenchyme. A. Excision of the area of the cardiac fold in a 21-somite-stage embryo. B. Separation by trypsinization, of the endoderm, E, containing the hepatic buds, HB. C. Grafting of the buds in the posterior part of the presumptive hepatic mesenchyme area, which has been isolated by an excision, Ex, of the lateral area. (The excision acts as an obstacle.) AIP, anterior intestinal portal; G, graft; H, heart; L, zone where the host liver differentiates; M, mesenchyme; HMA, presumptive hepatic mesenchyme. (Le-Douarin *Bull. Biol. Fr. Belg.* 98(4):543–583; 98(5): 589–676, 1964.)

In contrast, if it is associated with hepatic mesenchyme, the endodermal bud differentiates into cords of hepatic cells. The association of the two tissues can be accomplished *in ovo* or in vitro. If the isolated endodermal bud is grafted into the presumptive hepatic mesenchyme area, behind an obstacle (Fig. 17.6C), it differentiates into hepatic cords and invades the hepatic mesenchyme of the host (Fig. 17.7). The liver tissue which is formed is of mixed origin: the hepatic parenchyma comes from the grafted endoderm whereas the mesenchymal part is furnished by the host (133).

Furthermore, hepatic mesenchyme, isolated by an obstacle, may be transplanted from a 5-day-old embryo to the surface of a semisolid culture medium, and associated with the endoderm of a 20- to 22-somite stage embryo. Under these conditions a lobe of hepatic tissue develops in vitro (Fig. 17.8). Thus the hepatic mesenchyme exerts a morphogenetic action upon the endodermal cells of the hepatic buds, which in turn become capable of proliferating and differentiating into hepatocytes.

Association of endodermal buds with different heterologous mesenchymes (Le Douarin, 129, 131, 133) has shown

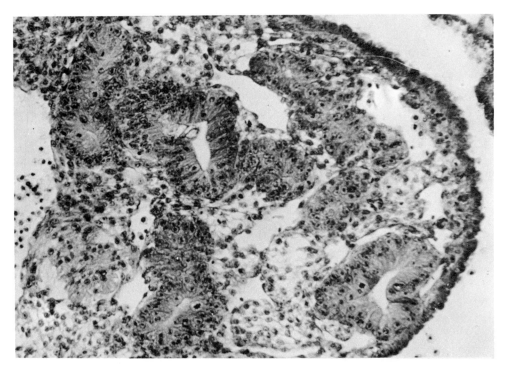

Fig. 17.7 Result of the association *in ovo* of hepatic mesenchyme with the endodermal liver primordium as represented in Fig. 17.6. At the 5th day of incubation the hepatic mesenchyme of the host is invaded by the hepatic epithelial cords of the graft. (Le Douarin, *Bull. Biol. Fr. Belg.* 98(4):543–583; 98(5):589–676, 1964.)

that the morphogenetic action exerted by hepatic mesenchyme is not strictly specific; certain mesenchymes from other parts of the embryo also permit further development of the endoderm. But it is remarkable that only those mesenchymes which are of the same embryonic origin as the hepatic mesenchyme, that is, mesenteric or peritoneal, permit the endodermal buds to develop and differentiate. The best differentiation, however, is obtained in the presence of homologous hepatic mesenchyme. All other types of mesenchyme, such as cephalic, somitic, and mesonephric, permit survival of the hepatic endoderm without permitting its differentiation.

On the other hand, the morphogenetic action of hepatic mesenchyme cannot induce other types of endoderm to differentiate into hepatocytes. Only hepatic endoderm responds to the stimulus of the mesenchyme.

Thus we can conclude that it is not the hepatic mesenchyme which determines the fate of the hepatic endoderm.

Determination of the Hepatic Endoderm

Recent experiments have shown that the determination of the hepatic endoderm takes place at the 4- to 5-somite stage and is due to the inductive action of the mesoderm of the cardiac area (Le Douarin, 130, 132, 133).

At presomite stages, indeed, the endomesoderm of the cardiac area differentiates sometimes into liver tissue when transplanted to the chorioallan-

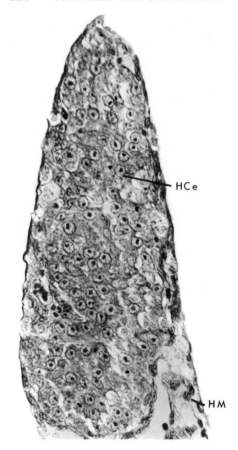

Fig. 17.8 Lobe of liver which has developed in vitro from the association of hepatic mesenchyme, HM, with the epithelial liver buds of a 21-somite-stage embryo. HCe, hepatic cells. (Le Douarin, *Bull. Biol. Fr. Belg.* 98(4):543–583; 98(5):589–676, 1964.)

results are obtained with endoderm isolated from stages up to the 4-somite stage. Thus, until the 4-somite stage, the endoderm is not determined, and may be termed "prehepatic endoderm." From the 5-somite stage onward the situation is different. The mesoderm of the cardiac area has induced the hepatic endoderm (132, 133), which now can interact with mesenchyme to produce hepatic cords.

One can thus distinguish two essential steps during the differentiation of the liver. The prehepatic endoderm is induced by the mesoderm of the hepatocardiac area and through the latter inductive stimulus it becomes able to react to the morphogenetic action of the hepatic mesenchyme (Fig. 17.13).

During the time period extending from the presomite stages to the first ap-

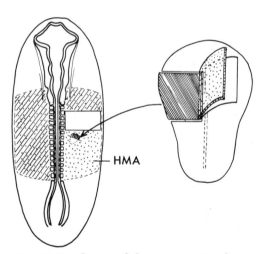

Fig. 17.9 Isolation of the presumptive hepatic endoderm at the head-process stage, and association *in ovo* of that endoderm with hepatic mesenchyme. In the blastoderm, on the right, a hepatic area is cut out. The endodermal part, separated by trypsinization, is then transplanted in the hepatic mesenchyme area, HMA, of a 12-somite-stage embryo, behind an excision of the lateral area. (Le Douarin, *Bull. Biol. Fr. Belg.* 98(4):543–583; 98(5):589–676, 1964.)

toic membrane (Rawles, 174). If it is grafted into the area of presumptive hepatic mesenchyme (behind a mechanical obstacle) the frequency of liver differentiation is increased (132, 133). In contrast, the hepatic endoderm, separated from the mesenchyme by trypsinization, and grafted into the presumptive area of the hepatic mesenchyme (Fig. 17.9) does not differentiate into hepatoblasts. It fuses with the host endoderm and acquires a digestive endodermlike structure (Fig. 17.10). Similar

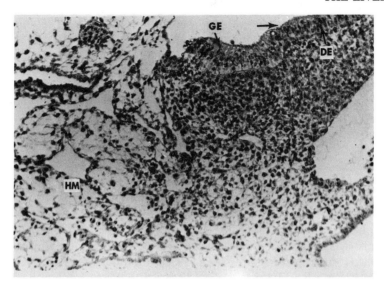

Fig. 17.10 Result of the experiment diagrammed in Fig. 17.9. Histological examination of the host embryo at the 5th day of incubation reveals that the grafted endoderm, GE, fuses (arrow) with the digestive endoderm of the host, DE. There is no hepatic histogenesis; the hepatic mesenchyme, HM, of the host remains devoid of epithelial cords. (Le Douarin, *Bull. Biol. Fr. Belg.* 98(4):543–583; 98(5):589–676, 1964.)

pearance of the primary hepatic bud, there are important changes in the distribution and degree of determination of the three cellular categories which are involved in liver differentiation. These three categories are the primary inductor (mesoderm of the hepatocardiac area), the secondary inductor (hepatic mesenchyme), and the prospective hepatic endoderm. At the head-process stage the heart-forming potencies, on the one hand, and the hepatic mesenchyme, on the other, are not yet segregated in the cardiohepatic area. Between the head-process stage and the 5-somite stage, a part of the splanchnic mesoderm migrates anteriorly toward the anterior endodermal fold. Thus the two cardiac primordia are brought together ventrally with respect to the embryonic pharynx. The migration of the precardiac mesoderm has recently been analyzed by DeHaan (51; Chapter 16) with the use of time-lapse microcinematography. During the same period the lateral endodermal areas, corresponding to the presumptive hepatic endoderm, meet ventrally in the cardiac fold (Bellairs, 11; Le Douarin, 133).

At the 5- to 6-somite stage the endodermal hepatic areas and the precardiac mesoderm are about to meet in the cardiac fold. The presumptive area of the hepatic mesenchyme remains more widespread. Segregation of the cardiac mesoderm and of the hepatic mesenchyme occurs during the migration of the precardiac mesenchyme. By that time only hepatic endoderm which is already incorporated into the fold has undergone primary induction. The prehepatic endoderm of the posterolateral areas is still undetermined (133).

Incorporation of the presumptive hepatic endoderm into the floor of the foregut continues in such a way that when the process is completed, the anterior intestinal portal contains the hepatic endoderm and part of the hepatic mesenchyme. The remainder of the mesenchyme extends laterally and posteriorly to reach the level of the 15th somite.

As to the two successive inductions which occur during the differentiation of the hepatic endoderm, it seems so far that the primary induction is specific; it can only be exerted by the mesoderm of the cardiac area, and only prehepatic endoderm can respond to it. However, although the first step is necessary for further development, it is not sufficient. At that time the hepatic endoderm is still incapable of autodifferentiation. It must undergo the second inductive stimulus by the hepatic mesenchyme. The secondary induction is less specific. One can compare the second step with the inductive influences which occur during the differentiation of other organs of endomesodermal origin such as the lung (Dameron, 49) and the pancreas (Golosow and Grobstein, 86). In these tissues, as in the liver, several heterologous mesenchymes can replace that of the primordium. In the case of the liver, the inductive influence of the mesenchyme upon the epithelium is followed by a reverse action of the hepatic epithelial cords upon the mesenchyme.

Transformation of Hepatic Mesenchymal Cells under the Influence of Endodermal Glandular Strands

If, as previously described, a transverse obstacle is placed in the anterior part of the presumptive hepatic area, the posterior hepatic mesenchyme, thus isolated, presents the following characteristics at the 5th day of incubation. It is formed by cellular strands radially arranged around the central vein. The mesh of the network thus formed delimits wide lacunae communicating with the vein (Fig. 17.4). These lacunae are similar to the hepatic sinusoids as seen in the liver of a 5-day-old embryo. The mesenchymal strands are limited by a layer of cells which play the role of an endothelium.

By grafting a hepatic endodermal primordium into the presumptive area of the hepatic mesenchyme of a 9- to 13-somite stage embryo, one can follow the transformation of the mesenchymal cells in contact with the hepatic cords. At the 4th day of incubation the epithelial cords begin invading the mesenchyme along the strands of mesenchymal cells. At least at the beginning of this process, the mesenchyme seems to determine the mode of ramification of the epithelial cords. In the central part of the strands the mesenchymal cells are pushed away by the invading parenchymal cells (Fig. 17.11). In the chick there is no enveloping process of the mesenchymal cells by the hepatic cells, as occurs in mammals (Mollier, 155; Damas, 45; Lipp, 140).

At the 6th or 7th day of incubation there are no more mesenchymal intratrabecular cells visible in the lobe of liver which has developed behind the obstacle. By that time the hepatic tissue is formed by only two cell types: the hepatoblasts and the endothelial cells of the blood sinusoids (Fig. 17.12). The absence of mesenchymal elements in the liver of the 6-day-old chick embryo is confirmed by observations with the electron microscope (Karrer, 115). In 1900, Minot (153) made the same observation, which suggests that the intratrabecular cells of the hepatic mesenchyme are incorporated into the border of the vascular sinusoids during the invasion process by the cords of hepatoblasts.

Embryonic hepatic hematopoiesis differs in different species according to the mode of invasion of the mesenchymal primordium by the endodermal elements. In mammals, where the mesenchymal cells are incorporated into the parenchyma, hematopoiesis is extravascular. In the chick, hematopoiesis is intravascular (Karrer, 115) and originates in the cells bordering the blood sinusoids.

Further Differentiation of Hepatic Tissue

The cytological changes which accompany the development of the liver have been studied in birds and mammals by several investigators. In the following section some recent data on the maturation of the hepatocytes and the hematopoietic cell line will be reviewed.

Cytodifferentiation of the Hepatoblast

Karrer (113, 114, 115) reported a study on the development of the hepatic cell in the chick embryo between 6 and 18 days of incubation. At the 6th day of incubation the hepatocyte does not yet possess all the characteristics of the adult liver cell. The Golgi apparatus is visible, but it becomes more important from the 7th day onward. Glycogen appears at about the 6th day in the form of granules (33 to 130μ in diameter) which become more and more numerous during later development and are finally dispersed through the whole cell. The endoplasmic reticulum is not fully constituted at these early stages. Between 6 and 8 days one finds only a few rough surfaces near the Golgi elements. Free ribosomes are abundant in the cytoplasm. In contrast to the adult, in which the mitochondria are dispersed through the whole cell, in embryonic liver they are grouped around the nucleus (North and Pollak, 163).

Development of the liver cell has been more extensively studied in mammals than in birds; however, the available information on hepatic cytodifferentiation is still fragmentary. Most work has been concerned with structural changes occurring in the liver cell at the time it acquires new functions such

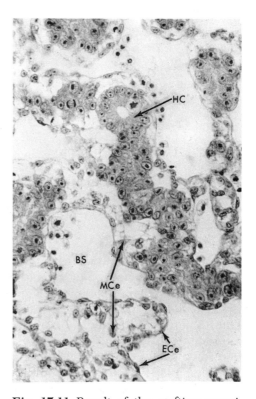

Fig. 17.11 Result of the grafting experiment represented in Fig. 17.6. Histological examination at the 5th day of incubation shows that the hepatic cords, HC, invade the mesenchymal strands. ECe, endothelial cells; BS, blood sinusoids; MCe, mesenchymal cells. (Le Douarin, *Bull. Biol. Fr. Belg.* 98(4):543–583; 98(5):589–676, 1964.)

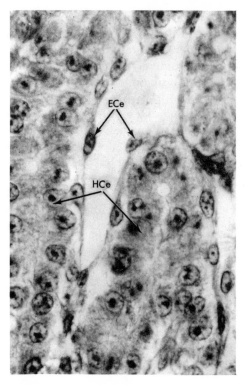

Fig. 17.12 Detail of the hepatic strands showing the hepatic cells, HCe, and the endothelial cells, ECe. Mesenchyme cells are no longer visible. (Le Douarin, *Bull. Biol. Fr. Belg.* 98(4):543–583; 98(5):589–676, 1964.)

as synthesis and accumulation of glycogen. With the beginning of glycogen storage there is an important increase in size of the hepatic cell (Du Bois, 62). During gestation the nucleoplasmatic ratio decreases as a result of the increasing volume of cytoplasm (Siess and Stegman, 185; Iversen and Thamsen, 107). The nuclear volume remains practically unchanged (Dadoune, 44; Dvorak, 64). The nucleolus is larger in the embryonic than in the adult liver cell (Ferreira, 74; Dadoune, 44). As in birds, the endoplasmic reticulum changes during development. Peters and co-workers (171) have shown that

in the liver of mouse embryo (15 days of gestation) the ergastoplasm is less important than at later stages. Great changes have been reported to take place in the ergastoplasm at the time when the liver begins to store glycogen (44, 64, 171). The mitochondria have been shown to increase in size and to change in form, structure, and localization during development (44, 64, Kafer and Pollak, 112; 171). The microbodies which were first described in kidney cells by Rhodin (176), and later in liver cells by Gansle and Rouiller (80), are more numerous in embryonic (74) and in regenerating liver (Rouiller and Bernhard, 180) than in normal adult liver tissue. The Golgi apparatus also develops markedly toward the end of the gestation period. At early stages the biliary ducts are scarce. In the mouse embryo they appear between the 12th and 15th days of gestation. They begin to develop near the branches of the portal vein (Wilson et al., 211). Whereas in the adult they are usually limited by two cells (Elias and Bengelsdorf, 69), in the young embryo the limit is constituted by four to eight cells. They reach their final definitive organization in the late embryonic period just before birth. The literature concerned with the occurrence of polyploid and binuclear cells in the liver at different stages during development has been reviewed by Doljanski (58).

The Endothelial Cells and Fetal Liver Hematopoiesis

In the embryonic liver of birds hematopoiesis is less important than in mammals. It is intravascular and originates in the endothelial cells of the sinusoids. Erythropoiesis, described in the 7- to 9-day-old chick embryo by Haff (98), has been studied recently by Kar-

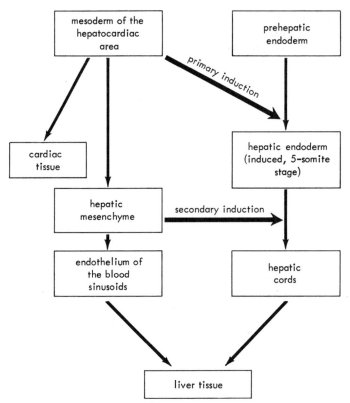

Fig. 17.13 Schema summarizing the different steps in the development of the liver. (Le Douarin, *Bull. Biol. Fr. Belg.* 98(4, 5) 1964.)

rer (115) with electronmicroscopy. According to these investigations, the endothelium of the sinusoids is continuous at the 6th day of incubation in embryonic chick liver; by the 8th day it becomes discontinuous. Some endothelial cells which are originally flat become rounded and are transformed into erythroblasts, which are liberated into the cavity of the sinusoids. The cytoplasm of the erythroblasts has a poorly differentiated ergastoplasm and possesses only a few mitochondria. Its iron content increases with maturation.

In mammals, hepatic hematopoiesis plays a more important role during embryonic life. It is essentially extravascular and takes place in the mesenchymal islets which are dispersed through the hepatic parenchyma. Sorenson (187, 188) reported a detailed study on hematopoiesis in the rabbit embryo in which organogenesis of the liver starts at the 10th day of gestation. By the 12th to 13th day, a few cells of the hematopoietic line can already be observed; fetal liver hematopoiesis reaches its maximum at about the 20th day. As early as the 15th day, the hematopoietic cells contain dispersed ferritin granules. The hemocytoblasts can be readily distinguished from the hepatocytes. Their cytoplasm is not very abundant, but is rich in free ribosomes; the nucleus and nucleolus are large. During differentiation of the erythroblast, the cell diameter decreases, the nucleus disappears, and hemoglobin is synthesized. According to Sorenson, the ferritin granules pass from the hepatoblasts to the erythroblasts by a process of pinocytosis. Other investigators (Grasso et al., 89) observed pictures which resemble the phenomenon of ropheocytosis as described by Policard and Bessis (173) in human bone marrow. The maturing erythroblasts migrate between the hepatoblasts and finally pass into the blood sinusoids.

The formation of megacaryocytes has been studied in the pig fetus by Akerman and Knouff (2). They appear to originate from dual sources: the mesenchymal cells of the septum transversum, and the endothelial cells of the blood sinuses.

Kupffer cells appear early during hepatic organogenesis (Sorenson, 187) and have a high phagocytic activity. One can observe the accumulation in the cytoplasm of ingested material composed mainly of debris of erythroid cells.

Biochemical Studies of Liver Development

Apart from a few isolated observations on the presence of certain enzyme activities at very early stages, most biochemical work has been concerned with later stages of liver development. During embryonic life the liver is characterized by a high rate of nucleic acid and protein synthesis. The incorporation of radioactive phosphorus (Wrba et al., 213–214) and of labeled amino acids (Burraston and Pollak, 23) is higher in embryonic than in adult liver. High mitotic activity, requiring the formation of new cellular material, accounts for the greater anabolic activity in embryonic cells. With increasing age, the anabolic and catabolic activi-

ties reach a dynamic equilibrium (Burraston and Pollak, 23), while the mitotic activity of the liver declines almost to zero (Doljanski, 58).

The changes in weight and chemical composition during development of the liver have been recently reviewed by Doljanski (58) and will not be fully documented here. The present section will be concerned mainly with the progressive appearance of specific proteins (for example, enzymes) during development of the liver in rat and chick embryos. As far as possible the data will be presented in correlation with the maturation of different liver functions.

Changes in Weight and Chemical Composition

The changes in weight during development have been expressed in two ways: absolute increase in liver weight, and relative weight of the organ (ratio of liver weight to body weight). In the rat the liver triples its weight between 16 and 22 days of gestation (Williamson, 208). The ratio of liver weight to body weight decreases during embryonic development in most mammals (58). The literature concerned with the changes in absolute liver weight at different developmental stages of the chick has been reviewed by Romanoff (179). In the chick, there is a steady increase in the LW : BW ratio between 9 and 17 days of incubation, interrupted by a plateau at 13–14 days. After the 17th day the ratio decreases until hatching (Weston, 207). The steady increase followed by a decrease after the 17th day has been confirmed by Croisille (36).

Earlier investigations on the changes in water, total protein, lipids, and ribonucleic and deoxyribonucleic acids during liver development have been reviewed by Doljanski (58). For a better understanding of the changes in some enzyme activities to be presented later, a few details on the synthesis and accumulation of glycogen will be recalled. In the rat the liver starts synthesizing glycogen at about the 16th day of gestation. From the 18th day, until birth, there is a huge accumulation of glycogen. During the first hours after birth the glycogen content of the liver decreases very rapidly until the end of the 2nd day. It then increases again, and by 5 to 6 days reaches the same level as at birth. At about the 10th day there is a second decrease, followed by an increase until the adult level is reached (Coquoin-Carnot and Roux, 34). In the chick liver, glycogen is first detectable at the 6th day of incubation (Grillo, 90). Then the glycogen content increases until the 10th day; during the period between 10 and 12 days there is a decrease of approximately 40 percent (Konigsberg, 123) followed by a tremendous increase between 14 days and hatching (Weston, 207). During the process of hatching there is a sharp fall in liver glycogen shown in Table 17.1 (Rinaudo, 177).

The following studies on changes in individual proteins, especially enzymes, will be presented with particular reference to the maturation of different liver functions.

Immunochemical Analysis of Liver Development

Thanks to their specificity and sensitivity, immunochemical techniques have become more and more useful in studies of the protein composition of different organ extracts. In recent years application of these methods has led to interesting observations on the dis-

TABLE 17.1   Liver Glycogen during Embryonic Development of the Chick[a]

AGE	MG GLYCOGEN/GR OF TISSUE
12-day embryo	5.72
14-day embryo	5.50
16-day embryo	29.60
18-day embryo	33.00
20-day embryo	42.75
1 hour after hatching	4.00
12 hours after hatching	1.70
36 hours after hatching	0.78
Adult liver	2.70

[a] According to Rinaudo, *Experientia* 17: 30–31, 1961.

tribution of different proteins in the different cellular fractions of the liver (Perlmann et al., 169, 170; D'Amelio et al., 46, 47; Mutolo and D'Amelio, 158; Vogt, 198, 199; Abeleev et al., 1). Unfortunately it has not always been established whether the different components are organ specific or held in common with other tissues. According to Vogt, the tissue-specific proteins of the microsome fraction occur exclusively in the membranes of the endoplasmic reticulum (198). This view is supported by the observations of Okada and Yamamura (164). Most of the above studies have dealt with adult liver, and will not be reported in detail.

In 1959 one of us (Croisille, 37–43) initiated an immunochemical investigation of the appearance of tissue-common and tissue-specific proteins during embryonic development of the chick liver. In the presence of an anti-adult chick liver serum, immunoelectrophoretic analysis, according to Grabar and Williams (88), permitted the demonstration of at least 16 different constituents in extracts of adult fowl liver, shown in Figure 17.14 (37, 38, 39). Of these components, six are al-

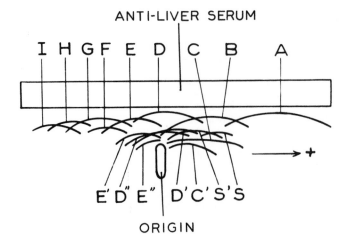

Fig. 17.14 Immunoelectrophoretic analysis of adult chick liver extract; schematic representation and nomenclature of the 16 precipitin lines which can be observed in the presence of an anti-adult chick liver serum. (Croisille, *Compt. Rend. Acad. Sci.* 249:1712–1714, 1959.)

ready present in the 6½-day embryo liver. The others appear progressively during development, shown in Figure 17.15 (38). As can be seen in Table 17.2, new components appear at about 8–9 days, 13–14 and 17–18 days of incubation. At hatching the picture is still incomplete and the pattern characteristic of adult liver will only be attained later on. Comparative experiments in which antiadult liver serum has been tested against chick serum and different organ extracts indicated that among the 16 components, four corresponded to serum proteins and five were held in common with other organs. The remaining seven constituents appeared to be specifically linked to the liver. However, recent data suggest that certain components might only be quantitatively liver specific, owing to the difficulty in ascertaining the complete absence of a given protein in heterologous extracts. However, no adult-type liver-specific component could be detected before the 9th day of development. At this point it must be emphasized that, with the technique used, only a minimum number of components could be detected. Attention must also be called to the possible ex-

istence of embryonic transitory constituents which, under the present experimental conditions, escape detection. The application of histochemical techniques permitted a better characterization of some constituents. The precipitin lines B and D have been found to be associated with esterase activity (40) and component E' has been identified as corresponding to the enzyme hypoxanthine dehydrogenase (41–43).

Recently D'Amelio and co-workers (48) reported a study on the antigenic components of the different cell fractions during the development of the chick liver. They also found that the different adult-type proteins appear progressively during development in the mitochondrial, microsomal, and cell sap fractions. In 1964, Okada and Yamamura (164) also confirmed the progressive appearance of the different components of the microsome fraction during development of the chick liver. No adult-type liver-specific protein could be detected in the microsome fraction before the 9th day of incubation. The organ-common components, however, are already present in the 6-day-old embryonic liver, two of them being associated with esterase activity. Thus the latter results completely support our own findings.

Except for the enzyme hypoxanthine dehydrogenase, which is known for its role in uric acid synthesis, no direct relation can be established between the appearance of the components described here and the first manifestation of a physiological function during development. We are thus led to studies of changes in enzyme activities, which can usually be more readily related to changes in metabolic processes during development.

Enzymological Studies of Liver Development

Because of their central position in cellular metabolism, enzymes have been extensively studied during development. However, as pointed out earlier, there are only a few observations on enzyme changes during the very early hours of liver development, most available information being concerned with the differentiation of the hepatic cell at later stages. Catayée (27) reported that in the 45-hour chick embryo there is a very high phosphomonoesterase activity in the septum transversum. Between 50 and 54 hours of development, that enzyme activity is high in the endodermal hepatic primordium, while it decreases sharply in the septum transversum. In the 70-hour chick embryo the hepatic primordium and the septum transversum have the same activity as a result of a new increase in the septum transversum, accompanied by a decrease in the hepatic endoderm. From that period onward, phosphomonoesterase activity increases in the hepatic cords while it decreases in the septum transversum. Thus important changes in enzyme ac-

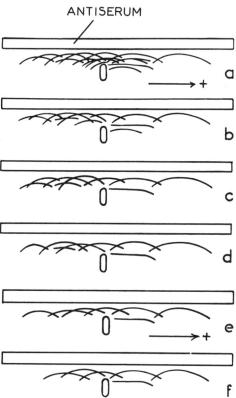

ANTISERUM

Fig. 17.15 Immunoelectrophoretic analysis of chick liver extracts from different development stages: a, adult chick liver; b, 5-day-old chicken liver; c, 17–18-day embryonic liver; d, 13–14-day embryonic liver; e, 8–9-day embryonic liver; f, 6½-day embryonic liver. (Croisille, *J. Embryol. Exptl. Morphol.* 8:216–225, 1960; *Pathol. Biol.* 9:253–264, 1961.)

tivity take place in the septum transversum at the time when it is invaded by the primary hepatic endoderm. Apart from that observation, and a few others relating to the presence of glucose-6-phosphatase (Kilsheimer et al., 118) and phosphorylase activity (Lövlie, 141) in the very early hepatic primordium, there is an important literature concerned with enzyme changes during later stages of liver development in avian and mammalian em-

TABLE 17.2   Appearance of Different Components during Embryonic Development of the Chick Liver[a]

STAGES	A	B	S	S'	C	C'	D	D'	D''	E	E'	E''	F	G	H	I
Adult liver	+	+	+	+	+	+	+	+	+	+	+	+	+	+	+	+
5-day chick liver	+	+	–	–	+	+	+	–	–	+	+	–	+	+	+	+
17–18-day embryo liver	+	+	–	–	+	–	+	–	–	+	–	–	+	+	+	+
13–14-day embryo liver	+	+	–	–	+	–	+	–	–	+	–	–	+	+	–	+
8–9-day embryo liver	+	+	–	–	+	–	+	–	–	+	–	–	–	+	–	+
6½-day embryo liver	+	+	–	–	+	–	+	–	–	+	–	–	–	+	–	–

CONSTITUENTS

[a]Croisille, *Pathol. Biol.* 9:253–264, 1961.

Components A,S,S', and H are serum proteins. The underlined components appeared to be organ specific. In recent experiments E' was found to be only quantitatively liver specific, since it exists at lower concentrations in the kidney, intestine, and pancreas. It has also been detected in trace amounts in embryonic liver from 8 days of incubation onward. (See the development of hypo-xanthine dehydrogenase activity in the section on nitrogen excretion during development.)

bryos. Numerous enzyme activities have been reported to appear or to increase at a given period of prenatal or postnatal life. Other enzyme activities have been shown to decrease or to disappear. Examples illustrating the appearance and disappearance of enzymes will be found later in the present review. Before describing the changes in enzyme activities which take place during the maturation of various liver functions, some recent observations on the changes in location of enzymes and on the existence of several enzymes in multimolecular forms will be briefly reported.

Changes in location of glutamic dehydrogenase activity during development of the chick liver have been reported by Solomon (186). Between 8 and 16 days of incubation that enzyme activity can be detected and found to increase in both the supernatant and mitochondrial fraction. At about the 16th day of development there is a sharp fall of activity in the supernatant fraction, accompanied by an increase in the mitochondrial fraction. From that period onward, practically the whole glutamic dehydrogenase activity of the liver cell is localized in the mitochondria. Changes have also been observed for alanine–glutamic acid transaminase in rat liver by Kafer and Pollak (112). These investigators found that in embryonic rat liver 55 percent of the total activity is localized in the mitochondria and 27 percent in the supernate, whereas in adult rat liver the situation is reversed, with 20 percent in the mitochondrial and 62 percent in the supernatant fraction. According to a cytochemical study by Conklin (33), lactic dehydrogenase activity also changes in location during development of the chick liver; in the 6-day embryonic chick liver all the LDH activity has been reported to be localized in the mitochondria. Between 12 and 18 days of development, liver LDH activity presents a dual localization in the mitochondria and in the cytoplasm. After hatching, the total activity is again confined to the mitochondria. Comparison of the latter results with electrophoretic data on the evolution of LDH isozymes during development of the chick liver (Nebel and Conklin, 161), reveals that the presence of extra-mitochondrial LDH coincides with the presence of one particular LDH isozyme (LDH 5). The change in LDH composition of the liver cell has been thought to indicate a shift from an anaerobic to an aerobic metabolism. This correlation between cytochemical and electrophoretic data seems premature, inasmuch as LDH 5, according to most other investigators, is present at all stages of chick liver development (see below).

With the discovery that several enzymes exist in multimolecular forms, a new era has been opened in the study of enzyme evolution during embryonic development. In 1957 Hunter and Markert (106) reported that starch gel electrophoresis permitted the separation of a family of proteins, all possessing esterase activity. In the mouse each organ appeared to have its characteristic zymogram. Some esterases are common to several organs, others only occur in a single organ; nearly all occur in the liver. During embryonic development of the liver and early postnatal life, the different esterases appear progressively, until the picture characteristic of the adult is completed when the tissue reaches maturity (Markert, 147;

Markert and Hunter, 148). Among several other enzymes which have been reported to exist in multimolecular forms, lactic dehydrogenase has undoubtedly been the most extensively investigated. In most vertebrates that enzyme has been described as existing in five electrophoretically distinct forms. Two major forms are usually recognized: one predominant in heart (form H or LDH 1), the other predominant in skeletal muscle (form M or LDH 5). In adult liver the predominant form varies according to the species. In the chick, LDH 1 is predominant (Philip and Vessel, 172, 197; Lindsay 138, 139; Cahn et al., 25; Croisille, 41, 42), whereas in the liver of most mammals it is usually form 5 which predominates. There are exceptions — beef liver, for example, containing almost all H type LDH. For a detailed analysis of the distribution of H and M type LDH in the livers of different mammals the reader is referred to the work of Fine and co-workers (75). During embryonic development of the liver, practically all mammals have LDH 5 predominant. In those species which contain LDH 1 in the adult stage, there is a shift from LDH 5 to LDH 1 at the time of birth. Among mammals, the human liver is an exception, since it seems to begin with LDH 1 during embryonic development (75); after birth it contains mainly LDH 5. The chick also begins with LDH 1 during embryonic development and maintains that form predominant in the liver throughout life. In a recent study Croisille (41, 42) found that starch gel electrophoresis of adult chick liver extracts reveals the existence of seven distinct bands, all staining positively for LDH activity. In addition to the forms characteristic of adult liver, embryonic chick liver possesses two more positively migrating forms, designated as E (Fig. 17.16). These two bands are only observed during embryonic life. They are clearly visible in embryonic liver between 6 and 16 days of incubation. From the 16th day on they tend to fade away and at hatching they have disappeared. Since it has not yet been determined whether E bands are true isozymes or reflect binding of some LDH molecules to another protein, it is premature to draw conclusions as to a possible role of the transitory components during embryonic life.

The physiological significance of LDH isozymes has been repeatedly discussed (Markert and Ursprung, 150; Cahn et al., 25; Fine et al., 75; Lindsay, 138, 139; Wilson et al., 210). On the basis of kinetic differences between LDH 1 and LDH 5, it has been proposed that organs depending more on an aerobic metabolism have LDH 1 predominant, whereas organs depending on an anaerobic metabolism have LDH 5 predominant. It seems, however, that the functional significance of the differential distribution of LDH in the livers of the different species is not yet fully understood.

Enzymes Involved in Carbohydrate Metabolism

As previously mentioned, glycogen synthesis and accumulation in the liver takes place earlier during development in birds than in mammals. Since glycogen storage and glucose redistribution is one of the primary functions of the liver, the developmental pattern of several enzymes which catalyze the different steps of glycogen synthesis and breakdown has been studied extensively in these two categories of animals. Most of the observations have

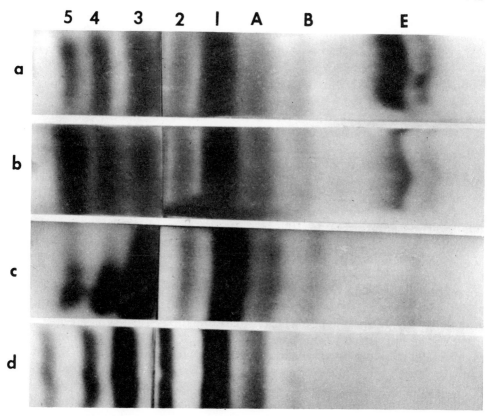

Fig. 17.16 Comparison of lactic dehydrogenase patterns at different stages during embryonic development of the chick liver: a, 10-day embryonic liver; b, 15-day embryonic liver; c, 20-day embryonic liver; d, adult chick liver. From the 15th day on the embryonic transitory bands, E, tend to fade away and at hatching they have disappeared. (Croisille, *Ann. Rept. Director Dept. Embryol., Carnegie Inst. Wash. Year Book*, 62:428–437, 1963.)

been made on rat and chick embryos.

In the rat, hexokinase activity is five times that of the adult liver in the 17-day embryo. During later development, the activity decreases and reaches the adult level 3 weeks after birth (Burch, 21). According to Walker (200), the liver of the fetal and newborn rat contains one hexokinase, whereas the mature adult liver contains two glucose-phosphorylating enzymes. The embryonic enzyme is a nonspecific hexokinase, having high affinity for glucose, but also phosphorylates fructose. The enzyme which develops after birth appears to be a specific glucokinase. Similar observations have been made by Oliver and Cooke (166). Fructokinase activity also is high in fetal liver and decreases to reach the adult level by 9 days after birth (21). Phosphoglucomutase has been reported to increase considerably between 17 days of gestation and birth (Ballard and Oliver, 7). Phosphorylase activity starts low in fetal liver and increases sharply during the day of birth and stays high in the adult (7,

21; Coquoin-Carnot, 35; Dawkins, 50). Uridine diphosphoglucose glycogen transglucosylase activity rises sharply between 17 and 20 days of gestation (7; Jacquot and Kretchmer, 109). That enzyme seems to be more active in fetal than in adult liver (Dawkins, 50). Glucose-6-phosphatase activity is low (3% of the adult level) in fetal liver. It increases tremendously (6000-fold) at birth and even more by the 4th day of postnatal life. Thereafter it decreases slightly to reach the adult value at 9 days (Coquoin-Carnot, 34; 109; 21; Nemeth 161; 50). Glucose-6-phosphate dehydrogenase activity is higher in fetal liver than in the adult (21). It is reported by Jacquot and Kretchmer (109) to decrease between 17 and 21 days of gestation. According to Burch (21), fructose-1,6-diphosphate aldolase is high in fetal liver and decreases to the adult level at birth. The enzymes of the Embden-Meyerhof pathway below fructose diphosphate aldolase, such as triosephosphate isomerase, glyceraldehydephosphate dehydrogenase, and lactic dehydrogenase, have high activity in the adult liver. The over-all changes in enzyme activities indicate a decreased capacity, with maturation, for glucose utilization, glycolysis, and oxidation via the pentose shunt; they support an increase in capacity for glycogenolysis, free glucose production, and lactate utilization (21). Experiments of Ballard and Oliver (7) also demonstrate that the synthesis of phosphoenolpyruvate from malate is nonexistent in the 20-day fetal rat liver. This synthetic capacity appears at birth and increases rapidly to reach the adult level. The radioactivity of the glycogen of liver slices incubated in the presence of pyruvate-C^{14} or glucose-C^{14} shows that glycogen cannot be synthesized from 3-carbon acids before birth. Fetal rat liver glycogen may be synthesized mainly from hexose units; the capacity for synthesizing glycogen from 3-carbon compounds does not appear until after birth.

The chick synthesizes and stores glycogen earlier than most mammals during embryonic development of the liver. As indicated earlier, glycogen appears at the 6th day of incubation. According to Grillo (91), the enzyme phosphorylase is first detectable at the 7th day of incubation. Between 10 and 19 days of incubation the activity rises threefold (7). Lövlie (141), however, mentioned very briefly that phosphorylase activity can be detected in the liver of the 3-day-old chick embryo. Uridine diphosphate glucose-glycogen synthetase appears at the time of the first appearance of glycogen in the liver tissue (Grillo and Ozone, 93). Then the activity increases threefold between 10 and 19 days of incubation (7). According to the same investigators, the activity of phosphoglucomutase also increases during the same period of time. Kilsheimer and co-workers (118) reported that glucose-6-phosphatase activity is present at 60 hours of incubation, appreciable activity being detected at the 7th day. According to Leibson and co-workers (137), the activity of that enzyme is higher in the embryo than in the neonatal chick. At the 9th day of incubation there is a very high activity which decreases during further development and reaches the adult level at hatching. After the embryo is hatched, the activity stays constant for at least 10 days. Fructose-1,6-diphosphatase activity also is higher in the embryonic than in the adult liver (Rinaudo, 177). It is detectable at 6 days of incubation, increases until it passes a maximum at about the 16th day, and finally gradually decreases. Ballard and Oliver (7) demonstrated that the ability to synthesize phosphoenolpyruvate from malate increases between 11 and 16 days of incubation, passes a maximum at 17 days, and drops until hatching. The synthesis of glycogen from pyruvate-C^{14} increases between 11 and 15 days, at which point it passes a maximum; after the 15th day it diminishes, reaching a minimum at 19 days. Thus there is an increasing importance of gluconeogenesis up to the 15th day of development, with a decrease toward hatching. In contrast to the rat embryo, the chick embryo seems to use 3-carbon compounds more readily than glucose during the period of active liver glycogen formation. Kilsheimer and co-workers (118) also found that pyruvate-C^{14} is utilized by the embryonic chick liver, labeled carbon being incorporated into glycogen, glucose, fatty acids, and CO_2.

It seems that in the rat and in the chick embryo early glycogen is preferentially synthesized through the UDP-glucose-glycogen pathway. Phosphorylase appears or is very active only when glycogen has already accumulated, and catalyses glycogen breakdown rather than its synthesis, at least in early stages. Since the discovery by Leloir and Cardini (137a) of the uridine diphosphate-linked pathway, it is generally accepted that the pathways for glycogen synthesis and breakdown are different (170a).

A very attractive problem is that of the stimuli which govern the mobilization of glycogen and the concomitant rise in glucose-6-phosphatase and phosphorylase activity at birth. According to Dawkins (50), the depletion of liver glycogen after birth is not directly related to the increase of glucose-6-phosphatase activity. If glucose-6-phosphatase activity is restricted by ethionine or insulin, this does not retard the mobilization of liver glycogen. However, if glycogen mobilization is prevented, the rise in glucose-6-phosphatase activity is also prevented. The latter observation is supported by the results of Jacquot and Kretchmer (109). These investigators found that if rat embryos are deprived of maternal and fetal corticoids (by adrenalectomy of the mother animal and decapitation of the embryo), their livers do not accumulate glycogen, and the enzyme glucose-6-phosphatase is absent. We are thus led to the problem of the hormonal control of carbohydrate metabolism.

Hormonal Influences on Carbohydrate Metabolism

Studies of Jost and Jacquot (108, 111) have clearly demonstrated that in the rabbit and rat embryos early liver glycogen accumulation is under hormonal control. Rat embryos, deprived of maternal and fetal corticoids, do not accumulate glycogen in their livers, but glycogen storage can be restored by cortisone administration. In the rabbit fetus the situation is more complicated. If the fetuses are decapitated at 25 days of gestation or before, cortisone does not induce glycogen accumulation. But at 26 days, cortisone induces the liver to synthesize more glycogen. Thus, until day 26 the presence of the pituitary permits the liver to respond to cortisone. Rat placenta extracts also permit cortisone to induce glycogen synthesis. According to Jost (110, p. 177) "the whole series of data are best explained by assuming that the storage of glycogen in the fetal liver is under the control of a synergistic action of a pituitary or a pituitarylike placental hormone and of adrenocortical steroids." The question then arises of how hormones exert their effects on fetal liver. A first answer to that question stems from the work of Jacquot and Kretchmer (109). These investigators have shown that in the corticoid-deprived rat fetus, phosphoglucomutase and glycogen synthetase activities are lower than in control livers. Glucose-6-phosphate dehydrogenase activity, which normally falls, is higher, and glucose-6-phosphatase activity stays low and does not undergo the normal dramatic rise on the 21st day of gestation. Whereas in normal embryos the utilization of glucose-6-phosphate through the hexosemonophosphate shunt diminishes at the time when glycogen begins to be synthesized, these metabolic changes do not take place in corticoid-deprived embryos. At this point it is interesting to cite the results of Sie and Fishman (184) demonstrating a stimulatory effect of cortisol on glycogen synthetase in the mouse liver.

In the early chick liver, glycogen synthesis proceeds without hormonal influence. Injection of various hormones such as cortisone (Leibson and Geloudkova, 134) and insulin (Grillo, 90) before the 6th day of development fails to accelerate glycogen deposition in the chick liver. Moreover, if the young chick liver is explanted on a nonhormonal medium (Lövlie, 141; Dieterlen-Lièvre, 54, 55) glycogen synthesis nonetheless takes place. Most remarkable is the fact that the chick liver synthesizes glycogen in vitro at earlier stages than in ovo. Three-day-old chick embryo liver produces glycogen within 24 hours when isolated in vitro, whereas normally the first glycogen is detected at the 6th day of incubation. According to Lövlie (141), if the whole 3-day-old embryo is cultivated in vitro, the liver does not accumulate glycogen. Thus the embryo as a whole seems to counteract or inhibit early liver glycogen synthesis, perhaps as a result of the need for glucose to meet various energy requirements. Several other explanations have been proposed, but none has so far received decisive experimental support.

Amphibian liver also synthesizes glycogen in vitro at earlier stages than in vivo (Beaumont, 9). The whole body of information on the first glycogen appearance during amphibian liver development has been reviewed recently by Beaumont (10).

As to the regulation of glycemia, the mammalian embryo (Jost, 110) has a very limited capacity to regulate its own blood glucose levels. Severe maternal hyperglycemia is accompanied by fetal hyperglycemia. In contrast, the chick embryo liver plays an active role in the regulation of glycemia, at least during the last third of embryonic development. The earlier literature on the development of the mechanisms for regulating the quantity of blood sugar by hormonal activity has been reviewed by Willier (209). From these observations it appeared that effective control is exerted when chemical integration has taken place, that is, from the 10th to the 13th day of development onward. Most of the more recent work supports this view. Bioassays, using the rat diaphragm technique, have shown that insulin is first detectable in the pancreas at the 12th day of development (Grillo, 92). Using the same technique, Leibson and Geloudkova (135) found that insulin appears in the plasma of the chick embryo at the 13th day of incubation. Another hormone which plays a role in the regulation of glycemia is adrenalin; it is first detected in the adrenals at the 9th day of incubation (Leibson and Stabrowsky, 136). According to Grillo (90), the injection of glucagon into chick embryos from 6 days onward produces a marked reduction of liver glycogen. The recovery of glycogen is slow up to the 12th day, and more rapid at later stages; between 6 and 12 days it can be accelerated by the injection of insulin. These observations are consistent with the view that during normal development insulin is first active at the 12th day of incubation. However, Thommes and Firling (193) induced hyperglycemia in the chick embryo by glucagon injection, and found that in the 6- to 10-day-old embryo, blood glucose as well as liver glycogen levels returned to normal in 1 or 2 days. These results tend to indicate that the early chick embryo does have the capacity to regulate its blood glucose and liver glycogen levels. In recent experiments Dieterlen-Lièvre (54, 55) demonstrated that the cells of the dorsal pancreatic primordium of the 3- and 4-day-old chick embryo contain alpha granules as revealed by electronmicroscopy. Moreover, if that primordium is associated with embryonic liver in vitro, it inhibits glycogen formation or causes rapid glycogen depletion in the liver explant. More recently (Dieterlen-Lièvre, 56), beta granules have been found to be present in the pancreas at the 4th day of incubation. Owing to the difficulty in detecting quantitative differences in glycogen, it could not be established if the 4-day-old embryonic pancreas is capable of enhancing glycogen deposition in the liver. Thus,

glucagon and probably insulin are secreted at earlier stages than hitherto accepted. But these two hormones are probably present in effective amounts only by the 10th to 12th day of development. Glucagon plays an important role in the transformation of phosphorylase from the inactive to the active form; the question of whether phosphorylase is present in the active or inactive form during early chick liver development has been considered by several investigators. The results of Grillo (91) suggested that at early stages phosphorylase is primarily present in the inactive form. The response of the embryo to glucagon injections demonstrates that the chick is capable of responding to the hormone as early as the 6th day of development (90, 193). Thus it seems that the enzyme phosphorylase can be activated by the hormone at these early stages. Guha and Wegman, however (95), reported that up to the 12th day of incubation the chick embryo liver contains phosphorylase only in the active form. According to these investigators, it is only at days 12 to 13 that phosphorylase exists in its two forms, with the inactive form predominating as in adult liver. Furthermore, the enzyme systems which maintain the equilibrium between the inactive and active forms also appear at that period.

Before leaving the problems concerned with glycogen synthesis and glucose redistribution in the embryo, and centering attention on the maturation of other liver functions, the existence during embryonic life of an early glycogen source must be mentioned. About 100 years ago Claude Bernard (11a,b) had shown that the placenta in mammals (1859) and the yolk sac in birds (1872) accumulate considerable amounts of glycogen. These reserves disappear approximately at the time of the onset of hepatic glycogenesis. On the basis of these observations, Bernard suggested that before the liver assumes its functions itself, the placenta and the yolk sac play the role of a "transitory liver," at least as far as glycogen storage is concerned. According to Jost (110) if, in mammals, the synthesis of liver glycogen is prevented by decapitation, the glycogen reserve of the placenta normally disappears. Thus there seems to be no direct correlation between the glycogen contents in the placenta and in the fetal liver. During the development of the chick embryo glycogen attains maximum concentration in the yolk sac membrane at the 8th day of incubation, and then diminishes. According to Zwilling (216), the yolk sac responds to insulin as the adult liver does. The injection of 5 units of insulin into the yolk sac at day 5 of incubation results in the diminution of all carbohydrate fractions in the embryo, accompanied by an increase in yolk sac membrane glycogen. By the 12th day the amounts of free sugar and glycogen return to normal in the embryo. In a study of the ontogeny of endocrine correlation, Willier (209, p. 611) concluded that in chick, during the phase extending from the 6th to the 10th day of incubation, "seemingly the processes concerned with the accumulation of carbohydrate in the liver and blood are to a high degree, if not entirely, independent of hormonal activity. These processes, although of obscure nature, are in some manner partly linked with the glycogenic and glycogenolytic functions of the yolk sac membrane." Recent experiments indicate the existence of other functional activities in the yolk sac membrane which are later more or less specifically linked to the liver. Sentenac and Fromageot (183a) reported a serinehydrolyase to occur in the yolk sac and in the liver of the embryonic and adult chick. High levels of dehydrogenases have been shown to occur in the yolk sac before the development of the liver begins (Solomon, 186a,b,c). In the yolk sac, cystein desulfhydrase activity increases steadily from 24 hours of incubation onward, passes a maximum at the 7th day, and then decreases until the 18th day of incubation. At the 7th day the activity starts increasing in the embryonic liver (186c). These changes occur in much the same manner as those observed for glutamic dehydrogenase (186a). During further development, cystein desulfhydrase activity is chiefly localized in the liver.

Nitrogen Excretion during Development

Whereas fats and carbohydrates are oxidized to water and CO_2 which are rapidly excreted, proteins and nucleic acids contain nitrogen which is excreted in various forms according to the physiology of the organism. Ammonia resulting from the deamination of amino acids is converted to uric acid in birds; in mammalian liver it is converted to urea through the Krebs-Henseleit cycle. The final product of purine excretion is uric acid in birds and in mammals. However, several mammals contain enzyme systems which permit the further transformation of uric acid into allantoic acid and allantoin. When does the capacity of eliminating nitrogen appear during embryonic development? Since the early work of Needham it has been accepted that in the chick embryo the mechanisms of nitrogen excretion are elaborated in three stages: the embryo first excretes ammonia, then urea, and finally uric acid. According to Fisher and Eakin (76) however, this schema cannot be fully accepted because uric acid appears to be the major product of excretion after the 5th day of development. Hypoxanthine dehydrogenase, a key enzyme in uric acid synthesis, has been shown to exist in very low concentration in embryonic liver, undergoing a dramatic increase only at the time of hatching (Morgan, 156; Kato, 116; Croisille, 41, 43). Thus the activity of the embryonic liver enzyme could not account for the total uric acid production during embryonic life. Also, it has been recently demonstrated that in the chick embryo, uric acid synthesis occurs essentially in the kidney (meso- and metanephros) (Chaube, 28, 41, 43). After hatching, the main activity is in the liver. The specific activity of arginase, an enzyme involved in the production of urea, decreases in the chick embryo from the 3rd day of incubation to the adult stage. Most of the total activity which remains in the newly hatched chick is found in the liver and in the kidney (Eliasson, 70–71).

In the rat, purine breakdown is very low in embryonic liver. The enzymes 5-nucleotidase, hypoxanthine oxidase, and uricase are absent or have very low activity during the whole embryonic period. (Donath, 59, 60). Several urea-cycle enzymes such as carbamylphosphate synthetase, ornithine transcarbamylase, arginase, and the arginine synthetase system have been investigated by Kennan and Cohen (117). Ac-cording to these authors, there is very little enzyme present during development of the rat liver. At birth the enzyme activities rise exponentially. Thus urea does not appear to be synthesized at a significant rate until late fetal life in the rat. In the pig embryo, in contrast, the enzyme activities increase during gestation to levels found in the adult.

Maturation of the Secretory Function (Glucuronide Synthesis)

Many aromatic compounds are excreted as derivatives of D-glucuronic acid. These derivatives are formed in the liver by the reaction of UDP glucuronic acid with the aglucone (nonsugar portion of the derivative). The main excretory pathway for bilirubin also involves conjugation with glucuronic acid. The enzyme which catalyses the conjugation is glucuronyl transferase.

Brauer and co-workers (15), by injection of S^{35}-labeled BSP (disodium phenoltetrabromphthalein di-S^{35}-sulfonate) have shown that conjugating and concentrating abilities are clearly present in the chick liver on the 8th or 9th day of incubation. The ability to secrete material into the bile does not appear until the 11th day.

In a comparative study of glucuronide synthesis in developing mammalian and avian liver, Dutton (63) found that the chick embryo resembles the adult mammal rather than the fetus. In contrast to the fetal guinea pig and newborn mouse, the liver of the chick embryo possesses UDP glucuronyl transferase activity early in development. The embryonic chick liver has the capacity to synthesize o-aminophenyl glucuronide from at least the 8th day of incubation onward; mammalian liver acquires that capacity only at birth or later.

Response of the Liver to Estrogen

Since most serum proteins are synthesized in the liver, their concentration in the blood may be considered to reflect the synthetic activity of the liver. It has been demonstrated that two new proteins, one being rich in phosphorus, appear in the serum of the hen in association with the onset of laying. These proteins also appear in the serum of immature fowls after estrogen treatment (see Common et al., 32).

Hosoda and co-workers (105) presented evidence that these proteins are synthesized in the liver. Specific antigenic properties, similar to serum phosphoprotein, are found only in the microsomal and supernatant fractions of livers from laying hens or from immature animals after estrogen administration. These antigenic properties do not exist in the nuclear and mitochondrial fractions of the laying hen's liver, nor in any of the subcellular fractions of the mature hen's spleen or mature cockerel liver.

In 1961 Schjeide and co-workers (183) raised the question of when the liver becomes capable of responding to estrogen. They followed the synthesis of three serum proteins (light lipoprotein, X1 phosphoprotein and X2 lipoglycoprotein) in the chick embryo from the 9th day of incubation onward. Injection of estrogen into embryos of 9, 10, 15, and 18 days of incubation produces an increased synthesis of the light lipoprotein fraction, the response becoming greater with increasing age. During the entire embryonic period, there is no production of X1 and X2 proteins. The capacity to synthesize

these two proteins, in response to estrogen stimulation, does not appear until hatching.

The Problem of Organ-specific Control of Growth

The observation that the ratio of organ weight to body weight is characteristic for each organ at each developmental stage raises the question of how organ size is regulated. The mechanisms controlling growth are not yet understood, but several hypotheses have been proposed and have been reviewed by Ebert (65) and Brachet (14).

According to Weiss (203, 204), protoplasmic synthesis yields (1) intracellular compounds (templates) for further reproduction and, (2) diffusible compounds (antitemplates) capable of inactivating the former. During the process of growth, antitemplates are continuously formed, and growth proceeds until an equilibrium between the intra- and extracellular populations of antitemplates is reached. Weiss has stated that this hypothesis was not proposed so much to explain the mechanisms of growth control as to promote further thinking and to help to devise new experimental approaches. There has been considerable discussion of this hypothesis, but under the stimulus of the considerations advanced, a great deal of experimental work has been done to demonstrate the existence of tissue-specific growth stimulators or inhibitors in liver extracts or in serum. According to the hypothesis, liver extracts were expected to contain both growth promoting and growth inhibiting substances, whereas serum should contain only the diffusible compounds, and therefore inhibit growth.

The Presence in Liver Extracts of Factors Affecting Growth

Normal adult liver extract injected into intact adult rats has been reported to have *no effects* on mitosis (Malmgren, 145; Blomqvist, 12; Lahtiharju, 124; Fisher and Fisher, 77), or *to stimulate* liver mitosis (Teir and Ravanti, 192; Paschkis et al., 168); a slight insignificant *depression* of the mitotic rate has been reported by Mac-Donald and co-workers (144). Administration of normal liver extract to rats which have been partially hepatectomized has been reported to increase the mitotic rate (Tumanishvili, 194; Lahtiharju, 124), or to inhibit mitosis (Saetren, 182; Stich and Florian, 190; Molimard, 154). Thus it has not been possible to detect consistent effects of injections of liver preparations on mitosis in the normal or regenerating liver. The variability of the results might depend on the age of the donor animals used. Teir and Ravanti (192) found that liver suspensions from 2-week-old rats produce a distinct stimulation of mitosis, whereas the effect of suspensions from 12-month-old animals is insignificant. Blomqvist (12) also found that homogenates of normal adult rat liver had no effect, whereas homogenates from newborn animals or from regenerating liver produced a highly significant stimulation of mitosis. Another factor which might be of importance in explaining the difference in results is the quantity of homogenate injected. As pointed out by Paschkis (167), both Teir and Blomqvist obtained mitotic stimulation with 3 to 30 mg of liver homogenate, whereas 800 mg was inhibitory in Stich's experiments.

More consistent effects have been obtained by grafts of adult liver ex-plants or injections of liver extracts during embryonic development of the chick. These procedures have been found uniformly to stimulate embryonic liver growth (Weiss and Wang, 205; Andres, 5; Tumanishvili et al., 195; Croisille, 36; Van Alten and Fennel, 196). The effects observed are not completely organ specific, but the growth stimulation of the homologous organ is constant, liver extracts mainly promoting liver growth (36). The significance of these findings with respect to the existence of organ-specific growth regulatory substances has been discussed by Ebert (66) and Ebert and Wilt (67). At present the results are perhaps best explained by the selective uptake of subcellular fractions (Ebert, 65; Walter et al., 201) or by a phenomenon of epigenetic recombination in which adult particles carry on synthesis in an embryonic environment (67).

Effects of Serum Injections on Liver Mitosis

Another approach to the problem of the existence of growth regulating substances has been to look for their presence in the serum. Injections of normal rat serum into intact rats have been reported to have no effect (Friedrich-Freksa and Zaki, 79; Glinos, 84; Moya, 157) or to stimulate mitosis (Fisher-Fisher and Saffer, 78). If injected into rats after partial hepatectomy, normal rat serum has either no effect (Mac-Donald and Rogers, 142) or inhibits liver mitosis (Stich and Florian, 190; Kohn, 122). The effects of posthepatectomy rat serum will be reported later in this paper, but the results are as inconsistent as those obtained with normal serum.

In a recent paper, Chaytor (29) presented evidence for the liberation of inhibitors into the serum during embryonic development of the chick. If chick embryos of 9 and 12 days of incubation are parabiosed, the younger embryo joined to the older partner shows a decrease of about 50 percent in liver mitotic frequency at the 16th day of development.

The data relating to the organ specificity of the effects observed and to the heat stability of the factors involved are contradictory. As already pointed out by Paschkis (167), the absence of effect on a single heterologous tissue should not be regarded as proof of organ specificity. From the available evidence, it is difficult to conclude that tissue-specific growth regulating factors exist in organ extracts. In 1960 Stich (189) commented on the difficulties of demonstrating such factors; crude extracts contain numerous compounds which can have general stimulating properties and thus obscure the presence of inhibitors and vice versa. The same confusion exists in the data related to the effects of kidney homogenates on renal growth (Goss, 87). As to the existence of growth inhibitory substances which are thought to be liberated into the serum, their organ-specific character cannot be easily established unless they are separated and purified. Until this aim is achieved, and the organ specificity of the effects firmly established, the release by the cells of organ-specific growth regulating substances must be regarded as problematical.

Regeneration of the Liver

Structural and Functional Changes in Regenerating Liver

In 1932 Higgins and Anderson (102) reported that the removal of two-thirds of the liver of the rat is followed within 24 hours by active cellular proliferation and complete restoration of the original liver mass in about 3 weeks. Since that original observation, the regenerating liver has been extensively studied in several respects. Initially, attention was paid to a morphological description, and to the changes in chemical composition and the essential liver functions. The bulk of the literature relating to these various aspects has been reviewed by Harkness (99), Glinos (84), and Weinbren (202). For the purpose of the present paper, the major structural and functional events during the first days of regeneration will be briefly summarized. In the second half of the first day after partial hepatectomy there is an increase in weight, followed by an outburst of cell division in the parenchymal cells. During the first day, when there is no cell division, the parenchymal cells increase in volume by about 50–100 percent. Cell division starts at 24 hours after operation and reaches a maximum frequency between 30 and 48 hours. The littoral cells undergo the same changes, but the changes are delayed in time. There is a rapid rise in total lipid, whereas the glycogen content falls sharply. Total liver protein decreases during the first 12 hours and then increases to reach a maximum between 12 and 24 hours after operation. The urea and bile output is reduced and the concentration of plasma protein falls.

In recent years the regeneration of the liver has been studied mainly from the biochemical point of view. A great deal of work has been done on the incorporation of labeled precursors into nucleic acids and proteins. These studies and others concerned with changes in enzyme activities during the very first hours of regeneration will be reported in some detail.

Biochemical Changes during Regeneration of the Liver

NUCLEIC ACID SYNTHESIS. In regenerating liver there is an increased synthesis of deoxyribonucleic acid preceding the onset of mitosis. The incorporation of labeled precursors into DNA has been studied by several investigators (Barnum et al., 8; Brody, 17; Bollum and Potter, 13; Holbrook et al., 104; Evans et al., 72; Kleinfeld and von Haam, 121; Grisham, 94; Nakamura et al., 159; Bucher et al., 20). There are some discrepancies with respect to the time at which DNA synthesis reaches its maximum. These discrepancies can be explained by the fact that the different investigators have used animals of different ages (20). From the work of Holbrook and co-workers (104) and Grisham (94) it appears that there are two waves of DNA synthesis in regenerating liver. According to Grisham, a great number of hepatocytes begin to synthesize DNA between 12 and 18 hours after partial hepatectomy, a peak being reached at about 20 hours. The peak of cells incorporating thymidine-H^3 preceded the peak of cells in mitosis by about 6 hours. A lag period of the same duration has been reported by Kleinfeld and von Haam (121). The synthesis of DNA in littoral and ductal cells begins later than in hepatocytes and reaches a peak between 36 and 48 hours. Grisham (94) estimated that 75 percent of the total DNA synthesis is associated with the hepatocytes.

Ribonucleic acid synthesis takes place earlier than DNA synthesis, but also in two waves. According to Hol-brook and co-workers (104), the peaks of incorporation of adenine-8-C^{14} into nuclear RNA occur at 19 hours and $42\frac{1}{2}$ hours after partial hepatectomy. In 1963 McArdle and Creaser (152) reported that the incorporation of P^{32} into the RNA fractions occurs in three stages. Over the first 4 hours after partial hepatectomy there is high incorporation of P^{32} into RNA of all the cell fractions: nuclei, microsomes, postmicrosomes, and supernate. From 4 to 8 hours there is a loss of radioactivity, interpreted as degradation of RNA. From 8 to 12 hours there is again considerable incorporation. Incorporation into nuclear RNA precedes incorporation into the bulk of cytoplasmic RNA. McArdle (151) reported that during the period from 8 to 12 hours a highly metabolically active RNA is first synthesized in the nuclear fraction and rapidly transferred to the cytoplasm. That RNA is compared to messenger-RNA and appears in the cytoplasm 6 to 8 hours after detection in the nucleus. Hoagland and Askonas (103) have shown that the pH 5 fraction, containing most of the soluble-RNA and activating enzymes, exhibits the same activity whether it is from normal or regenerating rat livers. But rat liver contains an RNA fraction which is more rapidly labeled than other cytoplasmic RNA and stimulates amino acid incorporation in microsomes. This fraction is more active when it comes from regenerating liver (20–24 hours after operation) than from normal liver. Even if most of its characteristics are different from those of bacterial messenger-RNA, the rapidly labeled RNA most probably represents messenger-RNA. Giudice and Novelli (in Giudice et al., 83) have presented evidence that up to 12 hours after partial hepatectomy there is synthesis of a specific messenger-RNA for DNA polymerase. The lag period between messenger-RNA synthesis and its utilization for enzyme synthesis is approximately 6 hours.

LIVER AND SERUM PROTEIN CHANGES DURING REGENERATION. Using paper electrophoresis, Guidotti and Clerici (96) have shown that the soluble proteins of the regenerating liver present the same electrophoretic pattern as those of the normal resting liver. They noticed, however, a faint albuminlike peak which appears 24 hours after surgery and disappears again 48 hours later. The liver glycoproteins have been found to decrease 24 hours after operation. At 60 hours two faint fractions reappear, and by 30 days glycoprotein is normal. In an analysis of the nuclear, mitochondrial, and supernatant fractions of normal and regenerating guinea pig liver, by agar gel electrophoresis, Gazzaniga and Sonnino (81) found that in the nuclear fraction two new components appear in the prealbumin zone 24 hours after partial hepatectomy. The mitochondrial preparations also reveal the appearance of a prealbumin component in regenerating liver 72 hours after surgery. In the supernatant fraction there are quantitative differences in the different protein components but there is also a new component which appears between the beta and gamma zones of migration. Using the immunoelectrophoretic technique, Gazzaniga and co-workers (82) found that in the cytoplasmic fraction some precipitin bands are not present in extracts of regenerating liver. In the mitochondrial fraction, a new band, which is always absent in normal liver, is visible. Thus there are proteins which disappear, or at least decrease in concentration, and new

components which appear, or increase in concentration, during the first hours of regeneration. The incorporation of labeled precursors into proteins is higher in regenerating than in normal resting liver. This increased synthesis of proteins is accompanied by a decreased catabolism of amino acids (Burke, 22).

There are some discrepancies in the results of studies on plasma protein synthesis during regeneration. Burke (22) found that the incorporation into plasma proteins is similar in regenerating and normal liver. Guidotti and co-workers (97) found that less albumin is released from 72-hour regenerating liver than from resting tissue. In regenerating liver, glycine incorporation into albumin is increased, suggesting that albumin turnover is faster. According to the latter investigators, the albumin level in the serum decreases, not because its synthesis in the liver is decreased, but because serum albumin is utilized by the liver itself to rebuild its tissue proteins. Braun and co-workers (16) reported a statistically significant increase in labeling of plasma albumin only in later stages of regeneration (72 and 144 hours after partial hepatectomy). At 14 and 24 hours after surgery there is a decrease in incorporation of C^{14} amino acids into plasma albumin. Thus, in early stages after partial hepatectomy, the liver preferentially synthesizes cellular or tissue protein. When the regenerative process is well under way, increased production of plasma albumin is favored (Drabkin, 61).

Studies of the incorporation of labeled amino acids into histones have shown that the specific radioactivity is six times higher in 48-hour regenerating than in normal rat liver (Okuda et al., 165). Using glycine-1-C[14] as a tracer, Holbrook and co-workers (104) studied incorporation into nuclear proteins at various intervals following partial hepatectomy. They found that the specific activities of the acid-insoluble nuclear proteins reached peaks at 19 and 37–43 hours. The incorporation into histones of regenerating liver nuclei is greater than the incorporation into other nuclear proteins and reaches a maximum at 22 hours after operation.

CHANGES IN ENZYME ACTIVITIES IN EARLY REGENERATING LIVER. As previously reported, total protein decreases during the first hours of regeneration. Most individual enzymes also decrease. However some enzymes, especially those concerned with nucleic acid synthesis, show a very rapid increase in activity. According to Bollum and Potter (13), there is a simultaneous increase in two enzymes required for the incorporation of thymidine into DNA: thymidine kinase and polymerase. DNA polymerase appears to increase at about 18 hours after partial hepatectomy, just at the time when DNA synthesis begins. There is an exponential rise of activity between 18 and 24 hours, followed by a slower increase up to 30 hours. Giudice and co-workers (83) found that 17 hours after operation, DNA polymerase activity is about 50 percent above normal; by 28 hours it is more than threefold normal. Deoxyribonuclease activity also increases during compensatory hyperplasia (Brody, 17); the increase is very rapid and starts at 12 hours after operation, reaching a peak by about 36 hours. Recondo and co-workers (175) found that in the serum of the partially hepatectomized rat deoxyribonuclease activity increases and passes a maximum at 36–48 hours after operation. RNA

polymerase activity has also been found to increase between 12 and 18 hours; it increases double during that period and by 48 hours has returned to the normal value (Busch et al., 24).

The activity of carbamyl phosphate aspartate transcarbamylase (CPAT) increases very rapidly during the first day after partial hepatectomy, reaches a maximum value by 48–56 hours, and drops to control values by the 15th day (Calva and Cohen, 26). The increase in carbamyl aspartate, which is an intermediate in the chain of reactions leading to the synthesis of pyrimidine nucleotides, appears to be correlated with the early synthesis of nucleic acids. Nazario and Cohen (160) proposed the hypothesis that the increase in CPAT activity together with a decrease in ornithine transcarbamylase activity (Kim, 119) might represent a regulatory mechanism by which more carbamyl phosphate is made available for pyrimidine biosynthesis. A higher rate of glycolysis in regenerating liver has been demonstrated by Clerici and Ciccarone (31) and Derache and co-workers (52, 53).

The Problem of the Stimulus to Regeneration

The mechanism whereby liver regenerates has received considerable attention. It has become increasingly clear that the factors which were initially thought to be of primary importance, such as the activity of endocrine glands and excretory products or nutritional factors, are not crucially involved (Swann, 191; Glinos, 84).

In recent years two different points of view have been defended and received experimental support. The first hypothesis is a corollary of the theory proposed by Weiss (203, 204), and suggests that partial removal of the liver results in a decrease of the extracellular concentration of organ-specific inhibitors which permits the remaining liver to resume growth. In contrast to this view is the idea of the liberation by the liver of a growth stimulating factor, and its accumulation in the serum.

EVIDENCE FOR THE INCREASE OF A STIMULATING AGENT. Evidence for the liberation of a growth stimulating factor stems largely from experiments of parabiosis, tissue cultures, and injections of posthepatectomy serum.

It has been shown that if one partner of a parabiotic pair of rats is partially hepatectomized, there is an increase in wet weight and number of hepatic cells (Wenneker and Sussman, 206) or an increase in mitotic rate (Bucher et al., 19) in the liver of the unoperated partner. In more recent experiments Wrba and co-workers (213–214) have demonstrated that liver explants from the operated member of a parabiotic pair take up 100 percent more labeled phosphate than explants from normal rat liver; in liver fragments of the same size from the second nonoperated member, the uptake of labeled phosphate is 50 percent above normal. Other evidence for the existence of a circulating factor comes from experiments of Boxer and Shonk (quoted in 26) in which it has been demonstrated that carbamyl phosphate aspartate transcarbamylase activity increases in the liver of partially hepatectomized rats and in the liver of untreated parabionts when the parabiotic partner has been partially hepatectomized. However, in several recent investigations no effect could be found on the liver of the unoperated member of a parabiotic pair. Fisher and co-workers (78) reported that there is no definite evidence of increased DNA synthesis in the intact normal member of a parabiotic pair following partial hepatectomy in the other. Similar results have been obtained by Alston and Thomson (4). Rogers and co-workers (178) found no increase in mitosis or DNA synthesis in the liver of the non-operated partner. Moreover, the latter investigators found that after sham operation in a member of a parabiotic pair of rats, there is greater hepatic DNA synthesis and mitotic activity in the nonoperated partner. Thus these authors insist that experiments on parabiotic animals must be compared to sham-operated controls, and emphasize the lack of such controls in earlier experiments. MacDonald and co-workers (144) noted the difficulties encountered in parabiosis experiments, in which 51 percent of the animals died, and others did not establish cross-circulation. Among the surviving pairs, 5 out of 19 showed some increase in DNA synthesis in the liver of the intact member joined in parabiosis to a partially hepatectomized partner. In 7 out of 15 other experiments, inhibition of DNA synthesis was found in the liver of the partially hepatectomized partner joined to normal animals. Thus, if several experiments tend to support the existence of a blood-borne stimulus to growth, others do not. From the positive findings, however, it appears that the liberation, by the regenerating liver, of a stimulating factor is highly probable. But, can this factor be regarded as the initial stimulus to regeneration, or is it produced as a result of the regenerative process which is itself triggered by other mechanisms?

Other evidence for the existence of a stimulating factor stems from tissue culture experiments. Posthepatectomy serum has always been found to be better than normal rat serum when added to tissue culture media (Akamatsu, quoted by Glinos, 84; Glinos and Gey, 85; Moya, 157). As pointed out by Glinos (84), the results of parabiosis and tissue culture experiments can be interpreted by the presence or increase of a growth stimulator, or by the absence or decrease of a growth inhibitor. Glinos and Gey (85) found a comparable outgrowth of liver explants in high concentrations of serum from partially hepatectomized rats and in low concentrations of normal rat serum. High concentrations of normal rat serum had inhibitory effects. From the experiments of Wrba and co-workers (213–215) it appears that normal rat serum does not inhibit the uptake of radioactive phosphorus in liver fragments cultivated in vitro. Liver tissue cultures incorporate the same amount of labeled phosphorus whether or not normal rat serum is added to the standard culture medium (chick embryo extract, calf serum, and Hank's solution). The addition of posthepatectomy serum stimulates the incorporation of P^{32} in normal and regenerating liver explants by about 30–40 percent as compared to cultures on normal serum. The stimulating action has been found to be organ specific, but not species specific; the factor is thermostable at $100°C$ for 5 minutes (214). The incorporation by embryonic and adult regenerating liver explants is about 130 percent above that of normal adult rat liver explants on all culture media. These experiments demonstrate that partial hepatectomy induces, in the remaining liver, an increase in metabolic activity which is observable after transplantation in vitro, and therefore does not appear to depend upon humoral regulation. But, if a direct action of hormones seems unlikely, at least for the continuation of the regenerative process, these experiments do not rule out the possibility that hormonal factors may be involved in the very early stages when the induction to regeneration takes place.

Whereas the results of tissue culture experiments consistently support the existence of a growth promoting agent in posthepatectomy serum, the results obtained by injections of serum into adult rats are more variable. Friedrich-Freksa and Zaki (79) injected posthepatectomy serum into normal rats and reported that the mitotic rate was increased in the liver by a factor of forty. These results have been confirmed by Laquerrière and Laumonier (125), but could not be confirmed by Glinos (84), MacDonald and co-workers (144), or Moya (157). Fisher-Fisher, and Saffer (78) reported that plasma obtained from hepatectomized donors and injected into normal rats resulted in an increase in mitosis of similar magnitude to that obtained when plasma from normal rats was injected. On the other hand, posthepatectomy serum injected into partially hepatectomized rats has been found to stimulate (Adibi et al., 3; Stich and Florian, 190) or to inhibit the mitotic rate in the liver (Kohn, 122).

Another indication of the liberation of a stimulating factor stems from the work of Ballantine (6) in which hepatectomy of the female rat at the 13th day of gestation was found to result in an increased weight of the livers in embryos at the 20th day of pregnancy.

EVIDENCE FOR THE DECREASE OF AN INHIBITOR. The findings of Glinos and Gey (85) indicated that high concentrations of normal rat serum are inhibitory. In a series of experiments, Glinos (84) has shown that if the concentration of the serum components is decreased by plasmapheresis, the number of cell divisions is increased in the resting liver of the adult rat. On the other hand, if the concentration of serum components is increased by depriving the animals of drinking, an effective inhibition of liver cell divisions is obtained in partially hepatectomized rats. These results were considered as evidence that the action of the factors controlling liver growth is inhibitory; partial removal of the liver causes a decrease in the concentration of inhibitors and thus the remaining liver resumes growth. Hemingway (100, 101) advanced the idea that the influence of plasma proteins may be due at least in part to the corticosteroids which are carried by the blood proteins. Repeating Glinos's experiments in combination with adrenalectomy, Hemingway came to the conclusion that corticosteroids represent the effective control agent of mitotic regulation in the liver. However, cortisone cannot be easily accepted as the only controlling agent, for its mitosis-inhibiting effect is not organ specific. It appears from the experiments that at least two factors contributed to the results obtained: a factor identical with that described by Glinos, and the corticosteroids. The latter group of experiments has one major shortcoming, inasmuch as the decrease in plasma proteins after partial hepatectomy is too slow and occurs only when other early signs of regeneration are already visible.

Whether there is liberation of a stimulator or decrease in the release of an inhibitor is not yet easy to decide. The two phenomena might occur together. But it seems that they are consequences of the regenerative process and occur when regeneration is already under way. As to the problem of the initial stimulus to regeneration, many factors have been shown to modify the regenerative rate, but none has been shown to be the effective controlling agent. As MacDonald and co-workers (144, p. 83) stated, "evidence to date is consistent with the hypothesis that control is exercised not through one crucial event, but through an interrelated series of conditions and events."

Summary

In the present paper some of the recent data related to the problems of liver development and regeneration have been reviewed. Three main sections have been devoted to the analysis of the information concerning the development of the liver in the chick and rat embryos.

The first section deals with a study of the inductive mechanisms intervening during early hepatic organogenesis in the chick embryo. The differentiation of the liver endoderm has been shown to depend upon two successive inductive stimuli. In a first step, which takes place at the time of the formation of the first somites, the prehepatic endoderm is induced by the mesoderm of the cardiac area. That primary induction which results in the determination of the prehepatic endoderm is necessary, but it is not sufficient for the further development of the hepatocytes. By that time, indeed, the hepatic endoderm remains still incapable of self-differentiation. The endodermal cells have to undergo a second inductive stimulus from the mesenchyme of the liver anlage which enables them to differentiate into hepatocytes. In addition, the epithelial cords exert a morphogenetic influence upon the mesenchymal part of the liver anlage; the result of the latter influence is the formation, by the mesenchymal cells, of the endothelium of the hepatic sinusoids.

The second section is mainly concerned with the description of some changes occurring in the different cellular structures during the further differentiation of the liver cell.

In a third section some biochemical changes accompanying the development of the liver have been analyzed. By means of immunochemical and enzymological techniques, several components characteristic of the adult liver have been shown to appear progressively during development. Other proteins have been demonstrated to disappear or to decrease in concentration. As far as possible, the changes in individual proteins, especially enzymes, have been correlated with the maturation of different liver functions.

Finally, the structural, functional, and biochemical changes accompanying the regeneration of the liver have been reviewed and the problems of the specific control of liver growth and of the initial stimulus to regeneration discussed.

References

1. Abelev, G. I., N. I. Khramkova, N. V. Engelhardt, and Z. A. Postnikova, "La Composition Antigénique des Cellules Normales et Tumorales du Foie," *Quelques Problèmes Posés par la Cellule Cancéreuse, Colloq. Franco-Soviétique, Moscow, 1962.* Paris: Gauthier-Villars pp. 77–90 (1963).
2. Ackerman, G. A., and R. A. Knouff, "Histochemical Differentiation of the Megacaryocytes in the Embryonic Liver," *Blood* 15:267–276 (1960).
3. Adibi, S., K. E. Paschkis, and A. Cantarow, "Stimulation of Liver Mitosis by Blood Serum from Hepatectomized Rats," *Exptl. Cell Res.* 18:396–398 (1959).
4. Alston, W. C., and R. Y. Thomson, "Humoral and Local Factors in Liver Regeneration," *Cancer Res.* 23:901–905 (1963).
5. Andres, G., "Growth Reactions of Mesonephros and Liver to Intravascular Injections of Embryonic Liver and Kidney Suspensions in the Chick Embryo," *J. Exptl. Zool.* 130:221–250 (1955).
6. Ballantine, E. E., "L'effet de l'Hepatectomie Partielle des Mères sur le Foie Fetal," *Intern. Course Regeneration, Athens* (1964).
7. Ballard, F. J., and I. T. Oliver, "Glycogen Metabolism in Embryonic Chick and Neonatal Rat Liver," *Biochim. Biophys. Acta* 71:578–588 (1963).
8. Barnum, C. P., C. D. Jardetzky, and F. Halberg, "Nucleic Acid Synthesis in Regenerating Liver," *Texas Rept. Biol. Med.* 15:134–147 (1957).
9. Beaumont, A., "Sur la Culture *in vitro* de Foie Larvaire d'Amphibien: Apparition du Glycogène en Milieu Synthétique," *Compt. Rend. Acad. Sci.* 243:676–677 (1956).
10. ———, "Etude Expérimentale de l'Apparition du Glycogène Hépatique chez les Larves d'Amphibiens Anoures," *Bull. Biol. Fr. Belg.* 94:268–395 (1960).
11. Bellairs, R., "Studies on the Development of the Foregut in the Chick Blastoderm. II. The Morphogenetic Movements," *J. Embryol. Exptl. Morphol.* 1: 369–385 (1953).
11a. Bernard Cl., "Recherche sur l'Origine du Glycogène dans la Vie Embryonnaire; Nouvelle Fonction du Placenta," *Compt. Rend. Soc. Biol.* 1:101–107 (1859).
11b. ———, "Glycogenèse Animale: Évolution du Glycogène dans l'Oeuf des Oiseaux," *Compt. Rend. Acad. Sci.* 75: 55–60 (1872).
12. Blomqvist, K., "Growth Stimulation in the Liver and Tumor Development Following Intraperitoneal Injections of Liver Homogenates in the Rat," *Acta Pathol. Microbiol. Scand. Suppl.* 121:1–65 (1957).
13. Bollum, F. J. and V. R. Potter, "Nucleic Acid Metabolism in Regenerating Rat Liver. VI. Soluble Enzymes which Convert Thymidine to Thymidine Phosphate

and DNA," *Cancer Res.* 19:561–565 (1959).

14. Brachet, J., *The Biochemistry of Development.* New York: Pergamon Press, (1960).

15. Brauer, R. W., L. M. Julian, and J. S. Krebs, "Maturation of Liver Function in the Chick Embryo as Explored with S³⁵-Sulfobromophthalein-Vascular Factors, Biliary Secretion and Conjugation," *Ann. N.Y. Acad. Sci.* 111:136–156 (1963).

16. Braun, G. A., J. B. Marsh, and D. L. Drabkin, "Synthesis of Plasma Albumin and Tissue Proteins in Regenerating Liver," *Metabolism* 11:957–966 (1962).

17. Brody, S., "Deoxyribonuclease Activity and Deoxyribonucleic Acid Synthesis in Normal, Regenerating, Precancerous and Cancerous Rat Liver," *Nature* 182:1386–1387 (1958).

18. Brouha, M., "Recherches sur le Développement du Foie, de la Cloison Mésentérique et des Cavités Hépato-Entériques chez les Oiseaux," *J. Anat. Physiol.* 34:305–363 (1898).

19. Bucher, N. L. R., J. E. Scott, and J. C. Aub, "Regeneration of the Liver in Parabiotic Rats," *Cancer Res.* 11:457–465 (1951).

20. ———, M. N. Swaffield, and J. F. Ditroia, "The Influence of Age upon the Incorporation of Thymidine 2-C¹⁴ into the DNA of Regenerating Rat Liver," *Cancer Res.* 24(3):509–512 (1964).

21. Burch, H. B., "Biochemical Changes in the Perinatal Rat Liver," *Ann. N.Y. Acad. Sci.* 111:176–182 (1963).

22. Burke, W. T., "Changes in Hepatic Metabolism Associated with Carcinogenesis or Regeneration in Rat Liver," *Cancer Res.* 22:10–14 (1962).

23. Burraston, J., and J. K. Pollak, "Aminoacid Incorporation into Embryonic Rat Liver," *Exptl. Cell Res.* 25:687–704 (1961).

24. Busch, S., P. Chambon, P. Mandel, and J. Weill, "The Effect of Partial Hepatectomy on the Ribonucleic Acid Polymerase of Rat Liver," *Biochem. Biophys. Res. Comm.* 7:255 (1962).

25. Cahn, R. D., N. O. Kaplan, L. Levine, and E. Zwilling, "Nature and Development of Lactic Dehydrogenases," *Science* 136:962–969 (1962).

26. Calva, E., and P. P. Cohen, "Carbamyl Phosphate Aspartate Transcarbamylase Activity in Regenerating Rat Liver," *Cancer Res.* 19:679–683 (1959).

27. Catayée, G., "De Quelques Aspects Graphiques des Variations Enzymatiques dans le Septum Transversum et dans les Formations Hépatiques au cours des Premières Heures du Développement de l'Embryon de Poulet," *Compt. Rend. Soc. Biol.* 156:1313–1316 (1962).

28. Chaube, S., "Hypoxanthine Dehydrogenase in the Developing Chick Embryonic Kidney," *Proc. Soc. Exptl. Biol. Med.* 111:340–342 (1962).

29. Chaytor, D. E. B., "The Control of Growth of the Chick Embryo Liver Studied by the Method of Parabiosis," *J. Embryol. Exptl. Morphol.* 11:667–672 (1963).

30. Choronshitzky, B., "Die Enstehung der Milz, Leber, Gallenblase, Bauchspeicheldrüse und des Pfortadersystems bei den verschiedenen Abteilungen der Wirbeltiere," *Anat. Hefte Abstr. 1*, 13:363–623 (1900).

31. Clerici, E., and P. Ciccarone, "Crabtree Effect in the Regenerating Liver of the Rat," *Nature* 201:1035–1036 (1964).

32. Common, R. H., and Mok. Chi-ching, "Phosvitin in the Serum of the Hen," *Nature* 183:1811–1812 (1959).

33. Conklin, J. L., "A Cytochemical Study of Lipid, Glycogen and Lactate Dehydrogenase in the Developing Liver," *J. Exptl. Zool.* 155:151–160 (1964).

34. Coquoin-Carnot, M., and J. M. Roux, "Taux du Glycogène et Activité de la Glucose-6-phosphatase dans le Foie du Rat à la Période Périnatale," *Compt. Rend. Soc. Biol.* 154:1763–1766 (1960).

35. ———, and ———, "Taux du Glycogène et Activité Phosphorylasique dans le Foie du Rat à la Période Périnatale," *Compt. Rend. Soc. Biol.* 156:442–445 (1962).

36. Croisille, Y., "Action de Différents Extraits d'Organes sur l'Embryon de Poulet et sur des Organes Embryonnaires Cultivés *in vitro*," *Arch. Anat. Microscop. Morphol. Exptl.* 47:359–400 (1958).

37. ———, "Etude, par la Méthode d'Immunoélectrophorèse, du Moment d'Apparition de Quelques Constituants Caractéristiques de l'Adulte dans le Foie de l'Embryon de Poulet," *Compt. Rend. Acad. Sci.* 249:1712–1714 (1959).

38. ——, "Etude Immuno-électrophorétique de l'Apparition Progressive de Quelques Constituants Caractéristiques de l'Adulte dans le Foie Embryonnaire du Poulet," *J. Embryol. Exptl. Morphol.* 8:216–225 (1960).

39. ——, "Etude Immuno-électrophorétique de l'Apparition de Quelques Constituants du Foie Adulte pendant le Développement Embryonnaire du Poulet," *Pathol. Biol.* 9:253–264 (1961).

40. ——, "Etude Immuno-électrophorétique des Estérases du Foie de Poulet Adulte et Embryonnaire," *Compt. Rend. Acad. Sci.* 254:2103–2105 (1962).

41. ——, "Developmental, Kinetic and Immunological Studies of Enzymes," *Ann. Rept. Director Dept. Embryol.*, Carnegie Inst. Wash., Year Book 62:428–437 (1963).

42. ——, "Formes Multimoléculaires de la Déshydrogénase Lactique chez le Poulet: Démonstration de l'Existence de Formes Transitoires chez l'Embryon," *Compt. Rend. Acad. Sci.* 258:2214–2217 (1964).

43. ——, "Hypoxanthine-Déshydrogénase dans les Organes du Poulet Adulte et Embryonnaire," *XII Colloq. Protides Biol. Fluids*, H. Peeters, ed., Amsterdam: Elsevier. pp. 199–202 (1964).

44. Dadoune, J. P., "Contribution à l'Étude au Microscope Électronique de la Différenciation de la Cellule Hépatique Chez le Rat," *Arch. Anat. Microscop. Morphol. Exptl.* 52:513–571 (1963).

45. Damas, H., "Les Premiers Stades de l'Hématopoièse dans le Foie (Cobaye)," *Arch. Biol.* 45:473 (1934).

46. D'Amelio, V., and P. Perlmann, "The Distribution of Soluble Antigens in Cellular Structures of Rat Liver," *Exptl. Cell Res.* 19:383–398 (1960).

47. ——, V. Mutolo, and A. Barbarino, "Immunological and Electrophoretic Analysis of Rat Liver Mitochondria and Other Cellular Fractions," *Exptl. Cell Res.* 29:1–16 (1963).

48. ——, ——, and E. Piazza, "A Serological Study of the Cell Fractions during the Embryonic Development of Liver in Chick," *Exptl. Cell Res.* 31:499–507 (1963).

49. Dameron, F., "Rôle du Mésenchyme dans la Différenciation de l'Ébauche Épithéliale du Poumon Embryonnaire de Poulet en Culture *in vitro*," *Pathol. Biol.* 10:811–816 (1962).

50. Dawkins, M. J. R., "Glycogen Synthesis and Breakdown in Fetal and Newborn Rat Liver," *Ann. N. Y. Acad. Sci.* 111:203–211 (1963).

51. DeHaan, R. L., "Migration Patterns of the Precardiac Mesoderm in the Early Chick Embryo," *Exptl. Cell Res.* 29:544–560 (1963).

52. Derache, R., M. F. Viala, and D. Gaillard, "Glycolyse Anaérobie dans la Phase Prémitotique du Foie de Rat en Hypertrophie Compensatrice," *Compt. Rend. Acad. Sci.* 258:2409–2411 (1964).

53. ——, and D. Gaillard, "Glycolyse Aérobie dans la Phase Prémitotique du Foie de Rat en Hypertrophie Compensatrice," *Compt. Rend. Acad. Sci.* 258:2674–2677 (1964).

54. Dieterlen-Lievre, F., "Influence du Pancréas Embryonnaire sur la Formation du Glycogène Hépatique chez le Poulet Étudiée par la Méthode des Parabioses *in vitro*," *Compt. Rend. Acad. Sci.* 250:1349–1351 (1960).

55. ——, "Démonstration de l'Activité Précoce des Cellules A du Pancréas chez l'Embryon de Poulet," *Compt. Rend. Acad. Sci.* 256:1597–1599 (1963).

56. Dieterlen-Lièvre, F., "Etude Morphologique et Expérimentale de la Différenciation du Pancréas chez l'Embryon de Poulet," *Bull. Biol.* 99:no. 1. In press (1965).

57. Dixon, M., and E. C. Webb, *Enzymes*. New York: Academic Press (1958).

58. Doljanski, F., "The Growth of the Liver with Special Reference to Mammals," *Intern. Rev. Cytol.*, G. H. Bourne and J. F. Danielli eds. New York: Academic Press, vol. 10, pp. 217–241 (1960).

59. Donath, R., "Anstieg der 5'–Nukleotidase Aktivität im Laufe der Entwickelung der Rattenleber," *Naturwissenschaften* 49:609–610 (1962).

60. ——, "Der Oxydative Abbau von Hypoxanthin und Harnsaüre durch Leberhomogenate im Laufe der Entwickelung der Rattenleber," *Acta Biol. Med. Ger.* 12:126–133 (1964).

61. Drabkin, D. L., "Kinetic Basis of Life Processes: Pathways and Mechanism of Hepatic Protein Synthesis," *Ann. N. Y. Acad. Sci.* 104:469–503 (1963).

62. Du Bois, A. M., "The Embryonic

Liver," *The Liver*. New York: Academic Press, vol. 1 (1963).

63. Dutton, G. J., "Comparison of Glucuronide Synthesis in Developing Mammalian and Avian Liver," *Ann. N.Y. Acad. Sci.* 111:259–273 (1963).

64. Dvorak, M. von, "Elektronen Mikroskopische Untersuchungen an embryonalen Leberzellen. *Z. Zellforsch.* 62:655–666 (1964).

65. Ebert, J. D., "Some Aspects of Protein Biosynthesis in Development," *Aspects of Synthesis and Order in Growth*, D. Rudnick, ed. Princeton, N.J.: Princeton University Press (1955).

66. ———, "The Acquisition of Biological Specificity," *The Cell*, J. Brachet and A. Mirsky, eds. New York: Academic Press, vol. 1, pp. 619–693 (1960).

67. ———, and F. H. Wilt, "Animal Viruses and Embryos," *Quart. Rev. Biol.* 35:261–312 (1960).

68. Elias, H., "Origin and Early Development of the Liver in Various Vertebrates," *Acta Hepatol.* 3:40–56 (1955).

69. ———, and H. Bengelsdorf, "The Structure of the Liver of Vertebrates," *Acta Anat.* 14:297–337 (1952).

70. Eliasson, E., "Arginase in Young Chick Embryos. I. The Nature of the Changes in Activity during Development," *Exptl. Cell Res.* 26:175–188 (1962).

71. ———, "Arginase in Young Chick Embryos. II. The Detailed Pattern of Early Arginase Accumulation," *Exptl. Cell Res.* 28:99–106 (1962).

72. Evans, J. H., D. J. Holbrook, and J. L. Irvin, "Changes in Content of Nuclear Proteins and Nucleic Acid in Regenerating Liver," *Exptl. Cell Res.* 28:126–132 (1962).

73. Felix, W., "Zur Leber und Pankreasentwicklung," *Arch. Anat. Entwickl.* pp. 281–323 (1892).

74. Ferreira, J. F. D., "A Diferenciaçao do Condrioma Aparelho de Golgi e Ergasto-Plasma," *Inst. Histol. Faculté Méd. Lisboa* (1959).

75. Fine, I. H., N. O. Kaplan, and D. Kuftinec, "Developmental Changes of Mammalian Lactic Dehydrogenase," *Biochemistry* 2:116–121 (1963).

76. Fischer, J. R., and R. E. Eakin, "Nitrogen Excretion in Developing Chick Embryos," *J. Embryol. Exptl. Morphol.* 5:215–224 (1957).

77. Fisher, B., and E. R. Fisher, "Local Factors Affecting Tumor Growth. I. Effects of Tissue Homogenates," *Cancer Res.* 23:1651–1657 (1963).

78. ———, ———, and E. Saffer, "Investigations Concerning the Role of a Humoral Factor in Liver Regeneration," *Cancer Res.* 23:914–920 (1963).

79. Friedrich-Freksa, H., and F. G. Zaki, "Spezifische Mitoseauslösung in normaler Rattenleber durch Serum von partiell hepatektomierten Ratten," *Z. Naturforsch.* 9b:394–397 (1954).

80. Gansler, H., and Ch. Rouiller, "Modifications Physiologiques et Pathologiques du Chondriome. Etude au Microscope Électronique," *Schweiz. Z. Allgem. Pathol. Bakteriol.* 19:217–243 (1956).

81. Gazzaniga, P. P., and F. R. Sonnino, "Agar Electrophoresis of Soluble Proteins Isolated from Cellular Fractions of Regenerating Guinea Pig Liver," *Experientia* 18/1:26–28 (1962).

82. ———, G. Di Macco, and F. R. Sonnino, "Immunoelectrophoresis of Soluble Proteins Isolated from Cellular Fractions of Regenerating Rat Liver," *Experientia* 19:419–420 (1963).

83. Giudice, G., F. T. Kenney, and G. D. Novelli, "Effect of Puromycin on Deoxyribonucleic Acid Synthesis by Regenerating Rat Liver," *Biochim. Biophys. Acta* 87:171–173 (1964).

84. Glinos, A. D., "The Mechanism of Liver Growth and Regeneration," *A Symposium on the Chemical Basis of Development*, W. McElroy, B. Glass, eds. Baltimore, Md.: The Johns Hopkins University Press, pp. 813–842 (1958).

85. ———, and G. O. Gey, "Humoral Factors Involved in the Induction of Liver Regeneration in the Rat," *Proc. Soc. Exptl. Biol. Med.* 80:421–425 (1952).

86. Golosow, N., and C. Grobstein, "Epitheliomesenchymal Interaction in Pancreatic Morphogenesis," *Develop. Biol.* 4:242–255 (1962).

87. Goss, R. J., "Mitotic Responses of the Compensating Rat Kidney to Injections of Tissue Homogenates," *Cancer Res.* 23:1031–1035 (1963).

88. Grabar, P., and C. A. Williams, "Méthode Permettant l'Étude Conjuguée des Propriétés Électrophorétiques et Immunochimiques d'un Mélange de Pro-

téines," *Biochim. Biophys. Acta* 10:193 (1953).

89. Grasso, J. A., H. Swift, and G. A. Ackerman, "Observation on the Development of Erythrocytes in Mammalian Foetal Liver," *J. Cell Biol.* 14:235–254 (1962).

90. Grillo, T. A. I., "Glycogen in the Chick Embryo and the Internal Secretions of the Pancreas," *Anat. Record* 136:202 (1960).

91. ——, "A Histochemical Study of Phosphorylase in the Tissues of the Chick Embryo," *J. Histochem. Cytochem.* 9: 386–391 (1961).

92. ——, "The Ontogeny of Insulin Secretion in the Chick Embryo," *J. Endocrinol.* 22:285–292 (1961).

93. ——, and K. Ozone, "Uridine Diphosphate Glucose-Glycogen Synthetase Activity in the Chick Embryo," *Nature* 195: 902–903 (1962).

94. Grisham, J. W., "A Morphologic Study of Deoxyribonucleic Acid Synthesis and Cell Proliferation in Regenerating Rat Liver; Autoradiography with Thymidine H³," *Cancer Res.* 22:842–849 (1962).

95. Guha, S., and R. Wegmann, "Phosphorylase in Chick Embryo Liver," *J. Histochem. Cytochem.* 9:454–455 (1961).

96. Guidotti, G., and E. Clerici, "Paper Electrophoresis of Soluble Proteins from Regenerating Rat Liver," *Experientia* 14: 341–342 (1958).

97. ——, ——, G. Sambo, and E. Bazzano, "Albumin Synthesis in Regenerating Rat Liver Cells," *Experientia* 15: 55–56 (1959).

98. Haff, R., "Bindegewebs und Blutbildungsprozesse in der embryonalen Leber des Huhns," *Arch. Mikroskop. Anat.* 84: 321–350 (1914).

99. Harkness, R. D., "Regeneration of the Liver," *Brit. Med. Bull.* 13:87–93 (1957).

100. Hemingway, J. T., "Withdrawal of Inhibition of Mitosis, as a Mechanism Influencing Normal and Pathological Growth," *Nature* 185:106–107 (1960).

101. ——, "Influence of Plasma Proteins in the Control of Mitosis Rates in Regenerating Liver," *Nature* 191:706–707 (1961).

102. Higgins, G. M., and R. M. Anderson, "Experimental Pathology of the Liver. Restoration of the Liver after Partial Removal and Ligation of the Bile Duct in White Rats," *Arch. Pathol.* 14:42–49 (1932).

103. Hoagland, M. B., and B. A. Askonas, "Aspects of Control of Protein Synthesis in Normal and Regenerating Rat Liver. A Cytoplasmic RNA-containing Fraction that Stimulates Amino-acid Incorporation," *Proc. Natl. Acad. Sci. U.S.* 49:130–137 (1963).

104. Holbrook, D. J., J. H. Evans, and J. L. Irvin, "Incorporation of Labeled Precursors into Proteins and Nucleic Acids of Nuclei of Regenerating Liver," *Exptl. Cell Res.* 28:120–125 (1962).

105. Hosoda, T., T. Abe, and T. Kaneko, "Antigenic Properties of Liver Cell Fractions Derived from Laying Hens and Estrogenized Chickens," *Proc. Soc. Exptl. Biol. Med.* 108:234–238 (1961).

106. Hunter, R. L. and C. L. Markert, "Histochemical Demonstration of Enzymes Separated by Zone Electrophoresis in Starch Gels," *Science* 125:1294–1295 (1957).

107. Iversen, S. and A. Thamsen, "The Nucleocytoplasmic Ratio in the Mouse Liver Cells," *Acta Pathol. Microbiol. Scand.* 38:96 (1956).

108. Jacquot, R., "Recherches sur le Contrôle Endocrinien de l'Accumulation de Glycogène dans le Foie chez le Foetus de Rat," *J. Physiol.* 51:665–692 (1959).

109. ——, and N. Kretchmer, "Relations entre Équipement Enzymatique, Teneur en Glycogène et État Endocrine dans le Foie Foetal du Rat," *Compt. Rend. Acad. Sci.* 257:2173–2175 (1963).

110. Jost, A., "Hormonal Factors Controlling the Storage of Glycogen in the Fetal Liver," *Perspectives in Biology*, C. F. Cori, V. G. Foglia, L. F. Leloir, S. Ochoa, eds. Amsterdam: Elsevier (1962).

111. ——, and R. Jacquot, "Recherches sur les Facteurs Endocriniens de la Charge en Glycogène du Foie Fetal Chez le Lapin," *Ann. Endocrinol.* 16:849–872 (1955).

112. Kafer, E., and J. K. Pollak, "Amino Acid Metabolism of Growing Tissues. II. Alanine-glutamic Acid Transaminase Activity of Embryonic Rat Liver," *Exptl. Cell Res.* 22:120–136 (1961).

113. Karrer, H. E., "Electron-Microscopic Observations on Developing Chick Embryo Liver. The Golgi Complex and Its Possible Role in the Formation of Glycogen," *J. Ultrastruct. Res.* 4:149–165 (1960).

114. ——, "Electron-microscopic Study of Glycogen in Chick Embryo Liver," *J. Ultrastruct. Res.* 4:191–212 (1960).

115. ——, "Electron-microscopic Observations on Chick Embryo Liver. Glycogen, Bile Canaliculi, Inclusion Bodies and Hematopoiésis," *J. Ultrastruct. Res.* 5:116–141 (1961).

116. Kato, Y., "Flavin Enzymes in the Chick Embryo and Hatched Chick," *Ann. Rept. Director Dept. Embryol.* Carnegie Inst. Wash., Year Book 60:397–399 (1961).

117. Kennan, A. L., and P. P. Cohen, "Biochemical Studies of the Developing Mammalian Fetus; Urea Cycle Enzymes," *Develop. Biol.* 1:511–525 (1959).

118. Kilsheimer, G. S., D. R. Weber, and J. Ashmore, "Hepatic Glucose Production in Developing Chicken Embryo," *Proc. Soc. Exptl. Biol. Med.* 104:515–518 (1960).

119. Kim, S., Ph.D Thesis, University of Wisconsin (1960).

120. Kingsbury, J. W., M. Alexanderson, and E. S. Kornstein, "The Development of the Liver in the Chick," *Anat. Record* 124:165–187 (1956).

121. Kleinfeld, R. G., and E. von Haam, "Nucleic Acid Metabolism in Regenerating Rat Liver Using Cytidine H^3," *Ann. Histochim.* 7 No. 3:89–96 (1962).

122. Kohn, R., "Effect of Administration of Rat Serum on Rat Liver Regeneration," *Exptl. Cell Res.* 14:228–230 (1958).

123. Konigsberg, I., "The Effects of Early Pituitary Removal by Decapitation on Carbohydrate Metabolism in the Chick Embryo," *J. Exptl. Zool.* 125:151–169 (1954).

124. Lahtiharju, A., "Influence of Autolytic and Necrotic Liver Tissue on Liver Regeneration in the Rat," *Acta Pathol. Microbiol. Scand. Suppl.* 150:1–99 (1961).

125. Laquerriere, R., and R. Laumonier, "Variations du Taux d'Acide Désoxyribonucléique dans le Foie du Rat Albinos après Injection de Sérum de Rat Hepatectomisé," *Compt. Rend. Soc. Biol.* 154:286–289 (1960).

126. Le Douarin, N., "Sur les Résultats d'Experiences de Radiodestruction Transversales Pratiquées chez l'Embryon de Poulet," *Compt. Rend. Acad. Sci.* 250:2064–2066 (1960).

127. ——, "Radiodestructions Partielles chez l'Embryon de Poulet aux Jeunes Stades et Localisation des Ébauches Digestives," *J. Embryol. Exptl. Morphol.* 9:1–8 (1961).

128. ——, "Données Expérimentales sur l'Organogenèse Hépatique chez l'Embryon de Poulet," *Compt. Rend. Acad. Sci.* 255:769–772 (1962).

129. ——, "Rôle du Mésenchyme dans l'Histogenèse Hépatique chez l'Embryon de Poulet," *Compt. Rend. Acad. Sci.* 257:255–257 (1963).

130. ——, "Action Inductrice Précoce du Mésoderme de l'Aire Cardiaque sur l'Endoderme Hépatique de l'Embryon de Poulet," *Compt. Rend. Acad. Sci.* 257: 1357–1360 (1963).

131. ——, "Isolement Expérimental du Mésenchyme Propre du Foie et Rôle Morphogène de la Composante Mésodermique dans l'Organogenèse Hépatique," *J. Embryol. Exptl. Morphol.* 12: 141–160 (1964).

132. ——, "Induction de l'Endoderme Pré-Hépatique par le Mésoderme de l'Aire Cardiaque chez l'Embryon de Poulet," *J. Embryol. Exptl. Morphol.* 12: 641–664 (1964).

133. ——, "Etude Expérimentale de l'Organogenèse du Tube Digestif et du Foie chez l'Embryon de Poulet," *Bull. Biol. Fr. Belg.* 98(4):543–583; 98(5), 589–676 (1964).

134. Leibson, L. G., and Z. P. Zheludkova, "Influence de la Cortisone sur la Fonction Glycogénique et la Sécrétion Biliaire du Foie de l'Embryon de Poulet, Evolution des Fonctions Physiologiques 17–21 Mars," *Acad. Sci. SSSR* (1959).

135. ——, and ——, "Sécrétion Pancréatique d'Insuline chez l'Embryon de Poulet," *Bjull. Exptl. Biol. Med. SSSR* 26:24–27 (1961).

136. ——, and E. M. Stabrowskij, "La Teneur en Adrénaline et Noradrénaline des Surrénales des Embryons de Poulet en Développement," *Fiziol. Zh. SSSR* 48:857–863 (1962).

137. ——, E. M. Plisetskaia, and L. G. Ogorodnikova, "Glucose-6-phosphatase of the Liver of Chick Embryos under Normal Conditions and Acted upon with Insulin," *Dokl. Akad. Nauk SSSR* 153: 240–242 (1963).

137a. Leloir, L. F., and C. E. Cardini,

"Biosynthesis of Glycogen from Uridine Diphosphate Glucose," *J. Am. Chem. Soc.* 79:6340–6341 (1957).

138. Lindsay, D. T., "Developmental Patterns and Immuno-chemical Properties of Lactate Dehydrogenase Isozymes from the Chicken." Dissertation, Johns Hopkins University, Baltimore (1962).

139. ———, "Isozymic Patterns and Properties of Lactate Dehydrogenase from Developing Tissues of the Chicken," *J. Exptl. Zool.* 152:75–89 (1963).

140. Lipp, W., "Die Entwicklung der Parenchymarchitektur der Leber," *Verh. Anat. Ges.* Jena, Germany: Fisher vol. 50, pp. 241–249 (1952).

141. Lövlie, A. M., "On the Functional Differentiation of the Hepatic Cells of the Chick Embryo: Glycogen Synthesis and Mitotic Activity," *Nytt Magasin Zool.* 8:5–24 (1959).

142. MacDonald, R. A., and A. E. Rogers, "Control of Regeneration of the Liver; Lack of Effect of Plasma from Partially Hepatectomized, Cirrhotic and Normal Rats upon Deoxyribonucleic Acid Synthesis and Mitosis in Rat Liver," *Gastroenterology* 41:33–38 (1961).

143. ———, ———, and G. Pechet, "Regeneration of the Liver: Relation of Regenerative Response to Size of Partial Hepatectomy," *Lab. Invest.* 11:544–548 (1962).

144. ———, ———, and ———, "Growth and Regeneration of the Liver," *Ann. N.Y. Acad. Sci.* 111:70–86 (1963).

145. Malmgren, R. A., "Observation on a Liver Mitotic Stimulant Present in Tumor Tissue," *Cancer Res.* 16:232–236 (1956).

146. Mandel, P., "Quelques Aspects de la Régulation de la Biosynthèse des Acides Nucléiques dans les Tissus Normaux et Cancéreux," *Colloq. Franco-Soviétique 1962.* Paris: Gauthier-Villars (1963).

147. Markert, C. L., "Chemical Concept of Cellular Differentiation," *Chemical Basis of Development*, W. McElroy, B. Glass, eds. Baltimore, Md.: The Johns Hopkins Press, pp. 3–16 (1958).

148. ———, and R. L. Hunter, "The Distribution of Esterases in Mouse Tissues," *J. Histochem. Cytochem.* 7:42–49 (1959).

149. ———, and F. Moller, "Multiple Forms of Enzymes: Tissue, Ontogenetic and Species Specific Patterns," *Proc. Natl. Acad. Sci.* 45:753–763 (1959).

150. ———, and H. Ursprung, "The Ontogeny of Isozyme Patterns of Lactate Dehydrogenase in the Mouse," *Develop. Biol.* 5:363–381 (1962).

151. McArdle, A. H., "Nucleoproteins in Regenerating Rat Liver: a Study of the Rapidly Labelled Ribonucleic Acid," *Biochim. Biophys. Acta* 68:569–577 (1963).

152. ———, and E. H. Creaser, "Nucleoproteins in Regenerating Rat Liver. Incorporation of ^{32}Pi into the Ribonucleic Acid of Liver during the Early Stages of Regeneration," *Biochim. Biophys. Acta* 68:561–568 (1963).

153. Minot, S. S., "On a Hitherto Unrecognized Form of Blood Circulation without Capillaries in the Organs of Vertebrata," *Proc. Bos. Soc. Nat. Hist.* 29:185–215 (1900).

154. Molimard, R., "Etudes sur le Mécanisme de la Régulation Pondérale des Organes. I. Freinage Spécifique de l'Hypertrophie Compensatrice du Foie Chez le Rat par un Extrait de Foie Homologue," *Rev. Fr. Et. Clin. Biol.* 4:652–660 (1959).

155. Mollier, S., "Die Blutbildung in der embryonalen Leber des Meisschen und der Säugetiere," *Arch. Mikroskop. Anat.* 74:474–524 (1909).

156. Morgan, E. J., "Xanthine Oxidase in the Avian Embryo," *Biochem. J.* 24:410–414 (1930).

157. Moya, F. J., "Inhibition of Growth by Post-hepatectomy Blood Serum. Effect on Regenerating Liver and on Tissue Cultures," *Exptl. Cell Res.* 31:457–469 (1963).

158. Mutolo, V., and V. D'Amelio, "Antigen Distribution in Rat Liver Mitochondria," *Experientia* 18:556–560 (1962).

159. Nakamura, R. M., D. S. Miyada, and D. L. Moyer, "Interrelationship of the Thyroid Gland to Liver Regeneration in Rats as Studied by Tritiated Thymidine Incorporation," *Exptl. Cell Res.* 34:410–414 (1964).

160. Nazario, M., and P. P. Cohen, "Effect of Thyroxine on Enzymes of the Urea Cycle in Regenerating Rat Liver," *Proc. Soc. Exptl. Biol. Med.* 106:492–495 (1961).

161. Nebel, E. J., and J. L. Conklin, "Development of Lactic Dehydrogenase Isozymes in the Chick Embryo," *Proc. Soc. Exptl. Biol. Med.* 115:532–536 (1964).

162. Nemeth, A. M., "Initiation of Enzyme Formation by Birth," *Ann. N.Y. Acad. Sci.* 111:199–202 (1963).

163. North, R. J., and J. K. Pollak, "An Electron-microscope Study on the Variation of Nuclear Mitochondrial Proximity in Developing Chick Liver," *J. Ultrastruct. Res.* 5:497–503 (1961).

164. Okada, T. S., and H. Yamamura, "Immunological Study on Progressive Appearance of Microsomal Constituents of the Developing Chicken Liver," *Embryologia* 8:115–128 (1964).

165. Okuda, J., D. Szafarz, and I. Khouvine, "Comparaison entre les Protéines Basiques et Acides d'une Fraction Extraite de Noyaux Isolés de Foie de Rat Normal et en Régénération," *Compt. Rend. Acad. Sci.* 257:2904–2905 (1963).

166. Oliver, I. T., and J. S. Cooke, "Rat Liver Glucokinase Activities in Starvation," *Biochim. Biophys. Acta* 81:402–404 (1964).

167. Paschkis, K. E., "Growth-promoting Factors in Tissues," *Cancer Res.* 18:981–991 (1958).

168. Paschkis, K. E., et al., "Growth-stimulating Actions of Liver Preparations," *Fed. Proc.* 16:98 (1957).

169. Perlmann, P., and V. D'Amelio, "Soluble Antigens in Microsomes and Other Cell Fractions of Rat Liver," *Nature* 181:491–492 (1958).

170. ——, T. Hultin, V. D'Amelio, and W. S. Morgan, "Distribution and Metabolism of Protein Antigens in Rat Liver," *Exptl. Cell Res. Suppl.* 7:279–295 (1959).

170a. Pesch, L. A., and Y. J. Topper, "The Liver and Carbohydrate Metabolism," *The Liver*, Ch. Rouiller, ed. New York: Academic Press, vol. 1 (1963).

171. Peters, V. B., G. W. Kelly, and H. M. Dembister, "Cytologic Changes in Fetal and Neonatal Hepatic Cells of the Mouse," *Ann. N.Y. Acad. Sci.* 111:87–103 (1963).

172. Philip, J., and E. S. Vessel, "Sequential Alterations of LDH Isozymes during Embryonic Development and in Tissue Culture," *Proc. Soc. Exptl. Biol. Med.* 110:582–585 (1962).

173. Policard, A., and M. Bessis, "Sur un Mode d'Incorporation des Macromolécules par la Cellule, Visible au Microscope Électronique: la Rophéocytose," *Compt. Rend. Acad. Sci.* 246:3194–3197 (1958).

174. Rawles, M. E., "A Study of the Localization of Organ-forming Areas in the Chick Blastoderm of the Head-process Stage," *J. Exptl. Zool.* 72:271–315 (1936).

175. Recondo, A. M., C. Frayssinet, and P. May, "Variations de l'Activité des Désoxyribonucléases Sériques au cours de l'Hypertrophie Compensatrice du Foie," *Compt. Rend. Acad. Sci.* 255:2667–2669 (1962).

176. Rhodin, J., "Correlation of Ultrastructural Organization and Function in Normal and Experimentally Changed Proximal Convoluted Tubule Cells of the Mouse Kidney," *Karolinska Inst. Aktiebolaget Godvil, Stockholm* (1954).

177. Rinaudo, M. T., "Fructose-1,6-Diphosphatase in the Liver of Chicken Embryos," *Experientia* 17:30–31 (1961).

178. Rogers, A. E., J. A. Shaka, G. Pechet, and R. A. MacDonald, "Regeneration of the Liver: Absence of a Humoral Factor Affecting Hepatic Regeneration in Parabiotic Rats," *Am. J. Pathol.* 39:561–578 (1961).

179. Romanoff, A. L., *The Avian Embryo: Structural and Functional Development.* New York: MacMillan Company (1960).

180. Rouiller, Ch., and W. Bernhard, "Microbodies and the Problem of Mitochondrial Regeneration," *J. Biophys. Biochem. Cytol.* 2:355–360 (1956).

181. Rudnick, D., "Thyroid-forming Potencies of the Early Chick Blastoderm," *J. Exptl. Zool.* 62:287–317 (1932).

182. Saetren, H., "A Principle of Autoregulation of Growth. Production of Organ Specific Mitose-inhibitors in Kidney and Liver," *Exptl. Cell Res.* 11:229–232 (1956).

183. Schjeide, O. A., S. Binz, and N. Ragan, "Oestrogen-induced Serum Protein Synthesis in the Liver of the Chick Embryo," *Growth* 24:401–410 (1961).

183a. Sentenac, A., and P. Fromageot, "La Serine Hydrolyase de l'Oiseau: Mise en Évidence dans l'Embryon et Mécanisme d'Action," *Biochim. Biophys. Acta* 81:289–300 (1964).

184. Sie, H. G., and W. H. Fishman, "Glycogen Synthetase: Its Response to Cortisol," *Science* 143:816–817 (1964).

185. Siess, M., and H. Stegmann, "Mes-

stecknische Untersuchungen über das Wachstum der Leber der Weissen Maus, als Grundlage für morphologisch funktionale Studien," *Virchows Arch. Pathol. Anat.* 318:534 (1950).

186. Solomon, J. B., "Changes in the Distribution of Glutamic, Lactic and Malic Dehydrogenases in Liver Cell Fractions during Development of the Chick Embryo," *Develop. Biol.* 1:182–198 (1959).

186a. ———, "Glutamic Dehydrogenase in the Developing Chick Embryo," *Biochem. Jour.* 66:264–270 (1957).

186b. ———, "Lactic and Malic Dehydrogenases in the Developing Chick Embryo," *Biochem. J.* 70:529–535 (1958).

186c. ———, "Constitutive Enzymes of the Chick Embryo. II. Cystein Desulphydrase," *J. Embryol. Exptl. Morphol.* 11:591–604 (1963).

187. Sorenson, G. D., "An Electron-microscopic Study of Hematopoiesis in the Liver of Fetal Rabbit," *Am. J. Anat.* 106:27–40 (1960).

188. ———, "Hepatic Hematopoiesis in the Fetal Rabbit: a Light and Electron-microscopic Study," *Ann. N.Y. Acad. Sci.* 111:45–69 (1963).

189. Stich, H. F., "Regulation of Mitotic Rate in Mammalian Organisms," *Ann. N.Y. Acad. Sci.* 90:603–609 (1960).

190. ———, and M. L. Florian, "The Presence of a Mitosis Inhibitor in the Serum and Liver of Adult Rats," *Canad. J. Biochem. Physiol.* 36:855–859 (1958).

191. Swann, M. M., "The Control of Cell Division: a Review," *Cancer Res.* 18:1118–1160 (1958).

192. Teir, H., and K. Ravanti, "Mitotic Activity and Growth Factors in the Liver of the White Rat, *Exptl. Cell Res.* 5:500–507 (1953).

193. Thommes, R. C., and C. E. Firling, "Blood Glucose and Liver Glycogen Levels in Glucagon-treated Chick Embryos," *Gen. Comp. Endocrinol.* 4:1–8 (1964).

194. Tumanishvili, G. D., "Stimulating Action of Tissue Extracts on Regenerative Processes," *J. Embryol. Exptl. Morphol.* 8:226–238 (1960).

195. ———, K. M. Dzhandieri, and I. K. Svanidze, "La Stimulation Spécifique des Organes de l'Embryon de Poulet sous l'Influence d'Extraits de Tissus," *Dokl.*

Akad. Nauk SSSR 106:1107–1109 (1956).

196. Van Alten, P. J., and R. A. Fennel, "The Effects of Chorioallantoic Grafts on the Developing Chick Embryo. I. Studies on Weight and Histology of Homologous and Heterologous Tissues," *J. Embryol. Exptl. Morphol.* 7:459–475 (1959).

197. Vessel, E. S., and J. Philip, "Isozymes of Lactic Dehydrogenase: Sequential Alterations during Development," *Ann. N.Y. Acad. Sci.* 111:243–257 (1963).

198. Vogt, P. K., "Distribution of Tissue Specific Antigens in Centrifugal Fractions of Rat Liver," *Nature* 182:1807–1808 (1958).

199. ———, "Die Immunologie der Lebermikrosomen. III. Die Lokalisation gewebespezifischer Antigene innerhalb der Strukturkomponenten des endoplasmatischen Retikulums," *Z. Naturfsch.* 15b:221–225 (1960).

200. Walker, D. G., "On the Presence of Two Soluble Glucose-phosphorylating Enzymes in Adult Liver and the Development of One of These after Birth," *Biochim. Biophys. Acta* 77:209–226 (1963).

201. Walter, H., D. W. Allman, and H. R. Mahler, "Influence of Adult Tissue Homogenates on Formation of Similar Embryonic Proteins," *Science* 124:1251–1252 (1956).

202. Weinbren, K., "Regeneration of Liver," *Gastroenterology* 37:657–668 (1959).

203. Weiss, P., "The Problem of Specificity in Growth and Development," *Yale J. Biol. Med.* 19:235–278 (1947).

204. ———, "Specificity in Growth Control," *Biological Specificity and Growth*, E. G. Butler, ed. Princeton, N.J.: Princeton University Press, pp. 195–206 (1955).

205. ———, and H. Wang, "Growth Response of the Liver of Embryonic Chick Hosts to the Incorporation in the Area Vasculosa of Liver and Other Organ Fragments," *Anat. Record* 79:62 (1941).

206. Wenneker, A. S., and N. Sussman, "Regeneration of Liver Tissue Following Partial Hepatectomy in Parabiotic Rats," *Proc. Soc. Exptl. Biol. Med.* 76:683–686 (1951).

207. Weston, J. C., "The Effect of Cortisone on Some Chemical Constituents of

Developing Chick Liver," *Growth* 20: 75–90 (1956).

208. Williamson, M. B., "Growth of the Liver in Fetal Rats," *Growth* 12:145–147 (1948).

209. Willier, B. H., "Ontogeny of Endocrine Correlation," *Analysis of Development*, B. H. Willier, P. A. Weiss, V. Hamburger, eds. Philadelphia: Saunders (1955).

210. Wilson, A. C., R. D. Cahn, and N. O. Kaplan, "Functions of the Two Forms of Lactate Dehydrogenase in the Breast Muscle of Birds," *Nature* 197:331–334 (1963).

211. Wilson, J. W., C. S. Groat, and E. H. Leduc, "Histogenesis of the Liver," *Ann. N.Y. Acad. Sci.* 111:8–22 (1963).

212. Wolff, Et., and K. Haffen, "Sur une Méthode de Culture d'Organes Embryonnaires *in vitro*," *Texas Rept. Biol. Med.* 10:463–472 (1952).

213. Wrba, H., H. Rabes, and W. Zintl, "Zur Biologie induzierter Wachstumsvorgänge in der Leber *in vivo* und in Explantat," *Virchows Arch. Pathol. Anat.* 336:12–15 (1962).

214. ——, ——, M. Ripoll-Gomez, and H. Ranz, "Die stoffwechselsteigernde Wirkung Von Seren Teilhepatektomierter Tiere auf Leber kulturen," *Exptl. Cell Res.* 26:70–77 (1962).

215. ——, and ——, "The Action of Serum from Partially Hepatectomized Rats on Explants of Liver and Tumors," *Cancer Res.* 23:1116–1120 (1963).

216. Zwilling, E., "Carbohydrate Metabolism in Insulin Treated Chick Embryos," *Arch. Biochem. Biophys.* 33:228–242 (1951).

18

Recent Work on Developing Lungs

SERGEI SOROKIN

Department of Anatomy
Harvard Medical School
Boston, Massachusetts

During the past decade we have improved our understanding of the process of development in the lung. Such progress has been achieved both through application of newly perfected techniques and through continued use of older methods. For all that, the accomplishments of earlier embryologists have yet to be equaled by their successors. At present the investigations being made on the developing lung fall into distinct although interdependent categories: (1) the general mechanisms of pulmonary development, (2) the acquisition of form specific to the lung of a given species, and (3) the differentiation of its cells. The last category may be subdivided into the differentiation of cells that are found in many tissues of the body, and of those that are specific to the lung. The approaches to these questions have been both descriptive and experimental. Much use continues to be made of reconstructions from a series of embryonic stages, particularly when this time-honored descriptive approach is combined with histochemistry or electronmicroscopy. Furthermore, methods for direct observation of morphogenesis, such as those of tissue and organ culture, have found renewed favor in both descriptive and experimental studies, while experiments involving dissociation and reaggregation of pulmonary tissues have come into prominence only recently.

Older Knowledge of Developing Lungs

Lungs, or homologous structures, are present in all major classes of vertebrates, from fishes to mammals; the respiratory organs of invertebrates, where present, are of different plan and different origins. In vertebrates the lungs arise from a ventral, primitively paired, pharyngeal bud (Marcus, 108) that appears between the sixth and seventh branchial arches shortly after closure of the ventral wall of the foregut. Some groups of fish provide exceptional examples of experimentation with lunglike structures derived from other, usually pharyngeal, diverticula, but as a rule the ventral bud is present. The sac produced is developed by fish into a swim bladder (Goodrich, 62). It may lose its connection with the pharynx; in the older orders of Actinopterygii and in primitive teleosts (Isospondyli) a passage remains (Young, 179). Swim bladders of lungfishes (Choanichthyes) are lunglike and functional in respiratory exchange. Without exception, lungs of higher vertebrates arise from the ventral bud. Usually there are two lungs, but the left one may be rudimentary, as in the burrowing caecilians and many snakes. They range in complexity from the functionally inadequate unilocular lungs of simpler urodele amphibians (*Proteus, Necturus*) to the highly efficient compound tubular lungs of birds and the compound lobular ones of mammals. The increase in complexity may be considered as achieved through successive reduplication of the inner, respiratory surface (Baudrimont, 17). Where lungs are absent, as in all plethodont urodeles (*Aneides, Batrachoseps*), the condition is thought to express either paedomorphosis or secondary change (Mekeel, 111; Noble, 121, 122). Thus, it has come to be known (1) that the lung begins to develop relatively early in embryonic life, (2) that in different species it develops similarly, although to different stages of complexity, and (3) that its complexity is related to the degree of internal subdivision. The starting point is the ventral pharyngeal bud; in the language of the classical germ layers, development of the lung is the consequence of interaction between the endoderm and the surrounding mesoderm. It proceeds through a process of centrifugal budding (Moser, 116), not-withstanding an older idea (Miller, 113) that in amphibians and reptiles later development involves the centripetal ingrowth of septa from the walls of a primitive unilocular lung sac.

The general theme and many details in the sequence of development have been worked out for the lungs of many species. The pharyngeal bud elongates, its tip swells, and it divides to form the precursors of the primary bronchus of each lung. These in turn elongate, swell, and subdivide, as do their descendents, until a large and arboreous system of tubules is formed — the early bronchial tree. From the outset, branching is not strictly dichotomous; the left primary bronchus veers more from the direction of the trachea than the right. The practical effect is to make room in the thorax for the heart, but this asymmetry in branching appears too early in embryonic life to be laid to mechanical pressure. Subsequent branchings of bronchi adhere awhile to the same rule: the smaller branch diverges more from the parent than the larger (Ewart, 53); the conducting portion of the lung is thus made to occupy as small a volume as possible (Barnett, 16). As the epithelium pushes out from the pharyngeal floor, it is accompanied by mesenchyme that originated beneath the laryngotracheal groove (Ham and Baldwin, 72). The invaded mesenchyme, a tissue relatively poor in cells, had migrated in from the median coelomic wall (Streeter, 161). It gradually condenses about the bronchial tree and differentiates into cartilage and adventitial connective tissue, as well as blood vessels and lymphatics.

The fetal lung in its earliest phase of development emphasizes the bronchial tree. It then resembles an exocrine gland, inasmuch as it possesses many ducts that end in sac-shaped expansions and lie embedded in connective tissue. The terminations resemble secretory acini in the cuboid shape, but not the fine structure, of their cells; they differ from exocrine glands in lacking a rich blood supply. During a second phase of development the major blood vessels enlarge and capillaries increase in number until the lung becomes the most vascular of all organs in the body. Finally, as best represented in mammals, alveoli are formed, and with their formation the lung becomes ready for its chief postnatal function. In birds there are no alveoli. Gaseous exchange takes place along respiratory capillaries that feed into posterior air sacs (Shepard et al., 149). These structures have their imperfectly developed counterparts in certain reptilian lungs, especially among the crocodiles. Like alveoli, they are developed last.

Details of the sequence of pulmonary development are available for several orders of vertebrates, the lungfishes (Kerr, 80), the amphibians (Ritter and Miller, 135; Gage, 58; Hempstead, 75; Moser, 116; Griel, 65), the reptiles (Moser, 116; Hesser, 76; Schmidt, 147), the birds (Locy and Larsell, 94), and the mammals. Possessing a more subdivided structure than the others, the mammalian lung has received more attention than the lungs of all other orders. Descriptions of pulmonary development may be found for prototherian (Narath, 118), metatherian (Bremer, 26, 27; McCrady, 105), and eutherian mammals. Among the latter, the insectivores (Willach, 170), the rodents (Robinson, 136; Narath, 119; Short, 150), the lagomorphs (Kölliker, 85; Narath, 119), the carnivores (Bender, 18; Boyden and Tompsett, 24), the ungulates (Flint, 57; Fauré-Fremiet and Dragoiu, 55; Clements, 40; Ham and

Baldwin, 72), and the primates (His, 78; Minot, 114; Galli, 59; Dubreuil et al., 48, 49; Palmer, 127; Amprino, 9; Amprino and Ceresa, 10; Barnard and Day, 15; Cooper, 41; Norris et al., 123; Short, 150; Engel, 52) have been considered. Of these accounts, that of Flint (57) is one of the more substantial.

Histochemical work on the developing lung has been published at various times, particularly on the topics of elastin or elastic fibers (Lenzi, 92; Linser, 93; Teuffel, 163; Klemola, 83; Amprino and Ceresa, 10), lipid (Fauré-Fremiet, 54; Granel, 63; Stewart, 160), and glycogen (Bernard, 20; Stewart, 160; Waddell, 168; Laumonier, 88; cf. review in Graumann, 64). Some of these studies are fragmentary. The investigations of Fauré-Fremiet and Dragoiu (55) on the lungs of sheep, however, remain outstanding.

Recent Contributions

Recent work on pulmonary morphogenesis has emphasized chemical embryology. The histochemistry of the lung has been explored more fully than in the past, and experiments have been devised to probe into mechanisms of pulmonary development. Speculation is rife concerning mechanisms that regulate the organ's development, but little is known for certain. Alexandrian refinement characterizes the descriptive work of the past few years. Elaborating on the classical studies, it has furnished new detail to challenge the developmental mechanist.

General Mechanisms of Development

THE LUNG AS A SELF-DEVELOPING ENTITY. One of the major contributions of studies with organ cultures has been to foster a conception of the fetal lung as a self-developing entity; for, separated from the embryo and the mother, rudiments of the lung develop in vitro to a fair likeness of the lung in vivo. Organ cultures that included lung had been grown earlier using grafts to the chorioallantoic membrane (Rudnick, 142) and to the anterior chamber of the eye (Waddell, 168), as well as using constant-perfusion techniques (de Jong and deHaan, 46); they have recently become popular because of technical improvements (Wolff, 176; Chen, 35). With fewer outgrowths to divert the energies of the explant (Wolff, 177) the cultures attain a higher degree of development. Benefiting from the improvements, investigators have learned that the fetal lung in vitro develops essentially all the cellular elements of the adult (Chen, 35). It proceeds to form a respiratory region (Sampaolo and Loffredo Sampaolo, 145, 146) and alveoli (Sorokin, 155). Successful cultures have been made from lungs of birds (Loffredo Sampaolo and Sampaolo, 95, 96, 97, 98, 99; Alescio, 2, 3, 5) and mammals (Chen, 35; Sampaolo and Loffredo Sampaolo, 145, 146; Loffredo Sampaolo and Sampaolo, 99; Alescio, 4; Chesterman and Franks, 36; Sorokin, 155). Parts of the respiratory system, such as the trachea (144; Aydelotte, 14) and the syrinx of birds (Em. Wolff, 171, 172, 173, 174, 175) have also done well in vitro. While most of these endeavors have been directed to the study of morphogenesis, attention has also been given the nutritional requirements of the explants (171; Croisille, 42; Loffredo Sampaolo and Sampaolo, 98). Other research related to embryology has also been carried out in organ cultures of lung. Wolff (177) and colleagues, in forming chimeras (Bresch, 28), as of chick and

mouse lung (Vakaet, 166), have shown that mutual attractions exist between epithelial cells, even from unrelated species. Such chimeras have also been formed between normal cultures and sarcomas (Schneider, 148). Using tobacco condensate and purified carcinogens, Lasnitzki (86, 87) demonstrated that striking metaplasias can be produced in the epithelium of pulmonary cultures.

Improved technical methods not only have made it possible to maintain organ cultures in good condition for periods longer than a few days but they have ensured success with younger starting material. Developmental studies with cultures have favored the idea that much, if not quite all, of the characteristics of pulmonary form, particularly that of a branching epithelial tree, lie implicit in the epithelium and mesenchyme of the tracheal bud. Once started, development seems to go on as a matter of course. This idea was first expressed by Rudnick (142), and subsequent work has strengthened it. It is still true, however, that the older the fetal lung fragments at the time of sowing, the better the prospects of obtaining an adultlike harvest. It is also true that in vitro the blood vessels do not develop to the extent they do in vivo. Nevertheless, growth rather than differentiation is limited. At first the cultures, grown either on a natural or good chemically defined medium, develop apace with the normal, intact controls of similar age (Loffredo Sampaolo and Sampaolo, 99), but after several days more even the best cultures fall behind (Alescio, 4). This disparity in growth between cultures and controls becomes even more apparent when the mitotic activities of pulmonary epithelium and mesenchyme are

TABLE 18.1   Mitotic Rates of Lungs Developing in vivo and in vitro

| | FETAL GUINEA PIG IN VIVO | | | | CULTURE OF 30-DAY GUINEA PIG | | |
| | DIVISIONS PER 1000 CELLS | | | | DIVISIONS PER 1000 CELLS | | |
AGE	EPITHELIUM	STROMA	E:S RATIO	DAYS IN VITRO	EPITHELIUM	STROMA	E:S RATIO
30	25.8	13.3	1.94	—	—	—	—
32	21.9	10.7	2.05	2	17.4	8.4	2.07
—	—	—	—	4	30.6	18.0	1.70
—	—	—	—	6	16.5	11.0	1.50
40a	17.4	8.9	1.96	11a	15.2	9.3	1.63
40b	18.0	9.9	1.82	11b	11.3	8.6	1.31
43	13.6	7.3	1.88	13	6.1	4.9	1.25
45	11.9	5.8	2.05	—	—	—	—

Mitotic figures were counted in slides of normally developing and cultured fetal guinea pig lungs. Each count listed is from an individual specimen. The gestation period of the animal is 68–70 days. (From Table 1, S. Sorokin, *Devel. Biol.* 3:60–83.)

considered. In general, early growth of the lung is achieved by cell division; during the period when the bronchial tree is undergoing rapid expansion, the epithelium branches because it divides more rapidly than the surrounding mesenchyme. In the rat and guinea pig about two epithelial divisions occur per mesenchymal division during early organogeny. Later this epithelium:stroma ratio increases, to decline toward unity (and a lower mitotic rate) sometime after birth (Sorokin et al., 159). Mitotic rates are lower in pulmonary cultures than in vivo. The explanted epithelium continues to divide more frequently than the stroma; but the epithelium:stroma mitotic ratios soon fall below those in the controls (Table 18.1), with the result that the cultures branch less often. In contrast, structural (Loffredo Sampaolo and Sampaolo, 96; Alescio, 5) and chemical differentiations (Sorokin, 155, Fig. 2) of pulmonary cells are so well matched in vivo and in vitro that the relative independence of differentiation from growth in this organ is readily perceived.

INDUCTIVE ACTIVITY. It is widely supposed but still unproved that the tracheal bud appears as a result of an initiating induction. Chemical changes in the area of the laryngotracheal groove precede morphological changes visible with the light microscope. These changes have been brought to light with the aid of histochemistry; the smallness of the laryngotracheal area has precluded effective study of it with biochemical techniques. The first events known to accompany formation of the tracheal bud are (1) an accumulation of glycogen in the cells of the epithelium and (2) appearance of certain enzymic activities, notably that for alkaline phosphatase (Moog, 115; McKay et al., 106, 107; Rossi et al., 140, 141; Hinsch and Knovacs, 77) in the epithelium and sometimes in the condensing mesenchyme. These, together with an increase in cytoplasmic ribonucleoprotein, constitute a chemical trinity that is found as well in various cephalic anlagen (Milaire, 112).

Concrete evidence has been found in more advanced fetal lungs to indicate that inductive activity occurs during pulmonary development. The experiments of Rudnick (142) with grafts of chick lung strongly suggested that budding of the bronchial tree does not take place when the epithelium is deprived of its investing mesenchyme. She concluded that factors necessary for the production of orderly branching of the endodermal bud lie within the surrounding mesoderm. Loffredo Sampaolo and Sampaolo (99) cultivating chick and rabbit lung on a defined medium, discovered that removal of the mesenchyme from the right lung interrupts the process of epithelial branching. It resumes once the mesenchyme has regenerated to replace the portion removed. The unaltered left lung, adjoining, continues to branch normally. Dameron (43, 44) indeed demonstrated that the epithelium of fetal lung, isolated in vitro, is incapable of morphogenesis. It forms spherical aggregations or spreads over the culturing surface. When the epithelium is recombined with pulmonary mesenchyme, development resumes. Recombination of the epithelium with other mesenchymes, from the chorioallantois, the somites, or the mesonephros, only checks the spread of the epithelium. Metanephrogenic mesenchyme, when similarly combined with epithelium, permits some degree of branching and epithelial differentiation to take place, but it is inferior to that produced by pulmonary mesenchyme.

Grover has studied the reaggregation process more fully. Using short-term cultures of cells dissociated from embryonic chick lung, he finds that when the medium is seeded, the cells begin to reaggregate into one mass. The epithelial cells settle in the center and within 48 hours exhibit functional activity (68). Optimum when starting material is obtained from 11–12-day chicks, the effectiveness of both dissociation and reaggregation decreases with increasing age (69, 70). The dissociated epithelium may be combined with varying amounts of mesenchyme; histogenesis is then seen to depend more upon the "proper balance" of the two than upon the time they are in culture (71). Mesenchyme, separated from fetal mouse lung and placed on plasma clots at some distance from the bare tracheobronchial tree, will migrate toward the epithelium and arrange itself about the epithelium. Following reassociation, epithelial branching proceeds. Furthermore, it is more hampered by γ-irradiation of the dissociated mesenchyme than of the freed epithelium, but it is maximally inhibited after irradiation of both components (Alescio et al., 8).

The preceding experiments indicate that, supplied in the right amount and at a certain stage in its maturity, the pulmonary mesenchyme is ideally suited to promote branching of the rudimentary bronchial tree. Depending on its state of differentiation, it possesses the capacity to limit branching as well. This has been demonstrated clearly by Alescio and Cassini (6, 7). If a section of mesenchyme from the tracheal bud is removed and replaced by mesenchyme taken from a bronchial bud, and if the grafted lung is cultivated in vitro, a supernumerary bud grows out from the epithelium beneath the grafting site. The results are visible within 6 hours (Fig. 18.1A). Subsequently, the bud elongates and eventually branches (Fig. 18.1B). Normally the trachea produces no extra branches. Deprived of its mesenchyme meanwhile, the donor bronchus is slower to branch than its intact neighbor. A similar experiment, in which mesenchyme

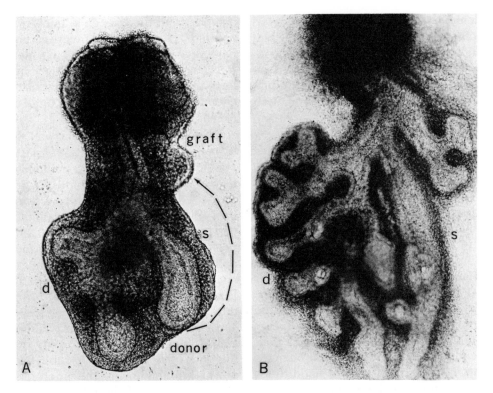

Fig. 18.1 Induction by bronchial mesenchyme. Cultures of 11-day fetal mouse lungs photographed alive. *A.* Bronchial mesenchyme removed from left, s, lung and grafted onto the trachea; right, d, lung intact. After 6 hours a supernumerary bud appears at the grafting site. *B.* After 3 days the tracheal bud has extended and branched. The right lung develops normally; the left is inhibited. ×65 (From Figs. 4a and 4c, T. Alescio and A. Cassini, *J. Exptl. Zool.* 150:83–94, 1962.)

from the normally budding lateral side of the left primary bronchus is grafted onto the normally inactive medial side, again results in the emergence of a supernumerary branch (7). The experiments indicate that the pulmonary epithelium is capable of budding, in a given region, for some time after it would normally stop. The pulmonary mesenchyme, on the other hand, exhibits different capacities to incite epithelial budding; that found nearest normally budding regions of the bronchial tree is most able to stimulate the epithelium. The response seems to be made through cell division, for mitotic figures in the epithelium surely are

most abundant in the terminal buds of the bronchial tree. It cannot be determined at present how the more mature, if less evocative, mesenchyme prevents epithelial budding in the trachea. Possibly the mesenchyme lowers production of stimulating chemicals or alters the extracellular material between itself and the epithelium. However, age changes in extracellular materials are measurable (Muir, 117) and the cells of connective tissue and epithelium increasingly become separated as they mature.

Summarizing, one can agree with Borghese and co-workers (22) that the experiments on pulmonary explants demonstrate that true inductive interaction takes place along with other cell and tissue interactions. The other interactions, revealed by the reaggregation experiments, are (1) a recognition of epithelial and mesenchymal cells for others of their kind and (2) a chemotactic attraction of mesenchyme to epithelium, expressed over a distance too great for induction to occur. The first results in the reorganization of like cells into tissues; the second is followed by a mass motion of mesenchyme toward the epithelium. Eventually one may expect that the epithelium will be shown to exert a secondary stimulation upon the mesenchyme.

PATTERNS OF DIFFERENTIATION. For the purposes of this review the term "differentiation" will be understood to mean those normally permanent structural and chemical changes that take place in cells at fixed times during the developmental period. It may be argued, nevertheless, that many such differentiations depend for their apparent permanence on the maintenance of certain conditions in the ambient. For example, the apparently stable cellular composition of the tracheal epithelium is readily unsettled in culture by changing the concentration of vitamin A in the medium (Aydelotte, 14; Fell and Mellanby, 56).

During development of the lung, differentiation of the epithelium spreads in a wavelike manner down the airways from the tracheal region to the terminal buds. As the mesenchyme condenses about the epithelial tubes, it differentiates into cartilage, smooth muscle, and the components of connective tissue; these differentiations also advance in a proximal-to-distal direction, but lag behind the epithelium. Thus, at any moment a gradient of maturity extends from the trachea to the terminal buds. Histochemical investigations have revealed these patterns in a clear light. In mammalian lungs, which have been more fully studied, similar histochemical patterns can be recognized in many species.

Glycogen and neutral fat are the principal storage materials to be encountered in developing pulmonary tissues. Since Claude Bernard (20) first described glycogen in the fetal respiratory epithelium, the subject of pulmonary glycogen has been taken up repeatedly (cf. Graumann, 64), principally with a view to learn whether or not the fetal lung serves as a "preportal liver" in storing carbohydrate during the prenatal period (Fauré-Fremiet and Dragoiu, 55; Szendi, 162; Parhon and Milcou, 128). It is fair to say that this role has not been established; newer information on the intermediary metabolism of the fetal lung (Villee, 167) suggests that the lung in man may indeed function in carbohydrate regulation, but only after the 11th week of gestation. There are two distinct patterns of glycogen deposition in the lung. The epithelial pattern is the more constant and the more significant for development; the mesenchymal is probably more important to the carbohydrate economy of the fetus (Sorokin et al., 159; Sorokin, 155). In the epithelium, glycogen is deposited as new cells are formed. It disappears after the cells mature, so that the terminal buds are richest in glycogen. In the mesenchyme, glycogen is variably concentrated by developing lungs of different species; in man it is abundant (Laumonier, 88), but in guinea pigs it is scarce (Angeli and De Biase, 11). Normally present in the rat's lung, it is absent when such lungs are grown in organ culture. Of the lipids in the lung, triglycerides undergo the greatest fluctuation during development. They accumulate slowly in the maturing connective tissue and cuboidal epithelium of the more distal pulmonary regions during later fetal life. In fetal human lungs only a little synthesis of lipid is measurable (Villee, 167). Phospholipids increase slowly with gestation. Where there are large accretions of fat in developing lungs, as in the rat during the postnatal period, the source appears to be dietary (Vacek et al., 164, 165). These decline at the time of weaning.

Histochemists have described changes in the activities of several enzymes present in the lung during development. Most of this work has been carried out on mammalian lungs and has considered the following enzymes: specific and nonspecific alkaline, neutral, and acid phosphomonoesterases, nonspecific esterases, indophenol oxidase, and the dehydrogenases for succinic acid, glucose-6-phosphate, and glyceraldehyde-3-phosphate. These studies have been reviewed recently by Rossi (137) in a substantial monograph on the histochemistry of enzymes during development. The enzymic studies have supported the concepts that (1) pulmonary differentiation occurs in a proximal-to-distal direction along the bronchial tree, and that (2) visible change is first seen in the epithelium. In evaluating the histochemical work it is well to remember that, by and large, the enzymes studied have been those for which methods existed at the time research was undertaken. Certainty in identifying and localizing the enzymic activity has increased with improvements in the histochemical methods, but it has not always been possible to ascribe to the enzyme a significant role in development. This may be said of the phosphomonoesterases, particularly acid and alkaline phosphatase, both of which have been extensively studied (Rossi et al., 138, 139, 140; Angeli and De Biase, 11; Sorokin et al., 159). Changing activity of the dehydrogenases, on the other hand, can more plausibly be related to mechanisms of pulmonary development, but the prospect of certainty is still distant.

Briefly presented, these studies on enzymes have revealed new patterns that occur in the developing lungs of several mammals. Alkaline phosphatase, first associated with the epithelium of the tracheal bud, continues to be active during early development in terminal buds, burgeoning glands, vascular endothelium, and other regions of intense cellular proliferation. In the rat the enzyme remains with the terminal buds for most of the prenatal period; in man it is there for the first 8 weeks (Sorokin, 154). Succinic dehydrogenase, weakly reactive in embryonic pulmonary tissues, increases in the maturing epithelium (Reale and Luzzato, 133), progressively from trachea to bronchiole (Sorokin et al., 159). Acid phosphatase, nonspecific esterases, indophenol oxidase, and glucose-6-phosphate dehydrogenase (Fig. 18.2) exhibit similar patterns of activity. In the adult lung the last five enzymes are localized not only in the epithelium but elsewhere according to their special character. Succinic dehydrogenase and indophenol oxidase are especially active at sites having synthetic or motor functions (tracheobronchial epithelium, glands, and pulmonary musculature); glucose-6-phosphate dehydrogenase is found in cells preparing secretory products (epithelium and great

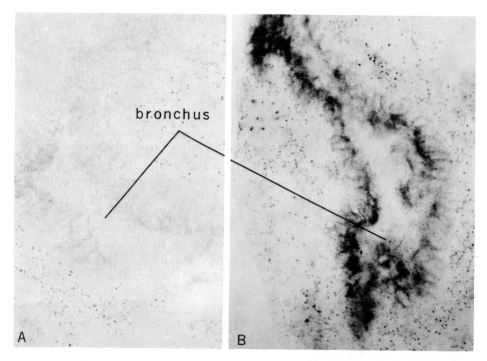

Fig. 18.2 Differentiation of glucose-6-phosphate dehydrogenase activity in organ cultures of rat lungs. *A*. 15-day fetal lung after 3 days in vitro. *B*. Similar lung after 7 days in vitro. Enzymatic activity is plainly elevated in the bronchial epithelium. ×465 (From Figs. 20 and 21, S. Sorokin, *Develop. Biol.* 3:60–83, 1961, published by Academic Press.)

alveolar cells) (Sorokin, 157); and acid phosphatase is reactive in areas exposed to airborne infection (epithelium and alveolar phagocytes).

INDICATIONS OF SOME DEVELOPMENTAL MECHANISMS IN THE LUNG. Physiological characteristics of the normal in vivo environment for pulmonary organogenesis are imperfectly known, but it is certain that the fetus develops at low oxygen tensions. As measured biochemically in human lungs, the activity of the citric acid cycle and the rate of oxidative metabolism appear to increase with gestation between 7.5 weeks and term (Villee, 167). That the lung is capable of developing to an advanced stage in an anaerobic environment has been shown by experiments with organ cultures of rat and guinea pig lung exposed to metabolic inhibitors (Sorokin, 155). Cultures grown in the absence of air or in the presence of cyanide or malonate did about as well as the controls; only those given fluoride fared poorly.

The preceding evidence provides factual, albeit still shaky, support for the following developmental scheme: One of the effects of early induction is to promote glycogen storage and rapid cell division in the epithelium of the lung. The glycogen-rich organ depends for some time on glycolysis as its main supply of energy during the early period of development, when a branching bronchial tree, composed of relatively undifferentiated cells, is under construction. The energy obtained from glycolysis is spent largely for synthesis of new protoplasm and for cell division. With an increase in the activities of the citric acid cycle, the cytochrome system, and the hexosemonophosphate shunt, signs of cellular differentiation become manifest in the epithelium; energy is diverted to operate the newly emerging cellular machinery, and the rate of cell division drops. From the histochemical localizations of succinic dehydrogenase, indophenol oxidase, and glucose-6-phosphate dehydrogenase, one might expect that the epithelium would be more affected than the mesenchymal derivatives by a decline in mitotic activity; hence, branching would no longer occur in the more differentiated spots, although it would continue in the undifferentiated terminal buds. In earlier development the epithelium would increase relative to the mesenchyme. Later on, the mesenchyme would increase relative to the epithelium. In the more mature regions of the epithelium, glycogen storage decreases near the time when activity of the three oxidative pathways increases. Possibly glucose-6-phosphate dehydrogenase competes successfully for glucose-6-phosphate with the uridine diphosphate glucose system (Leloir et al., 90) which requires it in order to synthesize glycogen. Whether or not cell death contributes significantly to pulmonary morphogenesis has not been critically assessed.

Specific Development of the Lung in Several Species

MODIFICATION OF DEVELOPMENTAL PATTERNS. It is apparent that the general form of the lung—the bronchial tree and the peripheral respiratory zone—may be built up through processes discussed in the previous section. Where the conducting airways are long in one species and short in another, or where there are other quantitative differences, certain developmental patterns seem to be modified in a manner to suit (for example, pulmonary alkaline phosphatase in man and rats). The lungs of distantly related animals are often only subtly different; some refined comparative studies on pulmonary development should be made before mechanisms to explain these interspecies differences are discussed further.

THE SHAPE OF THE BRONCHIAL TREE. The bronchial tree, its manner of branching, and its development have been of interest to embryologists since the anatomist Aeby (1) and the pathologist Ewart (53) presented opposing views on the plan of branching in the human lung. The first favored monopody; the second, a more complex scheme that invoked sympody, or unequal dichotomy. Aeby's views find support in other mammalian lungs. In the human lung, Heiss's interpretations (74) are felt to conform most closely with nature (Boyden, 23); development of an axis for each lung ceases with formation of buds for the secondary bronchi, three in the right and two in the left. Each bud subsequently develops its own pattern of branching. The frequency of variations from the prevalent mode is striking; they usually occur in subsegmental bronchi, that is, beginning with bronchi of the fourth or fifth order. The variations result from displacement, occur at predictable sites, and bring about changes in adjacent regions (Wells and Boyden, 169; Boyden, 23). The bronchial tree is subject to remodeling before it reaches adult configuration. In dogs the branches of the axial bronchus decrease in number after birth, probably due to formation of common stems for adjacent branches (Boyden and Tompsett, 24).

THE RESPIRATORY REGION. The respiratory region of the lung lies distal to the conducting passages and is characterized by the presence of a thin cellular barrier that separates the inspired air from the blood in the capillaries. In mammals the barrier is composed of a thin alveolar epithelial lining, a connective tissue space that at its thinnest contains only extracellular matrix and fine fibers, and the capillary endothelium. It has been a special concern of embryologists to learn how the terminal portion of the fetal lung becomes transformed from a region of budding tubules lined by a cuboidal epithelium into a region of blind sacs, or alveoli, that are lined principally by greatly flattened cells. Early investigations with the electron microscope (Low, 103; Karrer, 79) have led to acceptance of the continuity of the alveolar lining and of its epithelial character. Rigorous proof of its endodermal origin remains to be given, but at present there is no attractive alternative. The alveolar lining, moreover, shares certain characteristics with the epithelium of the airways (cf., Low and Sampaio, 104; Okada et al., 124, 125; Campiche et al., 34). Of two cell types present in the alveolar lining, however, one (Marinozzi, 109) or both (Policard et al., 131) have been considered to be of mesodermal origin.

Alveolar formation is related to the growth of the vasculature. It is first indicated in human fetuses at 18 weeks, when vascularization of the mesenchyme begins in earnest. Capillaries grow into the cuboid endodermal lining and appear to break it up by pushing loops through to reach the lumen of the airway (Loosli and Potter, 100, 101; Potter, 132). In the light microscope these loops seem bare; in the electron microscope they are entirely covered by a continuous lining that extends from the epithelial cells (Campiche et al., 34). Moreover, the epithelium and endothelium are separated by a basement membrane (Fig. 18.3). The capillary loops become more abundant with gestation (Barnard and Day, 15). The epithelium, known to be distensible (Bensley and Groff, 19), is stretched over them. The bodies of the stretched cells become tucked into spaces between the loops. These cells become the squamous alveolar epithelial cells (small alveolar cells, pulmonary epithelial cells, membranous pneumonocytes, type I cells) of the adult. The fetal cuboidal epithelium also becomes differentiated into a second type, a cell that does not become drawn into thin sheets but remains cubical or polygonal and produces characteristic lamellar inclusions (cytosomes) in its cytoplasm. This is the great alveolar epithelial cell (large alveolar cell, alveolar cell, granular pneumonocyte, type II cell, septal cell).

Using casts of the bronchial tree and three-dimensional reconstructions from sections to aid their dissections of dogs' lungs, Boyden and Tompsett (24) found that after birth the nonrespiratory peripheral bronchioles decrease in number by conversion into respiratory units. Preliminary evidence in man suggests that at birth the lung possesses the adult number of nonrespiratory generations (Boyden and Tompsett, 25; Bucher and Reid, 31). Terminal budding continues to produce new alveolar regions, but it is apparent

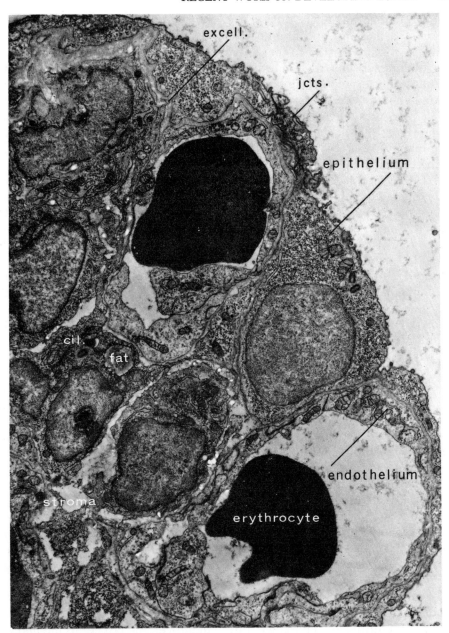

Fig. 18.3 Electronmicrograph of a stage in alveolar formation. Two capillaries are seen in cross section; they bulge into the epithelium. Between them an epithelial cell extends thin processes over the capillaries, where interdigitation, jcts., occurs with processes from other epithelial cells. The epithelium thus separates the capillaries from the air space. Between epithelium and endothelium the extracellular, excell., space is thin and consists of little more than basement laminar matter. Where this layer is thicker, fine reticular, but few elastic fibers are present. The stroma is cellular; in one fat-bearing cell a centriole is undergoing ciliogenesis, cil. ×5100.

that alveolar formation is in part the result of reshaping. The architecture of the respiratory region in the newly born differs substantially from that in the adult. For example, in infants, five or six generations of respiratory bronchioles are present; in adults, two or three (Engel, 51). Furthermore, the respiratory passages elongate after birth (Loosli and Potter, 101; Boyden and Tompsett, 24). This at first is due primarily to hyperplasia and later to hypertrophy (Neuhäuser and Dingler, 120). In man the number of alveoli continue to increase after birth (Kikuchi, 81), mainly in the first 8 years (Dunnill, 50), but the dimensions of the pulmonary zones and segments continue to expand until the age of 40 years (Demidov, 47).

THE BLOOD VESSELS. The blood vessels of the lung are derived from two sources. For their greater length, their origins can be traced to the plexiform network of vessels that develops in the pulmonary mesenchyme. Like the bronchi, the vessels are subject to variations in their course, which has been explained on the basis of selection of channels from the pre-existing network (Wells and Boyden, 169). Near their junction with the heart the pulmonary vessels have a cardiac origin. In man the development of the pulmonary veins has been re-examined recently (Los, 102). In rats an adventitial coat of cardiac muscle, which extends to the venules, becomes differentiated centrifugally along the pulmonary veins (Sorokin, et al., 158).

Cellular Differentiation

SPECIFIC AND NONSPECIFIC CELLS. The cells of the lung may be divided into those that are similar to cells in other parts of the body and those that are more or less specific to the lung. By morphological criteria the fibroblasts, chondrocytes, endothelial cells, pericytes, and smooth muscle cells clearly belong to the first category; they are all mesodermal derivatives.

Other cells, including the great alveolar, the squamous alveolar, and the nonciliated bronchiolar elements, belong to the second category; they are epithelial in nature and are probably all endodermal derivatives. With the assistance of recent studies in electronmicroscopy it is more evident than before that the more specifically pulmonary cells are epithelial. In the epithelium, furthermore, the cells most specific to the lung are located farthest out along the bronchial tree. This is readily appreciated when one reviews the cytology of this tree. In the trachea and bronchi the pseudostratified epithelium is composed of four types of cells, a ciliated, a goblet, a nonciliated (brush), and a short (basal) cell. It resembles other pseudostratified, ciliated, columnar epithelia of the body. In the bronchioles the columnar epithelium retains the ciliated cell, supplants the goblet cell by another that contains small apical secretory droplets (Clara, 37; Hayek, 73), and drops the others. Finally, the two cells present in the alveolar lining resemble no others in the body. One of these, the great alveolar cell, is thought to be the parent of the alveolar phagocyte (Bertalanffy, 21). During phagocytosis, moreover, the last cell is metabolically distinct from both polymorphonuclear and mononuclear phagocytes of the same species (Oren et al., 126; Dannenberg et al., 45). The preceding concept may be collated with the concept of centrifugal pulmonary development. Accordingly, the cells most specific to the lung (1) appear at positions physically far removed from the embryologically multipotent pharyngeal area and (2) are among the last to become differentiated.

PROGRESSIVE CHANGES IN THE ORGANELLES. Electronmicroscopy offers the embryologist an almost unique opportunity to follow the structural changes in organelles of cells that develop in heterogeneous tissues. Nevertheless, no study yet published on electronmicroscopy of the developing lung has included sufficient material to permit comprehensive analysis of changes in the organelles of differentiating pulmonary cells. It is evident, however, that some changes are coeval with the appearance of certain cellular functions. The differentiation—or the onset of function—of the great alveolar cell has been the main topic of several recent electronmicroscopic studies (Woodside and Dalton, 178; Campiche, 33; Groniowski and Djaczenko, 66; Groniowski and Biczyskowa, 67; Gautier et al., 60; Campiche et al., 34; Leeson and Leeson, 89; Klika, 84). One recognizes this cell in the prealveolar terminal epithelium by the appearance of phospholipid-containing multilamellar bodies (cytosomes) in its cytoplasm (Fig. 18.4). The bodies probably contain a secretory product made within membranous systems of the cytoplasm (Sorokin, 157). The product is thought to be identical to a surface-active material present in mature lungs (Klaus et al., 82). Cytosomes begin to appear in fetal human lungs during the 6th month of gestation (Gautier et al., 60) and in mice (Woodside and Dalton, 178) and rats (Groniowski and Djaczenko, 66; Leeson and Leeson, 89) a day or two before birth. This alveolar cell and the mucus-secreting elements

of the lung retain their embryonic cytoplasmic basiphilia. This ribonucleoprotein, even in the adult, is only partially associated with membranes of the endoplasmic reticulum. The other cells tend to lose their basiphilia as they mature. Woodside and Dalton (178) noted that many differentiating epithelial cells contain well-developed Golgi components. Leeson and Leeson (89) described increases in mitochondrial size and number in such cells; Campiche and co-workers (34), increase in number of epithelial organelles. Both reports stated that single specimens from younger age groups contain areas of greater and lesser differentiation.

Comparatively little attention has been granted to the differentiation of the less specific cells in the lung. Almost no structural changes occur in endothelial cells of lungs taken from 15 mm crown-rump to adult rats (Leeson and Leeson, 89). In the mesenchyme of fetal human lungs Campiche and co-workers (34) found slight evidence of differentiation and few organelles.

CELLULAR PRODUCTS. The first appearance and subsequent elaboration of certain secretory products by pulmonary cells have been recorded in recent histochemical surveys, as well as in papers that deal more specifically with mucus (Bucher and Reid, 32), with alveolar lining material (Pattle, 130), or with elastic fibers (Goldbach, 61; Matsumoto, 110; Loosli and Potter, 101). Deposition of the extracellular fibers occurs in maturing regions and follows the now-familiar proximal-to-distal sequence along the bronchial and vascular trees. From the electronmicroscopical research it is fairly certain that a continuous basement lamina separates the epithelium from the mesenchyme throughout development. Extracellular fibers are deposited in the tissue space that separates the basement membranes of epithelium and endothelium. They increase in amount with age, well into adult life (Briscoe and Loring, 29, 30).

The State of Pulmonary Development at Birth

Unless an organ is so undeveloped that it cannot function at all, one would not expect to find too close a correlation between the state of its development and the time of parturition. This is true of the lung. Few mammals begin life with lungs as simple in structure and as artless in histochemistry as the opossum (Sorokin, 156); but, once snug in the marsupium the babies suffer little from pulmonic immaturity. A respiratory surface ample for metabolic needs, a conducting and ventilating system, and a sufficient vasculature seem to be all that is required, but what is ample for one newborn animal need not be so for another. In lungs of animals with a long gestation period, compared to those with a short term, differentiative processes occupy a longer time. In spite of this equalizing effect, lungs from different newborn animals still are not necessarily comparable in maturity. The lung of the rat at term is similar to the lung of the 7th month human fetus; the lung of the sheep is somewhat more advanced than that of the newborn child. Postnatal development, including both growth and differentiation, is continuous with prenatal development and is fairly independent of the occurrences at birth. The accident of premature birth has no effect on the subsequent maturation of the lung (Lelong and Laumonier, 91).

Physiological changes in the lung at birth are concerned with expansion of the lungs and conversion of its low volume–high pressure fetal circulation to the high volume–low pressure system of the adult. Most of the studies on these topics have been performed on prenatal and newborn infants or on other large animals possessing relatively mature lungs at birth. They are of great importance to clinical medicine because respiratory difficulties (respiratory distress syndrome, hyaline membrane disease) are major causes of infant mortality. Work of recent years has tended to show that long before parturition the lung begins to ready itself for overcoming the difficulties of expansion. Flattening of the cells that line the respiratory region is not caused by the first breath; rather, it seems to be achieved principally by differential growth (Fig. 18.3), abetted by fetal inspiratory movements (Snyder, 152, 153), and possibly by contraction of pulmonary smooth muscle. Considerable attention has recently been turned to the subject of surface-active agents present (Pattle, 129, 130; Clements et al., 39; Avery and Mead, 13). These act to stabilize alveolar diameters and reduce the force necessary to expand the lungs. They contain a phospholipid moiety that includes dipalmitoyl lecithin and probably a protein (Clements, 38). The material is produced by the lung. In many cases of respiratory distress syndrome this material is missing (Avery, 12). Circulatory changes in this organ at birth seem to be the result of a complex of physiological mechanisms. One factor is the opening of many hitherto closed capillary channels on distension of the bronchial tree (Reynolds, 134) – a mechanical effect – but there

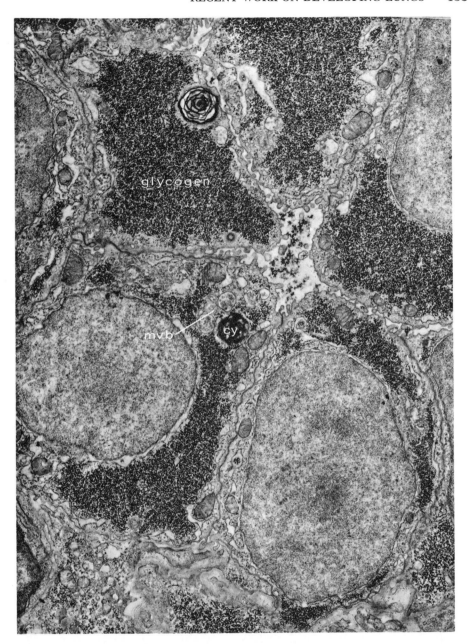

Fig. 18.4 Electronmicrograph of terminal bud epithelium from a 21-day fetal rat. A group of cells, linked by tight junctions, surrounds a small lumen. Nuclear chromatin is dispersed; cytoplasmic organelles (endoplasmic reticulum, Golgi apparatus, mitochondria, centriole) are displaced peripherally by large masses of glycogen, here stained with lead. Multivesicular bodies, mvb, are unusually abundant; they bear some relationship to the endoplasmic reticulum, the Golgi apparatus, and the cytosomes, cy, which are beginning to appear in the cells. ×10,200.

are chemical factors as well (Rudolph, 143). Expansion of the lung and conversion to the adult pattern of pulmonary circulation both begin in late fetal life, accelerate at birth (Smith, 151), and then continue for some days afterward.

Summary

This chapter surveys writings on developing lungs, some from earlier times, but most from the recent past. Attention is divided between studies that focus more generally on mechanisms of pulmonary morphogenesis and those that devote themselves more specifically to the development of the lung in a given species. Much of the recent work on fetal lungs has considered chemical changes that occur during development. It has been shown that inductive interaction between epithelium and mesenchyme is present during formation of the branching bronchial tree; other cell and tissue interactions take place as well. Expansion of the bronchial tree seems to result chiefly from mitotic activity that is heightened in the epithelium over the mesenchyme. Later on, the epithelial advantage decreases and the rate of branching declines. In the periphery of the lung, attenuation of the pulmonary epithelium is associated with the growth of pulmonary capillaries, which stretch the overlying epithelium as they lengthen to form loops that bulge into the primitive alveoli. Both conducting and respiratory regions of the lung, especially the latter, undergo considerable remodeling. Certain fluctuations in the levels of pulmonary enzymes and their substrates, demonstrated histochemically, complement this still-incomplete view of developmental mechanics. Among mammals there are great differences in the degree of pulmonary development attained at birth; the events of birth have only a secondary influence on the development of the lung. In the adult lung, the cells most specific to the organ are found in the smaller bronchioles and in the respiratory region. These specific cells include the two alveolar epithelial cells. To the developmental mechanist it is interesting that epithelial differentiation proceeds wavelike from trachea to alveolus and that the last-formed cells are the most unique.

References

1. Aeby, C., "Der Bronchialbaum der Säugethiere und des Menschen," Leipzig. W. Engelmann. (1880).

2. Alescio, T., "Osservazioni Preliminari sullo Sviluppo in vitro del Polmone di Pollo," Mon. Zool. Ital. Suppl. 68:199–206 (1959).

3. ——, "Culture Organotipiche di Polmone Embrionale di Pollo," Boll. Zool. 26:529–536 (1959).

4. ——, "Osservazioni su Culture Organotipiche di Polmone Embrionale di Topo," Arch. Ital. Anat. Embriol. 65: 323–363 (1960).

5. ——, "Sul Comportamento del Polmone Embrionale di Pollo Coltivato in vitro," Z. Zellforsch. 55:123–142 (1961).

6. ——, and A. Cassini, "Induction in vitro of Tracheal Buds by Pulmonary Mesenchyme Grafted on Tracheal Epithelium," J. Exptl. Zool. 150:83–94 (1962).

7. ——, and ——, "L'Interazione Epitelio-Mesenchimale nell'Organogenesi del Polmone Embrionale di Topo Coltivato in vitro," Z. Anat. Entwicklungsgeschichte 123:369–396 (1962).

8. ——, ——, and M. Ladu, "Ricerche sulla Riassociazione in vitro del l'Epitelio e del Mesenchima di Polmone Em-

brionale di Topo, Dopo Dissociazione Triptica ed Irradiazione con Raggi Gamma," *Arch. Ital. Anat. Embriol.* 68:1–44 (1963).

9. Amprino, R., "Come si Forma e come si Orgonizza la Struttura del Polmone nel Periodo Postnatale e Senile," *Arch. Ital. Anat. Embriol.* 38:447–458 (1937).

10. ——, and F. Ceresa, "Trasformazioni nella Struttura del Polmone nel Periodo Postnatale e Senile," *Arch. Ital. Anat. Embriol.* 38:428–446 (1937).

11. Angeli, F., and G. De Biase, "Lineamenti di Citochimica nel Polmone Fetale e alla Nascita come Premessa a Problemi di Citopatologia Polmonare," *Arch. Anat. Patol. Med. Clin.* 19:339–377 (1953).

12. Avery, M. E., *The Lung and Its Disorders in the Newborn Infant.* Philadelphia: Saunders (1964).

13. ——, and J. Mead, "Surface Properties in Relation to Atelectasis and Hyaline Membrane Disease," *Am. J. Diseases Children* 97:517–523 (1959).

14. Aydelotte, M. B., "The Effects of Vitamin A and Citral on Epithelial Differentiation *in vitro*. I. The Chick Tracheal Epithelium," *J. Embryol. Exptl. Morphol.* 11:279–291 (1963).

15. Barnard, W. G., and T. D. Day, "The Development of the Terminal Air Passages of the Human Lung," *J. Pathol. Bacteriol.* 45:67–73 (1937).

16. Barnett, C. H., "A Note on the Dimensions of the Bronchial Tree," *Thorax* 12:175–176 (1957).

17. Baudrimont, A., "Organisation Générale du Poumon et Structure des Alvéoles Pulmonaires des Vertébrés," *Arch. Anat. Histol. Embryol.* 39:97–136 (1956).

18. Bender, K. W., "Über die Entwicklung der Lungen," *Z. Anat. Entwicklungsgeschichte* 75:639–704 (1925).

19. Bensley, S. H., and M. B. Groff, "Changes in the Alveolar Epithelium of the Rat at Birth," *Anat. Record* 64:27–39 (1935).

20. Bernard, C., "De la Matière Glycogène Considérée comme Condition de Développement de Certains Tissus chez le Foetus avant l'Apparition de la Fonction Glycogénique du Foie," *J. Physiol.* 2:326–337 (1859).

21. Bertalanffy, F. D., "Respiratory Tissue: Structure, Histophysiology, Cytodynam-ics. I. Review and Basic Cytomorphology," *Intern. Rev. Cytol.* 16:233–328. New York: Academic Press, (1964).

22. Borghese, E., T. Alescio, and A. Cassini, "Experiments on Induction and Effect of Gamma Radiation in Mouse Lung Developing *in vitro*," *Cinemicrography in Cell Biology*, G. G. Rose, ed. New York: Academic Press, pp. 201–226 (1963).

23. Boyden, E. A., *Segmental Anatomy of the Lungs.* New York: McGraw-Hill, (1955).

24. ——, and D. H. Tompsett, "The Postnatal Growth of the Lung in the Dog," *Acta Anat.* 47:185–215 (1961).

25. ——, and ——, "Congenital Absence of the Medial Basal Bronchus in a Child: with Preliminary Observations on Postnatal Growth of the Lungs," *J. Thoracic Cardiovascular Surg.* 43:517–522 (1962).

26. Bremer, J. L., "On the Lung of the Opossum," *Am. J. Anat.* 3:67–73 (1904).

27. ——, "Postnatal Development of Alveoli in the Mammalian Lung in Relation to the Problem of the Alveolar Phagocyte," *Contrib. Embryol. Carnegie Inst. Wash.* 25:85–111 (1935).

28. Bresch, D., "Recherches Préliminaires sur des Associations d'Organes Embryonnaires de Poulet en Culture *in vitro*," *Bull. Biol. France Belg.* 89:179–188 (1955).

29. Briscoe, A. M., and W. E. Loring, "Elastin Content of Human Lung," *Proc. Soc. Exptl. Biol. Med.* 99:162–164 (1958).

30. ——, and ——, "Hydroxyproline Content of Human Lung and of Lung Collagen," *Federation Proc.* 18:470 (1959).

31. Bucher, U., and L. Reid, "Development of the Intrasegmental Bronchial Tree: The Pattern of Branching and Development of Cartilage at Various Stages of Intrauterine Life," *Thorax* 16:207–218 (1961).

32. ——, and ——, "Development of the Mucus-Secreting Elements in Human Lung," *Thorax* 16:219–225 (1961).

33. Campiche, M., "Les Inclusions Lamellaires des Cellules Alvéolaires dans le Poumon du Raton. Relations entre l'Ultrastructure et la Fixation," *J. Ultrastruct. Res.* 3:302–312 (1960).

34. ——, A. Gautier, E. I. Hernandez, and A. Reymond, "An Electron Microscope Study of the Fetal Development of Human Lung," *Pediatrics* 32:976–994 (1963).

35. Chen, J. M., "The Cultivation in Fluid Medium of Organised Liver, Pancreas, and Other Tissue of Foetal Rats," *Exptl. Cell Res.* 7:518–529 (1954).

36. Chesterman, F. C., and L. M. Franks, "Heterotransplantation and Organ Culture of Human Embryonic Lungs," *J. Pathol. Bact.* 79:123–129 (1960).

37. Clara, M., "Zur Histobiologie des Bronchalepithels," *Z. Mikroskop. Anat. Forsch.* 41:321–347 (1937).

38. Clements, J. A., *Remarks on Neonatal Respiratory Adaptation, Conference on Neonatal Respiratory Adaptation*, T. Oliver, ed. Washington, D.C.: National Institutes of Child Health and Human Development. In press (1965).

39. ——, E. S. Brown and R. P. Johnson, "Pulmonary Surface Tension and Mucus Lining of the Lungs: Some Theoretical Considerations," *J. Appl. Physiol.* 12: 262–268 (1958).

40. Clements, L. P., "Embryonic Development of the Respiratory Portion of the Pig's Lung," *Anat. Record* 70:575–595 (1938).

41. Cooper, E. R. A., "A Histological Investigation of the Development and Structure of the Human Lung," *J. Pathol. Bacteriol.* 47:105–114 (1938).

42. Croisille, Y., "Action de Différents Extraits d'Organes sur l'Embryon de Poulet et sur des Organes Cultivés *in vitro*," *Arch. Anat. Micros. Morphol. Exptl.* 47: 359–400 (1958).

43. Dameron, F., "Influence de Divers Mésenchymes sur la Différentiation de l'Epithélium Pulmonaire de l'Embryon de Poulet en Culture *in vitro*," *Compt. Rend. Acad. Sci.* 252:3879–3881 (1961).

44. ——, "L'Influence de Divers Mésenchymes sur la Différentiation de l'Epithélium Pulmonaire de l'Embryon de Poulet en Culture *in vitro*," *J. Embryol. Exptl. Morphol* 9:628–633 (1961).

45. Dannenberg, A. M., Jr., M. S. Burstone, P. C. Walter, and J. W. Kinsley, "A Histochemical Study of Phagocytic and Enzymatic Functions of Rabbit Mononuclear and Polymorphonuclear Exudate Cells and Alveolar Macrophages," *J. Cell Biol.* 17:465–486 (1963).

46. de Jong, B. J., and J. deHaan, "Organ and Tissue Differentiation in Perfused Cultures of Explants from the Esophagus-Stomach-Trachea Complex of Young Chicken Embryos," *Acta Neerl. Morphol.* 5:26–51 (1943).

47. Demidov, B. S., "Peculiarities of Development of the Pulmonary Zones and Segments in Man." (In Russian) *Tr. Konf. Vozrastnoi Morfol. Fiziol. Biokhim.* pp. 452–454 (1962).

48. Dubreuil, G., A. Lacoste, and R. Raymond, "Observations sur le Développement du Poumon Humain," *Bull. Histol. Appl.* 13:235–245 (1936).

49. ——, ——, and ——, "Les Étapes du Développement du Poumon Humain et de Son Appareil Élastique," *Compt. Rend. Soc. Biol.* 121:244–246 (1936).

50. Dunnill, M. S., "Postnatal Growth of the Lung," *Thorax* 17:329–333 (1962).

51. Engel, S., "The Structure of the Respiratory Tissue in the Newly-born," *Acta Anat.* 19:353–365 (1953).

52. ——, *Lung Structure*. Springfield, Ill.: Charles C Thomas (1962).

53. Ewart, W., *The Bronchi and Pulmonary Blood Vessels: Their Anatomy and Nomenclature*. London: Baillière, Tindall & Cox, Ltd. (1889).

54. Fauré-Fremiet, E., "A propos des 'Cellules à Graisse' de l'Alvéole Pulmonaire," *Compt. Rend. Soc. Biol.* 83:11–13 (1920).

55. ——, and J. Dragoiu, "Le Développement du Poumon Foetal chez le Mouton," *Arch. Anat. Microscop.* 19:411–474 (1923).

56. Fell, H. B., and E. Mellanby, "Metaplasia Produced in Cultures of Chick Ectoderm by High Vitamin A," *J. Physiol.* 119:470–488 (1953).

57. Flint, J. M., "The Development of the Lungs," *Am. J. Anat.* 6:1–138 (1906).

58. Gage, S. H., "Development of the Lungs in the Common Toad, *Bufo lentiginosus* and in the Tree Toads (*Hyla pickeringii* and *Hyla versicolor*)," *Science* 12:309 (1900).

59. Galli, R., "Ricerche Embriologiche sul Rivestimento dell'Alveolo Polmonare nell'uomo," *Arch. Ital. Anat. Embriol.* 34:376–403 (1935).

60. Gautier, A., M. Campiche, C. Bozic, E. Hernandez, A. Reymond, and C. Verdan, "Pulmonary Epithelium in the Human Fetus and Newborn," *Proc. 5th Intern. Congr. Electron Microscop. Philadelphia* New York: Academic Press, vol. 2, p. WW-6 (1962).

61. Goldbach, H. J., "Die Entwicklung der elastichen Fasern in der menschlichen Lunge," *Deut. Z. Ges. Gerichtl. Med.* 45:381–385 (1956).

62. Goodrich, E. S., *Studies on the Structure and Development of Vertebrates.* New York: Dover Publications (1956).

63. Granel, F., "Sur les Cellules à Graisse des Cavités Alvéolaires du Poumon," *Compt. Rend. Soc. Biol.* 82:1329, 1367 (1919).

64. Graumann, W., "Ergebnisse der Polysaccharidhistochemie: Mensch und Säugetiere," *Handbuch der Histochemie,* II/2 *Polysaccharide,* W. Graumann, K. Neumann, eds. Stuttgart: G. Fischer, pp. 341–350 (1964).

65. Griel, A., "Über die Anlage der Lungen, sowie der Ultimobranchialen (Postbranchialen, Supraperikardialen) Körper bei Anuren Amphibien," *Anat. Hefte* 29:445–506 (1905).

66. Groniowski, J., and W. Djaczenko, "Die Feinstruktur des Lungengewebes nach dem Beginn der Atmung," *Z. Zellforsch.* 53:639–644 (1961).

67. ———, and W. Biczyskowa, "Ultrastructure of the Blood-Air Barrier of the Neonatal Human Lungs," *Proc. 5th Intern. Congr. Electron Microscop. Philadelphia* New York: Academic Press, vol. 2, p. WW-5 (1962).

68. Grover, J. W., "The Enzymatic Dissociation and Reproducible Reaggregation *in vitro* of 11-day Embryonic Chick Lung," *Develop. Biol.* 3:555–568 (1961).

69. ———, "The Relation between the Embryonic Age of Dissociated Chick Lung Cells and Their Capacity for Reaggregation and Histogenesis *in vitro*," *Exptl. Cell Res.* 24:171–173 (1961).

70. ———, "The Influence of Age and Environmental Factors on the Behaviour of Reaggregated Embryonic Lung Cells in Culture," *Exptl. Cell Res.* 26:344–359 (1962).

71. ———, "Reaggregation and Organotypic Redevelopment of Dissociated Embryonic Chick Lung Cells in Short-Term Culture, *Symp. Or. Culture,* C. J. Dawe, ed. *Natl. Cancer Inst. Monograph 11.* Washington, D.C.: U. S. Dept. Health, Education, and Welfare, pp. 35–50 (1963).

72. Ham, A. W., and K. W. Baldwin, "A Histological Study of the Development of the Lung, with Particular Reference to the Nature of Alveoli," *Anat. Record* 81:363–375 (1941).

73. Hayek, H. V., "Cellular Structure and Mucus Activity in the Bronchial Tree and Alveoli," *Ciba Found. Symp. Pulmonary Structure Function,* A. V. S. de Reuck, M. O'Connor, eds. Boston: Little, Brown, pp. 99–102 (1962).

74. Heiss, R., "Zur Entwicklung und Anatomie der menschlichen Lunge," *Arch. F. Anat.* pp. 1–129 (1919).

75. Hempstead, M., "Development of the Lungs in the Frogs, *Rana catesbiana, R. silvatica,* and *R. virescens,*" *Science* 12: 309 (1900).

76. Hesser, C., "Über die Entwickelung der Reptilienlungen," *Anat. Hefte* 29: 215–310 (1905).

77. Hinsch, G. W., and S. Knovacs, "Alkaline Phosphatase in the Trachea and Esophagus of the Developing Chick," *Anat. Record* 138:357 (1960).

78. His, W., "Zur Bildungsgeschichte der Lungen beim menschlichen Embryo," *Arch. Anat. Entwicklungsgeschichte* 89–106 (1887).

79. Karrer, H. E., "The Ultrastructure of the Mouse Lung, General Architecture of Capillary and Alveolar Walls," *J. Biophys. Biochem. Cytol.* 2:241–252 (1956).

80. Kerr, J. G., "On Certain Features in the Development of the Alimentary Canal in *Lepidosiren* and *Protopterus,*" *Quart. J. Microscop. Sci.* 54:483–518 (1910).

81. Kikuchi, N., "Normal and Retarded Development of the Lung and Alveolar Hypoplasia in Neonatal Infants," *Tohoku J. Exptl. Med.* 77:99–119 (1962).

82. Klaus, M., O. K. Reiss, W. H. Tooley, C. Piel, and J. A. Clements, "Alveolar Epithelial Cell Mitochondria as Source of the Surface-Active Lung Lining," *Science* 137:750–751 (1962).

83. Klemola, E., "Über den Lungenbau der Frühgeburt und des ausgetragenen Kindes, vor allem mit Rücksicht auf die Entwicklung der elastichen Fasern und der Kapillaren," *Acta Pediat.* 21:236–249 (1937).

84. Klika, E., "Contribution to Histochemistry and Electron Microscopy of Lung Alveolus," *Čs. Morfol.* 12:190–193 (1964).

85. Kölliker, A., *Entwicklungsgeschichte des Menschen und die höheren Thiere*, 2d edition Leipzig: W. Engelmann, (1879).

86. Lasnitzki, I., "The Effect of 3-4, Benzpyrene on Human Foetal Lung Grown *in vitro*," *Brit. J. Cancer* 10:510–516 (1956).

87. ———, "The Effect of Carcinogens, Hormones, and Vitamins on Organ Cultures," *Intern. Rev. Cytol.* 8:80–121. New York: Academic Press (1958).

88. Laumonier, R., "Remarques sur la Structure Pulmonaire des Prématurés," *Semaine Hôp. Paris* 28:2047–2053 (1952).

89. Leeson, T. S., and C. R. Leeson, "A Light and Electron Microscope Study of Developing Respiratory Tissue in the Rat," *J. Anat.* 98:183–193 (1964).

90. Leloir, L. F., J. M. Olavarría, S. H. Goldemberg, and H. Carminatti, "Biosynthesis of Glycogen from Uridine Diphosphate Glucose," *Arch. Biochem. Biophys.* 81:508–520 (1959).

91. Lelong, M., and R. Laumonier, "Histological and Histochemical Evolution of the Foetal Lung," *Anoxia of the Newborn Infant, a Symposium*, J. F. Delafresnaye and T. E. Oppé, eds. Springfield, Ill.: Charles C Thomas, pp. 61–84 (1954).

92. Lenzi, L., "Sullo Sviluppo del Tessuto Elastico nel Polmone dell'Uomo," *Mon. Zool. Ital.* 9:213–220 (1898).

93. Linser, P., "Über den Bau und die Entwicklung des elastischen Gewebes in der Lunge," *Anat. Hefte* 13:309–334 (1900).

94. Locy, W. A., and O. Larsell, "The Embryology of the Bird's Lung, Based on Observations of the Domestic Fowl," *Am. J. Anat.* Part I, 19:447–504; Part II, 20:1–44 (1916).

95. Loffredo Sampaolo, C., and G. Sampaolo, "Colture Organotipiche di Polmone Embrionale di Pollo. Alcuni Aspetti Istologici e Istochimici," *Boll. Soc. Ital. Biol. Sper.* 32:797–801 (1956).

96. ———, and ———, "Indagini sulla Differenziazione in Coltura Organotipica della Trachea di Embrioni di Pollo," *Boll. Soc. Ital. Biol. Sper.* 33:173–176 (1957).

97. ———, and ———, "Les Aspects Histologiques de l'Appareil Respiratoire de l'Embryon de Poulet après Culture *in vitro*," *Compt. Rend. Assoc. Anat.* 44:448–460 (1957).

98. ———, and ———, "Colture Organotipiche di Abbozzi Precoci di Polmone Espiantati da Embrioni di Pollo Dallo Stadio 23 allo Stadio 27 su Terreni a Composizione Chimica Determinata," *Rend. Atti Accad. Sci. Med. Chir.* 114:3–11 (1960).

99. ———, and ———, "Indagini Sperimentali sullo Sviluppo del Polmone Embrionale (Pollo e Coniglio)," *Quaderni. Anat. Prat.* 17:1–43 (1961).

100. Loosli, C. G., and E. L. Potter, "The Prenatal Development of the Human Lung," *Anat. Record* 109:320–321 (1951).

101. ———, and ———, "Pre- and Postnatal Development of the Respiratory Portion of the Human Lung," *Am. Rev. Respirat. Diseases* 80:5–23 (1959).

102. Los, J. A., "De Embryonale Ontwikkeling van de Venae Pulmonales en de Sinus Coronarius bij de Mens," PH.D. Dissertation," Leiden (1958).

103. Low, F. N., "Pulmonary Alveolar Epithelium of Laboratory Mammals and Man," *Anat. Record* 117:241–263 (1953).

104. ———, and M. Sampaio, "The Pulmonary Alveolar Epithelium as an Entodermal Derivative," *Anat. Record* 127:51–64 (1957).

105. McCrady, E., Jr., "The Embryology of the Opossum," *Am. Anat. Mem.* Philadelphia: Wistar Inst., vol. 16, (1938).

106. McKay, D. G., E. C. Adams, A. T. Hertig, and S. Danziger, "Histochemical Horizons in Human Embryos. I. 5 mm. Embryo. Streeter Horizon XIII," *Anat. Record* 122:125–153 (1955).

107. ———, ———, ———, and ———, "Histochemical Horizons in Human Embryos. II. 6 and 7 mm. Embryos. Streeter Horizon XIV," *Anat. Record* 126:433–463 (1956).

108. Marcus, H., "Beitrage zur Kenntnis

der Gymnophionen; I. Über das Schlund-spaltengebiet," *Arch. Mikroskop. Anat.* 71:695–744 (1908).

109. Marinozzi, V., "La Structure de l'Al-véole Pulmonaire Étudiée au Moyen de la Technique de l'Imprégnation à l'Ar-gent," *Proc. 4th Intern. Congr. Electron Microscop. Berlin*, Berlin: Springer-Verlag, vol. 2, pp. 412–415 (1958).

110. Matsumoto, S., "A Histogenetic In-vestigation on the Lung of the Human Embryo, especially on the Elastic Fiber and Reticular Fiber," *Okajimas Folia Anat. Japon.* 30:275–289 (1957).

111. Mekeel, A. G., "A Pulmonary Vestige in the Lungless Salamanders," *Anat. Record* 34:141 (1926).

112. Milaire, J., "Prédifferenciation Cyto-chimique de Diverse Ébauches Céphal-iques chez l'Embryon de Souris," *Arch. Biol.* 70:587–730 (1959).

113. Miller, W. S., "The Structure of the Lung," *J. Morphol.* 8:165–188 (1893).

114. Minot, C. S., *Human Embryology.* New York: Wood, (1892).

115. Moog, F., "Localization of Alkaline and Acid Phosphatase in the Early Embryogenesis of the Chick," *Biol. Bull.* 86:51–80 (1944).

116. Moser, F., "Beiträge zur vergleichen-den Entwicklungsgeschichte der Wir-beltierlunge (Amphibien, Reptilien, Vögel, Säuger)," *Arch. Mikroskop. Anat.* 60:587–668 (1902).

117. Muir, H., "Chondroitin Sulphates and Sulphated Polysaccharides of Connective Tissue," *The Biochemistry of Mucopoly-saccharides of Connective Tissue. Bio-chem. Soc. Sympos.*, F. Clark, J. K. Grant, eds. Cambridge: Cambridge University Press. vol. 20, pp. 4–22 (1961).

118. Narath, A., "Die Entwicklung der Lunge von *Echidna aculeata*," Zoolo-gische Forschungsreisen in Australien u. dem Malayischen Archipel, R. Semon. II. *Denkschr. Medizinisch-naturw. Ge-sell. Jena* 5:247–274 (1896).

119. ———, "Der Bronchialbaum der Säugethiere und des Menschen," *Bibl. Med. A. Anat.* 3:1–380 (1901).

120. Neuhäuser, G., and E. C. Dingler, "Lungenwachstum im Saüglingsalter (Untersuchungen an der Albinoratte)," *Z. Anat. Entwicklungsgeschichte* 123:32–48 (1962).

121. Noble, G. K., "The Integumentary, Pulmonary, and Cardiac Modifications Correlated with Increased Cutaneous Respiration in the Amphibia: a Solution of the Hairy Frog Problem," *J. Morphol.* 40:341–416 (1925).

122. ———, *The Biology of the Amphibia.* New York: McGraw-Hill (1931).

123. Norris, R. F., T. T. Kochenderfer, and R. M. Tyson, "Development of the Fetal Lung," *Am. J. Diseases Children* 61:933–950 (1941).

124. Okada, Y., S. Ishiko, S. Daido, J. Kim, and S. Ikeda, "Comparative Morphology of the Lung with Special Reference to the Alveolar Epithelial Cells. I. Lung of the Amphibia," *Acta Tuberc. Japon.* 11:63–72 (1962).

125. ———, ———, ———, ———, and ———, "Comparative Morphology of the Lung with Special Reference to the Alveolar Epithelial Cells. II. Lung of the Reptilia," *Acta Tuberc. Japon.* 12:1–10 (1962).

126. Oren, R., A. E. Farnham, K. Saito, E. Milofsky, and M. L. Karnovsky, "Met-abolic Patterns in Three Types of Phag-ocytizing Cells," *J. Cell Biol.* 17:487–501 (1963).

127. Palmer, D. M., "The Lung of a Human Foetus of 170 mm. C. R. Length," *Am. J. Anat.* 58:59–72 (1936).

128. Parhon, C. I., and St. M. Milcou, "Rôle du Poumon Prérespiratoire dans le Mé-tabolisme du Sucre. Son Activité Pré-hépatique ou Concomitante avec Celle du Foie. Corrélations Pneumohépati-ques," *Compt. Rend. Soc. Biol.* 127:641–643 (1938).

129. Pattle, R. E., "Properties, Function and Origin of the Alveolar Lining Lay-er," *Proc. Roy. Soc. London Ser. B* 148:217–240 (1958).

130. ———, "The Formation of a Lining Film by Foetal Lungs," *J. Pathol. Bac-teriol.* 82:333–343 (1961).

131. Policard, A., A. Collet, and S. Préger-main, "Recherches au Microscope Élec-tronique sur les Cellules Pariétales Al-véolares du Poumon des Mammifères," *Z. Zellforsch.* 50:561–587 (1959).

132. Potter, E. L., "State of the Lungs at Birth," *J. Am. Med. Assoc.* 159:1341–1342 (1955).

133. Reale, E., and L. Luzzatto, "La Local-

izzazione Istochimica della Succinodeid-rogenesi in Alcuni Organi dell'Embrione e dell'Adulto de *Mus musculus albinus*," *Mon. Zool. Ital.* 64:95–106 (1957).

134. Reynolds, S. R. M., "The Fetal and Neonatal Pulmonary Vasculature in the Guinea Pig in Relation to Hemodynamic Changes at Birth," *Am. J. Anat.* 98:97–128 (1956).

135. Ritter, W. E., and L. Miller, "A Contribution to the Life History of *Autodax lugubris* Hallow., a Californian Salamander," *Am. Naturalist* 33:691–704 (1899).

136. Robinson, A., "Observations on the Earlier Stages in the Development of the Lungs of Rats and Mice," *J. Anat. Physiol.* 23:224–241 (1889).

137. Rossi, F., "Histochemie der Enzyme bei der Entwicklung," *Handbuch der Histochemie, VII/4 Enzyme* W. Graumann and K. Neumann, eds. Stuttgart, Germany: G. Fisher, pp. 109–298 (1964).

138. ——, G. Pescetto, and E. Reale, "La Localizzazione Istochimica della Fosfatasi Alcalina e le Sue Variazioni nel Corso dello Sviluppo Prenatale dell'-Uomo," *Z. Anat. Entwicklungsgeschichte* 115:500–528 (1951).

139. ——, ——, and ——, "La Reazione Istochimica per la Fosfatasi Acida nello Studio dello Sviluppo Prenatale dell'Uomo," *Z. Anat. Entwicklungsgeschichte* 117:36–69 (1953).

140. ——, ——, and ——, "Enzymatic Activities in Human Ontogenesis: First Synoptic Tables on Histochemical Research," *J. Histochem. Cytochem.* 5:221–235 (1957).

141. ——, and E. Reale, "The Somite Stage of Human Development Studied with the Histochemical Reaction for the Demonstration of Alkaline Glycerophosphatase," *Acta Anat.* 30:656–681 (1957).

142. Rudnick, D., "Developmental Capacities of the Chick Lung in Chorioallantoic Grafts," *J. Exptl. Zool.* 66:125–154 (1933).

143. Rudolph, A., *Remarks on Hemodynamic Changes in the Pulmonary Circulation at the Time of Birth, Conference on Neonatal Respiratory Adaptation*, T. Oliver, ed. Washington, D.C.: National Institutes of Child Health and Human Development. In press (1965).

144. Sampaolo, G., and C. Loffredo Sampaolo, "La Trachea di Feti di Cavia in Coltura Organotipica. Indagini Sugli Aspetti Istologici, Sugli Atteggiamenti Morfogenetici e Sulla Differenziazione *in vitro* dell'Epitelio e della Cartilagine," *Quaderni Anat. Prat.* 14:149–179 (1958).

145. ——, and ——, "Osservazioni Istologiche sul Polmone di Feti di Cavia Coltivato *in vitro*," *Quaderni Anat. Prat.* 14:212–224 (1958).

146. ——, and ——, "Observations Histologiques sur le Poumon de Foetus de Cobaye, Cultivé *in vitro*," *Compt. Rend. Assoc. Anat.* 45:707–714 (1959).

147. Schmidt, V., "Über die Entwickelung des Kehlkopfes und der Luftröhre bei Reptilien," *Anat. Hefte* 48:389–452 (1913).

148. Schneider, N., "Sur les Possibilités de Propagation d'un Sarcome de Souris sur des Organes Embryonnaires de Poulet à Différents Stades de Développement," *Arch. Anat. Microscop. Morphol. Exptl.* 47:573–604 (1958).

149. Shepard, R. H., B. K. Sladen, B. Peterson, and T. Enns, "Path Taken by Gases through the Respiratory System of the Chicken," *J. Appl. Physiol.* 14:733–735 (1959).

150. Short, R. H. D., "Aspects of Comparative Lung Growth," *Proc. Roy. Soc. London Ser. B* 140:432–441 (1952).

151. Smith, C. A., "The First Breath," *Sci. Am.* 209:27–35 (1963).

152. Snyder, F. F., "The Rate of Entrance of Amniotic Fluid into the Pulmonary Alveoli during Fetal Respiration," *Am. J. Obstet. Gynec.* 41:224–228 (1941).

153. ——, "Fetal Respiration during the Second Stage of Labor in Rabbits and the Origin of Pulmonary Hyaline Membrane," *Am. J. Obstet. Gynecol.* 75:1231–1243 (1958).

154. Sorokin, S. P., "Histochemical Events in Developing Human Lungs," *Acta Anat.* 40:105–119 (1960).

155. ——, "A Study of Development in Organ Cultures of Mammalian Lungs," *Develop. Biol.* 3:60–83 (1961).

156. ——, "A Note on the Histochemistry of the Opossum's Lung," *Acta Anat.* 50:13–21 (1962).

157. ——, "Activities of the Great Al-

veolar Cell," *Conference on Neonatal Respiratory Adaptation*, T. Oliver, ed. Washington, D.C.: National Institutes of Child Health and Human Developments. In press (1965).

158. ———, W. W. C. Green, and H. A. Padykula, Unpublished observations (1959).

159. ———, H. A. Padykula, and E. Herman, "Comparative Histochemical Patterns in Developing Mammalian Lungs," *Develop. Biol.* 1:125–151 (1959).

160. Stewart, F. W., "An Histogenetic Study of the Respiratory Epithelium," *Anat. Record* 25:181–200 (1923).

161. Streeter, G. L., "Developmental Horizons in Human Embryos. Description of Age Group XIII, Embryos about 4 or 5 Millimeters Long, and Age Group XIV, Period of Indentation of the Lens Vesicle," *Contrib. Embryol. Carnegie Inst. Wash.* 31:27–63 (1945).

162. Szendi, B., "Intrauterine Funktion der Lunge und Leber des Fetus," *Arch. Gynaekol.* 162:27–41 (1936).

163. Teuffel, E., "Zur Entwicklung der elastischen Fasern in der Lunge des Fötus und des Neugeborenen," *Arch. Anat. Entwicklungsgeschichte* pp. 377–392 (1902).

164. Vacek, Z., P. Hahn, and O. Koldovsky, "Role of the Lung in Metabolism of Fat during Ontogeny of the Rat," *Nature* 191: 85–86 (1961).

165. ———, ———, and ———, "Histological Study of Fat Distribution in the Small Intestine, Liver and Lungs Following Oral Fat Administration to Rats of Different Postnatal Ages," *Čs. Morfol.* 10: 30–45 (1962).

166. Vakaet, L., "Étude Expérimentale par la Méthode de Culture d'Organes des Réactions de l'Épithélium Bronchial de l'Embryon de Poulet," *Arch. Anat. Microscop. Morphol. Exptl.* 45:48–64 (1956).

167. Villee, C. A., "The Intermediary Metabolism of Human Fetal Tissues," *Cold Spring Harbor Symp. Quant. Biol.* 19:186–199 (1954).

168. Waddell, W. R., "Organoid Differentiation of the Fetal Lung," *Arch. Pathol.* 47:227–247 (1949).

169. Wells, L. J., and E. A. Boyden, "The Development of the Bronchopulmonary Segments in Human Embryos of Horizons XVII to XIX," *Am. J. Anat.* 95:163–201 (1954).

170. Willach, P., "Beiträge zur Entwicklung der Lunge bei Säugethieren." Osterwieck-Harz: A. W. Zickfeldt (1888).

171. Wolff, Em., "Sur la Croissance et la Différentiation en Milieu Synthétique de la Syrinx de l'Embryon de Poulet," *Compt. Rend. Soc. Biol.* 147:864–868 (1953).

172. ———, "Comparison entre les Valeurs Nutritives de l'Extrait d'Embryon et du Serum dans la Culture *in vitro* de la Syrinx de l'Embryon de Poulet," *Compt. Rend. Soc. Biol.* 148:2078–2080 (1954).

173. ———, "Amélioration de l'Extrait d'Embryons de Poulet par des Solutions Synthétiques dans la Culture *in vitro* de la Syrinx d'Oiseau," *Compt. Rend. Acad. Sci. Paris* 243:2154–2156 (1956).

174. ———, "Nouvelles Recherches sur la Culture Organotypique de la Syrinx d'Oiseau. Culture sur Différents Milieux Naturels et Amélioration de Ces Milieux par des Acides Aminés," *Arch. Anat. Microscop. Morphol. Exptl.* 46:1–38 (1957).

175. ———, "Analyse des Besoins Nutritifs d'un Organe Embryonnaire, la Syrinx d'Oiseau, Cultivée en Milieu Synthétique," *Arch. Anat. Microscop. Morphol. Exptl.* 46:407–468 (1957).

176. Wolff, Et., "Principe d'une Méthode de Culture d'Organes Embryonnaires en Milieu Synthétiques," *Compt. Rend. Soc. Biol.* 147:857–861 (1953).

177. ———, "Les Propriétés Génerales des Organes Embryonnaires en Culture *in vitro*," *Acta Anat.* 30:952–969 (1957).

178. Woodside, G. L. and A. J. Dalton, "The Ultrastructure of Lung Tissue from Newborn and Embryo Mice," *J. Ultrastruct. Res.* 2:28–54 (1958).

179. Young, J. Z., *The Life of Vertebrates.* Oxford: Clarendon Press (1950).

19

The Thyroid

THOMAS H. SHEPARD*

Department of Pediatrics
University of Washington
Seattle, Washington

This review of recent contributions to the knowledge of the developing thyroid will draw mainly on material introduced since the subject was last summarized (Willier, 81; Waterman and Gorbman, 79; Taki, 69; Jost, 27, 28; Mitskevich, 38; Romanoff, 53; Maraud and Stoll, 34; and Dieterlen-Lièvre, 9). Willier's review of 1955, although covering several animal species, analyzes work in anurans particularly. Waterman and Gorbman in 1956 published original work with the rabbit fetal thyroid and included a comprehensive review of the related literature. Taki in 1958 summarized much of the histological data available on the human fetal thyroid. Jost in 1957 and 1961 has summarized in French his ingenious studies of the early physiology and biochemistry in the rat and rabbit. Mitskevich has

contributed material on the comparative endocrinology of a group of animals and offers a number of thyroid weight measurements which are useful. Romanoff's material deals with the chick thyroid. In 1961 Maraud and Stoll (34) produced a comprehensive review of the histology, biochemistry, and physiology of the developing fetal thyroid and included in it their own work on the electronmicroscopy of the chick thyroid. The most recent review is by Dieterlen-Lièvre (9).

This chapter will place more emphasis on mammalian thyroid development, excluding all but strongly contributive work in birds and cold-blooded animals. This last restriction was made with the full understanding that many of the basic observations originated in birds and anurans. The author also apologizes to the many authors whose work could not be described more completely in this chapter. In many cases the most recent citations were used; thus earlier, and often more original, contributions have been omitted.

*The author's work was supported by grants from the National Institutes of Health. The friendly collaboration with Henning J. Andersen, Helge Andersen, and Franz Bierring of the University of Copenhagen, Denmark, has been very much appreciated.

493

Thyroid development can be divided into (1) the early stages which include separation of the anlage from the foregut and early differentiation, (2) later stages with production of colloid and follicle formation, (3) biochemical aspects, and (4) physiological and gross changes.

Early Development

Separation of Anlage from Foregut

The descriptions of the proliferation and evagination of the ventral foregut in the area of the truncus arteriosus at the level where the latter divides into two ventral aortae are remarkably similar in a wide number of mammalian species. In general this change in the foregut occurs during the early somite stage (Fig. 19.1) when the embryo is 2–3 mm in length (Table 19.1). The local tissue contributions and intrinsic changes leading to the proliferation of this epithelium are among the most important sequences in development (Figs. 19.2–19.4) but unfortunately, have not been extensively investigated in any animal except the chick (Rudnick, 56). Rudnick

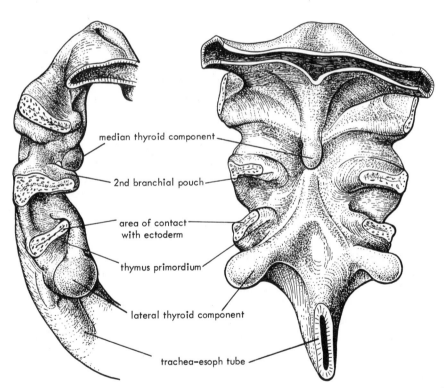

median thyroid component

2nd branchial pouch

area of contact with ectoderm

thymus primordium

lateral thyroid component

trachea–esoph tube

Fig. 19.1 The lateral (left) and ventral (right) aspects of pharyngeal and primordial epithelium of a 4-mm human embryo are shown to illustrate the positions of the endodermal invaginations. The mesodermal derivatives are not shown. (Figs. 19.1 through 19.6 are from G. L. Weller, "Development of the Thyroid, Parathyroid and Thymus Glands in Man," *Contributions to Embryology*, No. 141, Carnegie Institution of Washington 24:93–139, 1933, by Courtesy of Carnegie Institute of Washington.)

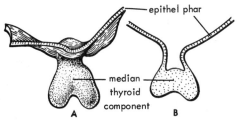

Fig. 19.2 A. Bilobed median thyroid component now attached to pharynx by a short pedicle. Embryo was 6.5 mm in crown-rump length. B. A single large cavity within pedicle communicates with the lumen of the pharynx.

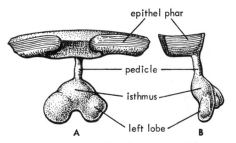

Fig. 19.3 Further development of the median thyroid in an embryo 8.2 mm in length. A. Ventral aspect. B. Right lateral view.

investigated the thyroid-forming potency of the blastoderm and noted a bilateral localization of the thyroid anlage after 72 hours. Early descriptions by Norris (42) in man and Sugiyama (66) in mice and rats stand essentially unchanged. Orts-Llorca and Genis Galvez (43) have described a variation in the shape of the early thyroid primordia in man. This variation consists of a tuberclelike projection of the thyroid into the lumen of the pharynx and resembles in some ways the usual case in the rabbit. The role of the proximity of the truncus arteriosus in induction of the anlage has not been investigated. Taki (69) has confirmed Norris' observation (42) of the presence of communicating cavities appearing within the solid primordium after the 6-mm stage in the human. Presumably these sinusoidallike structures are the cavities which are later invaded by blood vessels.

Because of the high content of glycogen, rapid multiplication, and the first appearance of function in later histological stages, it has been assumed that this tissue at this stage of early differentiation has none of the characteristics of mature thyroid. Gorbman and Merlini (17), however, have

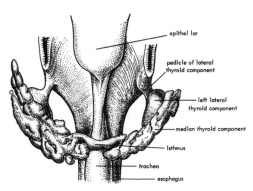

Fig. 19.4 The relationship of the lateral thyroid component (ultimobranchial body) to the median thyroid is shown in a 16-mm fetus.

pointed out that in ammocoetes larvae of the lamprey, structures similar to the primitive mammalian anlage secrete a thyroid hormonelike substance through a rudimentary duct into the pharynx, resulting in digestion and absorption of the hormone through the gastrointestinal tract. Perhaps more direct histochemical and radioautographic observations of the early mammalian anlage are indicated.

Later Stages, Production of Colloid, and Follicle Formation

Prefollicular Stage

During this period there is active growth and mitosis in the thyroid,

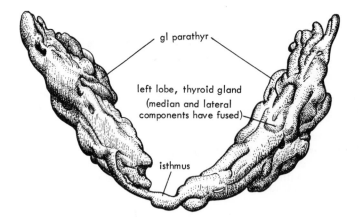

gl parathyr

left lobe, thyroid gland
(median and lateral
components have fused)

isthmus

Fig. 19.5 Structure of the gland in a 23-mm human fetus. Both Figs. 19.4 and 19.5 show the anastomosing of epithelial plates that constitute the thyroid at this stage.

which is formed by anastomosing cellular plates, two to three cells in thickness (Fig. 19.5). The limits of this time period in several animals and man are summarized in Table 19.1. The cytoplasm is scanty and large amounts of periodic acid-Schiff (PAS) positive, diastase-digestible materials have been observed in man by Taki (69), McKay and co-workers (36), and Shepard and co-workers (61). Also in man, acid phosphatase activity has been observed, but alkaline phosphatase activity is absent except in blood vessels (Rossi et al, 55; Jirásek, 26; and Shepard et al., 61). Lactic and succinic dehydrogenases have also been found to be active in this early stage (Shepard et al., 61).

Electronmicroscopic studies during this stage reveal a well-developed basement membrane surrounding the plates, scanty endoplasmic reticulum, and no evidence of a syncytium. The cell borders in the rat are interdigitated (Feldman et al., 10) whereas those of the human fetus are separated in some regions by spaces, and elsewhere are held together by desmosomes (Bierring and Shepard, 5). The latter authors observed that many of the ribonuclear particles were free and not attached to endoplasmic reticulum until later stages. A similar observation has been made in chick thyroid by Porte and Petrovic (52). The Golgi apparatus was present, but it occupied only rather a small area.

The contribution of the ultimobranchial body to development of the human thyroid has been reviewed by Sugiyama and co-workers (67) who concluded, as have others, that it contributes little, if anything, to the eventual mass of the mammalian gland. Moreover, the part which does remain during fetal life has a tendency to degeneration and cyst formation. Van Dyke (75) has reviewed comparative aspects of the ultimobranchial body. Machida and Sugiyama (33) have carefully studied the ultimobranchial body of the guinea pig. Their findings corroborate the observations in humans with lingual thyroid arrests that there is no I^{131} accumulation in the lower cervical region, and that hypothyroidism nearly always develops with removal of the lingual tissue (Ward et al., 78). There is, of course, the possibility that without the median thyroid's presence the lateral contributions cannot normally maintain themselves (Fig. 19.6).

TABLE 19.1 Histological and Functional Landmarks of the Fetal Thyroid in Various Animals

Animal (Developmental Period)	Evagination from Foregut	Prefollicular Stage	Intracellular Colloid	Follicles Appear	I¹³¹ Concentration	Organification[a] by Follicle	Thyroxine Production	References
Frog (30 days)	4 days (7-8 mm.)	4-17 days	11 days	17 days	8 days	8 days / Tailbud stage	16 mm.	Saxén (58) / Flickinger (11)
Chick (21 d.)	34-48 hrs.	2-11 d. / 9¼ d.	7-8 d.	9-11 d.	7 d. / 5 d.	8½ d.	9¼ days	Romanoff (53) / Trunnel and Wade (74)
Rabbit (32 d.)	10 d.	16-17 d.		16-17 d. / 18-19 d.	15-18 d. / 19-20 d.	17-19 d.	20-21 d.	Waterman and Gorbman (79) / Jost (28)
Mouse (19 d.) (19-20 d.)				16-17 d.	14 d.		16-17 d.	Jacobson and Brent (25)
Rat (22 d.)	11 d.	11-17 d.	16 d. / 17 d.	16-17 d. / 17-18 d.	15-16 d. / 17-18 d.	15-16 d.		van Heyningen (76) / Phillips and Schmidt (47)
					none at 16½ d.	17 d. / 17½-18½ d.	17½ d. / 17½-18½ d.	Nataf and Sfez (41)
Calf (285 d.)	22-26 d. (2-4 mm.)	52-72 d. (22-65 mm.)	75-88 d. / 64-72 d. (50-65 mm.)	75-88 d. / 72-80 d. (65-80 mm.)	60 d.		53-70 d.	Gelso (15) / Koneff et al. (31)
Man[b] (266 d.)	3-5 mm.	42-57 d.	58-64 d.	65-85 d.	70-84 d.		92-142 mm.	Shepard et al. (61) / (Yamazaki) (84) / Taki (69)

[a] Organification was assumed to occur if radioautographs from histologically fixed material were positive.
[b] Conversion of crown-rump length to gestational age was made from the data of Shepard and co-workers (60).

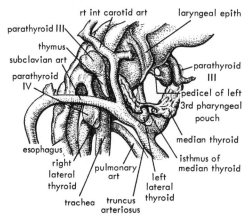

rt int carotid art   laryngeal epith

parathyroid III

thymus

subclavian art

parathyroid IV

parathyroid III

pedicel of left 3rd pharyngeal pouch

median thyroid

esophagus

isthmus of median thyroid

right lateral thyroid

pulmonary art

left lateral thyroid

trachea   truncus arteriosus

Fig. 19.6 Contribution of components from the 3rd and 4th pharyngeal pouches to the median thyroid and parathyroid glands. The close spatial relationship between the thyroid and the truncus arteriosis is shown.

Active Follicle Formation

Investigation of the appearance of follicles and colloid is complicated in mammals by the fact that there is very little synchrony of development from one area in the gland to another, as is seen in the chick. During most of early fetal life in man, for instance, all stages of early follicle formation may be seen in the same gland (Shepard et al., 61). The external portions of the lateral lobes are generally the most advanced in most mammals.

There is general agreement that colloid synthesis occurs in the rough-surfaced endoplasmic reticulum, which increases at the time of appearance of colloid. Herman (21) in the salamander, Stoll and co-workers (65), Porte and Petrovic (52) in explanted chick embryonic thyroid, and Bierring and Shepard (5) in explanted human fetal thyroid, have shown that thyrotropin stimulates an increase in the amount of endoplasmic reticulum and production of colloid. The role of the

Golgi apparatus in production of colloid is less clear. Feldman and co-workers (10) found that it expanded without evidence of vacuole formation in the fetal rat at the time of colloid production, whereas Bierring and Shepard (5) found it inconspicuous at all stages of early colloid formation in the human fetus.

Intracellular PAS-positive material which is not digested by amylase is the forerunner of follicles (anurans, Saxén, 58; rats, Phillips and Schmidt, 47; Carpenter, 6; chicks, Wollman and Zwilling, 83; Fujita and Machimo, 13; man, Taki, 69; Shepard et al., 61). The intracellular colloidlike particles have been reported to coalesce centrally, and contribute to formation of a colloid cavity in chicks (Fujita and Machimo, 13) and calf (Koneff et al., 31).

The formation of intracellular PAS-positive material analyzed in explanted embryonic chick thyroid by Gaillard (14), Tixier-Vidal (73), Bakker-Sauer (3), and Sobel and Leurer (63) has led to the conclusion that thyroid-stimulating hormone will increase the number of PAS-positive particles, but will not increase the general rate of differentiation. Mess and Hamori (37) used this phenomenon to develop a sensitive assay method for thyrotrophic hormone in the 8-day chick embryo. Thioamides, 1-goitrin and thiourea, when added to the chick organ cultures, were found by Shepard (Unpublished observations) to cause no change in either rate of development or amount of PAS-positive material accumulated, but a definite decrease in I^{131} accumulation was observed with 10^{-4} M 1-goitrin. Sobel and Leurer (63) claim to have observed decreased amounts of intracellular PAS-positive material after addition of unstated amounts of

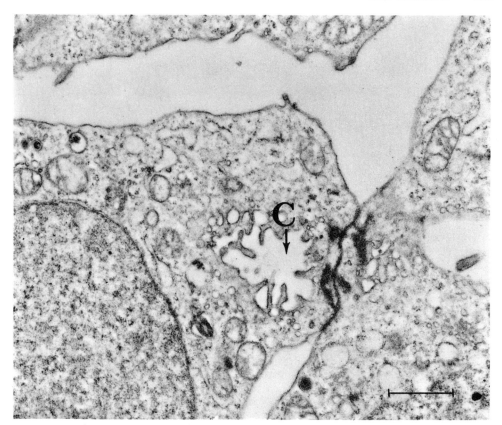

Fig. 19.7 Electronmicrograph from the thyroid of a 28-mm human fetus to illustrate an intracellular cavity C which is lined by coarse microvilli. Note the free ribosomes and large intercellular spaces. The marker signifies 1 μ in Figs 19.7–19.9.

thiouracil. Gonzales (16) has found iodinated products produced from embryonic chick explants. Rose and Trunnell (54) observed that the PAS-positive granules in the chick were resistant to diastase digestion, but did not concentrate radioiodine.

Hilfer (22) has raised an interesting point about the specific developmental influence by fibroblasts surrounding the thyroid. He found that fibroblasts from 17-day chick thyroid capsule had the capability of inducing follicles from dissociated epithelium in vitro. Fibroblasts from omentum did not have the same effect. In our own ex-

plants, vacuolization of the fibroblasts and epithelial necrosis was observed in chick explants exposed to thyrotropin (0.5 μ/ml of media), a finding similar to that of Gaillard (14).

Genesis of Central Colloid Cavities

What is the nature of these intracellular PAS-positive particles and how do they participate in follicle formation? It is accepted by most authors that they represent a colloid-like substance, perhaps in an immature state. Nadler and co-workers (40) have indicated that similar cell inclusions

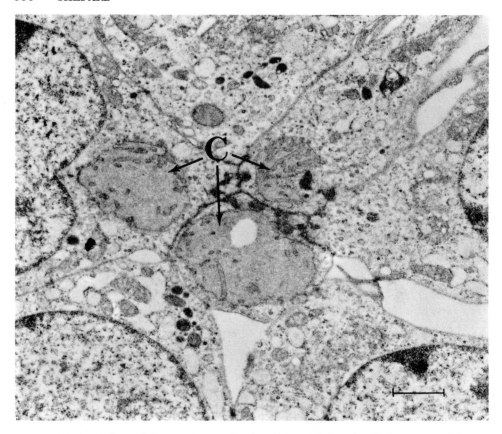

Fig. 19.8 Fetal thyroid from a 61-mm human fetus. The intracellular spaces C have enlarged and are now located close to the apex of the cell. Note the increased density of their contents.

in the adult rat may be uniodinated thyroglobin. In the 17-day rat fetus, these particles were immunologically specific for thyroglobulin but Feldman and co-workers (10) were unable to associate them with any specific ultrastructural component, and felt that the particles were retained perhaps in a dispersed state until the 20th day, when they were transferred to the colloid cavities. In the human, numerous intracellular canaliculi have been observed during the prefollicular stages (Bierring and Shepard, 5) and these structures, lined by microvilli, contain a thin granular substance (Figs. 19.7–19.10). With maturation, these cavities, which are thought to be a part of the smooth-walled endoplasmic reticulum, become more dilated, contain a denser substance and gradually move toward the apex of the cell. Subsequent stages are observed where these apical cavities have opened extracellularly, coalescing with similar adjacent structures. This gives a cloverleaflike outline on cross section (Fig. 19.9). These extruded intracellular spaces are maintained in a central location in the follicle by desmosomes that hold the apical edges of the cells together. From this mechanism of colloid

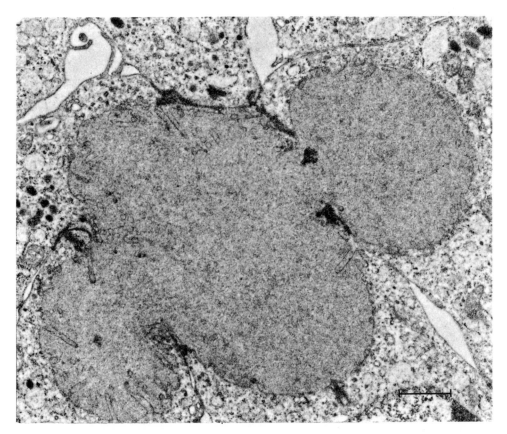

Fig. 19.9 Fetal thyroid from a 98-mm human fetus. The intracellular cavities are in the process of being disgorged into a central colloid cavity, a process which gives a clover-leaf pattern in cross section. Note the desmosomes which cause central retention of the colloid. The ribosomes are now mostly attached to endoplasmic reticulum.

cavity formation, a very close correlation between colloid production by the cell and central colloid cavity formation can be made; in fact, it could be stated that the secretory product of these cells is almost mechanically responsible for their organization into follicles. This intracellular canalicular mechanism of follicle formation has been observed only in the human fetus (5). No evidence of a similar sequence has been observed yet in the chick or rat (Petrovic and Porte, 46; Feldman et al., 10). The early follicular period in the human fetus is prolonged over a

30–40-day period while that of the chick and rat is only a few days; for this reason it may be that man and other animals with longer gestation periods will prove better subjects for study of the phenomenon of follicle formation.

The studies of the initial formation of colloid may contribute to the complex problem of origin of the dense colloid droplets. It has been suggested by Wissig (82) that these are thyroglobin, produced for transport to the colloid cavity by the Golgi of the cell. During early colloid cavity formation there

Evolution of colloid spaces from intracellular to extracellular location

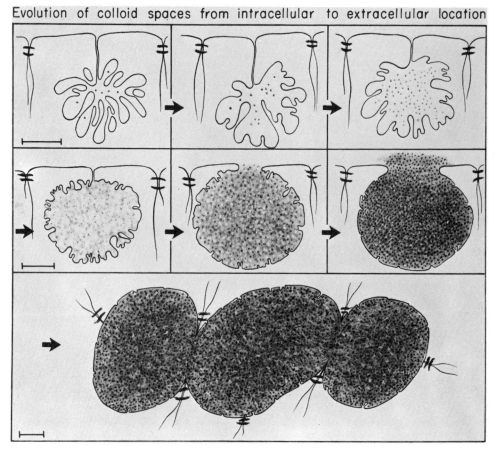

Fig. 19.10 Schematic diagram to show the evolution of the intracellular spaces toward the apex of the cell and their contribution to the formation of the central colloid cavity. The short parallel marks represent desmosomes.

are only very small numbers of colloid droplets in the rat and human fetus. This would support the work of Ponse (51) and Nadler and co-workers (40) who have produced evidence that dense droplets originate from material absorbed from the colloid cavity and are a means of transporting and hydrolyzing the thyroglobin in preparation for release of thyroxine from the gland. Bierring and Shepard (5) have commented on the structural similarity of these dense colloid particles to lysosomes.

During this stage of histogenesis there is also a rapid increase in the number of blood vessels between the follicles (Sugiyama, 66; Taki, 69; Shepard et al., 61). Thommes (72) has found that the vascular pattern of the chick thyroid is closely associated with the onset of its activity.

Antrum Formation

Explanted prefollicular embryonic chick thyroid, when exposed to thyroid-stimulating hormone (TSH) or pituitary explants, develops conspicuous intercellular dilations called antra, shown in Figure 19.11 (Bakker-Sauer, 3; Petro-

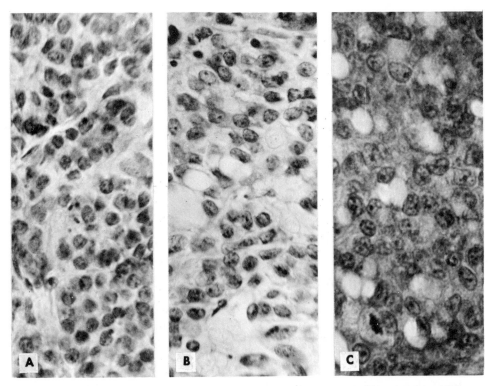

Fig. 19.11 Antrum formation in human and chick fetus. A. Control human thyroid from a 49-mm fetus. Maintained in vitro for 24 hours. B. Same thyroid exposed for 24 hours in vitro to 0.01 unit thyrotrophic hormone per ml of culture media. Note dilated spaces which displace the nucleus. C. Eight-day chick thyroid exposed to 0.1 unit thyrotrophic hormone per ml of culture media.

vic and Porte, 46; Thesingh, 70, 71; Daems and Thesingh, 8). This phenomenon occurs as early as 8 minutes after TSH exposure and disappears after 12–24 hours. The antra are larger than the nuclei and their clear contents have not been identified. The chick thyroid is responsive to as little as 10^{-5} units per ml of culture media and after the 10th day of incubation there is no antrum response to the stimulation. The antra can be identified by phase-contrast microscopy and also in vivo after TSH is added to the chorioallantoic membrane. Electronmicrographic studies by Petrovic and Porte (46) and Daems and Thesingh (8)

have shown that the antra are formed from small microvillous-lined cavities and are located extracellularly. In unpublished work, Shepard has found antra in human thyroid explanted from fetuses of 30–65 mm crown-rump length (Fig. 19.5A and 19.5B). A tempting explanation for the antrum formation is that small intracellular canaliculi, as described above in man (Figs. 19.1–19.3), are present also in the chick, and that they are stimulated to imbibe water at a rate which is greater than their rate of thyroglobin production. As a result, the small microvillous-lined cavities could, by the same mechanism as diagrammed in Figure

19.4 be disgorged into the intercellular spaces. Thesingh (71) has shown that sodium is pumped into explants of chick thyroid undergoing antrum formation, and that ouabain inhibits the production of antra; these findings support her theory that antrum formation is an expression of TSH stimulation of a sodium pump in the cell membranes bordering the antra.

The antrogenic effect of TSH is relatively resistant to heat. In addition, Thesingh (71) has studied a biologically inactive TSH preparation which retains its antrum-inducing activity.

Maturation of Follicles

The histological picture of the embryonic thyroid following follicle formation resembles that of the adult in many ways. In Table 19.1 an estimate of the time of occurrence for this period is detailed for various animals. The interfollicular spaces are now almost entirely filled with blood vessels. The follicular cells in humans are arranged around the colloid cavities and have lost their glycogen content (Taki, 69; Shepard et al., 61). The cytoplasm is more basophilic, reflecting an increase in ribonucleoprotein material. Shepard and co-workers (61) have measured the cell height during these stages in hope of finding evidence of an increase which could be related to thyrotropic hormone stimulation. No such increase was found; however, Taki (69) reports that epithelial cells were occasionally highly columnar at the beginning of the maturation period.

Acid phosphatase and nonspecific esterase activity appears more intense in the apical zones of the follicular cells than in adult thyroid epithelium (Jirásek, 26; Shepard et al., 61). Succinic and lactic dehydrogenase activities were found around the nucleus and also in the apical part of the cells, but no definite increase in activity could be shown histochemically during development (61). Alkaline phosphatase activity has not been detected in fetal thyroid epithelium but remains active in the endothelium (26; Rossi et al., 55; 61).

The colloid during this stage is also similar histochemically to adult colloid in its intensity of staining with PAS, mercury orange, toluidine, ninhydrin-Schiff, Millons, and Sakaguchi reagents. In the very early human stages, toluidine staining is weak in the colloid (61). Taki (69) has described a decreased amount of eosin and PAS staining. The diameter of the follicles at different stages of development in the human fetus have been given by Sugiyama and co-workers (68), Taki (69), and Shepard and co-workers (61). In correlating these last two works it is particularly important to note that Taki refers to crown-heel lengths in some cases, instead of crown-rump lengths.

The scalloplike vacuolization of the outer parts of the colloid cavity, indicative of utilization of thyroid hormone, was first seen in human fetuses of 70–80 mm crown-rump length (61).

Shepard and co-workers have observed intercellular rays radiating out from early colloid cavities (Bierring and Shepard, 5; 61). Some of these rays contain a substance histochemically resembling colloid. In electronmicrographs (Fig. 19.9) most of these spaces contain granular material of varying electron density but nearly always the substance is less dense than adjacent colloid spaces. Although separated only by desmosomes, no connections between the spaces and the colloid cavity have been found. It has been postulated that the formation of these intercellular spaces might act as an additional and emergency method by which the follicle could enlarge its circumference during periods of active growth of colloid cavities. Further studies are necessary before the significance of these findings can be evaluated.

The electronmicroscopic appearance of the thyroid during this maturation stage has been studied by Feldman and co-workers in the rat and Bierring and Shepard in man (10, 5). The usual characteristics of adult thyroid epithelium were seen. They consist of relatively large amounts of rough-surfaced endoplasmic reticulum, a few dense droplets, and microvillous projections into the central colloid cavity. No separate structures have been observed in the colloid.

Biochemical Maturation

In association with the early histogenesis of most fetal glands, sequential steps leading to the synthesis of thyroxine have been found (Table 19.1). The use of radioiodine has allowed the rapid exploration of this area. The earliest stage represented is that in which iodide is trapped, with no evidence of organic binding (calf, Koneff et al., 31; rabbit, Waterman and Gorbman, 79; mouse, Jacobson and Brent, 25; and man, Yamazaki et al., 84). In the fetal mouse (van Heyningen, 76) and in the rat (Geloso, 15) it has not yet been possible to demonstrate trapping before organic binding of iodide. Trun-

nel and Wade (74) have found trapping of iodide by the 5th day in the chick; on the 8th day monoiodotyrosine is detected, followed on the 9th day by diiodotyrosine. At 10 days thyroxine appears, along with the production of colloid. In the frog, Flickinger (11) has shown that monoiodotyrosine and diiodotyrosine appear before thyroxine. Both Geloso (15) and Nataf and Sfez (41) have shown that monoiodotyrosine and diiodotyrosine are present 1 day before thyroxine in the fetal rat thyroid. In human fetuses whose mothers received I^{131} before therapeutic abortions, Yamazaki and co-workers (84) have found iodide concentration at the 92-mm stage. In fetuses over 142 mm, monoiodotyrosine, diiodotyrosine, and triiodothyronine were present. In two 5-week fetuses, no iodide concentration was found. The presence of this sequential development of thyroxine precursors suggests that the enzymes responsible for their synthesis appear sequentially; unfortunately, our knowledge of these enzyme systems is still not fully enough developed to allow direct enzyme activity measurement. The studies of Stanbury (64) and others of patients with goiter have shown that specific steps in thyroxine synthesis may be congenitally absent.

Pickering and co-workers have investigated the later stages of fetal thyroid function in the monkey (48, 49, 50). They have found that radioiodine concentration is ten times higher in the fetal gland than in that of the mother. An increased gradient in the human fetal thyroid has been found by Beirwaltes and co-workers (4).

In monkeys, Pickering and co-workers (48) have shown that although the precursors and thyroxine are both synthesized, these products are retained in the fetal gland, and a larger amount of thyroxine is obtained from the mother's circulation (50). I believe this experimental approach allows an analysis of the actual events under normal conditions, in contradistinction to many of the physiological experiments to be discussed below which require substantial manipulations, and therefore abnormal conditions for analysis. There is a difference between what an organ is able to do and what it actually does.

The protein-bound iodine in fetal monkeys is 1.2 mg/100 ml at 75 days and 4.5 at 150 days (Pickering et al., 48). Although the role of thyroxine-binding protein has not been detailed in the monkey, it has been found by Andreoli and Robbins (2) to increase gradually after 60-mm crown-rump length in the human fetus. Protein-bound iodines of 1.9 and 3.4 mg/100 ml in fetuses of 67 and 117 mm respectively were found.

Numerous authors have reported the concentration of iodide in the human fetal gland (Chapman et al., 7; Hodges et al., 23; Andersen, 1). Although the precise stages have not been ascertained, there is a good correlation between the appearance of large numbers of colloid-filled follicles at 75–80 days of gestation (70–80-mm crown-rump length) and the concentration of iodide (Shepard et al., 61). In addition, there are several examples of radiologic thyroidectomy in the human fetus following treatment of the mother with I^{131} after the 70th gestational day (Russell et al., 57; Hammill et al., 20; Voorhess, 77). It should be pointed out that two of these four

children, in addition to and unrelated to their cretinism, developed a degenerative type of central nervous system disorder.

Another biochemical action of the fetal rat thyroid, the desulfuration of thiourea, was studied by Shepard (59) using radioisotope counting and radio-autographs to show concentration of the S^{35} of thiourea after the 17th day. On the 20th day, paper chromatograms gave evidence that the S^{35} from thiourea had been degraded by the thyroid to sulfate.

Physiological Aspects of Thyroid Development

Limitation of space prevents adequate coverage of this very interesting aspect of thyroid development. Descriptions by Waterman (80), Hwang and Wells (24), Jost (27, 28), and Osorio and Myant (44) contain the details of what is to be summarized below.

In general there are two stages of development. During the first, the thyroid is not sensitive to thyroid stimulation and develops, so to speak, on its own. The second stage, after colloid appears, is characterized by the appearance of a system in which the thyroid products control the production of thyroid-stimulating hormone via hypothalamic-pituitary centers. This control mechanism has been called a negative feedback system. During this stage in mammals there are two parallel negative feedback systems; one in the fetus and the other in the mother. By use of fetal decapitation (Jost, 27), or maternal hypophysectomy (Lampe et al., 32; Hamburger et al., 19; Knobil and Josimovich, 30) with or without thiomide or thyroxine administration (Peterson and Young, 45), it has been possible to study these interrelationships. It may be concluded that the maternal and fetal thyroid-stimulating hormones, although active, do not cross the placenta. However, thyroxine is capable of crossing in either direction. Although the fetal thyroid is reduced in size, it does develop without the fetal hypophysis (24, 28). The role of thyroxine-binding globulin in control of the availability of thyroxine to the fetus has been mentioned, but the analyses by Myant (39) and Osorio and Myant (44) should be cited here.

Certain experiments of nature allow for assumption of the same general relations in man. In anencephalic monsters who lack hypothalamic centers, the thyroid attains normal size at birth (Kind, 29). In limited observations, Henning Andersen and I have failed to observe thyroid hypertrophy in the fetuses of mothers receiving thioamides during the first 120 days of gestation, although during the last trimester of pregnancy it is well known that thioamides will induce fetal thyroid hypertrophy which is sometimes of severe nature. There are some examples of hypothyroid mothers whose condition improved because of the thyroid activity in their normal fetuses. In a reverse direction, the mothers of infants who are athyreotic cretins probably contribute significant amounts of thyroxine, since their children show only minor signs of hypothyroidism at birth (Grumbach and Werner, 18). The above aspects have been summarized by Smith and Montalvo (62) and French and Van Wyk (12).

In studies of interracial transplantation of fetal mouse thyroid, May and Jeanmaire have found that glands from the 16th day made positive implants, whereas glands before or after this period were rejected.

Size of the Thyroid during Development

Finally, in this section, reference will be made to the size of the thyroid gland during development. In the human, Shepard and co-workers (60) found that the thyroid-to-body ratio gradually increased from 0.02 percent at the 30-mm stage to 0.046 percent at the 80-mm stage, when colloid first becomes prominent. After the 80-mm stage, the ratio remains constant at a figure which is close to that of the adult, 0.036 percent. Mitskevich's data (38) on fetal thyroid and body weights for the guinea pig, Astrakhan sheep, rabbit, and rat demonstrate a decrease in all the ratios toward the end of gestation, but his measurements did not include glands before onset of function. The chick thyroid was exceptional in that from the 11th day through hatching it maintains a constant ratio (0.01%). Pickering (48) has found a relatively constant ratio (0.02–0.03%) in the fetal monkey between 75–150 days gestation.

Summary

This chapter has emphasized many of the contributions made during the past decade to understanding the development of the thyroid; earlier work has been briefly summarized.

Understanding of the mechanisms involved in separation of the thyroid primordium from the foregut has not particularly increased nor have specific differences in the primordial epithelium been demonstrated. The contribution of the lateral thyroid to the final substance of the thyroid gland is probably minimal in most mammals. In the prefollicular period it is now recognized, through the use of the electron microscope, that no syncytial arrangement of cells exists.

With the onset of colloid formation, the previously abundant glycogen disappears and cytoplasmic basophilia increases. Also at this point, larger amounts of endoplasmic reticulum appear as the free ribosomes decrease. In the earlier stages of colloid appearance, intracellular accumulation of PAS-positive material is observed with subsequent coalescing of these droplets toward the center of the immature follicle. This process, as observed in the human thyroid, consists of intracellular microvillous-lined canaliculi which gradually enlarge and accumulate an electron-dense material suggestive of colloid. In later stages, these intracellular canaliculi enlarge, move toward the apex of the cell, and disgorge themselves into a common central area which becomes the central colloid cavity. Desmosomes are found in places strategically located in order to contain the disgorged colloidlike material. The early colloid has the histochemical and immunological properties of colloid.

Antrum formation, a specific and extremely sensitive histological response of prefollicular thyroid epithelium to thyroid-stimulating hormone, is described in the chick and man and certain explanations of its mode of formation and role are offered.

Biochemical studies in a number of different species suggest that there is, with maturation, a sequential appearance of the ability of the gland to produce iodinated compounds. This sequence mimics the steps of synthesis of thyroxine in the mature gland. Thus in the earliest stage iodide is trapped, but not bound organically. Subsequently, a stage exists in which the iodotyrosines are made and, finally, a stage in which thyroxine can be synthesized is reached.

The extensive physiological studies of fetal thyroid function are reviewed briefly. A certain amount of evidence suggests that early organogenesis is not affected by thyroid-stimulating hormone, but later a negative feedback system is established between the fetal thyroid and pituitary. Although there is probably no exchange of fetal and maternal thyroid-stimulating hormone, the thyroid gland products, thyroxine and triiodothyronine, pass in either direction across the placenta. In the human it has been shown that the ratio of the thyroid weight to body weight gradually increases until the time of beginning function and thereafter remains relatively constant.

References

1. Andersen, H. J., "Studies of Hypothyroidism in Children," *Acta Pediat. Scand. Suppl.* 125:106–111 (1960).
2. Andreoli, M., and J. Robbins, "Serum Proteins and Thyroxine-Protein Interaction in Early Human Fetuses," *J. Clin. Invest.* 41:1070–1077 (1962).
3. Bakker-Sauer, E. K., "Some Effects of

Thyrotropic Hormone on Thyroid Tissue *in vitro*," *Koninkl. Ned. Acad. Wetenschap. Proc. Ser. C* 64:86–95 (1961).
4. Beierwaltes, W. H., M. T. J. Hilger, and A. Wegst, "Radioiodine Concentration in Fetal Human Thyroid from Fallout," *Health Phys.* 9:1263–1266 (1963).
5. Bierring, F., and T. H. Shepard, "Elec-

tron Microscopic Studies on Early Follicle and Colloid Formation in the Human Fetal Thyroid," *Acta. Pathol. Microbiol. Scand.*, In press (1965).

6. Carpenter, E. "Development of Fetal Rat Thyroid with Special Reference to Uptake of Radioactive Iodine," *J. Exptl. Zool.* 142:247–257 (1959).

7. Chapman, E. M., G. W. Corner, D. Robinson, and R. D. Evans, "Collection of Radioiodine by the Human Fetal Thyroid," *J. Clin. Endocrinol.* 8:717–720 (1948).

8. Daems, W. T., and C. W. Thesingh, "Electron Microscopy of TSH-stimulated Embryonic Chick Thyroids," *5th Intern. Congr. Electron Microscopy*, New York: Academic Press, pp. WW-2 (1962).

9. Dieterlen-Lièvre, F., "Le Rôle de la Thyroïde dans le Développement Embryonnaire des Oiseaux et des Mammifères," *Ann. Biol.* 2:17–34 (1963).

10. Feldman, J. D., J. J. Vazquez, and S. M. Kurtz, "Maturation of Rat Fetal Thyroid," *J. Biophys. Biochem. Cytol.* 11:365–383 (1961).

11. Flickinger, R. A., "Sequential Appearance of Monoiodotyrosine, Diiodotyrosine, and Thyroxine in the Developing Frog Embryo," *Gen. Comp. Endocrinol.* 4:285–289 (1964).

12. French, F. S., and J. J. Van Wyk, "Fetal Hypothyroidism," *J. Pediat.* 64:589–600 (1964).

13. Fujita, H., and M. Machino, "On the Follicle Formation of the Thyroid Gland in the Chick Embryo," *Exptl. Cell Res.* 25:204–207 (1961).

14. Gaillard, P. J., "Growth and Differentiation of Explanted Tissues," *Intern. Rev. Cytol.* 2:331–401 (1953).

15. Geloso, J. P., "Date de l'Entrée en Fonction de la Thyroïde chez le Foetus de Rat," *Compt. Rend. Soc. Biol.* 155:1239–1244 (1961).

16. Gonzales, F., "The Functional Differentiation of the Embryonic Chick Thyroid in Roller Tube Cultures," *Exptl. Cell Res.* 10:181–187 (1956).

17. Gorbman, A., "Problems in the Comparative Morphology and Physiology of the Vertebrate Thyroid Gland," *Comparative Endocrinology*, A. Gorbman, ed. New York: Wiley, pp. 266–282 (1959).

18. Grumbach, M. M., and S. C. Werner, "Transfer of Thyroid Hormone across Human Placenta at Term," *J. Clin. Endocrinol.* 16:1392 (1956).

19. Hamburgh, M., E. H. Sobel, R. Koblin, and A. Rinestone, "Passage of Thyroid Hormone across the Placenta in Intact and Hypophysectomized Rats," *Anat. Record* 144:219–228 (1962).

20. Hammill, G. C., J. A. Jarman, and M. D. Wynne, "Fetal Effects of Radioactive Iodine Therapy in a Pregnant Woman with Thyroid Cancer," *Am. J. Obstet. Gynecol.* 81:1018–1023 (1961).

21. Herman, L., "An Electron-microscopic Study of the Salamander Thyroid during Hormonal Stimulation," *J. Biophys. Biochem. Cytol.* 7:143–150 (1960).

22. Hilfer, S. R., "The Stability of Embryonic Chick Thyroid Cells *in vitro* as Judged by Morphological and Physiological Criteria," *Develop. Biol.* 4:1–21 (1962).

23. Hodges, R. E., T. C. Evans, J. T. Bradbury, and W. C. Keettel, "The Accumulation of Radioactive Iodine by Human Fetal Thyroids," *J. Clin. Endocrinol. Metab.* 15:661–667 (1955).

24. Hwang, U. K., and L. J. Wells, "Hypophysis-thyroid System in the Fetal Rat: Thyroid after Hypophyseoprivia, Thyroxin, Triiodothyronine, Thyrotrophin and Growth Hormone," *Anat. Record* 134:125–142 (1959).

25. Jacobson, A. G., and R. L. Brent, "Radioiodine Concentration by the Fetal Mouse Thyroid," *Endocrinology* 65:408–416 (1959).

26. Jirásek, J. E., "Die Histotopochemie Hydrolytischer Enzyme in der Fetalen Schilddruse des Menschen," *Acta Histochem.* 15:37–41 (1963).

27. Jost, A., "Le Problème des Interrelations Thyréohypophysaires chez le Foetus et l'Action du Propylthiouracile sur la Thyroïde Foetale du Rat," *Rev. Suisse Zool.* 64:821–832 (1957).

28. ———, "Physiologie des Hormones Thyroïdiennes chez les Foetus," *Colloque sur La Thyroide*, C. Chagas, L. C. Lobo, ed. Rio de Janeiro: Inst. Biofisica, Ofic. Gradica Univ. Brazil, pp. 81–112 (1961).

29. Kind, C., "Das endokrine System der Anencephalen mit besonderer Berücksictigung der Schilddrüse," *Helv. Paediat. Acta* 17:244–258 (1962).

30. Knobil, E., and J. B. Josimovich, "Placental Transfer of Thyrotrophic Hormone, Thyroxine, Triiodothyronine and Insulin in the Rat," *Ann. N. Y. Acad. Sci.* 75:895–904 (1958).

31. Koneff, A. A., C. W. Nichols, Jr., J. Wolff, and I. L. Chaikoff, "The Fetal Bovine Thyroid: Morphogenesis as Related to Iodine Accumulation," *Endocrinology* 45:242–249 (1949).

32. Lampe, L., L. Medveczky, and L. Kertész, "Storage of Iodine in the Foetal Thyroid," *Acta Physiol. Acad. Sci. Hung.* 20:385–391 (1961).

33. Machida, Y., and S. Sugiyama, "The Fate of the Ultimobranchial Body of the Guinea Pig and Its Relation to Thyroid Development," *Okajimas Folia Anat. Japon.* 38:73–88 (1962).

34. Maraud, R., and R. Stoll, "Sur la Fonction Thyroïdienne chez l'Embryon des Vertébrés Amniotes," *Biol. Méd. Paris* 50:313–352 (1961).

35. May, R. M., and R. Z. Jeanmaire, "Positive Interracial Grafts of Embryonic Thyroids Implanted into the Eye of Adult Mice." *Ann. N. Y. Acad. Sci.* 99:870–881 (1962).

36. McKay, D. G., E. C. Adams, A. T. Hertig, and S. Donziger, "Histochemical Horizons in Human Embryos II 6 and 7 Millimeter Embryos—Streeter Horizon XIV," *Anat. Record* 126:433–463 (1956).

37. Mess, B., and J. Hámori, "Bioassay of Thyrotrophic Hormone in Blood by I[131] autography in Embryonic Chick Thyroid," *Acta Physiol. Acad. Sci. Hung.* 20:299–303 (1961).

38. Mitskevich, M. S., "Glands of Internal Secretion in the Embryonic Development of Birds and Mammals," *Acad. Sci. USSR. Moscow* pp. 85–89 (1957). (English edition published for the Nat. Sci. Found. and the Dept. Health, Education, and Welfare, U.S.A., by the Israel Program for Scientific Translations (1959).

39. Myant, N. B., "The Passage of Thyroxine and Triiodothyronine from Mother to Foetus in Pregnant Rabbits, with a Note on the Concentration of Protein-bound Iodine in Foetal Serum. *J. Physiol.* 142:329–342 (1958).

40. Nadler, N. J., B. A. Young, C. P. Leblond, and B. Mitmaker, "Elaboration of Thyroglobin in the Thyroid Follicle," *Endocrinology* 74:333–354 (1962).

41. Nataf, B., and M. Sfez, "Début du Fonctionnement de la Thyroide Foetale du Rat," *Compt. Rend. Soc. Biol.* 155:1235–1238 (1961).

42. Norris, E. H., "The Early Morphogenesis of the Human Thyroid Gland," *Am. J. Anat.* 24:433–465 (1918).

43. Orts-Llorca, F., and J. M. Genis Galvez, "On the Morphology of the Primordium of the Thyroid Gland in the Human Embryo," *Acta Anat.* 33:110–121 (1958).

44. Osorio, C., and N. B. Myant, "The Passage of Thyroid Hormone from Mother to Foetus and Its Relation to Foetal Development," *Brit. Med. Bull.* 16:159–164 (1960).

45. Peterson, R. R., and W. C. Young, "The Problem of Placental Permeability for Thyrotrophin, Propylthiouracil and Thyroxine in the Guinea Pig," *Endocrinology* 50:218–225 (1952).

46. Petrovic, A., and A. Porte, "Sur la Formation, en Culture Organotypique, de Lacunes Intercellulaires dans la Thyroïde d'Embryon de Poulet de Six Jours et Demi Étude sous l'Influence de la Thyréostimuline. Étude au Microscope Électronique," *Compt. Rend. Soc. Biol.* 155:1848–1855 (1961).

47. Phillips, J., and B. Schmidt, "A Comparative Study of the Developing Pituitary and Thyroid Glands of the Fetal Rat," *J. Exptl. Zool.* 141:499–518 (1959).

48. Pickering, D. E., and N. E. Kontaxis, "Thyroid Function in the Fetus of the Macaque Monkey. II. Chemical and Morphological Characteristics of the Foetal Thyroid Gland," *J. Endocrinol.* 23:267–275 (1961).

49. ——, K. F. Settergren, and N. E. Kontaxis, "Thyroid Gland Function in the Infant Macaque Monkey," *Am. J. Diseases Children* 105:77–80 (1963).

50. ——, "Maternal Thyroid Hormone in the Developing Fetus," *Am. J. Diseases Children* 107:567–573 (1964).

51. Ponse, K., "L'histolophysiologie Thyroidienne," *Ann. Endocrinol.* 12:266–316 (1951).

52. Porte, A., and A. Petrovic, "Sur les

Caractères Ultrastructuraux de la Thyroïde d'Embryons de Poulets en Culture Organotypique et Leur Signification Fonctionelle," *Compt. Rend. Soc. Biol.* 155:1701–1705 (1961).

53. Romanoff, A. L., "The Thyroid Gland," *Avian Embryology*. New York: Macmillan, pp. 866–878 (1960).

54. Rose, G. G., and J. B. Trunnell, "Thyroid Epithelium in Tissue Cultures: Observations on the Morphology and Functional Capacities of Embryonic Chick Thyroids," *Endocrinology* 64:344–354 (1959).

55. Rossi, F., G. Pescetto, and E. Reale, "Enzymatic Activities in Human Antogenesis: First Synoptic Tables of Histochemical Research," *J. Histochem. Cytochem.* 5:221–235 (1957).

56. Rudnick, D., "Thyroid-forming Potencies of the Early Chick Blastoderm," *J. Exptl. Zool.* 62:287–318 (1932).

57. Russell, K. P., H. Rose, and P. Starr, "The Effects of Radioactive Iodine on Maternal and Fetal Thyroid Function during Pregnancy," *Surg. Gynecol. Obstet.* 104:560–564 (1957).

58. Saxén, L., "The Onset of Thyroid Activity in Relation to the Cytodifferentiation of the Anterior Pituitary," *Acta Anat.* 32:87–100 (1958).

59. Shepard, T. H., "Metabolism of Thiourea S³⁵ by the Fetal Thyroid of the Rat," *Endocrinology* 72:223–230 (1963).

60. ———, H. J. Andersen, and H. Andersen, "The Human Fetal Thyroid. I. It's Weight in Relation to Body Weight, Crown-rump Length, Foot Length and Estimated Gestation Age," *Anat. Record* 148:123–128 (1964).

61. ———, H. Andersen, and H. J. Andersen, "Histochemical Studies of the Human Fetal Thyroid during the First Half of Fetal Life," *Anat. Record* 149:363–380 (1964).

62. Smith, J. D., and J. M. Montalvo, "Maternal-Fetal Relationships in Normal and Abnormal Thyroid Development of the Newborn," *Am. J. Med. Sci.* 241:769–787 (1961).

63. Sobel, H., and H. Leurer, "Effects of Thyrotropin and Thiouracil on Embryonic Chick Thyroid in vitro," *Experimentia* 14:213–214 (1958).

64. Stanbury, J. B., *Familial Goiter in the Metabolic Bases of Inherited Disease*, J. B. Stanbury, J. B. Wyngaarden, D. S. Fredrickson, eds. New York: McGraw-Hill, pp. 273–320 (1960).

65. Stoll, R., R. Maraud, and A. Sparfel, "Recherches sur le Rôle des a Cytomembranes dans le Développement de la Thyroïde et dans Ses Tumeurs," *Arch. Anat. Microscop. Morphol. Exptl.* 48:1–24 (1959).

66. Sugiyama, S., "The Embryonic Development of the Thyroid Gland in the Albino Rat and the Mouse with Special Emphasis on Its Histogenesis," *Okajimas Folia Anat. Japon.* 20:465–506 (1941).

67. ———, A. Taki, Y. Machida, and N. Furihata, "The Significance and Fate of the Ultimobranchial Body in Man in Relation to the Development of the Thyroid Gland," *Okajimas Folia Anat. Japon.* 32:329–340 (1959).

68. ———, ———, A. Nakano, N. Sugiyama, and Y. Yamamoto, "Histological Studies of the Human Thyroid Gland in Middle and Late Prenatal Life," *Okajimas Folia Anat. Japon.* 33:75–84 (1959).

69. Taki, A., "Histological Studies of the Prenatal Development of the Human Thyroid Gland," *Okajimas Folia Anat. Japon.* 32:65–85 (1958).

70. Thesingh, C. W., "The Antrum Phenomenon: a Reaction of Embryonic Chick Thyroid Tissue to TSH Stimulation," *Gen. Comp. Endocrinol.* 2:621–622 (1962).

71. ———, "Antrumvorming in Embryonaal Kippeschildklierweefsel: een Reactie op Thyreotroop Hormoon." Thesis, Leiden pp. 1–82 (1964).

72. Thommes, R. C., "Vasculogenesis in Selected Endocrine Glands of Normal and Hypophysectomized Chick Embryos. The Thyroid," *Growth* 22:243–264 (1958).

73. Tixier-Vidal, A., "Étude Histophysiologique des Relations Hypophyse et Thyroide chez l'Embryon de Poulet," *Arch. Anat. Microscop. Morphol. Exptl.* 47:235–340 (1958).

74. Trunnell, J. B., and P. Wade, "Factors Governing the Development of the Chick Embryo Thyroid. II. Chronology of the Synthesis of Iodinated Compounds Studied by Chromatographic Analysis,"

J. Clin. Endocrinol. Metab. 15:107–117 (1955).

75. Van Dyke, J. H., "The Ultimobranchial Body," *Comparative Endocrinology*, A. Gorbman, ed. New York: Wiley, pp. 320–339 (1959).

76. van Heyningen, H. E., "The Initiation of Thyroid Function in the Mouse," *Endocrinology* 69:720–727 (1961).

77. Voorhess, M. L., "Congenital Hypothyroidism in Infant Following Maternal I^{131}," *J. Pediat.* 62:132–135 (1963).

78. Ward, G. E., J. R. Cantrell, and W. B. Allan, "The Surgical Treatment of Lingual Thyroid," *Ann. Surg.* 139:536–545 (1954).

79. Waterman, A. J., and A. Gorbman, "Development of the Thyroid Gland of the Rabbit," *J. Exptl. Zool.* 132:509–538 (1956).

80. ———, "Development of the Thyroid-Pituitary System in Warm-blooded Amniotes," *Comparative Endocrinology*, A. Gorbman, ed. New York: Wiley, pp. 351–367 (1959).

80a. Weller, L. G., Jr., "Development of the Thyroid, Parathyroid and Thymus Glands in Man," *Contrib. Embryol. Carnegie Inst. Wash.* No. 141, 24:93–139 (1933).

81. Willier, B. H., "Ontogeny of Endocrine Correlation," *Analysis of Development*, B. Willier, P. Weiss, V. Hamburger, eds. Philadelphia: Saunders, pp. 574–619 (1955).

82. Wissig, S. L., "The Anatomy of Secretion in the Follicular Cells of the Thyroid Gland. II. The Effect of Acute Thyrotrophic Hormone Stimulation on the Secretory Apparatus," *J. Cell. Biol.* 16:93–117 (1963).

83. Wollman, S. H., and E. Zwilling, "Radioiodine Metabolism in the Chick Embryo," *Endocrinology* 52:526–535 (1953).

84. Yamazaki, E., A. Naguchi, and D. W. Slingerland, "The Development of Hormonal Biosynthesis in Human Fetal Thyroids," *J. Clin. Endocrinol. Metab.* 19:1437–1439 (1959).

20

The Ontogenesis of the Endocrine Pancreas and Carbohydrate Metabolism

T. Adesanya I. Grillo

Department of Anatomy
University of Ibadan
Ibadan, Nigeria

In mammalian and avian embryos with 35–38 somite pairs, two thickenings or outpocketings of the endodermal lining of the gut represent the earliest morphological indications of the future pancreas. These embryonic buds arise on opposite sides of the early duodenum, at the level of the caudal hepatic diverticulum, to form the dorsal and ventral pancreatic rudiments. The dorsal primordium grows more rapidly than the ventral, extending deep into the mesenchyme of the dorsal mesentery. Soon the two primordia meet and unite, thus producing a joint organ. Grossly, the dorsal pancreas forms most of the mature gland.

Both pancreatic rudiments develop axial ducts, arising directly or indirectly from the duodenal wall. At the ends of the ducts, through branching and rearrangement of the endodermal cells, multiple buds or acini, and islets of Langerhans differentiate (Golosow and Grobstein, 34). This differentiation is dependent upon an interaction between the epithelial endoderm and the mesenchymatous components of the bud (Kallman and Grobstein, 57a; Wessels, 107a).

The islets of the pancreas were first described in 1869 by Langerhans (67) who thought that they were end-apparatus of nerve fibers. Laguesse, the same year, gave the name "Les îlots de Langerhans" to the group of cells and attributed an endocrine function to them. Diamare (25) described two types of cells in the islets but considered them to be the same cells in two different phases of secretory activity. Several important contributions came from Ssobolew (97). He found that after high-carbohydrate food was given to experimental animals the islets became more granular. He ligated the pancreatic duct in some dogs and found that the sclerotic process which affected the animal tissue did not implicate the islet cells. He also observed that glycosuria did not occur in dogs in which the pancreatic ducts had been ligatured. Finally, he observed that islets of Langerhans were absent from the pancreases of two human diabetics.

Ssobolew's experiments followed the discovery of glycogen by Claude Bernard (19). A definite link between carbohydrate metabolism and the internal secretion of the pancreas was therefore established. Ssobolew's experiment showed that the islet cells were parts of an endocrine system unconnected with the duct system of the pancreas, for ligation of the duct did not affect them. On the other hand, he showed that carbohydrate intake of the experimental animal affected the cytology of the islet cells. Finally, the absence of islets of Langerhans which he reported in human diabetics established the link between the islet cells and diabetes — a condition which had been known for many years previously as a disturbance of carbohydrate metabolism. Thus it was possible to attribute an endocrine function to the islet cells and to suggest that their internal secretion controlled carbohydrate metabolism.

Lane (66) described the two cell types, A and B, of the islets of the pancreas and Bensley (11) described a third type of cell which he termed "undifferentiated cells." Bloom (12), however, did not agree that they were undifferentiated cells and called them D cells.

Several attempts were made to isolate the hormone which was called "insulin." Banting and Best (5) prepared the active hormone of the islet system and Abel (1) succeeded in preparing crystalline insulin. Almost 20 years after, Sanger (92) worked out the chemical structure of the hormone.

Early Studies on the Functional Differentiation of β Cells

Investigations of the functional differentiation of the endocrine pancreas followed the first successful extraction of insulin by Banting and Best. Thus Potvin and Aron (89), in their research, set out to correlate the initial appearance of glycogen in embryonic liver cells with the differentiation of islet cells in the developing chick pancreas. Aron (3) had previously found that definitive islets of Langerhans first become evident in chick embryonic pancreas on the 10th day of incubation. He assumed that this cytological differentiation was sufficient evidence for the secretion of insulin.

Guelin-Shedrina (48) followed up the work of Potvin and Aron. She set out to investigate the theory that the initial secretion of insulin by the pancreas initiated glycogen storage in the liver. She injected insulin into the circulation of chick embryos 5–6 days old and fixed the embryos in Carnoy's fluid after 6–24 hours. She reported that glycogen could be detected in the liver of normal control embryos on the 8th day of incubation, and could not be induced earlier than that day by injecting insulin into young embryos. In addition, 3-day-old chick embryos grafted onto the chorioallantoic membranes of older embryos were shown to have liver glycogen earlier than on the 8th day, although they were, presumably, under the influence of the hormones of the host. Her findings were in conflict with those of Potvin and Aron, apparently because her techniques were more sensitive than theirs.

Dalton (23), in a histochemical investigation of chick embryonic liver, found that glycogenesis began in the liver on the 6th day of incubation. His finding has since been confirmed (Lee, 76; Grillo, 37). Although Dalton could not agree with Potvin and Aron that the initial storage of glycogen in the liver was influenced by the first secretion of insulin on the 12th day, he suggested that a relative increase in the utilization of carbohydrate as an energy source occurs between the 10th and 13th day of incubation—the implication being that the pancreatic islets might become functional during that period. Zwilling (110) made a day-to-day estimation of normal blood sugar levels of untreated chick embryos. He reported a rise of blood sugar level between the 12th and 14th days of incubation.

Histogenesis of the Islet Cells

The Chick Embryo

Apart from the investigations of Aron (3) already referred to, Villamil (102) made a histological study of the developing pancreas of the chick embryo. His findings were that on the 6th day of incubation the pancreatic cells were closely packed in cords and formed a solid mass at the distal end of the pancreatic area. From the 8th day of incubation, acinar cells began to differentiate from the primitive pancreatic cells, the process being marked by the appearance of zymogen granules and typical nucleoli. At the same stage (8th day) two kinds of islets become apparent, dark and light, both proceeding from the primitive pancreatic cells. The light islets, developing in small cellular clumps scattered throughout the whole pancreatic area, soon became isolated from the surrounding tissues by a basal membrane and increased in size by mitosis. From the 12th day onward, many cells degenerated and the remaining cells became loaded with β granules, which also began to appear on the 12th day. Dark islets developed only at the distal end of the pancreatic area. Many cells differentiated almost simultaneously at the beginning, while the remaining cells gradually underwent the same process during subsequent days. On the 8th day the α granules appeared, and D granules later on about the 14th day.

Ghiani (32) reported that paraldehyde-fuchsin-positive granules could be observed in chick pancreatic islet β cells from the 14th day of incubation onward.

Lievre (80), in a similar histological study of the chick embryonic pancreas, reported that α islets could be identified on the 8th day of incubation. These islets assume their definitive character on the 15th day. His quantitative study of the islet showed that it reached its greatest relative development at the beginning of organogenesis. The proportion of insular tissue suddenly declined from the 17th day until hatching. Alpha granules first appeared on the 15th day and were very abundant on the 17th day. Four days after hatching, α cells lost almost all of their granulation, but they reaccumulated granules again between the 4th and 11th days after hatching. The first β granulation appeared on the 17th day of incubation. It became very abundant 4 days after hatching but disappeared from the β cells again on the 7th day. On the 11th day after hatching these β granulations again appeared.

If granulation of β cells can be taken as a guide to functional activity, Lievre's data would suggest the 17th day of incubation for the initial secretion of insulin. This result is not in agreement with that of Villamil (102) who had suggested the 12th day of incubation.

The Rat Embryo

Hard (52) has made a similar study of the differentiation of islet cells in the developing pancreas of rat embryos. He described the outgrowth of islet cells from the ducts of the developing pancreas (Fig. 20.1). He noted that the β cells were the first of the islet cells to become recognizable as a specific cell type. According to Hard, these β cells could be seen on the 18th day shortly after the development of a capillary network within the islet. He found that the β granules were at first extremely minute and aggregate close to the nucleus, on the side directed toward the capillary. The Golgi apparatus was found to surround the nucleus of the cells which have these early β granules and appear to be connected with the production of the granules. The granulations increased sharply on the 20th day. There is also a similar increase in the number of β cells on that day.

Hard believed that the α cells do not differentiate fully until postnatal life. However, he pointed out the difficulty of distinguishing α cells from β cells until the latter have granules in them. DEVELOPMENT OF RAT EMBRYO PANCREAS IN VITRO. Several attempts have been made to grow fetal pancreas in organ culture. Pancreas of the rat

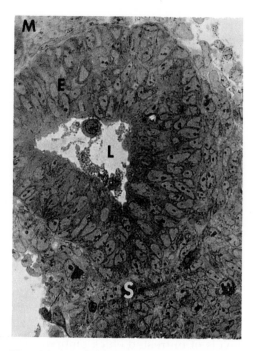

Fig. 20.1 A longitudinal central section through the pancreatic rudiment of an 11-day mouse embryo. The junction between the longitudinally arranged condensed mesenchyme, M, and the epithelium, E, is easily distinguished. The constricted portion of the epithelium, comprising a stalk, S, lies close to the attachment of the rudiment to the duodenal wall. The bulging distal portion of the duct, from which the acini and islets will bud, has an expanded lumen, L. Fixed in osmic-dichromate, dehydrated in acetone-permanganate, embedded in Epon, and stained with Azure II methylene blue. ×310 (From Kallman and Grobstein, *J. Cell Biol.* 20:403–ff., 1964.)

embryo has been cultured by Chen (18) and by Schweisthal, Ceas, and Wells (94). Pancreas of the mouse embryo has been cultured by Wells and Borghese (107) and by Golosow and Grobstein (34). In these investigations, islet cells have been observed in the cultures. The most recent of these investigations, that of Schweisthal, Ceas, and Wells (94) gave a detailed account of the in vitro development of islet cells of the rat embryo. These investigators were obtaining good growth of pancreatic islet, as shown by the increase in the size of islets, and in the number of cells per islet, as well as the increase in the number of islets. They observed that the rate of development of the islets was variable, being slower than that of in vivo growth in most cultured islets, equal in several cases, and faster in a few. They were able to observe granulation in explants. Since these explants were cultured early in development, that is, from the 13th day onward, they were growing completely outside other influences which will exist in vivo. The appearance of β granules in these islets showed that differentiation can occur without other influences outside the cells. Moreover, if taken as evidence for hormone synthesis, the islets may be said to be capable of independent insulin formation. It will be interesting to see when insulin can be detected either histochemically or biochemically in these explanted islets.

The Rabbit Embryo

Bencosme (8) made a careful histological study of the developing pancreas of the rabbit embryo. He described two generations of islets in the rabbit. "Primary" islets, which are derived from the primitive pancreatic cords, from 11½ to 22 days are formed exclusively of primitive β cells. "Secondary" islets appear after the formation of acinar cells. In the 38-mm rabbit embryo, that is, on the 18th day, Bencosme described the cytoplasm of β cells as devoid of granules, but stated that these cells, at that stage, had a "muddy" appearance and were basophilic. Definite granules, according to Bencosme, could not be seen in the

rabbit embryo until just before or after birth.

The Mouse Embryo

Munger (85) studied the pancreas of the mouse embryo with both the light and the electron microscope. Although he could not detect any tinctorial differentiation in both α and β cells by the 13th day, yet with the electron microscope he noticed a few round dense granules in an occasional cell. He suggested that these granules may represent the earliest stages of differentiation of β cells. Definite granules, according to Munger, could be detected with the electron microscope from the 15th day onward although at that stage no β granules could be stained or observed with the light microscope. Because the β granules lacked specific staining reaction to aldehyde fuchsin, he called the cells, on the 15th day, "immature beta cells." Characteristic β cells which could be stained with aldehyde fuchsin appeared on the 17th to 18th day. It is as yet difficult to be certain about what β granules really are. If they represent insulin in the cytoplasm then they must be aggregates of molecules of the hormone, for insulin was detected in embryonic pancreas before mature granulation occurred.

The Human Embryo

The histogenesis of the human pancreas was first studied by Pearce (87) who reported that the earliest appearance of islets occurred at the 54-mm stage. Weichselbaum and Kyrl (106) were the first to describe two cell types in the developing pancreatic islet. Ferner and Stoeckenius (30), in their investigation, found that the first differentiation of α and β cells occurs in the 130-mm embryo. At that stage the α cells outnumber the β cells, and all these cells were mainly in the intercalated ducts. They also described a third undifferentiated type of cell which was agranular.

The most recent comprehensive investigation of the development of the pancreatic islet was by Conklin (21). In his description he states that between the 30- to 40-mm stage (about the 8th week) many epithelial buds grow from the intralobular and intercalated ducts, and are located in the center of the lobule. At the 34-mm stage, some of the buds contain cells which are filled with argyrophilic granules. These argyrophilic cells are few in number, are widely scattered, and are located at the end of the tubules rather than along them. At the 55-mm stage, a few cells appear scattered in the buds; these cells contain granules which can be demonstrated with Masson A. These cells increase in number by the 85-mm stage. They were shown to contain tryptophan when stained by the dimethylaminobenzaldehyde technique and were therefore thought to be α cells. During this period of development, D cells become recognizable. They have large nuclei and stain positively with light green. It is also at the 85-mm stage that small cuboidal cells in the terminal buds show affinity for aldehyde fuchsin and acidic stains which give the cytoplasm and nucleus of the cells a grayish color. Conklin thinks that these may be a form of D cell which other investigators have called "muddy" cells.

Between 90 mm to 110 mm there is a great production of islets which are all still attached to their tubules of origin. All these islets contain the five different types of cells, that is, argyrophilic, α, β, D, and undifferentiated cells. The α cells, which are of the same size as argyrophilic cells, are oval in shape and about 20 μ in diameter. Greater variation in size is shown by D cells. Apart from being present in well-defined islets, all these cells could still be seen located in ducts. At this stage (90 mm to 110 mm) definite β cells with prominent purplish cytoplasmic granules staining with aldehyde fuchsin could be observed in the islets. These β cells assume a central position in the islets and are surrounded by the other cells, that is, they have the "mantelinsel" patterns. Some β cells could also be located within the walls of the ducts. There is an abundance of glycogen in the ducts at this stage.

The vascular pattern within the islets becomes better established between the 110-mm and 150-mm stage. The capillaries look like glomeruli having afferent and efferent capillaries, and sinusoids appear. It is possible that circulation within the islet is established at this stage. During this stage the β cells lose the mantelinsel pattern as adjacent islets fuse and other cell types migrate into the center of the islets. At the 160-mm stage, α cells become degranulated and argentiffin cells increase in number. But at about 180 mm, the argentiffin cells decrease in number. Conklin considers that the periodic degranulation of α and β cells which occurs at this stage may be evidence of secretion. The glycogen which had appeared in the ducts at an earlier stage begins to disappear during this period.

At term the islets are larger and more prominent than in the adult. Beta cells constitute about 60 percent, α cells 30 percent, D cells 5 percent and undifferentiated cells 5 percent of the islets.

Robb (91), Liu, and Potter (81) have confirmed the observations of Conklin and there is the suggestion that both α and β cells are fully developed during the first half of the intra-uterine life of man.

Histochemistry of the Developing Pancreas

The application of a battery of histochemical techniques to the study of the histogenesis of the pancreatic islet has yielded many good results. It is, however, not always easy to interpret the results.

Most histochemical investigations of the developing pancreatic islet have been concerned with demonstrating either (1) the products of the islet cells, that is, the hormones, or the components of these products; or (2) various enzymes thought to be either connected with the differentiation of the islet cells or with the production of the hormones.

Histochemistry of the Hormones

The purpose of the earlier histochemical investigations was to demonstrate some of the amino acids of the hormones. Thus, Barrnett, Marshall, and Seligman (6) employed their dihydroxy-dinaphthyl-disulfide (DDD) method to demonstrate sulfhydryl groups in the islet cells of fetal rat. They suggested that a positive DDD reaction in an islet indicates the presence of insulin in the islet cells. They successfully stained sulfhydryl groups on the 18th day of the development of fetal rat. They stated, however, that the acinar cells of the pancreas stained as heavily as the islet cells. Their finding, that sulfhydryl groups could be demonstrated from the 18th day in the fetal rat islet cells, has recently been confirmed (Grillo, 44).

The DDD reaction has also been used in a study of the histogenesis of the chick embryonic pancreas (Grillo, 41). Positive reaction was obtained from the 14th day of incubation. Thommes (100) reported that he obtained positive DDD reaction in β cells from the 7th day of incubation onward although the amount of stained material was very small. From the 11th to the 13th day he observed a marked increase in the DDD staining reaction as well as in β granulation.

The amino acids, tryptophan and methionine, are present in glucagon (p. 523) but not in insulin. It was therefore thought that a staining reaction for tryptophan would differentiate the glucagon-secreting α cells from the insulin-forming β cells. Glenner and Lillie (33) published their postcoupled *p*-dimethylaminobenzylidene reaction for tryptophan and applied it for the demonstration of α cells. Unfortunately this method has not so far proved successful in the study of the differentiation of cell types of fetal islets. Such an investigation was carried out on the developing pancreas of the chick embryo (Grillo, 40).

Schiebler and Schiessler (93) reported that the disulfide bonds of insulin can be oxidized with acidic permanganate to SO_3 groups which will then stain metachromatically with pseudoisocyanin. They claim that this staining reaction can be regarded as specific for insulin. In a recent investigation, the method was applied to sections of fetal rat pancreas and a positive staining reaction was obtained from the 16th day of gestation onward.

The most specific histochemical methods for hormones devised to date are immunohistochemical techniques. Such a method was developed for the in situ staining of insulin, but is not yet available for glucagon. The fluorescent antibody technique for insulin was developed by Lacy and Davies (61). By this method they obtained precise localized staining of insulin in β cells of islets. The method proved most useful in a recent investigation of the developing fetal rat pancreas. Insulin was successfully demonstrated by the fluorescent antibody technique in the islet of the fetal rat from the 14th day of gestation onward (Grillo, 44). Insulin has also been demonstrated in the pancreas of the 212-mm human embryo (Grillo, 45).

Enzyme Histochemistry of the Developing Islets

Alkaline phosphatase was reported to be present in the cells of the pancreatic islet but not in the β cells (Gomori, 35; Jacoby, 55). Since all cells in the islets of the fetal rat contain alkaline phosphatase which is lost in the cells that develop into β cells, McAlpine (83) has suggested that the loss of alkaline phosphatase may be used as an index of β-cell differentiation. He observed two phases related to the differentiation of β cells. During the first phase, there is a gradual accumulation of alkaline phosphatase within the cells, both α and β. In the second phase the amount of alkaline phosphatase present in the β cells decreases. Alkaline phosphatase has been associated with cell proliferation in the embryo (Willmer, 108; Moog, 83; Hamburger, 53). The disappearance of the enzyme may therefore mark the end of proliferation of undifferentiated cells and the specialization of β cells. The onset of this second phase is from the 16th day when the β cells gradually lose the alkaline phosphatase.

Gössner (36) demonstrated alkaline phosphatase in the damaged β cells of the alloxan-diabetic rat; hence the enzyme cannot be said to be directly associated with secretory function of β cells. Its disappearance before birth may indicate the beginning of the secretory phase.

Acid phosphatase has been demonstrated in islet cells of the pancreas of adult man, rabbit, and rat. Gössner (36) was unable to demonstrate the enzyme in the pancreas of the human fetus during gestation. The enzyme made its first appearance only during the 7th postnatal month. He reported that no acid phosphatase could be demonstrated in the pancreatic islet of a severe juvenile diabetic or in islets of the alloxan-diabetic rat. Although this result may be taken as evidence of a connection between acid phosphatase and insulin storage in the mature islet, the enzyme does not appear to be connected with the onset of insulin formation in the β cells. Moreover, other investigators have found that acid phosphatase is not exclusively restricted to islet cells, but is also present in the exocrine pancreas (Vorbrodt, 104; Lazarus, 72). Pearse (88) has suggested that the enzyme may take part in the formation of disulfide bonds of such proteins as insulin.

Glucose-6-phosphatase has been demonstrated exclusively in the β cells (Lazarus, 71). It is thought that the rate of insulin secretion depends on the amount of glucose-6-phosphatase available for metabolism in β cells. Glucose-6-phosphatase, which is a controlling factor in the formation of glucose-6-phosphate, will ultimately be of importance in insulin secretion.

Because of this possible relation of glucose-6-phosphatase to insulin secretion, an investigation of the enzyme in the islets of the developing pancreas was considered important as a likely index of the onset of β-cell functional activity. Such an investigation has been carried out. In the results of the investigation, reported recently (Grillo, 43, 44), glucose-6-phosphatase was detected histochemically in the pancreatic islet of the chick embryo from the 13th day of incubation onward. In the rat embryo the enzyme was first found in the islet about the 18th day.

Oxidative Enzymes in Islet Cells

The oxidative enzymes, nicotamide–adenine dinucleotide phosphate ($NADPH_2$) diaphorase, nicotamide–adenine dinucleotide (NAD) diaphorase, and glucose-6-phosphate dehydrogenase, have been demonstrated histochemically in the islets of adult animals (Lazarus and Bradshaw, 74). The presence of these enzymes suggests that the glucose metabolism of β cells is via the hexosemonophosphate shunt. It has been suggested (Lazarus and Volk, 75) that this pathway and the synthesis of reduced triphosphopyridine nucleotide may directly be connected with the formation of insulin in β cells. Hence an investigation of the oxidative enzymes in the developing pancreatic islet was of primary importance. Such an investigation was recently carried out (Grillo, 42, 43) and it was found that the enzymes could be demonstrated in the islet of the rat embryo from the 14th to 15th day of gestation and in that of the chick embryo from the 13th day of incubation onward. These dates are similar to those at which insulin was first detected in extracts of embryonic pancreas and the hormone localized in sections by the fluorescent antibody technique.

Biochemical Detection of Insulin in Extracts of Embryonic Pancreas

The development of very sensitive bioassay methods for insulin has made it possible to detect small quantities of the hormone in the embryonic pancreas. The latest methods for insulin assay, the immunoassay methods, have made is possible to detect such a small quantity of the hormone as 6 microunits in adult human serum (Hales and Randle, 51). This exotic technique has not yet been applied in the study of functional differentiation of the pancreas. However, the older biochemical methods of insulin assay have been used.

The rat diaphragm method of insulin assay is based on the observation that insulin increases the glucose uptake of skeletal muscle. Parallel with the enhanced glucose uptake is an increase in glycogen formation. A bioassay method for insulin, based on this observation, was devised by Randle (90). The original technique has been modified so that D-[$^{14}C_6$] glucose was introduced into the incubating medium, usually a bicarbonate buffer, (Battaglia and Randle, 7). The rat diaphragm method has been employed for the detection of insulin in extracts of embryonic pancreas.

Bioassay of Chick Embryonic Pancreatic Extracts

Insulin has been detected in the pancreas of the chick embryo by the rat diaphragm method (Grillo, 41). Extracts of the pancreas were made with acid alcohol following precipitation with trichloroacetic acid. Extracts of the pancreas of the 8-day-old chick embryo showed no insulin activity. Neither did the extracts of 10- or 11-day embryos. The extract of the pancreas of the 12-day-old chick embryo, however, showed strong activity of insulin. The activity increased until the 16th day, after which there was a drop. The activity at 2 days after hatching was less than at 16 days (Fig. 20.2).

From these results it can be concluded that the chick embryonic pancreas begins to synthetize insulin on the 12th day. Leibson, Zheludkova, and Chilingarian (77) have reported that they detected insulin in the blood of chick embryos from 13 days onward. Their results indicate that the secretion of insulin into the circulation probably began almost as soon as the initial synthesis of the hormone, that is, on the 12th day. The positive histochemical demonstration of oxidative enzymes in the islets on the 13th day supports this suggestion (Grillo, 44).

Extracts from the pancreases of rodents have similarly been investigated for insulin activity by the rat diaphragm method (Grillo, 44). Extract of fetal rat pancreas showed no activity of insulin until the 14th day of gestation. The activity of insulin was highest in the extract of 17-day fetal rat pancreas. There was a slight fall on the 18th day (Fig. 20.3).

Extract of fetal rabbit pancreas showed activity of insulin from the 18th day of incubation onward. The extract of the 16-, 17- and 18-day mouse fetal pancreas all showed insulin activity, as did extracts of fetal hamster pancreas.

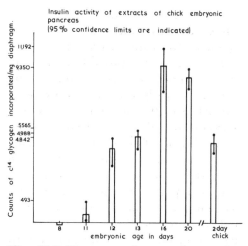

Fig. 20.2 Histogram showing the insulin activity of extracts of chick embryonic pancreas, assayed by the rat-diaphragm technique.

Relationship of Cytological Differentiation to Onset of Insulin Formation

It has been stated that cytological differentiation of β cells, as indicated by the appearance of mature β granulation, occurs late in development, while insulin formation has been found to take place early. In the chick embryo, although tinctorial recognition of β cells of the pancreas was possible on the 12th day, it was not until the 17th day of incubation that mature β granulation occurred. Insulin activity was detected from the 12th day onward.

In the rat embryo, β granulation could not be detected until the 18th day of gestation, yet a significant amount of insulin activity could be detected from the 14th day onward. The positive results obtained by the fluorescent antibody technique confirm the presence of insulin in the pancreatic islet of the 14-day rat embryo.

No definite β granulation was found

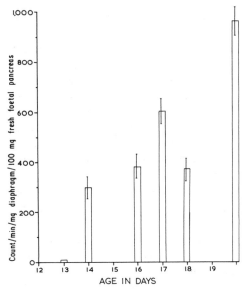

Fig. 20.3 Histogram showing the insulin activity of extracts of the fetal rat pancreas.

in the rabbit embryo throughout gestation, although β cells devoid of granules were reported to have a "muddy" appearance on the 18th day (Bencosme, 8). Insulin was also demonstrated in the fetal rabbit pancreas from the 18th day of gestation onward.

The α Cells and Glucagon

As far back as 1907, Lane described the two cell types of the pancreatic islet. It was, however, not until recently that any definite function was attributed to the α cells of the islets.

Macleod (82) first described the hyperglycemia which occurs immediately after an injection of the crude extract of the pancreas. The initial hyperglycemia was followed by the hypoglycemia known to be the true effect of insulin. Collip (20) confirmed the finding of Macleod. Kimball and Murlin (60) believed that the hyperglycemic effect was caused by a sec-

ond pancreatic hormone and suggested the name "glucagon" for it. Sopp (96) purified the extract and described it as a proteinlike substance which had chemical properties similar to those of insulin. Staub, Sinn, and Behrens (98) crystallized the protein. Three years later, Bromer, Sinn, Staub, and Behren (14) described the hormone as a protein of a minimum molecular weight of 3482, consisting of 29 amino acids. The notable difference from the polypetide of insulin was the absence of cystine, isoleucine, and proline. Instead of these amino acids, glucagon contained methionine and tryptophan. The frequent contamination of glucagon with insulin has been explained by the fact that zinc has a strong binding power and so unites the molecule of glucagon with the imidazole ring of the insulin molecule.

It is now generally accepted that glucagon is secreted by the α cells of the pancreatic islets. This conclusion has been arrived at by way of a number of experiments. The β cells of the pancreas of animals of some species have been destroyed with alloxan and the extracts of such alloxan-diabetic pancreases found to contain glucagon. To rule out the possibility of acinar tissues being the source of glucagon, this exocrine part of the pancreas was destroyed by ligation of the duct. Vuylstake, Cornelis, and de Duve (105) selectively destroyed the α cells of the pancreas with cobalt chloride. Ferner and Runge (29) used Synthaline A (decamethylendiguanidine dihydrochloride) to destroy the α cells. A marked reduction in the amount of glucagon was noticed in the extracts of pancreas treated with these chemicals. Bencosme, Liepa, and Lazarus (9) also made an important contribution by comparing two different portions of the pancreas of a dog. It had previously been observed, histologically, that the ucinate process of the pancreas of the dog is devoid of α cells. Bencosme, Liepa, and Lazarus therefore compared the extract of the ucinate process with the extract of other portions of the pancreas. They found that the ucinate portion contained no glucagon. All evidence therefore points to the α cells as the source of the second pancreatic hormone, glucagon.

The histogenesis of the α cells in the developing pancreases of man, some mammals, and the domestic fowl has already been described. In most of these animals α cells develop and become granulated during embryonic life. Among the few exceptions is the rat, for Hard (52) was unable to observe granulation in the α cells until after birth. Recently, however, Angervall, Hellerstrich, and Hellman (2) reported the luminescent granules in the islet of the fetal rat on the 18th day of gestation, although they could not observe granulation in α cells until after birth. Our unpublished observations agree with these reports, but we have occasionally noticed cells containing tryptophan in the islet of fetal rat from the 18th day of gestation on.

Biochemical Assay of Embryonic Pancreas for Glucagon

The absence of granulation at any particular stage of the development of the pancreas cannot be taken as complete evidence for the nonexistence of a hormone in islets. Hence, a biochemical assay of extracts of embryonic pancreas for the presence of glucagon was desirable.

Pancreatic extracts were prepared as described by Kenny (58), but with some modification to facilitate the use of small quantities of tissues. About 100 mg of pooled embryonic pancreas of the same age were weighed and homogenized in 1 ml of cold acid alcohol (750 ml of absolute ethanol, 250 ml of distilled water, and 15 ml of concentrated hydrochloric acid). The homogenate was allowed to stand overnight in the refrigerator at 4° C. On the next day the homogenate was centrifuged at 0° C. The supernatant was decanted and carefully kept at 4° C. The precipitate was re-extracted twice with 4 ml and 3 ml of acid alcohol for 1 hour, and 30 minutes, respectively. All the three supernatants were pooled, adjusted to pH 7.3 with ammonium hydroxide, and then filtered. The protein fraction was precipitated by adding to each 1 ml of the extract, 1.7 ml of absolute alcohol and 2.8 ml of ether. This mixture was allowed to stand at 0° for 24 hours. The protein precipitate formed was separated by centrifugation at 2000 rpm for about 50 minutes at 4° C. The precipitate was then dried in air and suspended in a solution containing one part of 0.1 M phosphate buffer at pH 7.4 and four parts of 0.9 percent NaA. The suspension was then centrifuged, its precipitate discarded, and the supernatant dialyzed against the saline-phosphate buffer mixture for 72 hours at 4° C. The dialyzate was then freeze-dried.

The procedure for assay was as follows: Well-fed young rabbits weighing 2 to 3 kg were anesthetized with pentobarbital and then bled. The liver was quickly removed, washed, and chilled in ice-cold saline solution for about 5 minutes. A lobe of the liver was blotted and cut into slices less than 1 mm in thickness and weighing 80–90 mg. The thin slices were placed in a chilled Petri dish lined with saline-moistened filter paper until ready for use. The slices were preincubated for 15 minutes in 10 ml of saline-phosphate buffer, pH 7.4 at 37° C. During the preincubation the flasks were stirred every 5 minutes. After 15 minutes of preincubation, the slices were transferred into individual beakers containing 2 ml of the saline-phosphate buffer to which was added 100 μg of glucagon-free insulin and either the unknown pancreatic extract or a known quantity of glucagon standard. The mixture was then incubated for 10 minutes at 37° C in a Dubnoff metabolic shaker at 110 oscillations per minute. At the end of 10 minutes of incubation the slices were washed in cold 0.05 M citrate buffer, pH 6.1, containing 0.1 M NaF, blotted on hard filter paper, and individually homogenized in 1.0 ml of the same citrate buffer. The homogenate was then centrifuged at 3000 rpm for 10 minutes at 0° C; the supernatant was carefully kept for phosphorylase de-

termination. This was performed, as described by Sutherland and Wosilait (99), by measuring the rate of glycogen synthesis from glucose-1-phosphate in the system, using the iodimetric method of Rull and Sutherland.

In a recent publication (Okuno et al., 86), it was discovered that whole rat embryo homogenate of 10–13 days of gestation showed no significant activity for glucagon. Extracts of the gastrointestinal tract and pancreatic tissue of rat embryos of from 14–18 days showed significant glucagonlike activity. The activity in embryonic extracts was higher than that in the gastrointestinal tract of either neonatal or adult rat, or adult spleen. There was a small increase in glucagonlike activity from the 14th day until the 17th day, when there was a sharp drop in the activity. But from the 18th day there was a sharp rise which reached a peak on the 19th day, after which there was a small decrease (Fig. 20.4). Preliminary results of the detection of glucagonlike activity in

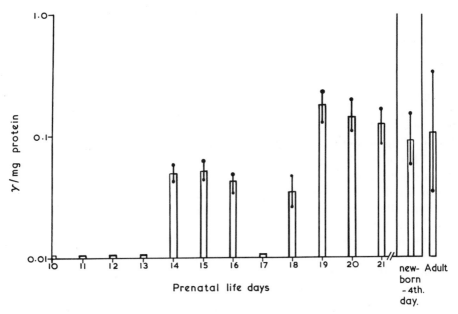

Fig. 20.4 Histogram of glucagonlike activity in the fetal rat.

the pancreas of the chick embryo have been reported elsewhere (Grillo, 40). Further investigations (Grillo, Okuno, Foa, and Price, 45) indicate that glucagonlike activity can be detected in the pancreas of the 9-day chick embryo. At two stages, on the 14th and 17th days, a sharp fall in activity was noticed. After the 17th day the activity rose gradually until hatching. Dieterlen-Livère (26) in a recent publication was able to recognize α granules in the dorsal pancreatic rudiment of the 3-day-old chick embryo and found that the glycogen formation in vitro was inhibited when 3-day pancreatic rudiment was incubated with liver from 6-day chick embryo donors. It has yet to be shown if the homogenate of whole 3-day-old embryos will exhibit glucagonlike activity. However there is no doubt that glucagonlike activity precedes insulinlike activity in the chick.

The Effects of Pancreatic Hormones on Embryonic Tissues

Effects of Insulin

The teratogenic effects of insulin on embryos have been studied by many investigators (Landauer, 63, 64, 65; and Zwilling, 112). The most pronounced effects observed have been on the inhibition of the growth of cartilage and bone. This effect has been obtained both in studies done in vivo as well as in vitro. Zwilling (112) observed that the chief effects of in vivo were a marked degeneration of chondrogenic tissue in the centers, the disturbance of matrix formation and hypertrophy of cartilage in the diaphyses. Zwilling considered that these effects were primarily responsible for the altered conditions of growth. Hay (54) studied the effects of growth hormone and insulin on the growth of embryonic long bones. She found that 0.016 IU of insulin per ml stimulated the growth in length of the bones at the beginning of the culture period. This stimulation of growth was temporary, for the final lengths of the treated bone were shorter than those of the controls. However, she found that insulin increased the wet and dry weights as well as the nitrogen content of the cultured bones. The glycogen formation in, and water content of the hypertrophic cartilage of insulin-treated limb buds were also increased. The results of the experiments of Zwilling and Hay showed that the effects of insulin on cartilage and developing bone were direct, rather than through the production of hypoglycemia. Sevastikoglou (95) in his in vivo experiments showed that injected insulin had an effect on the activity of alkaline phosphatase and on hydroxyproline—the activity of alkaline phosphatase being observed to rise more irregularly than in normal embryonic tibiae, while the level of hydroxyproline was lower than normal.

In addition to studies on the teratogenic effects of insulin, Zwilling, among other investigators, has produced results indicating that embryonic tissues respond early to the hormone. Thus, Zwilling (111) showed that insulin injected into the eggs during various stages of incubation increased the glycogen content of the yolk sac, but lowered the blood sugar level of the vitelline membrane.

The effects of insulin on the chick embryonic heart have recently been studied by Guidotti, Kanameishi, and Foa (50). These investigators found that glucose penetrates the heart of the 5-

day-old chick embryo freely and the intracellular hexokinase system becomes rapidly saturated, thus limiting the rate of glucose uptake. Moreover, the heart of the 5-day chick embryo does not seem to be sensitive to insulin, which did not significantly enhance glucose uptake. On the 7th day of incubation there seems to develop in the embryonic heart an insulin-sensitive glucose transport system which limits the glucose uptake of the heart. That is, from the 7th day onward the chick embryonic heart is no longer freely permeable to glucose, but is sensitive to insulin. This sensitivity to insulin was found to be greater in the 9-day embryo. What this limiting membrane is, is not clearly understood. Electronmicroscopic study of the developing chick embryo heart may prove useful.

Insulin has been found to increase the amount of glycogen in the heart and skeletal muscle of the 16-day chick embryo (Grillo, 37; also Dalton and Hanzal, 24).

Effects of Glucagon

One of the earliest studies on the effects of glucagon on the chick embryo was that of Cavellero (16) who reported that glucagon increased the weight of chick embryos. Elrick, Konigsberg, and Arai (28), on the other hand, have shown that chick embryos treated with glucagon weigh less than normal untreated embryos of the same age.

It is interesting to note that no teratogenic effect of glucagon has been reported. Embryos appear to be able to tolerate high dosages of the hormone. Chen (17) compared the effects of insulin on limb rudiments in tissue culture with the effects of glucagon. He reported that while the expected teratogenic effect of insulin was obtained, glucagon did not cause any abnormality of the limb rudiments.

The effects of glucagon on the levels of liver glycogen and blood sugar in the chick embryo have been studied by several investigators. Grillo (38, 40) reported that glucagon caused glycogenolysis in the liver and heart of chick embryos from 17 days of incubation onward. In the 9-day-old chick embryo, liver glycogen fell from 69 mg to 9 mg per gram wet weight in $1\frac{1}{2}$ hours after glucagon was pipetted onto the yolk sac. It was found that the drastic fall in liver glycogen could be reduced by simultaneous injection of insulin. In this case, liver glycogen decreased only to 27 mg per gram. The resynthesis of liver glycogen in the younger chick embryo, for example, the 9-day embryo, was very slow, recovery of normal level not being attained for over 8–10 hours. Although the effect of glucagon on liver glycogen in older embryos, that is, a 16-day chick embryo, is great (a rapid fall in level being obtained within $1\frac{1}{2}$ hours), the recovery to normal level was observed in a short time. Since the injection of insulin simultaneously with glucagon resulted in a quicker recovery of liver glycogen in the 9-day-old chick embryo, it is tempting to suggest that insulin secretion in older embryos leads to their faster recovery of liver glycogen. Such a slow resynthesis of liver glycogen had indeed been reported to follow the administration of glucagon to an alloxan-diabetic animal. But the slow glycogen resynthesis in young embryos may also reflect a deficiency of adrenocortical or pituitary hormones, which in normal mature animals enhance liver glycogen synthesis (Figs. 20.5–20.11).

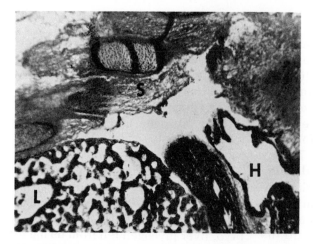

Fig. 20.5

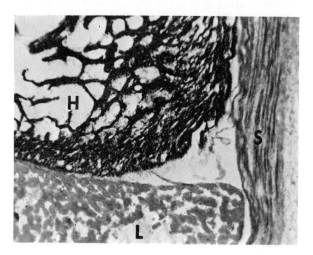

Fig. 20.6

Figs. 20.5–20.7 Parasagittal sections of 9-day chick embryos showing the effects of the injection of glucagon and insulin. **Fig. 20.5** Section of a 9-day-old embryo showing glycogen in L, liver, H, heart, and S, skeletal muscle. **Fig. 20.6** Section of a 9-day-old embryo showing glycogen in H, heart and S, skeletal muscle, but none in L, liver, 3 hours after the injection of 0.05 mg of glucagon. **Fig. 20.7** Section of a 9-day-old embryo showing glycogen in L, liver and S, skeletal muscle 3 hours after injection of 0.25 units of insulin.

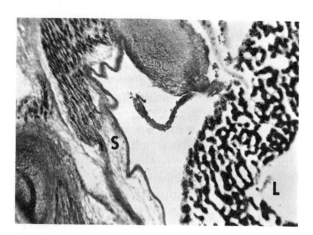

Fig. 20.7

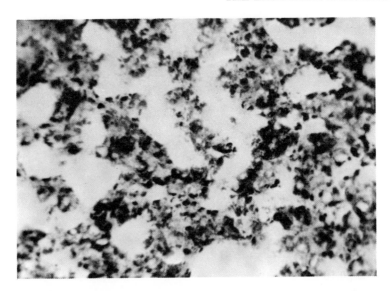

Fig. 20.8

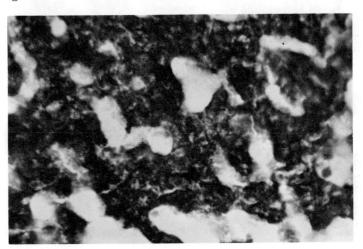

Fig. 20.9

Figs. 20.8–20.11 Sections of livers, stained by the PAS technique, of 11-day-old chick embryos treated in various ways. **Fig. 20.8** Embryo injected with normal saline 3 hours previously. Glycogen still present. **Fig. 20.9** Embryo injected with 0.05 mg of glucagon 3 hours before fixation. Glycogenolysis had occurred.

Thommes and Firling (101) have recently confirmed the findings of Grillo and have shown that chick embryos 6–10 days old require up to 10 days to recover normal levels of liver glycogen and blood glucose, while the 16-day chick embryo attains normal levels in only 6 hours. The ability to respond to glucagon and to synthetize glycogen strongly suggested that embryonic tissues have important enzymes directly connected with glycogen metabolism.

PHOSPHORYLASE IN EMBRYONIC TISSUES. Glucagon is now known to

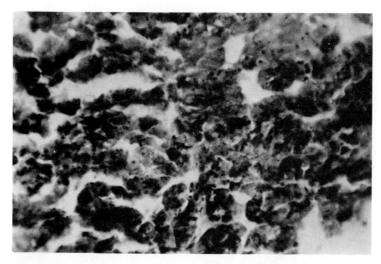

Fig. 20.10

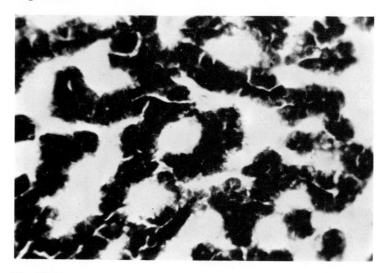

Fig. 20.11

Fig. 20.10 Three hours after the injection of 0.05 mg of glucagon and 0.25 units of insulin. Glycogenesis had begun. **Fig. 20.11** Ten hours after the injection of 0.05 mg of glucagon and 0.25 units of insulin, a greater amount of glycogen had been formed in the liver than found at the end of 3 hours.

stimulate phosphorylase activity in the liver (Sutherland, Wosilait, and Rall, 99) and in the heart (Cornblath, Morgan, and Randle, 22). The preceding report that glucagon causes glycogenolysis in the chick embryonic liver and heart and increases the blood sugar level indicates that phosphorylase would be present in these embryonic tissues. A series of reports have recently confirmed this suggestion. Bot, Andrassy, and Kovacs (13), by biochemical assay, showed that phosphorylase is present in the liver of chick and mammalian embryos. Grillo (37), in a histochemical study, reported that phosphorylase is present in the chick embryonic heart from the 3rd day, in the liver from the 7th day, and in skeletal muscle from the 14th day of incubation. These findings showed glycogen formation in these tissues preceded the appearance of the enzyme.

Okuno and co-workers (86) have recently reported a parallel rise in phosphorylase and glucagonlike activity in the rat embryo during development. This observation indicates a correlation between functional differentiation of α cells of the pancreas and the development of phosphorylase in rat embryonic tissues (Fig. 20.12).

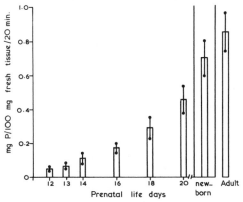

Fig. 20.12 Histogram of the levels of fetal rat liver phosphorylase.

EFFECTS OF GLUCAGON ON EMBRYONIC LIVER PHOSPHORYLASE. Since it is now known that glucagon mediates its glycogenolytic effect on the liver by stimulating the activity of phosphorylase, it was desirable to study the effect of glucagon on embryonic liver phosphorylase. Such an investigation is now in progress. Our preliminary results indicate that glucagon increases the activity of phosphorylase in chick embryo liver (Grillo, unpublished observations).

URIDINE DIPHOSPHATE GLUCOSE-GLYCOGEN SYNTHETASE IN EMBRYONIC TISSUES. It is now generally accepted that glycogen synthesis occurs via the enzymatic pathway of uridine diphosphate glucose (UDPG)–glycogen synthetase, while glycogenolysis occurs through the action of phosphorylase.

Recent investigations (Grillo, et al., 46; and Jacquot, et al., 57), both histochemical and biochemical, reveal that UDPG–glycogen formation begins in the tissues. Moreover, between the 10th and 14th days of incubation in chick embryo, a sharp increase in the activity of the enzyme was noted. This increase coincided with the onset of insulin secretion in the chick embryo and is in agreement with the view (Villar-Palasi and Larner 103) that insulin activates UDPG–glycogen synthetase (Figs. 20.13 and 20.14).

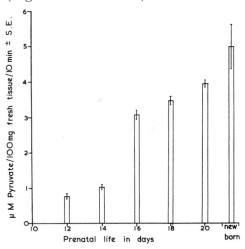

Fig. 20.13 Histogram of the levels of UDPG-glycogen synthetase in fetal rat liver.

Effect of Maternal Diabetes or Hypoglycemia on Fetal Pancreatic Islets

Carlson and Drennan (15) in their studies on the effects of pancreatectomy of pregnant dogs found that if the

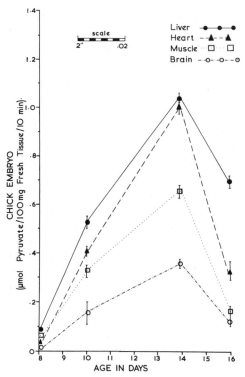

Fig. 20.14 Graph showing the level of UDPG-glycogen synthetase in the liver, heart, skeletal muscle, and brain of the chick embryo.

ternal circulation, (2) the utilization of excess insulin by the fetus, or (3) compensatory adjustments of hormonal mechanisms which are concerned in the regulation of maternal and placental carbohydrate metabolism (Willier, 108).

Dubrenil and Anderodias (27) were the first to describe hypertrophy and hyperplasia of the islets of newborn infants of a diabetic mother. Such a hyperplasia of islets has been experimentally produced in fetal rats either by pancreatectomy or alloxan diabetes of the mother rats (Hultguist, 55; Lawrence, 69; Kim, Rung, Wells, and Lazarow, 59; and Grillo, 42 and 43). The hyperplastic islets were degranulated and found to contain less insulin than islets of normal embryos of the same age (Grillo, 42 and 43). This observation has been interpreted as an evidence of the overactivity of the hyperplastic islets which probably had a rapid turnover of insulin to cope with the hyperglycemia resulting from maternal diabetes. However, the crucial evidence – the presence of a higher serum insulin level or a greater insulin utilization – still remains to be provided.

The effect of hyperinsulinism has been studied by several investigators. Best and Haist (11) found a drop in the insulin content of adult rat pancreas treated with insulin for a week. Frye (31), on the other hand, did not find any obvious degranulation in the islets of either maternal or fetal rats after a week's injection of insulin. The results of preliminary investigations (Grillo, 42) suggested that pancreas of fetuses of rats thus treated daily with insulin contained more insulin than pancreas of fetuses of untreated rats (Fig. 20.15). Latta and Harvey (68) have suggested

operation was performed in the later stages of pregnancy, the pregnant animals did not develop diabetes, while the nonpregnant controls become diabetic. Aron, Stulz, and Simon (4) confirmed their finding. Hultguist (55), in his study of diabetes and pregnancy in rats, observed that fetal loss was greatest if pancreatectomy was done before the 12th day. Lawrence (69) and Lawrence and Contopoulos (70) made a similar study and reported that if alloxan-diabetic rats became pregnant and carried their pregnancy to the 12th day, fetal loss through abortion became less. These results have been interpreted in various ways, as indicating (1) the passage of fetal insulin into ma-

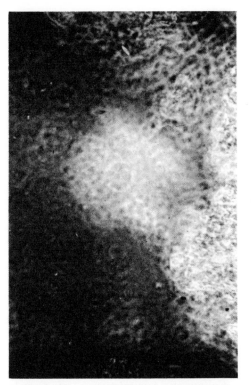

Fig. 20.15 Section of the pancreas of a 212-mm human fetus, showing insulin demonstrated in the islet by the fluorescent antibody technique. Printed from a color negative on Kodak Panatomic X paper, without color filters.

a decreased need for the formation of pancreatic insulin in rats daily receiving prolonged treatment with exogenous insulin. This problem needs to be resolved by future investigations.

Summary

The results of the investigations discussed strongly indicate that the embryonic endocrine pancreas is capable of producing insulin and glucagon. In some species, both insulin and glucagon were detected biochemically in extracts of fetal pancreas before the specific granules could be observed cytologically. Insulin was also detected during development by the fluorescent antibody method.

Pancreatic islets have been grown successfully in vitro. Cells of these islets, grown in organ culture, were observed to have β granules. If β granulation can be used as evidence of insulin formation, then it may be said that pancreatic islets are capable of self-differentiation in vitro.

Enzyme histochemistry of the embryonic pancreas revealed the presence of oxidative enzymes which are important in glucose metabolism. The presence of these enzymes and of glucose-6-phosphatase suggests that embryonic islets are capable of producing and secreting hormones in response to changes in blood glucose levels. Further proof of the secretion of insulin in the embryo has been obtained by the detection of the hormone in the blood of chick embryos.

That the secreted hormones can produce effects on their target organs was proved by the demonstration, in the tissues, of the presence of enzymes directly connected with glycogen metabolism, namely, phosphorylase and UDPG—glycogen synthetase. There appears to be a correlation in the appearance of enzymes in embryonic tissues and the secretion of the pancreatic hormones. Moreover, embryonic tissues have been shown to respond to pancreatic hormones. Thus, insulin increases the glycogen content of embryonic liver while glucagon produces glycogenolysis. Finally, embryonic pancreatic islets can respond to alterations in maternal blood sugar levels. Thus, fetal islets become hyperplastic and degranulated in response to maternal diabetes.

References

1. Abel, J. J., "Crystalline Insulin," *Proc. Natl. Acad. Sci. U.S.* 12:132–136 (1926).

2. Angervall, L., C. Hellerstrom, and B. Hellman, "Development of the Endocrine Pancreas of Rats as Manifested by the Appearance of Argyrophilia and Granulation," *Path. Microbiol. Basel* 25:389–399 (1962).

3. Aron, M. C., "L'evolution Morphologique et Fonctionelle de Îlot Endocrines du Pancreas Embryonnaire," *Arch. Anat. Hist. Embryol.* 1:69–113 (1922).

4. ——, E. Stulz, and R. Simon, "Fonctionnement du Pancreas Foetal après Ablation du Pancreas Maternal," *Compt. Rend. Soc. Biol.* 89:571–573 (1923).

5. Banting, F. G., and C. H. Best, "Pancreatic Extracts," *J. Lab. Clin. Med.* 7: 464–472 (1922).

6. Barrnett, R. J., R. B. Marshall, and A. M. Seligman, "Histochemical Demonstration of Insulin in the Islets of Langerhans," *Endocrinology* 57:419–437 (1955).

7. Battaglia, F. C., and P. J. Randle, "Regulation of Glucose Uptake by Muscle. 4. The Specificity of Monosaccharide Transport System in Rat Diaphragm Muscle," *Biochem. J.* 75:408–416 (1960).

8. Bencosme, S. A., "The Histogenesis and Cytology of the Pancreatic Islets in the Rabbit," *Am. J. Anat.* 96:103–152 (1955).

9. ——, E. Liepa, and S. S. Lazarus, "Glucagon Content of Pancreatic Tissue Devoid of Alpha Cells," *Proc. Soc. Exptl. Biol. Med.* 90:387–391 (1955).

10. Bensley, R. R., "Studies of the Pancreas of the Guinea Pig," *J. Anat.* 12:297–ff. (1911).

11. Best, C. H. and R. E. Haist, "The Effect of Insulin Administration on the Insulin Content of Pancreas," *J. Physiol.* 100: 142–146 (1941).

12. Bloom, W., "New Type of Granular Cells in Islets of Langerhans of Man," *Anat. Record* 49:363–372 (1931).

13. Bot, G., K. O. Andrassy, and E. F. Kovacs, "Enzymic Protein Synthesis in Embryonic Tissues *in vivo*. 1. Glucose-6-phosphatase, Phosphorylase, and Phosphoglucomutase Synthesis in the Liver of Mammalian and Avian Embryos," *Arch. Physiol. Acad. Sci. Hung.* 17:377–381 (1960).

14. Bromer, W. W., O. K. Sinn, A. Staub, and O. K. Behren, "The Amino Acid Sequence of Glucagon," *J. Am. Chem. Soc.* 78:3858–ff. (1956).

15. Carlson, A. J., and F. M. Drennan, "The Control of Pancreatic Diabetes in Pregnancy by the Passage of Internal Secretion of the Pancreas of the Foetus in the Blood of the Mother," *Am. J. Physiol.* 28:361–385 (1911).

16. Cavallero, C., "Pancreatic Islets and Growth," *Ciba Found. Colloq. Endocrinol. Internal Secretions of Pancreas,* (2) Boston: Little, Brown, Vol. 9, pp. 266–284 (1956).

17. Chen, J. M., "The Effect of Insulin on Embryonic Limb-bones Cultivated *in vitro*," *J. Physiol.* 125:148–162 (1954).

18. ——, "The Cultivation in Fluid Medium of Organised Liver, Pancreas and Other Tissues of Foetal Rats," *Exptl. Cell. Res.* 7:518–529 (1954).

19. Claude, B., "Sur le Mechanisms de la Formation du Sucre dans le Foie," *Comp. Rend. Acad. Sci.* 41:461–ff. (1855).

20. Collip, J. B., "Delayed Manifestation of the Physiological Effects of Insulin Following Administration of Certain Pancreatic Extracts," *Am. J. Physiol.* 63: 391–ff. (1923).

21. Conklin, J. L., *The Development of the Pancreas of the Human Foetus.* Ann Arbor, Mich.: University Microfilms Inc., pp. 61–2739 (1961).

22. Cornblath, M., H. E. Morgan, and P. J. Randle, "Glycogenolysis and Phosphorylase Activation by Glucagon and Anoxia in the Perfused Rat Embryo," *Federation Proc.* 20:85 (1961).

23. Dalton, A. J., "The Functional Differentiation of the Hepatic Cells of the Chick Embryo," *Anat. Record* 68:393–409 (1937).

24. ——, and R. F. Hanzal, "Carbohydrate Metabolism of Chick Embryo," *Proc. Soc. Exptl. Biol. Med.* 45:278–281 (1940).

25. Diamare, V., "Studii Comparativi Salle Isole di Langerhans del Pancreas," *Intern. Monotschr. Anat. Physiol.* 16:155 (1899).

26. Dieterlen-Lièvre, "Demonstration de l'Activite Precoce des Cellules a du Pancreas chez l'Embryon de Poulet," *Compt. Rend. Acad. Sci.* 256:1597–1599 (1963).

27. Dubrenil, G., and Anderodias, "Ilots de Langerhans Géants chez un Nouveau-né Tissue de Mere Glycosurique," *Compt. Rend. Soc. Biol.* 83:1490–1493 (1920).

28. Elrick, H., I. R. Konigsberg, and Y. Arai, "Effect of Glucagon on Growth of Chick Embryo," *Proc. Soc. Exptl. Biol. Med.* 97:542–544 (1958).

29. Ferner, H. and W. Runge, "Synthalin A as Selective Mitotic Poison Acting on α Cells of the Islets of Langerhans," *Science* 122:420 (1955).

30. ——, and W. Stoechkenius, "Die Cytogenese des Insetsystenis beim Menschen," *Z. Zellforsch. Mikroskop. Anat.* 35:147–175 (1951).

31. Frye, B. E., "The Differentiation of the Endocrine Pancreas in Foetuses of Alloxan Diabetes and Insulin-treated Rats," *J. Morphol.* 101:325–350 (1957).

32. Ghiani, P., "Evoluvione Citologica del Pancreas Endocrino Ricerche in Embrione di Pollo," *Atti Accad. Ligure Sci. Lettere* 13:1–16 (1956).

33. Glenner, G. G., and R. D. Lillie, "A Rhodocyan Technique for Staining the Anterior Pituitary," *Stan. Technol.* 32: 187–190 (1957).

34. Golosow, N., and C. Grobstein, "Epithelic-mesenchymal Interaction in Pancreatic Morphogenesis," *Develop. Biol.* 4:242–255 (1962).

35. Gomori, G. E., "Distribution of Phosphatase in Normal Organ and Tissues," *J. Cellular Comp. Physiol.* 17:71–84 (1941).

36. Gössner, W., "Zur Enzymchemie der Langerhans schen Insehin," *Verh. Dtsch. Ges. Pathol.* 42:125–130 (1959).

37. Grillo, T. A. I., *A Histochemical Study of Carbohydrate Metabolism in the Developing Chick Embryo.* Thesis for the degree of Ph.D. Cambridge University, England (1960).

38. ——, "The Response of Embryonic Tissues to Glucagon," *Am. J. Diseases Children* 102:568–569 (1961).

39. ——, "The Histochemical Study of Phosphorylase in the Tissue of the Chick Embryo," *J. Histochem. Cytochem.* 9: 389–391 (1961).

40. ——, "The Ontogeny of Function of the α Cells of the Pancreas of the Chick Embryo," *J. Anat.* 95:284 (1961).

41. ——, "The Ontogeny of Insulin Secretion in the Chick Embryo," *J. Endocrinol.* 22:285–292 (1961).

42. ——, "Foetal Pancreatic Insulin in Foetuses of Normal, Diabetic, Hyperinsulinic and Andrenalectomized Rodents," *J. Anat.* 97:155–156 (1963).

43. ——, "Enzymatic and Endocrine Correlation in the Development of Carbohydrate Metabolism," *Folia Histochem. Cytochem.* 1:125–126 (1963).

44. ——, "The Occurrence of Insulin in Pancreases of Foetuses of Some Rodents," *J. Endocrinol.* 31:67–73 (1964).

45. ——, Unpublished observations (1964).

46. ——, G. Okuno, P. P. Foa, and S. Price, "The Activity of Uridine Diphosphate Glucose–glycogen Synthetase in Some Embryonic Tissues," *J. Histochem. Cytochem.* 12:275–280 (1964).

47. ——, ——, ——, and ——, Unpublished observations (1964).

48. Guelin-Shedrina, A. "Fonction Glycogénique du Foie chez l'Embryon de Poulet," *Compt. Rend. Soc. Biol. Paris* 121:144–146 (1936).

49. Guidotti, G., and P. P. Foa, "Development of an Insulin-sensitive Glucose Transport System in Chick Embryo Hearts," *Am. J. Physiol.* 201:869–872 (1961).

50. ——, D. Kanameishi, and P. P. Foa, "Chick Embryo Heart as a Tool for Studying Cell Permeability and Insulin Action," *Am. J. Physiol.* 201:863–868 (1961).

51. Hales, C. N., and P. J. Randle, "Immunoassay of Insulin with Insulin-antibody Precipitate," *Biochem. J.* 88:137–145 (1963).

52. Hard, W. L., "The Origin and Differentiation of the Alpha Beta Cells in the Pancreatic Islets of the Rat," *Am. J. Anat.* 75:369–403 (1944).

53. Hamburger, V., "The Mitotic Patterns in the Spinal Cord of the Chick Embryo and Their Relation to Histogenetic Processes," *J. Comp. Neurol.* 88:221–283 (1948).

54. Hay, M. F., "The Effect of Growth Hormone and Insulin on Limb-bone Rudiments of the Embryonic Chick Cultivated *in vitro*," *J. Physiol.* 144:490–504 (1958).

55. Hultguist, G. T., "Diabetes and Pregnancy: an Animal Study," *Acta Pathol. Microbiol. Scand.* 27:695–719 (1950).

56. Jacoby, F., "The Pancreas and Alkaline Phosphorase," *Nature* 158:268–269 (1946).

57. Jacquot, R. L., N. Kretchmer, K. K. Tsuboi, I. C. Taylor, and H. McNamara, "Glycogen Metabolism in Fetal Liver," *Am. J. Diseases Children* 102:476–477 (1961).

57a. Kallman, F., and C. Grobstein, "Fine Structure of Differentiating Mouse Pancreatic Exocrine Cells in Transfilter Culture," *J. Cell Biol.* 20:399–413 (1964).

58. Kenny, A. J., "Extractable Glucagon of the Human Pancreas," *J. Clin. Endocrinol. Metab.* 15:1089–1105 (1955).

59. Kim, J. N., W. Runge, L. J. Wells, and A. Lazarow, "Pancreatic Islets and Blood Sugars in Prenatal and Postnatal Offspring from Diabetic Rats: Beta Granulation and Glycogen Infiltration," *Anat. Record* 138:239–248 (1960).

60. Kimball, C. P., and J. R. Murlin, "Aqueous Extracts of Pancreas. III. Some Precipitation Reaction of Insulin," *J. Biol. Chem.* 58:337 (1923).

61. Lacy, P. E., and J. Davies, "Demonstration of Insulin in Mammalian Pancreas by the Fluorescent Antibody Method," *Stan. Technol.* 34:85–89 (1959).

62. Laguesse, E., "Recherches sur l'Histogenie du Pancreas chez le Monton," *J. Anat. Physiol.* 32:209–255 (1869).

63. Landauer, W., "Insulin-induced Abnormalities of Beak, Extremities and Eyes in Chickens," *J. Exptl. Zool.* 105: 145–172 (1947).

64. ———, "Malformation of Chicken Embryos Produced by Boric Acid and the Probable Role of Riboflavin in Their Origin," *J. Exptl. Zool.* 120:469–508 (1952).

65. ———, "On the Chemical Production of Developmental Abnormalities and of Phenocopies in Chicken Embryos," *J. Cellular Comp. Physiol.* Suppl. 1, 34: 261–305 (1954).

66. Lane, M. A., "The Cytological Characters of the Areas of Langerhans," *Am. J. Anat.* 7:409–422 (1907).

67. Langerhans, P., "Beitrage zur Mikroskopischen Anatomie der Bauchspeicheldruse," Inaugural dissertation, Berlin: G. Lange (1869).

68. Latta, J. S., and H. T. Harvey, "Changes in the Islets of Langerhans of the Albino Rat Induced by Insulin Administration," *Anat. Record* 82:281–296 (1942).

69. Lawrence, A. M., "Studies in Reproductive Physiology of the Alloxan-Induced Diabetic Female Rat," Thesis for the degree of Ph.D. University of California, Berkeley, California (1957).

70. ———, and A. N. Contoponlos, "Reproductive Performance in the Alloxan-diabetic Female Rat," *Acta Endocrinol.* 33: 175–184 (1960).

71. Lazarus, S. S., "Demonstration of Glucose-6-phosphatase in Mammalian Pancreas," *Proc. Soc. Exptl. Biol. Med.* 101: 819–822 (1959).

72. ———, "Acid and Glucose-6-phosphatase Activity of Pancreatic β Cells after Cortisone and Sulfonylureas," *Proc. Soc. Exper. Biol. & Med.*, 102:303–306 (1959).

73. ———, H. Barden, and M. Bradshaw, "Enzymatic Histochemistry of Pancreatic β Cells and Mechanism of Alloxan Toxicity," *A.M.A. Arch. Pathol.* 73:210–ff. (1962).

74. ———, and M. S. Bradshaw, "Oxidative Pathways in Pancreatic β Cells," *Proc. Soc. Exptl. Biol. Med.* 102:463–468 (1959).

75. ———, and B. W. Volk, "Pancreas in Maturity—Onset Diabetes," *A.M.A. Arch. Pathol.* 71:44 (1962).

76. Lee, W. H., "The Glycogen Content of the Various Tissues in the Chick Embryo," *Anat. Record* 110:465–474 (1951).

77. Leibson, L. G., Z. P. Zheludkova, and L. I. Chilingarian, "Insulin Secretion of the Pancreas of the Chick Embryo," *Bull. Exptl. Biol. Med. USSR* 7:24–26 (1961).

78. Leloir, L. F., and S. H. Goldenberg, "Synthesis of Glycogen from Uridine Diphosphate Glucose in Liver," *J. Biol. Chem.* 235:919–923 (1960).

79. Levine, H. J., and G. G. Glenner, "Observations on Tryptophan Staining of the Pancreatic Alpha Cells," *J. Natl. Cancer Inst.* 20:63–68 (1958).

80. Lievre, F. D., "Contribution, a l'Histogenese du Pancreas Endocrine chez l'Embryon de Poulet," *Arch. Anat. Microscop. Morphol. Exptl.* 46:61–80 (1957).

81. Liu, H. M., and E. L. Potter, "Development of the Human Pancreas," *A.M.A. Arch. Pathol.* 74:439–451 (1962).

82. Macleod, J. J. R., "The Source of In-

sulin: A Study of the Effect Produced on Blood Sugar by Extracts of the Pancreas and Principal Islets of Fishes," *J. Metab. Res.* 2:149 (1962).

83. McAlpine, R. J., "Alkaline Phosphatase in the Developing Endocrine Pancreas of the Albino Rat," *Anat. Record* 109: 189–216 (1951).

84. Moog, F., "The Distribution of Phosphatase in the Spinal Cord of the Chick Embryo of One of Eight Days Incubation," *Proc. Natl. Acad. Sci. U.S.* 29:176–183 (1943).

85. Munger, B., "A Light and Electron Microscopic Study of Cellular Differentiation in the Pancreatic Islets of the Mouse," *Am. J. Anat.* 103:275–312 (1958).

86. Okuno, G., S. Price, T. A. I. Grillo, and P. P. Foa, "Development of Phosphorylase and of Phosphorylase Activating (Glucagon-like) Substances in the Rat Embryo," *Gen. and Comp. Endocrinol.* 4:446–451 (1964).

87. Pearce, R. M., "The Development of the Islands of Langerhans in the Human Embryo," *Am. J. Anat.* 2:445 (1903).

88. Pearse, A. G. E., *Histochemistry*, 2nd edition. Boston: Little, Brown, p. 182 (1960).

89. Potvin, R., and M. Aron, "Recherches sur l'Evolution Embryonnaire des Îlots Pancreatiques Endocrines chez le Poulet," *Compt. Rend. Biol.* 96:267–269 (1927).

90. Randle, P. J., "The Assay of Insulin *in vitro* by Means of Glucose Uptake of the Isolated Rat Diaphragm," *J. Endocrinol.* 14:82–86 (1956).

91. Robb, P., "The Development of the Islands of Langerhans in Man," *Arch. Diseases Children* 36:229–ff. (1961).

92. Sanger, F., "The Free Amino Groups of Insulin," *Biochem. J.* 39:507–515 (1945).

93. Schiebler, T. H., and S. Schiessler, "Über den Nachweis von Insulin mit den Metachromatisch Reagierenden Pseudo-isocyaninen," *Histochemie* 1:445–465 (1959).

94. Schweisthal, M. R., M. P. Ceas, and L. J. Wells, "Development of the Pancreas of the Rat Embryo *in vitro*: Islets and Acini," *Anat. Record* 147:149–155 (1963).

95. Sevastikoglou, J. A., "Biochemical Studies on the Skeleton Insulin-induced Micromelia in Chicken," *Acta Paediatric* 51:60–64 (1962).

96. Sopp, J. W., "Über das Glukagon, die Hyper Glykamisierende Substanz des Pankreas," *Z. Ges. Exptl. Med.* 96:817 (1935).

97. Ssobolew, L. W., "Über die Structur der Bauchspeicheldrüse unter Gewissen Pathologischen Bedingugen," *Contralbt. Allg. Pathol. Anat.* 11:202–ff. (1900).

98. Staub, A., L. Sinn, and O. K. Behren, "Purification and Crystallization of Hyperglycemic-Glycogenolytic Factor (H.G.F.)," *Science* 117:628–629 (1953).

99. Sutherland, E. W., W. D. Wosilait, and T. W. Rall, "The Relationship of Epinephrine and Glucagon to Liver Phosphorylase. I. Liver Phosphorylase; Preparation and Properties," *J. Biol. Chem.* 218:459–468 (1956).

100. Thommes, R. C., "A Histochemical Study of Insulin in the Chick Embryo Pancreas," *Growth* 24:69–80 (1960).

101. ———, and C. E. Firling, "Blood Glucose and Liver Glycogen Levels in Glucagon-Treated Chick Embryos," *Gen. Comp. Endocrinol.* 4:1–8 (1964).

102. Villamil, M. F., "Citogenesis del Pancreas Exoy Endocrine en Embriones de Polio," *Rev. Soc. Argent. Biol.* 18:416–424 (1942).

103. Villar-Palasi, C., and J. Larner, "Insulin-mediated Effect on the Activity of UDPG–glycogen Transglucosylase of Muscle," *Biochem. Biophys. Acta* 39: 171–173 (1960).

104. Vorbrodt, A., "Histochemically Demonstrable Phosphatase and Protein Synthesis," *Exptl. Cell Res.* 15:1–19 (1958).

105. Vuylstake, G. A., G. Cornelis, and C. de Duve, "Influence de Traitment su Cobalt sur le Contenu en Facteur. HGF du Pancreas de Cobaye," *Arch. Lutern. Physiol.* 60:128 (1952).

106. Wekhselbaum, A., and J. Kyrl, "Über das Verhalten der Langerhansschen Inseln des Menschlichen Pankreas im fötalen und Postfötalen Leben," *Arch. Mikroskop. Anat.* 74:223–258 (1909).

107. Wells, L. J., and E. Borghese, "Sviluppo Embrionale *in vitro* del Pancreas di Topo," *Bull. Zool.* 28:235–239 (1961).

107a. Wessells, N. K., "DNA Synthesis, Mitosis and Differentiation in Pancreatic

Acinar Cells *in vitro*," *J. Cell Biol.* 20: 415–433 (1964).

108. Willier, B. H., "Ontogeny of Endocrine Correlation," *Analysis of Development*, Philadelphia: Saunders, pp. 574–619 (1955).

109. Willmer, E. N., "The Localization of Phosphatase in Tissue Culture," *J. Exptl. Biol.* 19:11–13 (1942).

110. Zwilling, E., "Association of Hypoglycemia with Insulin Micromelia in Chick Embryo," *J. Exptl. Zool.* 109: 283–ff. (1948).

111. ———, "Carbohydrate Metabolism in Insulin-treated Chick Embryos," *Arch. Biochem. Biophys.* 33:228–242 (1951).

112. ———, "Micromelia as a Direct Effect of Insulin-evidence from *in vitro* and *in vivo* Experiments," *J. Morphol.* 104: 159–174 (1959).

21

Experimental Analysis of Lymphoid Differentiation in the Mammalian Thymus and Spleen

ROBERT AUERBACH[*]

Department of Zoology
University of Wisconsin
Madison, Wisconsin

An understanding of lymphoid differentiation is an essential prerequisite to cellular characterization of several crucial biological phenomena such as homograft rejection, antibody formation, leukemogenesis, and radiation recovery; yet the amount of basic experimental information on mammalian lymphoid morphogenesis is surprisingly scant. The descriptive literature concerning spleen and thymus development dates back to the early part of this century when such great histologists as Maximow, Beard, Hammar, Jolly, and Norris performed their classical studies on comparative lymphoid morphogenesis (Hammar, 27; Klemperer, 28; Maximow, 32, 33, 34; Ohno, 42; Thiel, 47). More recently, a most comprehensive and beautifully executed descriptive study of lymphoid development in the newborn opossum has been added to the literature (Block, 16), and in view of the fact that the opossum at birth is just beginning its lymphoid development, this study properly should be classed as embryological in nature. New descriptive information obtained through the use of electronmicroscopy is now available for mouse and hamster lymphoid embryogenesis (Shaw, 44).

In contrast to the excellent descriptive literature, the number of experimental investigations of thymus and spleen differentiation is quite re-

[*] Original research work reported in this paper was supported by grants C-5281 from the National Institutes of Health and G-19384 from the National Science Foundation. Technical assistance was provided by B. Alter, L. Kubai, E. M. Morin, and A. Tallungen.

stricted. Specific information comes primarily from tissue culture analysis of mouse embryonic rudiments, from transplantation of organs to chicken embryos, and to the anterior eye chamber of adult mice, from host responses to tissue grafts, from studies of regenerative phenomena after irradiation or hormone treatment, from differentiative changes induced by antigens, and from pathogenesis associated with tumorigenesis. Of these studies, only the first two groups are clearly concerned with embryonic processes; it is on these groups of experiments that this chapter will focus attention.

Control of Thymus Differentiation

The 12-day mouse thymus rudiment, comprised of about 4000 to 8000 cells, can readily be isolated by dissection and grown as a graft in the anterior eye chamber of adult mice (Auerbach, 3, 4) as a transplant on the chick chorioallantoic membrane (Auerbach, 4; Grégoire, 23) or in tissue culture, as shown in Figure 21.1 (Auerbach, 2, 3, 5, 10; Ball, 15). Seven days after transplantation — after an interval of time roughly equivalent to that needed for reaching neonatal life — such grafts or cultures develop from a simple epitheliomesenchymal rudiment to complex, mature lymphoid organs, complete with large, medium, and small lymphocytes, epithelial cells, and reticular material. During this development, all the transitions in histogenesis associated with normal differentiation in vivo take place in corresponding sequence. It should be noted that the discussion of these studies by Block (16) is based on photographs published for 7-day cultures and transplants. By this time the intermediate events have already taken place.

By using techniques of trypsin separation of tissue components the thymus has been separated into its epithelial and mesenchymal portions and these were subsequently grown in tissue culture either singly after recombination, or in combination with other test tissues, as in Figure 21.2A (cf. also Grégoire, 23, 24). When either component is isolated singly at a glass-clot interface, no further development takes place, mesenchyme spreading into a thin sheet and epithelium remaining rounded up with peripheral loss of cells (Fig. 21.2B). Recombination of the two tissues leads to the re-initiation of morphogenesis (Fig. 21.2C). Thus development of the thymus in vitro appears to depend on interaction of the two constituent tissues.

In order to determine the specificity of this tissue interdependence, various tissues from a wide variety of sources (mouse salivary gland mesenchyme, kidney mesenchyme, kidney epithelium, lung mesenchyme, lung epithelium, spinal cord, spleen, limb bud mesenchyme, chick salivary gland mesenchyme, chick bursa of Fabricius mesenchyme) were combined with thymus epithelium (Figure 21.2C–I). It was found that thymus epithelial morphogenesis required undifferentiated mesenchyme, but that mesenchyme from almost any of these sources was able to serve as a stimulus for differentiation. Interestingly, under the imposed conditions of culture each mesenchyme had its own characteristic impact on the morphogenetic pattern of epithelial outgrowth. Subsequent studies by McLoughlin, Gosolow and

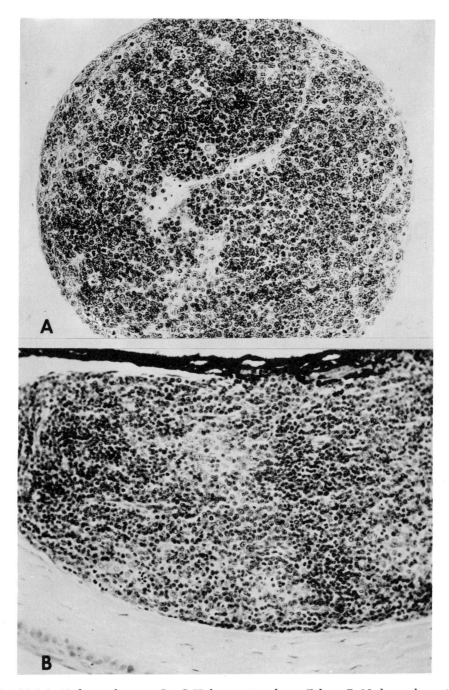

Fig. 21.1 *A*. 12-day embryonic C × C₃H thymus in culture, 7 days. *B*. 12-day embryonic C × C₃H thymus in anterior eye chamber of adult isologous male mouse.

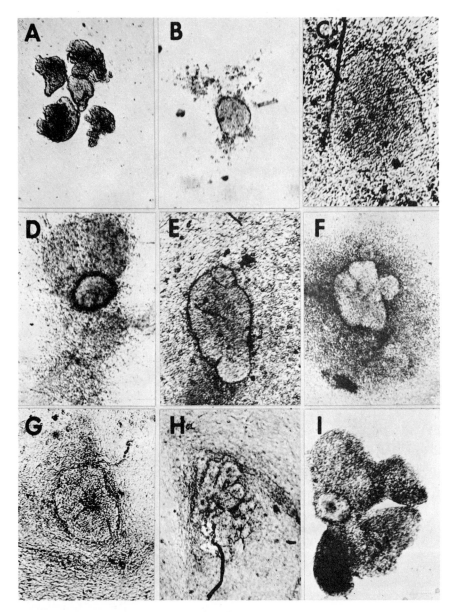

Fig. 21.2 *A.* Cluster culture at time of explantation, showing thymus epithelium surrounded by pieces of mesenchyme. *B.* Epithelial isolate, 4 days in vitro. *C.* Recombination of thymus epithelium with thymus mesenchyme, 4 days. *D.* Recombination of thymus epithelium with submandibular mesenchyme, 1 day. *E.* Same culture, 4 days. *F.* Recombination of thymus epithelium with lung mesenchyme, 4 days. *G.* Recombination of thymus epithelium with metanephrogenic mesenchyme, 4 days. *H.* Same culture, 6 days. *I.* Recombination of thymus epithelium with spinal cord, 4 days. Magnification, all ×40.

Grobstein, and Muthukaruppan suggest that response of epithelium to several types of mesenchyme is not a property unique to the thymus (cf. Auerbach, 2, 11). It would appear that morphogenetic pattern is more sensitive to mesenchymal variation than is histogenesis.

Further information on the nature of the mesenchymal influence was obtained through the interposition of millipore filter membranes between reacting tissues (Auerbach, 12). When epithelium and mesenchyme were placed on opposite sides of a 20 μ thick HA millipore filter, morphogenesis ensued. A critical extension of these studies to include filters of varying thickness and porosities (cf. Grobstein, 25, 26) has not been attempted but it is clear that cell infiltration and extensive cell contact are not required.

Origin of Lymphoid Cells in the Developing Thymus

The origin of thymic lymphocytes has long been discussed on the basis of histological observations, but critical experimental evidence has only recently become available. Since mouse and chick cells can be readily distinguished from each other by their differential stainability with hematoxylin as well as by their nuclear morphology and size, appropriate combinations of chick and mouse components were made and the composites grown either in vitro in chicken hosts or in normal or irradiated mouse hosts (Auerbach, 4, 9, 10). These studies have demonstrated that the mesenchyme, in addition to providing a stimulus to morphogenesis, gives rise to the stromal elements of the developing organ, but

that the epithelium is the main, if not the only, source of lymphoid cells of the developing thymus.[1]

While extrapolation from these experiments to in situ morphogenesis must of necessity be made with caution, it is reassuring that a number of different experimental approaches have yielded the same general results. It is important, however, to emphasize (cf. 4, 10) that the experimental findings are restricted to embryonic thymus rudiments. There is no reason to assume that a similar mechanism of cell origin applies to the functional thymus either of the neonatal animal or the adult — indeed it is likely that lymphoid kinetics after establishment of non-thymic lymphoid organs and a lymphoid circulation are quite different from the situation encountered during embryogenesis.

While the studies in tissue culture indicated that thymus lymphoid differentiation can proceed autonomously, and the studies of lymphoid development in grafts made into chicken embryos gave no indication of host cell contribution to the developing rudiment, it remained a distinct possibility that in isologous grafts made into adult mice, cells from the circulation might be entering the developing organ to add to the total cell population. To test this point, thymus rudiments were grafted into adult animals previously irradiated with lethal or sublethal doses of irradiation, into animals previously thymec-

[1] The comment by Ackerman and Knouff (1) that published photographs are consistent with mesenchymal lymphoid cells must be refuted. Their statement is based on photographs of a single culture (4) taken at a magnification which precludes identification of specific lymphocytes. At no time have we observed mesenchymal lymphocytes in combination cultures.

tomized, or into animals thymectomized as well as irradiated prior to
grafting (Auerbach, 6, 12). Morphogenesis of grafted rudiments was in
every way comparable in the different
groups, suggesting developmental
autonomy. Additional experiments involving the use of tritiated thymidine
as a marker of either host or graft cells
confirmed these findings (12). Thus
it appears not only that the thymus can
become lymphoid by self-differentiation but also that it does not sequester
lymphoid cells during embryogeny,
even when such cells are available.

Regenerative Processes in the Thymus

Developmental changes in the thymus can be readily induced by x-irradiation, for thymus lymphocytes are far
more sensitive to irradiation than are
the residual reticular and epithelial
cells. The descriptive features of thymic lymphoid regeneration have been
reported to involve both repopulation
by cells of extrinsic origin and by the
reinitiation of morphogenesis via the
intrinsic developmental pathway of
lymphoblasts to large, medium, and
small lymphocytes. The difficulties
inherent in the many descriptive developmental studies are unfortunately
equally apparent in these investigations, for in the absence of markers or
means of isolation of components,
interpretation of the observations is
difficult.

When comparison is made between
regeneration after low and high doses
of irradiation, it appears that at low
doses either cell immigration or enhanced division of residual small
lymphocytes is the most likely cause of
lymphoid regeneration (Auerbach, 6,
8). At high doses, on the other hand,

regeneration appears more probably
to be due to intrinsic differentiation
along a pathway not unlike that seen
in early embryogeny. Studies involving the regeneration of adult thymus
fragments in vitro would provide critical evidence on this question; such
studies are now in progress (Globerson, 19, 20).

Control of Spleen Lymphoid Differentiation

Analysis of spleen lymphoid differentiation is complicated by the fact
that the spleen erythropoietic and
myelopoietic activities are developed
well in advance of the appearance of
lymphoid cells (cf. Ohno, 42; Thiel, 47).
Thus studies of developmental interactions must of necessity be limited to
spleens already complex both in structure and function or, as an alternative,
spleen which must be capable of undergoing many consecutive transformations after experimental manipulation.
It is not surprising that virtually no
classical experimental data on mammalian spleen development are available. Understanding of the developmental mechanics underlying spleen
lymphopoiesis had not, until recently, progressed since the publication of such beautiful descriptive
studies as those of Thiel and Downey
and of Ohno (47, 42). In the last two
years, experiments involving tissue
culture and transplantation of the
embryonic mouse spleen have been
reported (Auerbach, 9, 10, 12). Spleen
rudiments from 13–14 day mouse
embryos are composed of an apparently
homogenous group of undifferentiated
mesenchymal cells and can readily be
isolated by dissection. When grown in
tissue culture at a glass-clot interface,

the cells spread rapidly to form a loose fibroblastic sheet. Use of a modified standing drop culture method designed to permit organ maintenance and lymphopoiesis and to prevent spreading and fibroblastic outgrowth leads to the survival and persistence of the spleen as an intact organ; such cultures examined at intervals from 4–28 days remain as an undifferentiated stromal mass of cells void of erythrocytes, lymphocytes, or granulocytes. Grafts of rudiments made to the chorioallantoic membrane of 9-day chick embryos and kept for 7 days show a similar lack of complex differentiation (Auerbach, 9, 13).

When equivalent spleen rudiments are grafted to the anterior eye chamber of adult mice, on the other hand, rapid development of grafts takes place, and within 7 days the grafts are found to be comprised of extensive granulocytic, erythroid, and lymphoid cell populations, as in Figure 21.3A (9, 13). In focusing attention on the lymphoid cells, it has been noted that the lymphocytes in such grafts appear mature and that lymphoblasts or large lymphocytes are lacking. The accumulation of lymphoid cells in these grafts, furthermore, is first associated with the vascular connections established after grafting—a histological manifestation very much akin to that observed during normal development in vivo.

To determine the origin of splenic lymphocytes in these grafts, host animals were irradiated with 950 r x rays prior to grafting in order to destroy host lymphocytes. Establishment and growth of grafted spleen rudiments was essentially normal (Fig. 21.3B). Such rudiments, however, although rich in myeloid and erythroid elements, were totally lacking in lympho-cytes, suggesting that the lymphoid cells associated with spleen differentiation in the eye were of host origin (9). In order to eliminate the possibility that the absence of spleen lymphoid cells in these grafts was the result of the absence of some humoral factor necessary for intrinsic spleen lymphopoiesis (cf. 9), experiments were performed involving tissues labeled with tritiated thymidine (Auerbach, 12). These experiments indicated that at least the large majority of lymphoid cells found in spleen grafts are of host origin and that few lymphocytes or none arise from the rudiment itself.

Functional Capacities of Spleen Lymphoid Cells

Since the grafting experiments indicated that spleen lymphoid cells arise by acquisition rather than self-differentiation, it was of interest to determine whether the acquired lymphoid cells possessed the capacity to function in immunological reactions (Auerbach, 13). To this end spleen rudiments obtained from Bagg alb. C embryos were grafted into either isologous adult C animals or into F_1 (C × C_3H) hosts. Grafts were recovered after 14 days; the individual grafts were cut into small fragments and these were then injected into 3-day-old F_1 (C × C_3H) animals for their capacity to produce the classical graft vs. host response. The results of assays performed 10 days after test grafting are shown in Table 21.1. Whereas rudiments grown in F_1 hosts failed to develop competence to produce a graft vs. host effect, rudiments grown in parental strain hosts developed this ability to a marked degree. In these experiments it is conceivable that C rudiments grown in C × C_3H host eyes became

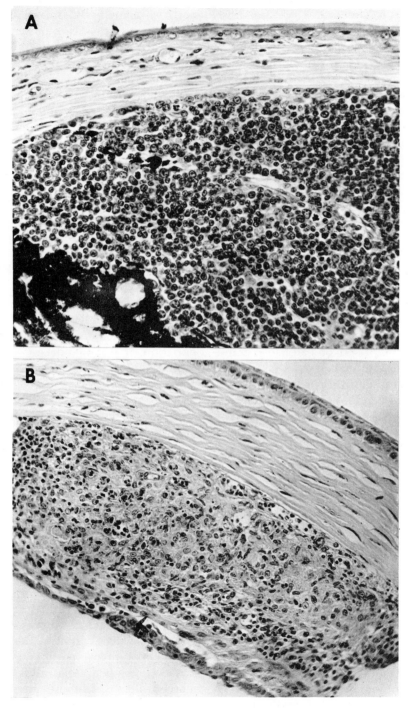

Fig. 21.3 *A*. Implant of 14-day embryonic spleen in anterior eye chamber of isologous adult mouse after 1 week of growth. *B*. Implant of similar spleen in anterior eye chamber of isologous adult mouse previously irradiated with 950 r.

TABLE 21.1 Graft vs. Host Assay Tissues Implanted in 3-day-old C × C₃H Mice

	ASSAY AFTER 10 DAYS	
DONOR TISSUE	RATIO SPLEEN WEIGHT / BODY WEIGHT	RATIO EXPER./CONTROL
C × C₃H adult spleen	0.0036	
C embryonic spleen in C × C₃H eye	0.0035	0.99
C embryonic spleen in C eye	0.0089	2.50
C adult spleen	0.0170	4.77

tolerant to C₃H antigens, but this appears to be an unlikely explanation in view of other experiments (cf. below). A reverse experiment involving the grafting of an F₁ (C × C₃H) rudiment into parental strain hosts would be most desirable. However, in such combinations, the initial graft becomes filled with vast numbers of host lymphocytes; organization of the graft is quite different, suggestive of graft splenomegaly, and the immunological test of such a graft would, therefore, not serve as a valid control.

Preliminary experiments have been performed in collaboration with A. Globerson to determine whether cells entering spleen grafts may carry information of previous immunological experience. Rudiments from Bagg alb. C embryos were grafted into adult isologous animals previously hyperimmunized against C₃H cells. After 5 days the host animals were injected with C₃H cells to elicit a secondary response. Two days later, grafts were removed from the hosts, placed in tissue culture, and combined with C (control) or C₃H (test) lymphocytes (cf. Bach, 14; Wilson, 50). Cultures were scored for activity after 2 days and the results are presented in Table 21.2. The experiments suggest that grafts can perform secondary responses

TABLE 21.2 Preliminary Data on Transfer of Immunological Activity from Host Animals to Grafted Embryonic Spleen Rudiments[a]

	EFFECT ON C₃H LYMPHOCYTES	
	+	−
Host spleen, not preimmunized	0	3
C spleen grafts grown in vitro after 7 days in C animals not preimmunized against C₃H cells	0	4
C spleen grafts grown in vitro after 7 days in C animals preimmunized against C₃H cells	5	3
Host spleen, preimmunized	3	0

[a]With A. Globerson.

in vitro after growth in preimmunized mice, indicating that cells either capable of giving a secondary response or cells already giving such a response enter the developing rudiment. Other preliminary experiments suggest that the secondary response may be elicited entirely in vitro from such grafted spleen rudiments.

Development of Spleen Rudiments as Homografts

In view of the unique behavior of thymus rudiments grown as homografts (Auerbach, 3, 10), spleen rudiments from Bagg alb. C, C_3H, or F_1 ($C \times C_3H$) embryos were grown in adult hosts of these three genetic constitutions and examined after 4, 7, and 10 days' growth in the anterior eye chamber. The results are presented in Table 21.3. Whereas isologous grafts differentiated in typical fashion (Figure 21.4A) grafts of C rudiments in C_3H animals or C_3H rudiments in C animals only demonstrated initial establishment. Growth never became fully lymphoid and the grafts were ultimately rejected by the host animals (Fig. 21.4B). Most interesting, however, was the behavior of F_1 rudiments grown in hosts of either parental strain. Such grafts grew to be extremely large, became filled with lymphocytes almost exclusively, and showed extreme signs of lymphoid disorganization with little evidence of lymphoid follicular organization. Only much later did graft rejection occur in this group.

This unique behavior of F_1 grafts is difficult to reconcile with the standard behavior of homografts since, if lymphocyte accumulation in the graft were a normal adjunct of graft rejection in this system, one would expect increased lymphocyte infiltration in the interstrain combinations also; in fact, the reverse is true, for in such grafts even the normal infiltration associated with typical spleen morphogenesis is reduced. More striking still is the behavior of chick embryo spleen grown as homografts in adult mice. Such spleen shows no signs of lymphocyte entry whatsoever, and grafts develop as healthy nonlymphoid organs.

As a tentative explanation one might suggest that the observed increase in lymphocytes in F_1 grafts grown in parental strain hosts represents a type of splenomegaly in some ways similar to that seen in chick embryos carrying grafts of homologous spleens on the chorioallantoic membrane. Here the splenomegaly is marked only if there is some degree of immunological identity, for grafts of turkey, pheasant,

TABLE 21.3   Results of Homotransplantation of Embryonic Spleen Rudiments to Anterior Eye Chamber of Adult Mice

| DONOR STRAIN | HOST STRAIN | | |
	C	$C \times C_3H$	C_3H
C	Normal (6)[a]	Normal (10)	Rejected (8)
$C \times C_3H$	Lymphoid hyperplasia (15)	Normal (18)	Lymphoid hyperplasia (8)
C_3H	Rejected (12)	Normal (41)	Normal (9)

[a] Number of cases examined histologically.

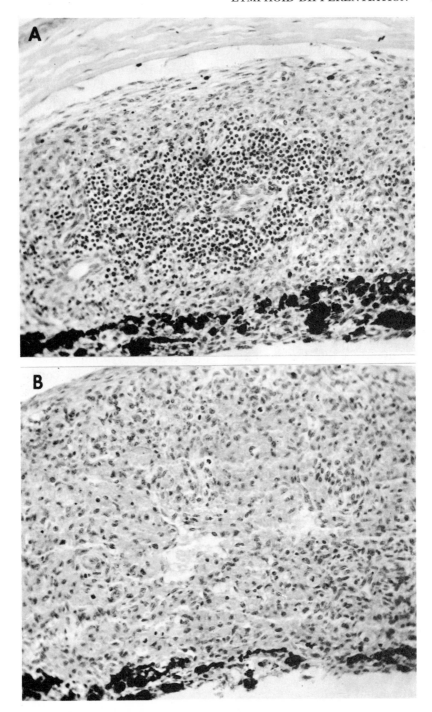

Fig. 21.4 *A*. Implant of 12-day embryonic C₃H thymus after 1 week of growth in the anterior eye chamber of C × C₃H adult mouse. *B*. Implant of similar C₃H rudiment after 1 week of growth in the anterior eye chamber of Bagg alb. C adult mouse.

rat, or guinea-pig spleens are less effective in inducing splenomegaly than are grafts of chicken spleens (Mun, 41a). In the present experiments, however, it would appear that enlargement is due primarily to immigrant cells, whereas in chicken embryos both donor and host components appear to contribute to splenomegaly.

The proposed explanation may also be applied to the incongruous results reported by McCulloch and Till in their beautiful studies of relative cloning efficiencies of hybrid and parental strain cells (McCulloch, 35). It may well be that lymphoid cell accumulation requires a certain degree of antigenic identity and that the sequestering of spleen lymphoid cells is, in fact, a selective process.

In this connection, it would be desirable to ascertain the degree of host and donor contributions to the observed graft enlargement. Unfortunately, initial experiments involving grafts of prelabeled spleen rudiments have for technical reasons (possible label dilution) given equivocal results.

Regeneration of Spleen Lymphoid Cells after Irradiation

The repair processes of the spleen after irradiation have been studied repeatedly, but the precise role of immigrant or intrinsic cells has never been defined. It is well known that injection of lymphoid cells into irradiated recipients leads to the colonization of these cells in the spleen, but evidence from such experiments does not permit valid inference for normal regenerative processes.

Recently it has been shown that the thymus plays an integral part in the restoration of the histological integrity of the spleen as well as in the recovery of the immune response (Auerbach, 7; Feldman, 18; Globerson, 21, 22; Miller, 40). Careful studies of Globerson and Feldman (18, 21), moreover, indicate that the thymus does not function primarily as a contributor of immunologically active cells. On the other hand, their studies do not attempt to distinguish between a thymic stimulation (humoral or cellular) of cells of nonsplenic origin which then enter the spleen, and a direct stimulation of spleen lymphoid precursor cells.

As is the case for the thymus, critical information on the mechanism of spleen lymphoid regeneration can readily be obtained in tissue culture. Such studies are now being performed by Globerson, and a preliminary report (20) indicates that spleen fragments isolated after x-irradiation fail to regenerate lymphoid cells in vitro, in contrast to tissue combinations which will be discussed below.

Interaction of Lymphoid Tissues in vitro

The early studies on thymus differentiation in vitro and in graft situations suggested the hypothesis that the thymus is the seat of immunologically competent cells which, during morphogenesis of the immune mechanism, migrate to the spleen and other lymphoid regions (Auerbach, 3). This hypothesis received initial support from the studies of Miller and of Good and his collaborators, who demonstrated that neonatal thymectomy is associated with a depression of the development of certain immunological functions (cf. Miller, 38, 39). Subsequent experiments suggested that the thymus might not be acting directly on the spleen via cell migration, but might rather exert its effect through humoral activity (De Somer, 17; Law, 29; Levey, 30, 31; Osoba, 43, cf. also Grégoire, 24). These studies are as yet fragmentary, but in view of the wide acceptance of the findings, a few critical comments are in order (cf. also Auerbach, 12).

The implication that all experiments on thymus function can be explained on the basis of hormone function (30) is unfortunate. Yunis and co-workers (51) have shown clearly that restoration of immunological competence in thymectomized mice by injection of thymus lymphoid cells is entirely due to the immunological activity of those cells themselves, as judged by activity of spleens subsequently tested by the discriminant spleen-assay method. Experiments of Taylor (45, 46) indicate further that thymus grafts contribute significantly to the development of lymph node cell populations in thymectomized animals.

At the present time, the published experiments are lacking in convincing controls. Critical tests for adjuvant properties of diffusion chambers carrying graft tissues have not been performed, nor is it clear in most instances that the chambers themselves were impervious to lymphoid cell leakage. The specificity of the action of thymus tissue in diffusion chambers is also in doubt, for in no instance have diffusion chambers carrying control tissues such as spleen, liver, marrow, or lymph node been examined for possible effects.

Perhaps most important to our understanding of presumed thymic humoral activity is the recognition that neonatal thymectomy is performed at a time when there are already circulating lymphocytes as well as marrow lymphoid cells. Even in neonatally thymectomized mice carrying no grafts or diffusion chambers, the *absolute* number of lymphocytes increases steadily with increasing body weight; only the *rate* of lymphoid cell increase is affected by the operation. This rate may well be influenced by humoral activity of thymus cells presumably of nonlymphoid type.

Thus the fact that neonatal thymectomy so drastically affects homograft reactions suggests either that the depression of total lymphocyte number is sufficient to lead to graft maintenance or, as has been suggested repeatedly, that there are several kinds of lymphocytes as well as several kinds of immunological responses. In this connection it is perhaps reassuring that the thymus at birth is not omnipotent, for neonatally thymectomized mice do respond in varied fashion to immunological stimuli of different sorts. Whether prenatal thymectomy would yield more absolute results is at present only a matter of conjecture.

With this discussion as background, it seems appropriate now to examine experiments involving interactions of lymphoid rudiments in vitro; in the tissue culture situation it may be possible by appropriate use of marked cells, millipore filters, and genetic strains ultimately to disentangle the various components of the differentiating immune system.

Spleen-Thymus Interaction

When thymus rudiments are grown in tissue culture, they become lymphoid and can be maintained for about 14 days, after which the lymphoid cells are gradually replaced by nonlymphoid elements (Fig. 21.5). Addition of spleen rudiments encourages

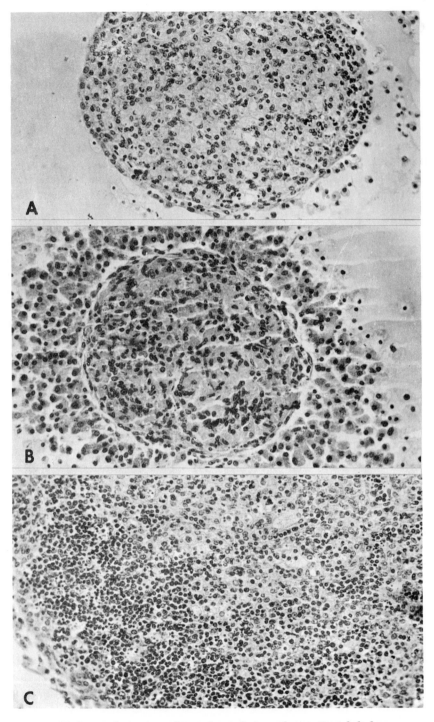

Fig. 21.5 *A*. 15-day embryonic spleen, 1 week in culture. *B*. Adult bone marrow, 1 week in culture. *C*. 15-day embryonic thymus, 1 week in culture.

growth and continued morphogenesis (Auerbach, 10). The effect of spleen on thymus, furthermore, is mediated across an intervening millipore filter (10). A reciprocal effect of thymus on spleen has not been observed. Recently, Globerson has demonstrated (20) that irradiated spleen fragments have a similar effect on regenerating adult irradiated thymus fragments.

Marrow-Thymus Interaction

When adult marrow is added to embryonic thymus cultures, the thymus tends to release lymphoid cells into the marrow channels. At the same time, the thymus appears to cause enhanced growth and maintenance of marrow explants.

Marrow-Spleen Interaction

The addition of adult marrow to embryonic spleen rudiments (Fig. 21.6A) leads to the subsequent localization of lymphoid cells within the spleen. The effect is particularly interesting in view of the fact that spleen by itself never becomes lymphoid and that marrow which is isolated singly fails to maintain lymphoid cells. The results again parallel the effects seen by Globerson (20) in combinations of adult marrow with irradiated spleen fragments.

Interaction with Lymph Node

Inguinal lymph nodes from adult mice have been combined with adult marrow, embryonic thymus, and embryonic spleen rudiments. In no combination has the lymph node appeared to exert a clear effect on other lymphoid organs, nor has it in turn been influenced by them. It must be cautioned, however, that in these cultures lymph node lymphocytes degenerated rapidly; the negative findings, therefore, may be due to technical reasons.

Marrow-Spleen-Thymus Interaction

Finally, three-way combinations involving embryonic spleen and thymus and adult marrow have been studied (Fig. 21.6B and C). These cultures show the most complex organization—the spleen becomes clearly lymphoid, the thymus healthy and active, and the marrow well differentiated with channels of lymphocytes. Marking experiments to clarify the origin of the various cells in this combination have not yet been performed.

The studies are clearly consistent with a pathway of migration from thymus to marrow to spleen. Furthermore, the effect of spleen on thymus may well mimic a function of the spleen normally associated with a local effect of the splenic milieu on cells entering the spleen via migration. On the other hand, the experimental system is now sufficiently far advanced that serious speculation seems unnecessary, for critical experiments involving functional tests with cultures obtained from combinations of appropriately chosen sources are feasible. Such experiments should be able to yield decisive information on the nature of tissue interaction during the development of a functional lymphoid system.

Summary

Experimental studies on thymus and spleen morphogenesis are presented. Thymus differentiation is seen as a result of inductive tissue interaction between epithelium and mesenchyme. Thymic epithelium is the source of

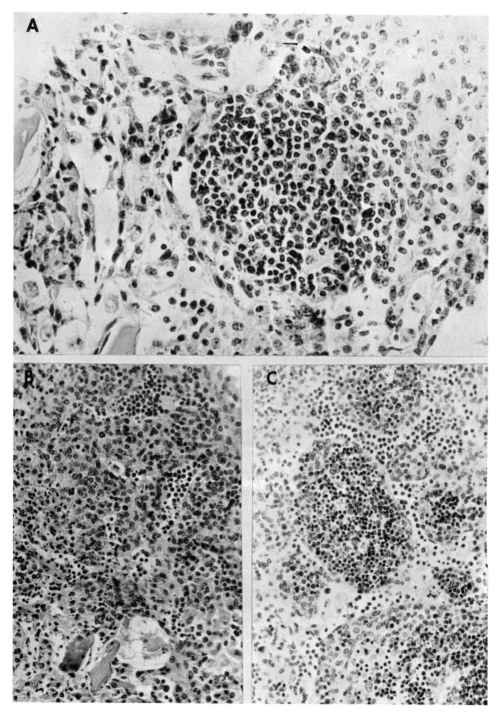

Fig. 21.6 *A*. Spleen-marrow combination. Note lymphoid follicle. *B*. Thymus-spleen-marrow combination — lymphoid cells in channels. *C*. Thymus-spleen-marrow combination — lymphoid follicle.

embryonic thymic lymphocytes, while mesenchyme provides the stromal material of the developing organ.

In contrast to the self-differentiation of the thymus, spleen development is seen to involve an extrinsic source of lymphocytes. Experiments are described which indicate that during spleen morphogenesis immunocompetent cells, as well as cells carrying immunological information, enter the spleen and are subsequently able to perform immunological reactions.

Studies involving combinations of thymus and spleen with bone marrow are described. These studies lead to the tentative suggestion that bone marrow may act as an intermediary in the transfer of cells from the thymus to the spleen. The embryological data are discussed in the context of origin of immune competence.

References

1. Ackerman, G. A., and R. A. Knouff, "Lymphocyte Formation in the Thymus of the Embryonic Chick," *Anat. Record* 149:191–216 (1964).

2. Auerbach, R. "Morphogenetic Interactions in the Development of the Mouse Thymus Gland," *Develop. Biol.* 2:271–284 (1960).

3. ———, "Genetic Control of Thymus Lymphoid Differentiation," *Proc. Natl. Acad. Sci. U.S.* 47:1175–1181 (1961).

4. ———, "Experimental Analysis of the Origin of Cell Types in the Development of the Mouse Thymus," *Develop. Biol.* 3:336–354 (1961).

5. ———, "Tissue Culture in the Analysis of Developmental Processes in Mammals," *New Developments in Tissue Culture*, J. W. Green, ed. New Brunswick, N. J.: Rutgers University Press, pp. 79–86 (1962).

6. ———, "Embryonic Thymus Development and Function," *Proc. 48th Ross Pediat. Res. Conf.* 47–54 (1965).

7. ———, "Thymus: Its Role in Lymphoid Recovery after Irradiation," *Science* 139: 1061 (1963).

8. ———, "A Quantitative Approach to Thymus Lymphoid Differentiation during Leukemogenesis and Regeneration," *Blood* 22:830–831 (1963).

9. ———, "Developmental Studies of Mouse Thymus and Spleen," *J. Natl. Cancer Inst.* 11:23–33 (1963).

10. ———, "Experimental Analysis of Mouse Thymus and Spleen Morphogenesis," *The Thymus in Immunobiology*, R. A. Good, A. Gabrielsen, eds. New York: Harper and Row (1964).

11. ———, "Continued Inductive Tissue Interaction during Differentiation of Mouse Embryonic Rudiments *in vitro*," *Wistar Inst. Symp.* Monograph I: 3–20 (1964).

12. ———, "On the Function of the Embryonic Thymus," *Wistar Inst. Symp.* Monograph II:1–8 (1964).

13. ———, Unpublished observations (1964).

14. Bach, F., and K. Hirschhorn, "Lymphocyte Interaction: A Potential Histocompatibility Test *in vitro*," *Science* 143:813–814 (1964).

15. Ball, W. D., and R. Auerbach, "*In vitro* Formation of Lymphocytes from Embryonic Thymus," *Exptl. Cell Res.* 20:245–247 (1960).

16. Block, M., "The Blood-Forming Tissues and Blood of the Newborn Opossum (*Didelyphys Virginiana*). I. Normal Development through about the One Hundredth Day of Life," *Ergeb. Anat. Entwicklungsgeschichte* 37:237–366 (1964).

17. De Somer, P., P. Denys, Jr., and R. Leyten, "Activity of a Noncellular Calf Thymus Extract in Normal and Thymectomized Mice," *Life Sciences* 11: 810–819 (1963).

18. Feldman, M., and A. Globerson, "The Role of the Thymus in the Restoration of Immune Reactivity and Regeneration of

the Lymphoid System in X-irradiated Adult Mice," *Ann. N. Y. Acad. Sci.* 120: 182–190 (1964).

19. Globerson, A., Unpublished observations.

20. ———, and R. Auerbach, "Interaction of Mouse Lymphoid Tissues *in vitro*," *Science* 139:1061 (1964).

21. ———, and M. Feldman, "The Role of the Thymus in the Restoration of Immune Reactivity and Regeneration of the Lymphoid System in X-irradiated Adult Mice" (1964).

22. ———, L. Fiore-Donati, and M. Feldman, "On the Role of the Thymus in Recovery of Immunological Reactivity Following X-irradiation," *Exptl. Cell Res.* 28:455–457 (1962).

23. Grégoire, Ch., "Recherches sur la Symbiose Lymphoépithéliale au Niveau du Thymus de Mammifère," *Arch. Biol. Liège* 46:717–820 (1935).

24. ———, and Gh. Duchateau, "A Study on Lympho-Epithelial Symbiosis in Thymus. Reactions on the Lymphatic Tissue to Extracts and to Implants of Epithelial Components of Thymus," *Arch. Biol. Liège* 67:269–296 (1956).

25. Grobstein, C., "Trans-filter Induction of Tubules in Mouse Metanephrogenic Mesenchyme," *Exptl. Cell Res.* 10:424–440 (1956).

26. ———, "Some Transmission Characteristics of the Tubule-inducing Influence on Mouse Metanephrogenic Mesenchyme," *Exptl. Cell Res.* 13:575–587 (1957).

27. Hammar, J. A., *Die normal-morphologische Thymus-forschung im letzten Vierteljahrhundert.* Munich: Johann Ambrosius Barth (1936).

28. Klemperer, P., "The Spleen," *Handbook of Hematology*, H. Downey, ed. New York: Paul B. Hoeber, Inc., vol. III, Sect. XXI, pp. 1591–1754 (1938).

29. Law, L. W., N. Trainin, R. H. Levey, and W. F. Barth, "Humoral Thymic Factor in Mice: Further Evidence," *Science* 143:1049–1051 (1964).

30. Levey, R. H., "The Thymus Hormone," *Sci. Am.* 211:66–77 (1964).

31. ———, N. Trainin and L. W. Law, "Evidence for Function of Thymic Tissue in Diffusion Chambers Implanted in Neonatally Thymectomized Mice: Prelimi-

nary Report," *J. Natl. Cancer Inst.* 31: 199–217 (1963).

32. Maximow, A., "Untersuchungen über Blut und Bindegewebe. II. Über die Histogenese der Thymus bei Säugetieren," *Arch. Mikroskop. Anat. Entwicklungsmech* 74:525–621 (1909).

33. ———, "Bindegewebe und blutbildence Gewebe," *Handbook Mikroskop. Anat. Mensch.* Vol. II, Part I, pp. 232–583 (1927).

34. ———, "The Lymphocytes and Plasma Cells," *Special Cytology* E. U. Cowdry, ed. Vol. I, pp. 320–367 (1928).

35. McCulloch, E. A., and J. E. Till, "Repression of Colony-Forming Ability of C 57 BL Hematopoietic Cells Transplanted into Non-isologous Hosts," *J. Cellular Comp. Physiol.* 61:301–308 (1963).

36. Metcalf, D., "The Autonomous Behavior of Normal Thymus Grafts," *Australian J. Exptl. Biol. Med. Sci.* 41:437–447 (1963).

37. ———, and R. Wakonig-Vaartaja, "Host-Cell Repopulation of Normal Spleen Grafts," *Lancet* 1:1012–1014 (1964).

38. Miller, J. F. A. P., "The Thymus and the Development of Immunologic Responsiveness," *Science* 144:1544–1551 (1964).

39. ———, and A. J. S. Davies, "Embryological Development of the Immune Mechanism," *Ann. Rev. Med.* 15:23–36 (1964).

40. ———, S. M. A. Doak, and A. M. Cross, "Role of the Thymus in Recovery of the Immune Mechanism in the Irradiated Adult Mouse," *Proc. Soc. Exptl. Biol. Med.* 112:785–792 (1963).

41. Mun, A. M., I. L. Kosin, and I. Sato, "The Effect of Spleens from Different Animals on the Growth of the Chick Embryo Spleen," *Anat. Record* 134:613–614 (1959).

41a. ———, "Enhancement of Growth of Chick Host Spleens following Chorioallantoic Membrane Grafts of Homologous Tissues," *J. Embryol. Exptl. Morphol.* 7:512–525 (1959).

42. Ohno, K., "Untersuchungen über die Entwicklung der Menschlichen Milz," *Z. Zellforsch. Mikroskop. Anat.* 10:573–603 (1930).

43. Osoba, D., and J. F. A. P. Miller, "The

Lymphoid Tissues and Immune Responses of Neonatally Thymectomized Mice Bearing Thymus Tissue in Millipore Diffusion Chambers," *J. Exptl. Med.* 119:177–194 (1964).

44. Shaw, B. S., D. I. Patt, and D. Shepro, "Ultrastructure of the Fetal Thymus in the Golden Hamster," *J. Morph.* 115: 319–354 (1964).

45. Taylor, R. B., "Immunological Competence of Thymus Cells after Transfer to Thymectomized Recipients," *Nature* 199:873–874 (1963).

46. ———, Unpublished observations.

47. Thiel, G. A., and H. Downey, "The Development of the Mammalian Spleen, with Special Reference to Its Hematopoietic Activity," *Am. J. Anat.* 28:279–339 (1921).

48. Tyan, M. L., and L. J. Cole, "Sources of Potential Immunologically Reactive Cells in Certain Fetal and Adult Tissues," *Transplantation* 2:241 (1964).

49. Wakonig-Vaartaja, R., and D. Metcalf, "The Origin of Mitotic Cells in Normal Thymus Grafts," *Lancet* 1302–1304 (1963).

50. Wilson, D. B., "The Reaction of Immunologically Activated Lymphoid Cells against Homologous Target Tissue Cells *in vitro*," *J. Cellular Comp. Physiol.* 62:273–286 (1963).

51. Yunis, E. J., H. Hilgard, K. Sjodin, C. Martinez, and R. A. Good, "Immunological Reconstitution of Thymectomized Mice by Injections of Isolated Thymocytes," *Nature* 201:784–786 (1964).

22

Morphogenesis of the Vertebrate Kidney

THEODORE W. TORREY*

Department of Zoology
Indiana University
Bloomington, Indiana

The kidney, or nephros, of vertebrates consists essentially of an aggregation of tubular units known as nephrons, which are derived embryonically from the intermediate mesoderm. Ideally, this mesoderm becomes segmented, each such segment being termed a nephrotome. Any given nephrotome contains a coelomic chamber, the nephrocoel, which opens to the adjacent splanchnocoel by way of a so-called peritoneal funnel. The conversion of a nephrotome to a nephron involves the following major events: from the dorsolateral wall of the nephrotome there arises a tubular outgrowth, the principal tubule, that communicates with the nephrocoel via a nephrostome—Goodrich (47) terms this the "nephrocoelostome" to distinguish it from the nonequivalent nephrostome of an annelid nephridium; the medial wall of the nephrotome invests a tuft of arterial capillaries

constituting the glomerulus, the wall itself then being identified as the renal (Bowman's) capsule. Although it has been traditionally held that Bowman's capsule is established by an invagination of the glomerular tuft into the wall of the nephrotome (a view going back over 100 years to Remak), recent studies by electronmicroscopy (Kurz, 71) indicate that invagination does not occur. Rather, the space between the ultimate filtering surface and the capsule arises as a cleft within a compact mass of epithelial cells, with the outer layer then becoming the capsular wall and the inner one reflected over the surface of the glomerulus. (See Dalton, 23, and Elias, 26, for details of the fine structure of the filtering surface.)

Although the question of its evolutionary origin remains unanswered (see Goodrich, 47, for a discussion of this issue), this is the type of tubular unit identified in fossil imprint in the oldest known vertebrates, the ostracoderms, and which, with many vari-

*Contribution No. 752 from the Zoological Laboratories, Indiana University.

ations, features the kidneys of all vertebrates from cyclostome to mammal (Fig. 22.1). It is beyond the province of this review to consider these variations in detail, but the following alternatives may be noted. The peritoneal funnel may be transitory or absent; the glomerulus (glomus, if large or consisting of numerous fused glomeruli) may be associated with the coelomic epithelium rather than the nephron proper; and nephrons may be entirely devoid of glomeruli (for example as in aglomerular fishes) so that the blood supply to the nephron is entirely venous.

The nephros of the first vertebrates presumably was composed of nephrons alike in kind throughout the length of the organ and opening independently to the exterior. But this arrangement is only hypothetical, for in all known vertebrates the nephrons empty into some variety of common drainage duct, that is, nephric duct. The situation is further complicated in modern vertebrates by reason of three variables. First, in the embryos of higher vertebrates, typical hollow nephrotomes are seldom formed; instead, nephrons differentiate without segmental arrangement within a continuous nephrogenic cord of intermediate mesoderm. Second, as the nephros develops embryonically, its entire length does not appear at one time; rather, the nephrons appear in sequence from front to rear and the first-formed anterior tubules disappear before the posterior ones arise. Third, the nephrons become structurally more complex progressively, from anterior to posterior.

With reference to amniotes, it has been customary to describe, as a manifestation of these variables, three distinct entities — pronephros, mesonephros, and metanephros — which dur-

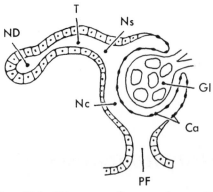

Fig. 22.1 Diagram of a nephron. Ca, capsule; Gl, glomerulus; Nc, nephrocoel; ND, nephric duct; Ns, nephrostome; PF, peritoneal funnel; T, tubule. (From Torrey, *Contrib. Embryol., Carnegie Inst. of Wash.* 35:175–197, 1954.)

ing ontogeny succeed each other in time and space, with the last alone being retained as the definitive adult kidney (Fig. 22.2). Moreover, this ontogenetic succession has been presumed to parallel the phylogenetic order of events in the vertebrates as a group. Accordingly, fishes and amphibians are said to possess first a pronephros that gives way to the final kidney, the mesonephros. Amniotes, then, add a third unit, the metanephros, with the previous two organs assuming provisional status. The facts are, however, that the morphological distinctions between the types of nephroi are vague indeed, so much so that while the terms pro-, meso-, and metanephros have considerable descriptive usefulness, the entities they refer to have no real significance other than as intergrading regions of a morphological continuum. The reader is referred to Fraser (38), Torrey (106), and Fox (36) for a full development of the argument for this interpretation. It is sufficient for the purpose of the present discussion to point up some morphological highlights only.

The nearest approach to the hypothetical ideal of a nephros composed of like nephrons throughout its length is found in the embryo of the myxinoid *Bdellostoma* (Price, 91, 92). Tubules arise from the nephrotomes from the 11th to the 82nd somite, the distal end of each tubule uniting with the one behind to form the excretory duct. At the opposite ends of the kidney the nephrons are distinctly different: anteriorly, glomeruli are lacking and peritoneal funnels are wide open to the splanchnocoel; pos-teriorly, the peritoneal funnels are closed and well-developed renal corpuscles occur. But this distinction is apparent only at the extremes, for at intermediate levels one type of nephron grades into the other. It is only as *Bdellostoma* enters adulthood that the anterior tubules become a compact isolated pronephros.

Conditions in lampreys are considerably more specialized. Studies (Torrey, 103) on the ammocoete larva of *Ichthyomyzon* reveal that young individuals bear a discrete pronephros consisting of a maximum of five tubules capable of picking up particulate matter from the coelom via ciliated peritoneal funnels and discharging it rearward through a patent nephric duct. As the larva ages, the tubules regress one by one, as does that portion of the nephric duct into which they drain, so at the time of metamorphosis only fragments of the system remain. Meanwhile, the mesonephros also appears and likewise undergoes change with the advancing age of the larva, that is, the most anterior and first-appearing tubules regress as those destined to comprise the definitive kidney of the adult appear on the developmental scene.

Among gnathostomes, a meaningful pronephros is usually found only in the embryos and larvae of the Actinopterygii, Dipnoi, and Amphibia. The only exceptions to this are the cases of certain teleosts (Emery, 27; Guitel, 63) in which functional pronephric tubules carry over into adult life. The pronephros ordinarily has functional significance only in those forms featuring free-living larvae, and among the amphibians, as Fox (36) has emphasized in a recent and thorough-going review of the pronephros in this vertebrate class, there has been an evolu-

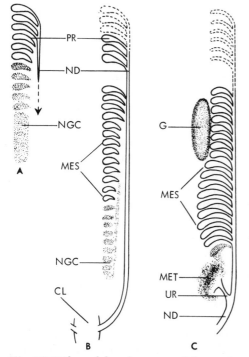

Fig. 22.2 Plan of development of the nephric system of vertebrates. *A*. Origin and mode of development of the nephric duct. *B*. and *C*. Relation of the nephric duct to other parts of the system. PR, pronephric units; ND, nephric duct; NGC, nephrogenic cord; G, gonad; MES, mesonephric units; MET, metanephros; UR, ureter; CL, cloaca. (From Burns, "Urinogenital System," in *Analysis of Development*, B. H. Willier, P. A. Weiss, and W. Hamburger, eds., W. B. Saunders, 1955.)

tionary diminution in form and function of the organ. Beginning with a primitive condition of about a dozen pronephrons in the gymnophionan *Hypogeophis*, there is a steady reduction in tubule number through various urodeles to a condition of two in the most specialized urodeles and three in the anurans.

In those anamniotes without larvae, for example, the elasmobranchs (and there are some interesting exceptions among those amphibians in which the larval stage has been suppressed), and in all the amniotes, the cranial end of the nephrogenic area shows only the most rudimentary development. Pronephric tubules have been described in embryos of a few representative reptiles, and of course the chick embryo has, since the days of Balfour, been described as exhibiting pronephric tubules of variable degrees of completeness from the 5th to 15th somites; nevertheless, it would seem that these two classes of vertebrates might be re-examined with profit. In the chick embryo especially, the transition between tubules judged to be pronephric and the first mesonephric tubules is so gradual as to cast doubt on the reality of the pronephric variety. As for mammals, with the exception of the marsupial *Trichosurus* in which 14–16 tubules have been described (Buchanan and Fraser, 11) and *Echidna*, for which 8 tubules have been recorded (Keibel, 68), the so-called pronephros consists at best of a variety of vaguely defined condensations, vesicles, or grooves (Torrey, 104). Most textbook descriptions to the contrary, the same is also true for the human embryo (Torrey, 106). Among amniotes, then, the pronephros, in the sense of the functional organ that

occurs in cyclostomes, a few fishes, and amphibians, no longer exists.

At the same time, the lower levels of the nephros show a steeper and steeper structural gradient. It has long been known, for example, that the posterior end of the adult selachian nephros is considerably more complex than the anterior and may in fact have a separate excretory duct. Similarly, in teleosts (Audigé, 1) there exists a whole series of types ranging from those with a continuous mesonephros to those in which a more complex "metanephric" posterior part, complete with separate blood supply and ureter, is isolated from the mesonephros. So it is also in amniotes, for example, the chick embryo, in which the last mesonephric tubules grade imperceptibly into the prospective metanephros behind. It was Graham Kerr (70) who long ago pointed out the lack of separation between mesonephros and metanephros in many forms and suggested that the term "opisthonephros" be applied to such situations, a term particularly appropriate to the definitive kidneys of adult fishes and amphibians.

Although the terms pro-, meso-, and metanephros have descriptive utility, the structural entities they refer to have no real significance other than as intergrading regions of a holonephros. The concept of the pronephros means little except in larval anamniotes; the metanephros of amniotes has reality only as the end product of a wave of differentiation along a nephric continuum. By the same token, there is little to distinguish the various categories of tubules in terms of fine structure and cellular functions. Leeson (73), for instance, in electronmicroscopy of the mesonephros of the 17-day rabbit embryo and metanephros of the adult, points to an extreme degree of similarity of glomeruli and tubule cells. Remembering, however, the great variation in extent of development of mammalian mesonephroi, ranging from the most rudimentary organ of the rat embryo (Torrey, 104) to the bulky organ of the pig embryo, and Bremer's (10) correlations of mesonephric form and function with placental types, an extension of Leeson's studies on a broadly comparative basis might be very revealing.

It is important to record that the concept of the holonephros is not based on comparative morphology alone. As will be noted in more detail elsewhere, the homogeneity of potency of the nephrogenic blastema has been demonstrated experimentally (Gruenwald, 60, 61; Cambar, 16), and nephrons of all types show a striking uniformity in their physiological performance (Gérard and Cordier, 41, 42). With respect to the latter, it has been shown that the cellular transport mechanism is fundamentally similar in pro-, meso-, and metanephric kidneys (Beyer et al., 6; Forster and Taggart, 35; Forster and Copenhaver, 33; Forster and Hong, 34; Jaffee, 66). It has been demonstrated through in vitro studies, for instance, that cellular transport in all types of nephrons takes place only when an adequate oxygen supply is present, thus indicating that the process is dependent upon aerobic metabolism. The role played by dehydrogenases in these oxidative reactions is pointed up by the inhibitive effects of iodoacetate and fluoride. The suppressive effects of cyanide and sodium azide suggest that a cytochrome oxidase system is operative in the transport process. That phosphate bond energy is employed in cellular transport is implied by the effects of various nitrophenol compounds. The reversible inhibition of dye (phenol red) transport by *para*-aminohippurate, uric acid, and penicillin suggests that these substances are not only excreted, but compete with phenol red for the transport mechanism. At the same time it should be made clear that many active cellular transport systems exist in nephrons of certain species and not in others. The voluminous literature on this issue has been summarized by Forster (32). The significant conclusion is, however, that the presence or absence of these excretory mechanisms cannot be correlated with cell structure, regional specialization of the nephron, or the kidney's status as a pro-, meso-, or metanephros. As Forster (32, p. 124) has put it, "whatever form may underlie these discrete functions must be sought for at the molecular, rather than at the cellular or organ, level."

The Nephric Duct

The issue of the origin and manner of development of the primary nephric duct becomes of paramount importance as one takes an overview of total kidney development. Not only is it the drainage channel for the pronephros, if and when this organ occurs, but even in the absence of definitive pronephrons, it is the first unit of the nephric system to appear and subsequently becomes involved with the mesonephros on two scores. First, it is the source of an inductive stimulus upon which the differentiation of mesonephrons largely depends (see section on integrative morphogenesis) and then, having been joined secondarily by mesonephrons, it serves as the excretory duct for the organ which these nephrons comprise. Moreover, in amniotes, the primary nephric duct is the source of the ureteric diverticulum that initiates the metanephros and ultimately provides the ureter for that organ. And, of course, in males the nephric duct becomes the vas deferens. So, in a very real way the primary nephric duct is a critical first phase in the total developmental history of the nephros, a phase that involves two separate problems – the manner of origin of the duct in the anterior reaches of the embryo, and the manner in which it finally arrives at the cloaca.

It seems clear that the primary nephric duct is primitively a segmental duct in the sense that it originates by the junction of the distal extremities of the anteriormost nephrons, that is, pronephrons. Such is the situation in lower vertebrates as exemplified by the myxinoid *Bdellostoma* (Price, 91, 92) and the gymnophionan *Hypogeophis* (Brauer, 9). Though there appears to be no reason to question this view of the original, primitive manner of origin of the duct, it has led to a generalization which, when extended to the vertebrates as a whole, simply does not square with the facts.

In amphibians, by far the most thoroughly analyzed, it has been shown that from the very start the nephric duct originates from nephrogenic mesoderm behind that which provides the pronephrons. Somite 5 marks the level of the duct primordium in anuran embryos (Dalcq, 22; van Geertruyden, 39; Cambar, 17), somites 5, 6, and 7 in urodeles. O'Connor (86), for instance, demonstrated that if the pronephric swelling below somites 3 and 4 in *Amblystoma* is vitally stained, the stain subsequently appears only in the pronephrons, whereas stain applied below somites 5–7 becomes confined to the duct. In a later experimental analysis on newt and salamander embryos, Holtfreter (64) showed that if an embryo is bisected between the levels of the 4th and 5th somites, the hindpiece, though devoid of pronephrons, still comes to contain a perfectly normal duct system.

In elasmobranchs, as already noted, pronephrons are vestigial, and the primary nephric duct is clearly the product of independent differentiation of the dorsolateral intermediate mesoderm at this, the pronephric, level. The story with respect to other types of fishes, however, is confusing to say the least. We have, for instance, the contention by Swaen and Brachet (102) that the nephric duct in *Salmo* represents a greatly elongated pronephric chamber. But Maschkowzeff (79) reports that in the sturgeon *Acipenser* the primary duct arises as a thickening of the dorsal side of the intermediate mesoderm, a thickening that is folded off and secondarily joined by solid strands of cells destined to become pronephrons. This account conforms essentially to Kerr's (70) view that in *Polypterus*, rudiments of the pronephric tubules unite secondarily with a previously established primordium of the nephric duct. All these early observations and interpretations of fishes leave much to be desired.

Descriptions of the origin of the nephric duct in the chick embryo and reptiles follow the convention of the junction of the distal ends of pronephric tubules. One may be reminded, however, that such descriptions date back 50 years and more to Balfour and Sedgwick (4) for the chick and to

Kerens (69) and Burland (12) for lizards and turtles respectively. This is not to say that these venerable accounts are necessarily wrong, but since the reality of the pronephros and this method of duct formation appear doubtful after comparative observations on other forms, a re-examination would seem to be in order. It is also pertinent to point out that a similar version of the origin of the nephric duct in the human embryo, dating from Felix (30), tends to persist to this day, yet it is clear that, not only are pronephrons lacking in the human embryo, but that the nephric duct originates by direct delamination from the dorsolateral side of the nephrogenic cord between the 9th and 13th somites (Torrey, 106). A similar situation exists in the embryo rat and is apparently widely true for other mammals as well (Torrey, 104). Allowing, then, for the questionable status of events in reptiles and birds and the truly unclear situation in fishes, especially teleosts, determination and differentiation of the nephric duct appear to proceed independently of pronephrons.

The question of how the nephric duct, once inaugurated, reaches the cloaca has been extensively explored. The voluminous literature pertaining to the issue has been organized by Fraser (38), Burns (14), and most recently by Fox (36), to whom the reader is referred. It is sufficient for the present discussion to record that historically there have been two views as to how the duct is extended: (1) new material is progressively added to it by differentiation in situ, (2) it elongates by free terminal growth. As Holtfreter (64) has remarked, the issue has been much like that which attended the controversy over the manner of

origin and elongation of nerve fibers in that progress toward a decision has come largely through the application of experimental methods. Generally speaking, these methods have involved extirpation of the primordial duct prior to outgrowth, blockage or reorientation of the duct in some fashion, localized vital staining, and explantation. That there have been discrepancies in the results reported by workers using one or more of these methods is not surprising when one considers the possibility of the uncontrollable spread of a vital stain or the nonprecision of an extirpation. Nevertheless, results have been sufficiently consistent (see tabulation by Burns, 14) to warrant the conclusion that the view of extension of the duct by independent caudal growth (according to Overton, 89, a migratory phenomenon) rather than by local accretion is the correct one. The one exception to this conclusion is found among amphibians, in instances of a short terminal piece of duct attached to the cloaca even when the main part of the duct has been prevented from forming. O'Connor (87, 88) believes such pieces are cloacal in origin.

Again, like the case of the outgrowing nerve fiber, the manner of elongation of the duct is not the whole story; there remains the question of the mechanism guiding the direction of growth. Certain of Holtfreter's (64) experiments are aimed at this second question. In amphibian neurulae and postneurulae where the continuity of the dorsal tissues is interrupted by a transverse cut, or where an anterior body fragment is reunited with a posterior one rotated through 90° or 180°, the nephric duct either stops advancing at the level of operation or finds its way into the hindpiece. In the latter event, the duct alters its direction, but finally reaches its normal topographic position and follows its normal route to the cloaca. (Comparable results have been reported by Tung and Ku, 107.) The assumption of a normal path after detours which sometimes appear strange suggests some sort of chemical attraction of the duct. Holtfreter, however, with the nerve fiber precedent in mind, believes the answer lies in contact guidance through selective cell adhesions rather than any form of chemotaxis. He has suggested the possibility of the blood vessels playing this role, but the question remains open for investigation. Resort to the vagueness of the "morphogenetic field" (Cambar, 18) is certainly not very satisfying.

Integrative Morphogenesis

The Mesonephros

Whatever the nature of the directive mechanism, the primary nephric duct normally follows a course just beneath the somites and dorsolateral to the nephrogenic cord on its way to the cloaca. Moreover, it is present prior to the appearance of the next generation of nephrons (mesonephric or opisthonephric, as the case may be) which, as they differentiate in the adjacent nephrogenic cord, join up with and thus take over the nephric duct. This fact long ago suggested that the primary nephric duct might serve as an inductor of differentiation of the mesonephrons.

The obvious test of this hypothesis was to prevent in some manner the topographic association of the duct with the nephrogenic cord. Such experiments have been carried out extensively in amphibian and chick embryos (see Fraser, 38; Gruenwald, 62; Burns, 14; and Fox, 36, for reviews) with results that are inconsistent, to say the least. Among urodele amphibians, reported results run the gamut from fully differentiated mesonephric tubules in grafts of duct-free mesonephrogenic tissue (Humphrey, 65) through irregular differentiation of tubules following extirpation of the pronephros and primordial duct (Burns, 13), to the formation of mere clumps of cells following obstruction of the elongating duct (Holtfreter, 64). Results with anuran embryos are somewhat more consistent—differentiation of mesonephrons appears in general to require an inductive stimulus by the duct, but here again there are variations. Thus, Miura (80) reports that after excision of the nephric duct in *Bufo* and *Rana* no tubules whatsoever appear; Shimasaki (99), following the same procedure but allowing the embryos to live longer, finds a rudimentary mesonephros; Waddington (108) reports only local condensations of cells after extirpation of the duct; and van Geertruyden (40) indicates that a blocked duct results in total failure of mesonephric differentiation (except at the extreme rear where the hindpiece of the duct grows forward from the cloaca).

There are also puzzling aspects of the results of experiments on the chick embryo. In agreement with similar results reported by Boyden (7), who destroyed the tip of the nephric duct by cautery, and later experiments by Waddington (108), who obstructed the duct by incision, Gruenwald (58)

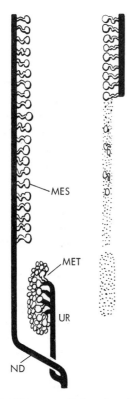

Fig. 22.3 Diagram of the developmental relations of the nephric organs. Those parts which, so far as known, develop independently, are shown in solid black; those which depend on others, in outline. The left side shows normal development and the right side shows the effects of cessation of growth of the nephric duct. Undifferentiated nephric tissues are stippled. MES, mesonephrons; MET, metanephrons; ND, nephric duct; UR, ureter. (Adapted from a figure by Gruenwald, "Development of the Excretory System," in *The Chick Embryo in Biological Research*, New York Academy of Sciences, 1952.)

reported that differentiation of nephrogenic tissue into mesonephros occurred only where that tissue was in contact with the duct (Fig. 22.3). However, Gruenwald (60) later reported that, in complete disagreement with his previous observations and those of other

investigators, the mesonephric blastema was capable of a considerable degree of self-differentiation, ranging all the way from small vestigial cell cords to conspicuous, well-developed groups of tubules and renal corpuscles. Calame (15) reached a similar conclusion. Though Gruenwald attributed a few such cases to possible induction by nervous tissue, this factor was judged not to be involved in most instances. But in a subsequent brief review, Gruenwald (62) tended to play down his earlier observations by saying "only a few scattered, vestigial nephrons may form in the absence of the duct" and went on to conclude that for its normal differentiation the mesonephros depends upon induction by the nephric duct.

One is hard put to resolve the differences in all these experimental results and come up with a common denominator. There may be built-in errors in many experiments that can be eliminated only by thorough reinvestigations. Then again, the role played by the duct may well vary in different genera and species or even varieties of animals. For instance, Gruenwald's (60) later experiments were conducted on Barred Rock chicks, whereas the earlier ones involved embryos of "unknown breeds." There is the possibility, too, that inductors other than the nephric duct may be variously involved. It has been shown, for example, that nervous tissue can induce mesonephrons in competent mesonephrogenic material in both the chick (Gruenwald, 60) and the frog (van Geertruyden, 40), and it is not unreasonable to suspect that other tissues such as somites might also be concerned. One is also reminded of the case of the lens of the eye, classically described as being initiated via an inductive stimulus provided by the optic vesicle, yet appearing in some species to exhibit self-differentiation. These latter cases having been shown to be manifestations of prior inductions by head mesoderm and lens formation in all species probably being elicited by the action of at least two supplementary or mutually reinforcing inductors of variable significance from one species to another emphasizes the relevant point that this may also be the case with the mesonephrons. They may be dependent upon the nephric duct and one or more supplementary inductors in varying degrees among genera and species.

It should also be remembered that all the information pertaining to induction of mesonephric tubules derives entirely from chick and amphibian embryos. There are no experimental analyses whatsoever on fishes and reptiles, and though the case of metanephric induction in mammals seems well established, induction of mesonephrons in this vertebrate class is only a presumption without documentation. In fact, Runner (98) presented some evidence against the likelihood of induction of mammalian mesonephrons by the nephric duct.

To this reviewer, then, it seems premature to accept a generalization that differentiation of vertebrate mesonephric tubules is *solely* dependent upon induction by the primary nephric duct. As favorable to this conclusion as evidence is, there remain important inconsistencies that need to be resolved in the results of experiments on chick and amphibian embryos. An extension of investigations to other classes of vertebrates, though posing technical difficulties, would seem to be called for.

The Metanephros

In embryos of reptiles, birds, and mammals, a ureteric diverticulum emerges from the nephric duct near its junction with the cloaca and pushes forward into the rear of the nephrogenic cord. The distal end of this diverticulum enlarges to form the so-called primitive renal pelvis and coincidentally, the nephrogenic tissue condenses around the pelvis as the metanephric blastema. Shortly afterward, the pelvis exhibits a progressively greater number of subdiverticula, around each of which the blastema continues to condense. Within these blastemal condensations, then, metanephrons differentiate. As they do so they open into the concomitantly elongating pelvic diverticula, which become collecting tubules. The metanephrons and collecting tubules together comprise the definitive kidney, or metanephros, drained by the ureter derived from the proximal portion of the original diverticulum.

As with the mesonephros, the appearance of the ureteric diverticulum and its invasion of the metanephrogenic tissue prior to the appearance of the metanephrons suggests the likelihood of an inductive relationship. Here the facts of experimentation and observation are consistent and clear. If the elongating primary nephric duct in the chick embryo is blocked so that its hinder portion is lacking and in consequence the ureteric diverticulum is also absent, though a blastema appears, metanephrons fail to form within it (Boyden, 7; Gruenwald, 58). This result conforms with those natural experiments leading to agenesis of a kidney in the human embryo. Congenital absence of a kidney is always accompanied by absence of the ureter on the corresponding side and, in males, by the absence of a vas deferens as well (Boyden, 8; Gruenwald, 59; Auer, 2). The obvious deduction is that through failure of the primary duct to form properly the ureteric diverticulum in turn is lacking and no metanephrons are induced. Conversely, double kidneys are always accompanied by double ureters (Wharton, 110), suggesting that in the event of anomalous double ureteric diverticula, duplicated inductions occur. These interpretations conform to the hypothesis advanced by Glucksohn-Schoenheimer (44) to explain the effects on the developing kidney of the *Sd* mutation in the mouse: kidney agenesis in homozygotes and reduction in kidney size in heterozygotes are related to aberrant development of the ureteric bud and decline or loss of its inductive capacity. The conclusion seems inescapable, then, that the ureter is essential to metanephric differentiation, a conclusion supported by a series of exquisite experiments on the metanephros of the embryonic mouse.

The experiments evolved from an earlier set of analyses of the development of the submandibular salivary gland (Grobstein, 48, 49, 50). Here the basic situation is similar to that in the primordial metanephros: an epithelial component is invested by a condensed mesenchymal capsule. The two components may be separated by treatment with trypsin. When the epithelial component alone is cultured in a clotting mixture of chicken plasma and nutrient medium, it simply spreads as a thin sheet, rather than undergoing its characteristic branching to form a tubular system. In combination with condensed mesenchyme of other rudiments such as lung or metanephros, or general mesenchyme, the epithelium still fails to undergo morphogenesis, though it does form a rounded mass or cyst, rather than spreading. Only submandibular mesenchyme is capable of inciting epithelial morphogenesis. In contrast, in heterogenous combination with submandibular epithelium, metanephric mesenchyme is stimulated to tubule production. This finding led to investigation of the metanephros itself (Grobstein, 51).

Preliminary tests showed that the intact metanephric primordium cultivated in vitro underwent characteristic morphogenesis, that is, the epithelial (pelvic) component formed a system of collecting ducts, the mesenchymal (blastemal) component formed coiled uriniferous tubules. But when the components are separated by trypsin and cultivated separately, neither shows ability to carry through morphogenesis. Apparently, then, a reciprocal inductive interaction normally operates. On the one hand, the branching of the primitive renal pelvis is dependent upon some property of the nephrogenic blastema; on the other, tubule differentiation within the blastema is dependent upon an inductive stimulus from the ureteric bud. In the first instance, the inductive capacity of the nephrogenic mesenchyme appears to be absolutely specific, for foreign mesenchyme is incapable of eliciting morphogenesis of the epithelial component (Grobstein, 49, 50). By contrast, the ureteric diverticulum shares its tubule-inducing capacity with some other tissues. Submandibular epithelium can induce kidney tubules (Grobstein, 50) as can embryonic spinal cord (Grobstein, 51). And particularly interesting is the ability of isolated metanephrogenic mesenchyme to form tubules when cultivated in the anterior chamber of the eye. Since none of the tissues of the eye appear to have inductive capacity, one is prompted to wonder from where the inducing factor within the eye chamber emanates. One also wonders whether it is the same factor as that involved in the demonstrated persistence of mesonephrons when implanted in the eye chamber (Runner, 98) and the promotion of differentiation toward maleness in intraocular grafts of sexually indifferent gonads (Torrey, 105). Certain suggestions coming from follow-up studies on the Sd mouse by Gluecksohn-Waelsch and Rota (46) are also pertinent to this question. Whereas there is failure of kidney development in embryos homozygous for this mutant gene, a failure attributed to aberrant development of the ureteric bud and loss of its inductive capacity (Gluecksohn-Schoenheimer, 44), intact kidney rudiments of Sd homozygotes do undergo a considerable measure of differentiation in vitro. Moreover, in reciprocal combinations of "normal" and "lethal" ureter with "normal" and "lethal" mesenchyme, the existence of inductive and reactive powers in both "lethal" components is demonstrated. That is, under these experimental conditions, the lethal gene does not suppress the inducing factors in either rudiment nor their ability to react. In attempting to account for the difference in performance of the nephric rudiments in vitro as compared with in vivo, there is only speculation that the in vitro environment may somehow neutralize a disharmony of inductive interaction or some spatial disarrangements ordinarily instigated by the Sd mutation.

As a first step toward gaining an understanding of the nature of the mechanism of tubular induction, Grobstein (51) and Grobstein and Dalton (57) set up cultures of metanephrogenic mesenchyme and embryonic spinal cord with interposed membrane filters of varying pore size. Phase-contrast and electronmicroscopy of sections of these preparations revealed a declining degree of cytoplasmic penetration with decline in pore size, yet with continuing tubule differentiation. Thus it was concluded that inductive activity is not dependent upon cytoplasmic contact. Follow-up studies (Grobstein, 53, 54, 55) not only verified that cytoplasmic contact was not required for induction, but created the definite impression that material of large molecular size, possibly protein, was secreted by the cells of the inductor into the immediate microenvironment and was involved as a mediator or carrier. These same studies also furnished some indication of the maximum distance through which the inductive factor can operate, namely, in the order of 80 μ. In this connection it is interesting to note that the maximum distance to which the amphibian nephric duct can be deviated from its normal course and still induce normal mesonephrons is also 70–80 μ (Cambar, 16). Herein may lie a clue to some of the inconsistencies in experimental analyses of the role of the primary nephric duct in the differentiation of mesonephrons.

These experiments are of multifold significance. It seems perfectly clear that differentiation of metanephrons requires an inductive stimulus. Normally this is provided by the branching renal pelvis, though under experimental conditions other tissues are capable of acting in this capacity. Moreover, the inducing principle is likely a diffusible substance. Although the chemical nature of this substance remains to be elucidated, it may well turn out to be similar to those possibly operating in other known cases of transfilter action. These are, notably, mesenchymal influence on growth and lobulation of thymus epithelia (Auerbach, 3), induction of cartilage from somitic cells by the spinal cord (Lash, Holtzer and Holtzer, 72), and dependence of differentiation of the epithelial component of the pancreas upon its surrounding mesenchyme (Grobstein, 56).

Concept of the Holonephros

Earlier in this review a favorable attitude was expressed toward the concept of the holonephros, a concept in which the pro-, meso-, and metanephros are intergrading parts of a continuum rather than discrete organs. Comparative morphology supports this view as does the commonness of functional operations in all types of nephrons. Some limited, but significant, observations relating to induction have a similar connotation.

In experiments involving blockage of the nephric duct in the chick embryo, Gruenwald (60) reported a single case of a nephric duct diverted by the blocking graft into the metanephrogenic mesenchyme which responded by producing nephrons of the mesonephric type. Subsequently, Gruenwald (61) demonstrated that grafted

nervous tissue also induced mesonephrons in metanephrogenic blastemata. (Incidentally, the tubule inductions in metanephrogenic mesenchyme by spinal cord that were obtained by Grobstein in his series of studies merit scrutiny. They are referred to simply as tubules and the implication is that they are metanephric. But *are* they?) Linked to these observations is the earlier report by Machemer (74) that when mesonephrogenic material in *Triton* is grafted into the pronephric area, it forms pronephrons. These data are scanty and to the best of this reviewer's knowledge the obvious converse experiments, for example, testing mesonephrogenic tissue with ureteric bud, have never been performed. But so far as they go, they suggest that the basic competence of nephrogenic tissue is the same at all levels and is one simply of producing generalized, nonspecific tubules, whereas the production of specific types of tubules in subregions of the continuum is a manifestation of locally operating inductors. In the case of mesonephrons, the primary nephric duct (plus other adjacent agents?) is the inductor; in the case of the metanephrons, it is the ureteric diverticulum.

Unfortunately, the key factor in the opening gambit in this succession of integrated events remains unknown. This refers to the agent or agents responsible for inciting the differentiation of the pronephrons (when it occurs) and, particularly, the primary nephric duct itself. It is an important missing key, for in the final analysis everything depends upon the nephric duct. It is a significant, if not exclusive, factor in the differentiation of mesonephrons; it is the material source of the ureteric bud which is the inductor of metanephrons.

Systematic analyses of amphibian and avian embryos by a host of investigators have revealed the topographic localizations of nephrogenic materials at successive stages of development as well as the progressive determination of these materials. (Papers by Pasteels, 90; Yamada, 111; Nieuwkoop, 85; Fales, 29; Muchmore, 83; Rudnick, 97; and Rawles, 94, are representative of such studies.) A detailed consideration of these matters is beyond the province of this review. Suffice it to say that nephrogenic potency is widely distributed at early stages of development and, in keeping with the early pluripotency of all embryonic materials, nephrogenesis can occur in a variety of tissues that normally have quite different prospects. Gradually, then, there is a progressive restriction in developmental potentials until nephrogenic ability becomes confined to a restricted area of the embryo in whose anteriormost reaches, that is, the prospective pronephric region, capacity for self-differentiation is acquired. So far, it has been impossible to nail down any one or combination of adjacent tissues — notochord, endoderm, neural plate, somitic mesoderm — that may be responsible for inciting this capacity. For the present, the problem of the basic mechanism underlying determination and differentiation of the pronephros, and particularly the nephric duct, remains unsolved.

Cellular and Functional Differentiation

It is difficult to extract from the enormous literature — increased by hundreds of papers each year — those observations on renal functions that have any obvious connection with the fundamental problem of morphogenesis. Fortunately, however, a winnowing is provided by the earlier reviews of Robinson (95), Smith (100), and Winton (109) dealing with the excretory, regulatory, and homeostatic aspects of the kidney's function as an organ; Forster's (32) recent summary has placed emphasis on individual cell processes. The availability of Forster's thorough review makes it possible to narrow attention to a few recent studies of those functional operations that either accompany morphogenesis or possibly may be fundamental to differentiation itself.

The paper by Gersh (43) stands as a landmark: first, in its provision of a summary of the earlier literature on the correlation of structure and function in the developing mesonephros and metanephros, and second, in its record of the onset of glomerular and tubular function in embryos of the chick and several mammals. With the use of ferrocyanide to test glomerular activity and phenol red for tubular activity, Gersh demonstrated that the mesonephros functions for a period, varying in length with the embryo, even as the metanephros assumes the same functions. There is, in other words, a functional overlap between the two tubule generations. Thus as the mesonephros declines structurally, the differentiating metanephros gradually assumes functional responsibility. The paper by Junqueira (67) pursues a similar theme by laying out in tabular form a variety of studies (and methods) pointing to the overlapping functions of meso- and metanephroi and correlating with these the rise and fall of acid and alkaline phosphatase in the developing chick embryo. Both phosphatases increase in the mesonephros from the 4th to 16th days of incubation and then decrease; in the metanephros there is an increase from the 11th to 16th day, a slow decrease to the 20th day, and then a rapid rise after hatching.

The case of the phosphatases has drawn a great deal of attention (see reviews by Moog, 81, 82), yet to this day the role played by these enzymes remains obscure, both with respect to their implication in tubule function and in the events of morphogenesis. Forceful arguments to the effect that phosphatases are involved in the phosphorylation-dephosphorylation processes concerned with glucose resorption have been offered (for example, see Davies', 24, studies on the functional correlation between the placenta, allantois, and mesonephros of the sheep), yet this is far from an established fact. Be that as it may, the involvement, if any, of the phosphatases in the basic operations of differentiation remains even more obscure (Eränkö and Lehto, 28; Rapola, Vainio, and Saxén, 93).

Over 30 years ago Needham (84) postulated that nitrogen excretion in the chick embryo occurred in three stages: the embryo first excretes ammonia, then urea, and, finally, uric acid, with urea thus being the major excretory product of the mesonephros. In a restudy of the situation, then, Clark and Fischer (20), while affirming the importance of uric acid as an end-product, obtained data pointing to the occurrence of all three products throughout development with a relatively greater significance of ammonia and urea at early stages. However, Fisher and Eakin (31) concluded that

ammonia and urea remain essentially constant after the 5th day of development, whereas uric acid increases steadily. That is, the stages of nitrogen excretion suggested by Needham actually do not exist; uric acid is the major end-product of excretion after the 5th day.

Since hypoxanthine dehydrogenase (HXDH) had been shown to be the key enzyme in the synthesis of uric acid, Chaube (19) was prompted to study the changes in activity of this enzyme in the nephros of the developing chick. Between the 5th and 7th days HXDH activity increased rapidly in the mesonephros and reached a maximum at the 14th day. Following the 15th day, it began to decline, a change correlated with the regression of the mesonephros. Meanwhile, with the differentiation of the metanephros, HXDH activity rose steadily in that organ through days 8 to 14, with a more abrupt rise at day 15, followed by a stable maximum. These data fit well indeed with older findings with respect to dye clearances and have recently been confirmed by Croisille (reported by Ebert, 25). Moreover, there appears to be complete immunochemical identity of HXDH whether from adult liver, adult kidney, embryonic mesonephros, or embryonic metanephros. Croisille (21) also reports, via immunoelectrophoretic studies, the presence of acetylnaphtoesterase activity in the chick mesonephros during the 11th and 12th days, with disappearance on the 16th day concomitant with its rise in the metanephros.

Looking to the fundamental problem of differentiation, the understanding we seek is that of the mechanisms, genetic or epigenetic, whereby the synthesis of specific protein molecules is brought about. Since the enzymatic content of a cell is a principal feature by which the state of biochemical differentiation is assessed, that is, genes express themselves in terms of enzyme production, there is profit in focusing on a particular enzyme. One which has been extensively investigated is lactate dehydrogenase (LDH), known to exist in at least five electrophoretically distinct molecular varieties, or isozymes, and having a ubiquitous distribution in the tissues of vertebrates (Markert, 75, 76; Markert and Møller, 77; Markert and Ursprung, 78). The specific characteristics of each tissue are based on the specific proportions of the several isozymes rather than the presence or absence of particular ones. Since the patterns of adult tissues are different, it follows that these patterns must arise during embryogeny. With respect to the developing kidney of the mouse, Markert and Ursprung (78) have demonstrated a gradual shift from a preferential synthesis of LDH-5 in fetuses 5 days prior to birth toward the LDH-1 and LDH-2 ends of the spectrum characteristic of the adult kidney. More recently, Croisille (reported by Ebert, 25) has described the presence of at least two additional isozymes in tissues of embryonic and adult chickens, isozymes which seem to disappear in progressively older mesonephroi.

Although there is a substantial body of data showing the hand-in-hand development of many enzymes and functional differentiation in embryos generally, the LDH case is really the first one in which a causal connection is strongly suggested, and hopefully, it points the way to the future. In fact, if this reviewer may be permitted a prediction, it is that some years hence, when his counterpart writes a progress report such as this, it will be a report couched largely in terms of differentiations of protein systems and their genetic control.

Summary

The kidney of vertebrates consists of an aggregation of tubular units known as nephrons, derived embryonically from the intermediate mesoderm. It has been hypothesized that the nephrons of the original vertebrates were all alike and opened independently to the exterior. But in all known vertebrates the nephrons empty into some variety of common drainage duct (nephric duct). Moreover, the nephrons exhibit increasing complexity from front to rear and, embryonically, appear in an anterior-posterior time sequence. In embryos of fishes and amphibians this sequence manifests itself in an early-appearing and transitory pronephros which is succeeded by an opisthonephros destined to become the definitive kidney; among amniotes the pronephros, rudimentary at best, is followed by a mesonephros which in turn is succeeded by the metanephros. That these various nephroi are actually only regions of a holonephric continuum rather than discrete organs is suggested by (1) their morphological overlap and intergradations of tubule types, (2) the uniformity of physiological performance of their constituent nephrons, and (3) the homogeneity of developmental potency of the nephrogenic blastema.

Although it is customarily said that the nephric duct originates by the junction of the distal extremities of the pronephrons, there are few well-documented cases of this actuality. Rather, the duct appears to differentiate directly within the intermediate mesoderm. There is good descriptive and experimental evidence supporting the conclusion that once initiated, the duct reaches the cloaca by free terminal growth. Enroute, the nephric duct is joined by later-appearing mesonephric (or opisthonephric) tubules. Much experimental evidence indicates that differentiation of mesonephrons is dependent upon induction by the primary nephric duct. However, inconsistencies and inadequacies within this evidence preclude a final conclusion to this effect. In contrast, the role played by the ureteric outgrowth from the nephric duct in the induction of metanephrons seems to be clearly positive. In fact, there is reason to believe induction of metanephrons is mediated by a chemical substance of such molecular size as to suggest it is proteinaceous. Recent studies of the coincidental rise of certain enzymes and functional differentiation of the kidney and other organs point the way to an understanding of differentiating protein systems and their genetic control.

References

1. Audigé, J., "Contribution à l'Étude des Reins des Poissons Téléostéens," *Arch. Zool. Exptl. Gén.* Ser. 5, 4:275–624, (1910).
2. Auer, J., "Bilateral Renal Agenesia, *Anat. Record* 97:283–292 (1947).
3. Auerbach, R., "Morphogenetic Interactions in the Development of the Mouse Thymus Gland," *Develop. Biol.* 2:271–284 (1960).
4. Balfour, F. M., and A. Sedgwick, "On the Existence of a Head-kidney in the Embryo Chick, and on Certain Points in the Development of the Müllerian Duct," *Quart. J. Microscop. Sci.* 19:1–20 (1897).
5. Beyer, K. H., R. H. Painter, and V. D. Wibelhaus, "Enzymatic Factors in the Renal Tubular Secretion of Phenol Red," *Am. J. Physiol.* 161:259–267 (1950).
6. ———, H. F. Russo, S. R. Gass, K. M. Wilhoyte, and A. A. Pitt, "Renal Tubular Elimination of n'-Methylnicotinamide," *Am. J. Physiol.* 160:311–320 (1950).
7. Boyden, E. A., "Experimental Obstruction of the Mesonephric Ducts," *Proc. Soc. Exptl. Biol. Med.* 24:572–576 (1927).
8. ———, "Congenital Absence of the Kidney. An Interpretation Based on a 10 mm. Human Embryo Exhibiting Unilateral Renal Agenesis," *Anat. Record* 52:325–350 (1932).
9. Brauer, A., "Beiträge zur Kenntniss der Entwicklung und Anatomie der Gymnophionen. III. Die Entwicklung der Excretionsorgane," *Zool. Jahrb. Abt. 2 Anat. Ontog. Tiere* 16:1–176 (1902).
10. Bremer, J. L., "The Interrelations of the Mesonephros, Kidney and Placenta in Different Classes of Animals," *Am. J. Anat.* 19:179–209 (1916).
11. Buchanan, G., and E. A. Fraser, "The Development of the Urogenital System in the Marsupialia, with Special Reference to *Trichosurus vulpecula*," *J. Anat.* Part I, 53:11–26 (1918).
12. Burland, T. H., "The Pronephros of *Chrysemys marginata*," *Zool. Jahrb. Abt. 2 Anat. Ontog. Tiere* 36:1–90 (1913).
13. Burns, R. K., "Development of the Mesonephros in *Amblystoma* after Early Extirpation of the Duct," *Proc. Soc. Exptl. Biol. Med.* 39:111–113 (1938).
14. ———, "Urinogenital System," *Analysis of Development*, B. H. Willier, P. A. Weiss, V. Hamburger, eds., Philadelphia: Saunders pp. 462–491 (1955).
15. Calame, S., "Contribution Expérimentale à l'Étude du Développement du Système Urogénital de l'Embryon d'Oiseau," *Arch. Anat. Strasbourg* 94:45–65 (1962).
16. Cambar, R., "Recherches Expérimentales sur les Facteurs de la Morphogenèse du Mésonéphros chez les Amphibiens Anoures," *Bull. Biol.* 82:214–285 (1948).
17. ———, "Données Récentes sur le Développement du Système Pronéphrétique chez les Amphibiens (Anoures en

Particulier)," *Ann. Biol.* 25:115–130 (1949).

18. ——, "Essai Expérimental de Déviation de l'Uretère Primaire au Cours de Son Développement chez les Amphibiens Anoures," *Compt. Rend. Soc. Biol.* 147:806–808 (1953).

19. Chaube, S., "Hypoxanthine Dehydrogenase in the Developing Chick Embryonic Kidney," *Proc. Soc. Exptl. Biol. Med.* 111:340–342 (1962).

20. Clark, H., and D. Fischer, "A Reconsideration of Nitrogen Excretion by the Chick Embryo," *J. Exptl. Zool.* 136:1–15 (1957).

21. Croisille, Y., "Etude Immunochemique de Quelques Constituants Charactéristique de l'Adult dans le Rein Embryonnaire de Poulet," *Compt. Rend. Soc. Biol.* 156:1221–1225 (1962).

22. Dalcq, A., "Contribution à l'Étude du Potentiel Morphogénétique chez les Anoures. III. Opérations Visant l'Ébauche Pronéphrétique au Seuil de la Gastrulation," *Arch. Biol.* 53:1–124 (1942).

23. Dalton, A. J., "Structural Details of Some of the Epithelial Cell Types in the Kidney of the Mouse as Revealed by the Electron Microscope," *J. Natl. Cancer Inst.* 11:1163–1185 (1951).

24. Davies, J., "Correlated Anatomical and Histochemical Studies on the Mesonephros and Placenta of the Sheep," *Am. J. Anat.* 91:263–299 (1952).

25. Ebert, J. D., "Developmental, Kinetic and Immunological Studies of Enzymes," *Carnegie Inst. Wash.*, Year Book 62:428–437 (1963).

26. Elias, A. H., "De Structura Glomeruli Renalis," *Anat. Anz.* 104:26–36 (1957).

27. Emery, C., "Le Specie del Genere *Fierasfer* nel Golfo di Napoli e Regione Limitrofe," *Fauna Flora Neapel* 2:1–76 (1880).

28. Eränkö, O., and L. Lehto, "Distribution of Acid and Alkaline Phosphatases in Human Metanephros," *Acta Anat.* 22:277–288 (1954).

29. Fales, D. E., "Experiments on the Development of the Pronephros of *Amblystoma punctatum*," *J. Exptl. Zool.* 72:147–173 (1935).

30. Felix, W., "The Development of the Urinogenital Organs," *Manual of Human Embryology*, F. Keibel, F. B. Mall, eds.

Philadelphia: Lippincott, vol. 2, chap. 19, pp. 752–979 (1912).

31. Fisher, J. R., and R. E. Eakin, "Nitrogen Excretion in Developing Chick Embryos," *J. Embryol. Exptl. Morphol.* 5:215–224 (1957).

32. Forster, R. P., "Kidney Cells," *The Cell*, J. Brachet, A. E. Mirsky, eds. New York: Academic Press, vol. 5 (1961).

33. ——, and J. H. Copenhaver, "Intracellular Accumulation as an Active Process in a Mammalian Renal Transport System *in vitro*," *Am. J. Physiol.* 186:167–171 (1956).

34. ——, and S. K. Hong, "*In vitro* Transport of Dyes by Isolated Renal Tubules of the Flounder as Disclosed by Direct Visualization. Intracellular Accumulation and Transcellular Movement," *J. Cellular Comp. Physiol.* 51:259–272 (1958).

35. ——, and J. V. Taggart, "Use of Isolated Renal Tubules for the Examination of Metabolic Processes Associated with Active Cellular Transport," *J. Cellular Comp. Physiol.* 36:251–270 (1950).

36. Fox, H., "The Amphibian Pronephros," *Quart. Rev. Biol.* 38:1–25 (1963).

37. Fraser, E. A., "Observations on the Development of the Pronephros of the Sturgeon, *Acipenser rubicundus*," *Quart. J. Microscop. Sci.* 71:75–112 (1927).

38. ——, "The Development of the Vertebrate Excretory System," *Biol. Rev. Cambridge Phil. Soc.* 25:159–187 (1950).

39. Geertruyden, J. van, "Quelques Précisions sur le Développement du Pronéphros et de l'Uretère Primaire chez les Amphibiens Anoures," *Ann. Soc. Roy. Belg.* 73:180–195 (1942).

40. ——, "Recherches Expérimentales sur la Formation du Mésonéphros Chez les Amphibiens Anoures," *Arch. Biol. Paris* 57:145–181 (1946).

41. Gérard, P., and R. Cordier, "Esquisse d'une Histophysiologie Comparée du Rein des Vertébrés," *Biol. Rev. Cambridge Phil. Soc.* 9:110–131 (1934).

42. —— and ——, "Recherches d'Histophysiologie Comparée sur le Pro- et le Mésonéphros Larvaires des Anoures," *Z. Zellforsch. Mikroskop. Anat.* 21:1–23 (1934).

43. Gersh, I., "The Correlation of Structure and Function in the Developing

Mesonephros and Metanephros," *Contrib. Embryol. Carnegie Inst. Wash.* 26: 33–58 (1937).

44. Gluecksohn-Schoenheimer, S., "Causal Analysis of Mouse Development by the Study of Mutational Factors," *Growth* Suppl. 9:163–176 (1949).

45. Gluecksohn-Waelsch, S., "Lethal Genes and Analysis of Differentiation," *Science* 142:1269–1276 (1963).

46. ――, and T. R. Rota, "Development in Organ Tissue Culture of Kidney Rudiments from Mutant Mouse Embryos," *Develop. Biol.* 7:432–444 (1963).

47. Goodrich, E. S., *Studies on the Structure and Development of the Vertebrates.* New York: Macmillan, chap. 13 (1930).

48. Grobstein, C., "Analysis *in vitro* of the Early Organization of the Rudiment of the Mouse Sub-mandibular Gland," *J. Morphol.* 93:19–44 (1953).

49. ――, "Epithelio-mesenchymal Specificity in the Morphogenesis of Mouse Sub-mandibular Rudiments *in vitro,*" *J. Exptl. Zool.* 124:383–414 (1953).

50. ――, "Inductive Epithelio-mesenchymal Interaction in Cultured Organ Rudiments of the Mouse," *Science* 118: 52–55 (1953).

51. ――, "Inductive Interaction in the Development of the Mouse Metanephros," *J. Exptl. Zool.* 130:319–340 (1955).

52. ――, "Trans-filter Induction of Tubules in Mouse Metanephrogenic Mesenchyme," *Exptl. Cell Res.* 10:424–440 (1956).

53. ――, "Some Transmission Characteristics of the Tubule-inducing Influence on Mouse Metanephrogenic Mesenchyme," *Exptl. Cell Res.* 13:575–587 (1957).

54. ――, "Autoradiography of the Interzone between Tissues in Inductive Interaction," *J. Exptl. Zool.* 142:203–213 (1959).

55. ――, "Cell Contact in Relation to Embryonic Induction," *Exptl. Cell Res.* Suppl. 8:234–245 (1961).

56. ――, "Cytodifferentiation and Its Controls," *Science* 143:643–650 (1964).

57. ――, and A. J. Dalton, "Kidney Tubule Induction in Mouse Metanephrogenic Mesenchyme without Cytoplasmic Contact," *J. Exptl. Zool.* 135:57–73 (1957).

58. Gruenwald, P., "Zur Entwicklungsmechanik des Urogenital Systems beim Huhn," *Arch. Entwicklungsmech. Or.* 136:786–813 (1937).

59. ――, "The Mechanism of Kidney Development in Human Embryos as Revealed by an Early Stage in the Agenesis of the Ureteric Buds," *Anat. Record* 75: 237–247 (1939).

60. ――, "Experiments on Distribution and Activation of the Nephrogenic Potency in the Embryonic Mesenchyme," *Physiol. Zool.* 15:396–409 (1942).

61. ――, "Stimulation of Nephrogenic Tissue by Normal and Abnormal Inductors," *Anat. Record* 86:321–339 (1943).

62. ――, "Development of the Excretory System," *The Chick Embryo in Biological Research. Ann. N.Y. Acad. Sci.* 55:142–146 (1952).

63. Guitel, F., "Recherches zur l'Anatomie des Reins des Gobiéscocidés," *Arch. Zool. Exptl. Gen.* 5:505–698 (1906).

64. Holtfreter, J., "Experimental Studies on the Development of the Pronephros," *Rev. Can. Biol.* 3:220–250 (1944).

65. Humphrey, R. R., "The Developmental Potencies of the Intermediate Mesoderm of *Ambystoma* when Transplanted into Ventro-lateral Sites in Other Embryos. The Primordial Germ Cells of Such Grafts and Their Role in the Development of the Gonads," *Anat. Record* 40: 67–102 (1928).

66. Jaffee, O. C., "Phenol Red Transport in the Pronephros and Mesonephros of the Developing Frog (*Rana pipiens*)," *J. Cellular Comp. Physiol.* 44:347–364 (1954).

67. Junqueira, L. C. V., "Phosphomonoesterase Content and Localization in the Meso- and Metanephros of the Chick Embryo," *Quart. J. Microscop. Sci.* 93: 247–257 (1952).

68. Keibel, F., "Über die Entwickelung des Urogenitalapparates von *Echidna,*" *Verhandl. Anat. Ges. Heidelberg* 14–19 (1903).

69. Kerens, B., "Recherches sur les Premières Phases du Développement de l'Appareil Excréteur des Amniotes," *Arch. Biol. Paris* 22:493–648 (1907).

70. Kerr, J. G., *Text-book of Embryology, Vertebrata with the Exception of Mammalia.* London: Macmillan, vol. 2 (1919).

71. Kurz, S. M., "The Electron Microscopy

of the Developing Human Renal Glomerulus," *Exptl. Cell Res.* 14:355–367 (1958).

72. Lash, J., S. Holtzer, and H. Holtzer, "An Experimental Analysis of the Development of the Spinal Column. VI. Aspects of Cartilage Induction," *Exptl. Cell Res.* 13:292–303 (1957).

73. Leeson, T. S., "The Fine Structure of the Mesonephros of the 17-day Rabbit Embryo," *Exptl. Cell Res.* 12:670–672 (1957).

74. Machemer, H., "Differenzierungsfähigkeit der Urnierenanlage von *Triton alpestris*," *Arch. Entwicklungsmech. Or.* 118:200–251 (1929).

75. Markert, C. L., "Epigenetic Control of Specific Protein Synthesis in Differentiating Cells," *Cytodifferentiation and Macromolecular Synthesis*, M. Locke, ed., *Ann. 21st Growth Symp.* New York: Academic Press, pp. 65–84 (1962).

76. ——, "Isozymes in Kidney Development," *Proc. 13th Ann. Conf. Kidney – Genetic, Developmental, and Immunological Aspects of Renal Disease*, J. Metcoff, ed. Evanston, Ill.: Northwestern University Press, pp. 54–63 (1962).

77. ——, and F. Møller, "Multiple Forms of Enzymes: Tissue, Ontogenetic, and Species Specific Patterns," *Proc. Natl. Acad. Sci. U.S.* 45:753–763 (1959).

78. ——, and H. Ursprung, "The Ontogeny of Isozyme Patterns of Lactate Dehydrogenase in the Mouse," *Develop. Biol.* 5:363–381 (1962).

79. Maschkowzeff, A., "Zur Phylogenie des Urogenitalsystems der Wirbeltiere auf Grund der Entwicklung des Mesoderms, des Pronephros, der Analöffnung und der Abdominalporen bei *Acipenser stellatus*," *Zool. Jahrb. Abt. 2, Anat. Ontog.* 48:201–272 (1926).

80. Miura, K., "Experimentelle Untersuchungen über die genetische Beziehung zwischen dem Wolffschen Gang und der Urniere bei Froschlarven," *Japan. J. Med. Sci. Anat.* 2:105–124 (1930).

81. Moog, F., "The Physiological Significance of the Phosphomonoesterases," *Biol. Rev. Cambridge Phil. Soc.* 21:41–59 (1946).

82. ——, "The Adaptations of Alkaline and Acid Phosphatase in Development,"

Cell, Organism, and Milieu, D. Rudnick, ed. New York: Ronald, pp. 121–155 (1959).

83. Muchmore, W. B., "Differentiation of the Trunk Mesoderm in *Amblystoma maculatum*," *J. Exptl. Zool.* 118:137–180 (1951).

84. Needham, J., *Chemical Embryology*. Cambridge: Cambridge University Press (1931).

85. Nieuwkoop, P. D., "Experimental Investigations on the Origin and Determination of the Germ Cells, and on the Development of the Lateral Plates and Germ Ridges in Urodeles," *Arch. Néerl. Zool.* 8:1–205 (1947).

86. O'Connor, R. J., "Experiments on the Development of the Pronephric Duct," *J. Anat.* 73:145–154 (1938).

87. ——, "Experiments on the Development of the Amphibian Mesonephros," *J. Anat.* 74:34–44 (1939).

88. ——, "An Experimental Study of the Development of the Amphibian Cloaca," *J. Anat.* 74:301–308 (1940).

89. Overton, J., "Studies on the Mode of Outgrowth of the Amphibian Pronephric Duct," *J. Embryol. Exptl. Morphol.* 7:86–93 (1959).

90. Pasteels, J., "New Observations Concerning the Maps of Presumptive Areas of the Young Amphibian Gastrula (*Amblystoma* and *Discoglossus*)," *J. Exptl. Zool.* 89:255–281 (1942).

91. Price, G. C., "Development of the Excretory Organs of a Myxinoid, *Bdellostoma stouti*, Lockington," *Zool. Jahrb. Abt. Anat. Ontog.* 10:205–226 (1897).

92. ——, "A Further Study of the Development of the Excretory Organs in *Bdellostoma stouti*," *Am. J. Anat.* 4:117–138 (1904).

93. Rapola, J., T. Vainio, and L. Saxén, "Viral Susceptibility and Embryonic Differentiation. IV. An Attempt to Correlate Viral Susceptibility with the Metabolism and Proliferation in Embryonic Tissues," *J. Embryol. Exptl. Morphol.* 11:757–764 (1963).

94. Rawles, M. E., "A Study in the Localization of Organ-forming Areas in the Chick Blastoderm of the Head-process Stage," *J. Exptl. Zool.* 72:271–315 (1936).

95. Robinson, J. R., *Reflections on Renal*

Function. Springfield, Ill.: Charles C Thomas (1954).

96. Romanoff, A. L., *The Avian Embryo. Structural and Functional Development.* New York: Macmillan (1960).

97. Rudnick, D., "Early History and Mechanics of the Chick Blastoderm," *Quart. Rev. Biol.* 19:187–212 (1944).

98. Runner, M. N., "The Development of the Mesonephros of the Albino Rat in Intraocular Grafts," *J. Exptl. Zool.* 103:305–320 (1946).

99. Shimasaki, Y., "Entwicklungsmechanische Untersuchung über die Urniere des *Bufo,*" *Japan J. Med. Sci. Anat.* 2:291–319 (1930).

100. Smith, H. W., *Principles of Renal Physiology.* London: Oxford University Press (1956).

101. Smith, C. H., and J. M. Kissane, "Distribution of Forms of Lactic Dehydrogenase within the Developing Rat Kidney," *Develop. Biol.* 8:151–164 (1963).

102. Swaen, A., and A. Brachet, "Études sur les Premières Phases du Développement des Organes Dérivés du Mesoblaste chez les Poissons Téléostéens," *Arch. Biol. Paris* 18:73–190 (1901).

103. Torrey, T. W., "The Absorption of Colloidal Carbon from the Body Cavity of Ammocoetes. A Study of the Structure and Function of the Larval Kidneys and Blood Forming Tissues," *J. Morphol.* 63:163–179 (1938).

104. ———, "The Development of the Urinogenital System of the Albino Rat. I. The Kidney and Its Ducts," *Am. J. Anat.* 72:113–147 (1943).

105. ———, "Intraocular Grafts of Embryonic Gonads of the Rat," *J. Exptl. Zool.* 115:37–58 (1950).

106. ———, "The Early Development of the Human Nephros," *Contrib. Embryol. Carnegie Inst. Wash.* 35:175–197 (1954).

107. Tung, T. C., and S. H. Ku, "Experimental Studies on the Development of the Pronephric Duct in Anuran Embryos," *J. Anat.* 78:52–57 (1944).

108. Waddington, C. H., "The Morphogenetic Function of a Vestigial Organ in the Chick," *J. Exptl. Biol.* 15:371–376 (1938).

109. Winton, F. R., *Modern Views on the Secretion of Urine.* Boston: Little, Brown (1956).

110. Wharton, L. R., "Double Ureters and Associated Renal Anomalies in Early Human Embryos," *Contrib. Embryol. Carnegie Inst. Wash.* 33:103–112 (1949).

111. Yamada, T., "Der Determinationszustand des Rumpfmesoderms im Molchkeim nach der Gastrulation," *Arch. Entwicklungsmech. Or.* 137:151–270 (1937).

The Reproductive System

A. SEXUAL DIFFERENTIATION

23

Genetic Control of Sexual Differentiation

in Vertebrates

L. G. Gallien*

Laboratoire d'Embryologie
Faculté des Sciences
Université de Paris
Paris, France

Sexual differentiation is an array of processes which in the course of development insures the organogenesis of gonads and of somatic organs associated in various ways with sexual reproduction. The singularity of sexual differentiation resides in a dual morphogenesis, that of male and that of female, which results in sexual dimorphism. This is based, in each species, upon a common hereditary foundation which is matched by a genetic dissymmetry, represented in the best cases by cytologically identifiable sex chromosomes. Therefore, the analysis of sexual differentiation imposes the consideration of the first elements which control it, genetic constitution and physiology of sex genes. Three

phenomena are interrelated in sexual organogenesis:

1. *The genetic substrate.* During normal development, it is the genome which controls the formation of sex, that is to say, it determines male or female differentiation.

2. *Intrinsic epigenetic factors of development.* These are essentially enzymatic systems, inductive substances and hormones which are characteristic of the ontogeny of the species being considered and which act normally at different phases of development.

3. *Extrinsic epigenetic factors of development.* These are environment, traumatic and teratogenic agents, drugs, surgical interventions, isolation, deficiencies, and recombinations. The use of these agents and the actions they provoke on the germinal system are ways of analyzing the mechanisms of sexual differentiation. Irradiation,

* The author expresses his gratitude to J. Bagnara of the Department of Zoology, University of Tuscon, Tuscon, Arizona, for his help in the English translation of the manuscript.

583

grafting, parabiosis, administration of steroid hormones, and organ cultures have been used for this type of experimentation.

The organs of sexual reproduction of the adult are linked by a chain of events in both differentiation and function. It is convenient to distinguish the following categories.

GONADS. The gonads carry the germinal cells and also act as a relay controlling the somatic sexual characters by means of the production of hormones. In the differentiation of the embryonic gonad two territories play a major role – the cortex and the medulla. These are potentially gynogenic and androgenic areas, respectively. After an indifferent period, sexual differentiation is expressed by dominance of one of these two territories, while the other involutes. Therefore, at the start of sexual differentiation the gonads are of ambisexual structure, having the potentiality of developing in either the male or female direction. It is the sex genes which control the direction of this development. This leads to the conception that the organism is on one hand genetically bisexual and on the other has a mechanism which insures the predominance of either cortex or medulla.

SOMATIC SEX CHARACTERS. The somatic sex characters intervene in various degrees in the physiology of reproduction. We must consider the genital tract (Wolffian and Müllerian ducts), the external organs used for mating (genital tubercle, callosities, ovipositor, gonopodium), and the sexual ornaments. It should be noted that for all these organs, initial ambisexuality is the rule.

The problem of genetic control of sexual differentiation presents itself from two points of view: the genetic structure of sex of the egg, and the physiology of genes controlling sexuality. By which path does genetic constitution express itself? In what measure can intrinsic and extrinsic epigenetic factors modify the expression of genetic information during the course of ontogeny?

The study of the genetic control of sexual differentiation is, understandably, quite broad. In the scope of this article, we have qualified this theme by selecting certain trends of research which are limited principally to the vertebrates. Among these, amphibians will be given particular attention. Ponse (95, 96) and Witschi (118), in the course of a colloquium on "Sexual Differentiation in Vertebrates" held in Paris in 1950, reviewed the genetic aspects of these problems. For a thorough analysis of the literature before 1950 and for a complete bibliography, we recommend these reviews. They are also valuable for providing a background which will facilitate the comprehension of the more recent developments.

Sex Chromosomes in Vertebrates

The genetic constitution of sex in vertebrates is classically based upon two principles. First of all, there is genetic dissymmetry. One of the parents is homogametic, while the other is heterogametic. This accounts for the sex ratio ($1♀ : 1♂$). Beyond this, fundamental sexual bipotentiality of inheritance is the rule. Every individual possesses, simultaneously, feminizing and masculinizing genes which are necessary to orient sexual differentiation, either in the female direction (ΣF), or in the male direction (ΣM). However, there is a prevalence in one of the sexualizing genes or the other, and it is this which dictates the direction of differentiation. In other words, we may speak of a genic balance (see Bridges, 8).

Karyotype and Heterochromosomes

Genetic dissymmetry may be expressed by a cytologically visible dimorphism in sex chromosomes. However, except in mammals in which sex chromosomes have been well observed, this situation is relatively rare among vertebrates (Matthey, 84; Becak et al., 4a; Weiler and Ohno, 108). Three lines of research have provided some new information in the field of sex chromosomes in vertebrates.

Lampbrush Chromosomes

Among urodele amphibians, studies on the lampbrush chromosomes of *Triturus cristatus* (Callan and Lloyd, 13) have revealed that the longest pair of giant chromosomes are quite distinguishable — one of the arms of the pair is heterochromatic and each component of the arm is characteristically different from the other. This observable dimorphism in a chromosome pair indicates that the karyotype of *Triturus cristatus* is ZZ, ZW. This is in agreement with observations made on the axolotl and *Pleurodeles* with other methods.

Sex Chromatin

Barr and Bertram (3) discovered a Feulgen-positive granule in the interphase nucleus of neurons of the female cat. This granule, called sex chromatin, is about 1 μ in diameter and does not exist in the male. The nature of this granule has recently been clarified (Ohno et al., 89; Davidson and Winn, 21; McKusick, 85a; Grumbach and Barr, 57, 57a), primarily in human cells. The granule is derived from one X chromosome, which is characterized by its peculiar behavior in mitosis: it is heterochromatic, and replicates relatively late. Persons with three X chromosomes have two late-replicating ones, and accordingly, two Barr bodies.

Kosin and Ishizaki (79) have observed the sex chromatin in birds.

Sex Chromosomes of Mammals

The study of mammalian karyotypes has been renewed by applying together the techniques of tissue culture and squashes of tissue pretreated with colchicine (Tjio and Levan, 105; Ford and Hamerton, 29).

In all mammals (Matthey, 84; Makino, 83; Tobias, 106) dimorphism of sex chromosomes is the rule, with the male always heterogametic (XY). The XO constitution has been observed in the mouse and in man, but these are cases of aneuploidy, except in the case of *Microtus oregani*. So far, some examples of mammals with compound heterochromosomes have been found: *Macropus ualabatus*, XY_1Y_2 (Agar, 1); *Sorex araneus* XY_1Y_2 (Bovey, 6); *Potourus tridactylus* XY_1Y_2 (Sharman et al, 103); *Gerbillus gerbillus* XY_1Y_2 (Matthey, 84a); *Microtus minutoides* $X_1X_2Y/\male$, $X_1X_2/\female$ (Matthey, 84b).

Experimental Analysis of the Genetic Constitution of Sex

Because cytological information is limited in the vertebrates, the hereditary structure of sex has been established from a genetic analysis which is based upon the use of appropriate crosses. The transmission of sex-linked characters has been studied in teleosts, birds, and mammals. This has permitted us to understand the nature of homo- and heterogametic sex for these classes. These historic methods are only mentioned in passing, however, since the following discussion will involve the use of techniques based upon the analysis of progeny of animals that had been sex reversed.

Amphibians

Crew (17) and Witschi (115) were able to obtain progeny of *Rana temporaria* hermaphrodites. The study of the sex ratio of these crosses established the fact that the homogametic sex was female. In the toad, *Bufo bufo*, Harms (59) and Ponse (94) were able to utilize the Bidder's organ, which is a vestigial ovary existing in both sexes. In males, after ablation of the testis, Bidder's organ became a functional ovary and later a complete feminization of the male was obtained. By crossing these neofemales with standard males, progeny was obtained. Unfortunately, the results of Harms and of Ponse differed radically and thus the homogametic sex could not be definitely established (see Ponse, 95, 96). It could only be concluded that these experiments demonstrated the genetic bipotentiality of sex.

Ambystoma

In a long series of well-known experiments on *Ambystoma*, Humphrey (62, 64), using a technique of transplanting gonad primordia at tailbud stages, was able to obtain a series of sex-reversed animals. These neofemales or neomales were crossed with standard males and females and the progeny was analyzed.

The principle which underlies this type of crossing is simple. For example, in *Ambystoma*, in which male homogamety has been demonstrated by this method, a normal cross insuring an even sex ratio (1 ♀ : 1 ♂) is written:

$$♂ \; ZZ \quad \times \quad ♀ \; ZW$$
$$50\% \; ♂ \; ZZ \quad 50\% \; ♀ \; ZW$$

If a female (ZW) is reversed into a functional neomale and is crossed with a standard female (ZW), the cross is written:

$$♀ \; ZW \quad \times \quad ♂ \; ZW$$
$$\text{(standard)} \quad \text{(neomale)}$$
$$♂ \; ZZ \quad ♀ \; ZW \quad ♀ \; ZW \quad ♀ \; WW$$
$$25\% ♂ \qquad 75\% \; ♀$$

A new type of female (WW) appears. Humphrey was able to obtain WW females reversed into neomales. They could be crossed with a standard female (ZW) or a female (WW).

If a genetic male (ZZ) is experimentally sex reversed into a functional neofemale, a cross of this animal with a standard male (ZZ) would be written:

$$♂ \; ZZ \quad \times \quad ♀ \; ZZ \quad \longrightarrow \quad 100\% \; ♂ \; ZZ$$
$$\text{(standard)} \quad \text{(neofemale)}$$

For this last cross, Humphrey (64) analyzed progeny of white axolotl genetic females which had been grafted with a small portion of a gonadal primordium from a black male. When these white females were crossed with standard white males, all the progenies of the black type were male. It is known that black is dominant over white. Thus, the ZZ gonocytes from the black donor differentiated into oocytes in the white female host. Since they had the male genotype (ZZ), the cross with a normal male resulted in 100 percent ZZ offspring.

Pleurodeles waltlii

Administration of estradiol to this species' during larval stages gives rise to individuals which are all females. The 1 ♂ : 1 ♀ sex ratio of controls indicates that, in reality, half of the females are genetic males which were transformed into neofemales (Gallien, 36, 38). Crossing these with standard males gives rise to progenies which are all males (Table 23.1).

The analysis of progeny indicates that in *Pleurodeles* the male sex is homogametic.

Xenopus laevis

The same experiment in which males were reversed to females by treatment with estradiol has been performed on the lower anuran, *Xenopus laevis* (Gallien, 39, 40; Chang and Witschi, 16). All results obtained with *Xenopus* (Table 23.2) indicate that the male sex is homogametic.

Mikamo and Witschi (86, 86a) have recently completed analysis of genetic constitution of sex in *Xenopus laevis*. Grafting a differentiated testis into a larva which has not yet undergone sex differentiation at first induces a marked inhibition of the host's gonads, whether or not it is male or

TABLE 23.1   Progeny of *Pleurodeles waltlii* after Inversion of Sexual Phenotype[a]

NUMBER OF FEMALES TESTED	GENETIC FEMALES (ZW) WITH BISEXUAL PROGENY			GENETIC MALES (NEOFEMALES ZZ) WITH UNISEXUAL PROGENY		
	NO. OF ♀	F_1 ♂♂	F_1 ♀♀	NO. OF ♀	F_1 ♂♂	F_1 ♀♀
22[b]	16	344		6	940	
			310			0
	16	344	310	6	940	0

[a] After Gallien, *Bull. Biol. France Belg.* 88:1–51, 1954.

[b] In addition to the 22 functional females, there were a number of sterile females which were actually transformed males. As a result, the sex ratio based upon 22 cases of fertile females is altered.

TABLE 23.2   Progeny of *Xenopus laevis* after Inversion of Sexual Phenotype[a]

NUMBER OF FEMALES TESTED	GENETIC FEMALES (ZW) WITH BISEXUAL PROGENY			GENETIC MALES (NEOFEMALES ZZ) WITH UNISEXUAL PROGENY		
	NO. OF ♀	F_1 ♂♂	F_1 ♀♀	NO. OF ♀	F_1 ♂♂	F_1 ♀♀
31	18	505		13	1624	
			457			0
	18	505	457	13	1624	0

[a] Combined results of Gallien, *Compt. Rend. Acad. Sci.* 240:913–915, 1955; *Bull. Biol. France Belg.* 90:163–183, 1956; Chang and Witschi, *Proc. Soc. Exptl. Biol. Med.* 89:150–152, 1955.

female. If this is followed by an ablation of the grafted testis, the gonadal
vestiges of the host, in some cases,
resume their development. As it happens, the medullary component which
is potentially androgenic becomes
prevalent, even in genetic females. As
a result, testes develop and neomales
are obtained. The genetic analysis of
sex-reversed *Xenopus* females was carried out in the same way as that for
Ambystoma by Humphrey. Of ten
animals which were grafted in this
way, and which behaved as males
during breeding experiments, eight
were genetic males (ZZ) and two were
genetic females (ZW). The results of
these breeding experiments are given
in Table 23.3.

males) or with standard females (ZW).
In the former, all progenies were
males, while in the latter an equal sex
ratio (1 ♂ : 1 ♀) was obtained.

Karyotypic observations in *Xenopus
laevis* have confirmed the conclusions
made from genetic analyses (Weiler
and Ohno, 108). The W chromosome
is larger than the Z chromosome and
is larger than any other chromosome.

Rana japonica

In Ranidae, administration of an
androgen (testosterone) to tadpoles
gives rise to individuals which are
all males. Recalling the experiment of
Gallien (34) on *Rana temporaria*, Kawamura and Yokota (77) were able to
raise individuals of *Rana japonica*

TABLE 23.3   Progeny of *Xenopus laevis* of Neomales and Neofemales[a]

TESTIS-IMPLANTED FATHERS	ZZ MOTHERS (ESTROGEN CONVERTS)				ZW MOTHERS (CONTROLS)			
	OFFSPRING							
	TOTAL FROGS	MALE		FEMALE		TOTAL FROGS	MALE		FEMALE	
		NO.	PERCENT	NO.	PERCENT		NO.	PERCENT	NO.	PERCENT
ZW (2 converts)	208	107	51.4 ±2.71	101	48.6 ±2.71	562	144	25.6 ±0.53	418	74.4 ±0.53
ZZ (8 genetic males)	539	539	100	0	0	758	382	50.4 ±1.07	376	49.6 ±1.07

[a] After Mikamo and Witschi, *Genetics* 48:1411–1421, 1963.

A neomale (ZW) crossed with a neofemale (ZZ), which was actually a
genetic male feminized with estrogens,
produced offspring with an equal
sex ratio (1 ♂ : 1 ♀). Crossing the same
neomale with a standard female (ZW)
produced offspring with a sex ratio of
1 ♂ : 3 ♀. The genotype of these progeny must have been 1 ZZ : 2 ZW : 1
WW. In eight cases the crosses were
those of ZZ males which had received testis grafts and which remained
male. These males were crossed either
with neofemales (ZZ, estrogenized

which were sex reversed (neomales)
by male hormone treatment (♀ → ♂).
Subsequent crosses showed that the
female sex was homogametic, XX : XY
(Table 23.4).

Teleost

Analyses comparable to those carried
out on amphibians have been performed by Yamamoto (127–130) on the
teleost, *Oryzias latipes*. The work of
Aida (2), based on the transmission of
sex-linked pigmentary factors, has
demonstrated that this species is of

TABLE 23.4   Progeny of *Rana japonica* after Sex Reversal[a]

NUMBER OF MALES TESTED	GENETIC MALES (XY) WITH BISEXUAL PROGENY			GENETIC FEMALES (NEOMALES XX) WITH UNISEXUAL PROGENY		
	NO. OF ♂	F_1 ♂♂	F_1 ♀♀	NO. OF ♂	F_1 ♀♀	F_1 ♂♂
12	4	147		8	399	
			184			1
	4	147	184	8	399	1[b]

[a] After Kawamura and Yokota, *J. Sci. Hiroshima Univ.* 18:31–38, 1959.
[b] Interpreted by the authors as a consequence of secondary epigenetic effect on a genetic female.

XX, XY type. In his studies, Yamamoto used both the analysis of progenies of parents which had been sex reversed and the transmission of genes which act as color markers. Sex reversal was carried out by treating the fry with estrone and methyltestosterone. In *Oryzias* there is a dominant gene, *R*, which gives the fish a pale red color and a recessive gene, *r*, which in the homozygous condition causes white coloration. *R* and *r* are carried on sex chromosomes and the two genes can be exchanged by crossing over of Y and X. In his experiments, Yamamoto used a strain in which *R* was carried by Y and *r* by X. These are the crosses:

Control

$$F_1 \quad \begin{array}{ccc} X_rX_r & \times & X_rY_R \\ X_rX_r & & X_rY_R \end{array} \quad \text{(type I)}$$
$$\quad\quad 24 \text{ ♀ white} \quad 22 \text{ ♂ Red}$$

In a second series of experiments the F_1 fry were feminized by adding estrone to the aquarium water.

$$\begin{array}{c} F_1 + \\ \text{estrone} \\ \text{(femini-} \\ \text{zation)} \end{array} \begin{array}{ccc} X_rX_r & \times & X_rY_R \\ X_rX_r & & X_rY_R \\ 26 \text{ ♀ white} & & 28 \text{ ♀ Red} \\ & & \text{(neofemales)} \end{array} \text{(type II)}$$

In this way, genetic males (F_1)

marked by the gene *R* were transformed into neofemales. These were then crossed with a standard male.

$$\begin{array}{ccc} & X_rY_R & \times & X_rY_R \\ & \text{(neofemale)} & & \text{(type III)} \end{array}$$
$$F_1 \quad X_rX_r \quad X_rY_R \quad X_rY_R \quad Y_RY_R$$
$$\quad\quad 21 \text{ ♀ white} \quad 51 \text{ ♂ Red}$$

The numerical proportion of sex was in the neighborhood of 1 ♀ : 3 ♂. However, the exact sex ratio was really 1 ♀ : 2.3 ♂. This result could be explained on the basis of a lower viability of Y_RY_R males. The red males obtained from this cross were systematically mated with white standard females (X_rX_r). Two types of progenies (IV and V) were obtained, corresponding to the two genotypes X_rY_R and Y_RY_R.

$$\begin{array}{ccccc} & \text{♀ } X_rX_r & \times & \text{♂ } X_rY_R & \text{(type IV)} \\ F_1 & 764 \text{ ♀ white} & & 900 \text{ ♂ Red} \end{array}$$

$$\begin{array}{ccccc} & \text{♀ } X_rX_r & \times & \text{♂ } Y_RY_R & \text{(type V)} \\ F_1 & & 72 \text{ ♂ Red} \end{array}$$

More recently, Yamamoto (129, 130) obtained reversal of genetic females into neomales. This was obtained by treating the progeny of a type I cross with male hormone (methyltestosterone).

$$X_rX_r \times X_rY_R$$

methyltestosterone

(type VI)

F$_1$ 100% ♂

white neomales   Red males

X_rX_r X_rY_R

X_rX_r × X_rX_r X_rY_R × X_rX_r

♀ standard   neomales   Red males   ♀ standard

X_rX_r X_rX_r X_rY_R

100% ♀ (1376)   50% ♀ (603)   50% ♂ (606)

♀ white   ♀ white   ♂ Red

Finally, Yamamoto (131) has succeeded in reversing sex differentiation of YY zygotes by estrone and has obtained YY females.

Thus, crosses have established that in *Oryzias latipes*, the male sex is heterogametic (XY) and the female sex is homogametic XX.

Conclusions

The results (Table 23.5) obtained from a variety of amphibians and from the teleost, *Oryzias latipes*, by the use of sex-reversal methods demonstrate: (1) The genetic constitution of sex is bisexual in nature. (2) For a given species, sex is homo- heterogametic in nature. (3) In amphibians, two modes of sex determination are represented: homogametic male (ZZ)–heterogametic female (ZW), exemplified by *Ambystoma*, *Pleurodeles*, and *Xenopus*; and homogametic female (XX)–heterogametic male (XY), as in the Ranidae. (4) The sexual form of gametes (spermatozoa and oocytes) is not a necessary consequence of the genotype of the gonia, but rather is the result of the nature of the gonadal territory in which they develop. This emphasizes the role of cortex and medulla respectively as gynogenic and androgenic inductor territories. (5) Animals with a female genetic constitution (ZW)

(WW) (XX) can undergo spermatogenesis just as individuals which are genetically male (ZZ) (XY) (YY) can undergo oogenesis. (6) Organisms with WW and YY genetic constitution which do not normally exist can be obtained. A sperm carrying a W chromosome, which is not normally produced by a species, is viable and has the capacity to fertilize eggs and an oocyte carrying a Y chromosome may be fertilized. (7) Eggs with a ZZ constitution and lacking a W chromosome can develop and differentiate into females just as WW eggs can develop into males. This demonstrates that the influence of sexual factors associated with heterochromosomes is not decisive for the differentiation of sex and that genes of sexuality of a type opposed to those of the heterochromosomes are present in the autosomes.

Heteroploidy and Genetic Control of Sex Differentiation

The mechanism of chromosome distribution, and especially of heterochromosomes, has been well established and the consequences of this distribution on the nature of sexuality have been elucidated; thus a new approach to the comprehension of the genetic control of sex differentiation is available. What is the consequence for the phenomenon of alterations in genome corresponding with heteroploidy? One knows that this term designated all deviations of the diploid number ($2n$) which is characteristic of a given species. Briefly, two major situations are to be considered. In polyploidy the number of chromosomes is a multiple of the fundamental haploid number (n). In this case, the equilibrium relative to the distribution of genes of sexuality can be disturbed. Aneuploidy is defined as the addition or the loss of one or more chromosomes. When this anomaly involves heterochromosomes, the genetic mechanisms controlling sex differentiation are altered. Finally, in the realm of het-

TABLE 23.5   Experimental Sex Reversal in the Teleost *Oryzias* and in Amphibians

NATURE OF EXPERIMENT	STANDARD TYPE *Ambystoma* *Pleurodeles* *Xenopus* ZZ : ZW ♂　♀[a]	NEW TYPE *Ambystoma* *Pleurodeles* *Xenopus*	NEW TYPE *Rana* *Oryzias*	STANDARD TYPE *Rana* *Oryzias* XX : XY ♀　♂	SPECIES	AUTHORS
Special cross Sex reversed ZW♂ ZW♀ · ZW♂		WW ♀			*Ambystoma* *Xenopus*	Humphrey (62) Mikamo and Witschi (86)
Neomale (XX) Hormonal treatment XX♀ → XX♂			XX ♂		*Rana* *Oryzias*	Kawamura and Yokota (77) Yamamoto (130)
Neomale (WW) Embryonic graft WW♀ → WW♂		WW ♂			*Ambystoma* *Xenopus*	Humphrey (63) Mikamo and Witschi (86a)
Special cross Sex reversed XY♀ XY♂ · XY♀			YY ♂		*Oryzias*	Yamamoto (128)
Neomale ZW♂ Embryonic graft ZW♀ → ZW♂		ZW ♂			*Ambystoma* *Xenopus*	Humphrey (62) Mikamo and Witschi (86)
Neofemale (XY) Hormonal treatment XY♂ → XY♀			XY ♀		*Oryzias*	Yamamoto (127– 129)
Neofemale (ZZ) Hormonal treatment Embryonic graft ZZ♂ → ZZ♀		ZZ ♀			*Pleurodeles* *Ambystoma* *Xenopus*	Gallien (38) Humphrey (62) Chang and Witschi (16) Gallien (39, 40)
Neofemale (YY) Hormonal treatment YY♂ → YY♀			YY ♀		*Oryzias*	Yamamoto (131)

[a] Formulae ZZ, ZW, and so on indicate genetic constitution; symbols ♂, ♀ indicate sexual phenotype and gametes.

eroploidy, one can classify certain other chromosomal aberrations: deficiencies and translocations which are beginning to be recognized in amphibians (Gallien et al., 52, 54, 55) and in the mouse (review by Russell, 99). Among the vertebrates, amphibians and mammals have been utilized in studies of the relationships of heteroploidy to disturbances in sex differentiation.

Amphibians

Amphibians have been utilized because heteroploidy can be produced experimentally, notably by application of cold or heat shock to eggs (reviewed by Fankhauser, 24, Gallien, 37, 45).

Humphrey and Fankhauser (66) have obtained in the axolotl ($2n = 28$) triploid females which apparently are of the three different genotypes: ZZW, ZWW, and WWW, and male triploids ZZZ. The males, which are often sterile, have normal spermatogenesis but their spermatozoa do not always pass into the deferent ducts. The retention of spermatozoa in the testis leads to sterility or near-sterility. However, by artificial insemination these sperm can fertilize diploid eggs, giving rise to progeny actually made up of lethal aneuploids possessing 29–40 chromosomes (Fankhauser and Humphrey, 26). In female triploids the development of the ovary is at first essentially normal, but after 3 months, when the oocytes progress beyond the zygotic stage, most of them begin to degenerate. A small number of them, however, reach maturity and can be fertilized. Therefore, triploidy is associated with a partial sterility. This is not the result of hormonal deficiency or lack of nutrition, but is due to an intrinsic alteration in physiology which is the result of the presence of supernumerary chromosomes.

The nature of the development of the ovary is the same for the three types of genetic constitution ZZW, ZWW, and WWW. Therefore, the degeneration of oocytes is not the result of an imbalance in the mechanism of sex determination, but the result of abnormal synapsis of chromosomes due to the polyploid state.

Crossed with diploid males, partially fertile female triploids give rise to progeny which are either aneuploids, tetraploids, or in some cases, pentaploids (Humphrey and Fankhauser, 67, 68, 69; Fankhauser and Humphrey, 25). Aneuploids are usually nonviable, while female tetraploids are viable and can produce eggs which are fertilizable. The ovaries of pentaploids are sterile.

Results similar to those with the axolotl were found with *Pleurodeles* (Gallien and Beetschen, 48). Female triploids could be fertile or could be completely sterile. Sterility of the ovary results in poor development of the genital tract. Crossing these females with either triploid or diploid males gives rise to aneuploid progeny which are generally lethal. In exceptional cases, certain aneuploid individuals can attain sexual maturity. A partial fertility of triploid individuals of *Triturus pyrrhogaster* was observed by Kawamura (75). In other polyploid urodeles which have been studied, sterility is the rule (Fankhauser, 24).

In triploid frogs the ovarian cortex does not develop normally. This leads to a complete reversal of ovaries to testes before metamorphosis in both *Rana pipiens* (Humphrey et al., 65) and *Rana japonica* (Kawamura and Tokunaga, 76).

The consequence of haploidy on sex differentiation has been impossible to analyze for a long time because the haploid embryos die prematurely. However, in certain rare cases haploid urodeles have achieved metamorphosis. In *Pleurodeles*, by grafting a haploid embryo in parabiosis with a normal diploid, it was possible to raise the former to sexual maturity (Gallien, 42, 47). The individuals studied were androhaploids. The testis differentiates, but bivalents cannot form and spermatogenesis is abortive (Gallien and Beetschen, 49; Gallien, 47).

In anurans, the few haploid larvae which have been obtained died prematurely. However, Miyada (87) with *Rana micromaculata* was able to raise 18 haploid individuals until metamorphosis and even beyond. In these, the sex of the gonad has been studied. These animals, being all gynohaploids, should have been females. However, Miyada found 14 females, 3 males, and 1 juvenile hermaphrodite. He suggests that the effect of recessive genes acting in a haploid individual results in inhibition of cortical development. The ovaries of 10 of these females were underdeveloped or were involuting.

In a general way, one can conclude that heteroploidy in amphibians leads generally to total sterility and in the best cases (triploidy–tetraploidy) to a partial fertility in some species. In haploids, spermatogenesis is abortive. In triploids and tetraploid females, aside from individuals with ovarian hypodevelopment, there are some cases in which oocytes attain sexual maturity and can be fertilized.

Mammals

Since 1959 a remarkable advance in cytogenetics of mammals has occurred as a result of progress in karyotypic techniques. This is especially true for man. In the mouse, a combination of karyotypic analysis and genetic experimentation has been made possible by the discovery of about 20 sex-linked gene markers.

Spontaneous and experimental heteroploidy was, of course, already known in mammals (reviewed in Beatty, 4). Cases of the effect of sex chromosome constitution on sex differentiation are more recent (reviewed in Russell, 99), but study of them would necessitate the survival of fetuses and young.

Mice

The discovery of monosomic females (XO) of the mouse was made by Russell and co-workers (102; Welshons and Russell, 109; Russell, 100). These females were detected by the fact that they presented a phenotype which is normally produced only in males by certain genes which serve as genetic markers. Russell (99) has analyzed the origin of the aberration. The genetic constitution was confirmed by observation of the karyotype. The XO females have 39 instead of 40 chromosomes. They are fertile and only slightly less viable than their XX litter mates. They appear with a frequency of 0.1 to 0.7 percent. Discovery of these XO females demonstrates the property of the male-determinant, Y chromosome. This is a situation different from that which is found in *Drosophila melanogaster*. Since the original discovery, other XO females have been described (McLaren, 85; Cattanach, 14, 15; Kindred, 78).

Russell and Chu (101) discovered a trisomic XXY mouse by the use of sex-linked markers. Study of the karyotype of this animal demonstrated the presence of 41 chromosomes instead of 40. It was a viable male of normal size. The male copulated regularly, but no female was inseminated, since there were no sperm in the ejaculate, and histological examination in a biopsy indicated that the testis did not contain any spermatogenic elements (Russell, 100). Thus, it was a sterile male. The constitution XXY confirms that the male properties are determined by the Y chromosome. Since the original discovery, Russell (100) obtained another XXY male, and Kindred (78) has reported two males which were presumably XXY. One of the XXY was verified by observation of the karyotype. The two animals were sterile. Cattanach (14, 15) described two XXY males capable of copulating, but sterile. McLaren (85) also reported the case of another XXY male. The occurrence of these XXY males is a result of a meiotic nondisjunction in the father. The frequency of their occurence (0.02%) is much lower than for XO mice (0.76%) in crosses in which the simultaneous detection of XO and XXY was possible.

Man

Analysis of aberrations in heterochromosomes which have an effect on sex differentiation can only be summarized here (reviewed in Ferguson-Smith, 27; Davidson and Smith, 20; Lejeune and Turpin, 80; McKusick, 85a). Manifestations of sexual dysgenesis show no simple relationship to chromosomal pattern. Thus we shall refer to typical cases, in order to make comparisons with similar cases in the mouse and in amphibians.

In man, three types of gonadal dysgenesis associated with a heteroploid sex chromosomal constitution have been described. In Turner's syndrome, with negative sex chromatin, the genetic constitution of the individual is XO, and the number of chromosomes is 45 (Ford et al., 30; Polani, 92; Stewart, 104). The phenotype is feminine; vagina, uterus, and oviducts are present, but the gonad is represented in each mesosalpinx by a fibrous connective tissue stroma situated in place of the ovary. This dysgenesis causes sterility. Other somatic anomalies are associated with the syndrome. The XO constitution in which the Y chromosome is absent corresponds to the type described in the mouse, in which case, however, females are fertile.

A second group of aberrations corresponds to Klinefelter's syndrome with positive sex chromatin. These individuals have 47 chromosomes and their constitution is XXY (Jacobs and Strong, 71; Nowakowski et al., 88; Stewart, 104). The phenotype is masculine and the testes show sclerosing tubular degeneration, hyperplasia of the Leydig cells, and some other somatic disturbances.

Ferguson-Smith and co-workers (28) have reported a case of Klinefelter's syndrome (with an XXXY sex chromosome constitution) in which mental retardation appears. The situation in these cases of Klinefelter's syndrome is comparable to that presented by sterile XXY mice and demonstrates the role of the Y chromosome in the expression of masculinity.

The study of color blindness in the chromosomal abnormalities XO and XXY provide information about the number and origin of X chromosomes present (Polani, 93; Stewart, 104).

A third case of heteroploidy of XXX constitution with 47 chromomsomes is known (Jacobs et al., 70). Genetically, this corresponds to a superfemale. The individual studied presented a feminine phenotype. The breasts were underdeveloped, the external genitalia infantile, the vagina was small and the uterocervical canal measured 6 cm.

The patient was observed because of secondary amenorrhea and was probably sterile.

Finally, in amphibians and in mammals, study of heteroploidy of sex chromosomes demonstrates that the situation is generally associated with a dysgenesis and sterility of the gonads. Only some cases of triploidy in amphibians and of monosomy (XO) in the mouse correspond with those individuals which are normally or partially fertile.

What is the mechanism which relates heteroploidy and gonadal dysgenesis? The interpretation suggested by Russell and Chu (101) concerning the fertility of XO mice and sterility of XXY males is based strictly on genetic considerations that XO and XXY individuals are nonintersexes.

One can at least suggest a mechanism concerning this situation, in the light of embryonic mechanisms of sex differentiation in the tetrapod vertebrates which combine the effects of sex genes and endocrine activities of the gonads.

In his study of experimentally induced dysgenesis of the gonads in urodeles, Houillon (61) showed that the aberration is the result of a medullary deficiency. In this case there is no intersexuality, but rather vestigial differentiation of male or female gonads, depending upon the genetic sex. That is to say, a synergism between cortex and medulla is necessary for the normal differentiation of the gonad. This situation corresponds to the case of Bidder's organ (vestigial ovary) in the toad, which is present in both male and female.

We can consider that the sexualizing factors, F, have an action on the growth of the cortex and that the M factors act in the same way on the medulla. Both territories are present in all gonads at the undifferentiated stage. In an organism $Z_M Z_M / Z_M W_F$ (urodeles) the double dose of masculinizing factors, M, dominate the F factors localized on the W chromosome and on autosomes, and lead to a medullary prevalence. In females, at the same time, the simple dose M is dominated by the F factors of the W chromosome and autosomes.

The fact that ZZ or WW individuals can become respectively female or male demonstrates that some factors F and M are localized in autosomes and that the system residing in heterochromosomes is not foremost in the differentiation of sex in urodeles.

If we compare this situation with that of mammals (XX, XY), we can consider that the X chromosomes carry F factors and that Y chromosomes carry M factors, with additional F and M factors distributed on the autosomes in a balanced manner ($X_F X_F : X_F Y_M$).

Thus in an XO individual, if Y controls the growth of the medulla, this territory is inhibited and we can conceive of the development of a vestigial female gonad in man, as in the case of *Pleurodeles*. This gonad will be sterile. Subsequently, as result of the lack of androgen secretion during the course of fetal life, the neutral sex type will develop, that is to say, the female type of mammals. This is essentially Turner's syndrome with negative sex chromatin. Presence of fertile ovaries in XO mice can be understood if the autosomes carry a sufficient quantity of masculinizing genes. In an XXY individual, there is an effect of the Y chromosome on the medulla in such a way that the XX factors acting on the cortex are diminished. Accordingly, this disturbance of the genetic balance on the corticomedullary system results in the formation of a sterile testis (azoospermy). This is Klinefelter's syndrome with positive sex chromatin. In this case the androgenic hormone of the fetus results in differentiation of male genitalia.

This is only speculation, for in mammals the presence of sexualizing genes on the autosomes has not been established. However, this situation is reminiscent of the case demonstrated by Winge (113) for the teleost, *Lebistes reticulatus*.

On the whole, in vertebrates in which consequences of heteroploidy have been observed, all abnormalities of the normal diploid chromosome set, and especially of heterochromosomes, lead generally to severe dysgenesis in gonad differentiation. Consequently, there are endocrine disturbances which lead to anomalies in the differentiation of the genital tract and external genitalia. Total or partial sterility is the rule, and exceptions are rare.

Physiological Activity of Sex Genes in the Course of Sexual Differentiation

Since the genetic constitution of sex in a vertebrate is defined for a given individual by genetic bipotentiality and by its homo- or heterozygotic character, the following question is raised: During the course of ontogenesis, what are the ways by which sex genes express physiological activity, activity which controls male or female morphogenesis?

Determination of the differentiation of gonads and somatic sex characters having been treated elsewhere, we will limit our analysis to facts which are related to genetic activity (for further discussions of this problem see reviews of Wolff, 122, 123; Jost, 73, 74;

Ponse, 95; Witschi, 116–120; Willier, 111; Burns, 9, 12; Gallien, 35, 44).

Relations between Genetic Constitution and Organogenesis of Somatic Sex Characters

THE NEUTRAL SEX.   Somatic sex characters (secondary sex characters) develop from primordia which are present in both male and female embryos. This situation should be considered as an expression of genetic bipotentiality. Ultimate development of these characters is controlled by the hormones of the ovary and testis.

How do these characters differentiate in the absence of the gonads and is there a relationship between genetic constitution and the neutral sex type? In amphibians, de Beaumont (5) castrated *Triturus cristatus* (ZZ, ZW) larvae at a stage at which gonads are not yet differentiated and obtained animals of an identical neutral form which were either genetically male or female. Both males and females conserved their Wolffian and Müllerian ducts. However, the posterior urogenital collecting ducts took the male form. In birds (ZZ, ZW), the neutral form possessed syrinx and tubercle typical of the male type (ZZ) while the gonoducts retained their ambisexual condition (Et. Wolff and Em. Wolff, 126). In mammals, Raynaud and Frilley (98), on the mouse, and Jost (72), on the rabbit, showed that the neutral sex type takes on the female condition (XX) with respect to gonoducts and external genitalia.

In general, differentiation of somatic sex characters continues after embryonic castration, and except for a few structures which remain ambisexual, the character of development corresponds with the homozygotic sex. It seems, therefore, that the gonads are endocrine relays which in the initial stages of development rule the differentiation of somatic sex characters.

Relations between Genetic Constitution and Gonadogenesis

The differentiation of gonocytes into spermatogonia and into oogonia requires the appropriate localization of primordial germ cells in the somatic territories of the gonad, the medulla, and the cortex. Primordial germ cells which wander away in the course of their migration do not multiply, do not differentiate (Witschi, 114; Houillon, 61), and finally disappear. If primordial germ cells are transplanted at a distance from the gonadal primordia (Willier, 110; Witschi, 116), they fail to undergo further development. This demonstrates that cytodifferentiation of these cells depends upon their contact with either the cortex or the medulla of a gonad. The functionally sex-reversed gonad permits us to study progeny. These experiments show that the genotypes of the organism and of the gonocytes ZZ, ZW, WW, XX, XY, and YY have no effect on the ultimate cytodifferentiation of spermatogonia or oogonia. This is controlled by the inductive effects of cortex and medulla where the germ cells are finally located.

medulla $\longrightarrow$ androgenic inductor $\longrightarrow$
testis $\longrightarrow$ spermatogonia
cortex $\longrightarrow$ gynogenic inductor $\longrightarrow$
ovary $\longrightarrow$ oogonia

This point is important because it concerns the question of the expression of the genetic code at the level of cytodifferentiation. At the level of the gonad, that is to say, the reproductive organ itself, it is not the genetic quality of the gonia which directs the organogenesis of the gonad into testis or ovary. Rather, it is the genetic nature of the gonadal primordia itself (as we are allowed to think from in vitro cultures) which controls the activity of the inductive territories and which insures the prevalence of one territory or the other.

genetically male embryo $\longrightarrow$
medullary prevalence $\longrightarrow$ testis
genetically female embryo $\longrightarrow$
cortical prevalence $\longrightarrow$ ovary

Stability of Genetic Sex Structure after Inversion of Sexual Phenotype

The analysis of progeny of sex-reversed organisms indicates that the genetic constitution of the individual remains unchanged. If this is correct, within the limited number of experiments which have been performed, the genetic nature of a gonocyte is not modified by its differentiation into a spermatogonium or oogonium. One can ask if this situation is maintained after the nucleus has been retained for a long time in cytoplasm in which the phenotype was reversed (that is, ZZ nucleus in ZZ cytoplasm induced to differentiate into an oocyte). The situation is effectively maintained. A *Pleurodeles* neofemale (ZZ) kept in my laboratory since 1949 and crossed with a standard male (ZZ) every year, always gives only male offspring. This fact has been verified using other neofemales (ZZ).

If the genetic constitution of a male nucleus is not apparently altered by the fact that it exists in essentially egg cytoplasm, it follows that chromosome morphology reflects the quality of the cytoplasm. In effect, the complement of chromosomes of a male nucleus takes on the lampbrush form when developing in a cell which becomes an oocyte. This form of chromosome morphology is specifically female and is absent during spermatogenesis.

One can still ask if substitution by nuclear grafting of a genetically male blastula nucleus for a genetically female nucleus in an oocyte (that is, ZZ nucleus in ZW cytoplasm) and vice versa, has any effect on the stability of the genetic sex structure of the nucleus. Briggs has obtained both normal males and females from implanting blastula nuclei in eggs from ZW females (Unpublished observations).

Interference between Genetic Effects and Epigenetic Factors

SYNERGISTIC AND ANTAGONISTIC EFFECTS IN GONAD ORGANOGENESIS. In the course of the establishment of the gonad, it has been demonstrated in certain species, notably *Pleurodeles* (Houillon, 61), that there exists an equilibrium between the cortical and medullary masses; that is to say, a synergistic effect is necessary for normal differentiation (Gallien, 41).

When the somatic constituents of the undifferentiated gonad appear, the gonad is morphologically equipotential. The direction of differentiation is the result of antagonistic effects which assures, as we have seen, the inductive dominance of one territory on the other, leading to final differentiation. This reaction translates the direction or prevalence of the genetic balance, that is to say, the consequences of the homo-heterozygotic genetic structure of sex.

EFFECTS OF EPIGENETIC FACTORS. Experimentation shows that the activity of genetic factors directing the chain of organotypic reactions can interfere with epigenetic factors. All extrinsic epigenetic action (namely, exogenous steroids, parabiosis, hypermaturity, teratogens) acting differentially on one of the two inductive territories can bring about a partial or total deviation, temporary or permanent, in the direction of sexual differentiation of the gonad. Among the epigenetic factors tested, two groups of experiments are to be remembered, those of parabiosis and those in which exogenous steroid hormones are administered during the course of differentiation of the gonads. The latter experiments require special attention since they are the only ones in which it has been shown that known chemical substances have a particular effect on the gonads. The general results are the following.

Steroid sex hormones exemplified by estradiol and testosterone and their derivatives have been shown to be capable, in a number of cases, of altering sex differentiation and in fewer cases, to be capable of causing sex inversion. This fact leads us to consider that these actions are not merely ordinary teratogenic effects. However, it has been shown in only a limited number of cases — in the fish, *Oryzias latipes*, and in a few amphibian species, *Rana japonica*, *Xenopus laevis*, and *Pleurodeles waltlii* — that a complete reversion of sex, as demonstrated by progeny studies, has been obtained. Similar results were obtained with *Ambystoma* (Humphrey, 62, 63) and with *Xenopus laevis* (Mikamo and Witschi, 86, 86a) after grafting a testis primordium. For other species of fishes and amphibians and for other classes of vertebrates, administration of hormones is either totally ineffective (placental mammals, certain amphibians such as *Bombina*) or partially effective (intersexuality of birds, Wolff, 121; opossum, Burns, 10,

11; and various amphibians, Gallien, 44). In some instances, the deviatory effect was only temporary.

Relative to temporary effects, two groups of experiments are striking: the case of a male becoming a female, in the birds (Wolff, 121), and in various amphibian species such as *Pelobates*, *Triturus* (Collenot, unpublished observations) and *Pleurodeles* (Gallien, 46). In the chick a strong intersexuality in the direction of ♂ → ♀ could be obtained after treating genetic male embryos with estrone (Dantchakoff, 19; Willier et al., 112; Wolff and Ginglinger, 124). However, the almost total inversion obtained is not stable and the gonad becomes a testis, even with continued treatment with feminizing hormone (Wolff, 121). Analysis of this phenomenon by the methods of tissue culture and intracoelomic grafts was undertaken by Wolff and Haffen (125) and by Haffen (58). In in vitro culture, a feminized male gonad (ZZ) placed under the same experimental circumstances as a normal ovary (ZW) does not develop like the latter. The cortex of the intersexual male gonad does not develop primary follicles and regresses rapidly, while the cortex of the ovary of a genetic female follows typical ovarian differentiation. If the cortex of an intersexual gonad (ZZ) is recombined with a medulla of a female embryo (ZW), the presence of this medulla does not interfere with the regression of the cortex. It seems probable, then, that the cause of involution of the cortex resides in the ZZ cortex itself.

The developmental potentialities of the cortical constituent of females (ZW) and intersexed (ZZ) gonads have been studied by intracoelomic grafts in successive hosts. After several passages, the cortex could attain an age of between 35 to 60 days. Under these conditions, if a female cortex (ZW) isolated at the age of 5 or 10 days – a period covering sex-differentiation – is grafted intracoelomically, it develops into a normal ovary after first giving rise to a weak medulla. On the other hand, a cortex of the ZZ type taken from intersexual gonads after 5–10 days of incubation at first acquired the cortical structure of a typical ovary with oogonia. But after the first passage, the oogonia did not continue their differentiation and during the course of the second and third passages they degenerated. This interesting work tends to show that the formation of primary follicles is an expression of intrinsic properties of the ovarian cortex. It is quite tempting to attribute this quality to the genetic nature of the cortex itself.

The instability of sex induced by hormone treatment in amphibians is marked by a reversal when sex inversion of gonads is not absolutely complete (strong intersexuality). In *Pleurodeles*, sex reversal of neofemales is generally permanent. However, a genetic male (ZZ) transformed into a functional female, and at first giving 100 percent male offspring (ZZ) can, after some years, develop a functional testis, while at the same time its ovarian tissue is completely destroyed. The (♂ → ♀) intersexes always end up by developing testes (Gallien, 46). *Pelobates* and *Triturus* also demonstrate this instability of sex reversal. These facts lead one to think that epigenetic effects can dominate, either partially or totally, and for at least a time, the genetic reactions which control sexual differentiation. However, the latter are not completely abolished. Genetic control is permanent; it continues to exert its effects during the entire life of the individual. Incidentally, the variation in the reactions obtained demonstrates that the force of effects of genetic determination varies with class and species.

In the cases in which partial or total inversion of the gonad was obtained after the action of steroid hormones, certain observations lead one to think that the success of inversion is not without connection with the genetic nature of sex. It is the homozygotic sex which appears to be more sensitive and which submits to a more characteristic sex reversal.

Therefore, for the XX–XY type exemplified by frogs, the male hormone masculinizes genetic females. This gives rise to functional neomales (XX). For the ZZ–ZW type, in urodeles, *Xenopus*, and birds, it is the female hormone which feminizes genetic males. This gives rise to functional neofemales (ZZ). The effects of female hormones on the XX–XY type and of male hormones on the ZZ–ZW type are either weak or paradoxical (differential teratogenic effect) (Gallien, 43).

There are exceptions to this generalization. In the teleost, *Oryzias latipes* (XX–XY), both male and female hormones are capable of completely reversing the sex of the gonad (Yamamoto, 127–130). In the opossum (XX–XY), the female hormone is feminizing (Burns, 10, 11). One must consider, however, that the embryonic process of gonad differentiation in teleosts is different from that of higher vertebrates. The opossum is a rare mammal in which the male possesses sex chromatin (Graham and Barr, 56).

Witschi (120) recalled these points, but emphasized that the epigenetic effects of steroid hormones and induction in parabiosis or in grafted gonads are often different. All in all, this question has not been clarified.

The administration of steroid hormones is frequently carried out at extraphysiological doses. This is confirmed by the fact that it leads to hyperdevelopment, corresponding to sexual maturity of the genital tract and its accessories. It is also confirmed by teratogenesis, especially agenesis. Some of these anomalies involve the Müllerian ducts, organization of the kidney, paradoxical effects on the gonads in urodeles, or of the genital tract of the opossum (Burns, 12). Various somatic malformations appear in the limbs of *Pelodytes* and *Bombina* (Collenot, unpublished observations). Reactions observed on the cortical and medullary territories in gonadogenesis should be interpreted in the light of these teratogenic actions.

In conclusion, deviations in the sex differentiation of the gonad obtained by epigenetic factors and particularly steroid hormones, represent teratogenic manifestations. These extrinsic factors may be interpreted more frequently as inhibitors, but they can in certain cases act as activators of the reactions controlled by the sexualizing genes.

Nature of Initial Reactions in Sex Differentiation as Controlled By Genetic Constitution

At this point of the analysis, we are confronted with the central problem of sex differentiation of the gonads. What is the nature of the reactions by which the genetic constitution is expressed and which lead to the prevalence in development of either cortex or medulla? What we know already about the nature of gene action suggests that genes act through specific enzymes. A second question follows. What are the substances elaborated by the cortex and the medulla which regulate the nature of cytodifferentiations and organogenesis?

The problem is still obscure. However, certain recent advances have increased our understanding. The aims of research have been to follow a series of biochemical manifestations from a very early stage, when the young gonads already elaborate identifiable steroid hormones, to the level of the homo- heterogametic genetic constitution of sex.

Experiments of embryonic castration, described earlier, have established that substances of hormonal nature are elaborated very early by gonads which have reached a sufficient degree of differentiation. This stimulates the researcher to identify the chemical nature of these substances. Gallien and Le Foulgoc (51, 53) have studied the problem for estrogens by spectrophotometric analysis and chromatography of extracts of large amounts of embryonic gonadal tissue. The methods applied to embryonic extracts were verified by using extracts of adult gonads as controls. When the amount of material extracted permitted, the biological test of Allen and Doisy was used as an additional control.

Estrogens were detected in the left ovary of adult hen, in that of the hatching chick (21 days), and in chick embryos at 10 and at 13 days of incubation. For amphibians, positive tests were obtained with *Xenopus laevis* for the very young ovaries present just after metamorphosis. These first indications emphasize the need for more refined techniques aimed at showing the presence of enzymes controlling biosynthesis of steroid hormones during the course of gonadogenesis.

In a first group of experiments, a pure steroid hormone was administered to embryos of a given stage. This was followed by chromatographic analysis of the steroids formed by the embryos after a given period of time. If new steroids are formed, we can say that the embryo already has the enzymatic system capable of transforming the original steroid substrate.

Breuer, Ozon, and Mittermayer (7) at first utilized in vitro incubation to analyze estrogen metabolism of adult *Pleurodeles*. They showed that the liver contained a 17β-hydroxysteroid dehydrogenase, a 16α- and 16β-hydroxysteroid dehydrogenase, and a 16α-hydroxylase. These results stimulated Ozon (90) to investigate the enzymes which intervene in in vivo estrogen metabolism in three different larval stages of *Pleurodeles*. The method consisted of adding a given estrogen, either estradiol-17β or 16-keto-17β-estradiol, to the water in which the larvae lived and identifying 24 hours later derivatives which were formed. The results were as follows:

STAGES	ENZYMES
34–49 Hatching to premetamorphosis. Undifferentiated gonads.	16α, 16β, 17β-ol dehydrogenase (DH)
49–55 Premetamorphosis. End of larval life. Period of gonad differentiation.	16α, 16β, 17β-ol DH + 17α−ol DH, 16α-hydroxylase
55 Metamorphosis completed.	16α, 16β, 17β-ol DH + 17α−ol DH, 16α-hydroxylase + enzymes of conjugation.

It seems from these studies that enzymes appear in a progressive manner in the course of larval development. Ozon thought that the presence of hydroxysteroid dehydrogenase in the first stages of development is probably not of great physiological significance, for this enzyme is widely distributed in animal tissues and in a number of microorganisms. However, the occurrence of new reactions at stage 49 marks an important step in the metabolism of sex hormones. In effect, it is after stage 49 that sex differentiation begins and this differentiation corresponds with the manifestations of newly formed enzymes already identified in adults, which are related to the biosynthesis of sex hormones.

These interesting experiments do not constitute proof that the steroid hormones which were studied are present in the stages considered; rather, they demonstrate the progressive appearance of enzymes which affect steroid metabolism.

Dale (18) indicates that in *Rana pipiens*, steroid hormones are secreted as early as stage 26 (larval life) but that their quantity is too low for identification. The demonstration of the presence of enzymes which are specific for the synthesis of androgenic and estrogenic steroids during the course of gonadal differentiation remains to be carried out.

In another trend of research, it has been shown by the use of specific histochemical reactions, according to the technique of Wattenberg (107) modified by Levy and co-workers (81), that a Δ^5-3β-hydroxysteroid dehydrogenase operates in steroid synthesis. The work was actually carried out on adult glands (adrenals, ovaries, testes). However, in the adrenals of *Xenopus laevis* (Rapola,

97; Pesonen and Rapola, 91) and *Pleurodeles waltlii* (Gallien et al., 50), the enzyme could be identified at very early stages in the first islets of interrenal tissue. A similar histochemical reaction has not been demonstrated in the embryonic gonad in amphibians.

To summarize, these recent works demonstrate that enzymes which control the biosynthesis of steroid hormones are present in the gonads at the moment of their differentiation or a little after. The formation of these enzymes probably represents the first step immediately preceding elaboration of steroids.

In *Drosophila melanogaster*, Fox (31, 32; Fox et al., 33) has observed specific serological reactions related to the presence of the X or Y chromosomes or to the dose of heterochromosomes (X and XX). If this is not related to the differentiation of the gonads, it remains that the genetic constitution of sex is expressed by the presence of sex-specific proteins. One is led to ask whether the same situation occurs in vertebrates during the differentiation of the gonads. There is as yet no experimental evidence in this respect; however, study of certain incompatibilities observed in the course of grafting skin between male and female mice of the same strain (Eichwald and Silmser, 22; Eichwald et al., 23) suggests the possible existence of specific proteins related to the genetic sex make-up (Hauschka, 60).

Summary

An understanding of the mechanisms which control sex differentiation of vertebrates has, during the course of the present century, permitted us by successive steps to associate the role of genetic structure, established by fertilization, with embryonic factors which play a part in the various stages of ontogenesis.

The first phase was the understanding of the sex *ratio* 1 ♂ : 1 ♀ based upon a mechanism of homo- heterogamy. In the most favorable cases, genetic dissymmetry can be seen cytologically. The most well-known cases are those of mammals. A second element of genetic control is represented by the bipotentiality of genetic structures. This is explained by the capacity of sex reversal. The two phenomena are associated in the concept of genic balance (see Bridges, 8).

With Lillie's (82) interpretation of the freemartin effect in cattle, the role of sex hormones elaborated by the embryonic gonad became important. The effect of sex reversal obtained with steroid hormones has become particularly striking since 1935.

In the course of these decisive steps, investigators were naturally led to assemble the results and to form theories of the mechanisms of sex differentiation (Wolff, 122, 123; Witschi, 116–120). In these attempts, because of the lack of sufficient experimental data, the relationship between the activities of the genetic substrate and hormonal mechanisms could not be, in our sense, sufficiently precise. In fact, except for a limited number of cases, we could not induce sex differentiation or insure the permanence of sex reversal obtained in vertebrates.

Two major events must be explained. The first concerns the tendency of sex-reversed animals to return to a gonadal morphology corresponding to the genetic sex and the other concerns the variability of responses to actions of steroid hormones in various classes and species. It seems clear to me that these phenomena impose considerations of the nature and of the permanence of genetic activities in the course of the life of an individual.

In addition, the study of heteroploidy has revealed the importance of the genetic substrate, for every abnormality of karyotype is followed by dysgenesis in gonadal differentiation. This dysgenesis is generally, but not always, associated with partial or total sterility. There is close unity in this respect with results obtained in both amphibians and mammals.

In the light of these considerations of actual facts, how can we conceive the chain of mechanisms in sex differentiation? The bipotential genetic structure of sex accounts for the ambisexuality of sex organ primordia. First of all, in the gonad this is expressed by the appearance of the corticomedullary bipotential system. In this way we can understand intersexuality and sex reversal. The anlagen of somatic sex organs are equally ambisexual. Their development is controlled by sex hormones.

The homo- heterogametic constitution of sex explains even the differentiation of the gonad into a testis or ovary. These points have been largely confirmed by modern research. In particular, the role of the Y chromosome as a determinant of the male sex in mammals has been clearly demonstrated.

In a first step, as proteins diversify during ontogenesis, specific proteins appear that are related to the dosage of X chromosomes (X or XX) and Y chromosome. This phenomenon, actually known for *Drosophila*, but not demonstrated in mammals, can be considered the first biochemical manifestation of the homo- heterogametic constitution of sex. The morphological manifestation of this phenomenon would be expressed by the prevalence of one of the elements of the cortico-medullary complex. However, it must be remembered that this is a speculative point, for we have limited experimental data.

In a second step, which corresponds to the period of gonad differentiation, it seems logical to suggest that an enzymatic system controlling the biosynthesis of steroid hormones in the embryonic gonad becomes functional. Various data provided by chromatographic analysis and histochemistry lead to the same conclusion. Thus far there have been no in situ demonstrations of the pathways of androgen and estrogen synthesis.

The third step is represented by the elaboration of estrogenic and androgenic steroid hormones at the level of the embryonic gonad. This point is well known. These embryonic hormones certainly control the development of somatic sex characters, as demonstrated by the observation of neutral sex and by the effects of steroid hormones on embryos. The action of these hormones on the differentiation of the gonads, however, must be clarified.

What is known about the intervention of exogenously administered steroids during sexual differentiation shows that they can dominate genetic control either partially, or totally, at least for a time. These results seem connected to the teratogenic effects of steroids. In general, it is conceivable that all exogenous epigenetic effects can inhibit or affect enzymatic function and in this way can consequently modify the direction of sex differentiation.

It must be emphasized that the genetic control of sex is never abolished. This is shown clearly by the return of intersexual gonads toward the genetic sex. Surely, completely reversed animals stay reversed. However, intersexed gonads return to the genetic sex when a small remnant of the gonad of the genetic sex type is present, even in the presence of steroid hormones of the opposite sex.

The function of the enzymatic systems is controlled by the genetic structure which can re-establish in a morphogenetic territory (vestigial medulla or cortex) the normal chain of enzymatic events, and thus lead to a final differentiation conforming to the genetic sex.

At this point is seems logical to consider the action of sex genes in their initial manifestation, which is, undoubtedly, the synthesis of proteins. In this case the proteins are the enzymes which necessarily precede steroid biosynthesis.

One last point should be emphasized. The cytodifferentiation of gonia is not directly controlled by the genetic constitution of these cells. This cytodifferentiation is the result of cytoinduction provided by the cortical or medullary territories in which the gonia are located. These are the ways in which we can best correlate the actual facts known about genetic control of sex differentiation in vertebrates.

References

1. Agar, W. E., "The Male Meiotic Phase in Two Genera of Marsupials (*Macropus* and *Petauroides*)," *Quart. J. Microscop. Sci.* 67:183–202 (1923).

2. Aida, T., "On the Inheritance of Color in a Fresh Water Fish, *Aplocheilus latipes* Temmick and Schlegel, with Special Reference to Sex-linked Inheritance," *Genetics* 6:554–573 (1921).

3. Barr, M. L., and E. G. Bertram, "A Morphological Distinction between Neurones of the Male and Female, and the Behaviour of the Nucleolar Satellite during Accelerated Nucleoprotein Synthesis," *Nature* 163:676–677 (1949).

4. Beatty, R. A., "Parthenogenesis and Polyploidy in Mammalian Development," *Monograph Exptl. Biol.* Cambridge: Cambridge University Press, vol. 7 (1957).

4a. Becak, W., M. L. Becak, and H. R. S. Nazareth, "Karyotypic Studies of Two Species of South American Snakes, *Boa constricta* and *Bothrops pararaca*," *Cytogenetics* 1:305–313 (1962).

5. Beaumont, J. de, "La Différenciation Sexuelle dans l'Appareil Uro-génital du *Triton* et Son Déterminisme," *Arch. Entwicklungsmech.* 129:120–178 (1933).

6. Bovey, R., "Un Type Nouveau d'Hétérochromosomes chez un Mammifère, le Trivalent Sexuel de *Sorex araneus* L.," *Arch. Julius Klaus-Stift. Vererbungsforsch* 23:506–510 (1949).

7. Breuer, H., R. Ozon, and C. Mittermayer, "Untersuchungen über den Stoffwechsel von Steroidhormonen bei Vertebraten. I. Vorkommen von Hydroxysteroid-Dehydrogenasen bei Fischen und Amphibien," *Z. Physiol. Chem.* 333:272–281 (1963).

8. Bridges, C. B., "The Genetics of Sex in *Drosophila*," *Sex and Internal Secretions*, E. Allen, R. M. Yerkes, eds. Baltimore: Williams & Wilkins, pp. 55–93 (1934).

9. Burns, R. K., "Hormones and the Differentiation of Sex," *Surv. Biol. Prog.* 1: 233–266 (1949).

10. ———, "Experimental Reversal of Sex in the Gonads of the Opossum *Didelphis virginiana*," *Proc. Natl. Acad. Sci. U.S.* 41:669–676 (1955).

11. ———, "Transformation du Testicule Embryonnaire de l'Opossum en Ovotestis ou en Ovaire sous l'Action de l'Hormone Femelle, le Dipropionate d'Oestradiol," *Arch. Anat. Microscop. Morphol. Exptl.* 45:173–202 (1956).

12. ———, "Role of Hormones in the Differentiation of Sex," *Sex and Internal Secretions*, 3rd edition, W. C. Young, G. W. Corner, eds. Baltimore: Williams & Wilkins, pp. 76–158 (1961).

13. Callan, H. G., and L. Lloyd, "Lampbrush Chromosomes of Crested Newts *Triturus cristatus* (Laurenti)," *Phil. Trans. Roy. Soc. London* 243:135–219 (1960).

14. Cattanach, B. M., "XXY Mice," *Genet. Res.* 2:156–158 (1961).

15. ———, "A Chemically-induced Variegated-type Position Effect in the Mouse," *Z. Vererh.* 92:165–182 (1961).

16. Chang, C. Y., and E. Witschi, "Breeding of Sex-reversed Males of *Xenopus laevis* Daudin," *Proc. Soc. Exptl. Biol. Med.* 89:150–152 (1955).

17. Crew, F. A., "Sex Reversal in Frogs and Toads," *J. Genetics* 11:141–181 (1921).

18. Dale, E., "Steroid Excretion by Larval Frogs," *Gen. Comp. Endocrinol.* 2:171–176 (1962).

19. Dantchakoff, V., "Sur les Effets Morphogénétiques de la Folliculine dans l'Ébauche Testiculaire du Poulet," *Compt. Rend. Soc. Biol.* 119:1117–1120 (1935).

20. Davidson, W. M., and D. Smith, *Proc. Conf. Human Chromosomal Abnormalities*, W. M. Davidson, D. Smith, eds. London: Staples (1961).

21. ———, and S. Winn, "The Relationship between the Sex Nodule and the Sex Chromosomes," *Proc. Conf. Human Chromosomal Abnormalities*, W. M. Davidson, D. R. Smith, eds. London: Staples, pp. 28–36 (1961).

22. Eichwald, E. J., and C. Silmser, "Discussion of Skin Graft Data," *Transplant. Bull.* 2:148–149 (1955).

23. ———, ———, and N. Wheeler, "The Genetics of Skin Grafting," *Ann. N.Y. Acad. Sci.* 64:737–740 (1957).

24. Fankhauser, G., "The Effect of Changes in Chromosome Number on Amphibian Development," *Quart. Rev. Biol.* 20:20–78 (1945).

25. ———, and R. R. Humphrey, "Chromosome Number and Development of Progeny of Triploid Axolotl Females Mated with Diploid Males," *J. Exptl. Zool.* 115: 207–250 (1950).

26. ———, and ———, "Chromosome Number and Development of Progeny of Triploid Axolotl Males Crossed with

Diploid Females," *J. Exptl. Zool.* 126: 33–58 (1954).

27. Ferguson-Smith, M. A., "Chromosomes and Human Disease," *Progr. Med. Genet.* 1:292–335 (1961).

28. ——, A. W. Johnsson, and S. D. Handmaker, "Primary Amentia and Microorchidism Associated with an XXXY Sex-chromosome Constitution," *Lancet* 2: 184–187 (1960).

29. Ford, C. E., and J. L. Hamerton, "The Chromosomes of Man," *Nature* 178: 1020–1023 (1956).

30. ——, K. W. Jones, P. E. Polani, J. C. DeAlmeida, and J. H. Briggs, "A Sex Chromosome Anomaly in a Case of Gonadal Dysgenesis (Turner's syndrome)," *Lancet* 4:711–713 (1959).

31. Fox, A. S., "Genetics of Tissue Specificity," *Ann. N.Y. Acad. Sci.* 73:613–634 (1958).

32. ——, "Genetic Determination of Sex-specific Antigens," *J. Natl. Cancer Inst.* 23:1297–1311 (1959).

33. ——, S. B. Yoon, and Ch. G. Mead, "Evidence for the Persistence in Protein Synthesis of an Information Transfer Mechanism after the Removal of Genes," *Proc. Natl. Acad. Sci. U.S.* 48:546–561 (1962).

34. Gallien, L., "Action Masculinisante du Propionate de Testostérone dans la Différenciation du Sexe chez *Rana temporaria* L.," *Compt. Rend. Acad. Sci.* 205:375–377 (1937).

35. ——, "Les Hormones Sexuelles dans la Différenciation du Sexe chez les Amphibiens," *La Différenciation Sexuelle Chez lès Vertébrés*, Colloq. Intern. Centre Nl. Rech. Sci. Paris. *Arch. Anat. Microscop. Morphol. Exptl.* Vol. 39, pp. 337–366 (1950).

36. ——, "Sur la Descendance Unisexuée d'une Femelle de *Pleurodeles waltlii* Michah. ayant subi pendant Sa Phase Larvaire l'Action Gynogène du Benzoate d'Œstradiol," *Compt. Rend. Acad. Sci.* 233:828–830 (1951).

37. ——, "L'hétéroploidie Expérimentale chez les Amphibiens," *Ann. Biol.* 29:5–22 (1953).

38. ——, "Inversion Expérimentale du Sexe sous l'Action des Hormones Sexuelles chez le Triton *Pleurodeles waltlii* Michah. Analyse des Conséquences Gé-

nétiques," *Bull. Biol. France Belg.* 88: 1–51 (1954).

39. ——, "Descendance Unisexuée d'une Femelle de *Xenopus laevis* Daud. ayant subi pendant sa Phase Larvaire l'Action Gynogène du Benzoate d'Œstradiol," *Compt. Rend. Acad. Sci.* 240:913–915 (1955).

40. ——, "Inversion Expérimentale du Sexe chez un Anoure Inférieur *Xenopus laevis* Daudin. Analyse des Conséquences Génétiques," *Bull. Biol. France Belg.* 90:163–183 (1956).

41. ——, "La Dissociation Médullo-corticale dans l'Organogenèse des Glandes Génitales des Amphibiens et le Problème des Gonades Vestigiales chez Certains Vertébrés," *Rev. Suisse Zool.* 64: 665–672 (1958).

42. ——, "Recherches sur Quelques Aspects de l'Hétéroploidie Expérimentale chez le Triton *Pleurodeles waltlii* Michah.," *J. Embryol. Exptl. Morphol.* 7: 380–393 (1959).

43. ——, "Etude Comparée des Activités des Hormones Stéroides dans la Différenciation Sexuelle des Amphibiens. Problème de Spécificité et Effets Paradoxaux," *First Intern. Congr. Endocrinol. Symp.* X:193–200 (1960).

44. ——, "Comparative Activity of Sexual Steroids and Genetic Constitution in Sexual Differentiation of Amphibian Embryos," *Gen. Comp. Endocrinol.* Suppl. no. 1:346–355 (1962).

45. ——, "Hétéroploidie et Sexualité chez les Vertébrés," *Ann. Biol.* 1:53–70 (1962).

46. ——, "Evolution chez le Triton *Pleurodeles waltlii* des Intersexués Obtenus après Traitement par l'Hormone Femelle," *Bull. Biol. France Belg.* 96:249–280 (1962).

47. ——, "Différenciation Sexuelle d'Individus Haploides du Triton *Pleurodeles waltlii* Michah. Mis en Parabiose. Effets de Compétition dans les Associations ♀ 2 n : ♂ n," *Compt. Rend. Acad. Sci.* 257:2890–2893 (1963).

48. ——, and J. C. Beetschen, "Sur la Descendance d'Individus Triploides Croisés entre Eux ou avec des Individus Diploides chez le Triton *Pleurodeles waltlii*," *Compt. Rend. Acad. Sci.* 248:3618–3620 (1959).

49. ——, and ——, "Différenciation Sexuelle et Gamétogenèse Abortive chez un Mâle Haploide d'Urodèle (*Pleurodeles waltlii*) Élevé en Parabiose," *Compt. Rend. Acad. Sci.* 251:1655–1657 (1960).

50. ——, Ph. Certain, and R. Ozon, "Mise en Évidence d'une Δ^5-3β-Hydroxystéroide-Déshydrogénase dans le Tissu Interrénal de l'Urodèle *Pleurodeles waltlii* Michah. aux Divers Stades du Développement," *Compt. Rend. Acad. Sci.* 258:5729–5731 (1964).

51. ——, and M. Th. Chalumeau-Le Foulgoc, "Mise en Évidence de Stéroides Œstrogènes dans l'Ovaire Juvénile de *Xenopus laevis* Daudin et Cycle des Œstrogènes au cours de la Ponte," *Compt. Rend. Acad. Sci.* 251:460–462 (1960).

52. ——, M. Labrousse, and J. C. Lacroix, "Aberrations Chromosomiques Associées à des Hypomorphoses Consécutives à l'Irradiation de l'Œuf par des Rayons γ chez l'Amphibien Urodèle *Pleurodeles waltlii* Michah.," *Compt. Rend. Acad. Sci.* 256:5413–5415 (1963).

53. ——, and M. Th. Le Foulgoc, "Activé Œstrogène dans l'Ovaire Embryonnaire du Poulet. Vérification par le Test Biologique de la Ratte Castrée (Allen-Doisy) de l'Identification Chimique d'Hormones Stéroides Œstrogènes dans l'Ovaire Gauche du Poulet à 21 Jours," *Compt. Rend. Acad. Sci.* 247:1776–1778 (1958).

54. ——, B. Picheral, and J. C. Lacroix, "Transplantation de Noyaux Triploides dans l'Œuf du Triton *Pleurodeles waltlii* Michah. Développement de Larves Viables," *Compt. Rend. Acad. Sci.* 256: 2232–2233 (1963).

55. ——, ——, and ——, "Modifications de l'Assortiment Chromosomique chez des Larves Hypomorphes du Triton *Pleurodeles waltlii* Michah. Obtenues par Transplantation de Noyaux," *Compt. Rend. Acad. Sci.* 257:1721–1723 (1963).

56. Graham, M. A., and M. L. Barr, "Sex Chromatin in the Opossum, *Didelphys virginiana*," *Arch. Anat. Microscop. Morphol. Exptl.* Suppl. 48 bis:111–121 (1959).

57. Grumbach, M. M., and M. L. Barr, "Cytologic Tests of Chromosomal Sex in Relation to Sexual Anomalies in Man," *Recent Progress in Hormone Research,* G. Pincus, ed. New York: Academic Press, vol. 14, pp. 255–334 (1958).

57a. ——, Congenital Malformations, M. Fishbein, ed. New York: International Medical Congress, pp. 62–67 (1964).

58. Haffen, K., "Sur les Greffes Cœlomiques du Constituant Cortical des Gonades Embryonnaires de Poulet Normales et Intersexuées," *Compt. Rend. Acad. Sci.* 256:3755–3758 (1964).

59. Harms, J. W., "Die Physiologie des Biddershen Organs in ein Ovarium beim Männchen von *Bufo vulgaris*," *Zool. Anz.* 53:253–265 (1923).

60. Hauschka, T. S., "Probable Y-Linkage of a Histocompatibility Gene," *Transplant. Bull.* 2:154–155 (1955).

61. Houillon, Ch., "Recherches Expérimentales sur la Dissociation Médullocorticale dans l'Organogenèse des Gonades chez le Triton *Pleurodeles waltlii* Michah.," *Bull. Biol. France Belg.* 90: 359–445 (1956).

62. Humphrey, R. R., "Sex Determination in Ambystomid Salamanders: a Study of the Progeny of Females Experimentally Converted into Males," *Am. J. Anat.* 76: 33–66 (1945).

63. ——, "Reversal of Sex in Females on Genotype WW in the *Axolotl* (*Siredon* or *Ambystoma mexicanum*) and Its Bearing upon the Role of the Z Chromosome in the Development of the Testis," *J. Exptl. Zool.* 109:171–185 (1948).

64. ——, "Male Homogamety in the Mexican Axolotl. A Study of the Progeny Obtained when Germ Cells of a Genetic Male are Incorporated in a Developing Ovary," *J. Exptl. Zool.* 134:91–102 (1957).

65. ——, R. Briggs, and G. Fankhauser, "Sex Differentiation in Triploid *Rana pipiens* and the Subsequent Reversal of Females into Males," *J. Exptl. Zool.* 115:399–428 (1950).

66. ——, and G. Fankhauser, "The Development and Functional Capacity of the Ovaries in Triploid Ambystomid Salamanders," *J. Morphol.* 79:467–510 (1946).

67. ——, and ——, "Tetraploid Offspring of Triploid Axolotl Females from Mating with Diploid Males," *Anat. Record* 94, no. 3:95 (1946).

68. ——, and ——, "Three Generations

of Polyploids in Ambystomid Salamanders," *J. Hered.* 40:7–12 (1949).

69. ——, and ——, "Structure and Functional Capacity of the Ovaries of Higher Polyploids (4 N, 5 N) in the Mexican *Axolotl (Siredon* or *Ambystoma mexicanum*)," *J. Morphol.* 98:161–198 (1956).

70. Jacobs, P. A., A. G. Baikie, W. M. Court Brown, T. N. MacGregor, M. B. Maclean, and D. G. Harnden, "Abnormalities of the Sex Chromosomes. Evidence for the Existence of the Human Super Female," *Proc. Conf. Human Chromosomal Abnormalities,* W. M. Davidson, D. R. Smith, eds. London: Staples, pp. 63–71 (1961).

71. ——, and J. A. Strong, "A Case of Human Intersexuality Having a Possible XXY Sex Determining Mechanism," *Nature* 183:302–303 (1959).

72. Jost, A., "Recherches sur la différenciation Sexuelle de l'Embryon de Lapin," *Arch. Anat. Microscop. Morphol. Exptl.* 36:151–200; 242–315 (1947).

73. ——, "Le Contrôle Hormonal de la Différenciation du Sexe," *Biol. Rev.* 23: 201–236 (1948).

74. ——, "Embryonic Sexual Differentiation," *Hermaphrodism, Genital Anomalies and Related Endocrine Disorders,* H. W. Jones, W. W. Scott, eds. Baltimore: Williams & Wilkins, pp. 15–45 (1958).

75. Kawamura, T., "Reproductive Ability of Triploid Newts with Remarks on Their Offspring," *J. Sci. Hiroshima Univ.* 12:1–10 (1951).

76. ——, and G. Tokunaga, "The Sex of Triploid Frogs *Rana japonica* Günther," *Proc. Imp. Acad. Tokyo* 13:121–128 (1952).

77. ——, and R. Yokota, "The Offspring of Sex Reversed Females of *Rana japonica* Günther," *J. Sci. Hiroshima Univ.* 18: 31–38 (1959).

78. Kindred, B. M., "Abnormal Inheritance of the Sex-linked Tabby Gene," *Australia J. Biol. Sci.* 14:415–418 (1961).

79. Kosin, I. L., and H. Ishizaki, "Incidence of Sex Chromatin in *Gallus domesticus,*" *Science* 130:43–44 (1959).

80. Lejeune, J., and R. Turpin, "Les Aberrations Chromosomiques Humaines," *Compt. Rend. Soc. Biol.* 154:1956–1960 (1960).

81. Levy, H., H. W. Deane, and B. L.

Rubin, "Visualization of Steroid 3β-oldehydrogenase Activity in Tissues of Intact and Hypophysectomized Rats," *Endocrinology* 65:932–943 (1959).

82. Lillie, F. R., "The Theory of the Freemartin," *Science* 43:611–613 (1916).

83. Makino, S., *A Review of the Chromosome Numbers in Animals.* Tokyo: Hokuryukan (1956).

84. Matthey, R., *Les Chromosomes des Vertébrés.* Lausanne: R. Rouge (1949).

84a. ——, "Un Nouveau Type de Chromosomes Sexuels chez un Mammifère," *Experientia* 10:18–20 (1954).

84b. ——, "Evolution Chromosomique et Speciation chez les Mus du sousguere *Leggada* Gray 1837," *Experientia* 20:657–665 (1964).

85. McLaren, A., "New Evidence of Unbalanced Sex-chromosome Constitutions in the Mouse," *Genet. Res.* 1:253–261 (1960).

85a. McKusick, V. A., "On the X-chromosome of Man," *Am. Inst. Biol. Sci. Wash.* (1964).

86. Mikamo, K., and E. Witschi, "Functional Sex-reversal in Genetic Females of *Xenopus laevis* Induced by Implanted Testes," *Genetics* 48:1411–1421 (1963).

86a. —— and ——, "Masculinization and Breeding of the WW *Xenopus,*" *Experientia* 20:622, 623 (1964).

87. Miyada, S., "Studies on Haploid Frogs," *J. Sci. Hiroshima Univ.* 19:1–55 (1960).

88. Nowakowski, H., W. Lenz, S. Bergman, and J. Reitalu, "Chromosome Studies in Klinefelter's Syndrome," *Proc. Conf. Human Chromosomal Abnormalities,* W. M. Davidson, D. R. Smith, eds. London: Staples, pp. 72–79 (1961).

89. Ohno, S., W. D. Kaplan, and R. Kinosita, "Formation of the Sex-chromatin by a Single X-chromosome in Liver Cells of *Rattus norvegicus,*" *Exptl. Cell Res.* 18: 415–418 (1959).

90. Ozon, R., "Analyse *in vivo,* du Métabolisme des Œstrogènes au Cours de la Différenciation Sexuelle chez le Triton *Pleurodeles waltlii* Michah.," *Compt. Rend. Acad. Sci.* 257:2332–2335 (1963).

91. Pesonen, S., and J. Rapola, "Observations on the Metabolism of Adrenal and Gonadal Steroids in *Xenopus laevis* and *Bufo bufo,*" *Gen. Comp. Endocrinol.* 2: 425–432 (1962).

92. Polani, P. E., "Exceptional Females," *Proc. Conf. Human Chromosomal Abnormalities*, W. M. Davidson, D. R. Smith, eds. London: Staples, pp. 45–53 (1961).

93. ——, "Paternal and Maternal Non-disjunction in the Light of Colour Vision Studies," *Proc. Conf. Human Chromosomal Abnormalities*, W. M. Davidson, D. R. Smith, eds. London: Staples, pp. 80–83 (1961).

94. Ponse, K., "L'évolution de l'Organe de Bidder et la Sexualité chez le Crapaud," *Rev. Suisse Zool.* 34:217–220 (1927).

95. ——, *La Différenciation du Sexe et l'Intersexualité chez les Vertébrés*. Lausanne: R. Rouge (1949).

96. ——, "La Génétique du Sexe chez les Batraciens, avec un Aperçu des Travaux de R. R. Humphrey," *La Différenciation Sexuelle chez les Vertébrés*, Colloq. Intern. Centre Natl. Rech. Sci. *Arch. Anat. Microscop. Morphol. Exptl.* 39:1–32 (1950).

97. Rapola, J., "Development of the Amphibian Adrenal Cortex," *Ann. Acad. Sci. Fennicae Ser.* A 64:1–81 (1962).

98. Raynaud, A., and M. Frilley, "Destruction des Glandes Génitales de l'Embryon de Souris par une Irradiation au Moyen des Rayons X, à l'Âge de 13 Jours," *Ann. Endocrinol.* 8:400–419 (1947).

99. Russell, L. B., "Genetics of Mammalian Sex Chromosomes," *Science* 133:1795–1803 (1961).

100. ——, "Chromosomes Aberrations in Experimental Mammals," *Prog. Med. Gen.* 2:230–294 (1962).

101. ——, and H. Y. Chu, "An XXY Male in the Mouse," *Proc. Natl. Acad. Sci. U.S.* 47:571–575 (1961).

102. Russell, W. L., L. B. Russell, and J. S. Gower, "Exceptional Inheritance of a Sex-linked Gene in the Mouse Explained on the Basis that the X/O Sex-chromosome Constitution is Female," *Proc. Natl. Acad. Sci. U.S.* 45:554–560 (1959).

103. Sharman, G. B., A. J. McIntosh, and H. N. Barber, "Multiple Sex-chromosomes in the Marsupials," *Nature* 166:996 (1950).

104. Stewart, J. S., "Mechanism of Meiotic Non-disjunction in Man," *Proc. Conf. Human Chromosomal Abnormalities*, W. M. Davidson, D. R. Smith, eds. London: Staples, pp. 84–96 (1961).

105. Tjio, J. H., and A. Levan, "The Chromosome Number of Man," *Hereditas* 42:1–6 (1956).

106. Tobias, P. V., *Chromosomes Sex Cells and Evolution in a Mammal*. London: Percy Lund, Humpries (1956).

107. Wattenberg, L. W., "Microscopic Histochemical Demonstration of Steroid 3β-ol-dehydrogenase in Tissue Sections," *J. Histochem. Cytochem.* 6:255–282 (1958).

108. Weiler, C., and S. Ohno, "Cytological Confirmation of Female Heterogamety in the African Water Frog (*Xenopus laevis*)," *Cytogenetics* 1:217–223 (1962).

109. Welshons, W. J., and L. B. Russell, "The Y-chromosome as the Bearer of Male Determining Factors in the Mouse," *Proc. Natl. Acad. Sci. U.S.* 45:560–566 (1959).

110. Willier, B. H., "Potencies of the Gonad Forming Area in the Chick as Tested in Chorio-allantoid Grafts," *Arch. Entwicklungsmech.* 130:616–649 (1933).

111. ——, "The Embryonic Development of Sex," *Sex and Internal Secretions*, 2nd edition, E. Allen, Ch. Danforth, E. A. Doisy, eds. Baltimore: Williams & Wilkins, pp. 64–144 (1939).

112. ——, T. F. Gallagher, and F. C. Koch, "Sex Modification in the Chick Embryo Resulting from Injections of Male and Female Hormones," *Proc. Natl. Acad. Sci. U.S.* 21:625–631 (1935).

113. Winge, O., "The Experimental Alteration of Sex Chromosomes into Autosomes and *vice versa* as Illustrated by *Lebistes*," *Compt. Rend. Trav. Lab. Carlsberg*, Ser. Phys. 21:1–49 (1934).

114. Witschi, E., "Studien ueber die Geschlechtsbestimmung bei Froeschen," *Arch. Mikroskop. Anat.* 86:1–50 (1914).

115. ——, "Uber die genetische Konstitution der Froschzwitter," *Biol. Zentralbl.* 43:83–96 (1923).

116. ——, "Genes and Inductors of Sex Differentiation in Amphibians," *Biol. Rev.* 9:460–488 (1934).

117. ——, "Modification of the Development of Sex in Lower Vertebrates and in Mammals," *Sex and Internal Secretions*, 2nd edition, E. Allen, Ch. Danforth, E. A. Doisy, eds. Baltimore: Williams & Wilkins, pp. 145–226 (1939).

118. ——, "Génétique et Physiologie de la Différenciation du Sexe," *La Différenciation Sexuelle chez les Vertébrés*, Colloq. Intern. Centre Natl. Rech. Sci. *Arch. Anat. Microscop. Morphol. Exptl.* 39:33–64 (1950).

119. ——, "The Inductor Theory of Sex Differentiation," *J. Fac. Sci. Hokkaido Univ. Ser. VI Zool.* 13:428–439 (1957).

120. ——, "Genetic and Postgenetic Sex Determination," *Experientia* 16:274–278 (1960).

121. Wolff, Et., "L'évolution après l'Éclosion des Poulets Mâles Transformés en Intersexués par l'Hormone Femelle Injectée aux Jeunes Embryons," *Arch. Anat. Hist. Embryol.* 23:1–28 (1936).

122. ——, "Essai d'Interprétation des Résultats Obtenus Récemment chez les Vertébrés sur l'Intersexualité Hormonale," *Experientia* 3:272–276; 301–304 (1947).

123. ——, "Le rôle des Hormones Embryonnaires dans la Différenciation Sexuelle des Oiseaux," *La Différenciation Sexuelle Chez les Vertébrés*, Colloq. Intern. Centre Natl. Rech. Sci. *Arch. Anat. Microscop. Morphol. Exptl.* 39:426–444 (1950).

124. ——, and A. Ginglinger, "Sur la Transformation des Poulets Mâles en Intersexués par Injection d'Hormone Femelle (Folliculine) aux Embryons," *Arch. Anat. Hist. Embryol.* 20:219–278 (1935).

125. ——, and K. Haffen, "Sur la Féminisation Induite par les Gonades Mâles Intersexuées chez l'Embryon de Poulet," *Arch. Anat. Hist. Embryol.* 44:275–302 (1961).

126. ——, and Em. Wolff, "The Effects of Castration on Bird Embryos," *J. Exptl. Zool.* 116:59–97 (1951).

127. Yamamoto, T., "Artificially Induced Sex Reversal in Genotypic Males of the Medaka (*Oryzias latipes*)," *J. Exptl. Zool.* 123:571–594 (1953).

128. ——, "Progeny of Artificially Induced Sex Reversals of Male Genotype (XY) in the Medaka (*Oryzias latipes*) with Special Reference to Y-Y Male," *Genetics* 40:406–419 (1955).

129. ——, "Artificial Induction of Functional Sex Reversal in Genotypic Females of the Medaka (*Oryzias latipes*)," *J. Exptl. Zool.* 137:227–265 (1958).

130. ——, "A Further Study on Induction of Functional Sex Reversal in Genotypic Males of the Medaka (*Oryzias latipes*) and Progenies of Sex Reversal," *Genetics* 44:739–757 (1959).

131. ——, "Induction of Reversal in Sex Differentiation of YY Zygotes in the Medaka, *Oryzias latipes*," *Genetics* 48:293–306 (1963).

24

Gonadal Hormones in the Sex Differentiation of the Mammalian Fetus

ALFRED JOST

Laboratoire de Physiologie Comparée
Faculté des Sciences
Université de Paris
Paris, France

The development of the sex glands and apparatus in either sex involves a complex chain of successive events. Many of our concepts in this field still owe much to early observations or interpretations which proceeded along several lines: descriptive and chronological studies of actual organogenesis, hormonal or inductive factors, and last but not least, genetics.

In the past, animal experiments were the main source of information. More recently, human clinical material has contributed a great deal to our information, and has also given rise to new questions.

The·aim of this paper is to evaluate some problems concerning sexual organogenesis in mammals; it will deal with sex differentiation of the gonads, with physiology of the fetal testis and its role in the differentiation of the genital tract, and finally, with some points concerning the genetics of sex.

Morphological Sex Differentiation of the Gonads

Most of our interpretations of gonadal sex differentiation have been based for many years on the concept of cortico-medullary antagonism, which Witschi began to develop and to demonstrate as early as 1914 (see Witschi, 55). As is well known, in this conception which was first based on amphibian material, the early undifferentiated gonadal primordium is composed of two components, the cortex and the medulla, which secrete antagonistic inductors; the dominant inductive system determines the sex of the developing gonad. Sex reversal may result from an impairment of the epistatic inductive system as well as from an enhancement of activity of the opposite component. A few experimental data pertaining especially to mammals or birds will be examined.

Embryonic Hormones during Gonadal Differentiation

Evidence that a developing gonad produces a humoral agent capable of interfering with gonadal organogenesis in the opposite sex was first found in freemartins (Lillie, 36, 37; Keller and Tandler, 35). The term "freemartin" is applied to the female of heterosexual twins of cattle. Under the influence of the male twin, the ovaries of the female fetus become profoundly inhibited and usually sterile. The ovarian cortex can be completely suppressed and replaced by a tunica albuginea; sometimes tubules resembling seminiferous tubules appear in the medullary part of the gonad (Willier, 54). These changes occur very early during sex differentiation; the youngest freemartin so far described was 32 mm in length (Bissonnette, 4).

The hormonal interpretation of freemartins rests on the assumption that the developing testis produces a hormone, which, in the female twin, has an initial effect of cortical inhibition.

More recently, inhibition of rat or rabbit fetal ovaries by fetal testes in combined grafts on adult hosts was also reported (Macintyre, 39; Holyoke, 17). Barton and Holyoke (2) obtained an extract of pig testes that inhibited the ovarian cortex of female mice fetuses; their preliminary report awaits confirmation.

In urodele amphibians, sex influences were studied in heterosexual pairs of parabiotic larvae or after orthotopic transplantation of gonadal anlagen (see Witschi, 55; Jost, 22). The usual dominance of the male over the female results in inhibition of the ovaries (freemartin effect) or in sex reversal. Unexpectedly, the testes of one animal may inhibit the testes as well as the ovaries of another animal (see Mikamo and Witschi, 40), an observation that still awaits adequate explanation.

In bird embryos, the ovaries feminize the testes to some extent after intracoelomic grafts of gonads (Wolff, 56), in vitro (Wolff and Haffen, 57), and in spontaneous freemartins developing in eggs with two yolks (Lutz and Lutz-Ostertag, 38; Ruch, 48).

The ovary is also the predominant organ in somatic sex differentiation of birds. In castrated duck embryos the sex characters become masculine, although the Müllerian ducts persist. That is, the neutral sex type developed in gonadless bird embryos is masculine (Wolff and Wolff, 59), as opposed to the feminine neutral sex type in mammals (Jost, 20, 21). One might then assume that during early gonadal organogenesis in birds the feminizing hormone is predominant, while in mammals, it is the masculinizing hormone or hormones.

Further speculation would suggest that in mammals and in birds the hormone produced by the heterozygous sex is predominant. However, this does not apply to urodele amphibians, in which the female is heterozygous, the neutral sex type in early castrates is predominantly masculine (De Beaumont, 3), and yet the male gonads prevail in parabiosis or grafts.

Analysis of the Cortico-medullary System in Birds

An analysis of the endocrine potencies of the medulla and of the cortex of the bird embryo gonad was pursued in Wolff's laboratory. Some of these results will be summarized:

The right gonad, which is essentially medullary in origin, produces a secretion which feminizes the sex characters (syrinx, genital tubercle) in hemicastrated duck embryos (Wolff and Wolff, 60); when associated with a testis in vitro, it feminizes it (Wolff and Haffen, 58). These results are especially interesting since it has been recognized for years that when the left ovary is removed in pullets, the right gonad masculinizes the animal, and eventually produces spermatozoa.

In keeping with the preceding observations, the ovarian medulla produces a feminizing secretion when grafted into the coelomic cavity of male chick embryos (Mintz and Wolff, 41).

In other experiments on duck embryos, the cortex was isolated by trypsinization from the medullary part of undifferentiated gonads (embryos of 5–7 days' incubation) and cultivated in vitro in combination with either a male or a female medulla taken from somewhat older embryos. The cortex from a male embryo associated with the medulla from a female embryo differentiates ovarian structures; associated with the medulla from a male embryo, it differentiates masculine structures (Haffen, 13).

It would appear that the medullary part of the ovary of the bird embryo does not antagonize the cortex, but actually produces a feminizing inductive substance. Moreover, the right gonad, which is predominantly feminizing in the embryo, later undergoes a shift and becomes potentially masculinizing in the pullet.

Sex Hormones and Gonadal Differentiation

After 1935, when sex differentiation could, to a large extent, be reversed in genetically male chick embryos by means of estrogens, several authors assumed that the genetically controlled gonadal inductors were the same hormones as those produced by adult gonads.

It is impossible to survey here the bulk of experiments devoted to the influence of sex hormones on the fetus and to discuss their significance. In the case of placental mammals, it has been impossible, so far, to reverse the sex of the gonads or to inhibit the ovaries with sex hormones. It must still be determined whether these hormones are incapable of altering early gonadal differentiation, or if the best conditions have not yet been devised.

The only case in which sex hormones altered gonadal differentiation was in opossums treated at early stages with estradiol dipropionate (Burns, 6). In the testes of these animals, the germinal epithelium of the early gonad persists and proliferates, while the central testicular part is profoundly inhibited and atrophied. It is hard to decide whether estradiol first inhibited the medullary part of the gonad, permitting the cortex to thrive, if it stimulated the cortex, or if it had both effects. It is also not yet possible to decide whether estradiol is the sex inductor in normal ovarian development of the opossum.

Conclusion

If one tries to summarize the present state of our knowledge concerning the inductors or hormones responsible for sexual differentiation of the gonadal primordium in higher vertebrates, the list of established facts is remarkably short. There is no evidence for a corticomedullary antagonism; only one type of secretion released during early sex differentiation has been uncovered so far. This is a feminizing (cortex-maintaining or stimulating) substance, produced by the ovarian medulla in birds, and an ovary-inhibiting secretion in mammals.

Taking these facts into consideration, the simplest theoretical interpretation of the *first steps* of sex differentiation of the gonad would postulate that one sex can develop in the absence of any hormonal stimulation. The development of the opposite sex is imposed by an inductor or inductors. During the first steps of gonadal differentiation in mammals, the fact that the ovaries first remain identical to the indifferent condition, while the testes undergo specific changes, would be consistent with this kind of an interpretation. These remarks remain speculative and should not conceal the necessity of new crucial experiments.

The Fetal Testicular Hormone

Older experiments concerning the role of the fetal gonads in sex differentiation of the genital tract will not be summarized again in detail. It is sufficient to recall that castration experiments on rabbit fetuses (Jost, 20, 21, 26) showed that the gonadless fetus acquires feminine features irrespective of its genetic sex (Fig. 24.1). Other lines of evidence supporting this view were obtained in mice embryos castrated *in utero* by a beam of x rays (Raynaud and Frilley, 47) or in rat tissues in vitro (Jost and Bergerard, 31; Jost and Bozic, 32; Price and Pannabecker, 46). These experiments showed that the ovaries play no leading role in feminine orga-

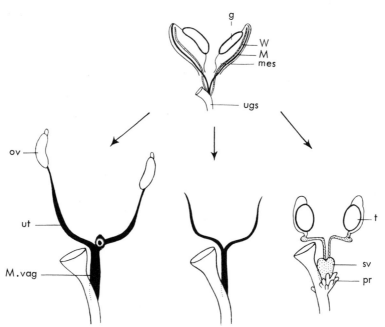

Fig. 24.1 Schematic presentation of sexual differentiation of the sex ducts in the rabbit embryo. From the undifferentiated condition (top) may arise either the female structure (bottom left), or the male structure (bottom right), or the gonadless feminine structure in castrated embryos of either sex (bottom middle). g, gonad; M, Müllerian duct; mes, mesonephros; M. vag, Müllerian vagina; ov, ovary; pr, prostate; sv, seminal vesicle; t, testis; ugs, urogenital sinus; ut, uterine horn; W, Wolffian duct (stippled). (After Jost, *Mem. Soc. Endocrinol.* No. 4:237–248, 1955.)

nogenesis, although they probably are not completely inactive. It is the testis which has the main responsibility in differentiating the sexes. For this reason, only testicular physiology will be discussed below.

Experimental Study of the Fetal Testicular Hormone

As has been stressed several times in the past (Jost, 21, 26, 27, 28), the part played by the fetal testis in imposing masculinity on the undifferentiated genital tract involves two different aspects: (1) The Müllerian ducts are suppressed, due to an inhibitory activity of the fetal testicular secretion on these ducts. This inhibition may actually result from the activation of the enzymatic systems involved in the regression of the Müllerian epithelial cells. (2) Masculine organogenesis is stimulated at the level of the Wolffian ducts, urogenital sinus, and external genitalia.

The second aspect is easily elicited in female fetuses submitted to androgenic steroids, although the Müllerian ducts are not suppressed (Jost, 21, 27, 28). The question thus arises whether the fetal testis produces only one hormone possessing both activities, or if two different hormones are secreted— an inhibitory hormone, inhibiting the Müllerian ducts, and an androgenic hormone, stimulating masculine organogenesis as do conventional androgenic steroids (Jost, 26, 28, 30). This question still remains incompletely answered, although various lines of evidence suggest that the fetal testis could produce two different substances.

PRODUCTION OF ADULTLIKE HORMONE BY THE FETAL TESTIS. The fetal testis of the rat, when grafted to the seminal vesicle of a castrated adult rat, stimulates the adult sex character as would testosterone or other androgens, as in Figure 24.2 (Jost, 23). The period of time allotted to the fetal testis in these experiments (16–21 days post-insemination) covers the period of sexual organogenesis in this species. The fetal testis did not produce conspicuous amounts of androgens when grafted to hypophysectomized hosts (Jost and Colonge, 34) unless gonadotropins were injected (Jost, 26). Under these

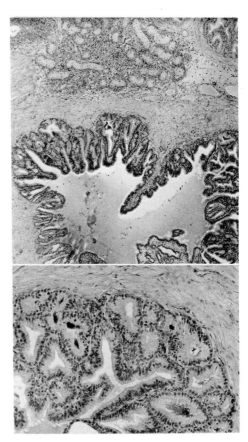

Fig. 24.2 Graft of rat fetal testis onto the seminal vesicle of an adult castrated animal. The testis taken from a 16-day-old fetus remained 5 days in the host. Top: General view. Bottom: Detail of the stimulated epithelium of the seminal vesicle. ×41 ×124 (Experiment by Jost, 1948.)

circumstances, the rat fetal testis behavior is that which would be expected from adult tissue.

A few biochemical studies in vitro pertaining to androgen production by human fetal testicular tissue have yielded interesting results. According to Bloch, Tissenbaum, and Benirschke (5) and to Acevedo, Axelrod, Ishikawa, and Takaki (1), the fetal testis may convert progesterone or 5-pregnenolone to testosterone and androstenedione at a stage when the fetus is 11 cm or 13 cm in crown-rump length. Since sex differentiation of the genital tract is completed at that time, investigations at earlier stages would be interesting.

The histoenzymatic demonstration of 3β-hydroxysteroid dehydrogenase in the fetal Leydig cells in mice is in keeping with the previous demonstrations of the ability of the fetal testis to synthesize steroid hormones (Hitzeman, 16).

THE FETAL INHIBITORY HORMONE. The possibility that the fetal testis produces an inhibitory hormone different from testosterone was suggested when the action of fetal testicular secretion and of adult androgenic steroids on the differentiating fetus was compared (Jost, 21, 26, 27, 28). Two series of experiments which were done on rabbits or on cows are reviewed.

Experiments on rabbit fetuses. Female fetuses were submitted to surgery on day 19 or 20, just before or at the beginning of sexual differentiation of the genital tract. Either a fetal testis, taken from another fetus of the same age, or a single crystal of testosterone propionate was placed near one ovary (Jost, 27, 28). The effect of these treatments was compared on day 28, when sexual organogenesis is, to a large extent, completed (Fig. 24.3).

The fetal testis and the crystal of testosterone both stimulated the Wolffian ducts or other masculine characters. The former displayed a more localized effect, the latter produced a more gen-

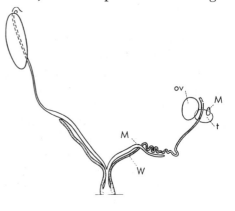

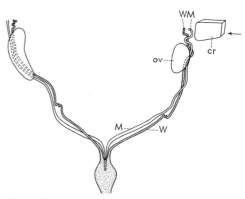

Fig. 24.3 Graphic reconstructions (slightly schematized) of the genital tract of two female fetuses 28 days old. Top: a fetal testis was grafted near the ovary on day 20. Partial inhibition of the Müllerian duct and partial maintenance of the Wolffian ducts resulted. (After Jost, *Arch. Anat. Microscop. Morphol. Exptl.* 36: 271–315, 1947.) Bottom: a crystal of testosterone propionate was implanted near the ovary on day 20. There was maintenance of the Wolffian ducts and no inhibition of the Müllerian ducts. cr, crystal of testosterone propionate; M, Müllerian ducts; ov, ovary; t, testicle; W, Wolffian duct (stippled). (After Jost, pp. 160–180 in *IIIe Reunion Endocrinol. Langue Francaise,* Masson et Cie, 1955.)

erally extended masculinization. These differences appeared to be of a quantitative rather than of a qualitative nature. However, the fetal testis inhibited the Müllerian ducts in its zone of influence, while the crystal of testosterone had no inhibiting effect at all.

Experiments on calf fetuses. More recently, experiments were done on calf fetuses (Jost, Chodkiewicz, and Mauléon, 33). This species was selected because it permitted comparison between naturally occurring freemartins—assumed to reveal effects of a fetal testicular hormone—and fetuses subjected to adult androgenic steroids.

Pregnant cows were injected intramuscularly with large amounts of steroids suspended in olive oil, starting on day 35–42 after mating. The doses were 1 gram per week for 3 weeks, then 3 grams per week for another 3-week period, and again 1 gram per week until sacrifice on day 105–110 after insemination. The steroids used were testosterone propionate, 9α-fluoro-11β-hydroxy-17-methyltestosterone (halotestin), and 17-methyltestosterone. A few cows were not pregnant, or aborted. Nine pregnancies produced nine single fetuses. Six of them exhibited only male characters and were considered males; three were intersexes and were considered females.

Two of these females (mother treated with halotestin) were completely masculinized in external appearance: the penis, retained under the abdominal wall, opened below the umbilicus; and the scrotum was present, although somewhat smaller than in normal males of the same age (Fig. 24.4). The third animal (mother treated with testosterone) had a free penis, similar macroscopically and microscopically to the penis of males of mammalian species

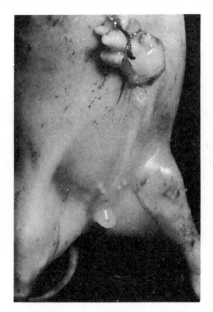

Fig. 24.4 External genitalia of a 106-day-old female calf fetus masculinized by halotestin given to the mother. (Beginning of treatment on day 40.) (After Jost, Chodkiewicz, and Mauléon, *Compt. Rend. Acad. Sci.* 256:274–276, 1963.)

which normally have a free penis. The internal structures looked female to the naked eye; ovaries and uterine horns of normal size were present (Fig. 24.5).

The whole genital tract was studied in serial sections and compared with normal females or males of the same age. No gross anomaly was observed in the ovaries (Figs. 24.6 and 24.7), tubes, or uterine horns. However, there were also well-developed Wolffian ducts with their derivatives—epididymis, vasa deferentia (Fig. 24.8), and seminal vesicles; and the posterior part of the genital tract was completely masculinized (prostate, Fig. 24.9).

When these animals are compared with freemartins, differences are evident. The main anomalies of the freemartins are inhibition of the ovaries

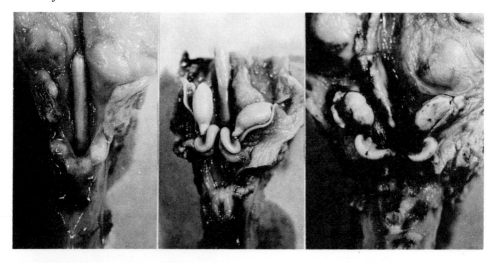

Fig. 24.5 Dissection of the internal sex organs of three female calf fetuses of approximately the same age. Middle: Control animal, showing ovaries, tubes, and uteri. Left: Freemartin collected at the slaughter house. Notice reduction of the ovaries and uteri. Right: Offspring of a mother which received halotestin. Notice normal size of ovaries and uteri. (After Jost, Chodkiewicz, and Mauléon, *Compt. Rend. Acad. Sci.* 256:274–276, 1963.)

and of the Müllerian ducts; the Wolffian ducts may persist and the seminal vesicles develop, but the other parts of the genital tract, especially the external structures, are not masculinized or are little masculinized. Apparently the testicular masculinizing hormone of the male twin reaches the freemartin in only limited amounts. In the androgen-treated fetuses the external genitalia are masculinized and all the internal male structures are fully developed, but the ovaries and Müllerian ducts are not inhibited.

It still is not certain whether the testicular factor which is responsible for the freemartin condition inhibits both the ovaries and the Müllerian duct, or whether it only alters the ovaries, which in turn inhibit the Müllerian ducts. In any case, in freemartins an inhibitory secretion is at work which cannot be replaced by conventional androgenic steroids given to the mother.

In future studies, the possibility of variations in the rate of placental transfer of steroid hormones according to gestational age should be considered.

The biological results presented in this section suggest that the fetal testis might produce two different kinds of secretions; such a possibility deserves further inquiry. The final proof of the existence of two factors requires their isolation.

Hormonal Interpretation of Some Sex Anomalies

A great number of anomalies of the external or internal genitalia among humans or animals can easily be interpreted as resulting from a faulty hormonal control during sexual organogenesis. The basic assumption of the interpretation developed after 1947 (Jost, 20, 24, 29) was that the fetal testis was necessary for imposing masculinity on the developing genital tract. A testicular deficiency allows feminine tendencies to appear.

GONADAL AGENESIS. The extreme case of testicular deficiency is that in which no testes at all develop in a genetically male subject. It was assumed that some "female" patients, suffering from complete gonadal agenesis might afford examples of such a condition (Jost, 20, 24). This has been confirmed on the basis of chromosomal studies (XY gonadal dysgenesis, Harnden and Stewart, 14), although most of the patients afflicted with Turner's syndrome exhibit chromosomal anomalies (for example, XO) and cannot be considered as genetic males or females (for references see Ford, 9; Sohval, 50).

Interestingly enough, gonadal dysgenesis can be accompanied by masculine trends of the body, which to some extent parallel the degree of development of interstitial tissue. It appears that sex characteristics in such patients are not directly controlled by local genetic factors, but obey hormonal control regardless of the chromosomal formula.

DIFFERENT VARIETIES OF MALE PSEUDOHERMAPHRODITISM. A wide variety of sex anomalies are found among patients possessing morphologically recognizable testes, but in whom different parts of the genital tract are feminized.

A hormonal interpretation of the condition of their genital tract can be tentatively considered. If one assumes that two different hormones are required for normal sexual differentiation, anomalies might result from the absence or deficiency of only one or of both of these hormones during fetal organogenesis. Anomalies might also result from lack of sensitivity of the receptor tissues to the appropriate hormone (Jost, 28). Lack of hormone or lack of sensitivity of the receptor tissues would result in the same final condition. Let us express the possibilities in terms of

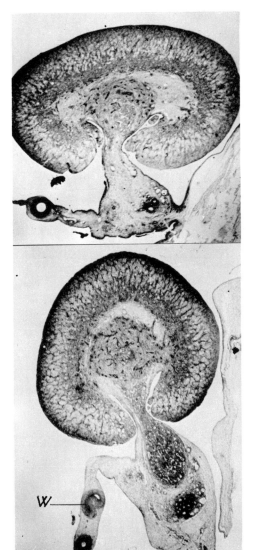

Fig. 24.6 Sections through the ovaries and tubes of two female calf fetuses. Top: A control animal. Bottom: A masculinized fetus (the same as in Fig. 24.4). W, Wolffian duct. ×14.

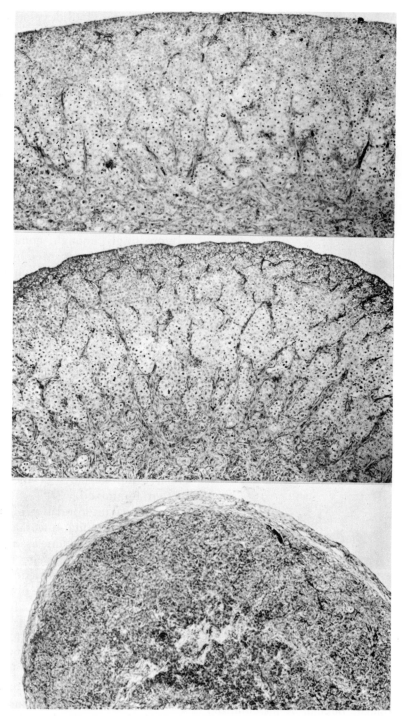

Fig. 24.7 Histological sections through the ovaries of a control fetus. Top: A control fetus. Middle: A fetus treated with halotestin (the same as in Fig. 24.5). Bottom: A freemartin. All fetuses were approximately the same age. ×72.

assumed hormonal deficiencies during fetal development.

Complete hormonal deficiency (absence of both inhibitory and androgenic hormones) should result in the genital tract being completely feminine, with no masculine organs other than testes. Several patients presenting such a condition have been described. An autopsy case of a sterile married "woman" was reported by Schwartz (49) a long time ago. Recently, another interesting case was studied by Ikkos, Tillinger, and Westman (19, case no. 2) under the title of "testicular feminization." The patient, who appeared female, had normal tubes and uterus, in addition to partially calcified testes; castration did not alter hormonal excretion.

More frequently, some enlargement of the clitoris or the presence of small parts of the epididymis are observed, which means that some androgenic hormone was actually produced. The condition is then intermediate to that described below. Such cases have been described in humans (Overzier, 44, p. 235), in a dog (Fralick and Murray, 10), and in a pig (Ferreira, 8).

Deficiency of the inhibitory hormone with normal production of the androgenic hormone should result in the whole set of masculine characters being normally developed, but with the tubes and uterus retained. A large number of human patients showing this anomaly have been reported. Nilson (43) surveyed 34 cases, and several others were reported more recently (Young, 61). It is of great interest that Prader (Personal communication) has found a familial example, which indicates that the disorder might be genetically controlled.

I recently studied the genital tract of a 3-month-old bull presenting the same

anomaly. External genitalia were masculine and the penis normally developed. At autopsy the genital tract showed testes, epididymes, large uterine horns and tubes, and apparently normal-sized seminal vesicles (Fig. 24.10). Sections were made at approximately every second centimeter between the testes and the junction of the uterine horns to verify that the male ducts were normally developed along their entire length.

This case is of special interest because (except for the gonads) it duplicates exactly the condition of the female calf fetuses subjected to androgenic steroids, referred to in a preceding section (Figs. 24.4–24.9).

Deficiency of the androgenic hormone with normal production of inhibitory hormone should result in complete absence of any masculine structure, and in feminine external genitalia and urogenital sinus; it also should result in the absence of the tubes and uterus. A complete lack of any genital duct between the testes and the blind end of the vagina in "female" subjects is to be expected. This condition of the sex organs is found in several patients which were classified under the term of testicular feminization (Morris, 42; recent review by Hauser, 15).

Most of these patients, reared as girls, develop feminine external sex characters (breasts) and estrogenized vaginal smears at puberty, but lack axillary and pubic hairs. Urinary estrogen output is at the lower end of the range for normal women; 17-ketosteroid secretion is normal. The testes are sterile but contain large numbers of Leydig cells. After removal of the testes, the output of estrogen decreases.

The condition is often familial. In a few instances it has been verified that the sex chromosomes are XY. At least

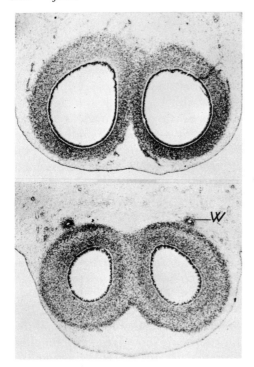

Fig. 24.8 Sections through the uterine horns, at the level of their junction, in a control female (top) and a masculinized female (bottom) which is the same animal as in Fig. 24.5. Notice the presence of the Wolffian ducts, W, in the latter.

two alternative explanations of this syndrome are possible:

1. It might be that during the period of sexual organogenesis the testis produced no androgenic hormone, and perhaps synthesized some estrogens instead. However, testicular tissue of one adult patient was able to convert progesterone into testosterone in vitro and failed to produce detectable estrogens (Griffiths, Grant, and White, 12).

2. It has been suggested that the feminine aspect of these patients might result from a lack of sensitivity to, or a resistance to androgens on the part of their tissues (Wilkins, 53; Prader, 45). It should be pointed out that the Mül-

lerian ducts should have been sensitive to the inhibitory action of the fetal testes, since they disappeared. But even this point cannot always be taken for granted because one does not know if some of these abnormal subjects ever developed any Müllerian ducts.

For the time being, it is impossible to choose between these possibilities, especially since there are probably different etiological subtypes among the so-called types of testicular feminization (for instance, some patients have pubic or axillary hairs, others do not).

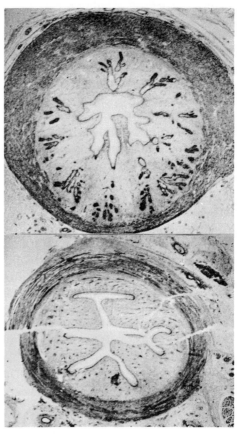

Fig. 24.9 Top: Section at the level of the prostate of a masculinized female calf fetus. Bottom: Section at approximately the same level in a control female fetus. ×17.

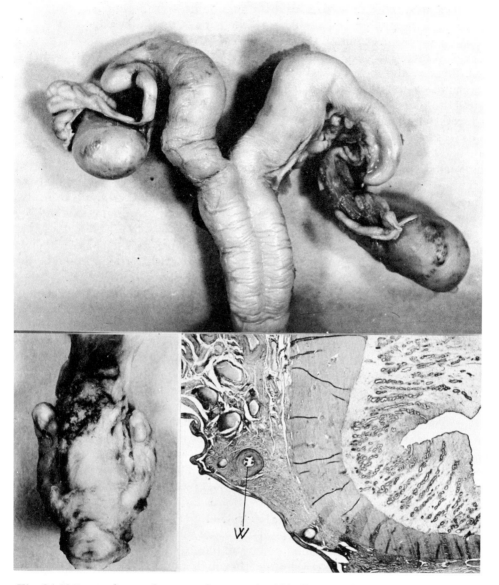

Fig. 24.10 Internal genital organs of a 3-month-old bull. Top: The uterine horns, testes, and epididymides are easily recognized. Lower left: The seminal vesicles. Lower right: Microscopical section showing the Wolffian duct (vas deferens), W, and the uterus. ×11.

A relative deficiency in fetal androgenic hormone is more frequent. The degree of feminization of the genital tract depends on the severity of the hormonal deficiency. The most frequent anomalies vary from completely feminine external genitalia with male internal structures, to different degrees of hypospadias. The same anomalies can easily be produced in rabbit fetuses when testicular functioning is depressed by decapitation (Jost, 25).

In conclusion, in the field of sex differentiation there is general agreement between the clinical findings and the hormonal theory of sexual differentiation. Some of the most typical human anomalies can be duplicated to a large extent in animal experiments, either by induced hormonal deficiencies in the fetus (castration or hypophysectomy at several stages, Jost, 29), or hormonal administration. Moreover, clinical cases not only afford information on some modalities of action of fetal hormones, they also give clues regarding genetically controlled testicular endocrine anomalies. A distinction between testicular organization and testicular physiology is suggested.

Various sex anomalies of the genital tract have been tentatively explained on the basis of a deficiency of fetal testicular hormones. On the assumption that there was an absolute metabolic block in the production of these hormones in some cases, it would appear that testicular organogenesis was possible even in their absence. Testicular organization should have been imposed on the undifferentiated gonadal primordium by other means. But in the best-studied human cases, some effects of the abnormal testes on the nearest parts of the genital tract are frequently observed (for instance, at the level of the epididymis). The available evidence does not exclude the possibility that minute amounts of these hormones might act locally, inside the developing gland, even if their production is not sufficient to control differentiation of the other parts of the genital tract during later stages of development.

The writer is quite aware of the fact that too many speculations may appear unwarranted; their object is only to recall the links between different assumptions and to emphasize some of the gaps in our knowledge.

Some Cytogenetic and Genetic Aspects of Sex Differentiation

The role of the heterochromosomes in the genetic determination of sex was first experimentally demonstrated in *Drosophila* and later in amphibians. For the latter, Humphrey (18) mated sex-reversed animals and studied the progeny; similar experiments were also performed by Gallien (11) and by Chang and Witschi (7).

In *Drosophila*, it has been known for years that sex is determined by the balance between the number of X chromosomes and the number of autosomes. More recently, other mechanisms have been discovered in plants and in animals. Welshons and Russel (51) demonstrated that in mice the Y chromosome is the "bearer of male determining factors." According to many chromosome studies, it also appears that in humans the Y chromosome is of foremost importance for testicular differentiation. It is impossible to review the literature here; reviews of this subject will be found in Sohval (50) and in Ford (9).

One probably does not distort the present state of our knowledge by stating that in (almost) all human subjects in which morphologically recognizable testes were found, at least one Y was present in the chromosomal formula. This does not apply to true hermaphrodites, since several XX cases have been reported, but further investigation is necessary.

The reciprocal proposition (presence of Y meaning presence of testes) also does not hold, since gonadal agenesis occurs occasionally in XY subjects.

However, the very important role of the Y chromosome in testicular organogenesis appears in Klinefelter's syndrome with XY, XXY, XXXY, XXXXY, or mosaic formulae. Moreover, several male pseudohermaphrodites possessing testes have been found to be XY (cf. Alexander and Ferguson-Smith, 1a).

It would appear that the Y chromosome bears factors determining the morphological differentiation of the testis, but it does not guarantee normal testicular functioning either in the fetus or in the adult. Spermatogenic or endocrine function can be abnormal. Familial cases of male pseudohermaphroditism or of testicular feminization suggest, in fact, that the secretion of the fetal testicular hormones may depend upon genetic control.

If the fetal testis actually produces two kinds of hormones, both necessary for normal sex differentiation of the body, and if under different genetic conditions either one or both may be deficient, it would appear that several genes must be involved in the control of testicular organogenesis and physiology.

Although the recent development of the cytogenetics of sex has provided exceedingly important data, the problem of the genetics of sex still has to be studied in terms of genes rather than whole chromosomes. The analysis of the role of different regions of the Y chromosome in the plant *Melandrium* *album* (Westergaard, 52) seems extremely interesting in this connection.

Summary

The causative factor or factors responsible for the sex differentiation of the early gonad primordium remain unknown. Moreover it cannot be assessed whether the inductor (inductors) or hormone (hormones) which control gonadal organogenesis are or are not the same as those which, at later stages, control the differentiation of the genital tract. In mammals the latter are mainly of testicular origin. Moreover, there is a suggestion that the fetal testis may produce two kinds of hormones.

The fetal testis is characterized both by its structure and by its endocrine capacities. Therefore, embryological or genetic studies of the differentiation of the testis should not be restricted to its morphological organization. A fetal testis that appears to be normally organized is not necessarily normal from the physiological point of view. Errors in metabolism are seldom evident under the microscope. The condition of the genital tract gives some indications concerning testicular activity at the time of sex differentiation.

Future work will have to determine what genetic and physiological causative factors are involved in morphological differentiation and in physiological specialization of fetal gonads.

References

1. Acevedo, H. F., L. R. Axelrod, E. Ishikawa, and F. Takaki, "Studies in Fetal Metabolism. II. Metabolism of Progesterone-4-C¹⁴ and Pregnenolone–7α–H³ in Human Fetal Testes," *J. Clin. Endocrinol. Metab.* 23:885–890 (1963).

1a. Alexander, D. S., and M. A. Ferguson-Smith, "Chromosomal Studies in Some Variants of Male Pseudo-hermaphroditism," *Pediatrics* 28:758–763 (1961).

2. Barton, J. M., and E. A. Holyoke, "An Experimental Study of the Effects of a Fetal Testes Extract on the Reproductive System of Embryonic Mice,"

Anat. Record 142:297, Abstr. (1962).

3. De Beaumont, J., "La Différenciation Sexuelle dans l'Appareil Uro-génital du *Triton* et Son Déterminisme," *Arch. Entwicklungsmech. Or.* 129:120–178 (1933).

4. Bissonnette, T. H., "Note on a 32-millimeter Freemartin," *Biol. Bull.* 54:238–253 (1928).

5. Bloch, E., B. Tissenbaum, and K. Benirschke, "The Conversion of [4-¹⁴C] Progesterone to 17α-Hydroxyprogesterone, Testosterone and Δ⁴-Androstene-3,17-dione by Human Fetal Testes *in vitro*," *Biochim. Biophys. Acta* 60:182–184 (1962).

6. Burns, R. K., "Transformation du Testicule Embryonnaire de l'Opossum en Ovotestis ou en Ovaire sous l'Action de l'Hormone Femelle, le Dipropionate d'Oestradiol," *Arch. Anat. Microscop. Morphol. Exptl.* 45:173–202 (1956).

7. Chang, C. Y., and E. Witschi, "Genic Control and Hormonal Reversal of Sex Differentiation in *Xenopus*," *Proc. Soc. Exptl. Biol. Med.* 93:140–144 (1956).

8. Ferreira, J. F., "Malformations du Système Uro-génital chez le Porc Domestique," *Folia Anat. Univ. Conimbrigensis* 12, no. 9:1–11 (1937).

9. Ford, C. E., "The Cytogenetics of Human Intersexuality," *Intersexuality*, Cl. Overzier, ed. New York: Academic Press, pp. 86–117 (1963).

10. Fralick, R. L., and R. C. Murray, "Pseudohermaphroditism in an Adult Dog," *Anat. Record* 100:741, Abstr. (1948).

11. Gallien, L., "Inversion Expérimentale du Sexe chez un Anoure Inférieur *Xenopus laevis* Daudin. Analyse des Conséquences Génétiques," *Bull. Biol. Fr. Belg.* 88:163–183 (1956).

12. Griffiths, K., J. K. Grant, and M. B. Whyte, "Steroid Biosynthesis *in vitro* by Cryptorchid Testes from a Case of Testicular Feminization," *J. Clin. Endocrinol. Metab.* 23:1044–1055 (1963).

13. Haffen, K., "La culture *in vitro* de l'Épithélium Germinatif Isolé des Gonades Mâles et Femelles de l'Embryon de Canard. II. Influence de la Médullaire sur la Différenciation de l'Épithélium Germinatif," *J. Embryol. Exptl. Morphol.* 8:414–424 (1960).

14. Harnden, D. G., and J. S. S. Stewart, "The Chromosomes in a Case of Pure Gonadal Dysgenesis," *Brit. Med. J.* 2:1285–1287 (1959).

15. Hauser, G. A., "Testicular Feminization," *Intersexuality*, Cl. Overzier, ed. New York: Academic Press, pp. 255–276 (1963).

16. Hitzeman, J. W., "Development of Enzyme Activity in the Leydig Cells of the Mouse Testis," *Anat. Record* 143:351–361 (1962).

17. Holyoke, E. A., "The Differentiation of Embryonic Ovaries and Testes Grafted Together in Adult Hosts in the Rabbit," *Anat. Record* 124:307 Abstr. (1956).

18. Humphrey, R. R., "Sex Determination in Ambystomid Salamanders: a Study of the Progeny of Females Experimentally Converted into Males," *Am. J. Anat.* 76:33–66 (1945).

19. Ikkos, D., K. G. Tillinger, and A. Westman, "Testicular Feminization," *Acta Endocrinol.* 32:222–232 (1959).

20. Jost, A., "Sur le Rôle des Gonades Foetales dans la Différenciation Sexuelle Somatique de l'Embryon de Lapin," *Compt. Rend. Assoc. Anat.* 34:255–263 (1947).

21. ———, "Recherches sur la Différenciation Sexuelle de l'Embryon de Lapin. III. Rôle des Gonades Foetales dans la Différenciation Sexuelle Somatique," *Arch. Anat. Microscop. Morphol. Exptl.* 36:271–315 (1947).

22. ———, "Le Contrôle Hormonal de la Différenciation du Sexe," *Biol. Rev. Cambridge Phil. Soc.* 23:201–236 (1948).

23. ———, "Activité Androgène du Testicule Foetal de Rat Greffé sur l'Adulte Castré," *Compt. Rend. Soc. Biol.* 142:196–198 (1948).

24. ———, "Recherches sur le Contrôle Hormonal de l'Organogenèse Sexuelle du Lapin et Remarques sur Certaines Malformations de l'Appareil Génital Humain," *Gynécol. Obstét.* 49:44–60 (1950).

25. ———, "Recherches sur la Différenciation Sexuelle de l'Embryon de Lapin. IV. Organogenèse Sexuelle Masculine après Décapitation de Foetus," *Arch. Anat. Microscop. Morphol. Exptl.* 40:247–281 (1951).

26. ———, "Problems of Fetal Endocrinol-

ogy: the Gonadal and Hypophyseal Hormones," *Recent Progr. Hormone Res.* 8: 379–418 (1953).

27. ———, "Modalities in the Action of Gonadal and Gonad-stimulating Hormones in the Foetus," *Mem. Soc. Endocrinol.* no. 4:237–248 (1955).

28. ———, "Biologie des Androgènes chez l'Embryon," *IIIe Réunion Endocrinol. Langue Française* Paris: Masson et Cie, pp. 160–180 (1955).

29. ———, "Embryonic Sexual Differentiation (Morphology, Physiology, Abnormalities)," *Genital Abnormalities, Hermaphroditism and Related Adrenal Diseases.* H. Jones, W. W. Scott, eds. Baltimore: Williams & Wilkins, pp. 15–45 (1958).

30. ———, "Hormonal Influences in the Sex Development of Bird and Mammalian Embryos," *Mem. Soc. Endocrinol.* Cambridge: Cambridge University Press, no. 7:49–61 (1960).

31. ———, and Y. Bergerard, "Culture *in vitro* d'Ébauches du Tractus Génital du Foetus de Rat," *Compt. Rend. Soc. Biol.* 143:608–609 (1949).

32. ———, and B. Bozic, "Données sur la Différenciation des Conduits Génitaux du Foetus de Rat Étudiée *in vitro*," *Compt. Rend. Soc. Biol.* 145:647–650 (1951).

33. ———, M. Chodkiewicz, and P. Mauléon, "Intersexualité du Foetus de Veau Produite par des Androgènes. Comparaison entre l'Hormone Foetale Responsable du Freemartinisme et l'Hormone Testiculaire Adulte," *Compt. Rend. Acad. Sci.* 256:274–276 (1963).

34. ———, and R. A. Colonge, "Greffe du Testicule Foetal de Rat sur l'Adulte Castré et Hypophysectomisé. Remarques sur la Physiologie du Testicule Foetal de Rat," *Compt. Rend. Soc. Biol.* 143:140–142 (1949).

35. Keller, K., and J. Tandler, "Über das Verhalten der Eihäute bei der Zwillingsträchtigkeit des Rindes. Untersuchungen über die Entstehungsursache der Geschlechtlichen Unterentwickelung von weiblichen Zwillingskälbern welche neben einem männlichen Kalbe zur Entwickelung gelangen," *Wiener Tierarztl. Wochschr.* 3:513–526 (1916).

36. Lillie, F., "The Theory of the Free-martin," *Science* 43:611–613 (1916).

37. ———, "The Freemartin, a Study of the Action of Sex Hormones in the Fetal Life of Cattle," *J. Exptl. Zool.* 23:371–452 (1917).

38. Lutz, H., and Y. Lutz-Ostertag, "Freemartinisme Spontané chez les Oiseaux," *Develop. Biol.* 1:364–376 (1959).

39. Macintyre, M. N., "Effect of the Testis on Ovarian Differentiation in Heterosexual Embryonic Rat Gonad Transplants," *Anat. Record* 124:27–45 (1956).

40. Mikamo, K., and E. Witschi, "Functional Sex Reversal in Genetic Females of *Xenopus laevis* Induced by Implanted Testes," *Genetics* 48:1411–1421 (1963).

41. Mintz, B., and E. Wolff, "Sur les Greffes Coelomiques de la Médullaire Ovarienne d'Embryons de Poulet: l'Évolution des Greffons et Leur Action Féminisante sur les Hôtes Mâles," *Compt. Rend. Soc. Biol.* 146:494–495 (1952).

42. Morris, J. McL., "The Syndrome of Testicular Feminization in Male Pseudohermaphrodites (82 Cases)," *Am. J. Obstet. Gynecol.* 65:1192–1211 (1953).

43. Nilson, O., "Hernia Uteri Inguinalis beim Manne," *Acta Chir. Scand.* 83:231–249 (1940).

44. Overzier, Cl., ed., *Intersexuality.* New York: Academic Press, (1963).

45. Prader, A., "Gonadendysgenesie und Testikulare Feminisierung," *Schweiz. Med. Wochschr.* 87:278–303 (1957).

46. Price, D., and R. Pannabecker, "Organ Culture Studies of Foetal Rat Reproductive Tracts," *Ciba Found. Colloq. Ageing* 2:3–13 (1956).

47. Raynaud, Alb., and M. Frilley, "Destruction des Glandes Génitales de l'Embryon de Souris par une Irradiation au Moyen des Rayons X, à l'Âge de 13 Jours," *Ann. Endocrinol.* 8:400–419 (1947).

48. Ruch, J. V., "Contribution à l'Étude des Modifications du Systeme Génital des Embryons Issus d'Oeufs Doubles de Poule (*Gallus domesticus*)," *Arch. Anat. Histol. Embryol. Strasbourg* 65:61–129 (1962).

49. Schwartz, E., "Sur un Cas d'Androgynoïde (Pseudohermaphrodite Masculin Complet)," *Bull. Acad. Méd.* 132:383–392 (1919).

50. Sohval, A. R., "Chromosomes and Sex

Chromatin in Normal and Anomalous Sexual Development," *Physiol. Rev.* 43: 306–356 (1963).

51. Welshons, W. S., and L. B. Russel, "The Y-chromosome as the Bearer of Male Determining Factors in the Mouse," *Proc. Natl. Acad. Sci. U.S.* 45: 560–566 (1959).

52. Westergaard, M., "The Mechanism of Sex Determination in Dioecious Flowering Plants," *Advan. Genet.* 9:217–281 (1958).

53. Wilkins, L., *The Diagnosis and Treatment of Endocrine Disorders in Childhood and Adolescence, 2d edition* Oxford: Blackwell (1957).

54. Willier, B. H., "Structure and Homologies of Freemartin Gonads," *J. Exptl. Zool.* 33:63–127 (1921).

55. Witschi, E., "Modifications of the Development of Sex in Lower Vertebrates and in Mammals," *Sex and Internal Secretions,* 2nd ed., E. Allen, ed. Baltimore: Williams & Wilkins, chap. IV, pp. 145–226 (1939).

56. Wolff, Et., "Recherches sur l'Intersexualité Expérimentale Produite par la Méthode des Greffes de Gonades à l'Embryon de Poulet," *Arch. Anat. Microscop. Morphol. Exptl.* 36:69–90 (1946).

57. ———, and K. Haffen, "Sur l'Intersexualité Expérimentale des Gonades Embryonnaires de Canard Cultivées *in vitro,*" *Arch. Anat. Microscop. Morphol. Exptl.* 41:184–207 (1959).

58. ———, and ———, "Action Féminisante de la Gonade Droite de l'Embryon Femelle de Canard en Culture *in vitro,*" *Compt. Rend Soc. Biol.* 146:1772–1774 (1952).

59. ———, and Em. Wolff, "The Effects of Castration on Bird Embryos," *J. Exptl. Zool.* 116:59–98 (1951).

60. ———, and ———, "Mise en Évidence d'une Action Féminisante de la Gonade Droite chez l'Embryon Femelle des Oiseaux par les Expériences d'Hémicastration," *Compt. Rend. Soc. Biol.* 145: 1218–1219 (1951).

61. Young, D., "Hernia Uteri Inguinalis in the Male," *J. Obstet. Gynaecol. Brit. Empire* 58:830–831 (1951).

25

The Role of Fetal Androgen
in Sex Differentiation in Mammals

DOROTHY PRICE AND EVELINA ORTIZ*

Zoology Department, University of Chicago, Chicago, Illinois
Biology Department, University of Puerto Rico, Río Piedras, Puerto Rico

Historical Background

It is almost 50 years since the epoch-making research of Lillie (30, 31, 32) and Keller and Tandler (28) on the female bovine intersex, the freemartin. This research focused attention sharply on the problem of the relation of fetal sex hormones to mammalian sex differentiation. However, the ensuing epoch in which such an impressive amount of scientific information was amassed did not begin immediately with experiments on mammals. Technical difficulties delayed analyses, but once testicular androgens and ovarian estrogens were isolated, chemically characterized and synthesized, an era of hormone administration to fetuses was initiated. Other experimental methods included grafting of fetal organs into postnatal hosts and the important and critical technique of extirpation of fetal gonads. All of this research was designed to modify or control the fetal endocrine environment and test the theory of fetal sex hormone control of sex differentiation. An experimental freemartin was never produced. Gonads were singularly unresponsive, but it was established that the sex ducts, urogenital sinus, and external genitalia respond to sex hormones in certain stages of prenatal development which are specific for each organ. It was shown that there are genetically determined basic sex differences in the responsiveness of homologous structures to sex hormones, and that differential sensitivity exists in various parts of the reproductive tract within the individual. Finally, fetal testes were found to secrete a male hormone. Early work was summarized by Moore (40).

By 1950 a solid basis was laid for an

* Our research on the fetal guinea pig was supported by grants from the Wallace C. and Clara A. Abbott Memorial Fund of the University of Chicago and by research grants GM-02912, GM-05335 and AM-03628 from the Division of General Medical Sciences, National Institutes of Health, Public Health Service.

understanding of the importance of testicular male hormone in mammalian sex differentiation. The subject was competently and thoroughly reviewed at that time for the rat (Wells, 67), mouse (Raynaud, 62), rabbit (Jost, 17), and opossum (Burns, 4; Moore, 41). It was evident, more particularly from the critical experiments of Wells and of Jost involving fetal gonad extirpation by surgical procedures and Raynaud's destruction of gonads by x ray, that testicular androgen plays a major role in sex duct differentiation, in development of derivatives of the urogenital sinus, and in the formation of the external genitalia. In subsequent experiments it was found possible to culture isolated reproductive tracts of rats (Price and Pannabecker, 55, 56; Price, 53) and mice (Brewer, 3) at very young stages and to demonstrate clearly the dependence of Wolffian duct maintenance and accessory gland development on fetal testicular androgen in these species. In the mouse, Brewer found evidence for male Müllerian duct inhibition by testicular hormone; this was also shown for the rabbit (Jost, 17). In both rat and mouse, differentiation of the sex ducts and urogenital sinus proceeded normally in the absence of the ovaries, as it did in Jost's ovariectomized rabbit fetuses.

The expanding field of fetal endocrinology early encompassed studies on pituitaries, thyroids, and adrenals, and evidence accumulated for prenatal onset of hormone secretion. Further, the pituitary axes with gonads, thyroids, and adrenals were found to be established before birth. This almost overwhelming volume of research on fetal endocrine physiology has been frequently reviewed. Excellent comprehensive reviews on various aspects, including comparative studies, have been written by Jost (18, 19, 20, 22, 23), Willier (73), Burns (5), Wells (69), Wolff (76), Moore (41), and Mitskevich (37, 38).

In spite of all these experimental studies on mammalian fetuses, many pertinent questions remain unanswered and await new approaches and more sophisticated and imaginative techniques of analysis. In the problem of sex differentiation there is the omnipresent question of the site of action of sex hormones, more particularly androgen, in the cells of end organs. By what mechanisms does the male hormone act to stimulate cells of Wolffian ducts and accessory glands and effect cell death in Müllerian ducts? What factors are responsible for the change in the Wolffian ducts of males (and females) from a hormone-independent status (as nephric ducts) to androgen dependency? How early in testis differentiation is androgen secreted and does it influence differentiation of the testis itself? Does the fetal testis secrete androgenic hormone or hormones which differ from androgens secreted by postnatal testes? Is fetal androgen species specific? Can it be a steroid? Finally, considering the well-established fact of sex hormone secretion by the adrenal cortex postnatally, is there a possibility that adrenals secrete androgen prenatally and that this source of androgen might be of significance in early stages of differentiation of gonads and sex ducts?

Studies on Sex Differentiation in the Fetal Guinea Pig

General Background

We selected the guinea pig as a suitable animal in which to attempt to answer some of the intriguing questions on sex differentiation. Not many studies have been made on this species, although some of the earliest research on hormone administration to fetuses was done on the guinea pig (Dantchakoff, 8, 9). The long gestation period and the relatively mature state of the young at birth are advantageous for comparing the sequence of events in sex differentiation in this rodent with rodents such as the rat, mouse, and hamster, and with the rabbit.

For the problem of determining the onset of secretory activity in fetal guinea pig testes, we had available a bioindicator technique which used cultures of reproductive tracts of 16½-day-old fetal rats and determined the androgenicity of the test organ by maintenance or regression of the rat Wolffian duct (Pannabecker and Price, 50). Figures 25.1 and 25.2 illustrate the maintenance of the duct by androgen from rat testes and the retrogression when testes were absent. Figures 25.3 and 25.4 show rat Wolffian duct maintenance by androgen from fetal mouse testes and demonstrate clearly the lack of species specificity in fetal testicular androgens in these mammals. More recently, a new and very sensitive method for detecting the presence of androgen has been developed. This method utilizes postnatal rat ventral prostate tissue in juxtaposed culture with test organs (Price et al., 60).

Our research program on the guinea pig has been designed to: (1) study the sequential stages in the early differentiation of the urogenital tract and adrenal glands, (2) determine the youngest stages of testis differentiation when androgenic secretion can be detected in culture, (3) examine the developing testes histochemically for steroidogenesis as shown by enzyme localization, (4) test for androgenicity and evidence for steroidogenesis in adrenal glands, and (5) describe the endocrine physiology of the young fetus in terms of onset of secretory activity in some other endocrine glands.

Sequential Stages in Differentiation of the Urogenital Tract

The stages in sex differentiation (Fig. 25.5) follow rather closely the pattern described for other laboratory rodents and for the rabbit. The gonads are cut off from the urogenital ridge between 22 and 23 days of fetal age. Differentiation of the testis follows rapidly and medullary cords form between 25 and 27 days; the ovary, as usual, is slower in differentiation and a conspicuous cortex is not present until about 31 days. Cell nests are organized by 35 days and by 50 days follicles are forming, but these do not become vesicular until some time after birth. The Müllerian ducts of males and females begin development at 23 days, and grow posteriorly and fuse with the urogenital sinus wall by 29 days. They join together to form the prostatic utricle in males and the uterovaginal canal in females between 29 and 31 days. Characteristically, degeneration of male Müllerian ducts begins at the anterior end while differentiation is still progressing posteriorly. By 35 days only small remnants of these ducts remain in the male.

The Wolffian ducts of females begin anterior degeneration at 29 days in some fetuses, but in others these ducts are still intact at 32 and 33 days and only a narrowing of the anterior region foreshadows degeneration, which then follows rapidly.

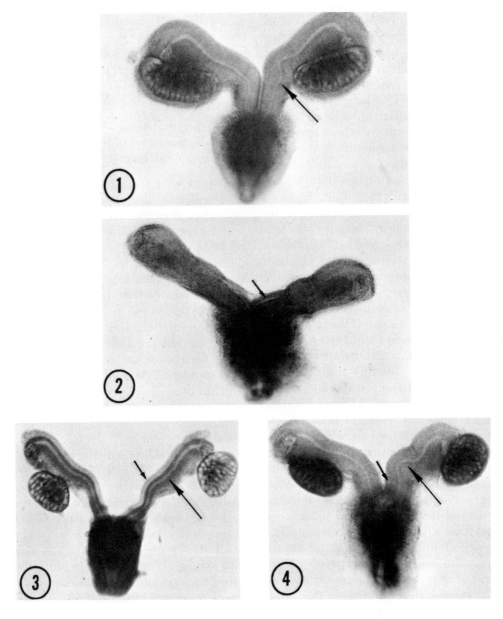

Figs. 25.1–25.4 Reproductive tracts of 16½-day-old male rat fetuses placed in culture and photographed on the medium. Large arrow indicates Wolffian ducts; small arrow, Müllerian ducts. ×32. **Fig. 25.1** Male tract cultured for 3 days with rat testes present; retention of Wolffian ducts. **Fig. 25.2** Male tract cultured for 3 days with no testes; retrogression of Wolffian ducts. **Fig. 25.3** Male tract at the time of explantation with 15½-day-old mouse testes. **Fig. 25.4** Explant shown in Fig. 25.3 after 3 days of culture; retention of Wolffian ducts. (From Price and Pannabecker, unpublished observations.)

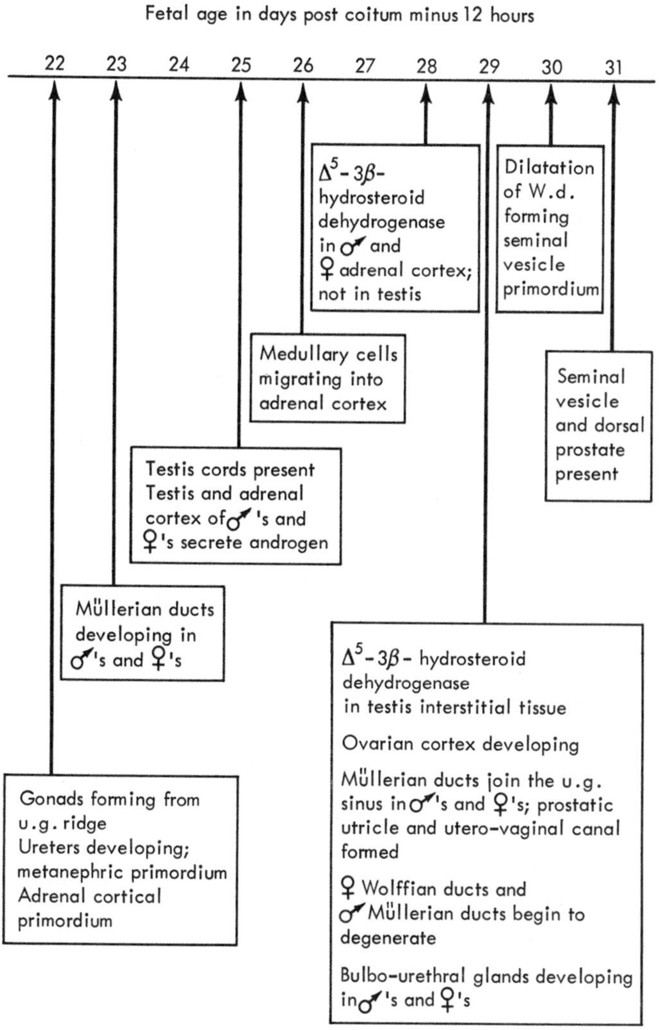

Fetal age in days post coitum minus 12 hours

Fig. 25.5 Stages in the differentiation of the urogenital tract of fetal guinea pigs.

The first male accessory glands to form are the bulbourethral at 29 days, but within the next 2 days seminal vesicle and prostatic development begins. No seminal vesicle or prostatic primordia were found in females, but bulbovestibular glands, homologous with bulbourethral were present at 29 days.

The adrenal cortical cells begin to group together at 22 days and the first detectable migration of medullary cells into the cortex occurs about 4 days later.

Testis Differentiation, Androgenicity, and Steroidogenesis

The formation of medullary cords occurs at variable times over a period of days, but in general, these cords are usually present by 26 or 27 days. Histochemical localization of alkaline phosphatases usually enables detection of testis cords at 26 days (Ortiz, 48). However, variability in testis development is marked even within litters, as shown in Figures 25.6, 25.9, and 25.10. This litter of five was 27 days of age. The testes in Figures 25.9 and 25.10 are recognizable by development of the tunica and seminiferous cords, but Figure 25.6 shows a testis which is not distinguishable from the ovaries in Figures 25.7 and 25.8. By 30 or 31 days the tunica and cords are well developed (Fig. 25.11) but the ovary is still not far advanced in its differentiation (Fig. 25.13).

In an attempt to test androgenic secretion by testes of fetal guinea pigs, the rat Wolffian-duct test was applied to testes of 45- and 31-day-old fetuses and to a few of 27 days (Price, Ortiz, and Pannabecker, 59). The results were clear at the two older ages and suggestive at 27 days. Figure 25.12 illustrates the retention of rat Wolffian ducts in culture by guinea pig testicular androgen. The lack of retention with an explanted ovary in culture is evident in Figure 25.14. The beginning of Wolffian duct degeneration is shown in this explant which was cultured for 2 days; on the subsequent day the ducts had retrogressed, as in Figure 25.2.

The earlier culture work has recently been repeated and greatly extended using postnatal rat ventral prostate tissue as an indicator for androgen (Price, Ortiz, and Zaaijer, 60, 61). The epithelium of the rat ventral prostate is highly responsive to androgen from testes, ovaries, and adrenals, and is androgen dependent for its maintenance in a histologically normal and functional state (Price and Williams-Ashman, 57). The new method confirmed earlier results and added information. Figure 25.15 illustrates a culture of guinea pig testis explanted at 31 days of age and cultured with rat ventral prostate tissue which was maintained in normal histological condition (Fig. 25.17) by androgen from the testis. Cultures of fetal ovaries at 31 days failed to stimulate juxtaposed prostate, which then retrogressed (Fig. 25.19). Prostate explanted alone or with guinea pig fetal urinary bladder as a control organ resembled the prostate shown in Figure 25.19. Cultures of younger testes, including 26-day-old, showed that they were secreting androgen.

The recent finding (Price, Ortiz, and Zaaijer, unpublished observations) that at 25 days testes gave positive tests, is more striking still. At this age testes are not detectably differentiated in most fetuses, but medullary cords are forming. In fact, our most recent results indicate that even 22-day-old gonads secrete androgen. It is apparent that the fetal guinea pig gonad, genetically determined as a testis, secretes androgen for a considerable period before the formation of primary cords.

The demonstration of androgenic secretory activity in fetal testes brought up the important question of whether this androgen could be a steroid; more specifically, whether fetal guinea pig testes have the potentiality of secreting steroidal androgens. This aspect was studied (Price, Ortiz, and Deane, 58) by the application of a histochemical method for visualizing the activity of the enzyme Δ^5-3β-hydroxysteroid dehydrogenase which is involved in the synthesis of most active steroid hormones. The first results demonstrated that interstitital cells of fetal

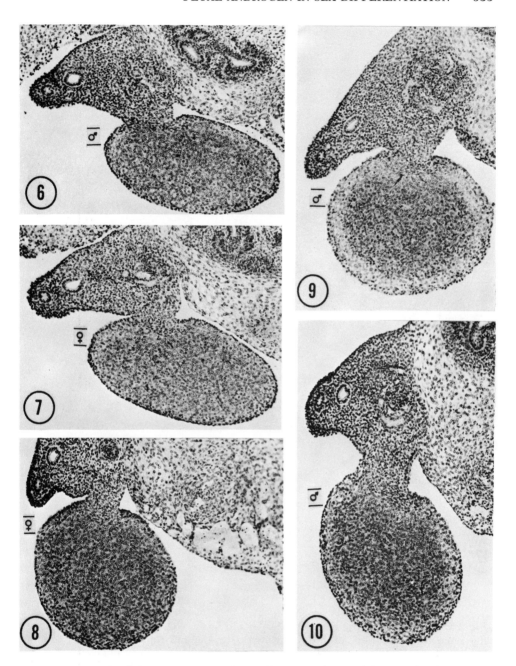

Figs. 25.6–25.10 Photomicrographs of gonads from a litter of five fetal guinea pigs aged 27½ days. The sex was determined by culturing the contralateral gonad with 16½-day-old reproductive tracts from fetal male rats and observing Wolffian duct retention or retrogression. ×87 (From Price and Pannabecker, unpublished observations.)

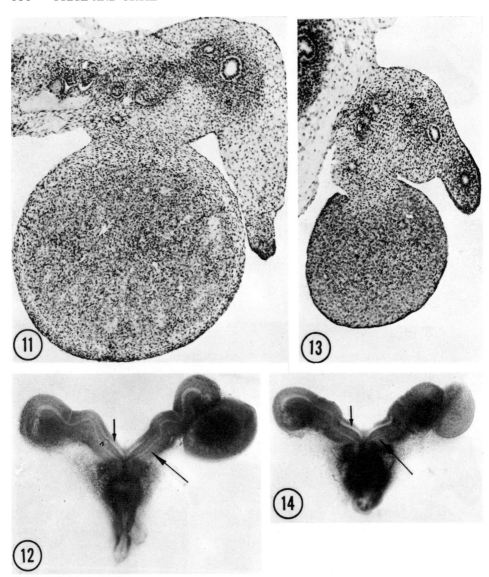

Fig. 25.11 Left guinea pig testis of a 31-day-old fetus. ×82. Fig. 25.12 Right testis of the same fetus cultured for 2 days against a 16½-day-old reproductive tract from a fetal male rat; Wolffian duct retention. ×30. Fig. 25.13 Left guinea pig ovary of a 31-day-old fetus (litter mate to the male fetus shown in Figs. 25.11 and 25.12). ×82. Fig. 25.14 Right ovary of the same fetus cultured for 2 days against a 16½-day-old reproductive tract from a fetal male rat; Wolffian duct retrogressing. Large arrows indicate Wolffian ducts; small arrows, Müllerian ducts. ×30 (From Price and Pannabecker, unpublished observations.)

testes showed positive reactions at 31, 45, and 50 days of age. Recent findings (Price, Ortiz, and Deane, unpublished observations) showed positive reactions in testes of 29½-day fetuses, but those of 28 days gave negative results, even after an incubation period of 24 hours. The intensity of the reaction increased with age. It is concluded that testes of fetal guinea pigs are capable of secreting steroidal androgen as early as 29½ days. The sensitivity of the method may be a limiting factor in detecting activity at younger ages. Fetal ovaries showed no reaction at corresponding ages. The oldest fetuses examined were 50 days old.

Adrenal Androgen Secretion and Steroidogenesis

Male and female adrenal glands were cultured with prostate in most experiments in which testes or ovaries were being studied (Price, Ortiz, and Zaaijer, 60, 61). They proved to be markedly androgenic (Figs. 25.16 and 25.18) in prostatic maintenance at all ages tested (26–32 days) and apparently were even more effective than testes. Male and female glands seemed equally androgenic. Subsequent experiments (Price, Ortiz, and Zaaijer, unpublished observations) have shown that at 22 and 25 days they are also secreting apparently high levels of androgen.

Histochemical studies were made and positive reactions for Δ^5-3β-hydroxysteroid dehydrogenase were demonstrated in male and female adrenal cortex in fetal glands 31, 45, and 50 days old (Price, Ortiz, and Deane, 58). Additional experiments (Price, Ortiz, and Deane, unpublished observations) showed that activity was present in adrenals of 28-day-old fetuses — the youngest age examined. There was no detectable difference between the activity in male and female glands, but activity increased with age. Thus the fetal adrenal cortex, as well as the testis, is capable of secreting steroidal androgens at an early stage.

In earlier work, Moog and Ortiz (39) concluded, on the basis of cell size and sudanophilia, that the adrenal cortex had the capacity to function by 36 days; maximum relative weight was reached at 32 days. There is no available information on the time of establishment of the pituitary-adrenal axis in fetal guinea pigs.

The adrenal medulla, incidentally, may be secreting hormone as early as 30 days (Langlois and Rehns, 29). Shepherd and West (64) identified noradrenalin in the adrenals of guinea pig fetuses of unspecified age (apparently near term) but no adrenalin was found.

Endocrine Physiology in Fetal Guinea Pigs during Sex Differentiation

The demonstration that testes and adrenals of fetal guinea pigs are secreting androgen before sex differentiation has begun, points up the question of the hormone milieu of the fetus, the onset of secretion in other endocrine glands, and the time of establishment of pituitary-gonad, pituitary-adrenal, and pituitary-thyroid axes. Figure 25.20 depicts graphically some rather fragmentary, and in some cases, indirect, evidence of functional activity in endocrine glands. Unfortunately, the only clear evidence for establishment of functional interrelationships relates to the time of development of the pituitary-thyroid axis.

In the guinea pig fetus, Ortiz (unpublished observations) observed ba-

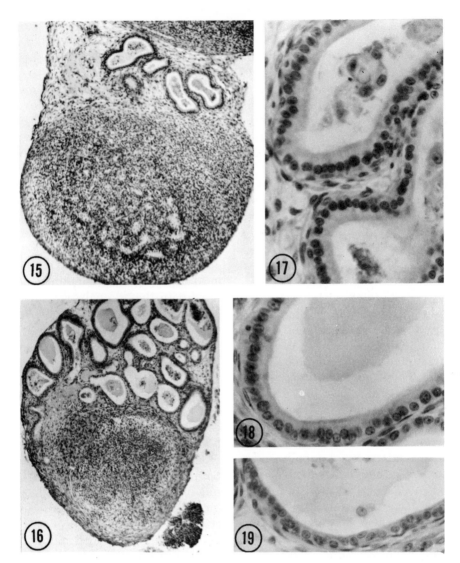

Fig. 25.15 Explant of a 31-day-old fetal guinea pig testis cultured for 5 days with 28-day-old (postnatal) rat ventral prostate tissue. ×64. **Fig. 25.16** Explant of a 27½-day-old fetal female guinea pig adrenal cultured for 6 days with 28-day-old (postnatal) rat ventral prostate tissue. ×64. **Fig. 25.17** Portion of the ventral prostate tissue shown in explant in Figure 25.15. Maintenance of normal histological structure by testicular androgen. ×400. **Fig. 25.18** Portion of the ventral prostate tissue shown in explant in Fig. 25.16. Maintenance of normal histological structure by adrenal androgen. ×400. **Fig. 25.19** Portion of a rat ventral prostate explanted with a 31-day-old guinea pig ovary and cultured for 5 days. Retrogression of the prostate epithelium. (From Price, Ortiz and Zaaijer, unpublished observations.)

sophils in the developing pituitary at 26 days of age. These were periodic acid-Schiff (PAS) positive (presumed gonadotrophs and thyrotrophs) but a few were also aldehyde-fuchsin (AF) positive (presumed thyrotrophs). Brilliant granules were conspicuous in the PAS-positive basophils at 31 days. A few acidophils had developed by 29½ days. The identification of these cell types gives no indication of whether the trophic hormones were being secreted and stored or released. The presence of granules in cells lining the residual lumen suggests storage of thyrotrophin.

Logothetopoulos and Scott (34) and Mitskevich (37, 38) reported the presence of colloid in the thyroid at 28 days, and at about the same age the organic binding of I^{131} was observed, indicating functional activity. They demonstrated clearly by administering a goitrogen to the pregnant females that the pituitary-thyroid axis was developed between 30 and 36 days. The experiments of Mitskevich showed that there was no increase in pituitary weights in goitrous fetuses until birth, but cytological changes were observed about the middle of the second half of the gestation period.

Ortiz (49) explored in a large series of fetal guinea pigs the consequences of the interruption of the pituitary-thyroid axis on growth and differentiation of the reproductive tract, adrenals, and pituitaries. Female guinea pigs were treated with propylthiouracil for varying periods of time and then mated. The goitrogen was administered continuously during pregnancy and the fetuses were examined at 45 and 60 days. Large maternal and fetal goiters were induced as expected, but the hypothyroid condition of the fetus did not affect weights of body, testes, ovaries, adrenals, uterus, or seminal vesicles. However, fetal pituitary weights were significantly increased at 45 days. No effects were observed on histological differentiation in any of the organs.

The period of sex differentiation in the guinea pig is marked by rapid onset of secretory activity in endocrine glands, probably led by secretion of androgen in testes and adrenals.

Pituitary-Thyroid and Pituitary-Adrenal Axes in Other Mammals

It is beyond the scope of this paper to review the extensive evidence for prenatal establishment of pituitary-thyroid and pituitary-adrenal axes in mammals. Among the many reviews are those of Willier (73), Jost (19, 21), Wells (68), and Noumura (46, 47). In general, these axes are developed in late fetal stages. However, Mitskevich (38) stressed the fact that fetal pituitary-thyroid axes are established relatively much earlier in mammals which are born well developed, such as the guinea pig and sheep, than in those in which the young are very immature at birth (rat and rabbit). The evidence for the prenatal existence of a pituitary-gonad axis is presented below.

Comparative Aspects of Sex Differentiation

The Pattern of Sex Differentiation in Fetuses

It is of interest to compare the sequence of events in sex differentiation in a representative group of laboratory mammals with varying periods of gestation (Fig. 25.21). An almost consistent pattern is evident. Morphological

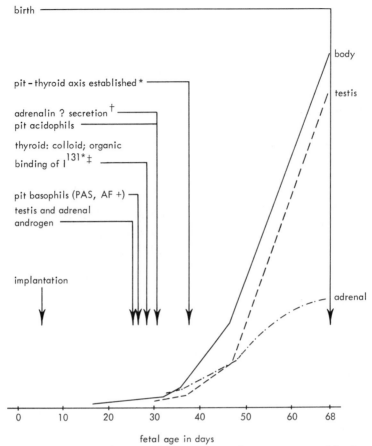

birth

body

pit - thyroid axis established *

testis

adrenalin ? secretion †
pit acidophils

thyroid: colloid; organic
binding of I^{131*}‡

pit basophils (PAS, AF +)
testis and adrenal
androgen

implantation

adrenal

| 0 | 10 | 20 | 30 | 40 | 50 | 60 | 68 |

fetal age in days

Fig. 25.20 Development of functional activity in endocrine organs of fetal guinea pigs in relation to growth of body, testis, and adrenal. *J. Logothetopoulos and R. F. Scott, *J. Endocrin.* 14:217–227. †J. P. Langlois and J. Rehns, *C. R. Soc. Biol.* 51:146–147. ‡M. S. Mitskevich, *Glands of Internal Secretion in Embryonic Development of Birds and Mammals,* Academy of Sciences of USSR, Moscow.

and functional differentiation of the testis (always accomplished earlier than ovarian differentiation) is, of course, the first step, and is followed in order by the beginning of degeneration of male Müllerian ducts, then female Wolffian ducts, and finally, by the development of primordia of male accessory glands and their homologues in some females. The sequence of these decisive stages is inextricably bound to the orderly pattern of organogenesis in the fetus; the ducts and glands of the definitive reproductive tracts are (especially in the male) a composite of bits and pieces taken over from the early nephric system and the primitive cloaca. Even the Müllerian ducts are phylogenetically (and probably ontogenetically) related to the nephric system. It is obvious that retrogression of Wolffian ducts in females cannot begin until mesonephric function (if the mesonephros functions in the spe-

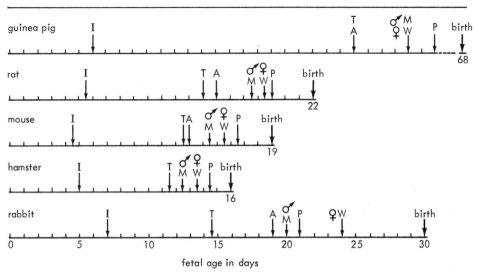

Fig. 25.21 Comparative sequence of developmental stages in mammalian sex differentiation. I, implantation; T, testis differentiation; A, androgen secretion; ♂ M, Müllerian duct degeneration in ♂ beginning; ♀ W, Wolffian duct degeneration in ♀ beginning; P, prostate.

cies) has been taken over by the meta-nephros. Sex differentiation then takes place within this framework and operates on indifferent or ambisexual gonads and duct systems.

The timing of the stages in this pattern is set by the onset of secretory activity in the testis and the release of this hormone into the body. Undoubtedly this occurs by diffusion into immediately adjacent tissues at very early stages, and only later does the hormone enter the blood stream in effective amounts. To act in controlling the sex differentiation of sex ducts and glands, testicular hormone must penetrate into the cells of these target organs and there affect metabolic processes at a time when the cells of each organ possess a special pattern of enzymes. These patterns have been established during the embryonic differentiation of each particular organ. Each target organ in embryogenesis passes suc-cessively through a stage of independent or "anhormonal" differentiation and then a stage in which the cells have developed the ability to respond to androgenic hormonal stimulation in very specific ways.

At this critical phase of onset of responsiveness to androgen, the cells of the Wolffian ducts of males respond and live, and the cells of the male Müllerian ducts respond and die. The continued presence or ultimate absence of the gonoducts is determined then. The cells of the Wolffian ducts of males (and females) are doomed to die in the absence of androgen; the cells of Müllerian ducts are doomed to die in its presence. However, once this critical stage is passed, the absence of androgen will not result in retrogression of Wolffian ducts of males or in retention of the Müllerian ducts. The Wolffian ducts are then stabilized but retain, of course, their ability to respond to androgen. In the female, the Wolffian ducts pass through a critical phase similar to that of the male ducts, and in the absence of androgen necrosis occurs. Absence of androgen also insures survival of the female Müllerian ducts.

The sequential pattern of sex differentiation represents, then, a developmental history of secretion of androgenic hormone acting in specific and unique ways in target organs at critical periods which are characteristic for each organ. In addition, convincing experimental evidence has shown that the hormone threshold differs in different end organs and in homologous sex ducts and glands in males and females.

It is not too surprising that the patterns of sex differentiation shown in Figure 25.21 are essentially similar in the four rodents and the domestic rabbit. However, it is interesting that the time span from morphogenesis of the testis through critical stages of duct differentiation to development of the prostate is almost the same in species with gestation periods as disparate as the guinea pig (68 days) and the hamster (16 days). The time span is 5–6 days in the guinea pig and about 4½ days in the hamster. This suggests a similar developmental rate in cellular differentiation in target organs and similar timing in male hormone action on the reproductive tracts of these different species.

The domestic rabbit has a different timing for degeneration of female Wolffian ducts. These ducts have a longer life span than in the rodents. It is noteworthy that an exactly similar pattern and timing of sex differentiation was described for a different species, the wild cottontail rabbit (*Sylvilagus floridans*), by Elchlepp (10). Here, as in the domestic species, the female retains Wolffian ducts up to 23 or 24 days of fetal age before retrogression begins. Gersh (11) has shown that the mesonephros of the domestic rabbit is functioning at 21 days of age (when metanephric function is just beginning) but that it is no longer functional at 23 days. Whereas the crucial stages in sex differentiation are completed in almost the same time span in the four rodents and the domestic and wild rabbits, the actual time of sex differentiation relative to the length of the gestation period differs markedly. In the hamster, two-thirds of gestation has passed before sex differentiation begins, but in the guinea pig fetus (which is born in a very well-developed condition) only a little over one-third of gestation has passed.

Critical Effects of Testicular Hormone on Ducts and Glands

The most critical analyses of the normal role of male hormone in duct and gland differentiation has come from experiments involving surgical gonadectomy, extirpation of gonads by x ray, or organ culture of whole, isolated reproductive tracts. All of these techniques are open to criticism from one point of view or another, but from the combined results, a relatively clear picture has emerged of sex differentiation in several species of mammals. Some of the most pertinent and direct evidence for placental mammals is summarized below.

EVIDENCE FROM EXPERIMENTS ON RABBITS. Jost showed clearly that castration of fetal males, if performed at 19 days, resulted in absence of Wolffian ducts, complete persistence of Müllerian ducts, and the total absence of prostatic buds (Jost, 17, 18, 23). Testis removal at later stages caused, depending upon the age of operation, more or less degeneration of Wolffian ducts, retention of Müllerian ducts, and development of the prostate. By 24 days of age Wolffian ducts were stabilized and Müllerian ducts were conditioned to retrogress. Castration at that time had no effect upon the differentiation of the male tract which was normal as studied at 28 days. In one case a fetal testis was grafted onto the mesosalpinx close to one ovary of a female fetus. Partial suppression of the adjacent Müllerian duct was obtained, as well as maintenance of the female Wolffian duct on that side. Removal of ovaries from fetal females did not affect normal sex differentiation. Jost concluded that fetal testis hormone was responsible for sex differentiation.

EVIDENCE FROM EXPERIMENTS ON RATS.   Wells and his collaborators castrated rat fetuses in late pregnancy at 18–19½ days of fetal age and observed some atrophy of Wolffian ducts, no retention of Müllerian ducts, development of fewer prostatic buds (no coagulating glands in some cases), and lack of flexure of the seminal vesicle (Wells, 67, 70; Wells and Fralick, 71; Wells, Cavanaugh and Maxwell, 72). They concluded that testis hormone was secreted prenatally in the rat and that it stimulated growth in accessory reproductive glands. But they did not assign to it a fundamental role in sex differentiation.

Price and Pannabecker (55, 56; Price, 53) explanted whole male and female reproductive tracts at ages of 14½–18½ days and cultured them for periods of 1–6 days. Sex differentiation proceeded essentially normally in male tracts with testes present, and in female tracts with or without ovaries. In male explants cultured without testes at all ages, the Wolffian ducts underwent anteroposterior retrogression (except at 14½ days, when they were retained), seminal vesicles were lacking, and only a few prostatic buds developed. Male Müllerian ducts retrogressed in all explants. Testes placed against female tracts caused local enlargement of the Müllerian ducts, slight stimulation of Wolffian ducts, and an increase in the number and length of prostatic buds. A female prostate stock of rats was used. Ovaries cultured with castrated male tracts had no stimulating or inhibiting effects. It was concluded that testicular hormone is essential in the rat for maintenance of the Wolffian ducts, stimulation of the primordia of seminal vesicles, and most, if not all, of the prostatic buds. The organ culture technique did not provide a critical test for possible effects of testicular androgen on male Müllerian ducts. In the youngest explants the Müllerian ducts were in a rapidly growing phase and were unstable under culture conditions in both males and females. In older stages, when the ducts had grown posteriorly to the urogenital sinus at the time of explantation, they were well maintained in cultures of female tracts but retrogressed in male explants. The critical period during which it might be possible to effect Müllerian duct retention by testis removal may be very short and probably occurs at a very early age. The work of Brewer (3) in the mouse suggests this. An added difficulty is that male Müllerian ducts of rats are never well developed anteriorly and do not form a lumen in segments adjacent to the testes. As a result, there is no true ambisexual stage in the duct systems of fetal male and female rats.

Fragments of rat gonoducts from males and females 15–16 days old were cultured by Jost and Bergerard (24) and Jost and Bozic (25). Müllerian ducts persisted in duct fragments of both sexes whatever the medium; Wolffian ducts were variable but showed signs of degeneration, except when cultured in blood serum of normal adult male rats or when a crystal of testosterone was added to the medium. In a different approach to the question of secretory activity of the fetal testis, Jost (16) grafted testes of 15–16-day-old rats on the seminal vesicle of adult castrated rats. He observed local stimulation of the seminal vesicle epithelium which did not occur if the hosts were hypophysectomized (Jost and Colonge, 26).

EVIDENCE FROM EXPERIMENTS ON MICE. The gonads of fetal mice were extirpated by x ray at 13 and 14 days of age (Raynaud, 62). At the younger stage, Müllerian ducts and anterior ends of Wolffian ducts of both sexes were completely destroyed by the irradiation. However, the remaining portion of Wolffian ducts of male fetuses were smaller than those of controls, and the seminal vesicles, coagulating glands, and prostates did not develop. At 14 days, irradiation of the testis (unilateral or incomplete destruction) resulted, on the gonadless side, in persistence of a portion of the Müllerian duct and a smaller Wolffian duct and seminal vesicle. Raynaud and his collaborators interpreted these findings as supporting evidence for the concept of fetal testicular hormone control of male differentiation.

In organ culture experiments, Céas (7) explanted male reproductive tracts of 11½–14½-day-old mice and cultured them for 3–6 days. Differentiation in culture was very limited and no accessory glands were found. When mouse placental extract was added to the medium, some slight effects were observed—more rapid retrogression of Müllerian ducts and the development of seminal vesicles and atypical prostate buds. The effects on Müllerian ducts and seminal vesicles were attributed to fetal testicular hormone but it was suggested that in the mouse, placental gonadotrophin might normally be stimulating the testis to secretory activity.

Brewer (3) explanted male and female mouse reproductive tracts in an extensive series. The results are of considerable interest and merit detailed description. Explantation was done at five different ages, beginning with an initial age of 12½ days and extending to 16½ days. The culture period was 3 days in most cases. At the youngest age, Wolffian ducts were completely retained in explants of both male and female tracts with and without gonads. In cultured male tracts removed from fetuses at ages of about 13–14½ days, the Wolffian ducts were retained only if testes were present. However, in tracts explanted from fetuses beyond this age, the Wolffian ducts remained even if testes were removed. Stabilization of the ducts was clearly demonstrated. In female explants put into culture at 13–14½ days with or without ovaries, the Wolffian ducts began anteroposterior involution, and when explanted at older ages they underwent rapid retrogression, as in vivo. No seminal vesicles developed. But if fetal testes were cultured with the ovariectomized female tracts at this critical period the Wolffian ducts were retained and stimulated and seminal vesicles appeared.

In male and female tracts explanted with or without gonads at $12\frac{1}{2}$ days, the developing Müllerian ducts failed to continue their posterior growth in culture. However, when explanted a day later (when the ducts have reached the urogenital sinus in vivo), the Müllerian ducts of females were stable and were retained in culture at this and all subsequent stages. Conversely, the Müllerian ducts in male tracts with testes began retrogression in cultured tracts explanted at $13\frac{1}{2}$–14 days. At older stages they almost completely disappeared during the culture period. But in this initial stage, between 13 and 14 days, removal of the testes from the tract before explantation resulted in partial or, in a few striking cases, total retention of the Müllerian ducts. At all older stages the ducts involuted, even when testes were absent. The retention of the Müllerian ducts obtained by testis removal during the critical period was variable but unequivocal. During a brief period of about 12 hours, the presence of a testis in the male tract imposed upon the Müllerian ducts an irreversible pattern of cell death through male hormone action. But this same testis placed against female tracts in culture not only did not inhibit the Müllerian ducts but actually stimulated them somewhat.

These experiments add materially to the evidence that in normal sex differentiation testicular hormone inhibits Müllerian ducts and stimulates Wolffian ducts during a critical stage and causes development of accessory glands. The successful demonstration of testicular androgen as an inhibitor of male Müllerian ducts in the mouse may have been attributable partly to the fact that an ambisexual stage of the ducts exists and for a time Müllerian ducts of males are as well developed as those of females. The failure of the fetal testis to inhibit female Müllerian ducts remains a problem. Possibly the critical stage when they could be inhibited is very brief.

The mechanisms by which testis hormone produces its effects on cells of Müllerian ducts is an intriguing problem of great current interest. Wolff (76), on the basis of extensive research on the chick in his laboratory, proposed a hypothesis involving direct determination of necrosis of the Müllerian ducts by proteolytic enzymes evoked or activated by the male hormone. Further studies have recently been made in experiments correlating the levels of enzymes and nucleic acids in Müllerian ducts of chicks with stages of stabilization or involution (Hamilton, 12). Hamilton discussed his results and those of others in terms of alternate hypotheses of mechanisms of male hormone action.

Control of Secretion of Testicular Hormone

Since testes secrete male hormone postnatally under the influence of gonadotrophic hormone from the anterior pituitary, the question was posed for fetal testes and the answer was sought mainly in research on rabbits, rats, and mice. Hypophysectomy was accomplished by techniques of decapitation (rabbit and rat) and x ray of fetal pituitaries (mouse). The results differed. In rabbits (Jost, 18, 19, 20, 23) there were abnormalities in the reproductive tract—reduction in the number of prostatic buds, and feminine development of external genitalia. Changes occurred in the interstitial cells of the testis and were correlated with the degree of defect in the tract. In contrast, the only result in the rat (Wells, 68, 69) was a slight change in testicular interstitial cells; little, if any, effect was found in the mouse following decapitation, even at 12 days of age (Raynaud, 63). Pituitary control of at least some of the testis secretory activity in the rabbit is indicated. In the rodents, the placenta might be a source of gonadotrophin, and maternal hormones cannot be entirely ruled out. The endocrine environment of the fetus is complicated and varies from species to species. Price (52) and Parkes (51) discussed some aspects of the fetal environment. It is impossible to say whether fetal testes are capable of autonomous secretory activity and the question is not solved by culturing gonads, since androgenic effects in explants may, and undoubtedly do, result at least partially from hormone residual in the testis at the time of explantation.

Ovarian Differentiation; Androgenic Effects

The many experiments designed to duplicate the structure of the freemartin ovary by administration of synthetic steroids to female fetuses were a signal failure (see review by Burns, 5). Ovaries were not inhibited or turned into ovotestes as are those of freemartins under the influence of fetal testicular hormone from the male co-twin. Nor did grafts of fetal gonads transplanted into postnatal hosts show clearly any specific effects of host sex hormones. Fetal ovaries showed evidence of sex reversal and the development of large medullary tubules regardless of whether hosts were normal or gonadectomized males and females (Buyse, 6; Moore and Price, 43; Torrey, 65). Holyoke (14), however, reported a somewhat greater tendency of masculinization of the ovary in male hosts.

These results suggested to some workers that the ability to cause sex reversal of fetal ovaries might be a unique property of a fetal testicular secretion which would be a medullary inductor of the type proposed many years ago by Witschi, and discussed recently (Witschi, 74). A series of experiments was done by Macintyre (35) and Macintyre, Hunter, and Morgan (36) in which heterosexual pairs of rat gonads were transplanted together into castrated adult male hosts. The inhibition or transformation of ovaries into testislike organs in these heterosexual pairs was taken as evidence that fetal testis secretion had an action similar to the postulated inductor "medullarin." However, the idea that these effects on fetal ovaries must result from the action of an embryonic inductor was effectively dispelled by Turner and Asakawa (66). They obtained differential effects on fetal rat ovaries grafted into kidneys or into testes of adult males and showed decisively that postnatal testis hormone has pronounced masculinizing effects. Ovaries were inhibited and large medullary tubules were formed under the influence of male hormone. The whole problem of inductor substances and embryonic hormones in sex differentiation has been ably reviewed by Burns (5).

The Identity of Fetal Testicular Hormone

The question remains as to the identity of fetal testicular hormone and whether more than one testicular hormone is involved in the inhibition and stimulation characteristic of androgenic effects in sex differentiation.

Varying opinions and the evidence that supports them are given by Jost (18), Burns (5), and Hamilton (12). Hamilton states, on the basis of experiments on chicks, that there is some evidence that embryonic sex hormones are "macromolecules of a size greater than steroids." However, our studies on the presence of Δ^5-3β-hydroxysteroid dehydrogenase in fetal guinea pigs demonstrated that the testes were capable of secreting steroidal androgen (Price, Ortiz, and Deane, 58). Similar experiments in the rat have shown that fetal testes can synthesize steroids (Niemi and Ikonen, 44, 45) and in the fetal mouse, testes have the same capability (Hitzeman, 13). In all cases the enzyme activity was localized in the interstitial tissue at early stages of sex differentiation. Bloch, Tissenbaum, Rubin, and Deane (2) reported Δ^5-3β-hydroxysteroid dehydrogenase activity in a testis from a human fetus 12 weeks old. These observations do not prove that fetal testis androgen is steroidal. However, they strongly suggest that there may be a steroid hormone present in the testis at crucial stages of differentiation of the testis and reproductive tract when it can be shown that the testis is secreting androgen. The ability of the fetal rabbit testis to synthesize testosterone before differentiation of the gonoducts begins has been reported recently (Lipsett and Tullner, 33). It was concluded that "enzymatic differentiation occurs in the gonad shortly after the time when the gonads can be identified morphologically."

Adrenal Androgen in the Fetus

The finding of androgen in male and female adrenals of very young guinea pig fetuses (Price, Ortiz, and Zaaijer, 60, 61) raises the old question of whether adrenal androgen might have any effects during normal sex differentiation in this or any other species of mammal. The well-known abnormal effects of adrenal hyperplasia in the human fetus are evident in varying degrees of masculinization of the female, including pseudohermaphroditism; in the male, sexual precocity results (Witschi, Nelson and Segal, 75; Howard and Migeon, 15).

The extensive findings on the sex hormones of the adrenal cortex and their effects on the reproductive system have been reviewed frequently in the past years. The excellent review by Howard and Migeon (15) brings the subject up to date. Of note is the observation that male reproductive glands in a number of species of rodents are responsive postnatally to adrenal androgen, as are also the prostate glands which are present in some female rats (Price and Williams-Ashman, 57).

Attempts were made to determine whether adrenals of fetal rats secrete androgen by the device of grafting them on the retrogressed seminal vesicles of castrated adult hosts. Moore (42) observed no stimulation of the seminal vesicle epithelium but Jost and Geloso (27), using castrated-adrenalectomized hosts, reported a very slight stimulation near the adrenal graft in a certain number of cases. Price and Ingle (54) obtained definite but localized stimulation of the epithelia of seminal vesicles, prostates, and coagulating glands of adult castrated rats by autotransplanting adrenals on the accessory glands.

The pituitary-adrenal axis is established prenatally in the rat (Wells, 68; Noumura, 46). Thus the pituitary secretes adrenocorticotrophin in the fetus and the adrenal cortex is stimulated to secrete corticoids. Little evidence is available on secretion of androgen. The extensive work of Wells and his collaborators showed that adrenalectomy had no effect on growth of the seminal vesicles; growth in adrenalectomized-castrated fetuses was similar to seminal vesicle growth in castrates (Wells, 68). It was concluded that the fetal adrenal did not secrete androgen or did not produce enough to prevent the retardation of growth following castration. Administration of adrenocorticotrophic hormone enlarged the fetal rat adrenals but did not affect the seminal vesicle growth. In young postnatal rats (see review by Price and Williams-Ashman, 57) adrenocorticotrophic treatment produced androgenic effects on the ventral prostate and seminal vesicles of castrates.

Fetal adrenal androgen has been considered as a possible source of stimulation for the prostates which develop in female rats of some strains (Price and Pannabecker, 56). Jost (18) commented on the question of adrenal androgen effects in the fetus and remarked upon the fact that in the castrated male rabbit the adrenals do not prevent retrogression of Wolffian ducts.

The recent research on androgenicity of fetal guinea pig adrenals (Price, Ortiz, and Zaaijer, 60, 61) leaves no doubt that high levels of androgenic hormone are present at very early stages of sex differentiation in this species. In addition, Price, Ortiz, and Deane (58) found Δ^5-3β-hydroxysteroid dehydrogenase activity in these glands and concluded that the adrenal cortex was capable of secreting steroidal androgen. However, it seems pointless to speculate at this time on whether adrenal androgen normally has any effect on sex differentiation in the guinea pig or any other mammal.

It is of interest that three C_{19} steroids were tentatively identified by paper chromatography as being present in male and female adrenals of human fetuses aged 11–19 weeks (Bloch, Benirschke, and Rosemberg, 1). Moreover, the concentration of these steroids decreased in older fetuses as glucocorticoid content increased. It was suggested (1, p. 632) that "the early fetal adrenal cortex synthesizes primarily weak androgenic steroids and a sodium retaining factor similar to aldosterone." Bloch, Tissenbaum, Rubin, and Deane (2) reported Δ^5-3β-hydroxysteroid dehydrogenase activity in human fetal adrenal tissue as early as the 9th week of gestation.

Summary

In surveying the case for the role of fetal testicular hormone in normal sex differentiation of placental mammals, it can be concluded that there is: (1) completely convincing evidence for critical effects in maintenance of Wolffian ducts and stimulation of development of accessory glands, (2) reasonably satisfactory evidence for inhibition of male Müllerian ducts, (3) inadequate evidence for inhibition of female Müllerian ducts—the only example is one case described by Jost (18) for the rabbit, and (4) no evidence for or against effects on differentiation of the indifferent gonad (genetically determined as male).

There is convincing evidence that fetal testes of several species have the ability to secrete steroidal hormones in early sex differentiation. In testes of fetal guinea pigs, the capacity for steroidogenesis parallels androgen secretion. Adrenals of fetal male and female guinea pigs are also secreting high levels of androgen very early and have a parallel capability for steroidogenesis. The function, if any, of this androgen during sex differentiation is unknown.

References

1. Bloch, E., K. Benirschke, and E. Rosemberg, "C_{19} Steroids, 17 α-Hydroxycorticosterone and a Sodium Retaining Factor in Human Fetal Adrenal Glands," *Endocrinology* 58:626–633 (1956).

2. ——, B. Tissenbaum, B. L. Rubin, and H. W. Deane, "Δ^5-3β-Hydroxysteroid Dehydrogenase Activity in Human Fetal Adrenals," *Endocrinology* 71:629–632 (1962).

3. Brewer, N. L., "Sex Differentiation of the Fetal Mouse *in vitro*," Ph.D. Thesis, University of Chicago (1962).

4. Burns, R. K., "Sex Transformation in the Opossum: Some New Results and a Retrospect," *Arch. Anat. Microscop. Morphol. Exptl.* 39:467–481 (1950).

5. ——, "Role of Hormones in the Differentiation of Sex," *Sex and Internal Secretions*, 3rd edition, W. C. Young, ed. Baltimore: Williams & Wilkins, pp. 76–158 (1961).

6. Buyse, A., "The Differentiation of Transplanted Mammalian Gonad Primordia," *J. Exptl. Zool.* 70:1–41 (1935).

7. Céas, M. P., "Lo Sviluppo *in vitro* dell' Apparato Riproduttore Maschile del Topo (*mus musculus*)," *Acta Embryol. Morphol. Exptl.* 4:327–345 (1961).

8. Dantchakoff, V., "Sur l'Édification des Glandes Annexes du Tractus Génital dans les Free-martins et sur les Facteurs Formatifs dans l'Histogenèse Sexuelle Mâle," *Compt. Rend. Soc. Biol.* 124:407–411 (1937).

9. ——, "Sur la Faculté des Tissus Induits par l'Hormone Mâle, d'Édifier de Nouvelles Structures chez l'Embryon de Cobaye Femelle," *Compt. Rend. Soc. Biol.* 124:516–518 (1937).

10. Elchlepp, J. G., "The Urogenital Organs of the Cottontail Rabbit (*Sylvilagus floridanus*)," *J. Morphol.* 91:169–198 (1952).

11. Gersh, I., "The Correlation of Structure and Function in the Developing Mesonephros and Metanephros," *Contrib. Embryol. Carnegie Inst. Wash.* 153:35–57 (1937).

12. Hamilton, T. H., "Hormonal Control of Müllerian Duct Differentiation in the Chick Embryo," *Proc. XIII Intern. Ornithol. Congr.* 1004–1040 (1963).

13. Hitzeman, J. W., "Development of Enzyme Activity in the Leydig Cells of the Mouse Testis," *Anat. Record* 143:351–361 (1962).

14. Holyoke, E. A., "The Differentiation of Embryonic Gonads Transplanted to the Adult Omentum in the Albino Rat," *Anat. Record* 103:675–699 (1949).

15. Howard, E., and C. J. Migeon, "Sex Hormone Secretion by the Adrenal Cortex," *Handbuch der Experimentellen Pharmakologie.* I. *The Adrenocortical Hormones, 1*, H. W. Deane, ed. Springer-Verlag, Berlin-Göttingen-Heidelberg, vol. 14, pp. 570–637 (1962).

16. Jost, A., "Activité Androgène du Testicule Foetal de Rat Greffé sur l'Adult Castré," *Compt. Rend. Soc. Biol.* 142:196–198 (1948).

17. ——, "Sur le Contrôle Hormonal de Différenciation Sexuelle du Lapin," *Arch. Anat. Microscop. Morphol. Exptl.* 39:577–598 (1950).

18. ——, "Problems of Fetal Endocrinology: the Gonadal and Hypophyseal Hormones," *Recent Progr. Hormone Res.* 8:379–418 (1953).

19. ——, "Hormonal Factors in the Development of the Fetus," *Cold Spring Harbor Symp. Quant. Biol.* 19:167–180 (1954).

20. ——, "Modalities in the Action of Gonadal and Gonad-stimulating Hormones in the Fetus," *The Comparative Physiology of Reproduction and the Effects of Sex Hormones in Vertebrates*, Mem. Soc. Endocrinol. 4, I. C. Jones, P. Eckstein, eds. Cambridge: Cambridge University Press, pp. 237–247 (1955).

21. ——, "The Secretory Activities of Fetal Endocrine Glands and Their Ef-

fect upon Target Organs," *Gestation,* C. A. Villee, ed. New York: The Josiah Macy, Jr. Foundation, pp. 129–171 (1957).

22. ——, "Hormonal Influences in the Sex Development of Bird and Mammalian Embryos," *Sex Differentiation and Development,* Mem. Soc. Endocrinol. 7, C. R. Austin, ed. Cambridge: Cambridge University Press, pp. 49–62 (1960).

23. ——, "The Role of Fetal Hormones in Prenatal Development," *Harvey Lectures* 55:201–226 (1961).

24. ——, and Y. Bergerard, "Culture *in vitro* d'Ébauches du Tractus Génital du Foetus de Rat," *Compt. Rend. Soc. Biol.* 143:608–609 (1949).

25. ——, and B. Bozic, "Données sur la Différenciation des Conduits Génitaux du Foetus de Rat Étudiée *in vitro,*" *Compt. Rend. Soc. Biol.* 145:647–650 (1951).

26. ——, and R. A. Colonge, "Greffe de Testicule Foetal de Rat sur l'Adulte Castré et Hypophysectomisé. Remarques sur la Physiologie du Testicule Foetal de Rat," *Compt. Rend. Soc. Biol.* 143: 140–142 (1949).

27. ——, and J. P. Geloso, "Recherche de l'Activité Androgène de la Surrénale par la Greffe sur la Vésicule Séminale de Rats Castrés," *Compt. Rend. Soc. Biol.* 148:474–477 (1954).

28. Keller, K., and J. Tandler, "Über des Verhalten der Eihäute bei der Zwillingsträchtigkeit des Rindes. Untersuchungen über die Enstehungsursache des Geschlechtlichen Unterentwicklung von Weiblichen Zwillingskälbern, welche Neben einem Männlichen Kalbe zur Entwicklung gelangen," *Wien Tierärztl. Wochschr.* 3:513–526 (1916).

29. Langlois, J. P., and J. Rehns, "Les Capsules Surrénales Pendant la Période Foetale," *Compt. Rend. Soc. Biol.* 51:146–147 (1899).

30. Lillie, F. R., "The Theory of the Freemartin," *Science* 43:611–613 (1916).

31. ——, "The Freemartin: a Study of the Action of Sex Hormones in the Fetal Life of Cattle," *J. Exptl. Zool.* 23:371–452 (1917).

32. ——, "Supplementary Notes on Twins in Cattle," *Biol. Bull.* 44:47–78 (1923).

33. Lipsett, M. B., and W. W. Tullner, "Capacity of Fetal Rabbit Gonad to Synthesize Testosterone during Embryonic Development," *Prog. 46th Meeting Endocrine Soc.* p. 35 (1964).

34. Logothetopoulos, J., and R. F. Scott, "Histology and Function of the Developing Foetal Thyroid in Normal and Goitrous Guinea Pigs," *J. Endocrinol.* 14: 217–227 (1956).

35. Macintyre, M. N., "Effect of the Testis on Ovarian Differentiation in Heterosexual Embryonic Rat Gonad Transplants," *Anat. Record* 124:27–46 (1956).

36. ——, J. E. Hunter, and A. H. Morgan, "Spatial Limits of Activity of Fetal Gonadal Inductors in the Rat," *Anat. Record* 138:137–141 (1960).

37. Mitskevich, M. S. *Glands of Internal Secretion in Embryonic Development of Birds and Mammals.* Acad. of Sciences of USSR, Moscow. Published in translation for the National Science Found. and Dept. of Health, Education and Welfare, USA, by the Israel Program of Scientific Translations (1959).

38. ——, "Hormonal Interrelations between Mother and Fetus in Mammals," *Gen. Comp. Endocrinol.* Suppl. 1:300–308 (1962).

39. Moog, F., and E. Ortiz, "The Duodenum of the Foetal Guinea Pig, with a Note on the Growth of the Adrenals," *J. Embryol. Exptl. Morphol.* 8:182–194 (1960).

40. Moore, C. R., *Embryonic Sex Hormones and Sexual Differentiation.* Springfield, Ill.: Charles C Thomas (1947).

41. ——, "The Role of the Fetal Endocrine Glands in Development," *J. Clin. Endocrinol.* 10:942–985 (1950).

42. ——, "Adrenal Cortical Secretions in Relation to the Reproductive System of Rats," *J. Clin. Endocrinol.* 13:330–368 (1953).

43. ——, and D. Price, "Differentiation of Embryonic Reproductive Tissues of the Rat after Transplantation into Postnatal Hosts," *J. Exptl. Zool.* 90:229–265 (1942).

44. Niemi, M., and M. Ikonen, "Steroid-3β-ol-dehydrogenase Activity in Foetal Leydig's Cells," *Nature* 189:592–593 (1961).

45. ——, and ——, "Cytochemistry of Oxidative Enzyme Systems in the Ley-

dig Cells of the Rat Testis and Their Functional Significance," *Endocrinology* 70:167–174 (1962).

46. Noumura, T., "Development of the Hypophyseal-adrenocortical System in the Rat Embryo in Relation to the Maternal System," *Japan J. Zool.* 12:279–299 (1959).

47. ———, "Development of the Hypophyseal-thyroidal System in the Rat Embryo and Its Relation to the Maternal System," *Japan J. Zool.* 12:301–318 (1959).

48. Ortiz, E., "Phosphatase Activity in the Gonad of the Guinea Pig during Development," *Anat. Record* 128:598–599 (1957).

49. ———, "The Effect of Propylthiouracil Treatment of Pregnant Guinea Pigs on the Development of the Fetus," *Anat. Record* 134:620 (1959).

50. Pannabecker, R., and D. Price, "Detection of Androgenic Hormone by Means of a Bio-indicator Method," *Anat. Record* 136:343 (1960).

51. Parkes, A. S., "Some Aspects of the Endocrine Environment of the Fetus," *Cold Spring Harbor Symp. Quant. Biol.* 19:3–8 (1954).

52. Price, D., "An Analysis of the Factors Influencing Growth and Development of the Mammalian Reproductive Tract," *Physiol. Zool.* 20:213–247 (1949).

53. ———, "Influence of Hormones on Sex Differentiation in Explanted Fetal Reproductive Tracts," *Gestation*, C. A. Villee, ed. New York: Josiah Macy, Jr. Foundation, pp. 173–186 (1957).

54. ———, and D. Ingle, "Androgenic Effects of Autotransplants of Adrenals in the Accessory Reproductive Glands of Adult Castrated Rats," *Ann. Soc. Suisse Zool.* and *Museum Hist. Nat. Genève* 64: 743–755 (1957).

55. ———, and R. Pannabecker, "Organ Culture Studies of Foetal Rat Reproductive Tracts," *Ciba Found. Colloq. Ageing* 2:3–13 (1956).

56. ———, and ———, "Comparative Responsiveness of Homologous Sex Ducts and Accessory Glands of Fetal Rats in Culture," *Arch. Anat. Microscop. Morphol. Exptl.* 48:223–244 (1959).

57. ———, and H. G. Williams-Ashman, "The Accessory Reproductive Glands of Mammals," *Sex and Internal Secre-*

tion, 3rd edition, W. C. Young, ed. Baltimore: Williams & Wilkins, pp. 366–448 (1961).

58. ———, E. Ortiz, and H. W. Deane, "The Presence of Δ^5-3β-Hydroxysteroid Dehydrogenase in Fetal Guinea Pig Testes and Adrenal Glands," *Am. Zool.* 4:327 (1964).

59. ———, ———, and R. Pannabecker, "A Study of the Relation of Age to Hormone Secretion in the Testes of Fetal Guinea Pigs," *Proc. 10th Intern. Congr. Cell Biol.* p. 158 (1960).

60. ———, ———, and J. J. P. Zaaijer, "Secretion of Androgenic Hormone by Testes and Adrenal Glands of Fetal Guinea Pigs," *Am. Zool.* 3:328 (1963).

61. ———, ———, and ———, "Vorming van androgene stoffen door Embryonale bijnieren van Caviae," *Ned. Tijdschr. Geneesk.* 108:1512 (1964).

62. Raynaud, A., "Recherches Expérimentales sur le Développement de l'Appareil Génital et le Fonctionnement des Glandes Endocrines des Foetus de Souris et de Mulot," *Arch. Anat. Microscop. Morphol. Exptl.* 39:518–569 (1950).

63. ———, "Effects of Destruction of the Fetal Hypophysis by X-rays upon Sexual Development of the Mouse," *Comparative Endocrinology*, A. Gorbman, ed. New York: Wiley, pp. 452–478 (1959).

64. Shepherd, D. M., and G. B. West, "Noradrenaline and the Suprarenal Medulla," *Brit. J. Pharmacol.* 6:655–674 (1951).

65. Torrey, T. W., "Intraocular Grafts of Embryonic Gonads of the Rat," *J. Exptl. Zool.* 115:37–58 (1950).

66. Turner, C. D., and H. Asakawa, "Differentiation of Fetal Rat Ovaries Following Transplantation to Kidneys and Testes of Adult Male Hosts," *Am. Zool.* 2: 270 (1962).

67. Wells, L. J., "Hormones and Sexual Differentiation in Placental Mammals," *Arch. Anat. Microscop. Morphol. Exptl.* 39:499–514 (1950).

68. ———, "Effect of Fetal Endocrines on Fetal Growth," *Gestation*, C. A. Villee, ed. New York: Josiah Macy, Jr. Foundation, pp. 187–227 (1957).

69. ———, "Functioning of the Anterior Hypophysis in the Fetal Rat," *Comparative Endocrinology*, A. Gorbman, ed. New York: Wiley, pp. 444–451 (1959).

70. ——, "Experimental Studies of the Role of the Developing Gonads in Mammalian Sex Differentiation," *The Ovary II*, S. Zuckerman, ed. New York: Academic Press, pp. 131–153 (1962).

71. ——, and R. Fralick, "Production of Androgen by the Testes of Fetal Rats," *Am. J. Anat.* 89:63–107 (1951).

72. ——, M. W. Cavanaugh, and E. L. Maxwell, "Genital Abnormalities in Castrated Fetal Rats and Their Prevention by Means of Testosterone Propionate," *Anat. Record* 118:109–134 (1954).

73. Willier, B. H., "Ontogeny of Endocrine Correlation," *Analysis of Development*, B. H. Willier, P. A. Weiss, V. Hamburger, eds. Philadelphia: Saunders, pp. 574–619 (1955).

74. Witschi, E., "The Inductor Theory of Sex Differentiation," *J. Fac. Sci. Hokkaido Univ., Ser. VI Zool.* 13:428–439 (1957).

75. ——, W. O. Nelson, and S. J. Segal, "Genetic, Developmental and Hormonal Aspects of Gonadal Dysgenesis and Sex Inversion in Man," *J. Clin. Endocrinol.* 17:737–753 (1957).

76. Wolff, E., "Le Déterminisme de l'Atrophie d'un Organe Rudimentaire: le Canal de Müller des Embryons Mâles d'Oiseaux," *Experientia* 9:121–133 (1953).

77. ——, "Experimental Modification of Ovarian Development," *The Ovary II*, S. Zuckerman, ed. New York: Academic Press, pp. 81–129 (1962).

26

Onset of Steroidogenesis in the Vertebrate Embryonic Gonads

GIOVANNI CHIEFFI[*]

Institute of Zoology and Comparative Anatomy
University of Camerino
Zoological Station
Naples, Italy

Various attempts have been made to establish the nature of secretion in the embryonic gonads of vertebrates. That such a secretion exists is now proved by a series of observations; the most significant are those concerning the effects of experimental parabiosis between embryos of opposite sexes.

The various hypotheses about the chemical nature of embryonic gonadal secretion have been tested from time to time with many techniques. These studies have been oriented mainly toward the discovery of steroids. They have not been concerned with assay-

ing the biological activities of any other chemical structure.

The reason for the trend in the direction of steroid research is the fact that it is possible to reverse the sex of many vertebrate species through administration of sex hormones to embryos or larvae. But the mechanism of action of steroid hormones on sexual differentiation is still only poorly understood. First of all, treatment with sex hormones does not always produce the expected results; for example, the androgens in many species do not have any effect (*Bufo, Xenopus, Triton, Discoglossus, Alytes, Pelobates, Pelodytes, Bombina*), or else show a paradoxical feminization, as in *Ambystoma, Pleurodeles, Hynobius* (Chieffi, 13; Gallien, 21). It is difficult to interpret these results.

Second, the property of causing sex reversal is not exclusive to the sex

[*] Part of the personal investigation was supported by research grant RG-06455, from the Division of General Medical Sciences, U.S. Public Health Service. Several investigations have been carried out with the collaboration of V. Botte, E. Cottino, and G. Materazzi and the technical assistance of Miss F. Valentino. The author is very grateful to Evelyn Shaw for translating the Italian manuscript.

hormones. It can be elicited through physical factors (for example, temperature; Witschi, 61) and through other chemical compounds, structurally similar to sex hormones, such as corticosteroids (Vannini, 55, 56; Witschi and Chang, 66) and even compounds not structurally similar, such as tryplaflavine (3,6-diamino-10-methylacridinium chloride) (Salzgeber, 52).

Finally a major criticism, valid until a few years ago, is that steroid hormones used experimentally on a variety of vertebrate species were isolated only from a few mammalian species. Doubt remained because the hormones taken from mammalian species might be completely different from the hormones of the species studied. However, recent studies appear to eliminate these doubts. The same steroid hormones as those found in mammals have now been isolated from the gonads and the adrenal cortex of fishes, amphibians, reptiles, and birds (Chester Jones and Phillips, 10; Chieffi and Lupo, 17). Since this doubt has been removed, it has been more than natural to continue with research on steroids in the embryonic gonads using new and more sensitive techniques.

The Secretory Activity of the Embryonic Gonads

Witschi (61) described the cortical and medullary tissues in the undifferentiated gonad in his earliest researches on the sexual differentiation of amphibians. Sexual differentiation depends on whether or not germ cells migrate into the medulla or remain within the cortex. Following this discovery, Goldschmidt (24, 25) distinguished "primary" from "secondary" sex inductors of masculinization and feminization. The former, identified as genetic factors, stimulate the cortex or the medulla to grow. In their turn, these regions produce secondary sex inductors, which Witschi (64) calls "corticin" and "medullarin," and which are believed to trigger differentiation in female or male direction, respectively.

This scheme of secretory activity of the embryonic gonad has been confirmed both in nature and through experimentation. The classical observations of Lillie (42), Keller and Tandler (36), Willier (60), and others on bovine freemartins are interpretable on the basis of the secretory activity of the testes of the male twin. The testicular secretion inhibits the development of the ovarian cortex of the female fetus, with consequent sterility.

The best-known experiments of parabiosis between amphibian larvae of opposite sex (Burns, 9; Witschi, 62) have confirmed the influence of the testis on the ovary, which shows a strong inhibition of cortical development. In birds, too, experimental and natural parabiosis causes intersexuality. In contrast to the bovines, the male and female bird twins inhibit each other mutually (Lutz and Lutz-Ostertag, 44; Wolff and Lutz-Ostertag, 72).

Many other experiments have confirmed the secretory activity of the embryonic testis of mammals. Castration, carried out before sexual differentiation of the male embryos of rabbit (Jost, 30), mouse (Raynaud and Frilley, 50), and rat (Wells, 58), inhibits the development of some secondary sex characters (Wolffian duct derivatives, prostate), while others (for example, urogenital sinus, external genitalia, and Müllerian duct derivatives) assume the female form. Jost (31) and

Jost and Colonge (33) transplanted rat embryonic testes as soon as they attained the stage of sexual differentiation (15th day). A testis was transplanted between the lobules of the seminal vesicle of an adult castrated male. The atrophied epithelium of the seminal vesicle rapidly returned to the normal appearance, evidently through the secretion of androgens by the embryonic testis. Price and Pannabecker (49) arrived at similar conclusions through experimental explanation of the rat reproductive tract.

In the literature one can find many other observations, but those reported here are sufficient to demonstrate the existence of secretory activity in the embryonic gonads either during or after sexual differentiation.

Much research appears to demonstrate, however, that the quality of gonadal secretion during and after sexual differentiation is not equivalent. We will return to this fundamental point later.

The Onset of the Biosynthesis of Steroid Hormones in the Gonads

Identification of Steroid Hormones

Research on steroids through the use of chemical methods has been very difficult because of the paucity of available material. Therefore most experiments have relied on histochemical methods, which not only permit precise localization of the substance in the tissue, but also are more sensitive than bulk chemical methods. However, histochemical techniques for steroids are specific only for cholesterol and its esters. Various methods for the demonstration of neutral and phenolic

steroids have been criticized and rejected as being nonspecific (Karnovsky and Deane, 35; Lison, 43).

The presence of cholesterol in large quantities in secretory tissues is considered an indicator of secretory activity. However, there can be steroid synthesis in the absence of detectable cholesterol if an important enzyme is present, namely, Δ^5-3β-hydroxysteroid dehydrogenase.

In the following sections, the nature and variety of steroids found in the embryonic gonads of vertebrates are characterized.

FISHES. The only histochemical studies are those of Chieffi (11) on *Scyliorhinus caniculus* (elasmobranch). Before sexual differentiation there appear, in the medulla of the gonads, a few sudanophilic granules, whereas the Schultz reaction for cholesterol and the Ashbel and Seligman reaction for carbonyl groups do not appear. Also, observations with polarized light before and after treatment with digitonin are negative.

After the beginning of sexual differentiation in the medulla, especially in the female (Fig 26.1), there appear many sudanophilic and Schultz-positive granules. In polarized light many birefringent needlelike crystals are evident. Such birefringence is not modified by treatment with digitonin; however, it is lost after staining with Sudan black B: the Schultz-positive reaction therefore corresponds to esterified cholesterol.

AMPHIBIANS. Chieffi (11, 12) examined the possible presence of lipid and steroid activity in the gonads of *Rana esculenta* tadpoles using histochemical methods. The results were negative before and during sexual differentiation. At the end of meta-

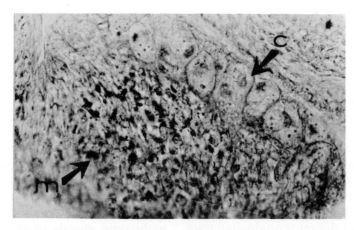

Fig. 26.1 *Scyliorhinus caniculus*, cross section of the ovary of a 34-mm embryo. Note the numerous sudanophilic granules in the medullary tissue, m; the cortex, c, is free of sudanophilia. ×600.

morphosis, a few sudanophilic granules were observed in the somatic cells of the gonads. More recently, Dale (20) extracted the following steroids from the water of tadpoles of *Rana pipiens*, grown in natural water and in water to which estradiol-17β had been added: hydrocortisone, aldosterone, androsterone, and estradiol-17β. The time of their initial presence coincides with the beginning of metamorphosis and sexual differentiation. It is necessary, however, to use caution in interpreting these results because, at the same developmental time, it is possible to demonstrate histochemically secretory activity of steroids in the interrenal gland of tadpoles (Chieffi, 11, 12; Chieffi and Botte, 15). Therefore there exists a strong probability that the steroids which Dale isolated are derived from the interrenal gland.

REPTILES. Chieffi and co-workers (Unpublished observations) found that the appearance of lipids and steroids in the gonads is very precocious in *Lacerta sicula*. By the 15th day of incubation numerous sudanophilic and Schultz-positive droplets are present in the medullary cells of the ovary (Fig. 26.2A). The same droplets are apparent in the somatic cells of the seminiferous tubules (Fig. 26.2B). The earlier stages, where sexual differentiation starts, have not been studied yet.

BIRDS. Among the more recent studies on birds are those of Gallien and Le Foulgoc (23) on the embryonic gonads of the chicken. Through the use of varied techniques (fluorimetry, colorimetry), these authors demonstrated the presence of estrogens of the estradiol-estrone group in the extracts of the left ovary taken from the 10th day of incubation. Sexual differentiation had already begun. In testicular extracts Zimmermann-positive substances are present, probably corresponding to 17-ketosteroids; but in this case the authors do not specify the day of incubation when the reaction appears.

Recently Weniger (59), through the use of the test of Allen and Doisy, isolated estrogenic substances from the

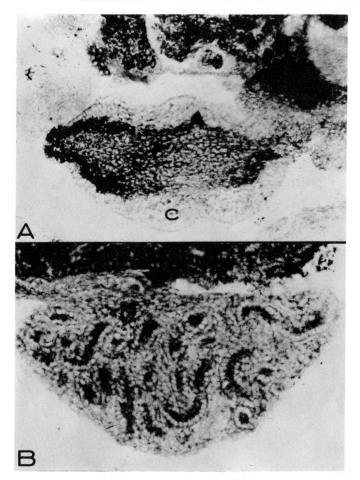

Fig. 26.2 A. *Lacerta sicula*, cross section of the ovary of a 34-mm embryo. Numerous sudanophilic granules in the medullary tissue; the cortex, c, is free of sudanophilia; top right, adrenal tissue; at the top, the mesonephric tubules show strong sudanophilia. ×400. *B.* Cross section of the testis of a 34-mm embryo: sudanophilia is present in the cytoplasm of the somatic cells of the seminiferous tubules, whose nuclei are unstained; at the top, the mesonephric tubules. ×625.

tissue culture media of female chick gonads removed on the 7th–10th day of incubation.

In chick gonads, Chieffi and coworkers (18) studied the distribution of lipids and cholesterol. These substances are found in the gonads after sexual differentiation, that is, from the 8th day of incubation, exactly in the somatic cells of the transformed primary sex cords of the ovary (Fig. 26.3A)

and in the stromal tissue of the testis (Fig. 26.3B).

MAMMALS. Among the mammals research is also scarce. Kudo (39) observed the appearance of sudanophilic and osmiophilic granules in the interstitial cells of the embryonic testis of guinea pig of 47 mm (Fig. 26.4A and B), after the stage of sexual differentiation (27 mm).

More recently, Jurand and Czubak

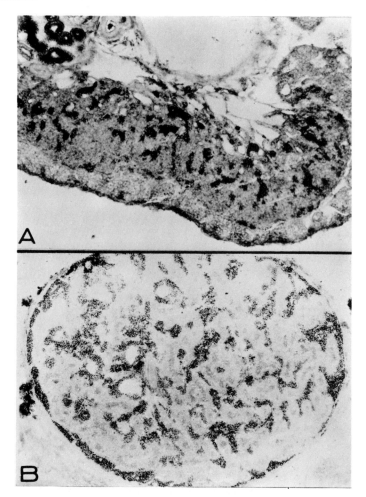

Fig. 26.3 A. Cross section of the ovary of a 15-day chick embryo. Sudanophilia is present in the clusters and cords of somatic cells of the transformed primary sex cords; cortical tissue is free of sudanophilia. ×189. B. Cross section of the testis of a 4-day chick. Sudanophilia is present only in the stromal tissue; the seminiferous tubules are unstained. ×100.

(34) investigated the appearance, through several histochemical techniques, of lipids and steroids in the adrenal cortex and in the gonads of rabbits from birth to sexual maturity. They observed a few birefringent, Schultz-, and Ashbel- and Seligman-positive granules, both in the follicular cells of the ovary and in the interstitial cells of the testis, only from the 2nd to the 6th week after birth.

Identification of Enzymes involved in Biosynthesis and Metabolism of Steroid Hormones

An indication of potential steroidogenic activity is shown by the presence of enzymes specific in the biosynthesis of steroid hormones. As with research on steroids, the demonstration of enzymes in the embryonic gonads through chemical methods is

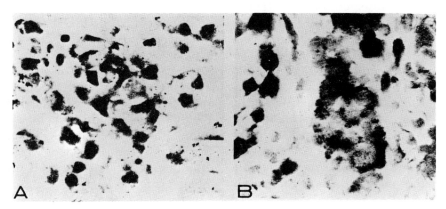

Fig. 26.4 Section of the testis of 47-mm (A) and 68-mm (B) guinea pig embryos. Note the large osmiophilic fat particles in the cytoplasm of the Leydig cells. ×567 (From Kudo, *Folia Anat. Japon.* 1:125–148, 1922.)

practically impossible because of the scarcity of available material. Therefore these researches are also histochemical, with the exception of human and bovine gonads, on which chemical methods have been employed.

Until now, techniques have been developed for the histochemical demonstration of three enzymes: Δ^5-3β-hydroxysteroid dehydrogenase (Δ^5-3β-HSDH), 17β-hydroxysteroid dehydrogenases (17β-HSDH), DPN- and TPN-dependent.

Together with Δ^5-3-ketoisomerase, Δ^5-3β-HSDH is involved in the transformation of pregnenolone to progesterone, one of the first steps of biosynthesis of all steroid hormones. This enzyme is universal in all the steroid-secreting tissues of all the vertebrates studied until now and it was demonstrated for the first time biochemically by Samuels and co-workers (53). Recently, Aoshima and co-workers (3) showed the presence of this enzyme in small quantities in the liver and the kidney of the rat, where it probably has metabolic significance. Then Wattenberg (57) introduced the technique for histochemical demonstration of

Δ^5-3β-HSDH, which was later modified by Levy and co-workers (41).

Both DPN- and TPN-dependent 17β-HSDH catalyze dehydrogenation of 17β-hydroxysteroids to 17-ketosteroids. They have been demonstrated biochemically, in the human placenta (Hagerman and Villee, 27; Hollander et al., 28; Langer and Engel, 40; Talalay et al., 54) and in the liver of amphibians and fishes (Breuer et al., 8), and histochemically in the human placenta (Kellog and Glenner, 37; Kleiner et al., 38) and in the rat liver and intestine (Pearson and Grose, 48). Both enzymes are characterized histochemically according to the method of Pearson and Grose (48) at pH 6.9, as adapted by Kleiner and co-workers (38).

The enzymes involved in the biosynthesis and metabolism of sex hormones have been investigated in the embryonic gonads of several representatives of the various vertebrate classes. Neither DPN- nor TPN-dependent 17β-HSDH has been found through histochemical methods. Therefore the latter enzymes will be discussed only if they have been found through biochemical methods.

FISHES. Research on Δ⁵-3β-HSDH has been carried out by Chieffi and co-workers (16) in the embryonic gonads of a few elasmobranchs: *Scyliorhinus caniculus*, *Scyliorhinus stellaris*, and *Torpedo marmorata*. Histochemical reaction is negative during and after sexual differentiation; it appears in the interrenal gland of *Scyliorhinus stellaris* at 5 cm in total length and in *Torpedo marmorata* when the yolk sac is almost completely absorbed.

AMPHIBIANS. The enzyme Δ⁵-3β-HSDH is absent in the gonad of *Rana esculenta* tadpoles during the period of sexual differentiation until after metamorphosis. Enzyme activity, however, appears very early in the interrenal gland at the stage just preceding the beginning of metamorphosis (Chieffi and Botte, 15). These observations have since been confirmed by Gallien and co-workers (22) in the urodele *Pleurodeles waltlii*.

It is important to note that the histochemical appearance of the enzyme in the interrenal gland coincides with the capacity of larvae of different species of amphibians to metabolize a number of steroids in vivo (Chieffi, 13, 14; Ozon, 47).

REPTILES. Δ⁵-3β-HSDH has been identified in the embryonic gonads of *Lacerta sicula* on the 15th day of incubation, with a total length of 18 mm (Chieffi et al., unpublished observations). After the start of sexual differentiation the ovarian medulla shows an intense enzyme activity, which is absent in the cortex (Fig. 26.5). In the testis the enzyme is localized in the somatic cells of the seminiferous tubules (Fig. 26.6). Nevertheless, it is absent in the interstitial spaces. We have not yet studied earlier stages, prior to sexual differentiation.

BIRDS. Also in the chick embryo, the activity of Δ⁵-3β-HSDH appears in the gonads after sexual differentiation (Chieffi et al., 18; Narbaitz and Kolodny, 45); in the somatic cells of the seminiferous tubules of the testis it appears from the 8th day of incubation (Fig. 26.7A). The histochemical reaction, initially very weak, becomes stronger in successive stages when the seminiferous tubules are well differentiated (Fig. 26.7B).

In the testis, as shown above, from the 8th day there is present among seminiferous tubules a stromal tissue that stains clearly for sudanophilic

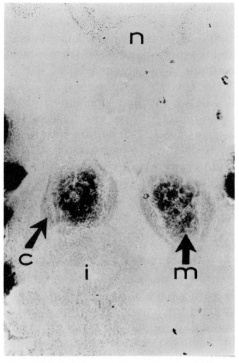

Fig. 26.5 *Lacerta sicula*, cryostat section of a 22-mm female embryo. Positive reaction for Δ⁵-3β-HSDH in the medullary tissue, m, of the ovaries; on both sides, strong nonspecific reaction in the mesonephric tubules; the cortex, c, is free of formazan deposit; i, intestinal lumen; n, nothocord. Counterstaining with carmalum. ×160.

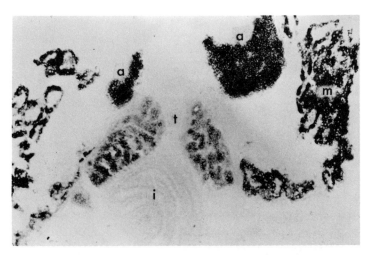

Fig. 26.6 *Lacerta sicula*, cryostat section of a 40-mm male embryo. Positive reaction for Δ^5-3β-HSDH in the somatic cells of the seminiferous tubules of the testes, t, and in the adrenocortical cells, a; the apparent activity of the mesonephric tubules, m, is nonspecific; i, intestine. Counterstaining with carmalum. ×160.

granules. However, it is always negative for Δ^5-3β-HSDH.

In the medullary tissue of the left ovary, from the 8th day of incubation there appear groups of cells in which the cytoplasm is rich with Δ^5-3β-HSDH (somatic cells of transformed primary sex cords), as shown in Figure 26.8A. The number of these clusters and cords of cells increases in successive stages and the cells persist in the newly hatched chick at least until 4 days (Fig. 26.8B). These cells are also sudanophilic. In the cortical region the reaction is negative, including sudanophilia and cholesterol. In the right ovary the reaction is positive in a few clusters of medullary cells only in the embryo of 8 days.

MAMMALS. The presence of the enzymes involved in the biosynthesis of sex hormones has been studied in the gonads of many species of mammals. Much research in vitro has shown that the fetal testis has the capacity to effect steroidal conversions, including testosterone synthesis. Acevedo

and co-workers (1, 2) have presented the first evidence for the functional capacity of the human fetal testis to synthesize male sex hormone. The isolation of several metabolites, by using progesterone or pregnenolone as substrates, showed that the following enzymes were present in the fetal testis: Δ^5-3β-HSDH, 17β-HSDH, side-chain splitting enzyme, 20α- and β-HSDH, 21-hydroxylase, 17α- and 16β-hydroxylases. Bloch and co-workers (6, 7) have obtained the conversion of progesterone to 17α-hydroxyprogesterone, Δ^4-androstenedione, and testosterone from testicular homogenates of a fetus of 15 weeks (13 cm crown-rump length). Subsequently, Bloch (5) studied the conversion of progesterone from human fetal testes 9–15 weeks old and isolated, besides testosterone and 17α-hydroxyprogesterone, 16α-hydroxyprogesterone.

All these researches were carried out on the fetal testis long after sexual differentiation, which occurs at 50–56 days.

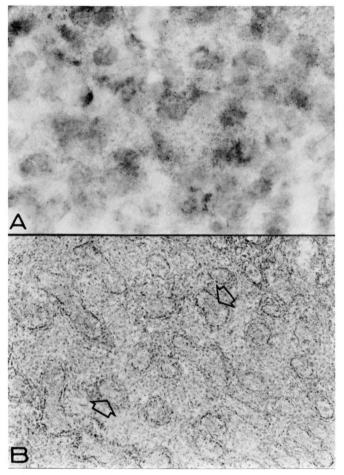

Fig. 26.7 A. Cryostat section of the testis of an 8-day chick embryo. The reaction for Δ⁵-3β-HSDH is very weak (few scattered formazan granules) in the cytoplasm of the somatic cells of the sex cords. Counterstaining with carmalum. ×2500. B. Cryostat section of the testis of a 4-day chick; weak positive reaction in the somatic cells of the seminiferous tubules. Counterstaining with carmalum. ×320.

In the rat and in the mouse testis (Niemi and Ikonen, 46; Chieffi et al., unpublished observations; Hitzeman, 29) Δ⁵-3β-HSDH appears respectively at 15 (Fig. 26.9A and B) and at $15\frac{1}{2}$ days of pregnancy; that is, after sexual differentiation. The latter occurs in the rat on the 14th day and in the mouse on the 12th day.

The ovary, on the other hand, does not appear to possess steroidogenic activity for almost the entire intra-uterine life of the embryo. In fact, ovarian homogenates of the human fetus of 9–19 weeks exhibited little metabolic activity toward progesterone. Only in the oldest fetus (19 weeks) was progesterone reduced to 20α-hydroxy-4-pregnene-3-one. On the other hand, this conversion can also be effected by several human fetal tissues.

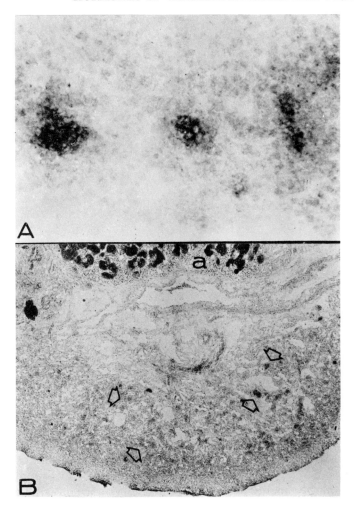

Fig. 26.8 *A.* Cryostat section of the left ovary of an 8-day chick embryo. Positive reaction for Δ^5-3β-HSDH in the clusters of somatic cells derived from the transformation of the primary sex cords. Counterstaining with carmalum. ×780. *B.* Cryostat section of the left ovary of a 4-day chick: positive reaction in the adrenocortical cells, a, and in the clusters of somatic cells of the transformed primary sex cords (arrows); cortex is free of activity. Counterstaining with carmalum. ×100.

These in vitro biochemical observations are in agreement with the failure to demonstrate, by histochemical methods, Δ^5-3β-HSDH in the ovary of the rat embryos (Chieffi et al., unpublished observations). Recently, Roberts and Warren (51) have demonstrated that the bovine fetal ovary (at least 1 month preterm) is capable of effecting 16α- and 17α-hydroxylations, 20α- and 17β-reductions, cleavage of the side chain, and aromatization.

Discussion

From the analysis of our results and those in the literature, it appears that embryonic and fetal gonads have the

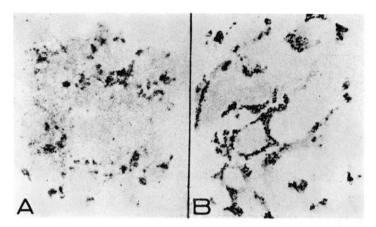

Fig. 26.9 Δ^5-3β-HSDH activity in the interstitial spaces of rat fetuses. *A.* 15-day-old fetus; sex cords unstained. ×127 *B.* 18-day fetus; seminiferous tubules unstained. ×77 (From Niemi and Ikonen, *Nature* 189:592–593, 1961.)

potential capacity to secrete, or actually do secrete steroid hormones, at least in the amniotes. In *Rana*, until after metamorphosis, the gonads do not show any signs of steroid metabolism. In the embryos of *Scyliorhinus*, however, lipids and cholesterol appear in the medulla of the gonad at the onset of sexual differentiation, while the results with Δ^5-3β-HSDH have been negative.

In the amniotes, histochemical techniques have shown that the steroidogenic activity is limited to the gonadal medulla and is absent in the cortex of all the species studied.

It is difficult to interpret the meaning of the different locations of Δ^5-3β-HSDH in the testis of reptiles, birds, and mammals; in reptiles and birds, the enzyme is present in the somatic cells of the seminiferous tubules; in the mammals when it appears, it is localized in the interstitial cells. In addition, in the embryo of *Lacerta* there is correspondence in the localization of Δ^5-3β-HSDH, sudanophilia, and cholesterol; in the chick embryo the lipids and cholesterol are present only in the stromal tissue (interstitial tissue?) among the seminiferous tubules, where the enzyme is absent.

In all the cases in which a steroidogenic activity has been noted in the embryonic gonads, it appears always in the stages succeeding sexual differentiation (Table 26.1). Therefore, within the limitations of techniques employed, we can exclude the possibility that hormones of the type secreted by adult gonads are involved in the process of gonadal sexual differentiation.

However, we could consider that the limitations of the techniques are inconsequential, because steroidogenic activity is evident in very early stages of development in the interrenal gland; for example, it is evident at the onset of metamorphosis in *Rana* tadpoles, at $4\frac{1}{2}$ days in the chick, and $12\frac{1}{2}$ days in the rat embryo (Chieffi et al., 15, 19 and unpublished observations).

It is interesting to note the correspondence of results between histochemical and biochemical methods,

TABLE 26.1   Onset of Lipid and Steroid Metabolism in the Gonads Compared to the Onset of Sex Differentiation of the Gonads and of Secondary Sex Characters

SPECIES	LIPID AND CHOLESTEROL METABOLISM			STEROID HORMONES	DIFFERENTIATION OF THE GONADS	DIFFERENTIATION OF S.S.C.
	SUDANOPHILIA	CHOLESTEROL	Δ^5-3βHSDH			
Scyliorhinus caniculus	31–32 mm. (o–t)	31–32 mm. (o–t)	After hatching?	?	31–32 mm.	31–32 mm.
Rana esculenta	Climax (o–t)	Climax (o–t)	After metamorphosis?	?	Incipient metamorphosis	After metamorphosis
Lacerta sicula[a]	18 days[c] (o–t)	18 days[c] (o–t)	18 days[c] (o–t)	?	13 days	18 days
Chick[a]	8 days (o–t)	8 days (o–t)	8 days (o–t)	10 days (o–t)	7 days	9 days
Mouse[b]	?	?	15½ days (o?–t)	?	12 days	15½ days
Rat[b]	?	?	15 days (t)	?	14 days	16 days
Human[b]	?	?	63 days[c] (t)	?	50–56 days	56 days to birth

[a] For *Lacerta* and chick, age is given as days of incubation.
[b] For mouse, rat, and human, age is given as days after fertilization.
[c] Earlier stages have not been examined.
? = no data available; (o–t) = present in both ovary and testis; t = present only in the testis.

particularly concerning the research of Δ^5-3β-HSDH. The latter cannot be demonstrated histochemically in the rat ovary; similarly, in the human fetal ovary of 9–19 weeks the metabolism of progesterone has not been elicited, except in the transformation to 20α-hydroxy-4-pregnene-3-one from older fetuses. However the embryonic testis of the same age has the capacity to convert pregnenolone and progesterone to different products, among which is testosterone.

In addition, the correspondence between histochemical and biochemical techniques is shown in the chick. The identification of 17-ketosteroids in the testicular extracts and of estrogens in the ovarian extracts and also in the fluid of ovarian tissue cultures corresponds to the presence of Δ^5-3β-HSDH both in the ovary and testis.

The appearance of steroidogenic activity in the gonads coincides with differentiation of secondary sex characters (s.s.c.) or just slightly precedes them (Table 26.1). In fact, in the chick, the earliest differentiation of Müllerian ducts appears about the 9th day of incubation. The Müllerian ducts regress in the male embryo, while they continue to enlarge and elongate in the female. Furthermore, the sudden regression of the Müllerian duct in the male embryo appears to be under the influence of male sex hormone. In fact, the regression has been obtained by Wolff and co-workers experimentally by coelomic grafts of embryonic testis (Wolff, 67), associations of testes with undifferentiated ducts in vitro (Wolff et al., 73), as well as by injection of androgens (Wolff et al., 74) or addition of androgens to the culture medium (Wolff and Lutz-Ostertag, 71). On the other hand, the maintenance of the Müllerian ducts in male embryos was achieved by injections of female crystalline hormones (Wolff and Ginglinger, 69), early castration (Et. Wolff and Em. Wolff, 75), and explants before the onset of sex differentiation (Wolff and Lutz-Ostertag, 71).

In the mouse embryo the genital ducts, the urogenital sinus, and external genitalia develop sex characteristics during the second half of the 15th day; in the rat embryo sex differences of s.s.c. can be seen at 16 days. In mammalian species (rabbit, mouse, rat) castration of the male fetus is followed by an almost complete failure of the differentiation of the s.s.c. (Jost, 30; Raynaud and Frilley, 50; Wells, 58).

In reptiles and elasmobranchs a time relation probably also exists between initiation of steroid secretion by the gonads and the differentiation of s.s.c. In *Rana* the late appearance of steroidogenesis coincides with the differentiation of the genital tract after metamorphosis.

The early biosynthesis of steroid hormones might throw light on the interpretation of the results obtained in the many experiments of explantation and transplantation of embryonic gonads and of the disagreement between these and the effects of natural and experimental parabiosis. The most recent works of Wolff and Haffen (70) and Haffen (26) have shown that the gonadal cortex of the duck embryo does not have the capacity to differentiate in vitro when it is isolated before sexual differentiation. However, when the cortex is associated with gonadal medullary tissue, taken from an embryo of 9–13 days—that is, after sexual differentiation—it always differentiates into an ovarian cortex, if it belongs to a female. The cortex of a male embryo differentiates into testicular cords or ovarian cortex, depending on the genetic sex of the medulla with which it is associated in culture.

Such results reflect those obtained following the administration of sex hormones in bird embryos. Also, in this case only estrogens are active. They feminize genetic males, whereas the female gonads do not respond to treatment with androgens (see Wolff, 68).

In the experiments of Haffen, since the associated female medulla was already differentiated, its feminizing effect on the male cortex may have been due to the onset of steroidogenesis.

Until we carry out experiments where the cortex and the medulla are associated in vitro, before they both start sexual differentiation, it is not possible to compare these experimental data with the natural processes of sexual differentiation in the gonad. These experiments must be carried out because in the natural and experimental parabiosis of birds, the female gonad does come under the influence of the male and vice versa.

Such considerations are applicable also to interpretation of the disagreement between the effects of natural parabiosis and the action of androgens on bovine female fetus. While in the freemartin there is an inhibition of the ovarian cortex and the oviducts, similar effects cannot be observed when the female fetuses are treated with strong doses of androgens by means of injections to the mother (Jost et al., 32). In this case the ovaries and the oviducts are not influenced and all the internal male s.s.c. are masculinized.

Many other observations indirectly show that the substances which induce gonadal sexual differentiation are different from sex hormones of the adults. Among these, I cite the ineffectiveness of androgens, including testosterone, on the sexual differentiation of the gonads in *Xenopus laevis*; on the other hand, immediately following metamorphosis, this hormone induces the precocious development of all male s.s.c. in both sexes (Witschi and Allison, 65).

Therefore, it appears that for gonadal sexual differentiation there is another hormone or hormones which are different from the one that induces secondary sex characters. The latter is probably steroid in structure, while the first is not yet identified.

The experimental sex reversal of the gonads obtained with sex hormones is probably not physiological; the effect of sex hormones might be pharmacological, by disturbing the development of the somatic tissues of the gonads.

Summary

Many histochemical and chemical studies have shown the early onset of steroidogenic activity in the embryonic gonads of vertebrates, but always after sexual differentiation of the gonads. Therefore the embryonic sex inductors, that is, the substances responsible for differentiating the gonads into male or female organs, are in all probability different from sex hormones of the adult.

The differentiation of secondary sex characters is probably under the influence of steroid hormones, secreted after sexual differentiation of the gonads.

Through the results of experiments on parabiosis, explantation, transplantation and treatment with hormones in vitro and in vivo, we can come to similar conclusions.

Finally, the chemical nature of the substance which induces gonadal differentiation is still obscure. It is now necessary to direct research toward the identification of substances, even those different from steroids.

That research along these lines will be fruitful is emphasized by the recent experiments of Barton and Holyoke (4)

who obtained definite inhibition or degeneration of the ovarian cortex of the female mouse embryo following injections of a lipid extract which was prepared from the testes of fetal pigs. The genital ducts differentiated normally. These results are in contrast to those which were obtained with testosterone, which masculinized male secondary sex characters, but did not affect the gonad.

References

1. Acevedo, H. F., L. R. Axelrod, E. Ishikawa, and F. Takaki, "Steroidogenesis in the Human Fetal Testis: the Conversion of Pregnenolone-7α-H³ to Dehydroepiandrosterone, Testosterone and 4-Androstene-3,17-dione," *J. Clin. Endocrinol. Metab.* 21:1611–1613 (1961).

2. ——, ——, ——, and ——, "Studies in Fetal Metabolism. II. Metabolism of Progesterone-4-C¹⁴ and Pregnenolone-7α-H³ in Human Fetal Testes," *J. Clin. Endocrinol. Metab.* 23:885–890 (1963).

3. Aoshima, Y., C. D. Kochakian, and D. Jadrijevic, "TPN- and DPN-specific 3α-hydroxy- and Δ⁵-3β-Hydroxysteroid Dehydrogenases of Liver and Kidney," *Endocrinology* 74:521–531 (1964).

4. Barton, J. M., and E. A. Holyoke, "An Experimental Study of the Effects of a Fetal Testes Extract on the Reproductive System of Embryonic Mice," *Anat. Record* 142:297 (1962).

5. Bloch, E., "Metabolism of 4-¹⁴C-Progesterone by Human Fetal Testis and Ovaries," *Endocrinology* 74:883–845 (1964).

6. ——, B. Tissenbaum, and K. Benirschke, "The Conversion of 4-¹⁴C-Progesterone to 17α-Hydroxyprogesterone, Testosterone and Δ⁴-Androstene-3,17-dione by Human Fetal Testes *in vitro*," *Biochim. Biophys. Acta* 60:182–184 (1962).

7. ——, ——, B. L. Rubin, and H. W. Deane, "Δ⁵-3β-Hydroxysteroid Dehydrogenase Activity in Human Fetal Adrenals," *Endocrinology* 74:629–632 (1962).

8. Breuer, H., R. Ozon and C. Mittermayer,

"Untersuchungen über den Stoffwechsel von Steroidhormonen bei Vertebraten. I. Vorkommen von Hydroxysteroid-Dehydrogenasen bei Fischen und Amphibien," *Hoppe-Seylers Z. Physiol. Chem.* 333:272–281 (1963).

9. Burns, R. K., "The Sex of Parabiotic Twins in Amphibia," *J. Exptl. Zool.* 42:31–90 (1925).

10. Chester Jones, I., and J. G. Phillips, "Adrenocorticosteroids in Fish," *Symp. Zool. Soc. London* 1:17–32 (1960).

11. Chieffi, G., "Nuove Osservazioni sull'Organogenesi della Medulla della Gonade nei Vertebrati: Ricerche Istochimiche in *Rana esculenta, Bufo viridis* e *Scyliorhinus canicula*," *Pubbl. Staz. Zool. Napoli* 27:62–72 (1955).

12. ——, "Contributo allo Studio dei Differenziatori Embrionali del Sesso. I. Ricerche Istochimiche nell'Interrenale e nelle Pieghe Genitali di Girini di *Rana esculenta*," *Riv. Biol.* 47:439–452 (1955).

13. ——, "Il Metabolismo degli Ormoni Sessuali da Parte degli Anfibi: Ricerche *in vivo* e *in vitro*," *Boll. Zool.* 23:121–130 (1956).

14. ——, "Experimental Sex Reversal of Amphibian Larvae and Sex Hormones Metabolism," *Proc. Intern. Congr. Zool. 15th London* pp. 600–601 (1958).

15. ——, and V. Botte, "Osservazioni Istochimiche sull'Attività della Steroide-3β-olo-deidrogenasi nell'Interrenale e nelle Gonadi di Girini e Adulti di *Rana esculenta*," *Riv. Istochim. Norm. Patol.* 9:172–174 (1963).

16. ——, ——, and T. Visca, "Attività Steroide-3β-olo-deidrogenasica nell'In-

terrenale di Alcuni Selacei," *Acta Med. Romana* 1:108–116 (1963).

17. ——, and C. Lupo, "Analisi Comparativa degli Ormoni Sessuali negli Ittiopsidi," *Excerpta Med. Intern. Congr. Ser.* 51:146–147 (1962).

18. ——, H. Manelli, V. Botte, and L. Mastrolia, "Il Differenziamento Istochimico dell'Interrenale e dei Tessuti Somatici della Gonade Embrionale di Pollo: Comportamento della Steroide-3β-olo-deidrogenasi," *Acta Embryol. Morphol. Exptl.* 7:89–91 (1964).

19. ——, ——, ——, and ——, "Osservazioni sul Precoce Differenziamento Funzionale dell'Interrenale nell'Embrione di Pollo," *Atti Accad. Naz. Lincei Rend. Classe Sci. Fis. Mat. Nat.* (In press).

20. Dale, E., "Steroid Excretion by Larval Frogs," *Gen. Comp. Endocrinol.* 2:171–176 (1962).

21. Gallien, L., "Analyse des Effets des Hormones Stéroïdes dans la Différenciation Sexuelle des Amphibiens," *Arch. Anat. Microscop. Morphol. Exptl.* 48 bis:83–100 (1959).

22. ——, P. Certain, and R. Ozon, "Mise en Évidence d'une Δ⁵-3β-Hydroxystéroïde Deshydrogénase dans le Tissue Interrénal de l'Urodele *Pleurodeles waltlii* Michah, aux Diverses Stades de Développement," *Compt. Rend.* 258:5729–5731 (1964).

23. ——, and Th. Le Foulgoc, "Détection par Fluorimétrie et Colorimétrie de Stéroïdes Sexuels dans les Gonades Embryonnaires de Poulet," *Compt. Rend. Soc. Biol.* 151:1088–1089 (1957).

24. Goldschmidt, R., *Die sexuellen Zwischenstufen*, Berlin: Springer-Verlag (1931).

25. ——, *Le Déterminisme du Sexe et l'Intersexualité.* Paris: Ancan (1932).

26. Haffen, K., "La Culture *in vitro* de l'Épithélium Germinatif Isolé des Gonades Mâles et Femelles de l'Embryon de Canard. II. Influence de la Médullaire sur la Différenciation de l'Épithélium Germinatif," *J. Embryol. Exptl. Morphol.* 8:414–424 (1960).

27. Hagerman, D. D., and C. A. Villee, "Separation of Human Placental Estrogen-sensitive Transhydrogenase from Estradiol-17β-dehydrogenase," *J. Biol. Chem.* 234:2031–2036 (1959).

28. Hollander, V. P., N. Hollander, and J. D. Brown, "Studies on the Estrogen-

sensitive Enzyme System from Placenta," *J. Biol. Chem.* 234:1678–1684 (1959).

29. Hitzeman, J. W., "Development of Enzyme Activity in the Leydig Cells of the Mouse Testis," *Anat. Record* 143:351–361 (1962).

30. Jost, A., "Recherches sur la Différenciation Sexuelle de l'Embryon de Lapin. III. Rôle des Gonades Foetales dans la Différenciation Sexuelle Somatique," *Arch. Anat. Microscop. Morphol. Exptl.* 36:271–315 (1947).

31. ——, "Activité Androgène du Testicule Foetal de Rat Greffé sur l'Adulte Castré," *Compt. Rend. Soc. Biol.* 142:196–198 (1948).

32. ——, M. Chodkiewicz, and P. Mauléon, "Intersexualité du Foetus de Veau Produite par des Androgènes. Comparaison entre l'Hormone Foetale Responsable du Free-martinisme et l'Hormone Testiculaire Adulte," *Compt. Rend.* 256:274–276 (1963).

33. ——, and R. A. Colonge, "Greffe de Testicule Foetal de Rat sur l'Adulte Castré et Hypophysectomisé. Remarques sur la Physiologie du Testicule Foetal de Rat," *Compt. Rend. Soc. Biol.* 143:140–142 (1949).

34. Jurand, A., and E. Czubak, "Histochemical Investigations into the Development of the Adrenals and Gonads of Rabbits," *Bull. Acad. Polon. Sci. Ser. Sci. Biol.* 2:15–18 (1954).

35. Karnovsky, M. L., and H. W. Deane, "Aldehyde Formation in the Lipide Droplets of the Adrenal Cortex during Fixation, as Demonstrated Chemically and Histochemically," *J. Histochem. Cytochem.* 3:85–102 (1955).

36. Keller, K., and J. Tandler, "Über das Verhalten der Eihäute bei der Zwillingsträchtigkeit des Rindes. Untersuchungen über die Entstehungsursache der geschlechtlichen Unterentwicklung von Weiblichen Zwillingskälbern, welche neben einen Männlichen Kalbe zur Entwicklung Gelangen," *Wien. Tieraerztl. Wochschr.* 3:513–526 (1916).

37. Kellog, D. A., and G. G. Glenner, "Histochemical Localization of Human, Term Placental 17β-Oestradiol Dehydrogenases: Implications for the Transhydrogenase Reaction," *Nature* 187:763–764 (1960).

38. Kleiner, H., P. Wilkin, and J. Snoeck,

"Lokalisierung der Steroid-Dehydro-genasen und der Leucin-amino-pepti-dase in der Menschlichen Plazenta," *Geburtsh. Frauenheilk.* 22:986–988 (1962).

39. Kudo, T., "Occurrence of the Intersti-tial Cells of the Testis in the Embryonic and Postnatal Life History of the Guinea Pig," *Folia Anat. Japon.* 1:125–148 (1922).

40. Langer, L. J., and L. L. Engel, "Human Placental Estradiol-17β-Dehydrogen-ase," *J. Biol. Chem.* 233:583–588 (1958).

41. Levy, H., H. W. Deane, and B. L. Rubin, "Visualization of Steroid-3β-ol-dehydrogenase Activity in Tissues of Intact and Hypophysectomized Rats," *Endocrinology* 65:932–943 (1959).

42. Lillie, F. R., "The Free-martin: a Study of the Action of Sex Hormones in the Foetal Life of Cattle," *J. Exptl. Zool.* 23:371–452 (1917).

43. Lison, L., *Histochimie et Cytochimie Animales.* Paris: Gauthier-Villars, (1960).

44. Lutz, H., and Y. Lutz-Ostertag, "Free-martinisme Spontané chez les Oiseaux," *Develop. Biol.* 1:364–376 (1959).

45. Narbaitz, R., and L. Kolodny, "Δ⁵-3β-Hydroxysteroid Dehydrogenase in Dif-ferentiating Chick Gonads," *Z. Zell-forsch. Mikroskop. Anat.* (In press).

46. Niemi, M., and M. Ikonen, "Steroid-3β-ol-dehydrogenase Activity in Foetal Leydig's Cells," *Nature* 189:592–593 (1961).

47. Ozon, R., "Analyse, *in vivo*, du Mé-tabolisme des Oestrogènes au Cours de la Différenciation Sexuelle chez le Triton *Pleurodeles waltlii* Michah," *Compt. Rend.* 257:2332–2335 (1963).

48. Pearson, B., and F. Grose, "Histo-chemical Demonstration of 17β-Hydroxy-steroid Dehydrogenase by Use of Tetra-zolium Salt," *Proc. Soc. Exptl. Biol. Med.* 100:636–638 (1959).

49. Price, D., and R. Pannabecker, "Organ Culture Studies of Fetal Rat Reproduc-tive Tract," *Ageing in Transient Tissues*, Ciba Found. Colloq. Ageing. Boston: Little, Brown pp. 3–13 (1956).

50. Raynaud, A., and M. Frilley, "Irradi-ation, au Moyen des Rayons X, des Ébauches des Glandes Génitales de l'Embryon de Souris, au Quizième Jour de la Vie Intrautérine," *Bull. Soc. Zool. France* 223:1187–1189 (1946).

51. Roberts, J. D., and J. C. Warren, "Ster-oid Biosynthesis in the Fetal Ovary," *Endocrinology* 74:846–852 (1964).

52. Salzgeber, B., "Action Sélective de la Tryplaflavine sur la Médullaire des Glandes Génitales de l'Embryon de Poulet, Cultivées *in vitro*," *Compt. Rend.* 236:1306–1308 (1953).

53. Samuels, L. T., M. L. Helmreich, M. B. Lasater, and H. Reich, "An Enzyme in Endocrine Tissues which Oxidizes Δ⁵-3-Hydroxysteroids to α, β Unsat-urated Ketones," *Science* 113:490–491 (1951).

54. Talalay, P., B. Hurlock, and H. G. Williams-Ashman, "On a Coenzymatic Function of Estradiol-17β," *Proc. Natl. Acad. Sci. U. S.* 44:862–884 (1958).

55. Vannini, E., "Primi Risultati sulla-Azione dell'Acetato di Desossicortico-sterone sullo Sviluppo delle Gonadi nell'Embrione di Pollo," *Acta Zool. Stockholm* 30:183–207 (1949).

56. ———, "Morfogenesi delle Gonadi nei Girini degli Anfibi ed Azioni Speri-mentali degli Ormoni Steroidi," *Prob-lemi dello Sviluppo*, Milano: Ambro-siana, (1954).

57. Wattenberg, L. W., "Microscopic Histo-chemical Demonstration of Steroid-3β-ol-dehydrogenase in Tissue Sections," *J. Histochem. Cytochem.* 6:225–232 (1958).

58. Wells, L. J., "Hormones and Sexual Differentiation in Placental Mammals," *Arch. Anat. Microscop. Morphol. Exptl.* 39:499–514 (1950).

59. Weniger, J. P., "L'Ovaire d'Embryon de Poulet Cultivé *in vitro* Sécrète une Hormone Oestrogène," *Compt. Rend. Soc. Biol.* 158:175–178 (1964).

60. Willier, B. H., "Structures and Homol-ogies of Free-martin Gonads," *J. Exptl. Zool.* 33:63–127 (1921).

61. Witschi, E., "Experimentelle Unter-suchungen ueber die Entwicklungsges-chichte der Keimdrusen von *Rana tem-poraria*," *Arch. Mikroskop. Anat.* 85: 9–113 (1914).

62. ———, "Sex Reversal in Parabiotic Twins of the American Wood-frog," *Biol. Bull.* 52:136–147 (1927).

63. ———, "Studies on Sex Differentiation

and Sex Determination in Amphibians. II. Sex Reversal in Female Tadpoles of *Rana sylvatica* Following the Application of High Temperature," *J. Exptl. Zool.* 52:267–291 (1929).

64. ——, "Range of the Cortex-medulla Antagonism in Parabiotic Twins of *Ranidae* and *Hylidae*," *J. Exptl. Zool.* 58:113–145 (1931).

65. ——, and J. Allison, "Responses of *Xenopus* and *Alytes* to the Administration of Some Steroid Hormones," *Anat. Record* 108:589 (1950).

66. ——, and C. Y. Chang, "Cortisone-induced Transformation of Ovaries into Testes in Larval Frogs," *Proc. Soc. Exptl. Biol. Med.* 75:715–718 (1950).

67. Wolff, Et., "Recherches sur l'Intersexualité Expérimentale Produite par la Méthode des Greffes de Gonades a l'Embryon de Poulet," *Arch. Anat. Microscop. Morphol. Exptl.* 36:69–90 (1947).

68. ——, "Le Déterminisme de l'Atrophie d'un Organe Rudimentaire: le Canal de Müller des Embryons Mâles d'Oiseaux," *Experientia* 9:121–133 (1953).

69. ——, and A. Ginglinger, "Sur la Production Expérimentale d'Intersexués par l'Injection de Folliculine à l'Embryon de Poulet," *Compt. Rend.* 200: 2118–2121 (1935).

70. ——, and K. Haffen, "La Culture *in vitro* de l'Épithélium Germinatif Isolé des Gonades Mâles et Femelles de Canard," *Arch. Anat. Microscop. Morphol. Exptl.* 48:331–345 (1959).

71. ——, and Y. Lutz-Ostertag, "La Différenciation et la Régression des Canaux de Müller de l'Embryon de Poulet en Culture *in vitro*," *Compt. Rend. Assoc. Anat.* 72:214–228 (1952).

72. ——, and ——, "Free-martinisme Spontané et Expérimental chez l'Embryon de Canard," *Arch. Anat. Microscop. Morphol. Exptl.* 50:439–468 (1961).

73. ——, ——, and K. Haffen, "Sur la Régression et la Nécrose *in vitro* des Canaux de Müller de l'Embryon de Poulet sous l'Action Directe des Hormones Mâle," *Compt. Rend. Soc. Biol.* 146:1793–1795 (1952).

74. ——, G. Strudel, and Em. Wolff, "L'Action des Hormones Androgènes sur la Différenciation Sexuelle des Embryons de Poulet," *Arch. Anat. Histol. Embryol.* 31:237–310 (1948).

75. ——, and Em. Wolff, "The Effects of Castration on Bird Embryo," *J. Exptl. Zool.* 116:59–97 (1951).

27

Fetal Hormones and Their Role in Organogenesis

LEMEN J. WELLS

Department of Anatomy
University of Minnesota
Minneapolis, Minnesota

The technique of organ culture, as used by Price and Ortiz (8), has the advantage that investigators may exclude such hormones of pregnancy as those of placental origin, those of maternal origin, and those from the embryonic adrenal. On the other hand, meaningful observations on endocrinology in the fetus are also obtainable from experiments performed in vivo. Furthermore, these observations contribute to the understanding of organogenesis. In the account which follows, the observations are largely those made in the Department of Anatomy at the University of Minnesota.

Organogenesis in vivo

Androgen from the Fetal Testis

Despite any placental and maternal hormones of pregnancy, the functioning of the testis of the rat embryo may

be shown by experiments in vivo (Wells, Cavanaugh, and Maxwell, 10). Castration of a fetus too young to have any prostatic buds reduces the number of prostatic buds which appear (Fig. 27.1A and B). This effect of castration may be prevented by implanting under the skin of the castrated fetus a pellet of testosterone propionate (Fig. 27.1C).

These observations suggest that the androgen of the developing testis is a steroid hormone and that it probably is identical with, or similar to, the androgen which is produced by the testis after birth.

Hypophysis-adrenal Axis

Similarly, despite any placental and maternal hormones of pregnancy, the functioning of the hypophysis-adrenal axis before birth may be demonstrated by experiments in vivo. In a fetal rat subjected to left adrenalectomy, the right adrenal undergoes a significant,

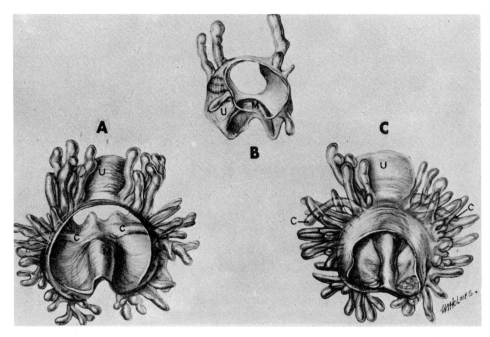

Fig. 27.1 Models of prostatic buds in three fetal rats of the same litter, which depict two observations: that castration prior to the appearance of any prostatic buds reduces the number of buds which develop; that this effect is preventable by an implanted pellet of testosterone propionate. C, coagulating gland; M, Müllerian tubercle; U, urethra. A. Unoperated, control fetus, 61 buds, many of which can be counted in the recorded view. B. Castrated fetus, 9 buds. C. Castrated fetus given subcutaneously a pellet of testosterone propionate, 62 buds. ×50 (After Wells, Cavanaugh, and Maxwell, *Anat. Record.* 118:109–133, 1954, with the permission of The Wistar Institute Press, publisher of *The Anatomical Record.*)

compensatory hypertrophy (Eguchi, Eguchi, and Wells, 2). Thus, in the data recorded in Figure 27.2, absence of the left adrenal for a period of 2 days caused a compensatory hypertrophy of 42 percent (group 1). After birth, there is temporarily a hiatus of 3 days, during which the functioning of the hypophysis-adrenal axis is significantly reduced (group 2) – a feature which deserves additional study.

The compensatory hypertrophy of the right adrenal in a fetus subjected to left adrenalectomy (Fig. 27.3A and B) may be prevented by an implanted pellet of cortisone (Kitchell and Wells, 6), as shown in Table 27.1. Also, in a normal fetus, an implanted pellet of corti-

sone not only retards the growth of the adrenal (Yakaitis and Wells, 12) but retards that of the hypophysis as well (Coetzee and Wells, 1).

Another line of evidence that the hypophysis-adrenal axis functions before birth may be obtained from experiments in which the fetal rat is subjected to hypophyseoprivus by decapitation *in utero* (Kitchell and Wells, 7). The hypophyseoprivus reduces the volume of the adrenal, and this effect may be prevented by a series of subcutaneous injections of ACTH (Table 27.2). Hypophyseoprivus alone, for a period of more than 4 days (gestation in the rat is about 21½ days), so retards the growth of the adrenal that the volume of the

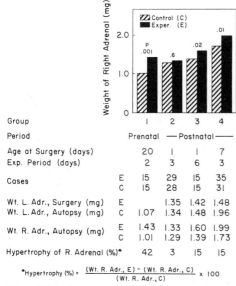

Group		1	2	3	4
Period		Prenatal	— Postnatal —		
Age at Surgery (days)		20	1	1	7
Exp. Period (days)		2	3	6	3
Cases	E	15	29	15	35
	C	15	28	15	31
Wt. L. Adr., Surgery (mg)	E		1.35	1.42	1.48
Wt. L. Adr., Autopsy (mg)	C	1.07	1.34	1.48	1.96
Wt. R. Adr., Autopsy (mg)	E	1.43	1.33	1.60	1.99
	C	1.01	1.29	1.39	1.73
Hypertrophy of R. Adrenal (%)*		42	3	15	15

$$*\text{Hypertrophy (\%)} = \frac{(\text{Wt. R. Adr., E}) - (\text{Wt. R. Adr., C})}{(\text{Wt. R. Adr., C})} \times 100$$

Fig. 27.2 Compensatory hypertrophy of the right adrenals in rats subjected to left adrenalectomy. Wt., weight. (After Eguchi, Eguchi, and Wells, *Proc. Soc. Exptl. Biol. Med.* 116:89–92, 1964, with the permission of the Board of Editors of the Society for Experimental Biology and Medicine.)

adrenal is only 39 percent of that in an untreated control fetus of the same sex, both fetuses being members of the same litter (Fig. 27.4A and B).

Hypophysis-thyroid System

From experiments performed in vivo, it may be shown that the hypophysis-thyroid system begins to function before birth. Thus, hypophyseoprivus by subtotal decapitation *in utero* retards the growth of the thyroid, and this effect may be prevented by giving the headless fetus a series of subcutaneous injections of thyrotrophin (Hwang and Wells, 4). Also, thyroidectomy of the fetus accelerates the development of the basophilic cells in the anterior lobe of the hypophysis and causes the partial degranulation of some of them (Hwang and Wells, 5). The combination of thyroidectomy and injected thyroxin does not produce any consistent changes in the hypophysis. In a normal fetal rat, injected thyroxin alone retards the development of the basophilic cells of the anterior lobe.

Somatotrophin and Growth of the Fetus

From experiments in vivo, it may be be shown that somatotrophin (growth hormone) from the developing hypophysis governs in part the prenatal growth of the fetus (Heggestad and Wells, 3). In a fetal rat, hypophyseoprivus induced by decapitating the fetus *in utero* retards the growth of the fetus. This effect may be prevented by giving the headless fetus a series of subcutaneous injections of somatotrophin obtained from bovine hypophyses. Indeed, it may be estimated that in the normal rat, shortly before birth, the somatotrophin from the fetal hypophysis is responsible for about 20 percent of the fetal growth.

Androgen and Sex Differentiation

Price and Ortiz (8) conclude that any possible role of androgen from the developing adrenal in sex differentiation in mammals is unknown. This conclusion is in harmony with the recorded observations of Kitchell and Wells (7). Bilateral adrenalectomy of a male rat embryo does not prevent the normal development of the seminal vesicle. Combined adrenalectomy and castration prevents the normal development of the seminal vesicle but not to any greater extent than castration alone.

Testicular Androgen and Differentiation of the Testis

Does androgen from the testis of the embryo further the differentiation of the testis itself? This question which is raised by Price and Ortiz (8) is not

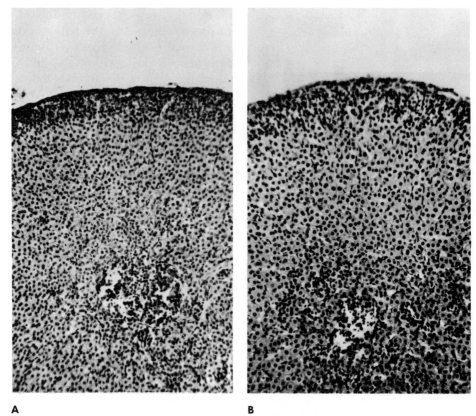

A   **B**

Fig. 27.3 Sections of adrenals of two fetal rats of the same sex and from the same litter (hematoxylin and eosin stain), which illustrate compensatory hypertrophy of the right adrenal after left adrenalectomy. A. Right adrenal of unoperated, control fetus. B. Right adrenal of experimental fetus. ×150 (After Kitchell and Wells, *Endocrinology* 50:83–93, 1952, with the permission of the J. B. Lippincott Co., publisher of *Endocrinology.*)

answered by them. It deserves special study.

We know, of course, that in a male mammal during postnatal life a series of injections of testosterone propionate may accelerate the formation of spermatozoa (Wells, 9). This effect may be demonstrated in an immature ground squirrel (*Citellus*). In a ground squirrel subjected to hypophysectomy, injections of testosterone propionate may cause the formation of spermatozoa.

Organogenesis in vitro

Physicochemical Differentiation before Morphological Differentiation

That physicochemical differentiation of the testis may antedate the morphologic differentiation of the testis, is indicated by the observations of Price and Ortiz (8). The evidence is that the explanted gonad of a male embryo can and does produce androgen before it is

TABLE 27.1 Compensatory Hypertrophy of the Right Adrenal of Fetal Rat Subjected to Left Adrenalectomy (Group A) and Its Prevention by Implanting a Pellet of Cortisone under the Skin of the Fetus (Group B)[a]

	Fetuses	Treatment	Body Weight (Grams)	Volume of the Right Adrenal ($mm^3 \cdot 10^2$)	$\left[\dfrac{VOL. (mm^3 \cdot 10^2)}{BODY\ WT. (GRAMS)}\right]$		
Group	Number		Average	Average	Average	E/C	p
A	14 E[b]	Unilateral (left) adrenalectomy	4.42	51.7	11.7		
	14 C	None	4.55	39.1	8.5	1.38	0.001
B	6 E	Unilateral (left) adrenalectomy and implanted cortisone	4.50	31.7	7.0		
	6 C	None	4.54	36.8	8.1	0.87	0.008

[a] From Kitchell and Wells (6), with the permission of J. B. Lippincott Co., publisher of *Endocrinology*.
[b] E, experimental; C, control of same litter, same sex.

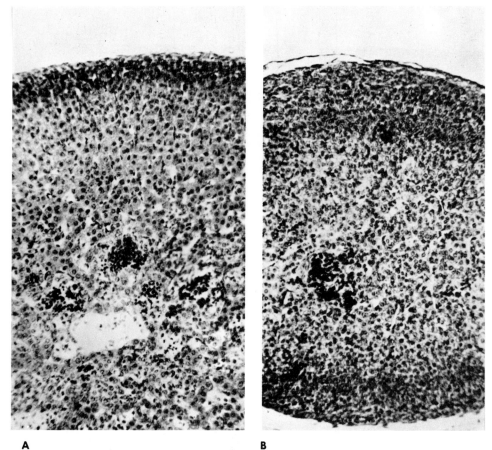

A   **B**

Fig. 27.4 Sections of adrenals of two fetal rats of the same sex and from the same litter (hematoxylin and eosin stain), which illustrate the retardation of growth of the adrenal after the fetus has been subjected to hypophyseoprivus by decapitation. A. Right adrenal of unoperated, control fetus. B. Right adrenal of experimental fetus. ×111 (From Kitchell and Wells, *Anat. Record.* 112:561–591, 1952, with the permission of The Wistar Press, publisher of *The Anatomical Record.*)

morphologically a testis. This sequence of differentiation, first physicochemical, and then morphological, is not surprising because a similar sequence has been reported for the pancreatic acinus (Wessells, 11). The dissociated elements of the pancreatic primordium of the mouse embryo, epithelial and mesenchymal, are grown symbiotically in

organ culture in such manner that these elements are separated from each other by a porous platform, a millipore filter. When a symbiosis of fewer than 36 hours is followed by a removal of the mesenchyme and by a continued cultivation of the epithelium, acini do not develop. In contrast, when the mesenchyme is removed after 36 hours of

TABLE 27.2 Reduction of Volume of the Right Adrenal of Fetal Rat Subjected to Hypophyseoprivus by Decapitation (Group A) and its Prevention by Giving the Operated Fetus a Series of Subcutaneous Injections of ACTH (Group B)[a]

FETUSES		TREATMENT		BODY WEIGHT (GRAMS)	VOLUME (mm³·10²)	$\left(\dfrac{\text{VOL. (mm}^3\cdot10^2)}{\text{BODY WT. (GRAMS)}}\right)$		
GROUP	NUMBER	KIND	HOURS	AVERAGE	AVERAGE	AVERAGE	E/C	P
A	28 E[b]	Hx[c]	65	2.90[d]	28.1	9.7		
	28 C	None		3.75[d]	47.3	12.6	.78	.001
B	6 E	Hx & ACTH	51	2.64[d]	74.6	28.8		
	6 C	None		2.93[d]	40.7	13.9	2.07	.009

[a] From Kitchell and Wells (7), with the permission of The Wistar Press, publisher of *The Anatomical Record.*
[b] E, experimental; C, control of same litter, same sex.
[c] Hx, hypophyseoprivus by decapitation.
[d] Weight of body minus head (C fetus decapitated just before weighing).

symbiosis and the epithelium alone grown in organ culture, acini develop. These observations are interpreted as follows. During a period of 36 hours of symbiosis the mesenchyme, acting as embryonic inducer, brings about a physicochemical differentiation of the epithelium. During a subsequent period of cultivation, this induced physicochemical differentiation is irreversible; it paves the way for the morphological differentiation of the epithelium.

Summary

Observations from experiments in vivo indicate that in the developing rat such endocrine glands as the testis, hypophysis, adrenal, and thyroid begin to function before birth. They point to the generalization that genesis of form and genesis of function tend to go hand in hand. Observations from experiments in vitro support the view that physicochemical differentiation may antedate morphological differentiation.

References

1. Coetzee, M. L., and L. J. Wells, "Hypophysis-adrenal System in the Fetal Rat: Effects of Hydrocortisone, Cortisone, DCA, Adrenalectomy and Maternal Hypophysectomy upon the Hypophysis," *Am. J. Anat.* 101:419–443 (1957).
2. Eguchi, Y., K. Eguchi, and L. J. Wells, "Compensatory Hypertrophy of Right Adrenal after Left Adrenalectomy: Observations in Fetal, Newborn and Week-old Rats," *Proc. Soc. Exptl. Biol. Med.* 116:89–92 (1964).
3. Heggestad, C. B., and L. J. Wells, "Experiments on the Contribution of Somatotrophin to Prenatal Growth in the Rat," *Acta Anat.* In press (1965).
4. Hwang, U. K., and L. J. Wells, "Hypophysis-thyroid System in the Fetal Rat: Thyroid after Hypophyseoprivia, Thyroxin, Triiodothyronine, Thyrotrophin and Growth Hormone," *Anat. Record* 134:125–141 (1959).
5. ——, and ——, "Hypophysis-thyroid System in the Fetal Rat: Hypophysis after Thyroidectomy and Thyroxin," *Arch. Anat. Microscop. Morphol. Exptl.* 48:123–132 (1959).
6. Kitchell, R. L., and L. J. Wells, "Reciprocal Relation between the Hypophysis and Adrenals in Fetal Rats: Effects of Unilateral Adrenalectomy and of Im-

planted Cortisone, DOCA and Sex Hormones. *Endocrinology* 50:83–93 (1952).
7. ——, and ——, "Functioning of the Hypophysis and Adrenals in Fetal Rats: Effects of Hypophysectomy, Adrenalectomy, Castration, Injected ACTH and Implanted Sex Hormones. *Anat. Record* 112:561–591 (1952).
8. Price, D., and E. Ortiz, "A Comparative Study of the Role of Fetal Androgen in Sex Differentiation in Mammals," *Organogenesis*, DeHann and Ursprung, eds. New York: Holt, Rinehart and Winston, Inc., chap. 25 (1965).
9. Wells, L. J., "Response of the Testis to Androgens Following Hypophysectomy," *Anat. Record* 82:565–585 (1942).
10. ——, M. W. Cavanaugh, and E. L. Maxwell, "Genital Abnormalities in Castrated Fetal Rats and Their Prevention by Means of Testosterone Propionate," *Anat. Record* 118:109–133 (1954).
11. Wessells, N. K., "DNA Synthesis, Mitosis, and Differentiation in Pancreatic Acinar Cells in vitro," *J. Cell Biol.* 20:415–433 (1964).
12. Yakaitis, A. A., and L. J. Wells, "Hypophysis-adrenal System in the Fetal Rat: Adrenals in Fetuses Subjected to Cortisone, DCA, Hypophyseoprivia and Growth Hormone," *Am. J. Anat.* 98:205–230 (1956).

28

Sexual Stabilization of Müllerian Ducts in the Chick Embryo

TERRELL H. HAMILTON AND CHING-SUNG TENG[*]
Department of Zoology
University of Texas
Austin, Texas

This is a review of some recent studies which deal with the role of hormones in the sexual differentiation of Müllerian ducts in the chick embryo. No attempt will be made to consider here the more general problem of hormone-regulated urogenital differentiation throughout the vertebrate class. For this the reader is referred to Dodd (4), Domm (5), Gallien (7), Hamilton (13), Jost (15–17), Price and Pannabecker (28), Wells (36), Willier (39), Witschi (40), and Wolff (41, 42).

More specifically, the objectives of this review are threefold: (1) to compare recent studies concerned with in vivo and in vitro aspects of differentiation of Müllerian ducts in the chick embryo (*Gallus*); (2) to consider the problem of ontogenetic stabilization or involution (regression or "death") of

these ducts as dual aspects of their differentiation; and (3) to stress, for the problem of embryonic hormone action and tissue competence, the model of modifier or inducer interaction with the genetic control mechanism of cellular metabolism. This chapter thus begins with an account of the in vivo pattern of sexual differentiation of the ducts, proceeds to experimental studies altering this pattern, and then relates to the recent and growing body of evidence that the actions of hormones and the specificity of tissues for responses to these phenomena are mediated in some way by DNA-dependent processes.

Sexual Pattern of Differentiation of Müllerian Ducts

Gross Morphology

Figure 28.1 illustrates the over-all pattern of differentiation of the chick

[*]In the preparation of this chapter we have benefited from discussions with F. L. Hisaw, C. M. Williams, Ernst Mayr, D. Price, J. Hopkins III, R. H. Barth, Jr., H. S. Forrest, R. Lockart, and, particularly, J. Tata and C. Widnell.

681

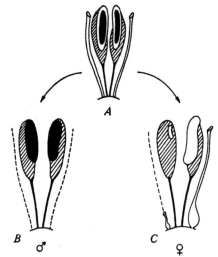

Fig. 28.1 Diagram of the sexual pattern of differentiation of the urogenital system in the chick embryo. Ventral view showing the changes in the neutral pattern after 9 days of incubation. Testes, black; ovary and ovotestes, white; Müllerian ducts, white; Wolffian ducts, black; embryonic kidneys, diagonal lines. (From Wolff, *Experientia* 9:121–133, 1958.)

urogenital system. The pattern is essentially one of paired structures common to both sexes during the early or neutral period, followed by sexual differences in the changes (cell movements, shifts in organ size, involution of ducts) of the structures during differentiation.

At a period of 5–6 days of incubation both male and female embryos possess undifferentiated *pairs* of gonads, Müllerian ducts, and Wolffian ducts. In the male embryo, the Wolffian ducts are retained after formation and become the vas deferentia of the adult, while *both* Müllerian ducts undergo involution and disappear by the 12th or 13th day of incubation. The gonads lose the cortical elements, and the medullary elements develop into testes. In the female embryo, the Wolffian ducts undergo involution and disappear after hatching at 20–21 days of incubation. By the 14th day the *right* female Müllerian duct is undergoing a slow anterior-to-posterior involution. A cloacal remnant of this duct persists in the adult female. The left Müllerian duct (the functional oviduct of the adult female) continues to develop, expanding in thickness with the shell gland forming in the cloacal region. In the female embryo, after the 8th day of incubation the right gonad (ovotestes) is distinguishable from the left one. By the 16th day the right gonad is reduced in size, and the left one has undergone a hypertrophic development in its cortical region, forming the ovary of the adult.

Changes in Tissue Levels of Nucleic Acids and Nucleases

Little work has been done correlating biochemical parameters with stabilization or involution of Müllerian ducts. Apart from early work by Wolff and co-workers (44) and Pfleger (26) demonstrating an effect of androgen on release of catabolic enzymes by Müllerian ducts in vitro, Brachet and co-workers (1) were the first to study the problem on a quantitative basis. Following the preliminary work of the latter, Scheib-Pfleger and Wattiaux (30) and Hamilton (13) reported on changes in amounts and activities of enzymes and nucleic acids for Müllerian ducts undergoing stabilization or involution. The analyses of the former workers (30) reveal that acid hydrolases (acid phosphatase, cathepsin, β-glucuronidase, acid ribonuclease) of these ducts are lysosome-contained (cf. De Duve, 3), and are released from such cytoplasmic particles in the course of involution. Hamilton (13), working with inactive (protein-bound), active (by urea treatment of cellular extracts), and soluble enzymes found the same pattern, and extended the analysis to include nucleic acids as well as nuclease (ribonuclease).

The comparative study (13) of tissue levels of RNA, lysosome-contained ribonuclease, soluble ribonuclease, and DNA is summarized in Figures 28.2 and 28.3. On a per unit weight basis for pooled Müllerian ducts, there is, between 7 and 9 days of incubation, a 300 percent rise in the cellular level of inactive or total ribonuclease in those ducts "destined to die" during subsequent embryogenesis — the two male and right female ducts. This marked rise does not occur in the stabilizing left female duct, which shows a further increase in RNA and DNA associated with its development (cf. Figs. 28.2 and 28.3). Inversely associated with the increase in ribonuclease in the male and right female ducts is a decrease in their levels of RNA and DNA (Fig 28.3). The concentration of the nucleic acids in these ducts indicates, in fact, a decrease at 9 days of incubation. Prior to onset of visible morphological involution at 9 days, the ducts concerned are already biochemically committed to autolysis and involution. Furthermore, the rise in ribonuclease activity for extracts from the ducts taken at 9 days of incubation and thereafter (for "yet uninvoluted" beads of tissue comprising the involuting ducts) only represents a shift of the enzyme from the inactive state (of being bound in or to lysosomes) to the active (or soluble) state. This increase in lysosomal-contained enzyme prior to onset of morphological involution in the ducts

destined to die represents, as it were, "metabolic preparation for death."

Thus not unexpectedly, the involution of chick Müllerian ducts during urogenital differentiation involves a sequential series of metabolic changes, and not a random collapse of the nucleic acids and enzymatic and structural protein systems of the cells. Undoubtedly, other biochemical units will show ordered shifts during involution when correspondingly studied. It would be of interest to know how the by-products of this cellular deterioration are assimilated or eliminated by the embryo. (Are phagocytes exerting a clean-up role here?) Despite the paucity of information concerning physiological and biochemical changes associated with the stabilization or involution of these ducts, it is clear from the data now at hand that here exists a remarkable example of "programmed death" (cf. Lockshin and Williams, 22) of an organ in embryogenesis, both between sexes and within a sex (namely, the unilateral involution of the right Müllerian duct in the female embryo; Fig. 28.1). The embryo's mechanisms for instrumenting this program remain to be discovered.

Survey of Recent Studies of Müllerian Duct Differentiation

Here we will consider several studies of the role of proximate physiological factors in the regulation of sexual differentiation of Müllerian ducts. The problem in general centers on the role of embryonic hormones, and on the commonly assumed belief that injected steroid hormones simulate, if not duplicate, the effects of the endogenous hormones. Thus, it is necessary to summarize the earlier studies in this area.

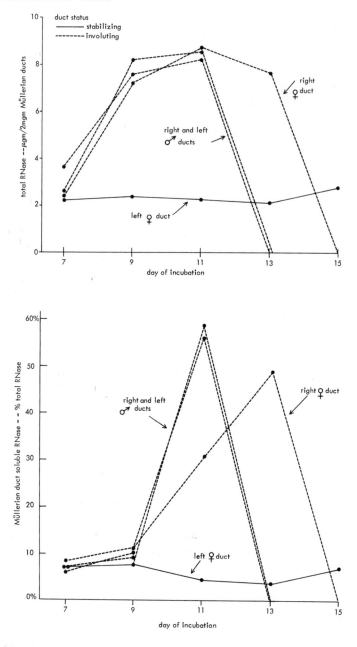

Fig. 28.2 Changes in lysosome-contained (top) and soluble (bottom) ribonuclease during the involution or stabilization of the right and left male and female Müllerian ducts to show the rapid shift of the enzyme to the active state during the 48 hours (for male ducts) and 4 days (for the right female duct) following onset of visible morphological involution during the 9th day of incubation. (From Hamilton, *Proc. XIII Intern. Ornith. Congr. Ithaca, N.Y.* pp. 1004–1040, 1963.)

Since 1935 it has been well known that injection of estrogens into male embryos prior to urogenital differentiation results in retention of the Müllerian ducts (feminization). Correspondingly, injection of androgens into female embryos results in the atypical involution or breakdown of the left female duct (masculinization). Except for the observation that androsterone, a potent androgen for growth induction of the chick comb, results (unlike testosterone, but like estrogen) in breakdown of the ducts in male embryos, the points cited above argue well for sex hormone control of Müllerian duct differentiation. (See Hamilton, 13, for a recent review of these experiments.)

During the 1940s and 1950s Et. Wolff and co-workers (for review, see

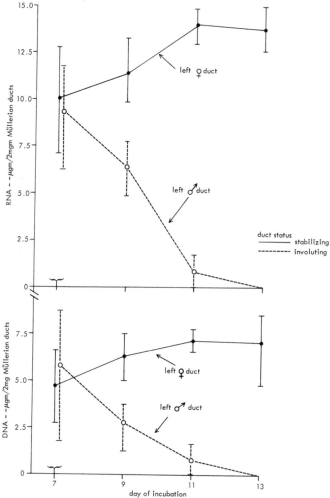

Fig. 28.3 Decrease or increase in RNA and DNA associated with involution or stabilization of Müllerian ducts. (From Hamilton, *Proc. XIII Intern. Ornith. Congr. Ithaca, N.Y.* pp. 1004–1040, 1963.)

Wolff, 41, 42), brought much order to this area of research in a series of experiments that began with in vivo experiments and transplantation studies, and ended with embryonic castration experiments and studies of the influence of steroid hormones on Müllerian ducts in vitro. The major conclusion from these studies was that in the absence of hormone both Müllerian ducts in each sex were retained. The workers cited found that a factor produced by the male gonads – presumably a diffusing hormone – in some way brought about autolysis and necrosis of the male ducts, and that hemicastration (of either the left or right gonad) of the female embryo failed to prevent the involution of the right Müllerian duct. Thus Wolff and his associates showed rather conclusively that a substance or factor (a male or masculinizing hormone?) produced by the gonads in both sexes is responsible for the involution of Müllerian ducts. Recent studies proceed from this point, and center around (1) the number and chemical nature of the embryonic hormone or hormones, and (2) the means by which endogenous hormones or exogenous steroid hormones induce or bring about the autolysis and breakdown of the ducts in vivo or in vitro.

In vitro Studies

In 1959 Wolff (42) summarized his studies and co-workers' studies of the influence of androgenic steroid hormones on Müllerian ducts cultured in vitro, when excised prior to in vivo differentiation or exposure to the endogenous hormone. He concluded that a male hormone or, at the minimum, a gonad hormone was responsible for the involution of the ducts in vivo. This conclusion on in vivo events was

an assumption based on the belief that androgenic steroid hormones duplicate in vitro events which occur in vivo. He thus interpreted his in vitro observation that isoandrosterone results in the release of proteolytic enzymes by Müllerian ducts as meaning that in vivo the gonad hormone activates a proteolytic enzyme which perpetrates an autolysis and necrosis of the hormone-sensitive ducts. Hamilton (12) has previously noted that, since tissues undergoing autolysis characteristically release acidophilic, catabolic enzymes, Wolff's observation may represent a result, not a cause, of breakdown of Müllerian ducts.

More recently, we have completed an in vitro analysis of the response of Müllerian ducts to varying doses of three naturally occurring steroid hormones: testosterone, androsterone, and estradiol-17β. For this work an in vitro technique was developed which permitted the culture and maintenance of individual ducts (closed system) for up to 20 days. The objective of the study was to determine dose-response curves for Müllerian ducts treated in vitro with the steroid hormones cited. In preliminary applications of this technique, it was found that Müllerian ducts taken from female embryos at 8 days, 11 hours of incubation, demonstrated in the course of in vitro culture a swelling response, coupled with a cloacal swelling in the posterior region of the duct (Fig. 28.4). In work with large numbers of ducts in vitro, population responses could be estimated, and it was to such control values that the influence of the three representative steroid hormones were compared.

Figure 28.5 shows the in vitro responses of Müllerian ducts (excised at 8 days, 11 hours of incubation) to con-

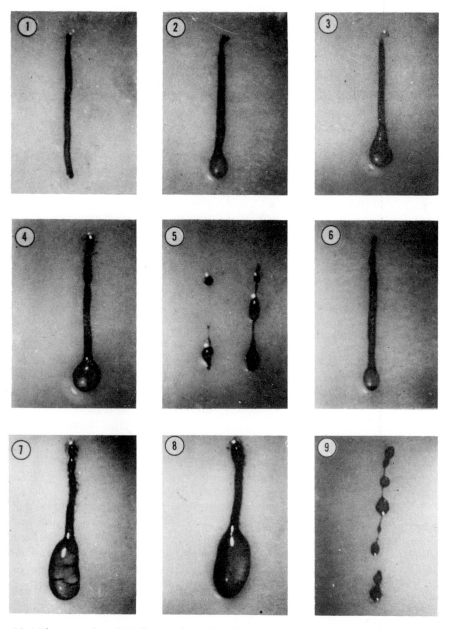

Fig. 28.4 Photographs of Müllerian ducts (Md) in control condition and after treatment with estradiol-17β. Responses to androgenic steroids are qualitatively similar. 1. Left ♀ Md after 2 days of culture. 2. Right ♀ Md after 3 days of culture. 3. Right ♀ Md after 5 days of culture. 4. Right ♀ Md after 7 days of culture. 5. ♂ Md after 7 days of culture. 6. Left ♀ Md after 2 days of culture in medium containing 10 μg/ml estradiol-17β. 7. Left ♀ Md after 5 days of culture in medium containing 1 μg/ml estradiol-17β. 8. Right ♀ Md after 7 days of culture in medium containing 1 μg/ml estradiol-17β. 9. ♂ Md after 7 days of culture in medium containing 10 μg/ml estradiol-17β. ×12.

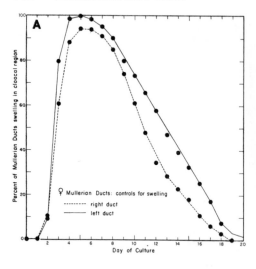

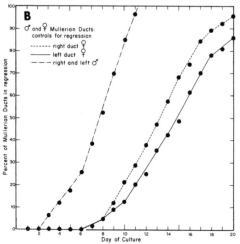

Fig. 28.5 In vitro development of Müllerian ducts in control medium (hormones absent). *A.* For right and left female Müllerian ducts, day of culture plotted against percent of ducts swelling in the cloacal region for the populations tested. *B.* For male and female Müllerian ducts, day of culture plotted against percent of ducts in regression for the populations tested.

trol medium (minus steroid hormones). In this and other experiments cited here, approximately 60 Müllerian ducts were individually cultured for

each of the following sexual or positional situations: right female duct, left female duct, and male duct (right and left). These were checked daily for evidence of visible swelling in the posterior or cloacal region and for regression. Regression in this instance refers to visible deterioration and collapse of the duct body (cf. Fig. 28.4, 9). The populations of ducts thus tested indicate the following: (1) Female ducts excised at the time period cited show a rapid swelling in the cloacal region reaching maximum percentage values by the 5th day of culture, and begin regressing on the 6th day. Here the right duct, which normally undergoes an in vivo involution, lags behind the left one in swelling, but regresses somewhat more rapidly. By 20 days of culture nearly all the female ducts have undergone regression. (2) Male ducts excised at 8 days, 11 hours of incubation, show almost no evidence of swelling in vitro. Rather, they fragment rapidly, and by 6 days of culture 97 percent of the ducts exhibit signs of regression or breakdown.

Results of dose-response experiments using female Müllerian ducts and estradiol, testosterone, and androsterone are summarized in Figures 28.6 and 28.7. These results are considered in greater detail elsewhere (Teng and Hamilton, 34), and will be discussed only briefly here. In general, each of the hormones tested exerted qualitatively the same influence on the female Müllerian ducts in vitro: small doses accelerated swelling and large doses (30 μg/ml to 100 μg/ml for estradiol and androsterone; 1.0 μg/ml to 100 μg/ml for testosterone) inhibited or suppressed swelling (Fig. 28.6). Small doses of these steroids (0.01 μg/ml to 0.05 μg/ml) delayed onset of in vitro regression, and large doses (0.05 μg/ml to 10 μg/ml) accelerated such regression. Large doses (above 10 μg/ml for estradiol and androsterone; 1.0 or more μg/ml for testosterone) inhibited swelling and induced rapid regression.

The surprising feature of these results is that they fail to correlate with the well-known in vivo effects of the hormones on the differentiation of Müllerian ducts. There is, in vitro, neither evidence for estrogenic maintenance of Müllerian ducts, nor evidence for their androgen-induced breakdown. In fact, testosterone is the most effective steroid in the sense that small doses (0.01 to 0.10 μg/ml) accelerate swelling and delay regression longer than comparable doses of estradiol and androsterone (cf., Fig. 28.7D with 28.7B and 28.7F). The results differ from those reported by Wolff (42), but different culture methods and hormones tested prevent comparison of the studies.

The observation that Müllerian ducts of the male embryo undergo a relatively rapid regression in the in vitro culture medium suggested that endogenous hormone had already reached the ducts and set the course of their differentiation (namely, death) by the time of their removal at 8 days, 11 hours of incubation. To check this point, and to determine whether the ducts excised at this time period are already committed to specific patterns of differentiation, ducts were taken from male embryos at 8 days, 0 hours of incubation. The results noted in Table 28.1 show that Müllerian ducts excised and cultured at this earlier time period fail to fragment and undergo regression as described above. At this time, male and female ducts respond comparably to steroid hormones. This observation indicates that male Müllerian ducts are committed in vivo to involution by a factor which reaches them between 8 days and 8 days, 11 hours of incubation. Ducts excised and cultured at 8 days are stimulated, not inhibited, by androgenic steroids such as androsterone (Table 28.1) or testosterone. Thus, the theory that the masculinizing hormone of the chick embryo is an androgenic steroid may be subject to criticism.

In vivo Studies

Four recent studies are of particular relevance to the present discussion. Morgan and Greb (24) have found in

TABLE 28.1 In vitro Responses of Müllerian Ducts to Androsterone

TIME OF REMOVAL OF MÜLLERIAN DUCTS FROM EMBRYOS	STATUS[a] AND NUMBER OF MÜLLERIAN DUCTS	TREATMENT	PERCENT REGRESSING IN FIRST 5 DAYS OF CULTURE
8 days, 11 hours	Right and left ♂ 67	Control	95%
8 days, 0 hours	Right ♂ and ♀ 24	Control	0%
8 days, 0 hours	Left ♂ and ♀ 24	Control	0%
8 days, 0 hours	Right ♂ and ♀ 24	Androsterone (5 μg/ml)	0%
8 days, 0 hours	Left ♂ and ♀ 24	Androsterone (5 μg/ml)	0%

[a] Status refers to position and sex of the ducts.

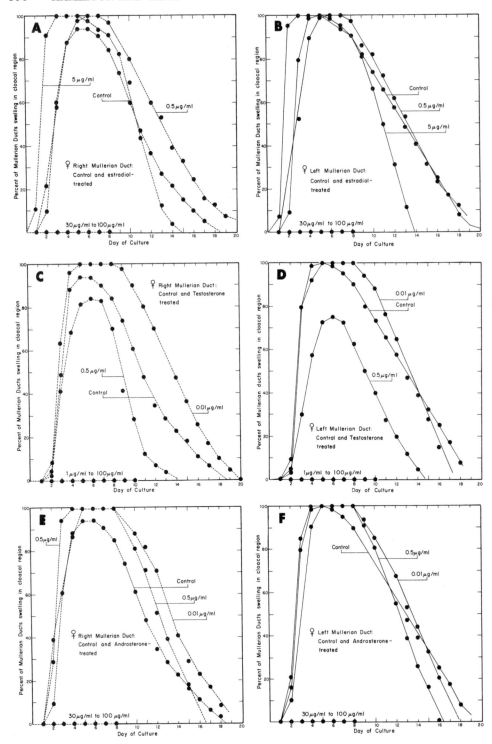

Fig. 28.6

inbreeding experiments evidence for a genotype or mutant which in some way *lengthens* the rudiment of the right female oviduct in adult chickens. This hints of genetic control of the degree of involution of the right duct in the female embryo. Hamilton has pointed out (13) that the importance of their finding to the problem of the asymmetrical nature of Müllerian duct differentiation in the avian embryo rests upon whether or not the genetic effects of inbreeding on the right female Müllerian duct operate for a lengthening of the cloacal remnant by post-differentiation growth, or by a decrease in the extent to which the duct undergoes anterior-to-posterior involution. The matter awaits analysis.

Kondo (19) has presented further evidence for the role of genetic factors in hormone responses by describing breed differences in responses to estrogens for the reproductive organs of chick embryos.

Proceeding from the earlier work of Raynaud (29) and Stoll (31), Hamilton (11) has conducted a quantitative analysis of the effects of varying doses of estradiol-17β, androsterone, and testosterone on Müllerian ducts, when injected into chick embryos prior to in vivo differentiation of their urogenital systems. Minimal doses of the steroids necessary per embryo for characteristic effects were: 10 μg, estradiol-17β; androsterone, 250 μg; and testosterone, 125–250 μg. Interaction studies were carried out, and it was noted that 10 μg estradiol could prevent the normal involution of Müllerian ducts in the male embryo even when co-administered with 1000 μg of testosterone. It was also noted that for female embryos, regardless of the time of injection or size of the dose of steroid hormone (androgen as well as estrogen), some involution of the right duct could not be prevented. This was interpreted as further evidence for a differential in competence to endogenous hormone for the right and left Müllerian ducts of the female embryo.

Groenendijk-Huijbers (9) has reported on results of surgical castration experiments. She concludes that in the female embryo a masculinizing hormone determines the anterior-to-posterior involution (female-type) of the right Müllerian duct, and that simultaneously a feminizing hormone protects the left Müllerian duct from posterior-to-anterior involution (male-type). Her interpretation is considered further in the following section.

Synthesis

Number and Nature of Embryonic Hormones

For the chick embryo, the most recent discussions of this problem are those of Wolff (42), Groenendijk-Huijbers (9), and Hamilton (13). Hamilton

Fig. 28.6 Summarized dose-response curves for in vitro female Müllerian ducts in the presence of estradiol-17β, testosterone, and androsterone. The measurement of the response is based upon the sensitivity of the swelling regions of ducts to the steroid hormones. Each dose-response curve represents day of culture plotted against percent of ducts swelling for the population tested. *A* and *B*. Represents the right and left female Müllerian ducts in response to different doses of estradiol-17β. *C* and *D*. Represents the right and left female Müllerian ducts in response to different doses of testosterone. *E*. and *F*. Represents the right and left female Müllerian ducts in response to different doses of androsterone.

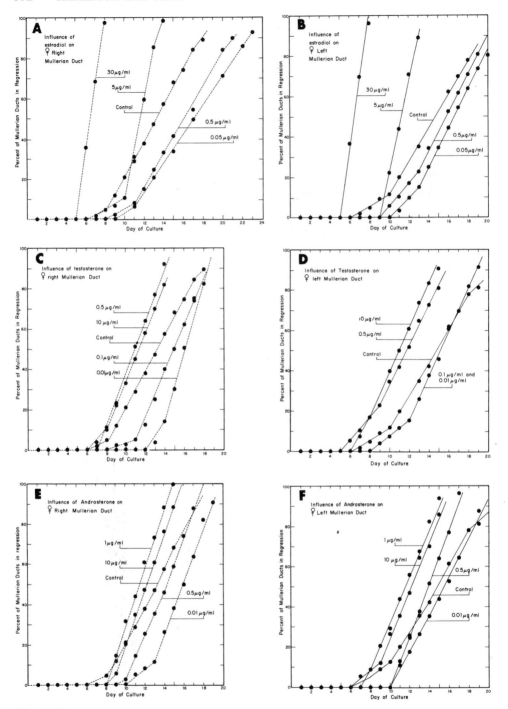

Fig. 28.7

compares the views of the three, and attempts to unify their ideas concerning the number of embryonic hormones in operation during the differentiation of the Müllerian ducts (Fig. 28.8). He suggests that there is at least one hormone, and perhaps two. Except as a stimulus for further discussion and experimentation, debates on such problems are often of little value. For example, when we know more of the biochemistry of differentiation, the concept of a "hormone" as a diffusing, biochemical unit may break down, with a variety of cellular and tissue metabolites being inducers, regulators, or modifiers to which other cells or tissues are adapted for responses at critical periods in their development or at onset of their specific functions (see below). For the present, at least, it seems obvious that at least one operationally defined factor or hormone is functioning in the differentiation of Müllerian ducts. This is the gonad hormone responsible for the involution of the male and right female ducts. Whether there is another, so-called feminizing hormone is uncertain.

Groenendijk-Huijbers (9, pp. 13–14), as noted, argues for the role of two hormones in the female embryo. She concludes that a "correct balance between masculinizing and feminizing hormones insures the phenotypic appearance of the female Müllerian ducts." She fails, however, to explain how the feminizing hormone could protect the left duct of the female embryo without also protecting the right one, which in fact does undergo involution. Our interpretation (13) at the present follows Wolff's view of one hormone in operation, with the addition that the asymmetrical nature of the differentiation of the female ducts is due to a differential in competence to hormone for the ducts – a differential thought to have a genetic basis.

As to the chemical nature of the embryonic hormone or hormones, little can be said with certainty, and it may well be that Hamilton (13) has already said too much on this problem, for which there is no direct experimental evidence. The weight of evidence from the early in vivo experiments argues for an androgenic steroid hormone. Hamilton (11, 13) has noted some seeming flaws in this idea, and has suggested that the embryonic hormone or hormones may be molecules larger than the steroid nucleus. Indeed, the results reported here in Table 28.1 show an influence of androgen on Müllerian ducts which is the *opposite* of the classical expectation (namely, stimulation, *not* inhibition of male ducts). It should be noted that (1) it can be argued that our results reflect pharmacological rather than physiological effects (in spite of the low dose range of hormones used in certain instances, Fig. 28.7*D*), and

Fig. 28.7 Summarized dose-response curves for in vitro female Müllerian ducts in the presence of varying doses of estradiol-17β, testosterone, and androsterone. The measurement of the response is based upon regression or deterioration in vitro. Each dose-response curve represents day of culture plotted against the percent of ducts in regression for the population tested. *A* and *B*. Representation of the right and left female Müllerian ducts in response to different doses of estradiol-17β. *C* and *D*. Representation of the right and left female Müllerian ducts in response to different doses of testosterone. *E* and *F*. Representation of the right and left female Müllerian ducts in response to different doses of androsterone.

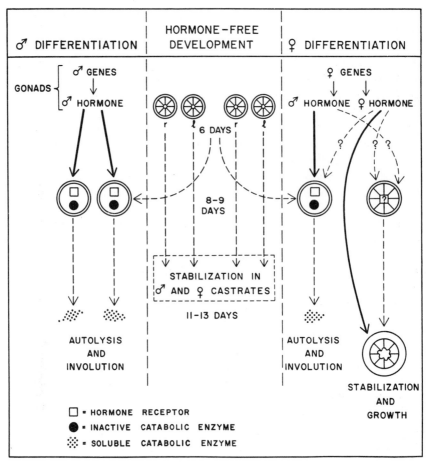

Fig. 28.8 Schematic diagram of factors that are thought to regulate sexual differentiation of Müllerian ducts (a modification of that used by Wolff, *Experientia* 9:121–133, 1958). To show (left) the hypothesized development of androgen-inhibited hormone receptors in the two male and right female ducts; (middle) the stabilization of the left female duct by means that seem independent of hormones; and (right) the rise and release of catabolic enzymes in the Müllerian ducts "destined to die." Arrows of broken lines denote for the female embryo possible actions of hormones which have yet to be proved or disproved by experimentation. Embryonic hormones (male, female) are defined on the basis of their operations, and thus their substantive properties are unknown. (From Hamilton, *Proc. XIII Intern. Ornith. Congr. Ithaca, N.Y.* pp. 1004–1040, 1963.)

that (2) Price and co-workers (27) have presented evidence for the presence of a hydroxysteroid dehydrogenase in the fetal guinea pig testis. This suggests that embryonic gonads have the potential, at least, to secrete androgenic steroids. The chemical nature of the embryonic hormone responsible for the differentiation of the Müllerian ducts remains unresolved.

The Mechanism of Embryonic Hormone Action

Concerning the means by which the endogenous hormone or exogenous injected steroid hormones might bring about the autolysis, necrosis, and associated involution of Müllerian ducts, Wolff (42) and his co-workers have argued that androgens activate or evoke a proteolytic enzyme, and that this in turn perpetrates an autolysis and necrosis of the ducts. We find two objections to this possibility: (1) It rests upon an in vitro demonstration that androgen brings about the regression of cultured Müllerian ducts. This is not the conclusion we draw from comparable, but (admittedly) not duplicative, in vitro experiments. Rather, we believe that the large doses of steroid hormone usually used in such experiments result in atypical or pharmacological-like inhibitory effects. This criticism is weakened, however, when it is recalled that in Wolff's experiments the Müllerian ducts, but not the Wolffian ducts, undergo autolysis when both sets of ducts are exposed together in vitro to androgen. (2) As previously noted (Hamilton, 12), tissues in autolysis characteristically release catabolic enzymes, and the demonstration of this in vitro by the workers cited may represent a result, not a cause, of deterioriation of Müllerian ducts. It has been suggested (Hamilton, 13) that, in view of the classic experiments in which estrogens and androgens are injected into embryos, Müllerian ducts may contain a cellular receptor site which is estrogen stimulated, but androgen inhibited (Fig. 28.8). Here the receptor site is thought to be genetic, or at least regulated by genetic factors. Morgan and Greb's finding (discussed above) provides some evidence for this. A possible flaw in this idea is why androsterone, unlike testosterone, has a feminizing influence on male embryos (Hamilton, 11). It has been noted (11) that the amount of androsterone necessary for induc-

tion of this in vivo response is much greater than for estradiol, and the speculation has been made that a small amount of estrogen is metabolically converted from androsterone by the embryo (13).

We will consider briefly what has recently been discovered concerning the primary actions of hormones at the cellular level, and how this may be related to the mode of action of the embryonic hormone or hormones considered in the present paper.

There are fashions in biological research, and one might even argue for cycles in fashions of research. For instance, it is a commonplace idea that hormones can influence other biological molecules (and thus cells and tissues) by influences on their function or formation. In the 1950s a lot was said and done with the idea that hormones influence pyridine nucleotide interactions and other enzyme-associated reactions (see, for example, papers cited by Hagerman and Villee, 10), and the possibility that hormones have a co-enzymatic action was tested. This was an emphasis on alteration of molecular function or activity; it seems not to have resulted in much progress. In the 1960s, however, following in the wake of molecular biologists and their inroads on the regulation of protein synthesis by nucleic acids, various workers began to test the role of hormones in stimulating RNA and protein synthesis in hormone-sensitive tissues. These studies, as is of course well known, were greatly aided (and simplified) by the availability of "good" inhibitors of RNA and protein synthesis (actinomycin-D and puromycin). Now it is fashionable to speak of the roles of hormones in the formation of other molecules (Moore and Hamilton, 23). As progress is made on the molecular basis of primary hormone action, we may see a return to the fashion of emphasizing effects on activity. After all, in any interaction between molecules some action must precede any subsequent change of events, whether they include changes in rate of formation or changes in activity.

Most invertebrate and vertebrate hormones have now been found to have their influence on specific tissues blocked by inhibition of RNA synthesis or of protein synthesis or of both (for example: thyroxine, Tata, 32; growth hormone, Korner, 20; estradiol, Ui and Mueller, 35; Hamilton, 14; testosterone, Liao and Williams-Ashman, 21; insulin, Wool, 44; adrenocorticotropin, Ferguson, 6; cortisone, Greengard et al., 8; and ecdysone, Karlson, 18). Even the plant hormone, indole acetic acid, is included in the list (Noodin and Thimann, 25). More could be cited, and for a review of the current dogma on the topic, the reader is referred to Williams-Ashman and co-workers (38).

We wish mainly to emphasize that if hormones exerting influences on stable and transitory tissues of the adult vertebrate do so through means of the DNA-dependent system regulating the cells' protein-synthesizing mechanism, then should we not expect comparable hormonal mechanisms (Fig. 28.9) to be in operation during embryogenesis? Perhaps the greatest contribution of the "central dogma" of molecular biology, as we know it today, will be to constantly remind us that through the DNA → RNA → protein synthetic axis there exists a means by which the multicellular organism can have its development with all its diverse differentiating processes regulated by genetic instructions, timed appropriately for their operations.

It is in this context that we emphasize the possibility — indeed probability — that the embryonic hormone responsible for the stabilization or death of Müllerian ducts does so through DNA-dependent means. Since the breakdown and atrophy of old organs, and their replacement by new and different ones is a normal aspect of the embryogenesis of the multicellular animal, it seems logical to expect given tissues or organs, such as the Müllerian ducts of the chick embryo, to have "built-in" through evolution a range of responses to hormones, including one

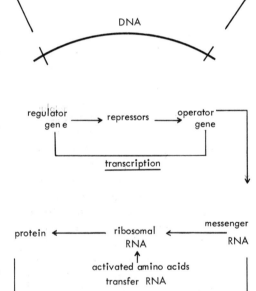

Fig. 28.9 Units and events involved in the regulation of protein synthesis by DNA and the three genera of RNA. At some point in this sequence, biological signals (hormones, inducers, and so on) are thought to interact in ways which lead to quantitative or qualitative changes, or both, in the production of RNA and proteins. (Modified from Tata, *Times Sci. Rev.* 54:3–6, 1964.)

which is death or involution. Viewed this way, the classic observation that Müllerian ducts of the chick live or die, depending upon slight molecular differences between the androgenic or estrogenic steroid nucleus when such hormones are injected into male embryos, seems not so dramatic. But the mechanisms for both the hormone action and the determination of tissue specificity are problems for the future. And when we replace the word hormone with such words as regulator, factor, chemical signal, modifier, or inductor substance (*sic*), the problem becomes essentially the same for all problems in organogenesis which involve stimulus-response systems.

Summary

Practically everything remains to be discovered concerning the biochemical and physiological mechanisms involved in sexual differentiation of Müllerian ducts. In this chapter we have (1) reviewed recent data pertaining to the topic and (2) speculated on the nature and number of embryonic hormones and a model through which both the action of the hormones and the specificity of tissue response can at least be viewed (if not explained) in keeping with recent progress in endocrine and protein synthesis research. The model derives primarily from the work of Jacob and Monod. Even though the model for control mechanisms of microorganisms will eventually have to be modified and changed in various ways to account for the mechanisms found in multicellular organisms (cf. Tata, 33) a preliminary expression (Fig. 28.9) is useful for experimental guidelines. Already there are signs of diversity of the basic units involved. For example, Widnell and Tata (37) have evidence for different RNA polymerase activities for rat liver nuclei. Hormones influencing growth and development of adult vertebrate tissues are being found to play a positive role in maintaining and regulating cellular levels of cytoplasmic ribosomes, the basic units of protein synthesis (Moore and Hamilton, 23; Tata, 33).

We believe much progress in the study of the role of hormones in embryogenesis will result from the application to embryonic tissues of the techniques used for the findings here cited for adult tissues. And there is no a priori reason not to expect some tissue-specific, hormone-influenced cellular control mechanisms to respond by metabolic preparation for death by autolysis and necrosis (involution of organs in embryogenesis), while others respond positively and anabolically in the course of their development. The embryonic origin of tissue specificity to hormones or other intercellular biological signals or inducers is, of course, another delightful problem for the future.

Appendix

The following technique was used for the in vitro culture of Müllerian ducts for the experiments described in this chapter.

PREPARATION OF CULTURE VESSELS. A modification of Chen's method (2) was used for in vitro culture of Müllerian ducts. Filter paper (W and R Balston, No. 1) was used in place of lens paper for support of the duct, and Pyrex culture tubes (1 cm in diameter, 7.5 cm in length, and 5 ml in volume; sealed by rubber stopper) were used for incubation. Filter paper was cut rectangularly to the size of 0.9 cm × 6.0 cm. It was prepared by washing in three changes of ether for 2 hours, followed by three changes of absolute alcohol for 2 hours and, finally, 20 changes of deionized water and 10 changes of glass-distilled water overnight. The paper was then dried in an oven (35° C) and sterilized by dry heat at 120° C for 1 hour.

THE MEDIUM.   Eagle's medium, enriched with 10 percent calf serum, 0.0005 percent phenol red, 100 units per ml of penicillin G potassium, and 83.33 units per ml streptomycin sulfate, was used in all experiments. The pH value was adjusted to 7.4. The total volume of medium in each tube was 2 ml. Steroid hormones (estradiol-17β, testosterone, or androsterone, dissolved in 1.0 percent ethyl alcohol) were added directly to the culture medium and mixed before use.

CULTURE OF THE MÜLLERIAN DUCTS.   Müllerian ducts were excised from embryos, and gently deposited by jeweler's forceps on the filter paper which had already been moistened in the medium. The filter paper, supported by the two edges of the culture tube, floated on top of the medium. Culture tubes which were sealed by rubber stoppers and placed at 15° angles on holding trays were then placed in incubators at 37° C and were checked daily thereafter for condition of the ducts.

MAINTENANCE OF CULTURES.   Mild tilting of each tube and its medium was done daily. This was for prevention of accumulation of metabolites in the filter paper. The enriched medium was replaced every 7 days for experiments running longer than a week.

References

1. Brachet, J., M. Decroly-Briers, and J. Hoyez, "Lysosomes and Embryonic Development," *Bull. Soc. Chem. Biol.* 40: 2039–2045 (1958).
2. Chen, J. M., "The Cultivation in Fluid Medium of Organized Liver, Pancreas and Other Tissues of Foetal Rats," *Exptl. Cell Res.* 7:518–529 (1954).
3. De Duve, C., "Lysosomes, a New Group of Cytoplasmic Particles," *Subcellular Particles*, T. Hayashi, ed. New York: Ronald, pp. 46–54 (1959).
4. Dodd, J. M., "Genetic and Environmental Aspects of Sex Determination in Cold-blooded Vertebrates," *Mem. Soc. Endocrinol.* 7:17–44 (1960).
5. Domm, L. V., "Recent Advances in Knowledge Concerning the Role of Hormones in the Sex Differentiation of Birds," *Recent Studies in Avian Biology*, A. Wolfson, ed. Urbana, Ill.: University of Illinois Press, pp. 146–167 (1955).
6. Ferguson, J., Jr., "Protein Synthesis and Adrenocorticotropin Responsiveness," *J. Biol. Chem.* 238:2754–2760 (1963).
7. Gallien, L., "Comparative Activity of Sexual Steroids and Genetic Constitu-

tion in Sexual Differentiation of Amphibian Embryos," *Gen. Comp. Endocrinol.* Suppl. 1:346–355 (1962).
8. Greengard, O., M. Smith, and G. Acs, "Relation of Cortisone and Synthesis of Ribonucleic Acid to Induced and Developmental Enzyme Formation," *J. Biol. Chem.* 238:1548–1551 (1963).
9. Groenendijk-Huijbers, M. M., "The Cranio-Caudal Regression of the Right Müllerian Duct in the Chick Embryo as Studied by Castration Experiments and Estrogen Treatment," *Anat. Record* 142: 9–20 (1962).
10. Hagerman, D. D., and G. A. Villee, "Metabolic Studies of the Mechanisms of Action of Estrogens," *Endocrinology of Reproduction*, C. W. Lloyd, ed. New York: Academic Press, pp. 317–334 (1957).
11. Hamilton, T. H., "Studies on the Physiology of Urogenital Differentiation in the Chick Embryo. I. Hormonal Control of Sexual Differentiation of Müllerian Ducts," *J. Exptl. Zool.* 146:265–274 (1961).
12. ———, "Sexual Differentiation of Mül-

lerian Ducts of the Chick Embryo," *Nature* 193:88–89 (1962).

13. ———, "Hormonal Control of Müllerian Duct Differentiation in the Chick Embryo," *Proc. XIII Intern. Ornith. Congr. Ithaca, N.Y.*, pp. 1004–1040 (1963).

14. ———, "Sequences of RNA and Protein Synthesis during Early Estrogen Action," *Proc. Natl. Acad. Sci. U.S.* 51:83–90 (1964).

15. Jost, A., "Le Contrôle Hormonale de la Différentiation du Sexe," *Biol. Rev.* 23:201–236 (1948).

16. ———, "Problems of Foetal Endocrinology: the Gonadal and Hypophyseal Hormones," *Recent Progr. Hormones Res.* 8:379–413 (1953).

17. ———, "Hormonal Influences in the Sex Development of Bird and Mammalian Embryos," *Mem. Soc. Endocrinol.* 7:49–62 (1960).

18. Karlson, P., "New Concepts on the Mode of Action of Hormones," *Perspectives Biol. Med.* 6:203–207 (1963).

19. Kondo, K., "Breed Differences in the Responses of the Male Reproductive Organs of Chick Embryos to Estrogen," *J. Exptl. Zool.* 141:1–14 (1959).

20. Korner, A., "Regulation of Rate of Synthesis of Messenger RNA by Growth Hormone," *Biochem. J.* 92:449–456 (1964).

21. Liao, S., and H. G. Williams-Ashman, "An Effect of Testosterone on Amino Acid Incorporation by Prostatic Ribonucleoprotein Particles," *Proc. Natl. Acad. Sci. U.S.* 48:1956–1964 (1962).

22. Lockshin, R., and C. M. Williams, "Programmed Cell Death. II Endocrine Potentiation of the Breakdown of Intersegmental Muscles of Silk Moths," *J. Insect Physiol.* 10:643–649 (1964).

23. Moore, R. J., and T. H. Hamilton, "Estrogen-induced Formation of Uterine Ribosomes," *Proc. Natl. Acad. Sci. U.S.* 52:439–446 (1964).

24. Morgan, W. C., and R. Greb, "Evolutionary Import of a Newly Discovered Mutation Affecting the Genital System in Poultry," *Proc. Intern. Congr. Genet. 10th Montreal*, pp. 193–194 (1958).

25. Noodin, and K. Thimann, "Evidence for a Requirement for Protein Synthesis for Auxin-induced Cell Enlargement," *Proc. Natl. Acad. Sci. U.S.* 50:194–199 (1963).

26. Pfleger, D., "Etude de l'Influence des Hormones Sexuelles sur l'Activité Envmatique des Autolysats de Canaux de Müller chez l'Embryo de Poulet," *Compt. Rend. Soc. Biol.* 146:932–935 (1952).

27. Price, D., E. Ortiz, and H. W. Deane, "The Presence of Hydroxysteroid Dehydrogenase in Foetal Guinea Pig Testes and Adrenal Glands," *Am. Zool.* 4:232 (1964).

28. ———, and R. Pannabecker, "Comparative Responsiveness of Homologous Sex Ducts and Accessory Glands of Fetal Rats in Culture," *Arch. Anat. Microscop. Morphol. Exptl.* 48:223–243 (1959).

29. Raynaud, M., "Effets d'un Mélange de Dipropionate d'Oestradiol et de Propionate de Testostérone sur la Différenciation Sexuelle de l'Embryon Male du Poulet," *Compt. Rend. Acad. Sci.* 211:489–492 (1940).

30. Scheib-Pfleger, D., and R. Wattiaux, "Étude des Hydrolases Acides des Conadex de Müller d'Embryos de Poulet. I. Activités Total et Solubles des Canaux d'Embryos de 8 à 10 Jours d'Incubation," *Develop. Biol.* 5:205–217 (1962).

31. Stoll, R., "Sur la Différenciation Sexuelle de l'Embryo de Poulet," *La Différenciation Sexuelle chez les Vertébrés.* Paris: Masson et Cie, pp. 233–243 (1951).

32. Tata, J., "Inhibition of the Biological Action of Thyroid Hormones by Actinomycin-D and Puromycin," *Nature* 4873:1167–1168 (1963).

33. ———, "Hormonal Control of Growth and Development," *Times Sci. Rev.* 54:3–6 (1964).

34. Teng, C., and T. H. Hamilton, unpublished observations (1965).

35. Ui, H., and J. Mueller, "The Role of RNA Synthesis in Early Estrogen Action," *Proc. Natl. Acad. Sci. U.S.* 50:256–259 (1963).

36. Wells, L. J., "Hormones and Sexual Differentiation in Placental Mammals," *La Différenciation Sexuelle chez les Vertébrés.* Paris: Masson et Cie, pp. 317–335 (1951).

37. Widnell, C., and J. Tata, "Evidence for Two DNA-dependent RNA Polymerase Activities in Isolated Rat-liver Nuclei," *Biochem. Biophys. Acta* 87:531–533 (1964).

38. Williams-Ashman, H. G., S. Liao, R. L. Hancock, L. Jurkowitz, and D. A. Silverman, "Testicular Hormones and the Synthesis of Ribonucleic Acid and Proteins in the Prostate Gland," *Recent Prog. Hormone Res.* 20:247–292 (1964).

39. Willier, B. H., "The Embryonic Development of Sex," *Sex and Internal Secretions*, E. Allen, C. Danforth, E. Doisy, eds. Baltimore: Williams & Wilkins, pp. 64–144 (1939).

40. Witschi, E., "Modifications of the Development of Sex in Lower Vertebrates and Mammals," *Sex and Internal Secretions*, E. Allen, C. Danforth, E. Doisy, eds. Baltimore: Williams & Wilkins, pp. 145–226 (1939).

41. Wolff, Et., "Le Determinisme de l'Atrophie d'un Organe Rudimentaire: le Canaux de Müller des Embryons Mâles de'Oiseaux," *Experientia* 9:121–133 (1958).

42. ———, "Endocrine Function of the Gonad in Developing Vertebrates," *Comparative Endocrinology*, A. Gorbman, ed. New York: Wiley, pp. 568–573 (1959).

43. ———, Y. Lutz-Ostertag, and K. Haffen, "Sur la Régression et la Nécrose *in vitro* des Canaux de Müller de l'Embryon de Poulet rons l'Effet de Substances Hormonales," *Compt. Rend. Soc. Biol.* 146:1793–1795 (1952).

44. Wool, I. G., "Effect of Insulin on Nucleic Acid Synthesis in Isolated Rat Diaphragm," *Biochem. Biophys. Acta* 68: 28–33 (1963).

29

Hormonal Control of Sex Differentiation in Invertebrates

HELENE CHARNIAUX-COTTON

Laboratoire de Genetique Evolutive et de Biometrie
Gif-sur-Yvette, (S. et O.) France

The endocrinology of invertebrates, once considered as nonexistent, has developed to a surprising extent during the past 40 years and now occupies a large part of the surveys on comparative endocrinology (see, for example, Gorbman and Bern, 54). However, until about 10 years ago, the invertebrates were considered as lacking in sexual hormones. This opinion was based on two lines of evidence. On the one hand, in insects (the only group of bisexual invertebrates on which surgical castration has been performed) castrated larvae give rise to adults with normal secondary sexual characters, even when castrated at a very early stage. On the other hand, the existence among insects of gynandromorphs and of sexual mosaics was considered as conclusive evidence against the circulation of sexual hormones in the blood.

However, parasitic sex reversal in insects and crustaceans indicated that sexual characters can be influenced by internal conditions. We may recall that the male or female *Andrena*, when invaded by *Stylops*, acquires an intersexual appearance (Perez, 94). Male crabs, parasitized by *Sacculina*, become feminized (Giard, 51). Reinhard (97), in an exhaustive article on parasitic castration in crustaceans, showed that this phenomenon was very differently interpreted by different authors. Finally, Goldschmidt's theory (53), which had a great impact, can be transcribed in terms of hormones, since that author thought that sexual genes act through the production of male- or female-determining substances.

The first experimental proof of the existence of a sexual hormone in an invertebrate was given in an amphipod crustacean, *Orchestia gammarella*, with evidence of the endocrine function of the ovary (Charniaux, 23) and the discovery of a new gland, the androgenic gland (A.G.) (Charniaux-Cotton, 24). The very recent experimental conversion of sex by Naisse (90, 91) in a beetle, *Lampyris noctiluca*, showed that insects also possess an endocrine control of sexual differentiation. Finally, evidence that gametogenesis is controlled by a masculinizing substance in *Hydra* allows the conclusion that hormonal control of sexual differentiation is probably general in invertebrates.

In this article we are concerned only with endocrine control of sexual differentiation, not of reproduction, in Crustacea Malacostraca, insects, and *Hydra*.

Crustacea Malacostraca

In 1952 I succeeded in performing the surgical castration of the male and female amphipod *Orchestia gammarella* (Charniaux, 23). In castrated females the ovigerous hairs disappeared. After the implantation of an ovary into a castrated female, the ovigerous hairs reappeared at the time of vitellogenesis. These experiments furnished the first experimental proof of the existence of hormonal control of the gonads on an external sexual character in a bisexual invertebrate.

The implantation of testes into a female was without effect. However, an ovary implanted into a male was transformed into a testis. The results were the same when the male was castrated (Charniaux-Cotton, 24). This led me to examine the terminal region of the vasa deferentia which I had left in place in the castrated males. An organ of glandular appearance was found to be attached to each of them. A series of experiments brought proof that these organs controlled all the male differentiation. I called them "androgenic glands" (Charniaux-Cotton, 26). They had never before been described.

Since then, A.G. have been observed in all suborders of the higher crustaceans, except for the Syncarida which have not yet been examined. In all the orders studied, except for certain isopods, the A.G. is attached to the subterminal region of the vas deferens, and is of the holocrine type. Up to now, histological studies have not yielded results of special interest (Charniaux-Cotton, 28, 30, 31, 35, 36; Juchault, 62; Meusy, 83). A descriptive monograph of the A.G. is now available (Charniaux-Cotton, Zerbib, and Meusy, 45). The experimental studies were performed with Talitridae and isopods. In decapods, except for proterandric hermaphrodites, transplantation and removal of A.G. have given so far only partial results which we shall not report here. Demeusy (47, 48, 49) observed the presence of the A.G. in very young male *Carcinus maenas*, and an inhibitory action of the eyestalks on growth of these glands.

Amphipod Talitridae

Sexual Dimorphism of *Orchestia gammarella*

Sexual dimorphism of *Orchestia gammarella* is very pronounced. As in other Malacostraca, the external sex characters can be divided into two groups: (1) those exhibiting presence of an organ in only one sex, for example, oostegites in the females, genital apophyses in the male; and (2) those exhibiting difference of form from one sex to another of an organ or sexual variant. This is the case with the first and second thoracic legs (gnathopods) and the last legs. In the male the second gnathopods form two powerful claws and the last legs are enlarged.

The gonads are two tubes situated

under the pericardial septum on both sides of the digestive tube and stretching from the 2nd to the 7th thoracic segment (Fig. 29.1). They are formed from the same anlage in both sexes and the structure is very similar from one sex to the other. The female genital pores are situated on the 5th sternite, male apertures on the sternite of the 7th thoracic segment.

O. gammarella molts and grows all its life. Sexual differentiation occurs progressively. Differentiation of the gonads is completed before that of the external sex characters (Fig. 29.2); the latter continue differentiating during the entire life of the male. One cannot speak of puberty in *O. gammarella*, only of genital maturity.

SEXUALLY UNDIFFERENTIATED PHASE. At hatching, the young has specific form but shows no sexual differentiation. The gonad is a strand of mesodermal cells extending from the 2nd to the 7th thoracic segment (Fig. 29.3A). It contains gonia in its anterior region. They are anlagen of the oviduct and spermiduct. The anlage of the spermiduct is the posterior region of the mesodermal strand; it ends just at the level of the A.G. All individuals have precursor cells for this gland, connected with the end of the vas deferens (Charniaux-Cotton, 32). The differentiation of the genital apparatus starts during the 2nd molt. On the other hand, the external morphology remains the same in all individuals until the 5th molt, as is shown by the biometric study of the growth of sexual variants (Charniaux-Cotton, 29). At the 5th molt, the genital papilla appear in the male, and oostegites in the female.

MALE DIFFERENTIATION. The first cells of the A.G. develop into organs during the 2nd intermolt. Then, the vasa deferentia thicken and the gonia remain blocked in the anterior region. Afterward, spermatogenesis starts and the vasa deferentia acquire a lumen (Fig. 29.3B). Their posterior extremities grow and induce genital papillae, which appear at the 5th molt. Spermatozoa are present at the next intermolt. Then, the vas deferens divides into a seminal vesicle and an ejaculatory duct. The latter has a muscular sheath on its exterior and an internal epithelium which secretes mucopolysaccharides (Zerbib, 107). The A.G. is then completely separated from the spermiduct, and well defined. At the 7th molt, the genital apparatus has acquired its final structure.

The male growth of the sexual variants (Charniaux-Cotton, 29, 38) starts after the 5th molt (the molt at which the genital papillae appear), that is, when the differentiation of the genital apparatus is almost completed. The relative growth of the second male gnathopod is divided into two phases of allometric growth separated by an important discontinuity. During this discontinuity, the claw of the gnathopod acquires its definite (adult) form. The male growth of the last leg starts after the achievement of the adult form of the claw. The male cannot copulate unless he has an adult claw which helps him hold the female – almost four intermolts after genital maturity.

The testis is a tube surrounded by a thin connective sheath, which has an identical structure from one end to the other (Charniaux-Cotton, 29; Meusy, 82, 84, 85). A germinative zone, situated against the connective sheath, runs from one end of the gonad to the other. It is formed by a thread of mesodermal cells enclosing primary gonia. The remaining part of the gonadal tube is occupied by two or three longitudinal regions superimposed on each

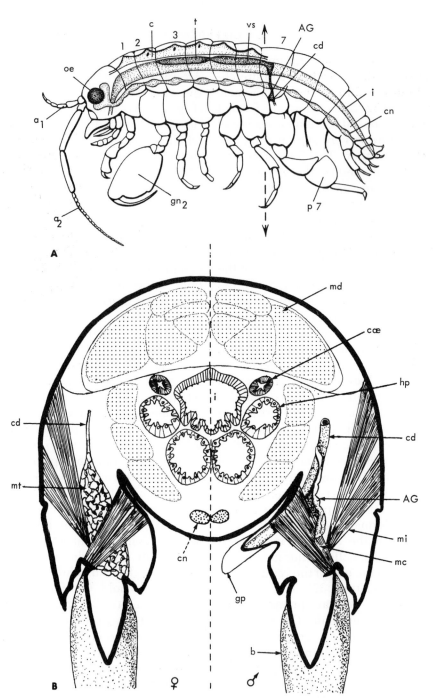

Fig. 29.1 Genital apparatus and androgenic gland of *Orchestia gammarella*. *A.* Lateral view showing relation of genital apparatus to general anatomy. *B.* Transverse section through the last thoracic segment at the level indicated in *A* by arrows and seen from the anterior end. a₁, a₂, antennae; AG, androgenic gland; b, basipodite of the 7th pereiopod; c, heart; cae, intestinal cecum; cd, vas deferens; cn, ventral nerve cord; gp, genital papilla; gn₂, 2nd gnathopod; hp, hepatopancreas; i, intestine; mc, muscles of the coxopodite; md, dorsal muscles; mi, muscles for the insertion of the 7th pereiopod; mt, mesenchymatic tissue with the primordial cells of the AG; oe, eye; p₇, 7th pereiopod; t, testis; vs, seminal vesicle. (From Charniaux-Cotton, pp. 411–447 in *The Physiology of Crustacea*, T. H. Waterman, ed. Academic Press, 1960.)

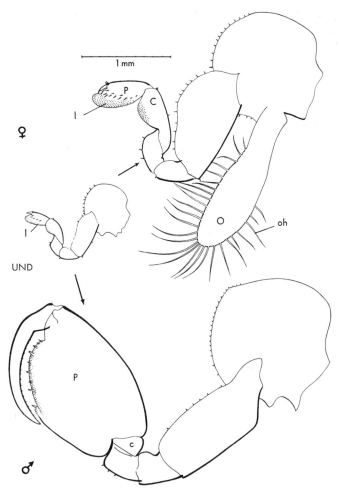

Fig. 29.2 *Orchestia gammarella.* Second gnathopod of a sexually undifferentiated animal, und; a mature female (top) and a mature male (bottom). C, carpopodite; I, lobe of the propodite; O, oostegite; oh, ovigerous hair; P, propodite. (From Charniaux-Cotton, pp. 411–447 in *The Physiology of Crustacea,* T. H. Waterman, ed. Academic Press, 1960.)

other and formed by germinal cells at the same stage of spermatogenesis. Each region is surrounded by a follicle. Cross sections are therefore identical from one end of the gonad to the other (Fig. 29.4).

The primary gonia undergo mitoses during the entire life span of the male. The gonia periodically leave the germinative zone and become secondary gonia. The departure of the gonia is accompanied by increasing synthesis of

nuclear RNA, as has been shown histochemically and by injection of tritiated uridine (Meusy, 82, 86). The gonia go into mitosis and a follicle is constituted around them. They synchronously start meiosis while new spermatogonia leave the germinative zone. At time of diakinesis, follicle cells grow and their nuclei swell, probably by polyploidization. They secrete a mucus which coats the spermatozoa.

The duration of spermatogenesis has

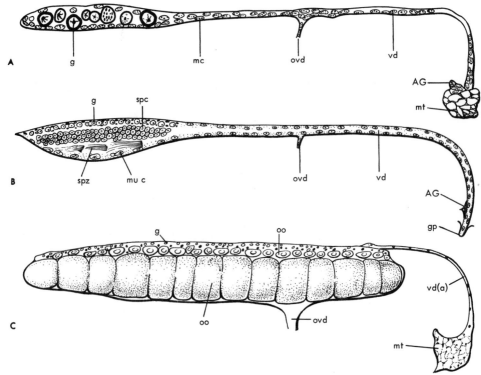

Fig. 29.3 Organogenesis of the genital apparatus in *Orchestia gammarella*. A. Undifferentiated stage. B. Young male at the 6th molt; the seminal vesicle is not differentiated. C. Female in vitellogenesis. AG, androgenic gland; g, gonia; gp, genital papillae; mc, mesodermic cell; mt, mesenchymatic tissue with the primordial cells of the AG; mu c, mucus cell; oo, oocyte; ovd, oviduct; spc, spermatocyte; spz, spermatozoa; vd, vas deferens; vd(a), anlage of the vas deferens. (Redrawn from Charniaux-Cotton, *Bull. Soc. Zool. France* 84:105–115, 1959, and from Zerbib, *Bull. Biol. France Belg.* 157:391–408, 1964.)

been determined by radioautography (Meusy, 85). The injection of thymidine labeled with tritium allowed us to determine that 10 days are the minimum time to obtain labeled spermatids. Since the incorporation of thymidine stops at the preleptotene stage, these 10 days are the duration of a testicular cycle (from phase 5 to phase 4, Fig. 29.5). The period of spermatogenesis, being about two testicular cycles, lasts, therefore, about 20 days.

FEMALE DIFFERENTIATION. In the female the rudiments of the vas deferens and the A.G. do not develop and are not modified during the life of the animal (Fig. 29.3C). During the 2nd intermolt, gonia undergo mitosis and migrate in the mesodermal strand as far as the 6th thoracic segment. It is quite probable that this migration occurs because, contrary to the male spermiduct, the female spermiduct does not show cell multiplication. Oogenesis soon takes place in all gonads. Each oocyte is surrounded by a follicle. The posterior end of the ovary loses its continuity with the anlage of the spermiduct (which explains why testes of masculinized females cannot evacuate their spermatozoa). At the 5th molt, ovary and oviduct are completely

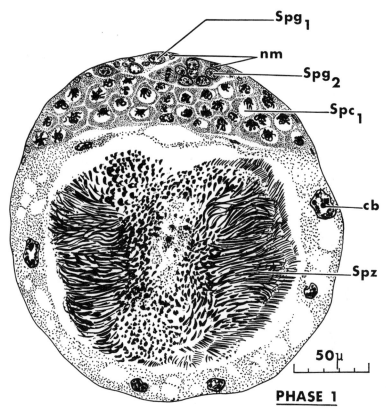

PHASE 1

Fig. 29.4 Testis of *Orchestia gammarella* in phase 1 (see Fig. 29.5), transverse section. cb, mucus cell; nm, mesodermal cell; Spc_1, spermatocyte; Spg_1, primary spermatogonia (in germinative zone); Spg_2, secondary spermatogonium; Spz, spermatozoa. (From Meusy, *Bull. Soc. Zool.* 88:197, 1963.)

differentiated. When the oocytes reach a diameter of 200 μ, their growth stops. The second growth phase, or vitellogenesis, does not start until the 9th or 10th molt, and is controlled by neurosecretion.

At the 5th molt, the oostegites appear on the coxopodites of the 2nd, 3rd, 4th, and 5th pereiopods. These oostegites grow at every molt. The oostegites of young females, and those of mature females in period of sexual repose, are bordered by juvenile hairs (0.02 mm long). During the reproductive season the oostegites bear, instead, ovigerous hairs (0.8 mm long). These ovigerous hairs are temporary

secondary sex characters associated with the incubation of embryos.

The growth of sexual variants in the female is similar to the growth of sexual variants during the undifferentiated phase; the second gnathopods of a female are similar to those at hatching, except for the presence of an oostegite.

The ovaries have a structure similar to that of testes (Fig. 29.6). When gonia leave the germinative zone, they do not effect mitoses but carry out oogenesis. During the reproductive season at the beginning of each intermolt the oocytes which have reached the size of 200 μ begin vitellogenesis; egg laying occurs after the next molt

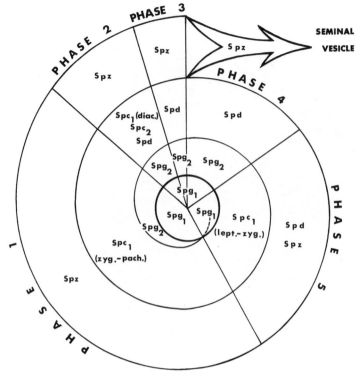

Fig. 29.5 Functional cycle of the testes of *Orchestia gammarella*. The five phases of the cycle are represented by sectors whose angle is proportional to duration of the phase. The circle in the center represents the germinative zone. Lettering as for Fig. 29.4. Spd, spermatids; lept, leptotene stage; pach., pachytene stage; zyg., zygotene stage. (From Meusy, *Bull. Soc. Zool.* 88:197, 1963.)

(Charniaux-Cotton, 29; Campbell-Parmentier, 19).

Hormonal Control of Sex Differentiation

CONTROL OF MALE DIFFERENTIATION BY ANDROGENIC HORMONE. The androgenic glands are the exclusive source of a hormone responsible for the differentiation of all male primary and secondary sex characters. This was established by experiments of implantation and removal of these glands. The testes are without action on sex differentiation (Charniaux-Cotton, 25, 26, 27, 29, 40).

Gland location and structure. The androgenic gland is attached to the subterminal region of the vas deferens (Fig. 29.1). It is separated from the muscular sheath of the vas deferens by connective tissue and has no communication with it. The gland is made up of cellular strands folded upon themselves (see Fig. 29.14A). The nuclei, about 7 or 8 μ in diameter, are peripheral in location. In newly formed parts the cells are linearly arranged. Mitoses are seen. Later the cells increase in size, becoming vacuolated. Finally, the nuclei become pycnotic and the cells degenerate.

Implantation of androgenic gland in a female. Transplantation of testis or of a portion of the vas deferens without androgenic gland into a female *O.*

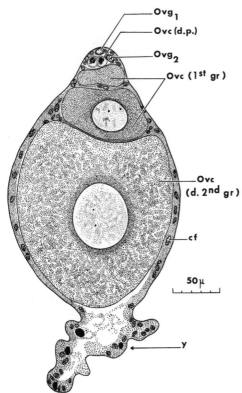

Labels on figure: Ovg₁ — Ovg_1; Ovc (d.p.); Ovg_2; Ovc (1st gr); Ovc (d. 2nd gr); cf; 50μ; y

Fig. 29.6 Transverse section of an ovary of *Orchestia gammarella*, at the beginning of yolk deposition. cf, follicular cell; Ovg_1, primary oogonium (in germinative zone); Ovg_2, secondary oogonium; Ovc (d.p.), oocyte at the beginning of the prophase; Ovc (1st gr), oocyte in the first growth; Ovc (d. 2nd gr), oocyte at the beginning of yolk deposition; y, follicle after egg discharge. (From Meusy, *Bull. Soc. Zool.* 88:197, 1963.)

gammarella does not affect the host. In contrast, implantation of the A.G. into both immature and mature females brings about masculinization of the primary and secondary sex characters of the hosts. If the female is ovariectomized before implantation, masculinization of the vas deferens (Zerbib, 107) and of the external sex characters still takes place, indicating that the A.G. acts directly on the secondary sex characters and not through

the gonad. I did not notice any difference between masculinization of a young female and of a female which had already laid eggs.

Masculinization of the ovaries. Masculinization of the female starts with the genital apparatus. If the female is in the reproductive period, the onset of the next vitellogenesis is inhibited.

Reversal of the ovaries into testes begins approximately 3 weeks after implantation of A.G. Some gonia, after leaving the germinative zone, undergo mitosis and soon form spermatocyte clusters (Fig. 29.7A). This process shows that the androgenic hormone (A.H.) acts at the level of the gonia. When a gonium leaves the germinative zone, it is determined as a spermatogonium or an oogonium according to whether it has received A.H. or not. The presence of many abnormal germ cells in an ovary early in reversal is probably due to a partial action of A.H.

It is the germ cells which control the differentiation of somatic cells of the gonad, not the other way around (Charniaux-Cotton, 38). In fact, in the region of spermatid clusters, the follicular cells are transformed into cells that secrete mucus (Fig. 29.7B). Degenerating oocytes are phagocytized by their follicular cells. Moreover, follicles are not necessary for spermatogenesis; the first cluster of spermatocytes undergo meiosis synchronously without follicles (Fig. 29.8).

About 2 or 3 months after the graft of an A.G., the female gonad has the structure of a normal testis. However, sperm cannot be released, and accumulate in the gonad, because the vas deferens is nonfunctional.

Masculinization of the vas deferens. The cells of the anlage of the vas de-

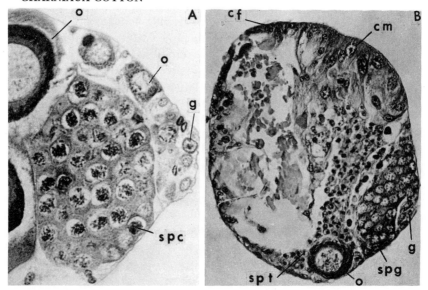

Fig. 29.7 Two stages in the masculinization of the ovary of *Orchestia gammarella* following the grafting of an androgenic gland. *A*. The first generation of male germinal cells is in meiotic prophase. *B*. The ovary has almost acquired testicular structure; some follicular cells are changing into mucus cells (top), while others (left) are phagocytizing the yolk debris. Note the absence of any equivalent of a cortex and a medulla; the gonia lie in the same germinative zone. cf, follicular cells; cm, mucus cells; g, gonia in the germinative zone; o, oocyte; spc, spermatocyte; spg, secondary spermatogonium; spt, spermatid. (From Charniaux-Cotton and Kleinholz, in *The Hormones*, G. Pincus, K. V. Thimann, eds., Academic Press, 1963.)

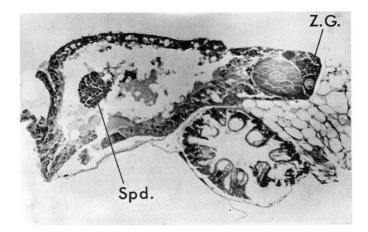

Fig. 29.8 Transverse section of an ovary of a mature female *Orchestia gammarella* masculinized by implantation of an androgenic gland. The spermatids, Spd., occupy the region of a degenerating oocyte and are without follicle. Below the ovary is a section of hepato-pancreas. Z. G., germinative zone.

ferens multiply and secrete mucus under the influence of A.H. The posterior end of this anlage grows, and the genital papilla appears. The time of this appearance varies, being more precocious in young females. If the female is mature at the time of implantation, organogenesis of spermiducts stops. If the female is young, the vas deferens acquires a lumen and a muscular sheath, but this lumen is not in continuity with the gonad. By implanting A.G. in the female at the time of the appearance of oostegites (5th molt), this continuity is retained. However, the lumen of the spermiduct is never continuous. Thus, masculinized females which have male sexual behavior and mate with normal females cannot inseminate them.

Nevertheless, spermatozoa that are formed by such testes are fertile because eggs can be artificially fertilized by sperm from masculinized females. In fact, 33 males and 33 females have been obtained by this procedure. The female sex thus appears to be heterogametic (Charniaux-Cotton, 33; Charniaux-Cotton and Ginsburger-Vogel, unpublished observations).

Response of androgenic gland anlage. The initial cells of the A.G. cannot be distinguished in mesenchyme of a normal female (Fig. 29.3C). But in a masculinized female, these cells respond to A.H. just like the cells of the rudiment of the spermiducts. They multiply and secrete mucus in the same fashion (Charniaux-Cotton, 40). They arrange themselves more or less into a hollow organ. When the graft is made into a young female, before the 3rd or 4th molt — that is, before external female differentiation — the anlage of the A.G. forms a small canal, so that the extremity of

the vas deferens becomes bifurcated. The anlage from a masculinized female implanted into a normal female has no effect. Therefore, a masculinized female does not acquire functional A.G. We will see, however, that masculinized females of terrestrial isopods do acquire functional A.G.

Masculinization of external sexual characters. After an androgenic gland is transplanted, the appendages of the female progressively acquire the male form, their development being similar to that in a normal male. The gnathopods start to be masculinized after the beginning of masculinization of ovaries. At the second postoperative molt (approximately 6 weeks after implantation) the propodite of the second gnathopod is bigger than that of a normal female. It acquires the adult male form after two or three intermolts.

Complete removal of androgenic gland. Complete removal of the androgenic glands indicates that these glands are the exclusive source of the male hormone. Differentiation of the external sex characters ceases. If the gnathopod is amputated, it regenerates in undifferentiated form. In the testis, spermatogenesis decreases and then stops. Some oocytes appear (Charniaux-Cotton, 42). An ovary implanted into a male deprived of its A.G. survives without modification, whereas in a normal male it is transformed into a testis. The presence or absence of the testes does not modify these results, again demonstrating that the testes are without hormonal activity.

CONTROL OF EXTERNAL FEMALE CHARACTERS BY OVARIAN HORMONES

Temporary characters. Total ovariectomy of a female during the reproductive period is always followed by complete replacement of the ovigerous hairs by juvenile hairs at the first or second postoperative ecdysis.

The converse experiment, implanting an ovary or a portion of one into a castrated female, has also been carried out. When yolk deposition in a series of oocytes takes place in the implanted ovary, the oostegites bear ovigerous hairs at the following molt. Castration carried out at different stages of the intermolt cycle shows that liberation of the hormone takes place during the D_0 stage (Charniaux-Cotton, 29).

Basically, the genesis of oostegite marginal hairs is identical with that of hairs in other locations. When the molting hormone acts alone, juvenile hairs are formed. When the effect of the ovarian factor is added to that of molting hormone, the trichogenic matrices are stretched out greatly and so form ovigerous hairs. If the quantity of hormone does not attain a certain threshold (as after a partial ovariectomy, when only two or three oocytes in the remaining portion of the ovary deposit yolk), the elongation of the matrices is only partial and, as a result, the length of the hairs is intermediate.

The fact that any portion of the ovary in vitellogenesis is capable of inducing the formation of ovigerous hairs suggests that the source of hormone concerned is well distributed throughout the gonad. The follicular cells would be the most likely source of the hormone responsible for the formation of the longer hairs since they are the only components of the ovary outside of the germ cells.

Permanent characters. The oostegites persist in a castrated female; moreover, when a pereiopod is amputated, it regenerates with its oostegite. But, if an ovary from an immature or maturing female is implanted into a male whose A.G. have been removed, oostegites appear at the first or second postoperative ecdysis. It should be noted that oostegites never appear in males which have only been deprived of their A.G. Any portion of the ovary is able to induce oostegites. The source of the hormone controlling the permanent characters is probably the young follicles (Charniaux-Cotton, 26).

The appendages of a normal female have the same form as those of a castrated female, or an undifferentiated individual (Fig. 29.2). Thus the growth of the appendages apparently occurs without intervention of a hormone in the female. However, after the graft of an ovary into a male deprived of its A.G., the propodite of the 2nd gnathopod acquires a female lobe. This suggests that the ovarian hormone is able to induce the female form of the gnathopod, although in the normal female this induction is unnecessary because the gnathopod form is similar to the undifferentiated gnathopod.

OVARIAN   SELF-DIFFERENTIATION. The ovarian hormones have never shown any action on the germ cells of a testis. Neither graft of an ovary into a male of *O. gammarella* deprived of its A.G. nor graft of a testis into a female has an effect. Ovarian differentiation is a spontaneous process which occurs in the absence of A.H.; it is a self-differentiation.

Experimental proof of this statement has not been achieved with *O. gammarella*. As a matter of fact, after complete removal of the A.G., spermatogenesis slows down. Six months later, oocytes appear in some parts of the testis. Very few operated animals survive beyond this period.

It has not yet been possible to remove the A.G. before testis differentiation takes place because of the smallness of these animals. Therefore we tried with another species of *Orchestia*, *O. montagui*. In this species, as in almost all Talitridae, the testes possess an anterior ovarian region (Fig. 29.9). This region is highly developed in the winter, when the A.G. are small; it disappears completely in the summer, when the A.G. become bigger. The gonads possess only one germinative zone. Spermatogenesis extends more or less forward, according to the titer of hormone. It seemed logical, then, to expect that in the absence of male hormone the posterior gonia would give rise to oocytes. This hypothesis was confirmed by removal of the A.G. One month after removal, the testes were completely transformed into ovaries; all the gonia gave rise to oocytes (Fig. 29.9). This result is the more remarkable because the diffuse structure of the

apical regions of the A.G. did not permit their complete removal.

Thus, in two species of the same genus the response of the gonia to male hormone is different: in *O. gammarella* the gonia are able to maintain spermatogenesis for a long time after the disappearance of male hormone, while the gonia of *O. montagui* need a constant titer of hormone. The in vitro culture of a testis of *Talitrus saltator* without oocytes shows also that in the absence of A.G. oocytes appear in the gonad (Berreur-Bonnenfant, 11, 12).

Ovarian self-differentiation may thus be reduced to the fact that before the gonia have received any ovarian hormone, they develop toward oogenesis. The oocytes then determine follicular structure, that is, ovarian structure.

NORMAL SEXUAL ORGANOGENESIS. The experimental results reported in the preceding section are summarized

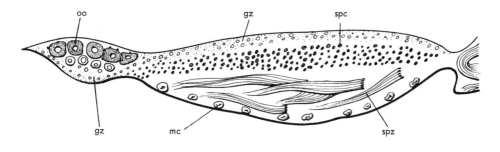

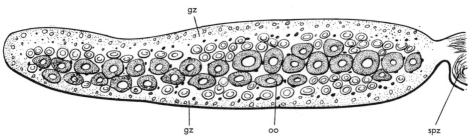

Fig. 29.9 Schematic view of the testis of *Orchestia montagui*. Top: Normal male in winter. Bottom: Male deprived of its androgenic glands. gz, germinative zone; mc, mucus cell; oo, oocyte; spc, spermatoycyte; spz, spermatozoa.

in Figure 29.10. In the male, the A.G. anlage develops, and its secreted hormone controls all male differentiation. Experiments (Charniaux-Cotton, 38) have shown further that this hormone has an inhibitory action on external female characters; in fact, after amputation of a thoracic leg in a normal or castrated female *Orchestia*, the leg regenerates with an oostegite, but in masculinized females the oostegite does not regenerate (Charniaux-Cotton, 38). Further, it is interesting to note that in certain intersexes of *Orchestia*, genetic mutations can transform these inhibitory properties of the A.G. into inductive properties (Charniaux-Cotton, 39). Finally, A.H. inhibits the onset of vitellogenesis; this is the first effect after a gland is grafted into a female (Charniaux-Cotton, 29). In species where testes have an ovarian portion, these inhibitory effects constitute double assurance for the male sex;

males of such species have no external female characters, and oocytes cannot mature.

In the female, the primordium of A.G. does not develop. This permits ovarian differentiation. The ovaries are endocrine, and control the secondary female characters.

In organogenesis of the normal male gonad, the A.H. acts as an inductor by contact. Indeed, it is in direct contact with the spermiduct anlage (Fig. 29.3). Androgenic hormone probably progresses along the spermiduct, and is responsible for the morphology of the genital male apparatus by blocking the gonia in the anterior region. The hormone does not induce differentiation of a special region for spermatogenesis. It is the germinal cells which control the disposition of somatic cells around them.

In *O. gammarella*, spermatogenesis occurs along the entire length of the

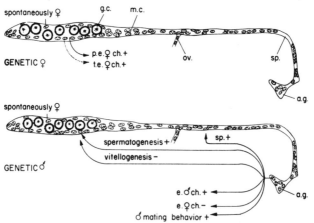

Fig. 29.10 Diagram of endocrine control of sex differentiation in Talitridae. The arrows indicate the stimulating (+) or inhibiting (−) effects of ovarian and androgenic hormones; one of two ovarian hormones is secreted only during vitellogenesis (dashed arrow). a.g., androgenic gland (the androgenic gland does not develop in the female); e. ♀ ch., external female characters, p.e. ♀ ch., permanent external female characters; t.e. ♀ ch., temporary external female characters; e. ♂ ch., external male characters; g.c., germ cell; mc., mesodermal cells; ov., oviduct; sp., sperm duct. (From Charniaux-Cotton, pp. 135–198 in *The Hormones,* G. Pincus and K. V. Thimann, eds. Academic Press, 1963.)

gonad. In contrast, in *O. mediterranea* (Charniaux-Cotton, 32) and *O. cavimana* (Graf, 55), oogenesis takes place at first in the gonad because the amount of male hormone is not sufficient. Spermatogenesis begins during the 3rd intermolt in the posterior region. Hence, an ovarian anterior region is formed. The gradient of responsiveness of the germinative zone to A.H. which exists throughout the life of *Orchestia* has not been explained.

Only after the 5th molt do sexual variants of *O. gammarella* begin their male growth, that is, when genital organogenesis is almost finished and after the A.G. has separated from the spermiduct. It is probable that male hormone was not present in the blood before that time, since if an A.G. is implanted into a young male whose gnathopods are not yet differentiated, the male precociously acquires claws of the adult form (Charniaux-Cotton, 38).

Endocrinology and Genetics of Sex

OVARIAN HORMONE SECRETION BY A TESTIS CONVERTED INTO AN OVARY. We have seen that in the absence of A.H. a testis can be converted into an ovary. On the other hand, an ovary grafted into a male deprived of its A.G. leads to the appearance of oostegites. Can the testis of a male deprived of its A.G. secrete ovarian hormone and induce the appearance of oostegites? Recent experiments are affirmative.

The males of *O. montagui* and of *Talitrus saltator* deprived of A.G. never acquire oostegites, although the gonad is converted into an ovary. In these species, however, the A.G. have a diffuse form which does not permit complete removal. The lack of oostegites can be explained by the inhibitory property of A.H. which is secreted by small residual portions of the glands.

In *O. gammarella*, complete removal of the A.G. is possible, but as I have pointed out, spermatogenesis continues for a long time. I obtained only two or three oocytes in each testis. These males, deprived of their A.G., never acquired oostegites. Therefore, testes of *T. saltator* were grafted into males of *O. gammarella* which had been deprived of their A.G. Eight males received one testis each; six of these testes contained oocytes. After the 1st or 2nd postoperative molt, five operated animals acquired oostegites, including the two males provided with oocyteless testes (Fig. 29.11). In these animals, the grafted testes were converted into ovaries. In the three males which had not acquired oostegites, the grafts had degenerated.

Thus, a testis of *T. saltator*, protected from A.H. action, becomes an ovary and secretes ovarian hormone. These experiments indicate that the male phenotype is converted into the female phenotype by suppression of A.H. (Charniaux-Cotton, 41, 42).

COMPARATIVE ACTION OF MALE AND FEMALE HORMONES. There are two regions in the genital apparatus of the Talitridae which can secrete sex hormone: the gonadal region in the female and the A.G. in the male. Androgenic and ovarian hormones are not equivalent. The experimental sex inversions show that in the presence of A.H. male differentiation takes place, whatever the genetic sex of the individual. In the absence of this hormone female differentiation ensues, even in a genetically determined male. This female differentiation begins with ovarian self-differentiation. The ovary becomes endocrine and produces ovarian hormone, which in turn evokes external female differentiation.

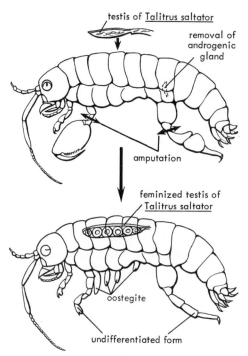

testis of <u>Talitrus saltator</u>

removal of androgenic gland

amputation

feminized testis of Talitrus saltator

oostegite

undifferentiated form

Fig. 29.11 Diagram of the experiments which prove the secretion of an ovarian hormone by a testis reversed into an ovary. The host is a male *Orchestia gammarella* (see text).

It is therefore the presence or absence of A.H. that determines the male or female sex. The A.H. alone has the capacity to convert a female into a male. The ovarian hormone is just a link in the female differentiation and has no effect whatsoever on the male.

CONTROL OF SEX GENE ACTIVITY BY ANDROGENIC HORMONE. Since experimental sex inversions in Talitridae have shown that each individual has the genetic information for both male and female differentiation, including that for secretion of ovarian hormone, we must assume that the male and female have genes for both sexes. Thus their genomes differ only in the genetic control of morphogenesis of the A.G. (Fig. 29.12). The presence or absence

of A.H. regulates the activity of the sex genes. In the absence of A.H., it is the genes for female morphogenesis which act; in the presence of A.H., it is the genes for male morphogenesis which act.

The germ cells offer a particularly clear example of these mechanisms. The gonia undergo spermatogenesis or oogenesis according to whether or not they have received A.H. They must therefore possess both male and female gene complements; the activity of one or the other is governed by the titer of A.H.

SEX DETERMINATION. We know that there exists a genetic difference between male and female which is responsible for sex determination. Since it is the presence or absence of A.H. which determines sex, it must be assumed that the genetic difference is responsible for the development or nondevelopment of the A.G. This in turn might depend directly on the genetic constitution of the A.G. cells. This seems to be the case in *O. gammarella* in which the rudiments of the A.G. of a masculinized female never develop into functional A.G. It may also depend on hormonal control, which differs in male and female. This is probably the case in isopods and insects, as we shall see.

Since the genetic difference between male and female is responsible simply for the presence or absence of A.H., there is no reason to consider sex determination the result of a balance of male and female genes. This classic concept of "genetic balance of sex" (see Johnson, 61; Tinturier-Hamelin, 102) confuses the existence in all individuals of genes for all sex characters with the genetic system controlling the activity of these genes.

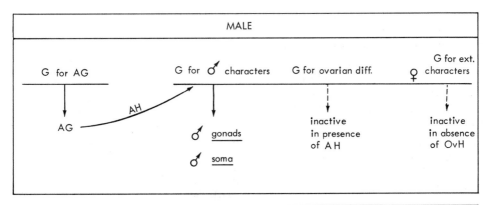

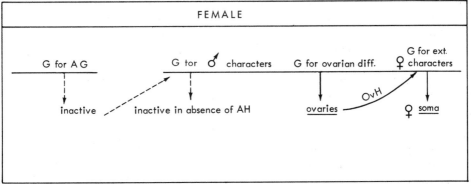

Fig. 29.12 Genetic and endocrine controls of sex differentiation in Talitridae. AG, androgenic gland; AH, androgenic hormone; OvH, ovarian hormones; G, genes whose activity leads to the organogenesis of androgenic gland.

Isopods

The first successful surgical castration of a crustacean was done by Takewaki and Nakamura in 1944 (101) on a terrestrial isopod, *Armadillidium vulgare*. In neither sex did such castration lead to modification of the external sexual characters. Later, Lattin and Gross (71) grafted testes into mature females of *Oniscus asellus* and obtained external male characters. Thus, the testes of oniscoids were considered as the source of male hormone by these authors, and also by Legrand (73b, 74). This hormone has only a limited action on the ovary, inducing degeneration of the oocytes while it produces develop-

ment of the vas deferens. Likewise, ovaries grafted into males (Legrand, 73a) exhibit oocyte degeneration, but the gonia are not directed toward spermatogenesis and do not induce modification of the host. Therefore, for many years isopods were thought to differ from amphipods in the following ways: (1) no specific A.G. was known, (2) testes appeared to be the source of male hormone, and (3) this hormone did not control primary sexual characters.

However, in 1958 Balesdent-Marquet (6) described an A.G. in *Asellus aquaticus*, the location of which is homologous to the A.G. of the *Orchestia gammarella*. When grafted into a female, this gland produced external masculinization. A short time later, androgenic tissue was identified histologically in some species of oniscoids as three pairs of A.G. attached to the apex of the three testicular lobes (Legrand, 76). Homoplastic grafts of these A.G. into females of *Armadillidium vulgare* (Katakura, 66) and of the *Metoponorthus pruinosus* (Shimoizumi, 99) brought about external masculinization, just as with whole testes.

In 1960 Katakura (67) obtained transformation of ovaries into testes in *Armadillidium vulgare* by grafting A.G. into young females. Thus, with respect to the control of male differentiation, the isopods appear more similar to the amphipods than was once thought.

Dimorphism of Genital Apparatus and Location of Androgenic Glands

The gonads of the primitive isopods *Anthura* and *Gnathia* are tubular in form in both sexes, as in amphipods and decapods (Vandel, 103). In the higher isopods this is true for the female, but in the male the undifferentiated gonad differentiates into three tubular testes in which spermatogenesis takes place, plus a seminal vesicle and vas deferens (Legrand and Vandel, 81).

At hatching, the gonads are composed of two strands of mesodermal cells with gonia. The gonads are identical in all individuals, recalling the condition in *Orchestia gammarella*. Along the external side of each mesodermal strand are thin lateral cellular filaments, one in each of the seven thoracic segments (t1 . . . t7). At the 3rd molt, sexual differentiation begins. In the male, cells begin proliferating in the filaments t1 . . . t3, and gonia migrate into these filaments which become the testicular tubes. In the female, each strand with gonia becomes an ovary. The filaments do not develop, except for t5 which gives rise to the oviduct (Figs. 29.13 and 29.15). External sex differentiation starts with the 4th molt in *Porcellio*, in the 3rd in *Helleria*.

The location of the A.G. varies with suborders of isopods. In the Gnathiidea, *Paragnathia formica* (Bonnenfant, 14, and Legrand and Juchault, 79), the male gonad is a tube. The A.G. is comparable to that of the amphipods with respect to location and structure. In the Anthuridea, *Cyathura carinata*, in which each male gonad has two testicular tubes, the A.G. is a cord of cells inserted at the level of the 5th segment (Legrand and Juchault, 79). In many Flabellifera Sphaeromidae, each gonad has two A.G., one at the level of the 5th segment, another at the 7th segment (Legrand and Juchault, 79). In the Flabellifera Cymothoadae, *Meinertia oestroïdes* (Bonnenfant, 14, 15; Berreur-Bonnenfant, 9, 10) and *Anilocra physodes* (Remy and Veillet, 96) the A.G. stretches along the vas deferens. In the Valvifera, *Idotea viridis*, the A.G. are formed by two groups of cells in the 6th and 7th segments (Legrand and Juchault, 79). In the Asellota, *Asellus aquaticus*, the A.G. form many clusters along the vas deferens, seminal vesicle, and testes (Balesdent-Marquet, 6). In the Oniscoidea, the location of the A.G. is still more anterior, attached to the anterior end of the testicular tubules. In the Oniscoidea of the "serie tylienne," the vas deferens consists of two cellular strands (5th and 7th segments) in *Helleria brevicornis*, and only one (5th segment) in *Tylos latreilli* (Legrand and Juchault, 78). In the Trichoniscidae (Legrand and Juchault, 78) the A.G. are located either along the vas deferens, or along the vas deferens and at the apex of the testes. Finally, in most of the other Oniscoidea, the A.G. are found only at the cephalic end of each testis, as in Figures 29.13 and 29.14A (Legrand and Juchault, 78; Katakura, 68; Shimoizumi, 99). The displacement of the A.G. along the genital apparatus from

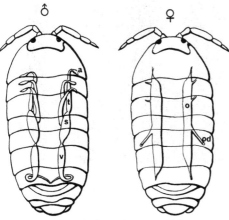

Fig. 29.13 Genital apparatus of the terrestrial isopod, *Armadillidium vulgare*, dorsal view. a, androgenic gland; s, seminal vesicle; v, vas deferens; t, testicular tubule; o, ovary; od, oviduct (Redrawn from Katakura, *Annotiones Zool. Japon.* 34:60–71, 1961.)

the posterior to the anterior region, proceeding from lower to higher isopods, has not received any explanation. Legrand and Juchault (78) have suggested that the A.G. differentiate by cellular proliferation in one or more of the seven segmental filaments of the undifferentiated gonad, and that they are endocrine "diastematic" glands similar to the interstitial tissue of vertebrates. Experimental studies have shown that the role of the A.G. is the same wherever it is found.

Control of Male Differentiation

As noted, an A.G. transplanted from a mature male to a mature female causes external male sexual characters to appear in the form of spermiducts and a penis. The ovaries are not converted into testes, but ova degenerate. In 1960 Katakura (67) transformed ovaries into testes by grafting A.G. into young females of *Armadillidium vulgare*. The testes developed from the three pairs of cell filaments (Fig. 29.14*B*). Three normal females, after copulating with such a masculinized female, produced only female offspring (Katakura, 69).

In recent experiments, Juchault and Legrand (63, 64) confirmed the experiments of Katakura, and obtained two important new results which separate isopods from amphipods: (1) the A.G. which develop in masculinized female testes have androgenic activity, and (2) this development is indispensable for the conversion of the ovary into a testis.

Experiments have been performed on the two oniscoid species *Helleria brevicornis* and *Porcellio dilatatus*. The former (which belongs to the tylienne series) possesses two A.G., respectively in the 5th and 7th segments. In *Porcellio* the A.G. is situated at the anterior end of the testicular tubules. Androgenic glands taken from adult males and grafted into young females almost at the time of external sex differentiation convert these females into functional males. After mating with normal females, the progeny are female, as in *Armadillidium*. In both species the A.G. have developed in their usual position. These induced A.G. may masculinize a female.

In *Helleria brevicornis* (in which the A.G. differentiate in t5 and t7) the

AG

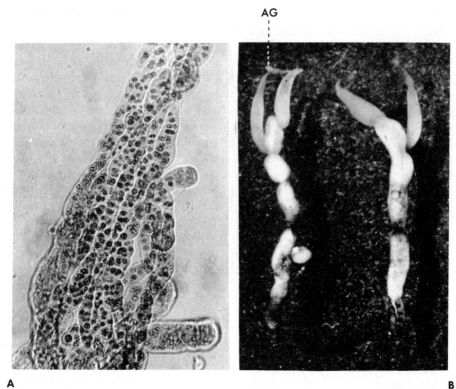

A   **B**

Fig. 29.14 *Armadillidium vulgare.* A. Androgenic gland of normal male; it is formed by about ten cords of cells. (From Katakura, *Annotiones Zool. Japon* 34:60–71, 1961.) B. Genital apparatus of sex-reversed female; the developed testes are accompanied anteriorly with newly formed androgenic glands, AG. (Katakura, personal communication.)

pairs of undifferentiated gonads taken out at hatching were grafted into adults, one into a male, the other into a female. In one series of experiments, only the anterior part was grafted. This part did not have primordia of A.G. or oviducts. Two months after the operation, the grafts, whatever their genotype or that of the host, showed an atypic ovarian structure poor in gonia. In another series, the gonads were grafted with "t5." After 3 months, all the gonads grafted into males were differentiated into testes. Among gonads grafted into females, 50 percent were testes, 50 percent were ovaries. The interpretation is that gonads taken from genetic

males differentiate into testes in all recipient animals. Gonads taken from genetic females differentiate into ovaries in a female host and into testes in a male host. The diagram in Figure 29.15 sums up the experiments made on the oniscoids.

Legrand (77) interprets these results in a rather complex way. To explain the differentiation of an A.G. in a sex-reversed female, he supposes that A.H. has a chemical composition close to the "inducteur nucleaire male," and therefore causes cells of the androgenic primordia to develop into A.G. The male hormone would act on the genetic complex $\Sigma F/\Sigma M$ of the female either

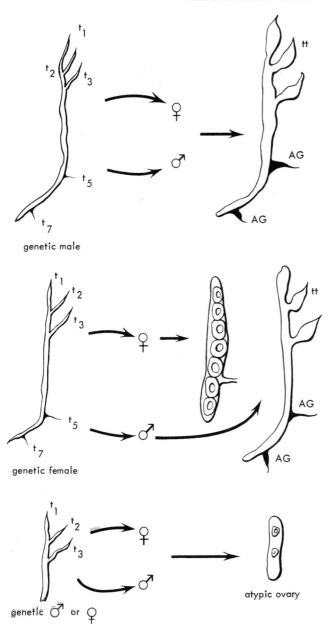

Fig. 29.15 Diagram of the experiments with the terrestrial isopod *Helleria brevicornis* (see text). The undifferentiated gonad with or without (bottom) the rudiments of the androgenic gland (t_5, t_7) is implanted into male or female as indicated by the curved arrows. AG, androgenic gland; t_1, t_2, t_3, segmented filaments; tt, testicular tubule.

by inhibiting the female genes or by reinforcing the male genes. The mesenchymal tissue of the female androgenic anlage soon loses its ability to react toward the male hormone, which is why the latter must act early. The fact that ovaries cannot be masculinized directly by a male hormone circulating in the hemolymph of a grafted female, led Legrand to suggest that the autochthonous A.G. secretes a substance early in its differentiation which differs chemically from the adult male hormone, and that it is this early substance which is the male sexual inductor. Finally, the fact that the gonoducts are induced directly by the male hormone in the adult female indicates that the sexual inductor and the male hormone are chemically related.

By taking into account the results obtained with the amphipods and insects, I propose another interpretation: It may be that the initial cells of the A.G. are equally secretory in the male and the female, and their multiplication is under hormonal control. In the insect, in fact, this control appears to be via a neurosecretion. Neurosecretion may thus be the point of impact of genetic sex determination.

The development of the anlage of the A.G. in young females provided with A.H. could be explained by a mitotic effect of this hormone on the cells of the genital tract. We know, in fact, that in *O. gammarella*, A.H. evokes multiplication of the initial cells of the A.G. of the female. But then these cells respond like those of the vas deferens, failing to organize themselves into an A.G., indicating that they differ from cells in the male.

Finally, if A.H. cannot directly masculinize a young ovary of *Helleria* deprived of the anlage of the A.G., it is probably due to the fact that the gonadal anlagen respond only to contact with A.G. *tissue*.

Control of Female Differentiation

CONTROL OF EXTERNAL SEX CHARACTERS. In isopods, the large size of the oostegites is a temporary character connected with incubation. After surgical castration, females of *Armadillidium vulgare* (Legrand, 75) and *Asellus aquaticus* (Balesdent-Marquet, 6) no longer develop a brood pouch. However this reappears after implantation of an ovary. Therefore in isopods, as in amphipods, the temporary sex characters appear to be under ovarian control. In *Asellus aquaticus*, Balesdent-Marquet (7) claims that an annex gland of the oviduct controls permanent external sex characters.

OVARIAN SELF-DIFFERENTIATION. Ovarian differentiation seems to be autonomous in the isopods, as it is in the amphipods. In fact, an undifferentiated male gonad of *Helleria brevicornis* (Juchault and Legrand, 64) without an androgenic anlage develops into an ovary in a male as well as in a female (Fig. 29.15).

Gonad Territory

Legrand (77) considers that in isopods the gonia give rise to oocytes or to spermatozoa according to whether they are localized in the axial part of the gonad or in testicular utricles. In males or in masculinized females, A.H. would have merely the role of provoking the development of utricles-into which the gonia migrate, after being first localized in the axial tube.

However, Berreur-Bonnenfant (10), studying the gonad of a hermaphroditic Cymothoidae, *Meinertia oestroides*, has observed oocytes in the testicular utricles at the time of sex reversal of the male phase to the female (Fig. 29.16). Moreover, the gonad of the *Anilocra physodes* (another Cymothoidae) taken from young males long before sex reversal, and cultivated in vitro, exhibited active oogenesis in the testes after 15 days (Berreur-Bonnenfant, 12, 13). Thus, development of a gonium toward spermatogenesis does not depend on location only; it also requires A.H.

Since spermatogenesis has never been observed in the axial region of

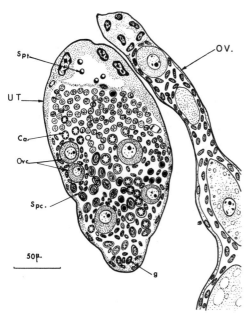

Fig. 29.16 Transverse section of the gonad of the hermaphroditic isopod Flabellifera, *Menertia oestroides*, at the time of sex reversal (see Fig. 29.18*B*). Ca., abnormal cell; g, gonia; OV., ovarian region, Ovc, oocyte; Spc., spermatocyte; Spt, spermatid; UT, testicular tubule with oocytes. (From Berreur-Bonnenfant, *Bull. Soc. Zool. France* 87:253–259, 1962.)

the gonad, the hypothesis that the filaments which develop into testicular tubes are the only territory competent to transmit the action of A.H. to gonia must be considered.

Functional Proterandric Hermaphrodites

The Malacostraca are generally bisexual. However, several decapod species, like the prawns *Lysmata* and *Pandalus*, and the two isopod groups Cymothoidae and Cryptoniscidae, are functional proterandric hermaphrodites. The two phases of gametogenesis occur in the same gonad. Studies have shown that the A.G. are present during the male phase, and disappear before the female phase is established.

From the results obtained in Talitridae, we know that this disappearance suffices to explain sex reversal, for it permits complete transformation of the gonads into ovaries. These secrete ovarian hormone, which in turn induces the external female characters.

Decapods

The modalities of sex reversal have been described for *Lysmata seticaudata* (Charniaux-Cotton, 30, 34; Veillet, 104) and for *Pandalus borealis* (Carlisle, 20, 21, 22). Sex reversal proceeds to an extent which is specific for each species. Degeneration of the A.G. occurs during the male phase, and ultimately affects all cells of the gland. Within one or several molts, the external male sex characters disappear, the female characters appear, and vitellogenesis starts.

It was known early that the gonad during the male phase included an ovarian portion. But the physiology of this ootestis had not been interpreted correctly. In *Lysmata* (Charniaux-Cotton, 37) and *Pandalus* (Charniaux-Cotton, unpublished observations) each gonad is tubular, and a germinative zone runs along the wall, from one end to the other, just as in amphipods.

During the male phase, the gonad of *Lysmata* resembles that of the talitrid, *Orchestia montagui*. Along the germinative zone, there is a gradient of response to the A.H., so that the anterior gonia develop into oocytes, the posterior ones become spermatozoa. For a brief period, spermatogenesis can occur in the entire gonad, with the anterior gonia also forming spermatozoa. However, after the A.G. have disappeared, oogenesis progresses toward the posterior region. Nonetheless, even in old females, the most posterior gonia continue to develop into spermatozoa, just as in the testis of *Orchestia gammarella.*

In *Pandalus*, the germinative zone does not show a gradient of response to the A.H. During the male phase the

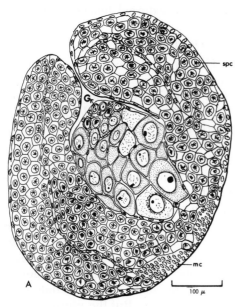

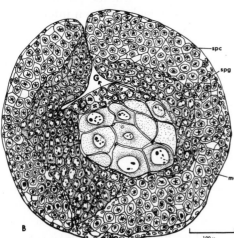

Fig. 29.17 Transverse section of the gonad of the hermaphroditic prawn *Pandalus borealis* during the male phase. *A.* Oogenesis. *B.* Spermatogenesis (see text). G, primary gonium, (in the germinative zone); mc, mucus cell; spc, spermatocyte; spg, secondary spermatogonium.

germinative zone exhibits alternations of spermatogenetic and oogenetic activities (Fig. 29.17) along its length. Oocytes remain near the germinative zone, enclosed in their follicles. When spermatogenesis begins, the secondary spermatogonia move in from either side to surround this ovarian center. These processes are responsible for the characteristic structure of the gonad, with an ovarian "medulla" surrounded by a testicular "cortex" (Aoto, 2). It should be emphasized, however, that oocytes and spermatocytes derive from the same germinative zone. After the disappearance of the A.G., spermatogenesis stops and the gonad becomes an ovary.

In both species only the oocytes accomplish their first growth during the male phase, since vitellogenesis is inhibited by the A.H. Once they have reached their maximum size after this first growth, they are phagocytized by their follicle cells.

Sex reversal, then, poses the problem of how the disappearance of the A.G. is controlled. Various experiments suggest that this disappearance is not under hormonal control.

Eyestalk removal during the male phase in *Pandalus* (Aoto and Nishida, 3; Carlisle, 21) is without effect, the A.G. remaining active even at the 2nd postoperative molt (Charniaux-Cotton, 34). Females do not possess an inhibitor of the A.G., as shown by the fact that a gland implanted into female *Lysmata* survives and masculinizes the host (Charniaux-Cotton, 33, 34, 37). It is probable that the A.G. disappear after the processes of regeneration fail to counterbalance degeneration.

Isopods

The cymothoid, *Meinertia oestroides,* an external parasite of fish, has been studied in detail by Bonnenfant (14, 15), and Berreur-Bonnenfant (10). At hatching, the young have a tubular gonad. There is a bud of an A.G. at the posterior end of the deferent canal, but it is inactive. The young do not exhibit male external characters, and oogenesis begins in the gonad. Then, the A.G. develop. The testicular utricles form as swellings from the germinative zone (Fig. 29.18A), and the external sex characters appear. Thus the testicular utricles develop from re-gions of the germinative zone that are competent to respond to the A.H.

During the male phase, the A.G. show histological variations indicating intermittent activity. Alternations of spermatogenesis in the utricles, and of oogenesis in the tubular part of the gonad, correspond to these variations. This is reminiscent of the shrimp, *Pandalus*, although here gametogenesis starts from specialized regions of the germinative zone.

When sex reversal begins, the A.G.

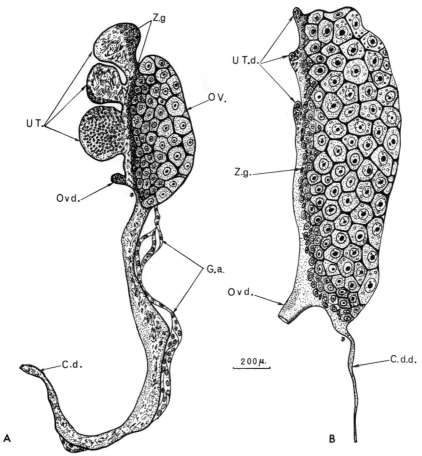

Fig. 29.18 Gonad of the hermaphroditic isopod *Menertia oestroides*. A. Male phase. B. Sex reversal. C.d., vas deferens; C.d.d., degenerated vas deferens; G.a., androgenic gland; OV., ovarian region; Ovd., oviduct; UT., testicular tubules; UT.d., degenerated testicular tubules; Z.g., germinative zone. (Redrawn from Berreur-Bonnenfant, *Bull. Soc. Zool. France* 87:253–259, 1962.)

progressively disappear. In the testicular utricles spermatogenesis comes to a halt, and oocytes appear, accompanied by numerous atypical germ cells whose nuclei are blocked at diakinesis (Fig. 29.16). The utricles regress, and their germinative zones regain their original position (Fig. 29.18*B*). The gonad has become an ovary again. Thus, A.H. is necessary both for the development and the maintenance of the testicular utricles.

In *Anilocra physodes*, another cymothoid, regression of the A.G. at the onset of sex reversal has also been observed (Remy and Veillet, 96). When A.G.'s are implanted into females of this species, the male phase is re-established (Legrand and Juchault, 80).

Discussion

The gonad of hermaphroditic crustaceans has been considered to include a female and a male region, with the latter being functional only during the male phase (Aoto, 2). At the onset of sex reversal, the ovarian region becomes functional, and the testicular region disappears.

The studies summarized in the preceding section, however, show that there is only one germinative zone. Above a certain titer of A.H., spermatogenesis occurs; below this titer, oogenesis. The threshold of sensitivity to A.H. may be the same along the entire length of the germinative zone, as in *Pandalus*, which is characterized by successive waves of spermatogenesis and oogenesis during the male phase. Or else the threshold may vary along the germinative zone as in cymothoids and *Lysmata*. In the latter shrimp, spermatogenesis can occur along the entire gonad during the male phase, provided the titer of A.H. is high enough.

The hermaphrodites are entirely comparable to males of *Orchestia montagui* or *Talitrus saltator*. Their testes show oogenesis which varies with the season, and the males turn into females after experimental removal of the A.G. The only difference between a hermaphrodite and a male talitrid is that in the former the A.G. disappear at a given time of its life span, whereas they persist in the latter.

And that is where a question arises: Is the hermaphroditism of the Malacostraca primitive, or are we dealing with bisexual species whose females have disappeared? For the females to disappear from a species, it is necessary that the male be the homogametic sex, and that the disappearance of its A.G. at a given time in its life span permit it to function as a female. This is certainly the case in hermaphroditic shrimps. In fact, in certain populations of *Pandalus borealis*, there is still a small percentage of true females (see Charniaux-Cotton, 33). In *Lysmata seticaudata*, no true female has ever been described, and reproduction is therefore solely guaranteed by the genetic males.

Insects

Ever since the discovery, in vertebrates, of the role of the gonads in the realization of secondary sex characters, experiments involving castration and gonad transplantation have been performed in insects (Oudemans, 92, Kopec, 70, Geigy, 50). However, these operations never produced modification of sex characters in the adult, even when done in young larvae.

It was for this reason that insects were thought to be devoid of sex hormones. Furthermore, the contributions of geneticists, notably those of Morgan and Bridges on gynandromorphs (87) have led biologists to consider it a fact that sexual differentiation is controlled directly by the genetic constitution of the cells. This probably explains why the work of Paul (93) has often been doubted, and never repeated. This author transplanted a wing imaginal disc from a female butterfly larva (*Orgyia antiqua*) into a male larva whose own disc had been removed. The transplanted disc developed into a male wing. In the reciprocal experiment (that is, transplantation of a male wing disc into a female), the sex of the implant was not reversed. This suggested the existence of a male hormone.

Recent experiments by Bergerard (8) in *Carausius morosus*, an orthopterous insect with constant thelyotokous parthenogenesis, have shown that more or less masculinized individuals can be obtained by keeping the eggs at 30° C during the first third of their embryonic life. Thus, genetically female eggs can develop into males under the influence of an external factor.

Finally, the brilliant experiments carried out by Naisse (90, 91) on the coleopterous insect *Lampyris noctiluca* have proved, beyond doubt, the existence of a sex hormone in an insect. This author has also localized the source of this hormone, and obtained data relevant to the control of its secretion. Before presenting this work, it is necessary to describe in more detail the sexual differentiation in lampyrids, which has been studied carefully by Naisse (91).

Sexual Differentiation of *Lampyris noctiluca*

EXTERNAL DIMORPHISM. At hatching, all larvae look alike. There are 4 larval molts in the male and 5 in the female. The size of the female ex-

ceeds that of the male. The nymphal and imaginal molts lead to adults with a very pronounced sexual dimorphism. The female is apterous, but still an adult, clearly differentiated from a larva by its cuticle and its luminescent organs located on the last three sternites. The male has two pairs of wings. Its eyes are larger than those of the female, and its luminescent organs are located on the last sternite only.

DEVELOPMENT OF THE GONADS. Naisse distinguishes three phases in the postembryonic development of the gonads, from hatching until the imaginal molt.

1. *Phase of undifferentiation.* During the first three intermolts, the gonads of all individuals are identical. The genital follicles form, and the gonia.

2. *Phase of differentiation.* Starting after the 3rd molt, male and female gonads can be distinguished by their external appearance, as well as by the structure of their follicles.

In the male, the mesoderm cells located at the apex of the follicles proliferate and soon occupy half of the testicular follicle. This apical tissue has a secretory appearance and becomes vacuolized; this condition is maintained until the nymphal molt. The apical tissue thus is present only during stages 4 and 5.

In the ovarian follicles of the female, the apical cells do not proliferate, and in fact degenerate. The follicle becomes completely filled with gonia.

3. *Gametogenesis.* After the nymphal molt, the spermatogonia proliferate. The apical tissue regresses, and the spermatogonia occupy the entire follicle. The cysts form, and spermatogenesis takes place.

In the female, shortly before the

nymphal molt, the oogonia located next to the mesodermal cells of the base of the follicle develop into oocytes.

Experimental Demonstration of the Androgenic Function of the Testis

Thus, the first difference between male and female is the development of the apical tissue in the former, but not in the latter. Could this very tissue be the source of a male hormone? Naisse (90, 91) has done various implantation experiments in order to answer this question.

IMPLANTATION OF TESTES INTO FE-MALE LARVAE.   One or two testes of a male larvae were implanted into the abdomen of a female larva. Testes coming from larvae of stage 4 or 5 completely masculinized female larvae of stage 4, 5, or 6. Such female larvae develop into adults with a normal male appearance and functional testes. After implantation, apical tissue develops in the ovarian follicles, which become organized like testicular follicles. The only residual indication of female development is the presence of a few degenerating oogonia.

Testes obtained from larvae close to the nymphal molt, or from nymphae or adults, do not exhibit masculinizing activity. Thus a testis is capable of inverting the sex of a female larva, but only if its apical tissue is well developed. Naisse consequently considers this tissue as the source of an "androgenic hormone."

Nymphae cannot be masculinized, which is probably explained by the fact that after the nymphal molt the gonia are engaged in oogenesis.

If female larvae are ovariectomized prior to the implantation of testes, they also become masculinized. A normal ectodermal sperm duct forms. However it does not establish contact with the mesodermal sperm ducts of the implanted testes. These experiments show that the androgenic tissue of the implant acts directly upon the secondary characters.

IMPLANTATION OF OVARIES INTO MALE LARVAE.   Ovaries from larvae of stage 4 or 5 were implanted into male larvae of stage 4 or 5. They did not have any influence on the host, but were transformed into testes.

In another experimental series, male larvae were castrated before implantation of ovaries. These larvae developed into normal adult males. The transplanted ovaries became transformed into testes, but with only few spermatozoa. Is this inversion due to a residue of A.H.? This is uncertain, because after the disappearance of the apical tissue, that is, at the nymphal stage, the male interior milieu does not transform an implanted ovary.

Could the development of the apical tissue itself be under the control of yet a different endocrine system? In an attempt to answer this question, Naisse carried out a histophysiological study of the neurosecretory cells.

Role of the Neurosecretory System

SEXUAL DIFFERENCES AMONG CERTAIN NEUROSECRETORY CELLS.   Naisse (89) observed that the "small grain" variety of neurosecretory cells behave differently in males and females. In the male, these cells start their activity at the 3rd molt, and their secretion remains conspicuous until the adult stage. In the female, they are less numerous, less active, and only begin secreting at stage 5.

EXTIRPATION OF THE CORPORA CARDIACA ALLATA.   The corpora cardiaca and allata has been removed bilaterally in larvae of both sexes. Female larvae metamorphose into normal adult females. However, male larvae are also converted into adult females, provided the extirpation is done near the time of the 3rd molt. If the operation is carried out later, normal male adults form. Thus the apical tissue cannot develop when the small-grain neurosecretion is not present at the 3rd molt.

Conclusions

The results obtained by Naisse establish for the first time the existence, in an insect, of an endocrine control of sexual differentiation. The apical tissue of the testicular follicles secretes early in the larval life an androgenic hormone responsible for the entire sexual differentiation of the male. In the absence of this hormone, a female is produced.

The development of this apical tissue appears to be under the control of a secretion produced by neurosecretory cells of the male. In the absence of this secretion, the apical tissue does not develop. Naisse considers female differentiation as anhormonal, that is, differentiation in the female direction occurs in the absence of A.H.

Coelenterates

Even in *Hydra*, the simplest metazoan, determination of the sex germ cells has been shown to be under hormonal influence.

Sexuality of *Hydra*

The modalities of sexuality in *Hydra* have been studied very carefully by Brien (16, 17). Certain species are bisexual, others hermaphrodites.

In the hermaphroditic species *Hydra*

viridis, the testicular zone is in the distal part of the animal, the zone of the ovary below. Since *Hydra* grows continuously from the subhypostomal region, the same interstitial cells give rise, during their descent toward the base of the animal, first to spermatogonia and then to oogonia.

The bisexual species, *Hydra attenuata*, exhibits a hermaphroditism, which is similar to that described for crustaceans. The females are always normal, but the males sometimes contain oocytes (Brien, 17; Brien and Reniers Decoens, 18). Ovarian spots can appear on one side of the stalk of the male. However, occasionally they may pervade the entire polyp, which becomes totally converted into a female. After several weeks, these animals become normal males again.

These observations on the sexuality of *Hydra* can be interpreted within the conceptual framework outlined for crustaceans. Spermatogenesis would be dependent upon an androgenic substance. In the absence of this substance, oogenesis would occur spontaneouly. In hermaphroditic species, the androgenic substance must be present only just below the hypostomal region. In bisexual species, a genetic system ensures the absence of the androgenic substance in females, and its presence in males. In males, however, ovarian tissue could appear if there were a deficiency of the substance.

This interpretation of the sexuality of *Hydra* has been advanced by Brien (17) and is entirely shared by the present author. It is confirmed by experiments involving parabiosis.

Sexual Inversion by Parabiotic Grafts

In *Hydra fusca*, a stable bisexual species, parabioses between polyps of different sexes have been done by Pirard (95) for the first time. Each polyp is opened longitudinally. The two individuals are then placed against each other and held together by platinum wires. On the following day, the two individuals have fused. The double hydra then consists of a single stalk. The number of tentacles is regulated by fusions, two by two. This double hydra is now placed at 8° C to initiate gametogenesis, with the result that the female half is always masculinized. Spermatogenesis can be seen progressing into the female part, starting at the two contact zones. The more limited the contact zones, the longer it takes for the masculinizing influence to cover the female side. The gonia of the female side may all be directed to sperm formation simul-

taneously, or those furthest from the male half may have time to begin oogenesis and growth. These cytolyze when spermatogenesis takes over their zone (Fig. 29.19). However, if growth of the oocytes is fairly advanced, they may fuse into a typical oocytic plasmodium, in which case an egg will form and be autofertilized.

Experimental sex inversion of a female hydra by a male is reminiscent of the conversion of an ovary into a testis by A.H. in *Orchestia gammarella*. These experiments indicate the existence of a masculinizing substance capable of diffusing from the male into the female. Like the androgenic hormone, this substance blocks oogenesis, but not oocyte growth already under way. It imposes a male tendency on the gonia.

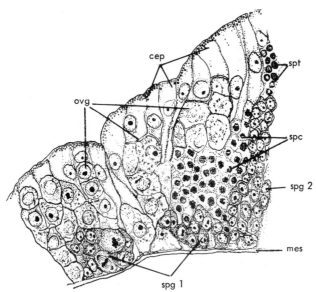

Fig. 29.19 Part of a section through the female portion of a parabiotic pair: *H. fusca* ♀ × *H. fusca* ♂ . Oogenesis had begun in the region shown, and some interstitial cells have already become oogonia, ovg. However, as spermatic induction reaches the interstitial cells, they transform, in place, into spermatogonia, spg 1. These proliferate rapidly, pressing the oogonia toward the periphery, where they undergo histolysis. cep, epithelial cells; mes, mesoglea; spg 1 and spg 2, primary and secondary spermatogonia pressing against the oogonia; spc, spermatocytes in meiosis; spt, Spermatids. (From Brien, *Bull. Biol. France Belg.* 97:214–283, 1963.)

Conclusions

The parabiosis experiments show that there is an androgenic substance in *Hydra* which is capable of imposing a male orientation onto female gonia. Furthermore, the observations on hermaphroditism show that in the absence of the masculinizing substance, oogenesis takes place spontaneously.

Thus in *Hydra*, as in crustaceans and in *Lampyris*, the gonia carry all the genes needed for male or female gametogenesis. The activity of genes is controlled by the presence or absence of a single androgenic substance.

The primitive position of *Hydra* among metazoans attributes general significance to this type of control of sexual differentiation.

Hermaphroditic Forms

The theory has long been accepted that germ cells develop into eggs or sperm according to their genetic constitution. This theory made the interpretation of hermaphrodites obscure, because in a hermaphrodite, all gonia carry the same genome. It was assumed that, contrary to the situation in bisexual species, the gonia are directed toward one sex or the other by trophic factors in the milieu (Ancel, 1).

It has been shown in crustaceans, insects, and hydroids that the development of a gonium does not depend on its male or female genetic constitution, but rather on the presence or absence of a hormone or androgenic substance. Hermaphroditism and gonochorism are no longer incompatible ideas.

Control of the Differentiation of Gonia

Several recent experiments with various groups of hermaphrodites favor the concept that sexual differentiation of germ cells is controlled by an androgenic substance, even though the authors have not interpreted their results in this sense.

In the oligochaete annelid, *Eisenia foetida*, in which male and female gametogenesis occur in separate gonads, removal of the cerebroid ganglia is followed by arrest of gametogenesis. After the brain has regenerated, the gonads become active again. However, before this occurs a temporary oogenesis begins in the testes (Herlant-Meewis, 60). Thus it appears that, in addition to neurosecretion, an androgenic substance is necessary for spermatogenesis. Moreover, the secretion of this substance by the testes comes to a halt after removal of the brain. In its absence, oogenesis sets in.

In ascidian tunicates, culture of gonads in vitro together with the neural gland complex also suggests a hormonal control of gametogenesis (Sengel and Kieny, 98).

In pulmonate gastropods, the two phases of gametogenesis proceed in each acinus of the gonad, starting from the same germinal epithelium (Aubry, 4). This may be interpreted to mean that each spermatogenic wave exhausts the androgenic substance, and that oogenesis follows by autodifferentiation. Oogenesis ceases when the germinal epithelium is again provided with androgenic substance. This interpretation is supported by results of Guyard and Gomot (56) on organotypic cultures of gonads of *Helix aspersa*. When the gonad is cultured alone, spermatogenesis ceases and is completely replaced by oogenesis. On the other hand, when the gonad is cultured in association with the cephalic complex, spermatogenesis is favored and may occupy the entire acinus. A second spermatogenic wave may even follow immediately, without the intermittent oogenesis which will normally occur.

In the echinoderm, *Asterina gibbosa*, spermatogenesis and oogenesis occur successively in the same gonad, starting from the same germinative zone. If a gonad in which spermatogenesis has begun is transplanted, oogonia begin to form (Delavault, 46). This result may be interpreted as a disturbance of the secretion of masculinizing substance.

Control of Somatic Maturity

In hermaphrodites there are characters that play an important role in reproduction and which develop only at sexual maturity.

In earthworms, for example, the ventral glands and clitellum develop only at sexual maturity. Avel (5), after successful castration of *Allolobophora*, demonstrated that these sex characters are independent of the gonads. If they are removed at juvenile stages and transplanted heterotopically to older animals, they develop synchronously with those of the host. A "clitellogenic factor," absent in the young, appears at sexual maturity. Herlant-Meewis (58, 59) removed cerebroid ganglia experimentally and showed that this hormonal factor originates in the brain and is probably secreted by the so-called "a" cells of the brain.

In pulmonate snails, graft experiments have shown that the hermaphroditic gonad secretes, at sexual maturity, a hormone responsible for the glandular activity of the genital ducts (Laviolette, 72).

Conclusions

These results concerning the control of sexual differentiation of germ cells in hermaphrodites are as yet ambiguous, but argue in favor of hormonal control by the presence or absence of a masculinizing substance. If current investigations confirm our interpretation, the mechanisms of orientation of germ cells may prove to be uniform among all invertebrates.

The endocrine control of sex characters developing at the time of sexual maturity in gastropods and oligochaetes has been confirmed. It is interesting to emphasize that in the former, the hormone is secreted by the gonads, in the latter, by neurosecretory cells.

Discussion

That sexual differentiation in invertebrates is under hormonal control has now been established by means of experimental sex reversal in such diverse groups as the higher crustaceans, coleopterans, and hydroids. In crustaceans and insects, experimental sex reversal has been accomplished in both directions. The results can be summarized as follows: a female may be masculinized completely by grafting the tissue responsible for the secretion of male hormone. In crustaceans this is the androgenic gland; in insects, it is the testis, which contains the androgenic tissue. A male crustacean is transformed into a female after removal of the androgenic gland; its testes are transformed into ovaries and then secrete the hormones responsible for the secondary sex characters of the female. A male insect can be transformed into a female if its androgenic tissue does not develop as a result of experimental suppression of neurosecretion. In hydras, the existence of a hormonelike substance, produced by the male and capable of inducing spermatogenesis in the female, has been demonstrated by parabiosis.

These results have both endocrinological and genetic implications. Which sex is expressed in an organism depends on the presence or absence of only one hormone, the male hormone. In crustaceans, a female hormone also exists, but it does not control sex, and is not capable of inverting a male. This hormone is secreted by the ovary after its autodifferentiation in the absence of male hormone, and controls the formation of the secondary sex characters.

Every individual, male or female, possesses all the genes necessary for the differentiation of primary and secondary characters of both sexes. The activity of this hermaphrodite genome is regulated by the male hormone. In its presence, those genes controlling the differentiation of primary and secondary male characters are active; in its absence, "female genes" are active. In crustaceans, those genes involved in the formation of external female characters are activated by the ovarian hormone.

Since sex is under genetic control in crustaceans and insects, it is logical to assume that the secretion of androgenic hormone in the male, and its absence in the female, are due to genetic differences between the sexes. In *Lampyris*, this difference does not concern those genes directly controlling the development of androgenic tissue; rather, it involves the genes controlling the secretion of the cerebral hormone, which in turn is required for the formation of androgenic tissue. This neurosecretion occurs only in the male. The female probably has the genes involved in the organogenesis of androgenic tissue. In fact, this tissue does develop in a masculinized female. Similarly, in crustaceans an active androgenic hormone forms in female isopods masculinized by an implanted androgenic gland. It is worth noting that in birds similar results were obtained: a male gonad feminized by a female hormone secretes itself female hormone (Haffen, 57; Wolff and Haffen, 106).

In the amphipods and probably decapods, the genetic difference between male and female appears to concern the genes that control directly the organogenesis of the androgenic glands. In fact, in a masculinized female, the androgenic hormone stimulates cellular multiplication in the primordia of the androgenic glands, but an active gland does not form. Unpublished results by Charniaux-Cotton and Costlow indicate that in the crab, *Callinectes sapidus*, the removal of the neurosecretory tissue of the eyestalks or sinus gland in a very young megalops does not impede its metamorphosis into an adult crab with normal sex characters. Thus, neurosecretion is not necessary for the development of androgenic glands. Therefore, genetic determination of sex in *Lampyris*, crustaceans, and hydroids consist of the genetic control of secretion of an androgenic hormone. These genes should not be confused with those possessed by all individuals—the genes that are responsible for the formation of male and female sex characters. The concept of regulation of gene activities in a hermaphrodite genome by the titer of androgenic hormone leads to unity in sexuality, applying to hermaphrodites and at the same time explaining intersexuality (Charniaux-Cotton, 39).

Several experiments on hermaphrodites suggest the existence of a substance which induces spermatogenesis in the gonia. The absence of this "male substance" results in oogenesis. In segregated gonads, this substance is produced only in the male regions. In nonsegregated gonads, it is depleted periodically by waves of spermatogenesis that alternate with oogenesis. In species with sex reversal, the masculinizing substance is secreted only during a limited part of the life span.

The transition from hermaphroditism to bisexuality may be explained by postulating a genetic mechanism which prevents the secretion of androgenic substance in certain individuals—that is, females. This genetic mechanism could consist of a single pair of alleles, as in the mosquito, *Culex molestus* (Gilchrist and Haldane, 52). In general, however, it is more complex; the sexes may differ in some chromosomal segment, or even an entire chromosome (Staiger and Bocquet, 100). In the isopod, *Asellus aquaticus*, sex determination appears to be controlled by a polygenic system (Montalenti, 88).

A frequent type of intersexuality is characterized by the presence of oocytes in the testes of males. This would be explained if the gonia did not receive sufficient male hormone early enough, and therefore began to develop toward oogenesis. On the other hand, spermatogenesis never occurs in a female because females cannot synthesize male hormone. Similarly, the proterandric hermaphroditism of certain malacostracans may be explained by the disappearance of the androgenic glands at a certain phase of the animal's life.

Finally, the regulation of the activity of genes involved in sex differentiation by the titer of androgenic hormone can be compared to the control of larval and adult forms of insects by the titer of juvenile hormone. As stressed by Wigglesworth (105, p. 319), "the juvenile hormone is responsible for maintaining in action those genes which cause the appearance of the larval form; that is, those genes which favor the production of the enzymes necessary to larval syntheses. In the absence of juvenile hormone the gene system necessary for the production of the adult form becomes active."

Thus, sexual organogenesis, like all other organogenesis, comprises the regulation of gene activity by the titer of inducers or hormones. The peculiarity of sexual organogenesis is that in bisexual organisms the absence of the hormone is assured genetically in one category of individuals.

Summary

The androgenic glands, first discovered in the amphipod *Orchestia gammarella*, are found to exist in higher crustaceans. At hatching, the young *Orchestia gammarella* is sexually undifferentiated, and possesses a primordium of the androgenic gland at the end of the sperm duct. Experiments involving grafts or ablations of the androgenic glands in *Orchestia gammarella* show that the androgenic hormone controls the differentiation of primary and secondary male sex characters. Experiments involving grafting or removal of ovaries in the same organism show that the ovaries (but not the testes) have endocrine function and control both temporary and permanent external female characters.

In amphipods (Talitridae), testes become converted to ovaries in the absence of androgenic hormone. Thus, ovarian differentiation can be classified as an autodifferentiation. This explains the frequent presence of oocytes in the testes of crustaceans. A testis that has been converted to an ovary secretes ovarian hormone. Thus, in amphipods, sex is controlled by the presence or absence of male hormone alone. In the presence of androgenic hormone the male sex is differentiated, regardless of the genetic sex of the individual. In the absence of the androgenic hormone, the female sex forms.

In many terrestrial isopods, androgenic glands occupy an exceptional site at the anterior end of the testes. In young females that have been masculinized by grafting androgenic tissue, the primordia of the host androgenic glands become active.

In proterandric hermaphroditic malacostracans, sexual inversion is caused by the disappearance of the androgenic glands. In the coleopteran, *Lampyris noctiluca*, the gonads are undifferentiated during the first three larval instars. At the 3rd molt, an apical tissue in the testicular follicles develops. When the testes of 4th or 5th instar males are grafted into a female larva, the host develops into a functional male adult. Female differentiation is an autodifferentiation. The development of the (apical) androgenic tissue appears to be controlled by neurosecretion.

In hydras, parabiosis demonstrates the existence of a hormonelike substance secreted by males and capable of inducing spermatogenesis in females. Oogenesis appears to involve an autodifferentiation.

It is concluded that each individual possesses the genes for the characters of both sexes. The activity of these genes is regulated by the titer of androgenic hormone. The sexes differ only in their genetic information controlling the secretion of androgenic hormone. In insects, this information seems to act via a neurosecretion.

References

1. Ancel, P., "Histogenèse et Structure de la Glande Hermaphrodite d'*Helix pomatia* L.," *Arch. Biol.*, 19:389–652 (1963).
2. Aoto, T., "Sexual Phases in the Prawn, *Pandalus kessleri* Czerniavski, with Special Reference to the Reversal Sex," *J. Fac. Sci. Hokkaido Univ. Ser. VI*, 11:1–20 (1952).
3. ——, and H. Nishida, "Effect of Removal of the Eyestalks on the Growth and Maturation of the Oocytes in a hermaphroditic Prawn, *Pandalus kessleri*," *J. Fac. Sci. Hokkaido Univ. Ser. VI*, 12: 412–424 (1956).
4. Aubry, R., "Étude de l'Hermaphrodisme et de l'Action Pharmacodynamique des Hormones de Vertébrés chez les Gastéropodes Pulmonés." Thesis, University of Strasbourg (1962).
5. Avel, M., "Recherches Expérimentales sur les Caractères Sexuels Somatiques des Lombriciens," *Bull. Biol. France Belg.* 63:149–318 (1929).
6. Balesdent-Marquet, M.-L., "Présence d'une Glande Androgène chez le Crustacé Isopode *Asellus aquaticus* L.," *Compt. Rend. Acad. Sci.* 247:534–536 (1958).
7. ——, "Identification et Rôle d'une Glande Annexe de l'Appareil Génital Femelle chez le Crustacé Isopode *Asellus aquaticus*," *Compt. Rend. Acad. Sci.* 257:4053–4056 (1963).
8. Bergerard, J., "Intersexualité Expérimentale chez *Carausius morosus* Br. (Phasmidae)," *Bull. Biol. France Belg.* 45:273–300 (1961).
9. Berreur-Bonnenfant, J., "Essai de Culture *in vitro* de Gonades de Crustacé," *Bull. Soc. Zool. France* 87:377 (1962).
10. ——, "Glande Androgène et Différenciations Sexuelles Mâle et Femelle

chez le Crustacé Isopode *Meinertia oestroïdes*," *Bull. Soc. Zool. France* 87: 253–259 (1962).

11. ———, "Survie et Activité des Gonades et de la Glande Androgène des Mâles d'*Orchestia gammarella* en Culture Organotypique," *Compt. Rend. Acad. Sci.* 256:2244–2246 (1963).

12. ———, "Autodifférenciation Ovarienne dans les Gonades Mâles de Crustacés en Culture *in vitro*," *Bull. Soc. Zool. France* 88:235–238 (1963).

13. ———, "La Culture *in vitro* de Gonades de Crustacés et Son Intérêt pour l'Étude Endocrinologique," *Gen. Comp. Endocrinol.* 3:6 (1963).

14. Bonnenfant, J., "La Glande Androgène de Deux Isopodes: *Paragnathia formica* et *Meinertia oestroïdes*," *Compt. Rend. Acad. Sci.* 252:1518–1520 (1961).

15. ———, "Evolution de l'Appareil Génital de *Meinertia oestroïdes*," *Bull. Soc. Zool. France* 86:292–293 (1961).

16. Brien, P., "Étude d'*Hydra pirardi* (nov. spc.). Origine et Répartition des Nématocytes. Gamétogenèse. Involution Postgamétique. Evolution Réversible des Cellules Interstitielles. *Bull. Biol. France Belg.* 95:301–367 (1961).

17. ———, "Contribution à l'Étude de la Biologie Sexuelle chez les Hydres d'Eau Douce. Induction Gamétique et Sexuelle par Méthode des Greffes en Parabiose," *Bull. Biol. France Belg.* 97: 214–283 (1964).

18. ———, M. Reniers Decoen, "La Gamétogenèse et l'Intersexualité chez *Hydra attenuata* (Pallas)," *Ann. Soc. Roy. Belg.* 87:285–327 (1951).

19. Campbell-Parmentier, F., "Vitellogenèse, Maturation des Ovocytes, Accouplement et Ponte en Relation avec l'Intermue chez *Orchestia gammarella* Pallas (Crustacé Amphipode *Talitridae*)," *Bull. Soc. Zool. France* 88:474–488 (1963).

20. Carlisle, D. B., "On the Sexual Biology of *Pandalus borealis* (Crustacea Decapoda). I. Histology of Incretory Elements," *J. Marine Biol. Assoc. United Kingdom* 38:381–394 (1959).

21. ———, "On the Sexual Biology of *Pandalus borealis* (Crustacea Decapoda). II. The Termination of the Male Phase," *J. Marine Biol. Assoc. United Kingdom* 38:481–491 (1959).

22. ———, "On the Sexual Biology of *Pandalus borealis* (Crustacea Decapoda). III. The Initiation of the Female Phase," *J. Marine Biol. Assoc. United Kingdom* 38: 493–506 (1959).

23. Charniaux, H., "Castration Chirurgicale chez un Crustacé Amphipode (*Orchestia gammarella*) et Déterminisme des Caractères Sexuels Secondaires. Premiers Résultats," *Compt. Acad. Sci.* 234:2570–2572 (1952).

24. Charniaux-Cotton, H., "Implantation de Gonades de Sexe Opposé à des Mâles et des Femelles chez un Crustacé Amphipode (*Orchestia gammarella*)," *Compt. Rend. Acad. Sci.* 238:953–955 (1954).

25. ———, "Découverte chez un Crustacé Amphipode (*Orchestia gammarella*) d'une Glande Endocrine Responsable de la Différenciation des Caractères Sexuels Primaires et Secondaires Mâles," *Compt. Rend. Acad. Sci.* 239:780–782 (1954).

26. ———, "Le Déterminisme Hormonal des Caractères Sexuels d'*Orchestia gammarella* (Crustacé Amphipode)," *Compt. Rend. Acad. Sci.* 240:1487–1489 (1955).

27. ———, "Déterminisme Hormonal de la Différenciation Sexuelle chez les Crustacés," *Ann. Biol.* 32:371–399 (1956).

28. ———, "Existence d'un Organe Analogue à la Glande Androgène chez un Pagure et un Crabe," *Compt. Rend. Acad. Sci.* 243:1168–1169 (1956).

29. ———, "Croissance, Régénération et Déterminisme Endocrinien des Caractères Sexuels d'*Orchestia gammarella* Pallas (Crustacé Amphipode)," *Ann. Sci. Nat. Zool. Biol. Animale* 19:411–559 (1957).

30. ———, "La Glande Androgène de Quelques Crustacés Décapodes et Particulièrement de *Lysmata seticaudata*, Espèce à Hermaphrodisme Protérandrique Fonctionnel," *Compt. Rend. Acad. Sci.* 246:2814–2817 (1958).

31. ———, "Contrôle Hormonal de la Différenciation Sexuelle chez les Crustacés Supérieurs," *Bull. Soc. Zool. France* 83: 314–336 (1958).

32. ———, "Étude Comparée du Développement Post-embryonnaire de l'Appareil Génital et de la Glande Androgène chez *Orchestia gammarella* et *Orchestia mediterranea* (Crustacés Amphipodes). Auto-

différenciation Ovarienne," *Bull. Soc. Zool. France* 84:105–115 (1959).

33. ———, "Masculinisation des Femelles de la Crevette à Hermaphrodisme Protérandrique *Lysmata seticaudata*, par Greffe de Glandes Androgènes. Interprétation de l'Hermaphrodisme chez les Décapodes. Note préliminaire," *Compt. Rend. Acad. Sci.* 249:1580–1582 (1959).

34. ———, "Physiologie de l'Inversion Sexuelle Chez la Crevette à Hermaphrodisme Protérandrique Fonctionnel, *Lysmata seticaudata*," *Compt. Rend. Acad. Sci.* 250:4046–4048 (1960).

35. ———, "Sex Determination *The Physiology of Crustacea*, T. H. Watermann, ed., New York: Academic Press, vol. I, pp. 411–447 (1960).

36. ———, "La Glande Androgène du Crustacé Stomatopode: *Squilla mantis*," *Bull. Soc. Zool. France* 85:110–114 (1960).

37. ———, "Physiologie de la Gonade de *Lysmata seticaudata* (Crevette Protérandrique) chez les Individus Normaux et les Femelles Masculinisées," *Compt. Rend. Acad. Sci.* 252:199–201 (1961).

38. ———, "La Croissance et la Morphogenèse des Caractères Sexuels des Crustacés Supérieurs et l'Hormone Androgène," *Bull. Soc. Zool. France* 86:484–499 (1961).

39. ———, "Déterminisme de l'Intersexualité Chez les Crustacés Supérieurs et Particulièrement Chez les Amphipodes *Talitridae*," *Bull. Soc. Zool. France* 87:338–366 (1962).

40. ———, "Androgenic Gland," *Gen. Comp. Endocrinol.* Suppl. 1:241–247 (1962).

41. ———, "Démonstration Expérimentale de la Sécrétion d'Hormone Femelle par le Testicule Inversé en Ovaire de *Talitrus saltator* (Crustacé Amphipode). Considérations sur la Génétique et l'Endocrinologie Sexuelle des Crustacés Supérieurs," *Compt. Rend. Acad. Sci.* 256:4088–4091 (1963).

42. ———, "Endocrinologie et Génétique du Sexe chez les Crustacés Supérieurs," *Ann. Endocrinol.* 25:36–42 (1964).

43. ———, T. Ginsburger-Vogel, "Preuve Expérimentale de l'Autodifférenciation Ovarienne chez *Orchestia montagui* Audouin (Crustacé Amphipode)," *Compt.*

Rend. Acad. Sci. 254:2836–2838 (1962).

44. ———, and L. H. Kleinholz, "Hormones in Invertebrates (Other than Insects)," *The Hormones*, G. Pincus, K. V. Thimann, eds. New York: Academic Press, pp. 135–198 (1963).

45. ———, Ch. Zerbib, J-J. Meusy, *Monographie de la Glande Androgène des Crustacés Supérieurs. Crustaceana* 8 (1965).

46. Delavault, R., "Recherches Expérimentales sur la Sexualité des Hermaphrodites chez *Asterina gibbosa* Greffes de Glandes Génitales," *Arch. Anat. Microscop. Morphol. Exptl.* 52:470–495 (1963).

47. Demeusy, N., "Recherches sur la Mue de Puberté du Décapode Brachyoure *Carcinus maenas* Linné," *Arch. Zool. Exptl. Gén.* 95:253–491 (1958).

48. ———, "Pédoncules Oculaires, Glande de Mue et Appareil Génital chez *Carcinus Maenas* L.," *Compt. Rend. Acad. Sci.* 248:2652–2654 (1959).

49. ———, "Différenciation des Voies Génitales Mâles du Crabe *Carcinus maenas* Linné. Rôle des Pédoncules Oculaires," *Cahiers Biol. Marine* 1:259–277 (1960).

50. Geigy, R., "Action de l'Ultra-violet sur le Pôle Germinal dans l'Oeuf de *Drosophila melanogaster* (Castration et Mutabilité)," *Rev. Suisse Zool.* 38:187–288 (1931).

51. Giard, A., "De l'Influence de Certains Parasites Rhizocéphales sur les Caractères Sexuels Extérieurs de Leur Hôte," *Compt. Rend. Acad. Sci.* 103:84–86 (1886).

52. Gilchrist, B. M., and J. B. S. Haldane, "Sex Linkage and Sex Determination in a Mosquito, *Culex molestus*," *Hereditas Lund* 33:175–190 (1947).

53. Goldschmidt, R., *Die Sexuellen Zwischenstufen*. Berlin: Springer-Verlag, p. 528 (1931).

54. Gorbman, A., and H. A. Bern, *A Text Book of Comparative Endocrinology*. New York: Wiley (1962).

55. Graf, F., "Développement Post-embryonnaire des Gonades et des Glandes Androgènes d'*Orchestia cavimana* (Heller). Crustacé Amphipode," *Bull. Soc. Sci. Nancy* 17:223–261 (1958).

56. Guyard, A., and L. Gomot, "Survie et

Différenciation de la Gonade Juvénile d'*Helix aspersa* en Culture Organotypique," *Bull. Soc. Zool. France* 89: 48–55 (1964).

57. Haffen, K., "Associations Hétérosexuées d'Épithélium Germinatif et de Médullaire de Gonades Embryonnaires de Canard, en Culture *in vitro*," *Compt. Rend. Soc. Biol.* 154:315–318 (1960).

58. Herlant-Meewis, H., "Reproduction et Neurosécrétion Chez *Eisenia foetida* Sav.," *Ann. Soc. Roy. Zool. Belg.* 87:151–183 (1956).

59. ———, "Influence de la Nutrition Chez *Eisenia foetida*," *Compt. Rend. Acad. Sci.* 255:2187–2188 (1962).

60. ———, "Endocrine Relationships between Nutrition and Reproduction in the Oligochaete, *Eisenia foetida*," *Gen. Comp. Endocrinol.* 2:608 (1962).

61. Johnson, G., "Contribution à l'Étude de la Détermination du Sexe chez les Oniscoïdes: Phénomènes d'Hermaphrodisme et de Monogénie," *Bull. Biol. France Belg.* 95:177–271 (1961).

62. Juchault, P., "Sur la Glande Androgène d'un Certain Nombre de Péracarides (Cumacés, Mysidacés, Tanaïdacés)," *Compt. Rend. Soc. Biol.* 157:613 (1963).

63. ———, and J-J. Legrand, "Transformation de Femelles Génétiques en Mâles Physiologiques chez les Oniscoïdes *Porcellio dilatatus* et *Helleria brevicornis*," *Compt. Rend. Acad. Sci.* 258: 2197 (1964).

64. ———, and ———, "Mise en Évidence d'un Inducteur Sexuel Mâle Distinct de l'Hormone Adulte et Contribution à l'Étude de l'Autodifférenciation Ovarienne chez l'Oniscoïde *Helleria brevicornis*," *Compt. Rend. Acad. Sci.* 258: 2416–2419 (1964).

65. ———, and ———, "Démonstration de l'Homogamétie Femelle par Croisement de 2 Femelles Génétiques, chez les Oniscoïdes *Porcellio dilatatus* et *Helleria brevicornis*," *Compt. Rend. Acad. Sci.* 258:2685–2686 (1964).

66. Katakura, Y., "Masculinization through Implanting Testis into the Female *Armadillidium vulgare*, an Isopod Crustacean," *Proc. Japan. Acad.*, 35:95–98 (1959).

67. ———, "Transformation of Ovary into Testis Following Implantation of Androgenous Glands in *Armadillidium vul-*

gare an Isopod Crustacean," *Annotationes Zool. Japon.* 33:241–244 (1960).

68. ———, "Hormonal Control of Development of Sexual Characters in the Isopod Crustacean *Armadillidium vulgare*," *Annotationes Zool. Japon.* 34:60–71 (1961).

69. ———, "Progeny from the Mating of the Normal Female and the Masculinized Female of *Armadillidium vulgare* and Isopod Crustacean," *Annotationes Zool. Japon.* 34:197–199 (1961).

70. Kopec, St., "Untersuchungen über Kastration und Transplantation bei Schmetterlingen," *Arch. Entwickl. Mech.* 33:1–166 (1911).

71. Lattin, G., de, and F. J. Gross, "Die Beeinflussbarkeit Sekundärer Geschlechts Male von *Oniscus asellus* durch die Gonaden," *Experientia* 9:338–339 (1953).

72. Laviolette, P., "Rôle de la Gonade dans le Déterminisme Humoral de la Maturité Glandulaire du Tractus Génital chez Quelques Gastéropodes *Arionidae* et *Limacidae*," *Bull. Biol. France Belg.* 88:310–332 (1954).

73a. Legrand, J. J., "Etude Expérimentale de la Différenciation du Sexe chez les Crustacés Isopodes Terrestres par Implantation Homoplastique et Hétéroplastique d'Ovaires chez les Mâles," *Compt. Rend. Acad. Sci.* 239:108–110 (1956).

73b. ———, "Effets de l'Implantation d'un Testicule chez les Femelles des Crustacés Isopodes Terrestres," *Compt. Rend. Acad. Sci.* 239:321–323 (1954).

74. ———, "Rôle Endocrinien du Tissu Nourricier dans le Testicule des Crustacés Isopodes Terrestres," *Compt. Rend. Acad. Aci.* 240:120–122 (1955).

75. ———, "Rôle Endocrinien de l'Ovaire la Différenciation des Oostégites chez les Crustacés Isopodes Terrestres," *Compt. Rend. Acad. Sci.* 241:1083–1085 (1955).

76. ———, "Mise en Evidence Histologique et Expérimentale d'un Tissu Androgène chez les Oniscoïdes," *Compt. Rend. Acad. Sci.* 247:1238–1241 (1958).

77. ———, "La Différenciation Sexuelle chez les Oniscoïdes Gonochoriques," *Compt. Rend. Soc. Biol.* 158:340–343 (1964).

78. ———, and P. Juchault, "Disposition

Métamérique de Tissu Sécréteur de l'Hormone Mâle chez les Différents Types d'Oniscoïdes," *Compt. Rend. Acad. Sci.* 250:764–766 (1960).

79. ——, and ——, "Sur la Glande Androgène d'un Certain Nombre de Peracarides et en Particulier d'Isopodes Marins," *Compt. Rend. Soc. Biol.* 155: 1360 (1961).

80. ——, and ——, "Etude Expérimentale des Facteurs de l'Inversion Sexuelle chez *Anilocra physodes* L. Premiers Résultats," *Compt. Rend. Acad. Sci.* 253: 1275–1277 (1961).

81. ——, and A. Vandel, "Le Développement Post-embryonnaire de la Gonade chez les Isopodes Terrestres Normaux et Intersexués. I. Evolution Morphologique de la Gonade," *Bull. Biol. France Belg.* 82:79–94 (1948).

82. Meusy, J. J., "Evolution de la Teneur en Acide Ribonucléique des Cellules Germinales au Cours de la Gamétogénèse chez *Orchestia gammarella* Pallas (Crustacé Amphipode)," *Compt. Rend. Acad. Sci.* 255:2297–2299 (1962).

83. ——, "La Glande Androgène de Deux Crustacés Péracarides *Paramysis noveli* (Labat) (Mysidacé) et *Eocuma dollfusi* Calman (Cumacé)," *Compt. Rend. Acad. Sci.* 256:5425–5428 (1963).

84. ——, "La Gamétogénèse chez *Orchestia gammarella* Pallas (Crustacé Amphipode)," *Bull. Soc. Zool.* 88:197 (1963).

85. ——, "Détermination de la Durée de la Spermatogenèse d'*Orchestia gammarella* Pallas, Crustacé Amphipode, par Injection de Thymidine Tritiée et Autoradiographie," *Arch. Anat. Microscop. Morphol. Exptl.* 53:252–260 (1964).

86. ——, "Etude de l'Incorporation de l'Uridine Tritiée au Niveau du Testicule d'*Orchestia gammarella* Pallas. (Crustacé Amphipode)," *Arch. Anat. Microscop. Morphol. Exptl.* 53:287–299 (1964).

87. Morgan, Th., and C. L. Bridges, "The Origin of Gynandromorphs," *Carnegie Inst. Wash. Publ.* 278:1–122 (1919).

88. Montalenti, G., "Alcune Considerazioni sull'Evoluzione della Determinazione del Sesso," *Accad. Nazion. Lincei Italia* 47:153–181 (1960).

89. Naisse, J., "Neurosecretion and Corpora Cardiaca corpora Allata during Postembryonic Development in *Lampyris noctiluca* L. (Insect Coleoptère)," *Gen. Comp. Endocrinol.* 2:630–631 (1962).

90. ——, "Détermination Sexuelle Chez *Lampyris noctiluca* L. (Insecte Coléoptère Malacoderme)," *Compt. Rend. Acad. Sci.* 256:799–800 (1963).

91. ——, "Contrôle Endocrinien de la Différenciation Sexuelle chez les Insectes," *Arch. Anat. Microscop. Morphol. Exptl.* (1964).

92. Oudemans, J. T., "Falter aus Kastierten Raupen, wie sie aussehen und wie sie Sich Benehmen," *Zool. Jahrb. Abt. Syst.* 12:71–85 (1889).

93. Paul, H., "Transplantation und Regeneration der Flügel zur Untersuchung ihrer Formbildung bei einem Schmetterling mit Geschlechtsdimorphismus," *Arch. Entwicklungsmech. Or.* 136:64–111 (1936).

94. Pérez, J., "Des Effets du Parasitisme des *Stylops* sur les Apiaires du Genre *Andrena*," *Mém. Soc. Nat. Bordeaux* 3 (1880).

95. Pirard, E., "Induction Sexuelle et Intersexualité chez une Hydre Gonochorique (*Hydra fusca*) par Méthode des Greffes," *Compt. Rend. Acad. Sci.* 253: 1997–1999 (1961).

96. Remy, C., and A. Veillet, "Evolution de la Glande Androgène chez l'Isopode *Anilocra physodes* L.," *Bull. Soc. Sci. Nancy* 1:53–80 (1961).

97. Reinhard, E. G., "Parasitic Castration of Crustacea," *Exptl. Parasitol.* 5:79–107 (1956).

98. Sengel, P., and M. Kieny, "Rôle du Complexe Formé par la Glande Neurale et le Ganglion Nerveux et l'Organe Vibratile sur la Différenciation Sexuelle des Gonades de *Molgula manhattensis* (Tunicier Ascidiacé)," *Bull. Soc. Zool. France* 87:615–628 (1962).

99. Shimoizumi, M., "Studies on the Sexuality of Land Isopod *Metoponorthus pruinosus*. VII. Masculinization of the Females through the Implantation of Androgenous Gland," *J. Gakugei Tokushima Univ. Nat. Sci.* 11:1–9 (1961).

100. Staiger, H., and C. Bocquet, "Cytological Demonstration of Female Heterogamety in Isopods," *Experientia* 10:64–66 (1954).

101. Takewaki, K., and Nakamura, N., "The Effects of Gonadectomy on the Sex Char-

acters of *Armadillidium vulgare*, an Isopod Crustacean," *J. Fac. Sci. Imp. Univ. Tokyo Sec. IV*, 6:369–382 (1944).

102. Tinturier-Hamelin, E., "Polychromatisme et Détermination Génétique du Sexe chez l'Espèce Polytypique *Idotea balthica* (Pallas) (Isopode valvifère)," *Cahiers Biol. Marine* IV:473–591 (1963).

103. Vandel, A., "Recherches sur la Sexualité des Isopodes. Les Conditions Naturelles de la Reproduction chez les Isopodes Terrestres," *Bull. Biol. France Belg.* 59:317–371 (1925).

104. Veillet, A., "Inversion Sexuelle et Glande Androgéne chez Quelques Crustacés," *Bull. Soc. Sci. Nancy* 18:200–203 (1958).

105. Wigglesworth, V. B., "Hormones in Relation to Metamorphosis," *Gen. Comp. Endocrinol.* Suppl. I. 316–321 (1962).

106. Wolff, E., and K. Haffen, "Sur la Féminisation Induite par les Gonades Mâles Intersexuées, chez l'Embryon de Poulet," *Arch. Anat. Histol. Embryol.* 44:275–302 (1961).

107. Zerbib, Ch., "Evolution Post-embryonnaire de la Voie Déférente Mâle chez le Mâle et la Femelle Normale et Masculinisée d'*Orchestia gammarella* Pallas (Crustacé Amphipode)," *Bull. Biol. France Belg.* 157:391–408 (1964).

B. PLACENTATION

30

Organogenesis of the Human Placenta

P. G. WILKIN

*Laboratory of Experimental Gynecology
and Clinic of Gynecology and Obstetrics
St. Pierre Hospital
University of Brussels
Brussels, Belgium*

The general architecture of the human placenta is conditioned first of all by the morphology of its fetal circulation. To understand the development of this particularly complex vascular system and its intimate relationships with the maternal placental circulation, it is necessary to recall the various phases of placental organogenesis based upon the works of Hertig (36, 37), Hertig and Rock (39–42), Hamilton and Boyd (32, 33), Hamilton, Boyd, and Mossman (34), and upon our own observations (Wilkin, 84).

For didactic purposes it is possible to divide placental organogenesis somewhat arbitrarily into periods as follows:

Previllous period (6th–13th day)
1. Prelacunar stage (6th–9th day)
2. Lacunar stage (10th–13th day)
Villous period (14th day to term)
1. Stage of elaboration (14th day to 4th month)
  a. 14th–18th day
    Formation of primary villi
    Formation of intervillous space
  b. 19th–21st day
    Formation of secondary and tertiary villi
    Formation of the cytotrophoblastic shell
  c. 22nd day to end of 4th month (approximately)
    Formation of chorion laeve and frondosum
    Formation of the fetal cotyledons
    Regression of villous, chorionic, and columnar cytotrophoblast
    Formation of the intercotyledonary septa (maternal cotyledons)
2. Stage of maturity (5th month to term)

743

Previllous Period

Prelacunar Stage

From the 6th or 7th to the 9th day of development, the implanted ovum consists of a bilaminar embryonic disc protruding into a cavity, the lecithocele. This cavity is enclosed by the trophoblast, which is actively proliferating at the embryonic pole, but reduced to a thin membrane at the abembryonic pole. Even at this early stage, the trophoblast is made up of two morphologically distinguishable elements: the primary cytotrophoblast formed by large, clear, polyhedral cells, located near the lecithocele, and the primary syncytiotrophoblast. The latter is located at the periphery, is more abundant, and forms a dark cytoplasmic sheet without cell limits. Although both types of trophoblast evidently originate from the trophoblastic cells previously differentiated in the blastocyst, it seems well established that, at this stage of placental morphogenesis, the syncytiotrophoblast is formed at the expense of mononucleated trophoblastic cells, morphologically identical to the primary cytotrophoblastic cells. Multinucleated cells which probably represent transitional forms between the cytotrophoblastic cells and the syncytial undivided mass have, for example, been observed (Fig. 30.1) at a later stage (3 months).

The further growth of the syncytiotrophoblast, however, seems to result from differentiation at the expense of the primary cytotrophoblast and from

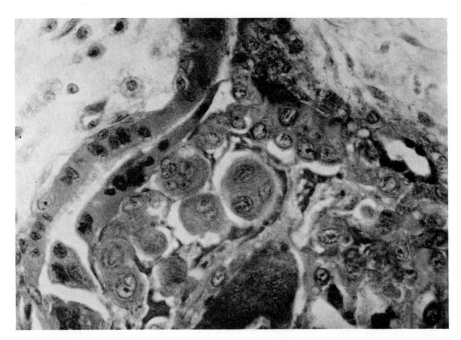

Fig. 30.1 Multinucleate cells, probably intermediate stages between Langhans' cells and syncytiotrophoblast. 3-month placenta. Detail of a proliferative trophoblastic area around a sclerotic villous axis, devoid of fetal capillaries. At the left top corner is a normal villus with loose stroma, several Hofbauer's cells, and a few normal Langhans' cells.

amitotic division of the syncytial nuclei (Boyd and Hamilton, 15). The peripheral trophoblast is thus originally a true syncytium rather than a plasmodium.

It is to be noted that in the hands of Wislocki and Dempsey (87) and of Bargmann and Knoop (6), electron-microscopic sections failed to show any evidence of intercellular walls in the syncytiotrophoblastic layer. Quite recently, on the other hand, Carter (20) presented preparations suggesting the secondary dissolution of intercellular membranes between cytotrophoblastic cells. Studies with thymidine-H³ injection in the macaque by Midgley, Pierce, Deneau, and Gosling (54) bring further arguments in favor of syncytial formation at the expense of cytotrophoblast.

Lacunar Stage

From the 10th to the 13th day of placental development, lacunae become evident in the syncytiotrophoblast (lacunar stage).

Villous Period

Stage of Elaboration

During the period between day 14 and day 18, the lacunae merge into one another, forming a single cavity, almost entirely bordered by syncytiotrophoblast. This cavity bears the name of intervillous space because its formation is concomitant with the formation of the villi. The latter are formed through the proliferation of cytotrophoblastic elements into syncytial trabeculae which at first limit the trophoblastic lacunae (primary villi).

19TH–21ST DAY. The proximal end of the primary villus consists of a central cytotrophoblastic core in active mitotic proliferation at its proximal end, and a covering layer of syncytium. At its distal end, it exhibits syncytial tissue only. The villi acquire the characteristics of secondary villi through ingrowth, into their central cytotrophoblastic core, of mesoblastic trabeculae which are continuous with the primary extraembryonic mesoblast (Fig. 30.2). With the appearance of vessels and the formation of blood islands in the mesoblast (19th to 21st day) the secondary villi are transformed into definitive, tertiary villi.

During these fundamental changes in structure, the villous cytotrophoblast continues proliferating at the distal end of the villi, building dense columns of cells (the cytotrophoblastic cell columns), covered by syncytial tissue facing the intervillous space. The distal elements of the cytotrophoblastic cell columns, upon reaching the maternal tissue, give off lateral expansions in all directions, soon forming a more or less continuous cytotrophoblastic shell surrounding the ovum.

The cytotrophoblastic shell thus divides the primary syncytiotrophoblast into a definitive syncytium located on the embryonic side of the cytotrophoblastic shell, and a peripheral syncytium, much less abundant, lying between the shell and the decidua reflexa and decidua basalis, respectively (Fig. 30.3).

The definitive syncytium forms an almost complete lining of the intervillous space. It covers the chorion, the tertiary villi, and the embryonic surface of the cytotrophic shell. Many of the tertiary villi are attached to the cytotrophoblastic shell and are called anchoring villi. The few villi whose distal ends are unattached and floating

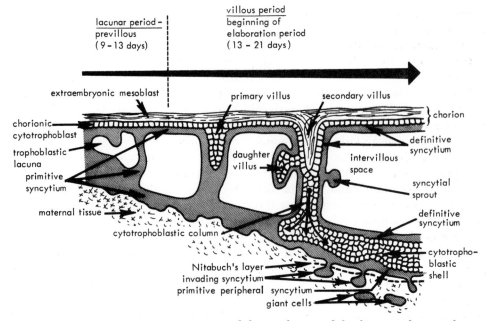

Fig. 30.2 Diagrammatic representation of the evolution of the human placenta from the 9th day to the 21st day.

in the intervillous space are called free villi. The definitive syncytium on the surface of the villi gives off numerous syncytial buds. These are sometimes accompanied by cytotrophoblastic and mesoblastic proliferation (Fig. 30.2) and are thus the origin of daughter villi. Occasionally these buds are pinched off to form free syncytial masses. These may be carried away by the maternal blood stream which has meanwhile been established in the intervillous space (Douglas et al., 24). Salvaggio and co-workers (67) have shown multinucleated trophoblastic cells in cord blood and fetal circulation and a recent publication of Boyd and Hamilton (16) suggests that the passage of trophoblastic masses or even of entire villous fragments in the fetal circulation is caused by the existence of stromal trophoblastic buds in the immediate vicinity of fetal vessels.

The peripheral syncytium also gives rise to multinucleated buds which break through the fibrinoid layer of Nitabuch (15th-day ovum, Johnstone, 45). The latter is the demarcation line between the fetal elements and the maternal decidual cells. Numerous multinucleate cells, originating from those buds or directly from the cytotrophoblastic shell, invade the decidua as early as the 13th day. These are the so-called placental site giant cells. Later these infiltrate the myometrium in the vicinity of the decidua basalis.

The fetal placental circulation becomes functional around the 21st day when the villous vascular system establishes connections with the embryonic heart through the chorioallantoic vessels. On the other hand, the erosion of the capillaries and of the superficial venous sinuses, typical of the endo-

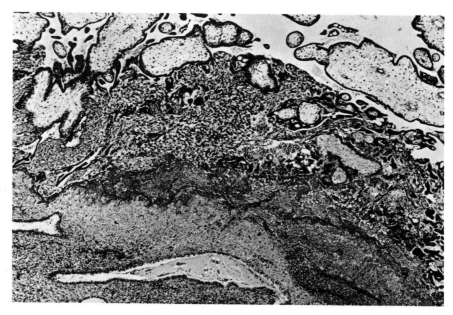

Fig. 30.3 Basal plate of a 3½ months' in situ placenta. From top to bottom, intervillous space, basal cytotrophoblast, Nitabuch's layer, and decidua. (Wilkin, p. 43 in *Le Placenta Humain, Aspects Morphologiques et Functionels*, J. Snoeck, ed. Masson et Cie, 1958.)

metrium during the luteal phase (Wilkin, 83, 85), allows the eruption of maternal blood into the trophoblastic lacunae as early as the 11th–12th day. The maternal placental circulation, however, becomes fully functional only around the 14th–15th day, with the opening of the spiral arteries. These arteries are called thereafter the uteroplacental arteries, and are the seat of important modifications which we will discuss later.

22ND DAY TO END OF 4TH MONTH. From the 22nd day to the end of the 4th month (approximately) various important modifications take place, giving rise to the characteristic structure of the full-term placenta. These are: (1) degeneration of the villi in the decidua reflexa and formation of the chorion laeve; (2) branching of the villi and formation of fetal cotyledons with their characteristic vascular arborization; and (3) changes occurring in the cytotrophoblastic layer, leading to the development of the intercotyledonary septa (maternal cotyledons).

1. Degeneration of villi in the decidua reflexa and obliteration of the uterine lumen. For reasons still ill defined (which perhaps include unfavorable maternal circulatory conditions), the chorionic villi toward the decidua reflexa degenerate as early as the end of the 2nd month, leaving the chorion on this side smooth and avascular. This so-called chorion laeve is made up of the extraembryonic parietopleure and a layer of cytotrophoblastic cells derived from the primary cytotrophoblast. In this layer it is still possible to recognize hyalinized, avascular cores of degenerated chorionic villi.

The villi on the side adjacent to the decidua basalis, on the other hand, continue to proliferate. That part of the chorion which gives rise to them, the chorion frondosum, is discoidal in shape and corresponds to the placenta stricto sensu (Fig. 30.4).

When the blastocyst implants in the endometrium with its embryonic pole in contact with the surface epithelium, the connecting stalk (ventral pedicle) will subsequently suspend the amnion, the embryonic disc, and the primary yolk sac from the inner aspect of the chorion frondosum. The umbilical cord is derived from the body stalk. It is covered with amniotic epithelium and in it the allantoic diverticulum has differentiated. Less commonly, the embryonic pole of the blastocyst is not the first area to come in contact with the endometrial lining. Then the insertion of the umbilical cord lies on the chorion laeve, beyond the fetal aspect of the placenta (velamentous insertion).

Blastocyst implantation deep within the endometrium makes possible, according to some authors, the persistence of villi toward the decidua reflexa, thus leading to the formation of an abnormally diffuse placenta or placenta membranacea. As tempting as this thought may be, it remains, nevertheless, only a hypothesis and does not preclude a priori the idea that genetic factors may partly determine the shape of the placenta just as they do the majority of fetal characteristics.

Some authors (Hertig, 38) suggest that an abnormally superficial implantation of the blastocyst, on the contrary, prevents sufficient development of the fetal aspect of the placenta through the usual growth process. This, then, leads to a compensatory proliferation of the villi, deep in the decidua, at the placental margin, giving rise to the placentae extrachoriales (placenta marginata and circumvallata). It should be noted, however, that to our knowledge no such anomalies have been observed in the macaque placenta, in which species the implantation of the blastocyst is always superficial.

At the end of the 3rd month, as a consequence of the development and distention of the amniotic cavity and concomitant with the disappearance of the extraembryonic coelom, the decidua reflexa comes into contact with the decidua vera or decidua parietalis, thus obliterating the uterine lumen.

From this time on, the placenta resembles a cake, is more or less discoidal, and is attached to the uterine wall through its maternal aspect or basal plate. Its fetal aspect or chorionic plate is covered by the amniotic epithelium and extends beyond the placental margin (where the three deciduae join) into the placental membranes. These are—from the amniotic cavity toward the myometrium—the amnion, the splanchnopleura and the extraembryonic parietopleura, the chorionic cytotrophoblast with its degenerated villous cores, and the fused deciduae reflexa and parietalis.

2. The branching of the villi and the formation of the fetal cotyledons. After the formation of the chorion laeve, there remain only a fixed number of villous pedicles on the chorion frondosum (20–40 according to Wilkin, 82; Crawford, 21). These villous pedicles, arising from the chorionic plate and going toward the basal plate of the placenta, probably represent the tertiary anchoring villi mentioned in the preceding section. The daughter villi,

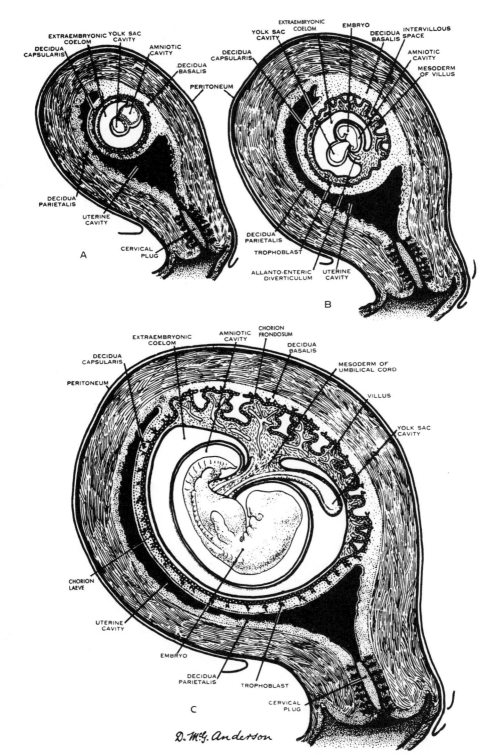

Fig. 30.4 Scheme to show the relationships of the chrionic sac, amnion, and developing embryo to the endometrium and uterine cavity at successive stages of pregnancy.

and anchoring and free villi, which at this stage of placental organogenesis number about 1000 (or about 25–50 per parent villus) are proliferating radially in all directions in the vicinity of the chorionic extremity of the primary anchoring villi. Most of these villi proceed toward the basal plate (floor of the intervillous space), adhere to it by their trophoblastic outer layer, and curve upward and lose themselves in the intervillous space after a short distance. The part of the parent tertiary villus lying between the chorionic plate (roof of the intervillous space) and the point of origin of most of the daughter villi hypertrophies and becomes the villous pedicle or villous trunk of first order (according to our own terminology, or "truncus chorii" according to Bøe, 11). The proximal parts of the daughter villi, which in turn undergo a dichotomous subdivision, become villous trunks of second order ("rami chorii" of Bøe). The distal extremities of the daughter villi, of which the greater number adhere to the cytotrophoblast of the basal plate, become, finally, villous trunks of third order. Together the villous pedicle and the subordinate trunks form the fetal cotyledon (Fig. 30.5). Within the trunks of first, second, and third order, the vessels are surrounded by dense collagenous material which probably plays a role of support (Tenzer, 78).

There exist originally 20–40 such cotyledons, and this number remains unchanged until the termination of pregnancy. Placental growth, once the differentiation of the chorion into its two varieties is achieved, occurs only through the growth and hypertrophy of these cotyledons. Although this situation appears, at first sight, to be unfavorable for eventual compensatory regeneration, it can be explained

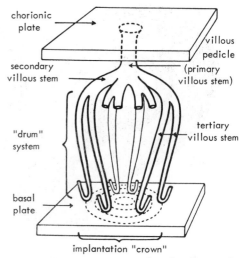

Fig. 30.5 Diagrammatic sketch of a single fetal cotyledon. (Wilkin, p. 48 in *Le Placenta Humain*, J. Snoeck, ed., Masson et Cie, 1958.)

if one remembers that placental growth must necessarily be synchronous with uterine growth. During the latter, the implantation area of the placenta increases greatly. As a result, the implantation sites of the villous trunks of third order are spread apart, farther and farther, in all directions. As these trunks move apart they form what we have called the "drum systems," that is, a symmetrical arrangement of anchoring villi around a central axis (Wilkin, 82). The existence of these drum systems has been confirmed by several authors who have studied the general architecture of the placenta (Mayer, Panigel and Leclerc-Polyak, 52; Palliez, Delecour, Fovet, and Depreux, 61; Thoyer-Rozat and Martin, 80; Nold, 57, 58; Vartapetova, 81; Arts, 4; Crawford, 22; Smart, 69).

The insertions of the third-order trunks, taken together, form the implantation crowns (Wilkin, 82). The genesis of these crowns can be explained through the same mechanism as that which led to the formation of the drum systems (Fig. 30.6).

It follows from our description of the fetal cotyledons that their central part, devoid of villous trunks, must also be relatively poor in terminal villi. Quite often this becomes evident when macroscopic sections are made in planes which are either perpendicular or parallel to the placental plates. The central regions of the fetal cotyledons then often appear as "caverns" (see also Crawford, 22, and Spanner, 71).

The globular, drumlike shape of the fetal cotyledons is further corroborated by the macroscopic aspect of placental sections in cases of fetal death *in utero*, due to extraplacental causes. Such placental sections show whitish, rounded areas caused by ischemia of the fetal cotyledons which are in contact with the basal plate, but do not reach as far as the chorionic plate. The paleness of these areas contrasts sharply with the dark hue of the subchorionic zone of the intervillous space, which is full of maternal blood.

Placental growth during the periods of elaboration and maturity can be seen as an increase in the area of the placental surfaces (basal and chorionic plates) and as an increase in the thickness of the placenta. The determination of the actual value of these dimensions at various stages of pregnancy is open to several sources of error, not the least of which is the fact that the dimensions of the placenta (diameter, thickness, and volume) after delivery are greatly different from those of the functional organ in situ because of the collapse of the intervillous space. Thus, a variety of conflicting measurements have been obtained (Grosser, 31; Arey, 2; Spanner, 71; Stieve, 74; Hamilton and Boyd, 32). However, we agree with Hamilton and Boyd that, whereas the

area of the plates increases progressively throughout gestation, the thickness of the placenta increases at a particularly rapid rate between the 4th and 7th month.

This phenomenon of placental growth occurs through the development of the individual fetal cotyledons. Crawford (22) reckoned that between the 12th and 40th week each fetal cotyledon goes through a five hundred-fold increase. According to our observations, this cotyledonary development results, on the one hand, from the lengthening of existing villous trunks and proliferation of new second- and third-order trunks, at the expense of the existing primary trunks; and on the other hand, from the formation of new drum systems from the original villous pedicle. It follows (Wilkin, 82) that the small cotyledons (mainly peripheral) are made up of a single drum system, whereas the large cotyledons (mainly central) may include as many as five of these systems.

Our description of the cotyledonary growth in the foregoing paragraph accounts for the large discrepancies between the number of cotyledons reported by different authors. If one regards each pedicle or first-order trunk as the source of only one fetal cotyledon, single or multiple, then the number of cotyledons is equal to the number of pedicles (20–40) and is immutably fixed as soon as the chorion frondosum is formed. If, on the other hand, one regards each drum system by itself (subcotyledon of Smart, 69) as one fetal cotyledon, then the number of these cotyledons increases during the gestation period to reach a value of 80–90 near term.

The drum systems become ramified with the appearance of multiple branches, often formed at acute angles

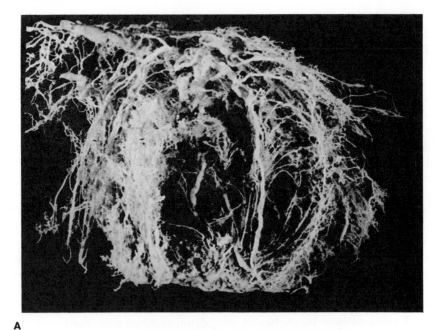

A

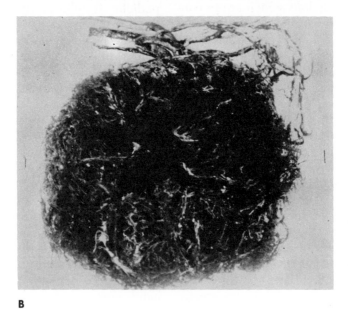

B

Fig. 30.6 *A.* Vertical section of a single fetal cotyledon, with only one "tambour" system. Venous cast with 7 percent plexene. Corrosion preparation. (Wilkin, *Gynecol. Obstet.* 53:239, 1954.) *B.* Basal view of a single fetal cotyledon showing the "implantation crown." Plexene 10 percent. Arterial and venous injection. Corrosion preparation. (Wilkin, *Gynecol. Obstet.* 53:239, 1954.)

of the third-order trunks, and running chiefly toward the periphery. The main branches may follow a course parallel to that of the third-order trunks, from which they originate, either toward the chorionic plate or toward the basal plate; in the vicinity of which they may, like the third-order trunks, make an upward curve. The smaller branches produce, over their entire length, multiple offshoots which are directed toward the periphery of the drum system. Finally, both types of preterminal centrifugal branches, originating from second- and third-order trunks, end in multiple villous tufts. Each of these terminal tufts is made up of ten or a dozen villi.

These villi begin to grow as buds ("growing ends" of Crawford) and at first receive their blood supply only through the paravascular capillary network sheathing the preterminal branches (Bøe, 10). Later they differentiate into two main types, depending on their location and the time of their appearance during organogenesis. The villi, located in the subchorionic region, appear as fingerlike expansions, long and thin (the future digitaliform or fingerlike villi). Those villi, located in the juxtabasal portion of the intervillous space, are thicker and generally shorter and give rise to numerous circumvolutions (the future "villosités en massue" or clublike villi).

3. *Changes in the cytotrophoblastic layers.* During the period of placental elaboration (22nd day to the end of the 4th month) the various types of cytotrophoblast undergo profound changes.

The chorionic cytotrophoblast stops proliferating and often shows signs of degeneration. The cytotrophoblast of the villi, which at first forms a continuous unilaminar layer of cells, the so-called Langhans' cells, becomes progressively sparser and ends up by leaving an ever-dwindling number of isolated Langhans' cells.

The cytotrophoblastic columns progressively disappear as early as the end of the 2nd month, to be replaced by connective tissue originating from the core of the villi. In similar fashion, the cytotrophoblastic shell becomes thinner. After the 4th month there remain only a few cytotrophoblastic elements still clearly recognizable among the maternal decidual cells.

Contrasting with the retrogression of the Langhans' layer and the basal cytotrophoblast (cytotrophoblastic columns and shell), one observes during this phase of placental elaboration the appearance of new cytotrophoblastic elements: the cytotrophoblastic islets (Fig. 30.7). The nature, genesis, and meaning of these rounded cell clusters are still matters of debate. They show, according to our own observations, an important common characteristic – the presence within the islets of small, sclerotic, avascular, villous cores. A hyaline substance which is eosinophilic and strongly PAS positive (the so-called fibrinoid substance) is also quite often observed on the periphery of these islets. These cytotrophoblastic islets are usually located at the periphery of the cotyledonary drum systems. It seems unlikely that they are of maternal origin since they appear within an intervillous space surrounded on all sides by fetal tissue. More probably, they originate by proliferation within certain terminal villi, located at the periphery of the drum systems. However, we agree with Stieve (73, 75) and Stieve and von Der Heide (76, 77) that, from the 4th month onward, they progressively

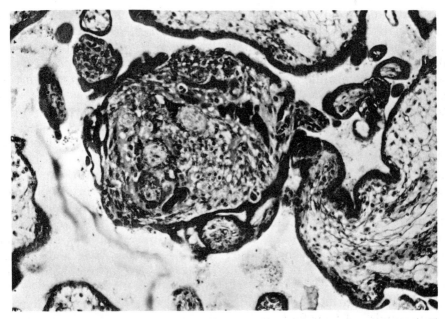

Fig. 30.7 Cytotrophoblastic islet from a 5-month placenta. Several avascular villi of small diameter amidst the cytotrophoblastic cells. (*Vokaer*, p. 72 in *Le Placenta Humain*, J. Snoeck, ed. Masson et Cie, 1958.)

merge into one another to form incomplete cellular partitions around the fetal cotyledons (the intercotyledonary septa) (Figs. 30.8 and 30.9).

The mode of formation of the septa has been a matter of dispute, but we believe that the mechanism just stated satisfactorily explains their morphogenesis and morphological characteristics. The following confirmatory points may be cited: (1) The septa late appear in the course of placental organogenesis, at a time when the intervillous space has already been long in existence. It is hard to believe, in contradistinction to the assertions of some authors (Grosser, 31), in the persistence of decidual trabeculae to this stage. (2) The septa are discontinuous and incomplete (Becker and Jipp, 9). (3) The septa are usually absent in the subchorionic portion of the intervillous

space and the great majority of the terminal villi originate from third-order trunks. The first- and second-order trunks are devoid of terminal offshoots.

The septa merge with the cytotrophoblast of the basal plate at the time the definitive syncytium disappears from the floor of the intervillous space. The basal extremities of the septa are thus originally composed only of cytotrophoblastic cells. Because of the thickening of the placenta and consequent increase in the distance between the floor and the roof of the intervillous space, part of the basal plate, including both its degenerative cytotrophoblastic layer and its decidual basalis (maternal), may be included in the septal base between the 4th and 7th months (Fig. 30.9). The opening of the uteroplacental veins into the intervillous space, which

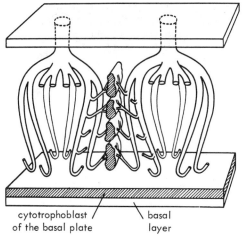

cytotrophoblast
of the basal plate

basal
layer

Fig. 30.8 Diagrammatic representation of the spatial relationships between the fetal cotyledonary systems and the cytotrophoblastic islets.

is initially located at the level of the basal plate, may thus later be shifted to another aspect of a septal foot (Fig. 30.10). It is understandable that the secondary inclusion of maternal ele-ments (decidual cells and maternal vessels) in the base of the septa has led some authors to attribute an exclusively maternal origin to these septa. Similarly, studies of the sex chromatin of cells located in the septal bases would be expected to demonstrate Barr's corpuscles, even in cases of male fetuses (Sadowsky et al., 66; Klinger et al., 48, 49). Nonetheless, it is easy to distinguish cytologically between the decidual elements, with their clear cytoplasm, and the trophoblastic cells, with their dark, strongly basophilic cytoplasm (Fig. 30.10).

The septa subdivide the primitive blood pool of the intervillous space into a variable number of cotyledonary or even subcotyledonary cavities, communicating with each other through an undivided subchorionic pool. Cleavage of some of these septa, during the expulsion of the placenta, disclose on the maternal (uterine) aspect of the placenta 12 or more polygonal fields of

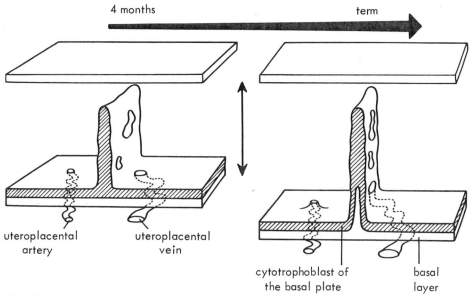

4 months

term

uteroplacental
artery

uteroplacental
vein

cytotrophoblast of
the basal plate

basal
layer

Fig. 30.9 Diagrammatic representation of the development of the intercotyledonary septa. From the 4th month to term.

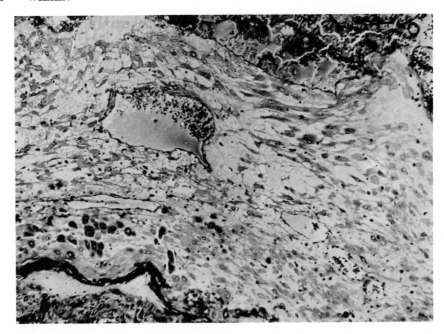

Fig. 30.10 Juxtabasal part ("foot") of an intercotyledonary septum from a full-term placenta. In the left bottom corner are several dark-staining cytotrophoblastic cells and in the central part of the septum, a maternal vein. The clear cells are maternal decidual cells.

widely different sizes—the maternal cotyledons. The number of maternal cotyledons does not exactly correspond to the number of fetal cotyledons since the arrangement of the septa is not constant, and since some septa which remain intact in the process of delivery may not appear on the maternal aspect of the placenta.

Stage of Maturity

From the end of the 4th month to full term (period of maturity) the placenta retains the structure which we have described in previous paragraphs, and which is represented diagrammatically in Figure 30.11. This picture, which differs only slightly from that proposed in 1954 (Wilkin, 82) diverges widely from the conceptions of Bumm (18), Stieve (72), and Spanner (71). On the other hand, it exhibits similarities to those of Nold (58) and Smart (69) with regard to structure of the villous network, and to that of Ramsey (63) with reference to the maternal circulation in the intervillous space.

It is impossible to give here a complete critical review of the placental structures which have been proposed (Romney and Reid, 65; Franken, 29; Florange and Höer, 27). However, substantial agreement seems now to have been reached on the structural unit which we have called drum system, and which is sometimes described as "onionlike" (Mayer et al., 52) or "ball-like" (Nold, 58).

The "chandelier" arrangement of the fetal cotyledonary tree (Spanner, 71) has been unanimously discarded, as have the labyrinthine arrangement de-

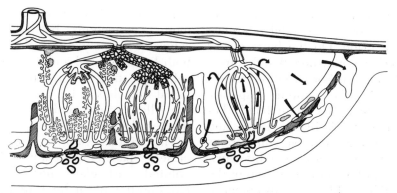

Fig. 30.11 Diagrammatic representation of the general structure of the human placenta. Top: Chorial plate (amniotic epithelium, chorial connective tissue, allantochorionic vessels with anastomosis between the umbilical arteries, chorial cytotrophoblast (hatched), and Langhans' fibrinoid layer (dotted). Bottom: Basal plate (basal cytotrophoblast with intercotyledonary septa), Rohr's fibrinoid layer (dotted), Nitabuch's fibrinoid layer (stippled line), basal decidua with uteroplacental arteries (heavy line), and uteroplacental veins (light line). The intervillous space is limited by the chorial and the basal plates. The diagram shows on the left a multiple fetal cotyledon (only two "tambours" systems are sketched), and on the right, a single fetal cotyledon (the arrows point out the direction of the maternal blood flow inside the intervillous space).

scribed by Stieve (72) for the fetal vascular system, and the arteriovenous anastomoses reported by Danesino (23).

On the other hand, the upward curving of the third-order trunks at the level of the basal plate, and the formation of the implantation crowns which we were the first to describe, are not yet unanimously accepted. However, Crawford, who in his earlier publications denied the existence of these anatomical structures, writes in his last paper on the subject (22, p. 1551) ". . . there is little doubt that a proportion of these most peripheral or fixing trunks inserted into the decidua do travel in the decidua horizontally for a time and then curve upward to bear more divisions, ending in capillary structures." However, he agrees with Arts (3, 4) in thinking that anchoring villous trunks, obliterated by endar-

teritis (?) were not filled in the casts we have described, and that this artifact accounts for the implantation crowns. However, he gives no basis for this argument. This difference in opinion seems to us simply to result from an incorrect translation, and the lack of histological studies by Crawford and Arts. Smart (69, p. 931), making use of an injection technique similar to ours, has corroborated our outline in every detail: "The subcotyledon [our drum system] takes the form of a hollow globe. . . . The primary villous arteries at the maternal pole . . . turn sharply back in the same plane. Their many branches form a dense cortex around a central, irregular core which communicates with the exterior through a small hole at the maternal pole, which is ringed by the recurrent vessels."

THE FETAL CAPILLARY NETWORK. We must now turn to a description of the fetal capillary network to which, up to now, only incidental reference has been made. On the basis of our 1954 work, we may note that the first-, second-, and third-order villous trunks have a veillike ("en voilette") capillary network which lies immediately beneath their trophoblastic layer, and which forms anastomotic connections with the main arteries and veins coursing through the central portion of the trunks (Fig. 30.12). The physiological significance of this veillike network (or paravascular plexus of Bøe, 10, 11) is still unknown; however, it gives rise to the primary capillary network of the growing villous buds.

When the villi, stricto sensu, are fully mature, they show evidence of a more complex capillary network. This network is made up of capillaries

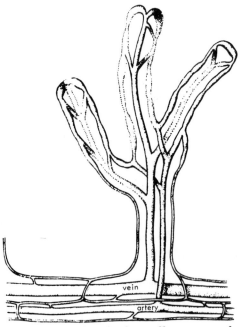

Fig. 30.12 The fetal capillary network. (After Arts, *Am. J. Obstet. Gynecol.* 82:147, 159, 1961, published by the C. V. Mosby Co., St. Louis.)

which form short transverse anastomotic connections between themselves. The network is then linked both by an arterial and a venous vessel, originating from the trunk preterminal branches to the main vessels of the villous trunks, and also directly to the veillike network.

The villous capillary network is closely spaced and elaborately convoluted, particularly near the juxtabasal portion of the intervillous space, and the periphery of the drum systems, that is, in areas where the villi assume a clublike shape (Fig. 30.13). Close to the subchorionic region of the intervillous space—where the fingerlike villi are formed—the villous capillaries are less closely spaced and less convoluted (Fig. 30.14). However, they still show the same characteristics. Each villus has 2–8 capillaries, according to its diameter; the length of the villous capillary network varies between 0.2–0.8 mm.

Some authors (Crawford, 22; Mayer et al., 52) have noticed marked variations in the diameter of the villous network capillaries after intravascular injections of India ink. These variations do not appear in our own material (our casts being made from relatively viscous plastics) and were probably due to vasomotor activity of the villous vessels. Such activity was directly observed and filmed by ten Berge (79).

THE MATERNAL PLACENTAL CIRCULATION. As we mentioned earlier, the maternal placental circulation becomes functional with the opening of the spiral arteries into the intervillous lacunae, at about the 14th and 15th day of gestation. The endometrial capillaries and superficial venous sinuses are eroded earlier (9th–13th day) by the trophoblast.

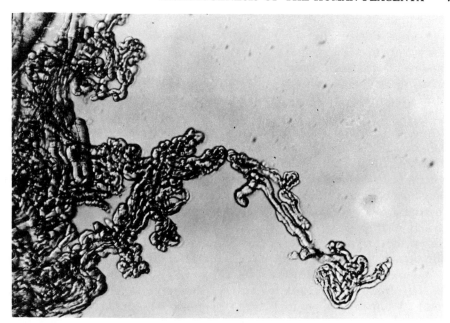

Fig. 30.13 Juxtabasal villous tuft. Casting in polyester resin. Villus *"en massue."* ×84 (Wilkin, *Gynécol. Obstét.* 53:239, 1954.)

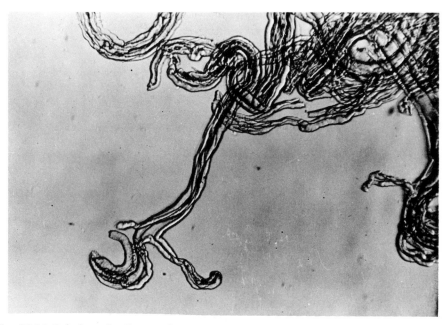

Fig. 30.14 Subchorial villous tuft. Casting in polyester resin. Corrosion preparation. Fingerlike villus. ×84 (Wilkin, *Gynécol. Obstét.* 53:239, 1954.)

The spiral (uteroplacental) arteries exhibit great differences along their course within the placental basal plate. At the level of the deciduomyometrial junction, their diameter does not exceed 20 μ and they still possess their muscular wall. Within the basal plate, they lose their musculature and their diameter increases considerably, running to about 200 μ. Their endothelium degenerates, and their wall is finally reduced to a layer of fibrinoid material containing a few necrotic cells (Figs. 30.15 and 30.16).

During the first half of pregnancy, the uteroplacental arteries are invaded along their entire course through the basal plate from the decidua toward the arterial lumen, shown in Figure 30.17 (Boyd, 13; Boyd and Hamilton, 14; Wilkin, 85). In 1956, Boyd (13) and Wislocki (13) ascribed an endothelial origin to these cells; however, McKay (53) recognized their trophoblastic origin. The endovascular giant cells observed in the hamster by Orsini (59) are apparently similar.

Boyd and Hamilton (14) suggest that this arterial narrowing protects the intervillous space against the violence of sudden changes in blood pressure. The intra-arterial cytotrophoblastic cells gradually disappear, carried by the blood stream toward the intervillous space. They probably take part in the formation of the projection cone which we have sometimes observed at the opening of the uteroplacental arteries in the intervillous space. These cones have often been mistaken for the foot of the septa in nonserial histological sections. This is what led to Bumm's (18) erroneous interpretation of the maternal placental circulation.

The number and disposition of the openings of the uteroplacental arteries

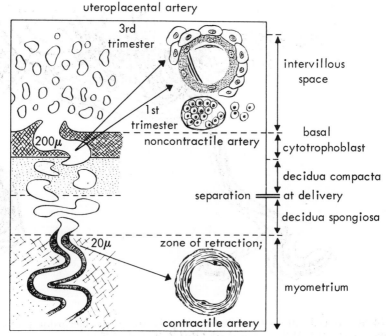

Fig. 30.15 Diagrammatic sketch of the uteroplacental artery.

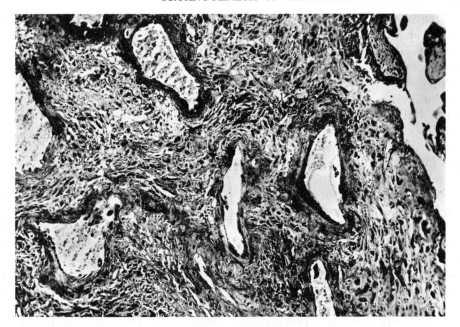

Fig. 30.16 Uteroplacental artery inside the basal plate. Intervillous space on the right. Fibrinoid degeneration of the arterial wall. 7-month placenta.

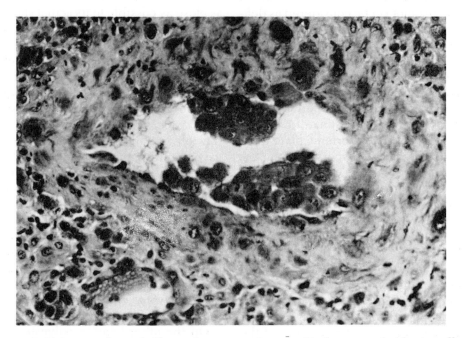

Fig. 30.17 Two and one-half month in situ placenta. Dark cytotrophoblastic cells invading the lumen of a uteroplacental artery.

into the intervillous space has been a subject of controversy. Spanner's (71) figure of 500 is probably much exaggerated. Boyd (13) at first estimated the number of these openings to be 180–320, but now considers that it must be nearer 100 (Smart, 69).

If this view proves to be true, there should exist approximately as many uteroplacental arteries as cotyledonary drum systems, which suggests a very interesting and morphogenetic relation between the respective locations of these structures. It is tempting to imagine that the uteroplacental arteries are open in the center of the implantation crowns and that the arterial blood is injected into the intervillous space in the middle of the drum systems. Although Bøe (10), Franken (28), and our own observations corroborate the frequency of arterial openings in the center of the maternal cotyledons, the spatial relationship mentioned above cannot yet be considered as definitely established.

The maternal blood, pouring from the uteroplacental arteries under high pressure (70–80 mm Hg, according to Alvarez and Caldeyro, 1), enters the intervillous space intermittently as jets (Borell and Westman, 12). The blood reaches the chorionic plate without notable lateral dispersion (Ramsey, 62, in the monkey; Wilkin, unpublished observations) and far too rapidly to consider that it traverses a capillary network, as suggested by Hörmann (44). Ramsey and co-workers (64) have established that the uteroplacental arteries in the monkey are not all functionally permeable at the same time, and give off blood streams independently of each other. This crucial observation is reminiscent of the condition of the spiral arteries of the endometrium during menstruation (Markee, 51) and explains the heterogeneous composition of the intervillous blood (Fuchs, Spackman, and Assali, 30).

We have been able to study the maternal circulation during a Porro operation on a 5-months' pregnant woman with a cervical carcinoma. Injection of India ink into the uterine arteries confirmed Borell's jets, as well as the heterogeneity of the arterial blood diffusion within the intervillous space. Serial sections showed that some areas of the intervillous space were devoid of India ink; the subchorionic blood lake and marginal region were rich in injected material – an observation suggesting an important slowing of circulation in these areas. The close parallelism between the third-order trunks and the arterial streams was also demonstrated.

This placenta was still adherent to the uterine wall and was in a condition as close as possible to its actual state in vivo. The pregnant uterus had been frozen in toto, immediately after its removal. All the vascular pedicles were ligated at nearly the same time. It was cut into 1-cm slices with a Gigli saw, to avoid collapse of the intervillous space. Histometry (by means of the integration plate) of this placenta gave figures approximately twice as high for the intervillous space as those found in expelled placenta (60% instead of 37.7%). It follows that the volume of the intervillous space of the placenta in its functional state must be approximately twice as large as that of the delivered placenta. According to our calculations, this volume is 177–265 ml, a value which is similar to that published by Jonen (46).

On the other hand, a polyester cast of the intervillous space of an in situ placenta (hysterectomy for uterine rupture at 8 months' gestation) shows the intervillous space as a labyrinth, occupying more than half of the total placental volume).

Because of the basic structure of the cotyledonary villous arborization, the subchorionic region of the intervillous space and the marginal area—which is its continuation—are poorest in villi. The names "subchorionic blood lake" and "marginal sinus" which were applied to these areas by Spanner are therefore easy to understand. The maternal blood of the intervillous space goes from these areas to the openings of the uteroplacental veins. These are located over the entire surface of the basal plate, as shown by the preparations of Hamilton and Boyd (32), Ramsey (62), Kladetzky-Haubrich (47), and of ourselves (Wilkin, 84). However, these venous openings are particularly wide at the marginal area of the placenta, close to the placental periphery

where the uteroplacental arteries are virtually absent. The idea of venous drainage exclusively through the marginal region of the placenta (marginal sinus) is no longer considered tenable by most authors.

Quite often, the uteroplacental veins open into the intervillous space after having traveled for some distance within the basal plate in a direction parallel to the floor of the intervillous space (Fig. 30.18). During a uterine contraction, the hydrostatic pressure within this space increases (Caldeyro-Barcia and Poseiro, 19; Hendricks et al., 35) and it seems probable that these veins are then shut by a valve mechanism which prevents the collapse of the intervillous space. Masses of villous tissue which have been sucked into the lumen of these veins are also frequently observed.

The number of these venous openings is not well known. According to Spanner (71), it is 170; Franken (28)

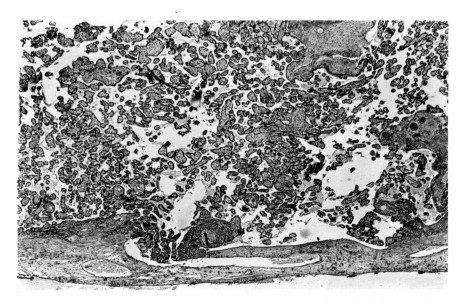

Fig. 30.18 Venous opening in the central part of the basal plate of a full-term placenta. (Wilkin, p. 58 in *Le Placenta Humain*, J. Snoeck, ed. Masson et Cie, 1958.)

counts only 79. Their arrangement in relation to the maternal cotyledons and to the drum systems is a matter of dispute (cf. Ramsey, 62; Boyd, 13; Arts, 4). We agree with Bøe (10) and Franken (28) that these openings are chiefly grouped at the periphery of the maternal cotyledons, especially near the septa.

The abundance of venous orifices near the periphery of the placenta can readily be explained since this periphery is formed by the juxtaposition of the peripheral portions of the maternal marginal cotyledons. These openings can be seen macroscopically in the delivered placenta and have been named "abscission windows" by Schneider (68).

The circulatory pattern within the intervillous space is ultimately the end result of a progressive decrease in the hydrostatic pressure gradient. This pressure, as high as 80 mm Hg at the level of uteroplacental arteries, decreases progressively along the arterial streams and the basal plate to the chorionic plate, to reach a mean value of 10 mm Hg in the rest of the intervillous space between uterine contractions, and 30–50 mm Hg during contractions. The blood is finally forced into the uteroplacental veins, having a pressure of only 8 mm Hg.

The maternal blood flow in the placenta is extremely important, since it reaches 600 ml per minute according to the estimation of Browne and Veall (17). On the other hand, Ramsey (64) has shown that during uterine contractions, the placental blood flow is curtailed or even abolished.

Lastly, it must be pointed out that the hydrostatic pressure within the villous capillaries, lying between the hydrostatic pressure within the umbilical arteries (48 mm Hg) and the pressure within the umbilical vein (24 mm Hg) is considerably higher than the pressure in the intervillous space. It follows that at least near term, both the villi and umbilical cord are permanently turgescent in vivo. This difference between the pressure within the fetal capillaries and the pressure within the intervillous space remains essentially at the same level during uterine contractions (Margolis and Orcutt, 50).

FUNCTIONAL CONSEQUENCES OF HUMAN PLACENTAL MORPHOLOGY AND OF THE PATTERN OF ITS CIRCULATORY SYSTEMS. Our description of human placental morphology and the pattern of circulatory systems (Wilkin, 84) provides grounds upon which to reject the hypothesis that the fetal and maternal blood flow in the placenta, on the two sides of the exchange membrane, runs parallel but in opposite directions. Such a pattern has been reported in the rabbit by Mossman (55) and Noer (56); in the sheep by Barcroft and Barron (5), and in the rat by Holmes and Davies (43), and suggested as applicable to the human by Falkiner (25, 26) and Beck (8). This arrangement, which is eminently favorable to fetomaternal exchanges, is not present in man. On the contrary, we were able to show on mathematical grounds (Wilkin, 84) that the human placenta has at its disposal another anatomic device particularly suitable for exchanges by diffusion. Indeed, the villous capillary network in the human placenta cannot be assimilated to a continuous channel with a single arterial inlet and a single venous exit. On the contrary, it is formed of a great many villous capillaries (about 50 million in the full-term placenta, Wilkin and Bursztein, 86), each with its arterial inlet and its venous outlet. The arterial extremity of each villous capillary network, whatever its position within the intervillous space, is subject to roughly similar concentration and hydrostatic pressure gradients.

This system has recently been called a "multivillous stream system" by Bartels and co-workers, (7) who applied our analysis of the diffusion phenomenon to an artificial system equivalent to a simplified model of the human placenta (Fig. 30.19). They were able to corroborate the superiority of such an arrangement over a diffusion system based on parallel flow in the same directions.

Summary

Study of human placental organogenesis aids in interpreting the basic structure of the mature placenta. This structure is essentially determined by the disposition of the fetal circulatory system, which has the cotyledonary drum system as a morphological unit.

Maternal circulation within the intervillous space takes place through uteroplacental arterial and venous openings distributed over the entire surface of the basal plate, and as a result of a decreasing gradient in hydrostatic pressure.

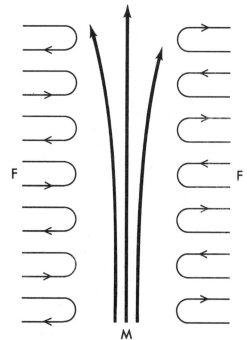

Fig. 30.19 A simplified system exhibiting the anatomical relationships between fetal, F, and maternal, M, circulations in the human placenta, showing "multivillous stream systems." (Bartels et al., *Am. J. Obstet. Gynecol.* 84:1714, 1962.)

The anatomical arrangement of the maternal and fetal circulations in the human placenta gives rise to an exchange system which appears to be particularly well adapted to diffusion phenomena.

References

1. Alvarez, H., and R. Caldeyro, "Contractility of the Human Uterus Recorded by New Methods," *Surg. Gynecol. Obstet.* 91: 1 (1950).

2. Arey, L. B., *Obstetrics and Gynecology*, A. H. Curtis, ed. Philadelphia: Saunders, chap. 14 (1933).

3. Arts, N. F. Th., "Een Onderzoek over het Vaatstelsel van de Placenta," (Centrale Drukkery n.v.) p. 148. Nymegen (1958).

4. ———, "Investigations on the Vascular System of the Placenta. I. General Introduction and the Fetal Vascular System. II. The Maternal Vascular System," *Am. J. Obstet. Gynecol.* 82:147, 159 (1961).

5. Barcroft, S., and D. H. Barron, "Observations upon the Form and Relations of Maternal and Fetal Vessels in the Placenta of the Sheep," *Anat. Record* 94:569 (1946).

6. Bargmann, W., and A. Knoop, "Elek-

tronenmikroskopische Untersuchungen an Plazentarzotten des Menschen (Bemerkungen zum Synzytiumproblem," *Z. Zellforsch.* 50:472 (1959).

7. Bartels, H., W. Moll, and J. Metcalfe, "Physiology of Gas Exchange in the Human Placenta," *Am. J. Obstet. Gynecol.* 84: 1714 (1962).

8. Beck, A. C., "The Obstetrician's Responsibility for the Hazards of the First Few Days of Life with Special Reference to Anoxia and Prematurity," *Am. J. Obstet. Gynecol.* 51:173 (1946).

9. Becker, V., and P. Jipp, "Ueber die Trophoblastschale der Menschlichen Plazenta," *Geburtsh. Frauenheilk.* 23:466 (1963).

10. Bøe, F., "Studies on the Vascularization of the Human Placenta," *Acta Obstet. Gynecol. Scand. Suppl.* 5, 32 (1953).

11. ———, "Vascular Morphology of the Human Placenta," *The Mammalian Fetus; Physiological Aspects of Development.* Cold Spring Harbor Symp. Quant. Biol. New York: The Biological Laboratory, Vol. XIX (1954).

12. Borell, U., and A. Westman, "Eine Arteriorgraphische Studie des Plazentarkreislauf," *Geburtsh. Frauenheilk.* 18:1 (1958).

13. Boyd, J. D., "Morphology and Physiology of the Uteroplacental Circulation," *Gestation,* Trans. 2nd Conf. C. A. Villee, ed. New York: The Josiah Macy Jr. Foundation, p. 132 (1956).

14. ———, and W. J. Hamilton, "Cells in the Spiral Arteries of the Pregnant Uterus," *J. Anat. London* 90:595 (1956).

15. ———, and ———, "The Giant Cells of the Pregnant Human Uterus," *J. Obstet. Gynaecol. Brit. Empire* 67:208 (1960).

16. ———, and ———, "Stromal Trophoblastic Buds," *J. Obstet. Gynaecol. Brit. Commonwealth* 71:2 (1964).

17. Browne, J. C. M., and N. Veall, "The Maternal Placental Blood Flow in Normotensive and Hypertensive Women," *J. Obstet. Gynaecol. Brit. Empire* 60: 141 (1953).

18. Bumm, E., "Ueber die Entwicklung des Mütterlichen Blutkreislaufes in der Menschlichen Plazenta," *Arch. Gynäekol.* 43:181 (1893).

19. Caldeyro-Barcia, R., and J. J. Poseiro, "Physiology of the Uterine Contraction," *Clin. Obstet. Gynecol.* 3:386 (1960).

20. Carter, J. E., "Morphologic Evidence of Syncytial Formation from the Cytotrophoblastic Cells," *Obstet. Gynecol.* 23:647 (1964).

21. Crawford, J. M., "A Study of Human Placental Growth with Observations of the Placenta in Erythroblastosis *foetalis,*" *J. Obstet. Gynaecol. Brit. Empire* 66:885 (1959).

22. ———, "Vascular Anatomy of the Human Placenta," *Am. J. Obstet. Gynecol.* 84:1543 (1962).

23. Danesino, V., "Blocking and Arteriovenous Anastomosis Arrangements of the Fetal Vessels in the Human Placenta," *Arch. Obstet. Gynecol.* 55:251 (1950).

24. Douglas, G. W., I. Thomas, M. Carr, M. N. Cullen, and R. Morris, "Trophoblast in the Circulating Blood during Pregnancy," *Am. J. Obstet. Gynecol.* 78: 960 (1959).

25. Falkiner, N. M., "Circulation of the Maternal Blood through the Placenta," *Irish J. Med. Sci.* 6:59 (1939).

26. ———, "Placental Circulation," *Proc. Roy. Soc. Med.* 37:417 (1947).

27. Florange, W., and W. Höer, "Die Menschliche Placenta, Gefässverlauf und Placentaschema. I. Der Gefässverlauf in der Menschlichen Placenta," *Ann. Univ. Saraviensis Med.* 6:106 (1958).

28. Franken, H., "Beitrag zur Veranschaulichung von Struktur und Funktion der Placenta," *Zbl. Gynäekol.* 76:729 (1954).

29. ———, "Die Menschliche Placenta, Gefässverlauf und Placentaschema (Struktur und Funktion)," *Ann. Univ. Saraviensis Med.* 6:7 (1958).

30. Fuchs, F., T. Spackman, and N. S. Assali, "Complexity and Nonhomogeneity of the Intervillous Space," *Am. J. Obstet. Gynecol.* 86:226 (1963).

31. Grosser, O., "Frühentwicklung, Eihaubtbildung und Plazentation des Menschen und der Saügetiere," München: Bergmann, p. 454 (1927).

32. Hamilton, W. J., and J. D. Boyd, "Observations on the Human Placenta," *Proc. Roy. Soc. Med.* 44:489 (1951).

33. ———, and ———, "Development of the Human Placenta in the First Months of Gestation," *J. Anat. London* 94:297 (1960).

34. ———, ———, and H. W. Mossman, *Human Embryology,* Heffer, ed. Cam-

bridge: Cambridge University Press (1952).

35. Hendricks, C. H., E. J. Quilligan, C. Tyler, and G. J. Tucker, "Pressure Relationship between the Intervillous Space and the Amniotic Fluid in the Human Term Pregnancy," *Am. J. Obstet. Gynecol.* 77:1028 (1959).

36. Hertig, A. T., "Angiogenesis in the Early Human Chorion and in the Primary Placenta of the Macaque Monkey," *Contrib. Embryol. Carnegie Inst. Wash.* 25:37 (1935).

37. ———, "On the Development of the Amnion and Exocoelomic Membrane in the Previllous Human Ovum," *Yale J. Biol. Med.* 18:107 (1945).

38. ———, "Pathological Aspects," *The Placenta and Fetal Membranes*, C. A. Villee, ed. Baltimore: Williams & Wilkins, p. 109 (1960).

39. ———, and J. Rock, "The Human Ova of the Previllous Stage, Having an Ovulation Age of about Eleven and Twelve Days Respectively," *Contrib. Embryol. Carnegie Inst. Wash.* 29:127 (1941).

40. ———, and ———, "On the Development of the Early Human Ovum, with Special Reference to the Trophoblast of the Previllous Stage: A Description of Seven Normal and Five Pathologic Human Ova," *Am. J. Obstet. Gynecol.* 47:149 (1944).

41. ———, and ———, "Two Human Ova of the Previllous Stage, Having a Development Age of about Seven and Nine Days Respectively," *Contrib. Embryol. Carnegie Inst. Wash.* 31:65 (1945).

42. ———, and ———, "On a Human Blastula Recovered from the Uterine Cavity Four Days after Ovulation," *Anat. Record* 94, Suppl. 25 (1946).

43. Holmes, R. P., and D. V. Davies, "The Vascular Pattern of the Placenta and Its Development in the Rat," *J. Obstet. Gynaecol. Brit. Empire* 55:583 (1948).

44. Hörmann, G., "Zur Systematik einer Pathologie der Menschlichen Plazenta," *Arch. Gynäekol.* 191:297 (1958).

45. Johnstone, R. W., "Contribution to the Study of the Early Human Ovum Based upon the Investigation of I, a Very Early Ovum Embedded in the Uterus and II, a Very Early Ovum Embedded in the Infundibulum of the Tube," *J. Obstet.*

Gynaecol. Brit. Empire 25:231 (1914).

46. Jonen, P., "Experimentalle Untersuchungen über die Kapazität des Intervillösen Raumes der Menschlichen Plazenta," *Arch. Gynäekol.* 129:610 (1922).

47. Kladetzky-Haubrich, A. L., "Beobachtung über den Venösen Abfluss aus der Plazenta an Hand von Befunden an einer in situ Fixierte Plazenta aus dem 5," *Monatsh. Acta Anat. Basel* 14:168 (1952).

48. Klinger, H. P., and K. S. Ludwig, "Sind die Septen une die Groszelligen Inseln der Plazenta aus Mütterlichen oder Kindlichen Gewebe Aufgebaut," *Z. Anat. Entwicklungsgeschichte* 120:95 (1957).

49. ———, ———, and H. G. Schwarzacher, "Neue Ergebnisse der Sex-Chromatin-Forschung an Placenta und Eihäuten," *Gynaecologia* 146:328 (1958).

50. Margolis, A. J., and R. E. Orcutt, "Pressures in Human Umbilical Vessels *in utero*," *Am. J. Obstet. Gynecol.* 80:573 (1960).

51. Markee, J. E., "Morphological and Endocrine Basis for Menstrual Bleeding," *Progress in Gynecology* J. V. Meigs and S. M. Sturgis, eds. New York: Grune & Stratton, vol. 2 (1960).

52. Mayer, M., M. Panigel, and H. Leclerc-Polyak, "Observations sur l'Aspect et la Disposition des Vaisseaux et des Capillaires Foetaux dans le Placenta Humain," *Gynécol. Obstét.* 55:257 (1956).

53. McKay, D. G., *Gestation*, Trans. 2nd. Conf., C. A. Villee, ed. New York: The Josiah Macy Foundation (1956).

54. Midgley, A. R., Jr., G. B. Pierce, Jr., G. A. Deneau, and J. R. G. Gosling, "Morphogenesis of Syncytiotrophoblast *in vivo*," *Science* 41:349 (1963).

55. Mossman, H. W., "The Rabbit Placenta and the Problem of Placental Transmission," *Am. J. Anat.* 37:433 (1926).

56. Noer, R., "A Study of the Effect of Flow Direction on the Placental Transmission, Using Artificial Placenta," *Anat. Record* 96:383 (1946).

57. Nold, B., "Ueber den Fetalen Plazentarkreislauf. Morphologische Studien an Normalen Plazenten verschiedener Schwangerschaftsdauer," *Z. Geburtshilfe Gynäekol.* 150:146 (1958).

58. ———, "Ein Neues Schema des Placentarkreislaufes," *Gynaecologia Basel* 149:265 (1960).

59. Orsini, M. W., "The Trophoblastic Giant Cells and Endovascular Cells Associated with Pregnancy in the Hamster," *Am. J. Anat.* 94:273 (1954).

60. Oshizaki, Y., "Isolated Vestiges of Calcified Syncytial Knots (Orphan Bodies) in the Stroma of Chorionic Villi. Their Genesis and Implication," *Obstet. Gynecol.* 15:528 (1960).

61. Palliez, R., M. Delecour, A. Fovet, and R. Depreux, "Étude de la Vascularisation Placentaire au Cours des Grossesses Normales et Pathologiques," *Gynécol. Obstét.* 55:312 (1956).

62. Ramsey, E. M., "Distribution of Arteries and Veins in the Mammalian Placenta," *Gestation,* Trans. 2nd Conf., C. A. Villee, ed. New York: The Josiah Macy Jr. Foundation, p. 229 (1956).

63. ———, "Circulation in the Intervillous Space of the Primate Placenta," *Am. J. Obstet. Gynecol.* 84:1649 (1962).

64. ———, G. W. Corner, and M. W. Donner, "Serial and Cineradioangiographic Visualization of Maternal Circulation in the Primate (Hémochorial) Placenta," *Am. J. Obstet. Gynecol.* 86:213 (1963).

65. Romney, S. L., and D. E. Reid, "Observations on the Fetal Aspects of Placental Circulations," *Am. J. Obstet. Gynecol.* 61:83 (1951).

66. Sadowsky, A., D. M. Serr, and G. Kohn, "Composition of the Placental Septa as Shown by Nuclear Sexing," *Science* 126:609 (1957).

67. Salvaggio, A. T., G. Nigogosyan, and H. C. Mack, "Detection of Trophoblast in Cord Blood and Fetal Circulation," *Am. J. Obstet. Gynecol.* 80:1013 (1960).

68. Schneider, C. L., "Rupture of the Marginal Sinus of the Placenta: Abscission Windows," *Obstet. Gynecol.* 11:715 (1958).

69. Smart, P. J. G., "Some Observations on the Vascular Morphology of the Foetal Side of the Human Placenta," *J. Obstet. Gynaecol. Brit. Commonwealth* 69:929 (1962).

70. Snoeck, J., *Le Placenta Humain. Aspects Morphologiques et Fonctionels,* Paris: Masson et Cie (1958).

71. Spanner, R., "Mütterlicher und Kindlicher Kreislauf der Menschlichen Plazenta und seine Strombahnen," *Z. Anat. Entwicklungsgeschichte* 105:163 (1935).

72. Stieve, H., "Neue Beobachtungen über des Bau der Menschlichen Placenta (Vorläufige Mitteilung)," *Zbl. Gynäekol.* 59:434 (1935).

73. ———, "Neue Untersuchungen über die Plazenta, besonders über die Entstehung der Plazentarsepten," *Arch. Gynäekol.* 161:160 (1936).

74. ———, "Ueber das Wachstum des Menschlichen Plazenta," *Anat. Anz.* 90:225 (1940).

75. ———, "Die Entwicklung und der Bau der Menschlichen Plazenta. I. Zotten, Trophoblastinseln und Scheindewände in der Ersten Hälfte der Schwangerschaft," *Z. Mikroskop. Anat. Forschr.* 48:287 (1940).

76. ———, and von Der Heide, "Ueber die Entwicklung der Septen in der Menschlichen Plazenta," *Anat. Anz.* 92:1 (1941).

77. ———, and von Der Heide, "Anatomie der Plazenta und der Intervillösen Raumes," *Seitz-Amreich Biologie und Pathologie des Weiber,* Berlin: Urban & Schwartzenberg, vol. 7, p. 109 (1952).

78. Tenzer, W., "Graphishce Rekonstruktion des Bindegewebigen Stützskeletts der Menschlichen Plazenta," PH.D. Inauguration dissertation Medicine, Kiel (1962).

79. ten Berge, B. S., "L'activité Capillaire dans les Villosités Placentaires," *Bull. Soc. Roy. Belge Gynécol. Obstét.* 26:210 (1956).

80. Thoyer-Rozat, J., and Martin, "A Propos de l'Étude de la Circulation Foetale dans le Placenta par l'Injection de Résines Synthétiques," *Gynécol. Obstét.* 55:255 (1956).

81. Vartapetova, V. G., *Vop. Ohrany Materin Dets.* 65. *Excerpta Med.* 15:862 Abstr. (1960).

82. Wilkin, P., "Contribution à l'Étude de la Circulation Placentaire d'Origine Foetale," *Gynécol. Obstét.* 53:239 (1954).

83. ———, "Some Aspects of the Vascularization of the Human Endometrium During the Luteal Phase of the Menstrual Cycle," *Bull. Soc. Roy. Belge Gynécol. Obstét.* 25:402 (1955).

84. ———, *Le Placenta Humain, Aspects Morphologiques et Functionels,* J. Snoeck, ed. Paris: Masson et Cie (1958).

85. ———, "La Vascularisation de l'Endo-

mètre Humain au Cours de la Phase Progestéronique du Cycle Mentruel et au Cours de la Nidation Ovulaire," *Les Fonctions de Nidation et Leurs Troubles* Paris: Masson et Cie, p. 331 (1960).

86. ———, and M. Bursztein, "Méthode Quantitative de l'Évolution, au Cours de la Grossesse, de la Superficie de la Membrane d'Échange du Placenta Humain," *Compt. Rend. Assoc. Anat. Leyde* 44: 830 Extr. (1957).

87. Wislocki, G. B., and E. W. Dempsey, "Electron Microscopy of the Human Placenta," *Anat. Record* 123:133 (1955).

31

The Principal Interchange Vessels
of the Chorioallantoic Placenta
# of Mammals

H. W. MOSSMAN[*]

Department of Anatomy
Bardeen Medical Laboratories
University of Wisconsin
Madison, Wisconsin

A labyrinthine chorioallantoic placenta provides for an essentially complete interchange of oxygen and carbon dioxide, and of certain other substances between the fetal blood circulating in a capillary of a terminal allantoic villus and maternal blood circulating in an adjacent trophoblastic tubule. The apposed walls of the capillary and of the trophoblastic tubule comprise the "separation membrane" or "barrier" through which this interchange takes place (Fig. 31.1). It is almost certain that in all such placentae the blood in the fetal capillaries flows in the opposite direction to that in the adjacent maternal tubule (Fig. 31.3), thus providing the advantage of counterflow

to the exchange mechanisms, whether they involve simple diffusion, osmosis, pinocytosis, or active transport.

Physiological interchange between mother and fetus in the labyrinth is, to an appreciable extent, always dependent upon the nature of this separation membrane. Because of this, great effort has been directed toward determination of the kind and number of layers of which it is composed, both definitively and during its development. Yet, with all this past effort, the few studies that have now been made utilizing electronmicroscopy have shown that we were often very wrong in our interpretations of even the number of these layers. Also, electronmicroscopy is confirming and elaborating the information, provided through many years by physiological studies, show-

[*] Aided by grant HD 00277-08, National Institute of Health.

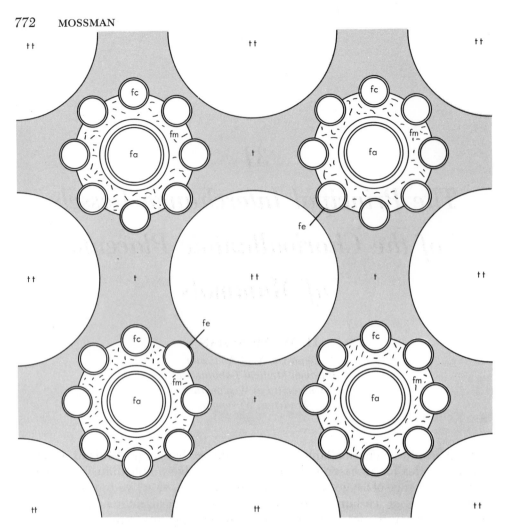

Fig. 31-1A

Fig. 31.1 Diagram to compare the relation of the maternal to fetal blood streams in the interchange area of: (*A*) a hemochorial labyrinthine placenta, and (*B*) a hemochorial villous placenta. fa, fetal arteriole (central arterial vessel of mesenchymal villus); fc, fetal capillary (capillary of interchange); fe, fetal capillary endothelium; fm, fetal mesenchyme (stroma of villus); is, intervillous space occupied by circulating maternal blood; t, trophoblast (syncytium or syntrophoblast of villus); tt, trophoblastic tubule occupied by circulating maternal blood (corresponds to is).

ing that interchange (except of oxygen and carbon dioxide) is seldom a matter of simple diffusion or osmosis. The technique indicates clearly that active transport mechanisms exist in these separation membranes or barriers. In fact, the ultrastructure of these layers also clearly confirms the physiological evidence that the placental labyrinth is an organ of very high metabolic activity in synthesis as well as in transport.

In view of these things, it is obvious that placental morphology and physi-

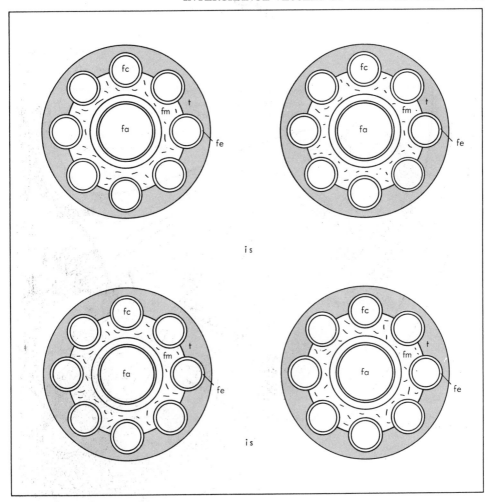

Fig. 31-1B

ology offer a challenging and rewarding field for research with more modern and sophisticated methods. It may not be so obvious that there are still a number of unanswered questions relating directly to the vessels of interchange, and to the barrier. These questions have never been investigated adequately and must be answered if one is to understand thoroughly the functional mechanism of placental interchange.

We can speak of these anatomical and physiological unknowns as "placental constants." A few examples of these constants are: the diameter of the fetal and maternal vessels of interchange, their length, the relative number of each, the linear rate of blood flow through each, the volume per minute flow, the pressure in each, the corpuscle-plasma ratios on entering and leaving these vessels, the oxygen uptake capacity of each blood stream, and so on.

Some determinations of these values

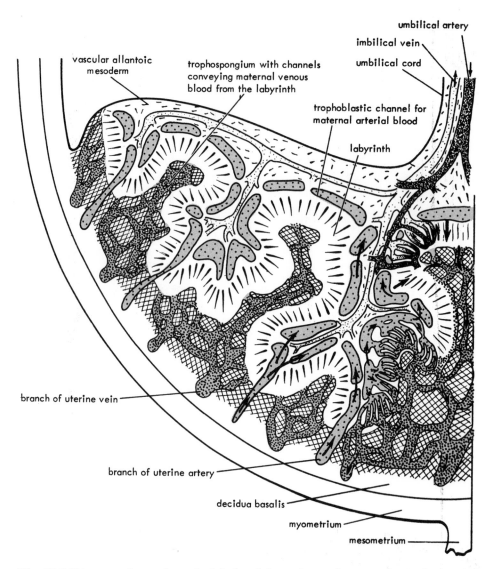

Fig. 31.2 Diagram of a moderately lobulate labyrinthine placenta of a medium-sized rodent, such as the muskrat. Note the homology of the fetal and intralobular surface of the labyrinth with the fetal surface in Fig. 31.3, and the homology of the basal *and* interlobular trophospongium with the entirely basal trophospongium of Fig. 31.3. Labyrinth, striate; trophospongium and trophoblastic giant cell layer, cross-hatched; vascular allantoic mesoderm, flecked. At the right, one small portion shows the fetal capillaries of interchange and another the maternal tubules of interchange. Fetal arterial (depleted) blood, dense stipple, small dots; fetal venous (oxygenated) blood, light stipple, small dots; maternal arterial blood, light stipple, large dots; maternal venous blood, dense stipple, large dots. Arrows indicate the direction of blood flow.

have been attempted in a few placental types; but for most of these, and for many placental types not mentioned, such determinations have not been attempted. No single placental type has been studied intensively enough to give us a total coherent idea of its labyrinthine anatomy and function. Some of these constants would be extremely difficult to obtain, even with present-day instrumental techniques. Others would be easily available, even by such unsophisticated methods as injection and wax-plate reconstruction.

Length of Interchange Vessels

For a long time I have believed that in a given species the interchange vessels of the labyrinthine placenta at the definitive stage should have a length only sufficient to effect complete interchange; that to be much longer than necessary would be wasteful and nonadaptive, and to have a wide range of lengths would be unthinkable biologically. I also realized that for some years my general impression of what this length would be had been far too great, and I have the impression that others have erred likewise. Certainly at present the area of the effective interchange membrane in any given type of placenta is unknown. Total trophoblastic surface area for the human placenta has been calculated several times (Wilkin and Bursztein, 18), but this may have little meaning in respect to the principal areas of interchange, the terminal villi.

I have been impressed by the apparently uniform length of these interchange vessels in an individual placenta, and even in placentae of different types in various species. Although no accurate measurements of these vessels could be made directly from the histological material at hand, I have nevertheless attempted to establish the approximate limits within which these vessel lengths must fall. In most of the simpler small labyrinthine placentae the thickness of the true labyrinth gives some idea of these limits, while in larger lobulated placentae, the thickness of the true labyrinthine portions of the lobules indicates these limits (Figs. 31.3 and 31.4). In other labyrinthine, and in some villous placentae, one-half the average distance between small allantoic villi containing central vessels is an approximation of the length of the small terminal villi. These are no doubt the principal functional ones so far as interchange is concerned. They are the ones that correspond to the interchange vessels of a labyrinth lobule, or of a simple labyrinth. Some varieties of placental labyrinths, because of their peculiar structure, defy any attempt to make measurements on histological sections which would yield even an approximate notion of the interchange vessel length; yet cleared vascular injections of many of these could provide measurable material.

Using these concepts, a series of rough measurements and estimates of interchange capillary and maternal tubule lengths, and of terminal villous lengths, were made on a variety of mammalian placentae, either in late pregnancy, near term, or at term. For purposes of summary, these measurements are presented for placentae having labyrinths of each of four rather distinct types (Tables 31.1 to 31.4). Since the villous regions of villous placentae correspond to the true labyrinths of labyrinthine placentae, these regions have been measured in appro-

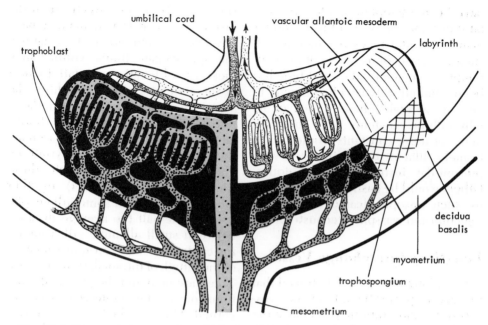

Fig. 31.3 Diagram of a simple nonlobulate labyrinthine placenta of a small rodent, such as a hamster. The labyrinth is the portion occupied by the maternal and fetal vessels of interchange. The trophospongium is occupied only by venous channels draining maternal blood after it has passed through the labyrinth. Except for a small amount of fetal mesenchyme and endothelium in the labyrinth, both portions are made up of trophoblast. The maternal blood flow through the trophoblastic tubules is diagrammed on the left side, the fetal blood flow through the capillaries of interchange is represented on the right. Both, of course, occur throughout the labyrinth. Note that the maternal and fetal blood streams flow in opposing directions in the tubules and capillaries of interchange. The extreme right side of the placenta is represented schematically to correspond to Figure 31.4. Blood indicated as in Fig. 31.2. Trophoblast, black. Arrows indicate direction of blood flow.

priate ways, and have been included.

When no estimated lengths for the interchange vessels are given, there were no available criteria on which to estimate these lengths. For instance, these vessels in bats are known to be exceedingly tortuous, in carnivores they are netlike, and in the ruminant cotyledonary placentae they probably run at right angles to the long axes of even the smaller villi, as was shown by Hamilton, Harrison, and Young (7) in *Dama dama*. If this is not true of the cotyledonary types, then one has the problem of accounting for the ex-

tremely long straight terminal villi of the elk (*Cervus canadensis*). If the vessels really parallel these villi, they could well be several times longer than seems to be the case in many other ruminants, or in any other mammalian group. It should also be remembered that these lengths are derived from measurements of paraffin-embedded and sectioned material, which means that because of tissue shrinkage estimates of vessel length are no doubt at least 20 percent less than they would have been if measured in the living condition.

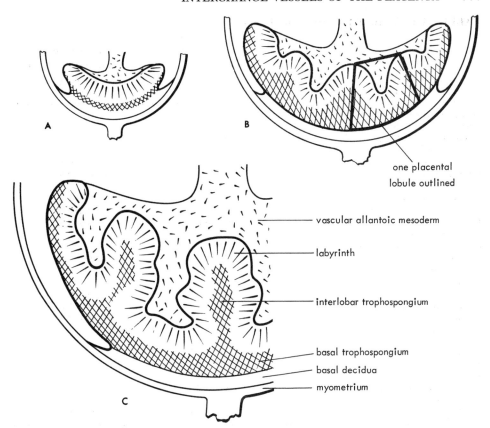

one placental
lobule outlined

vascular allantoic mesoderm

labyrinth

interlobar trophospongium

basal trophospongium

basal decidua

myometrium

Fig. 31.4 Diagrams to show the manner in which the basic structure of a simple small labyrinthine placenta (A) is modified to form a large lobulate labyrinthine placenta (C) without change in length of the tubules of interchange. Note that the basally located trophospongium and/or giant cell layer in the simple placenta becomes largely interlobular in the lobulate placenta. Labyrinth, striate; trophospongium and/or trophoblastic giant cell layer, cross-hatched; vascular allantoic mesoderm, flecked.

It seems probable, on the basis of these admittedly very crude data, that the length of the interchange vessels in mammals ranges from not much less than 0.05 mm to not much over 1 mm in length; indeed, it seems probable that they are usually considerably less than 1 mm in length. One millimeter is exceptionally long for capillaries in general.

This concept of interchange vessel length as being under a millimeter bears on a number of placental problems. For one thing, it explains why

the larger placentae must develop in one of four patterns or combinations of patterns: some form of lobulation; long complexly and finely branched villi; numerous cotyledons with very long villi having circumferentially arranged interchange capillaries; or a very wide area studded with short villi.

Counterflow

This problem of vessel length also shows the error in applying the counterflow concept on too gross a

TABLE 31.1 Typical Labyrinthine Types

Taxonomic Group	Approximate Labyrinth Thickness in mm	Estimated Interchange Vessel Lengths in mm
Hemicentetes semispinosus (tenrec)[a]	1.7	
Soricidae (red-toothed shrews)	1.0–1.8	
Tupaiidae (tree shrews)	0.7–2.3	
Chiroptera (bats)	1.0–3.0	
Ochotona princeps (pika)	0.5–2.3	0.3–0.8
Leporidae (rabbits)	1.7–7.5	0.6–0.8
Aplodontia rufa (mountain beaver)	2.0–3.5	
Sciuridae (squirrels)	0.7–6.5	0.3–1.2
Castor canadensis (beaver)	5.0–19.0	0.2–0.8
Pedetes cafer (jumping "hare")	6.0–8.0	0.4–0.5
Cricetidae (mice, rats, hamsters)	0.5–1.4	
Ondatra zibethicus (muskrat)	2.0–2.5	
Muridae (mice and rats)	0.8–2.1	
Zapus hudsonicus (jumping mouse)	0.5–0.8	
Jaculus (sp?) (jerboa)	0.7–1.0	
Erethizon dorsatum (porcupine)	12.0–15.0	0.5–0.7
Cavia cobaya (guinea pig)	4.0–7.0	0.5–1.0
Chinchilla (sp?)	2.5–6.0	0.4–0.8
Canis familiaris (dog)	2.5–3.5	
Ursus americanus (black bear)	1.0–3.0	
Procyon lotor (raccoon)	2.0–3.0	
Mustelidae (mink, weasels)	1.0–3.0	
Felidae (cats)	2.2–5.5	
Procavia capensis (hyrax)[b]	1.0–3.0	
Trichechus latirostris (manatee)[c]	2.0–5.0	
Limits	0.4–19.0	0.2–1.2

[a] Goetz, *Z. Anat. Entwicklungsgeschichte* 108:161–200, 1937.
[b] Wislocki, *Contrib. Embryol. Carnegie Inst.* 122:85–95, 1930.
[c] Wislocki, *Mem. Museum Comp. Zool. Harvard College* 54, no. 3:159–178, 1935.

TABLE 31.2 Trabecular and Villous Placentae of the Anthropoidea and Dasypodidae

Taxonomic Group	Approximate Labyrinth Thickness in mm	Estimated Interchange Vessel Lengths in mm
Saguinus (sp?) (marmoset)[a]	0.5–1.5	
Ateles[b]	5.0–8.0	
Papio cynocephalus (Guinea baboon)[c]	20.0–30.0	
Gorilla gorilla[d]	19.0	
Homo	10.0–30.0	0.2–0.7
Dasypus novemcinctus (armadillo)[e]	3.0–4.5	0.3–0.7
Limits	0.5–30.0	0.2–0.7

[a] Benirschke provided slides of placentae.
[b] Wislocki, *Contrib. Embryol. Carnegie Inst.* 133:173–192, 1930.
[c] Hillemann, *Oregon State Monographs, Studies in Zool.* 8:1–47, 1955.
[d] Ludwig, *Acta Anat.* 45:110–123, 1961.
[e] Enders, *J. Anat.* 94:34–45, 1960.

TABLE 31.3   Broad or Diffuse Placentae, Usually with Short, Stout, Relatively Sparcely Branched Villi

TAXONOMIC GROUP	APPROXIMATE LABYRINTH THICKNESS IN MM	ESTIMATED INTERCHANGE VESSEL LENGTHS IN MM
Talpidae (moles)	0.3–3.0	0.2–0.5
Lemuroidea (loris, galago)	0.4–2.2	0.4–0.5
Tursiops truncatus (bottlenosed porpoise)[a]	0.5–1.5	0.2–0.4
Orycteropus (aardvark)	2.0–4.0	0.2–0.4
Equidae (horses)[b]	0.6–1.5	0.3–0.7
Tapir[c]	1.6	0.2
Sus scrofa (pig)	0.2–0.4	0.1–0.2
Camelidae[d]	0.5–1.5	
Tragulus (chevrotain)	0.4–2.0	0.3–0.8
Limits	0.2–4.0	0.1–0.8

[a] Wislocki and Enders, *Am. J. Anat.* 68:97–125, 1941.
[b] Morton provided slides of placentae.
[c] Schauder, *Morphol. Jahrb.* 89:407–456, 1945.
[d] Morton, *J. Anat.* 95:200–209, 1961; and Lennep, *Acta Morphol. Neerl. Scand.* 5:373–379, 1963.

TABLE 31.4   Cotyledonary Placentae

TAXONOMIC GROUP	APPROXIMATE LABYRINTH THICKNESS IN MM	TERMINAL VILLUS LENGTHS	ESTIMATED INTERCHANGE VESSEL LENGTHS IN MM
Cervus canadensis (elk)	15.0–25.0	6.0–8.0	
Dama virginiana (white-tailed deer)	7.0–13.0	0.5–1.0	
Bos bovis (domestic cow)	13.0–15.0	0.5–1.0	
Bison bison	5.0–8.0	0.3–0.5	
Ovis aries (sheep)[a]	5.0–8.0	0.5–1.0	
Limits	5.0–25.0	0.3–8.0	

[a] Wimsatt, *Am. J. Anat.* 87:391–458, 1950.

scale. The work of Hamilton and co-workers (7) indicates that, if counterflow exists in ruminants, it is probably not oriented along the long axes of the villi, even of the terminal ones, but is oriented in a generally circumferential direction. Somewhat in line with this is Lennep's (11) observation that a spiral capillary net is characteristic of at least certain parts of the villi of the dromedary.

As applied to the monkey and human placenta, it means that the really significantly directed countercurrent, if such exists, must involve primarily the capillaries of the smallest or terminal villi and the minute intervillous interstices between them; in other words, that the anthropoid placenta possesses an enormous number of very small lobules at the tips of its extremely complex system of villous branches (Figs. 31.5 and 31.6).

On the basis of injection techniques and study of both normal and pathological placentae, Hörmann (10) ar-

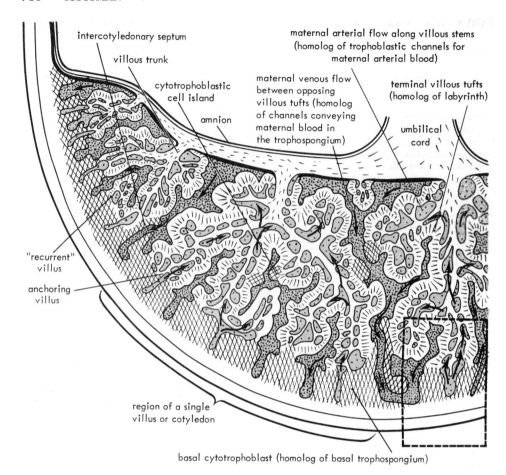

Fig. 31.5 Diagram of a multilobulate villous hemochorial placenta, such as that of man or a higher anthropoid. The terminal villous tufts are indicated as making up continuous, complexly lobulated zones, homologous to the labyrinthine zones of labyrinthine placentae. The alleged arterial flow of maternal blood along the villous stems is homologous to the flow in arterial trophoblastic channels along the fetal and intralobular zone of the labyrinth, as shown in Figs. 31.2 and 31.3. The drainage of maternal blood into the interlobular portions of the maternal blood space is homologous to the venous drainage through the interlobular portions of the trophospongium, as shown in Fig. 31.2. The basal cytotrophoblast is homologous with the basal trophospongium (cf. Fig. 31.2), and the cytotrophoblastic cell islands and intervillous septa are comparable to the interlobular trophospongium of the labyrinthine placenta (cf. Fig. 31.2). See Fig. 31.6 for a more detailed explanation of the area in the "box."

rived at about the same concept of the functional portion of the human placenta that has been presented here. He particularly stressed the capillary nature of the interchange portion of the intervillous space, which he called the "intervillöses Capillarsystem," and the anatomical stabilization of this system by the frequent syncytial anastomoses between the terminal villi. He attributed the wide spaces usually seen between the terminal villi to

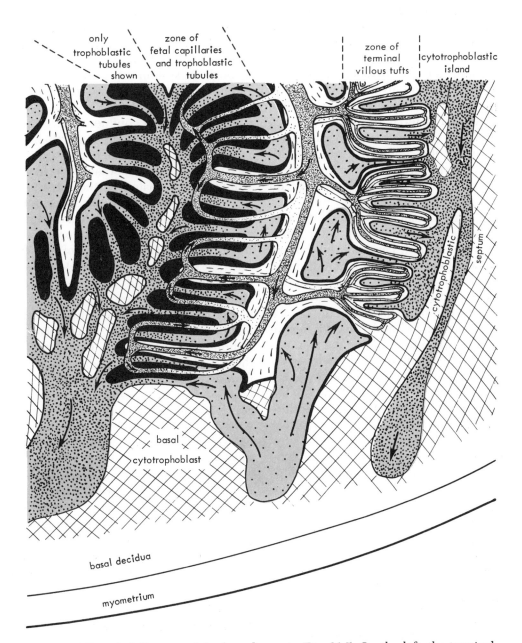

Fig. 31.6 Detailed diagram of the boxed area in Fig. 31.5. On the left, the terminal villous area and intervillous space is diagrammed as it would be in a labyrinthine placenta. On the right, schematic terminal villus tufts are shown with their very narrow intervillous clefts of interchange corresponding to trophoblastic tubules. The intervillous space is shown with a "cell island" and a "septum" which correspond to the trophospongium. Blood indicated as in Fig. 31.2.

shrinkage and distortion by technical procedures. He thought that this shrinkage and inadvertent pressures before and during fixation might also account for the relative scarcity of maternal blood usually observed in this portion of the intervillous space in sectioned material.

Wilkin (17) gives 0.2–0.8 mm as the length of the capillary net in the villi of the terminal tufts of the human placenta. This is in close agreement with my own estimate of 0.2–0.7 mm.

In the human placenta the tufts of short terminal villi with their interchange capillaries and intervillous maternal blood interstices of a millimeter or less in length correspond to the lobules of interchange capillaries and maternal tubules of labyrinthine placentae (Figs. 31.2 and 31.6). It is here in these minute lobules that the countercurrent flow must operate to be effective. That it does is indicated at present most clearly by evidence from comparative placentology. The lower anthropoids (marmosets and certain other New World monkeys) have either labyrinthine placentae or the intermediate trabecular type, rather than the villous placentae characteristic of higher anthropoids (Hill, 8; Wislocki, 20). The vascular patterns in these lower anthropoid labyrinthine types are entirely characteristic of placentae having counterflow; so it is almost certain that they do possess this feature, although no injection studies have ever been made on them to positively demonstrate it. Except for the lack of fusion of the trophoblast of adjacent villi to one another, which confines the maternal blood to definite labyrinthine channels, the villous placentae of the higher anthropoids have the same basic allantoic villous pattern as these lower forms, and hence should have a similar circulatory design. If maternal arterial blood reaches the terminal tuft villi, it matters little whether it flows through a system of capillary-sized trophoblastic tubules or whether, as in the higher anthropoids, it flows between the villi in confluent spaces of capillary thickness. Gruenwald (6) has made the suggestion that some capillary resistance to maternal blood flow would be eliminated by the substitution of confluent intervillous spaces for trophoblastic tubules. Such a design would certainly require less pressure to provide a given amount of blood flow per unit of time, and would allow the maternal blood to move more slowly because the cross-sectional area of the blood space would be greater for the same number, size, and distribution of villi (Fig. 31.1). Conversely, there could be more villi per volume of maternal blood, as theoretically less space would be occupied by trophoblast. It would also seem that essentially free terminal villi without trophoblastic anastomosis would favor a more uniform thickness of separation membrane (placental barrier) as in Figure 31.1. These advantages of terminal free villi over a terminal labyrinthine system may well have played a part in the adaptive evolution of the anthropoid hemochorial villous placenta from the labyrinthine type.

Circulation in the Villous Hemochorial Placenta

It is important to our understanding of the hemodynamics and physiology of the human placenta to know whether or not the terminal villi are truly the principal region of interchange, and whether or not the counterflow principle is utilized. We have seen that comparative evidence indicates that both are true, but we are still confronted by the question of how the maternal blood flow is directed through the spongework of villi in such a way that it will pass by the capillaries of the terminal villi in a direction opposed to that of fetal blood in these capillaries. Reference to Figures 31.5 and 31.6 will help in understanding how this can happen. As stated by Wilkin (17), evidence points to an arterial current of maternal blood along the villous trunks and branches, probably from distal to proximal along the anchoring villi (secondary and tertiary trunks), but certainly distalward along most of the recurrent villi and along the numerous small branch villi. In other words, arterial maternal blood enters the central basal region of the cotyledon and flows toward its upper and lateral surfaces. (See Wilkin's and Crawford's figures 16 and 17 of the cotyledonary "tambours" or "drums.") Such a direction of maternal blood flow distalward to the terminal villous tufts is exactly the pattern known in lobulated labyrinthine placentae. After passing through the narrow capillary-sized spaces between the villi of the terminal tufts or lobules, the venous maternal blood would then flow past the distal surfaces of these tufts to accumulate between adjacent groups. Eventually, it would reach the margins and base of the cotyledon where it would enter veins in the trophoblastic septa, or those penetrating the basal trophoblast in a fashion homologous to the drainage of maternal venous blood through the trophospongium (basal trophoblast) of a labyrinthine placenta (Figs. 31.2 and 31.3). The hemochorial villous placenta of anthropoids is thought of as a labyrinthine placenta in which the trophoblast of the labyrinth has been reduced so that it individually clothes allantoic villi, but no longer connects them to one another (Fig. 31.1), and in which the interlobular trophospongium has been reduced to a few cell islands and intercotyledonary (interlobular) septa (Figs. 31.5 and 31.6). It is apparent that, if this is true, such small villi as those indicated by the question mark in Figure 31.5 could not have the normal maternal blood supply unless they anastomose broadly with neighboring villi which are themselves connected to the basal plate of cytotrophoblast.

If the maternal blood flows distalward between the terminal villi, then the fetal blood in the more superficial capillaries of these terminal villi should be flowing proximalward. It is in general true that the terminal villi do contain a more central arteriole or arterial capillary which feeds a superficial net in which the blood does flow proximalward. This net is connected at intervals of a few tenths of millimeters with deeper venous capillaries or venules. However, this capillary pattern does not always seem to be as clearly adapted to counterflow as has just been indicated (Bøe, 3), and it may also be true that some of the superficial capillary nets of the branch villi themselves are likewise involved in the interchange system. Yet one must keep in mind that these capillaries of the branch villi may be largely nutritive to these villi, rather than functional in interchange. Furthermore, many of the smaller villi with seemingly randomly arranged capillaries described by Bøe may be young growing villi or sprout villi which have not yet reached their definitive condition.

There is little doubt that the elaboration of new functional terminal villi continues practically up to the actual moment of parturition.

There seems to be nothing about the known structure of human and higher anthropoid placentae, or about the dynamics of their blood flow (see the works of Ramsey and her collaborators, 14) which negates the concepts presented above. The most puzzling thing is how the maternal blood can be directed through the maze of villi occupying the intervillous space of a cotyledon in an exact enough manner to reach the terminal tufts or lobules from the proper direction, and for each small portion to pass accurately through one, and only one, villous tuft during one circulatory cycle, as it does in labyrinthine placentae. It seems necessary to assume that in the living hemochorial villous placenta the arrangement of the villi provides patent and reasonably constant flow-ways for the maternal blood, flow-ways which correspond to the arterial and venous channels formed in the trophoblast of hemochorial labyrinthine placentae (cf. Figs. 31.2, 31.3, 31.5–31.6). The interesting patterns of spread of x-ray-opaque media in monkey placenta, as demonstrated by Ramsey, must in some way be a manifestation of the more gross channeling of maternal blood through these potential flow-ways. It seems unlikely that the finer pattern of maternal blood flow can be illuminated by x-ray methods. Other techniques must be developed to demonstrate exactly the flow in the regions of principal interchange.

One can argue that the vascular conditions in an anthropoid villous placenta may be such that counterflow would make little difference in the efficiency of interchange. An enormously greater volume of maternal blood than fetal blood (somewhat as envisioned by Bartels et al., 2, in their "multivillous" schema), or a much greater rate of maternal flow than of fetal flow, would indeed negate the advantage of counterflow. But we have no evidence that such conditions do exist. Certainly, to increase the volume of blood or its rate of flow would seem wasteful of space or energy compared to the biologically economical situation made possible by the countercurrent design.

The case that has just been made for the presence of the counterflow pattern in the regions of principal interchange in the anthropoid and human hemochorial placenta is necessarily based on very general terms as far as the dynamics of placental interchange are concerned. For detailed discussions of the great variety of morphological and physiological factors involved in this, one may consult Wilkin and Bursztein (18) and Bartels and co-workers (2).

Finally, it must be obvious to all that no one has spoken in terms of experimental or causative ontogenesis of the fetal membranes and placenta, nor of their genetics, simply because no one has ever used the mammalian fetal membranes for such investigations. They might offer a fertile field for such work, especially for study of regulatory factors. They present the opportunity, not only to test the effects of basic anatomic elements (germ layers, and somatopleure and splanchnopleure) upon one another within the same individual, but also to study the interactions of these elements with another genetically different individual, the maternal organism.

Summary

Comparative evidence is presented which suggests, but by no means proves, that a common denominator of all mammalian chorioallantoic placentae is a multitude of interchange vessels (maternal channels and fetal capillaries), of less than 1 mm in length, which lie adjacent to and essentially parallel to each other, and in which the two blood streams flow in opposing directions. It is suggested, that to be really intelligible, studies on the mechanisms of placental transmission must often be correlated intimately with the structural and quantitative nature of these vessels and of the barrier separating their two blood streams. It is also suggested that, in view of the scarcity of specific morphological data on these interchange structures, anatomical investigation in depth must eventually be made on them to determine certain anatomical placental constants of each species being used for physiological studies.

References

1. Barcroft, J., and D. H. Barron, "Observations upon the Form and Relations of the Maternal and Fetal Vessels in the Placenta of the Sheep," *Anat. Record* 94: 569–595 (1946).
2. Bartels, H., W. Moll, and J. Metcalfe, "Physiology of Gas Exchange in the Human Placenta," *Am. J. Obstet. Gynecol.* 84:1714 (1962).
3. Bøe, F., "Studies on the Vascularization of the Human Placenta," *Acta Obstet. Gynecol. Scand. Suppl.* 5, 32:1–92 (1953).
4. Enders, A. C., "Development and Structure of the Villous Haemochorial Placenta of the Nine-banded Armadillo (*Dasypus novemcinctus*)," *J. Anat.* 94: 34–45 (1960).
5. Goetz, R. H., "Studien zur Placentation der Centetiden. III. Die Entwicklung der Fruchthüllen und der Placenta bei *Hemicentetes semispinosus* (Cuvier)," *Z. Anat. Entwicklungsgeschichte* 108:161–200 (1937).
6. Gruenwald, P., Personal communication. (1964).
7. Hamilton, W. J., R. J. Harrison, and B. A. Young, "Aspects of Placentation in Certain Cervidae," *J. Anat.* 94:2–33 (1960).
8. Hill, J. P., "The Developmental History of Primates," *Phil. Trans. Roy. Soc. London Ser. B* 221:45–178 (1932).
9. Hillemann, H. H., "Organization, Histology, and Circulatory Pattern of the Near-term Placenta of the Guinea Baboon, *Papio cynocephalus*, Demarest," *Oregon State Monographs, Studies in Zool.* 8:1–47 (1955).
10. Hörmann, G., "Ein Beitrag zur funktionellen Morphologie der Menschlichen Placenta," *Arch. Gynaekol.* 184: 109–123 (1953).
11. Lennep, E. W. van, "The Placenta of the One-humped Camel (*Camelus dromedarius* L.) during the Second Half of Gestation," *Acta Morphol. Neerl. Scand.* 5:373–379 (1963).
12. Ludwig, K. S., "Beitrag zum Bau der Gorilla-placenta," *Acta Anat.* 45:110–123 (1961).
13. Morton, W. R. M., "Observations on the Full-term Fetal Membranes of Three Members of the Camelidae (*Camelus dromedarius* L., *Camelus bactrianus* L. and *Lama glama* L.)," *J. Anat.* 95:200–209 (1961).
14. Ramsey, E. M., G. W. Corner, Jr., and M. W. Donner, "Serial and Cineradioangiographic Visualization of Maternal Circulation in the Primate (Hemochorial) Placenta," *Am. J. Obstet. Gynecol.* 86: 213–225 (1963).
15. Schauder, W., "Der gravide Uterus und die Placenta des Tapirs mit Vergleich von Uterus und Placenta des Schweines und Pferdes," *Morphol. Jahrb.* 89:407–456 (1945).
16. Wilkin, P., "Morphogénèse," *Le Placenta Humain*, J. Snoek, ed. Paris: Masson et Cie, pp. 23–70 (1958).

17. ———, "Organogenesis of the Human Placenta," *Organogenesis*, DeHaan and Ursprung, eds. New York: Holt, Rinehart and Winston, Inc., chap. 30 (1964).

18. ———, and M. Bursztein, "Étude Quantitative de l'Évolution, au Cours de la Grossesse de la Superficie de la Membrane d'Échange du Placenta Humain," *Le Placenta Humain*, J. Snoek, ed. Paris: Masson et Cie, pp. 211–248 (1958).

19. Wimsatt, W. A., "New Histological Observations on the Placenta of the Sheep," *Am. J. Anat.* 87:391–458 (1950).

20. Wislocki, G. B., "On the Placentation of Primates, with a Consideration of the Phylogeny of the Placenta," *Contrib. Embryol. Carnegie Inst.* 111:51–80 (1929).

21. ———, "On an Unusual Placental Form in the Hyracoidea: Its Bearing on the Theory of the Phylogeny of the Placenta," *Contrib. Embryol. Carnegie Inst.* 122:85–95 (1930).

22. ———, "On a Series of Placental Stages of a Platyrrhine Monkey (*Ateles geoffroyi*) with Some Remarks upon Age, Sex, and Breeding Period in Platyrrhines," *Contrib. Embryol. Carnegie Inst.* 133:173–192 (1930).

23. ———, "The Placentation of the Manatee (*Trichechus latirostris*)," *Mem. Museum Comp. Zool. Harvard College* 54, no. 3:159–178 (1935).

24. ———, and R. K. Enders, "The Placentation of the Bottle-nosed Porpoise (*Tursiops truncatus*)," *Am. J. Anat.* 68:97–125 (1941).

Index

Index